ELECTRONIC CIRCUITS

mcgraw-hill electrical and electronic engineering series

Frederick Emmons Terman, Consulting Editor
W. W. Harman, J. G. Truxal, and R. A. Rohrer, Associate Consulting Editors

Electronic Circuits: Physical Principles, Analysis, and Design

PAUL M. CHIRLIAN
Professor of Electrical Engineering
Stevens Institute of Technology

McGRAW-HILL BOOK COMPANY

New York
St. Louis
San Francisco

Düsseldorf
London
Mexico

Panama
Sydney
Toronto

ELECTRONIC CIRCUITS

Library of Congress Catalog Card Number 73-118393
10797

1 2 3 4 5 6 7 8 9 0 M A M M 7 9 8 7 6 5 4 3 2 1 0

This book was set in Times New Roman, and printed
on permanent paper and bound by The Maple Press
Company. The designer was Edward Zytko; the
drawings were done by John Cordes, J. & R. Technical
Services, Inc. The editors were B. G. Dandison, Jr., and
Margaret LaMacchia. Peter D. Guilmette supervised
production.

To Barbara, Lisa, and Peter

Preface

This book is an undergraduate college textbook on the physical principles and circuits of electronic devices for use in junior or senior level courses. Its purpose is to provide the student with a thorough understanding of the physical principles of electronic devices and the operation of their circuits. Both integrated and discrete circuits are discussed at length. The basic principles of the design of electronic circuits are also presented in detail. Although by no means a design handbook, since most of the discussions are of the physics and analysis of electronic circuits, there are numerous design examples and discussions. It is hoped that the student will obtain a general design philosophy from these sections. The book can also be of considerable help to the practicing electronics engineer. Although a design example is not given for every circuit, such things as amplifier design (including the effects of bypass capacitors), feedback system stabilization, and oscillator design are discussed in considerable detail. Numerous other thorough design discussions are also given.

    Portions of this book are based on the author's previous book "The Analysis and Design of Electronic Circuits," but there have been many substantial changes. Four chapters on the physics and basic principles of electronic devices have been added. A thorough discussion of the field-effect transistor has been included and is integrated throughout the book. The linear models of the bipolar junction transistor have been thoroughly revised.

The fundamental high-frequency model used to analyze common-emitter transistor circuits is the hybrid-pi model. In addition, an *h*-parameter model, derived from the hybrid-pi model, is also used. This model has the accuracy of the hybrid-pi model and at times is more convenient to use.

The vacuum tube has been greatly deemphasized, particularly in those areas where it has been almost completely replaced by semiconductor devices, e.g., receiving tubes and low-power amplifiers. However, some brief discussion of vacuum tubes is given, and, in many instances, the analysis of vacuum-tube circuits is very similar to that of field-effect-transistor circuits. This is pointed out, so that the reader can gain an understanding of vacuum-tube circuits from the discussion of the field-effect transistor. Problems emphasizing this are included in the homework.

There is considerable amplification of material covered in "Analysis and Design of Electronic Circuits." For instance, amplifier noise is now covered. A thorough discussion of complementary symmetry in push-pull circuits has been included. The section on basic principles of feedback systems has been expanded greatly. Additional material on oscillators has been included. A greatly expanded discussion of the physical principles of switching in semiconductor circuits has been added. A computer application of logic circuits is now included also. Many homework problems have been added.

A unified treatment of transistors, field-effect transistors and vacuum-tube circuits is given wherever possible. (In many circumstances, the vacuum-tube circuit can be omitted from classroom discussion and merely be assigned for reading.) When fundamental differences exist between transistor, FET, and vacuum-tube circuits, they are stressed. Particular emphasis is placed upon the approximations which can be made in electronic circuits.

Chapter 1 discusses the physical principles common to all electronic devices. Here, the basic conduction processes that take place in a vacuum or in a solid are presented and discussed. A quantum-mechanical approach is used.

Chapters 2 to 4 describe the basic physical principles of electronic devices. Vacuum tubes are briefly discussed in Chap. 2. The basic semiconductor devices are discussed in Chap. 3. Thorough treatments of *p-n*-junction diodes, the bipolar junction transistor, and the FET are given, with both qualitative and quantitative discussions. These are given in sequence so that the reader first obtains a "picture" of the device and then learns its fundamental equations. In Chap. 4, the basic parameters of integrated devices are presented. This chapter discusses the fabrication of all semiconductor devices, discrete and integrated.

Chapters 5 to 7 develop the basic techniques for the analysis of electronic circuits. Chapter 5 presents graphical analysis techniques. The analysis of nonlinear distortion is also discussed.   Linear models are discussed in Chap. 6.   Various forms of low- and high-frequency models are developed, and their advantages and disadvantages are discussed.   Linear-circuit theory is related to the linear models of electronic devices.   The hybrid-pi model is presented as the basic high-frequency common-emitter model for the junction transistor.   The *h*-parameter model is used for low frequencies.   A high-frequency *h*-parameter model, derived from the hybrid-pi model, is also presented, permitting the low- and high-frequency models to be related. Some basic amplifier circuits are also given in this chapter.   Chapter 7 consists of a study of piecewise-linear models.   Such models for the commonly used electronic devices are developed.

Chapter 8 is an introduction to electronic amplifiers.   Basic terminology and amplifier structures are given.   Decibel notation, logarithmic plots, and concepts of efficiency are also introduced.

Chapter 9 discusses linear class A amplifiers.   This is a lengthy chapter, since an attempt has been made at completeness.   The analysis and design of many amplifier configurations are discussed.   In addition, poles and zeros are introduced, and their relation to the transient response is given.   The ideas of transformed gain and time functions are also presented, along with general discussion of random noise and electronic-device noise.

Chapters 10 and 11 discuss the analysis and design of power amplifiers.

Chapter 12 introduces signal-flow graphs.   They are used in Chap. 13, which is a discussion of feedback.   Every attempt is made in this chapter to present a rigorous, accurate discussion of feedback amplifiers.   Although the mathematical theory of feedback cannot be completely presented on an undergraduate level, sufficient material is included to enable the student to have a basic understanding of what he is doing.   For instance, stability is discussed in terms of poles and zeros.   The Nyquist criterion is presented as a procedure for determining the differences between the number of right half-plane zeros and poles.   In addition, the design of feedback systems is presented in some detail.   Design in terms of gain and phase margin is thoroughly discussed, and techniques for improving the margins are given.   The use of corrective networks is also discussed.   A complete discussion of voltage, current, series, and shunt feedback and their effects on impedance levels is given.

Chapter 14 uses and simplifies the principles of Chap. 13 in a discussion of sinusoidal oscillators.   Thorough discussions of both resonant-circuit and phase-shift oscillators are given.

Pulse and switching circuits are discussed in Chap. 15.   Although discussion of these circuits has been limited to avoid undue length, the fundamentals of semiconductor switching are presented.   Several basic switching, counting, logic, and waveshaping circuits are then discussed.   A section on the application of logic circuits to adders is included.

Amplitude, frequency, and phase modulation are discussed in Chap. 16.

The mathematics of these modulation systems is rigorously given. Modulation and demodulation systems are discussed in considerable detail. Pulse modulation and its applications are discussed here.

Chapter 17 consists of a discussion of power supplies. This chapter contains not only the analysis and design of rectifiers and filters but also regulated-power supplies and controlled rectifiers.

If the instructor wishes, he need not exactly follow the order of these chapters. For instance, Chap. 7 can be omitted until pulse circuits (Chap. 15) are discussed. Chapters 10 and 11 can follow the discussion of feedback in Chap. 13. Much of the discussion of power supplies can precede the chapters on amplifiers.

Instead of including the characteristics of electronic devices in an appendix, they are distributed throughout the text where they are most useful, and the student should encounter no difficulty in finding the characteristics necessary for the solution of problems. Usually, the characteristics are close to the problems themselves. In any event, the necessary characteristics are referred to (by figure number) in a specific problem or set of problems. Many varied problems have been included at the end of each chapter.

The author would like to express his gratitude to his colleagues Profs. Alfred C. Gilmore, Jr. and Gerald J. Herskowitz for many helpful discussions held with them during the writing of this book. The author would also like to express his gratitude to Profs. John Truxal and George Anner for their very many fine suggestions which have been incorporated in this book.

Loving gratitude and many heartfelt thanks are again due my wife Barbara, who not only provided me with continuous encouragement and saw to it that my time was free from interruption but also typed the rough draft and the final draft of the manuscript and corrected the punctuation and grammar of the copy.

PAUL M. CHIRLIAN

Contents

ELECTRONIC CIRCUITS

1

Conduction Processes in a Vacuum and in Solids—Atomic Structure

In this book we shall discuss electronic devices and the circuits which use them. These circuits are of fundamental importance to all communication systems such as radio, telephone, and television. In addition, they are very important in medical applications. For instance, diagnostic devices such as electrocardiographs and electroencephalographs use them. In addition, electronic devices in the form of transistor circuits are sometimes implanted within the body in a device called a *pacemaker* used to regulate the beat of the heart when a part of the body's nervous system fails. Very large modern computers would not be possible were it not for the development of the transistor. The integrated circuit makes it possible to design computers capable of doing much more than those developed previously.

In the preceding paragraph we mentioned some of the applications of electronic circuits. Of course, there are many more. In this book, we shall first discuss the physical principles of these devices, and then we shall consider circuits using them. An important part of this discussion will concern the design of these circuits. We shall consider circuits which are basic to almost all electronic devices.

In this chapter, we shall discuss some physical principles a knowledge of which is fundamental to understanding the operation of electronic devices. In the following chapters, we shall apply these fundamentals to the development of the characteristics of these devices.

We shall start our discussion by considering some fundamental particles of nature. The motion of charged particles in a vacuum will then be studied, followed by the study of the motion of charge carriers in solids.

1-1   SOME FUNDAMENTAL PARTICLES

All electronic devices involve the motion of charged particles. In this section we shall consider some fundamental particles. In subsequent sections methods of controlling the motion of charged particles will be discussed.

All atoms consist of a *nucleus*, containing positive and electrically neutral charges, and one or more *electrons*, which travel about the nucleus. The electron is fundamental to the operation of electronic devices. Every electronic device involves the motion and/or control of electrons.

The electron is extremely small and possesses a negative charge $-e$, whose magnitude is 1.602×10^{-19} coul. At times the electron acts as a particle, while at other times its behavior is that of a wave. The mass m of the electron at rest is 9.107×10^{-31} kg. The ratio of charge to mass of an electron appears in many relations. It is $e/m = 1.759 \times 10^{11}$ coul/kg.

A particle which is a part of the nucleus of an atom is the *proton*, which has a positive charge equal in magnitude to that of the electron and a rest mass of 1.68×10^{-27} kg. The mass of the proton is 1845 times that of the electron.

A third particle, called the *neutron*, is believed to be obtained from the combination of a proton and an electron. The neutron is electrically neutral. That is, its effective charge is zero.

The nucleus of an atom consists of protons, neutrons, and some other fundamental particles. If the entire atom is to be electrically neutral, the number of electrons must equal the number of protons. If electrons are removed from the atom, it will have a net positive charge. A charged atom is called an *ion*. In subsequent sections of this chapter we shall consider atomic structure in much greater detail. Here we simply mention it to discuss some charged particles.

The particle description of the components of the atom is called the *classical* model. This representation can generally be used to calculate the motion of charged particles over relatively large distances. However, if motion within solids is considered, then, to obtain accurate results, electrons must be considered to be wavelike. Quantum mechanics, rather than newtonian mechanics, must be applied in these cases. This will be discussed further subsequently.

1-2 ELECTROSTATIC FIELDS—POTENTIAL

It has been experimentally determined that a charged particle in the presence of other charged particles will experience a *force*. If there are only two charges Q_1 and Q_2 coul, then the magnitude of force on either of them will be

$$\mathscr{F} = \frac{Q_1 Q_2}{4\pi\epsilon r^2} \qquad (1\text{-}1)$$

where $\mathscr{F}$ = magnitude of force, newtons
    r = distance between charges, meters
    ϵ = permittivity of medium surrounding charges
The permittivity of free space is $10^{-9}/36\pi$ farad/meter. The direction of the force is along the line drawn between the two charges. The charges repel each other if they are of like sign and attract each other otherwise. In this book, we shall use boldface script letters to indicate vectors. Lightface script letters indicate the magnitude of vectors. Thus, we can modify Eq. (1-1) to give the force on Q_1 as

$$\mathscr{F} = \mathscr{U}_r \frac{Q_1 Q_2}{4\pi\epsilon r^2} \qquad (1\text{-}2)$$

where $\mathscr{U}_r$ is a unit vector which lies along the line from Q_1 to Q_2 and points away from Q_2.

  If a charged body is in the presence of other charged bodies, it will experience a force which is the vector sum of the forces due to the individual charges. We can state that a charged body experiences a force because it is in an *electric field*. That is, we can *define* an electric field in terms of the force on a unit positive charge in the following way:

$$\mathscr{E} = \frac{\mathscr{F}}{Q} \qquad (1\text{-}3)$$

For instance, let us determine the electric field at point P_2 of Fig. 1-1. A charge of Q coul is placed at P_1. Then, from Eqs. (1-2) and (1–3), we have

$$\mathscr{E} = \mathscr{U} \frac{Q}{4\pi\epsilon r^2} \qquad (1\text{-}4)$$

Fig. 1-1 The electric field about a point charge.

where the unit vector $\mathcal{U}$ lies along the line $P_1 P_2$ and points away from P_1.

If the magnitude and direction of the electric field are constant within a region, then the electric field there is called a *uniform electric field*. Such a field can be set up between two charged parallel plates which are infinite in area. In practice, an electric field which approximates a uniform one can be established by charging two parallel plates whose dimensions are much greater than the spacing d between them. Such a *parallel-plate capacitor* is shown in Fig. 1-2. The field is very uniform except for the regions near the ends of the plates.

If a field does not vary with time, it is called a *static* field. Thus a time-invariant electric field is called a *static electric field* or an *electrostatic field*.

Potential A charged particle in an electric field will have a force on it. Thus, in general, work will be done if the charge is moved. The *difference of potential* between two points is defined as the work done in moving a unit positive charge from one point to the other. The potential difference between two points a and b is written as V_{ab}. When positive work is done by the field in moving a positive charge from a to b, then V_{ab} is said to be a positive potential drop or a negative potential rise. An alternative name for potential rise or drop is *voltage rise* or *voltage drop*. The unit of potential is the *volt*, where

$$\text{Volt} = \frac{\text{joules}}{\text{coulombs}}$$

It is an experimentally determined fact that when the electric field does not vary with time, the work done in moving a unit charge between any two points is independent of the path taken. Such fields are called *conservative*. Thus, in an electrostatic field, the difference of potential between two points

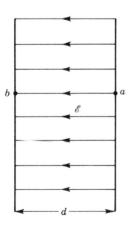

Fig. 1-2 A parallel-plate capacitor with a uniform electric field. Fringing of the electric field at the edges of the capacitor has been neglected.

is independent of the path taken by the unit positive charge used to determine the potential.

As an example, let us find the difference of potential between points a and b in Fig. 1-2. The magnitude of the force on a unit positive charge is

$$\mathscr{F} = 1\mathscr{E}$$

Thus, as a voltage rise, the potential is

$$V'_{ab} = -\mathscr{E}\, d \qquad\qquad (1\text{-}5a)$$

and, as a voltage drop,

$$V_{ab} = \mathscr{E}\, d \qquad\qquad (1\text{-}5b)$$

The prime is used to indicate a voltage rise. Usually we shall use voltage drops. If the electric field is not uniform and/or the path between the points in question is not a straight line, we can still compute the potential between two points. Consider Fig. 1-3, where a curved path is drawn through a nonuniform electric field. Approximate the curved path by a series of connected straight line segments as shown. The segments should be taken short enough so that the electric field can be considered approximately uniform along each of them. Call the length of each segment Δl. Then the work done in moving a unit positive charge along the first segment is

$$-\mathscr{E}_1 \cos\theta_1\, \Delta l$$

Note that negative work means that the particle is "pulled along" by the field. We can repeat this calculation for each segment in turn. Thus, the potential rise V'_{ab} is approximately given by

$$V'_{ab} \approx -\sum_{k=1}^{N} \mathscr{E}_k \cos\theta_k\, \Delta l \qquad\qquad (1\text{-}6)$$

Note that θ_k is the angle between $\mathscr{E}_k$ and the kth line segment. As the length

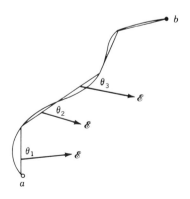

Fig. 1-3 A curved path in a nonuniform electric field.

of the straight-line segments Δl is decreased, Eq. (1-6) becomes more accurate. In the limit, as Δl approaches zero, we write

$$V'_{ab} = -\int_a^b \mathscr{E} \cos \theta \, dl \tag{1-7}$$

Equation (1-7) is called a *line integral*. It is *defined* as the limit of Eq. (1-6) as Δl approaches zero.

As a further example, let us compute the potential difference between points a and b in Fig. 1-4. We can use any path between the points to compute the potential. We shall use the one shown by the dashed line since, as we shall demonstrate, this simplifies the calculations. The first part of the path consists of a circle of radius r_a whose center is at Q. The force on a unit charge, and hence the electric field, is everywhere perpendicular to the path. Thus, no work is done in moving along it. The electric field along line bc is [see Eq. (1-4)]

$$\mathscr{E} = \frac{Q}{4\pi\epsilon r^2}$$

where r is the distance from point Q. Then, the potential rise from point c to point b is V'_{cb};

$$V'_{cb} = \int_{r_c}^{r_b} \frac{Q}{4\pi\epsilon r^2} \, dr \tag{1-8a}$$

where $dr = -dl$ in Eq. (1-7). No work is done in moving the charge over the arc ac. Thus,

$$V'_{cb} = V'_{ab}$$

$$V'_{ab} = \int_{r_c}^{r_b} \frac{Q}{4\pi\epsilon r^2} \, dr$$

Noting that $r_c = r_a$, we obtain

$$V'_{ab} = \frac{Q}{4\pi\epsilon} \left(\frac{1}{r_b} - \frac{1}{r_a} \right) \tag{1-8b}$$

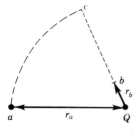

Fig. 1-4 A path used to compute the voltage drop V_{ab}. A charge of Q coul is placed as shown.

Note that the potential difference depends only upon the radial distance of the points from the charge. Thus, the potential difference between any two points equidistant from Q is zero. Therefore, if the electric field is due only to Q, the potential difference between any two points on a sphere whose center is the charge Q is zero. In general, even for an arbitrary configuration of charges, we can find a set of surfaces each one of which is such that the potential difference between *any* two of its points is zero. Such a surface is called an *equipotential surface*.

The work done in moving a charge along an equipotential surface is zero. Thus, the electric field must be *perpendicular* to an equipotential surface at all points in space.

Equation (1-7) can be used to determine the potential difference between any two points in space. Let us now consider that one of these is fixed but the other can vary through space. For instance, suppose the path is parallel to the x axis. Then $\mathscr{E} \cos \theta$ represents $\mathscr{E}_x$, the x component of the electric field. Equation (1-7) can be written as

$$V(x) = -\int_a^x \mathscr{E}_x \, dx \tag{1-9}$$

That is, $V(x)$ represents the potential difference between point a and a point on the x axis whose x coordinate is x. $V(x)$ is called the *potential distribution*. Differentiating partially, we obtain

$$\mathscr{E}_x = -\frac{\partial V}{\partial x} \tag{1-10a}$$

In a similar way, we can state

$$\mathscr{E}_y = -\frac{\partial V}{\partial y} \tag{1-10b}$$

$$\mathscr{E}_z = -\frac{\partial V}{\partial z} \tag{1-10c}$$

Thus, the electric field can be determined by partially differentiating the potential distribution.

1-3 MOTION IN A UNIFORM ELECTROSTATIC FIELD

Let us now consider that a charged particle is placed in a uniform electrostatic field and determine its motion. From Newton's second law we have

$$\mathscr{F} = ma \tag{1-11}$$

where $\mathscr{F}$ = force, newtons
$\quad\quad m$ = mass, kg
$\quad\quad a$ = acceleration, meters/sec^2

The force on a particle whose charge is q in a uniform electric field is

$$\mathscr{F} = q\mathscr{E} \tag{1-12}$$

Thus,

$$a = \frac{q}{m}\mathscr{E} \tag{1-13}$$

As an example, consider the parallel-plate-capacitor system of Fig. 1-5. We assume that the electric field is uniform in the region between the plates. A three-dimensional coordinate system is also shown in Fig. 1-5. Assume that the origin lies at point P. The electric field will lie in the x direction. We shall write any vector in terms of its three coordinates. For instance,

$$\mathscr{E} = \mathscr{U}_x\mathscr{E}_x + \mathscr{U}_y\mathscr{E}_y + \mathscr{U}_z\mathscr{E}_z \tag{1-14}$$

where $\mathscr{U}_x$, $\mathscr{U}_y$, and $\mathscr{U}_z$ are unit vectors which point in the x, y, and z directions, respectively. In Fig. 1-5 $\mathscr{E}_y = \mathscr{E}_z = 0$.

The potential difference between the two plates is established by the battery to be V volts. Then, from Eq. (1-5) we have

$$\mathscr{E}_x = -\frac{V}{d}$$

The minus sign appears because the electric field points in the negative x direction.

Now consider that an electron is injected into the space between the plates, at point P, with a velocity in the x direction of v_{0x}. From Eq. (1-13) we obtain

$$a_x = -\frac{e}{m}\left(-\frac{V}{d}\right) \tag{1-15}$$

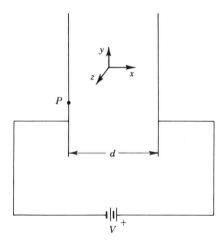

Fig. 1-5 A uniform electric field into which an electron is injected.

where $-e$ is the charge of the electron. Since $a_x = dv_x/dt$, we have

$$\frac{dv_x}{dt} = \frac{eV}{md} \tag{1-16}$$

Integration yields

$$v_x = \int \frac{eV}{md} dt \tag{1-17a}$$

or

$$v_x = \frac{eV}{md} t + C_1 \tag{1-17b}$$

where C_1 is a constant. At $t = 0$, the electron is injected into the region with velocity v_{0x}. Hence,

$$v_{0x} = 0 + C_1$$

Therefore

$$v_x = \frac{eV}{md} t + v_{0x} \tag{1-17c}$$

Now let us determine the position of the electron as a function of time:

$$v_x = \frac{dx}{dt}$$

or

$$x = \int v_x \, dt \tag{1-18}$$

Integrating Eq. (1-17c), we obtain

$$x = \frac{1}{2} \frac{eV}{md} t^2 + v_{0x} t + C_2$$

The x coordinate of the left-hand plate is 0. Thus, at $t = 0$, $x = 0$. Hence, $C_2 = 0$, and

$$x = \frac{1}{2} \frac{eV}{md} t^2 + v_{0x} t \tag{1-19}$$

The electron will not be accelerated indefinitely but will eventually strike the right-hand plate. Let us compute the time T required for this to occur. Substituting $x = d$ into Eq. (1-19), we obtain

$$d = \frac{1}{2} \frac{eV}{md} T^2 + v_{0x} T \tag{1-20}$$

Solving for T, we have

$$T = \frac{md}{eV}\left(-\mathcal{v}_{0x} \pm \sqrt{\mathcal{v}_{0x}{}^2 + \frac{2eV}{m}}\right) \tag{1-21}$$

Since T is positive, the plus sign of the square root must be chosen. If $\mathcal{v}_{0x} = 0$, Eq. (1-21) becomes

$$T = d\sqrt{\frac{2m}{eV}} \tag{1-22}$$

Since the charge-to-mass ratio of the electron is very small, very small electric fields will produce very large acceleration. For instance, if $d = 1$ meter and $V = 1$ volt, then [see Eq. (1-15)]

$$a_x = 1.759 \times 10^{11} \text{ meters/sec}^2 \tag{1-23}$$

Let us again consider Fig. 1-5 but now assume that the electron is injected with components of velocity in both the x and y directions, $\mathcal{v}_{0x}$ and $\mathcal{v}_{0y}$. In this case, the motion in the x direction is as just computed and given by Eqs. (1-17c) and (1-19).

There is no electric field in the y direction. Hence there is no force on the electron in this direction. Thus,

$$\mathcal{v}_y = \mathcal{v}_{0y} \tag{1-24}$$

independent of time. Since the y coordinate of point P is $y = 0$, then

$$y = \mathcal{v}_{0y}t \tag{1-25}$$

1-4 THE ELECTRON VOLT AS A UNIT OF ENERGY

The work done on a charged particle in moving it between two points depends only upon the charge and the potential difference between those points. The work is independent of the path. If a particle is accelerated by an electric field, the kinetic energy it gains is equal to the potential energy it has lost. Very often, in electronic devices, the charged particles are electrons. If an electron is accelerated through a potential difference of V volts, the kinetic energy it gains will then be eV joules. In general, eV will be an extremely small number. Since e is constant, all the information about the electron's kinetic energy is known if V is known. Thus, the kinetic energy of an electron is often given in terms of the potential difference through which it has been accelerated. This unit of energy is called the *electron volt* (eV). For instance, an electron which has been accelerated by a 1-volt potential difference has acquired 1 eV of energy, or 1.602×10^{-19} joule. The symbol W will be used for energy in joules, and E will be used for energy in electron volts.

Let us consider the velocity of an electron starting from rest and accelerated through V electron volts. The kinetic energy of the electron is $\frac{1}{2}mv^2$. Equating this to the potential energy, we have

$$\frac{1}{2}mv^2 = eV \tag{1-26}$$

Then,

$$v = \sqrt{\frac{2e}{m}}\sqrt{V} \tag{1-27a}$$

Substituting for e/m, we obtain

$$v = 5.93 \times 10^5\sqrt{V} \quad \text{meters/sec} \tag{1-27b}$$

Thus, a small accelerating potential can produce large velocities because of the large charge-to-mass ratio of the electron.

1-5 FORCES IN A MAGNETIC FIELD

If a charged particle moves in a magnetic field, it will experience a force in addition to that produced by any electric fields which may be present. It has been found experimentally that the force due to the magnetic field is given by

$$\mathscr{F} = \mathscr{U}_p Q v \mathscr{B} \sin \theta \tag{1-28}$$

where $\mathscr{F}$ = force, newtons
  Q = charge, coul
  v = velocity, meters/sec
  $\mathscr{B}$ = magnetic flux density, webers/meter^2

θ is the angle between the v and $\mathscr{B}$ vectors, and $\mathscr{U}_p$ is a unit vector. The direction of $\mathscr{U}_p$ is perpendicular to the plane formed by the $\mathscr{B}$ and v vectors and is in the same direction that a right-handed screw would move if it were aligned along $\mathscr{U}_p$ and turned from v to $\mathscr{B}$ through the smaller angle. This is illustrated in Fig. 1-6.

Now let us discuss the force on a wire carrying current. The current is made up of the flow of many electrons. Let us consider that the magnetic field is uniform, i.e., constant throughout the space in question, and that the wire is a straight right-circular cylinder of length L and cross-sectional area

Fig. 1-6 Force on a moving charge in a magnetic field.

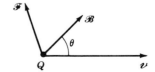

A. Assume that the density of the electrons making up the current is n electrons per cubic meter of wire and all the electrons are moving with velocity v. The force on any one electron is

$$\mathscr{F}_e = -\mathscr{U}_p ev\mathscr{B} \sin\theta \tag{1-29}$$

where $-e$ is the charge of a single electron and θ is the angle between v and $\mathscr{B}$. The total number of electrons in the wire is given by the density of the electrons n multiplied by the volume of the wire AL. Thus, the total force on the wire is

$$\mathscr{F} = -\mathscr{U}_p enALv\mathscr{B} \sin\theta \tag{1-30}$$

The total current I past any point in the wire is given by the product of the total number of electrons in 1 meter of the wire, the average velocity of the electrons, and the charge of an electron. Thus,

$$I = -enAv \tag{1-31}$$

Substituting in Eq. (1-30), we have

$$\mathscr{F} = \mathscr{U}_p I\mathscr{B}L \sin\theta \tag{1-32}$$

where θ is the angle between the wire and the magnetic field and $\mathscr{U}_p$ is perpendicular to the plane established by the wire and the magnetic field. Its direction is established as it was for a single charge.

1-6 MOTION IN A UNIFORM MAGNETOSTATIC FIELD

Let us consider that a charged particle is injected into a uniform magnetic field. We shall assume for the time being that the velocity of the particle is perpendicular to the magnetic field, as is illustrated in Fig. 1-7. Assume that the magnetic field is zero to the left of the dashed line and uniform and into the paper to the right of it.

The force will be perpendicular to the direction of the velocity. Thus, no work is done. Therefore, the magnitude of the velocity will not change. In addition, the force is also perpendicular to the magnetic field. Thus, it lies in the plane of the paper, so that the particle will remain in that plane. Hence, the angle between v and $\mathscr{B}$ will remain constant at 90°. Therefore, the magnitude of the force and the magnitude of the acceleration will be constant. Their direction will be perpendicular to the direction of motion. A particle which is accelerated in this fashion will move in a circle. Let us compute its radius. The magnitude of the acceleration of a particle moving in a circle of radius R with constant speed v is v^2/R. Hence, using Newton's second law,

$$\mathscr{F} = m\frac{v^2}{R} \tag{1-33}$$

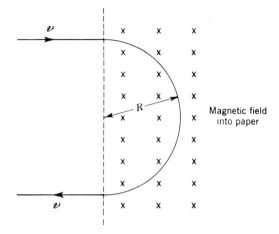

Fig. 1-7 Circular motion of a charged particle in a uniform magnetic field.

Substituting Eq. (1-28), noting that $\theta = 90°$, and solving for R, we obtain

$$R = \frac{mv}{\mathscr{B}Q} \tag{1-34}$$

If the charged particle were in a magnetic field that was uniform throughout all space, it would continuously move in a circular path. The time T required for it to make one complete revolution is given by the ratio of the circumference $2\pi R$ of the path to the magnitude of the velocity. Hence,

$$T = \frac{2\pi m}{\mathscr{B}Q} \tag{1-35}$$

T is called the *period* of the motion. The *frequency* is given by the number of revolutions per second. This is

$$f = \frac{1}{T} = \frac{\mathscr{B}Q}{2\pi m} \tag{1-36}$$

Now let us assume that the initial velocity of the particle is not perpendicular to the magnetic field. In this case, we can express the velocity as a sum of two components $v + v_1$, where v is perpendicular to the magnetic field and v_1 is parallel to it. The perpendicular component results in circular motion, as discussed above. The component of velocity parallel to the magnetic field does not lead to any force. Thus, the particle moves in the parallel direction with constant velocity v_1. Hence, the particle moves in a helix whose radius is given by Eq. (1-34). The pitch of the helix is $v_1 T$, where T is given by Eq. (1-35).

1-7 MOTION IN COMBINED ELECTROSTATIC AND MAGNETOSTATIC FIELDS

Let us now consider the motion of a charged particle in a region where there are both uniform electrostatic and magnetostatic fields. We shall start by considering two special cases: (1) the electric and magnetic fields are parallel, and (2) the two fields are perpendicular.

Parallel electrostatic and magnetostatic fields Let us consider that the electric and magnetic fields are both parallel to the x axis with magnitudes $\mathscr{E}$ and $\mathscr{B}$, respectively. A particle of charge Q is injected into this region with velocity v_0, where the x component of v_0 is v_{0x} and the component of v_0, which lies in the yz plane, is v_{0P}. Hence, using vector addition,

$$v_0 = v_{0x} + v_{0P} \tag{1-37}$$

The electric field will accelerate the particle in the x direction. This component of velocity is parallel to the magnetic field. Hence, it does not interact with it. Thus, the motion in the x direction is independent of the magnetic field. Let us call the origin of the coordinate system that point where the charged particle is injected. The electric force on the particle will be $Q\mathscr{E}_x$. Hence,

$$\frac{dv_x}{dt} = Q\mathscr{E}_x \tag{1-38}$$

Then proceeding as before, we obtain

$$v_x = \frac{Q\mathscr{E}_x}{m} t + v_{0x} \tag{1-39a}$$

and

$$x = \frac{1}{2} \frac{Q\mathscr{E}_x}{m} t^2 + v_{0x}t \tag{1-39b}$$

The magnitude of the particle's velocity in a direction perpendicular to the magnetic field will remain constant at v_{0P}. Its direction will remain perpendicular to the magnetic field. Hence (see Sec. 1-6), the projection of the path of the particle on the yz plane will be a circle. Its radius is [see Eq. (1-34)]

$$R = \frac{mv_{0P}}{\mathscr{B}Q} \tag{1-40}$$

The total motion of the particle is a helix whose pitch varies with time.

Perpendicular electrostatic and magnetostatic fields When the electric and magnetic fields are perpendicular to each other, the result is more complex than the parallel case since the effects of the two fields interact. Let

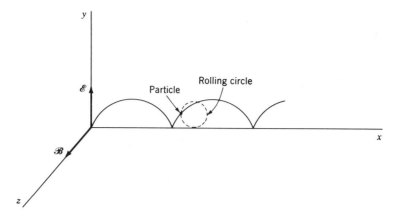

Fig. 1-8 The cycloidal motion of a charged particle in perpendicular electrostatic and magnetostatic fields. The initial velocity of the particle is zero in this figure.

us assume that the electric field is in the y direction while the magnetic field lies in the z direction. This is illustrated in Fig. 1-8. If the particle is initially at rest, there will be no force due to the magnetic field. However, the particle will be accelerated in the y direction by the electric field. As soon as this occurs, the y component of velocity will interact with the magnetic field. This will now result in force in the x direction, etc.

Let us now perform a mathematical analysis. We shall assume that the particle is injected at the origin of Fig. 1-8 with x and y components of velocity v_{0x} and v_{0y}. Since there will be no force in the z direction, we have assumed, for simplicity, that v_{0z} is zero.

The force in the x direction at any time is given by [see Eq. (1-28)]

$$\mathscr{F}_x = Qv_y\mathscr{B} \tag{1-41}$$

The force in the y direction is the sum of the forces due to the electric and magnetic fields. Thus,

$$\mathscr{F}_y = Q(\mathscr{E} - v_x\mathscr{B}) \tag{1-42}$$

Now, applying Newton's second law of motion, we obtain

$$m\frac{dv_x}{dt} = Q\mathscr{B}v_y \tag{1-43a}$$

$$m\frac{dv_y}{dt} = Q(\mathscr{E} - v_x\mathscr{B}) \tag{1-43b}$$

Let us now make the substitution

$$\omega = \frac{\mathscr{B}Q}{m} \tag{1-44}$$

Note that this corresponds to the *angular* frequency of Eq. (1-36). Substituting into Eq. (1-43), we have

$$\frac{dv_x}{dt} = \omega v_y \tag{1-45a}$$

$$\frac{dv_y}{dt} = \frac{Q\mathscr{E}}{m} - \omega v_x \tag{1-45b}$$

Differentiate Eq. (1-45b) with respect to time and then substitute Eq. (1-45a) for dv_x/dt. (Note that $Q\mathscr{E}/m$ is a constant.) This yields

$$\frac{d^2 v_y}{dt^2} = -\omega^2 v_y \tag{1-46}$$

The solution to this differential equation is

$$v_y = A_1 \sin \omega t + A_2 \cos \omega t \tag{1-47}$$

where A_1 and A_2 are arbitrary constants. Let us evaluate them. At $t = 0$, $v_y = v_{0y}$. Thus,

$$A_2 = v_{0y} \tag{1-48}$$

To obtain A_1, differentiate Eq. (1-47) with respect to time and evaluate the derivative at $t = 0$. This yields

$$\left.\frac{dv_y}{dt}\right|_{t=0} = \omega A_1 \tag{1-49}$$

From Eq. (1-45b), we have

$$\left.\frac{dv_y}{dt}\right|_{t=0} = \frac{Q\mathscr{E}}{m} - \omega v_{0x} \tag{1-50}$$

Solving Eqs. (1-49) and (1-50) for A_1 and substituting it and Eq. (1-48) into Eq. (1-47), we obtain

$$v_y = \left(\frac{Q\mathscr{E}}{m\omega} - v_{0x}\right) \sin \omega t + v_{0y} \cos \omega t \tag{1-51}$$

To obtain v_x, differentiate Eq. (1-51) with respect to time and substitute it into Eq. (1-45b). Manipulation yields

$$v_x = \frac{Q\mathscr{E}}{m\omega} + \left(v_{0x} - \frac{Q\mathscr{E}}{m\omega}\right) \cos \omega t + v_{0y} \sin \omega t \tag{1-52}$$

To obtain the displacements x and y as functions of time, we integrate v_x and v_y, respectively. Doing this and substituting the initial conditions

$$x = y = 0 \qquad \text{at } t = 0$$

yields

$$y = \left(\frac{Q\mathscr{E}}{m\omega^2} - \frac{v_{0x}}{\omega}\right)(1 - \cos \omega t) + \frac{v_{0y}}{\omega} \sin \omega t \qquad (1\text{-}53a)$$

and

$$x = \frac{Q\mathscr{E}}{m\omega} t + \left(\frac{v_{0x}}{\omega} - \frac{Q\mathscr{E}}{m\omega^2}\right) \sin \omega t + \frac{v_{0y}}{\omega} (1 - \cos \omega t) \qquad (1\text{-}53b)$$

Equations (1-53) are the parametric equations for the path of the particle.

Before we discuss the general expression for the path, let us consider the special case where

$$v_{0x} = v_{0y} = 0$$

Equations (1-53) then become

$$y = \frac{QE}{m\omega^2} (1 - \cos \omega t) \qquad (1\text{-}54a)$$

$$x = \frac{QE}{m\omega^2} (\omega t - \sin \omega t) \qquad (1\text{-}54b)$$

These are the parametric equations of a cycloid, which is illustrated in Fig. 1-8. A cycloid is generated by a point on the circumference of a circle as it "rolls along" the x axis. The center of the rolling circle moves at the constant velocity $Q\mathscr{E}/m\omega$. The radius is $Q\mathscr{E}/m\omega^2$.

If the initial velocity of the particle is not zero, Eqs. (1-53) are used to obtain its path. In this case, the path will be either a prolate cycloid or a curate cycloid. These curves can also be considered to be generated by a rolling circle, but now the point which traces the curve does not lie on its circumference. These curves are illustrated in Fig. 1-9a and b. Note that the circle rolls on a line that is parallel to the x axis.

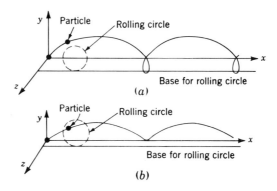

Fig. 1-9 (a) A prolate cycloid and (b) a curate cycloid.

Unaccelerated motion If v_{0x} and v_{0y} have certain values, the particle will be unaffected by the fields. Let us demonstrate this. Choose

$$v_{0y} = 0 \tag{1-55a}$$

and

$$v_{0x} = \frac{Q\mathscr{E}}{m\omega} = \frac{\mathscr{E}}{\mathscr{B}} \tag{1-55b}$$

Substituting into Eqs. (1-51) to (1-53b), we have

$$v_y = 0 \tag{1-56a}$$

$$v_x = \frac{QE}{m\omega} \tag{1-56b}$$

$$y = 0 \tag{1-57a}$$

$$x = \frac{QE}{m\omega} t \tag{1-57b}$$

Thus, the particle moves as though there were no fields present. Actually, in this case, the forces due to the electric and magnetic fields just cancel each other.

Arbitrary orientation of electrostatic and magnetostatic fields
If the electric and magnetic fields are neither parallel nor perpendicular to each other, the problem can be solved by a superposition of the two preceding cases. That is, the electric field can be resolved into two components, one parallel to the magnetic field and the other perpendicular to it. Since motion parallel to the magnetic field does not interact with it, we can consider this motion as though there were only an electric field and then consider another case with perpendicular electric and magnetic fields.

1-8 RELATIVISTIC EFFECTS

In the preceding sections, we assumed that the masses of the particles were constant. If the velocity is much less than the velocity of light, this is a valid approximation. However, it was shown by Lorentz and later by Einstein (in the special theory of relativity) that the mass of a particle is a function of its velocity, as viewed by an observer. The mass is given by

$$m = \frac{m_0}{\sqrt{1 - v^2/c^2}} \tag{1-58}$$

where m_0 = mass of particle at rest
v = observed magnitude of particle's velocity
c = invariant velocity of light = 2.998×10^8 meters/sec

As the velocity of the particle approaches that of light, its mass becomes infinite. Thus, the particle cannot be accelerated to speeds greater than that of light. Note that if $v = 0.1c$, then $m = 1.005m_0$. Thus, the mass has increased by only 0.5 percent. Usually, if v is equal to or less than $0.1c$, relativistic considerations can be ignored.

Let us now consider computations of velocity when we must use relativistic corrections. The special theory of relativity states that mass can be converted into energy and vice versa. The relation between mass and energy is

$$W = mc^2 \tag{1-59}$$

where W is the total energy of the particle. At rest, a particle will have an energy of

$$W_0 = m_0 c^2 \tag{1-60}$$

Thus, if a particle is accelerated from rest to a velocity v, its kinetic energy has increased by

$$W - W_0 = mc^2 - m_0 c^2 \tag{1-61}$$

If the particle is accelerated by an electric field, the gain in kinetic energy must equal the loss in potential energy QV, where V is the potential through which the charge Q has been accelerated. Equating kinetic and potential energies, we obtain

$$VQ = mc^2 - m_0 c^2 \tag{1-62}$$

Substituting m from Eq. (1-58) and solving for v, we obtain

$$v = c\sqrt{1 - \frac{1}{(1 + VQ/m_0 c^2)^2}} \tag{1-63}$$

In electronic devices, the particles in question are often electrons. Substitution of constants for the electron into Eq. (1-63) yields

$$v = c\sqrt{1 - \frac{1}{(1 + 1.957 \times 10^{-6} V)^2}} \tag{1-64}$$

A voltage of approximately 2500 volts will accelerate an electron to about $0.1c$. Thus, relativistic considerations must be applied when greater accelerating potentials are used. Accelerating potentials considerably greater than 2500 volts are often found in many electronic devices, including television receivers.

Let us demonstrate that, for small accelerative potentials, Eq. (1-63) reduces to Eq. (1-27a), which was calculated using newtonian mechanics. Let us call the velocity calculated this way v_N. From Eq. (1-27a), we have

$$v_N = \sqrt{\frac{2QV}{m_0}} \tag{1-65}$$

Substituting in Eq. (1-63) for VQ/m_0 and manipulating, we have

$$v = v_N \sqrt{\dfrac{1 + \dfrac{1}{4}\dfrac{v_N^2}{c^2}}{\left(1 + \dfrac{1}{2}\dfrac{v_N^2}{c^2}\right)^2}} \tag{1-66}$$

If $v_N \ll c$, the square root is essentially unity and v approximates v_N, as it should.

1-9 THE CATHODE-RAY TUBE—DEFLECTION

One type of vacuum tube extensively used in television receivers, radar receivers, and measuring equipment is the *cathode-ray tube*. It is used to portray visually voltages or currents which vary in accordance with some information. For instance, in a television receiver, the picture is established by the cathode-ray tube.

A sketch of a typical cathode-ray tube is shown in Fig. 1-10. The entire device is enclosed in an envelope which is evacuated so that there is a nearly perfect vacuum within it. The leftmost element is called an *electron gun*. Its purpose is to supply a narrow beam of electrons. It contains a *cathode*, which acts as a copious source of electrons, plus other electrodes which accelerate the electrons (see Sec. 1-3) and focus them into a narrow beam. In Secs. 1–10 and 1-20 we shall discuss cathodes and the focusing of electron beams. If there were no other electrodes in the cathode-ray tube, the electrons in the beam would leave the electron gun and travel in an unaccelerated path until they struck the front face of the tube. This is coated with a phosphorescent material which glows where the beam strikes it. In addition, the envelope of the cathode-ray tube is coated with a conductive material. This enables the electrons which strike the front face of the tube to return to the

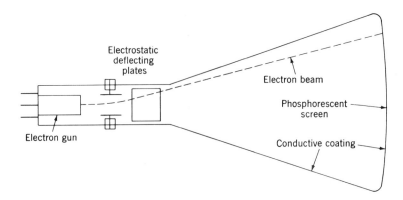

Fig. 1-10 A diagrammatic representation of a cathode-ray tube with electrostatic deflection.

cathode. If this were not done, the front face would acquire a large negative charge which would eventually repel the electron beam.

Let us now consider the electrostatic-deflecting plates. There are two sets of them. One, positioned horizontally, is called the *vertical-deflecting plates*, and the other positioned vertically, called the *horizontal-deflecting plates*. If a potential is impressed across either pair of these plates or both pairs, the beam will be deflected. Thus, if signal information in the form of a varying voltage is applied to a pair of plates, the electron beam will be deflected in accordance with the signal. Hence, the location of the glowing spot on the face of the screen can be controlled by a signal. Note that this deflection is called electrostatic. However, the signal voltage will, in general, vary with time. Thus, the fields will not be static. Nevertheless, for the usual type of operation, the signal voltages vary very slowly in comparison with the time it takes for an electron to pass through the region between the deflection plates. Thus, each individual electron essentially experiences a constant electric field there.

At times, a pair of coils is placed around the neck of the tube (in essentially the same position that the deflecting plates would be). Current in these coils sets up a magnetic field, which deflects the electron beam. Such deflection is called *magnetostatic deflection*. (The electrostatic-deflecting plates are omitted from tubes designed for magnetic deflection.) Magnetostatic deflection is used in almost all television receivers.

Electrodes within the electron gun can vary the intensity of the electron beam, which, in turn, varies the intensity of the spot on the face of the cathode-ray tube. Thus, the intensity, as well as the position, of the spot can be varied by a signal. This is of fundamental importance to the formulation of a television picture.

Let us now consider deflection systems in greater detail. In any electron beam we shall assume that the spacing between the electrons is large enough so that the force on any one electron due to the other electrons can be neglected. This is usually a valid assumption.

Electrostatic deflection To study electrostatic deflection we shall use the structure represented in Fig. 1-11 and the coordinate system shown there. The x axis is parallel to the deflection plates, and the origin is at the left end of them. Assume that the electrostatic field set up by the deflection plates is uniform and exists only in the region between the plates. The electrons are accelerated by a potential V_a in the electron gun. Thus, if we neglect relativistic effects, the velocity of the electrons as they leave the electron gun is [see Eq. (1-27a)]

$$v_x = \sqrt{\frac{2V_a e}{m}} \tag{1-67}$$

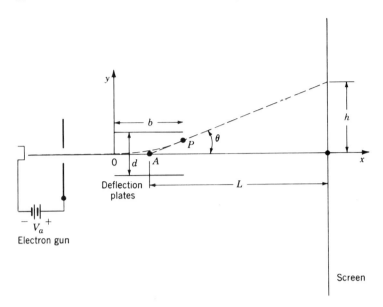

Fig. 1-11   A representation of an electrostatic deflection system.

When the electrons pass between the plates, they experience an acceleration in the y direction. If the potential difference between the upper plate and the lower plate is V_d volts, with the upper plate positive with respect to the lower one, then the electric field will be [see Eq. (1-5)]

$$\mathscr{E}_y = -\frac{V_d}{d} \tag{1-68}$$

The electron will experience an acceleration

$$a_y = -\frac{e\mathscr{E}_y}{m} = \frac{e}{m}\frac{V_d}{d} \tag{1-69}$$

Once the electrons leave the electron gun, their velocity in the x direction remains constant at v_x. Thus, the electrons will remain in the region between the plates for only T sec, where

$$T = \frac{b}{v_x} = b\sqrt{\frac{m}{2V_a e}} \tag{1-70}$$

Thus, as an electron leaves the region between the deflection plates, it will have a y component of velocity $a_y T$ and a y displacement $\frac{1}{2}a_y T^2$. Hence, at point P

$$v_{yP} = V_d\frac{b}{d}\sqrt{\frac{e}{2V_a m}} \tag{1-71}$$

$$y_P = \frac{b^2}{4d}\frac{V_d}{V_a} \tag{1-72}$$

We shall assume that the electric field is zero outside the region between the deflection plates. Thus, the electron travels in a straight line once it leaves the region between the deflection plates. The slope of the straight line is v_{yP}/v_x. Let us assume that the center of the deflection plates is L meters from the face of the tube. Then h, the total displacement of the electron, is

$$h = \left(L - \frac{b}{2}\right)\frac{v_{yP}}{v_x} + y_P$$

Substituting and manipulating, we obtain

$$h = L\frac{V_d}{V_a}\frac{b}{2d} \tag{1-73}$$

Often, the cathode-ray tube is operated so that all potentials except V_d are held constant. V_d is varied in accordance with some input signal. The deflection should be proportional to the input V_d. Equation (1-73) shows that this is so.

It is often desirable to obtain a large deflection when V_d is small. A figure of merit which is used to rate cathode-ray tubes is the *electrostatic-deflection sensitivity* S_e. It is defined as the amount of deflection produced by 1 volt of V_d. Thus,

$$S_e = \frac{Lb}{2V_a d} \tag{1-74}$$

It may appear as though any desired sensitivity could be obtained by manipulating the parameters. However, practical considerations limit S_e. For instance, as L is increased, the length of the cathode-ray tube increases. Thus, for practical reasons, some maximum limit is imposed upon L.

If the ratio b/d is reduced, the maximum value of h is limited. The electrons cannot be deflected more than $d/2$ in the region between the plates since they then would strike the plates and not reach the screen. To analyze this consider the angle θ shown in Fig. 1-11. Thus,

$$\tan \theta = \frac{v_{yP}}{v_x}$$

Now assume that an electron is released at point A between the plates with velocity v_{yP} and v_x but is unaffected subsequently; i.e., it travels in a straight line with slope v_{yP}/v_x. It will strike the screen at a displacement of Lv_{yP}/v_x. Substitution of Eqs. (1-67) and (1-71) yields, for the deflection, the same h as for the actual one. Thus, the electron can be considered to travel in a straight line from point A. (Since the actual straight-line path has the same slope as the fictitious one and they pass through the same point at the screen, the two straight lines must be the same.) Hence, a straight line drawn from point A to the screen at height h will have a slope tan θ. Thus, the maximum value of θ is limited by the relation

$$\tan \theta|_{\max} = \frac{d}{b} \qquad\qquad (1\text{-}75)$$

Hence, the maximum value of b/d is limited by the maximum deflection angle desired.

If V_a is reduced, S_e will increase. However, the intensity of the spot produced in the phosphorescent screen varies directly with V_a. Thus, it cannot be reduced too much.

Magnetostatic deflection Another type of deflection system uses magnetic rather than electric fields to deflect the electron beam. Such cathode-ray tubes are built without electrostatic-deflection plates. A pair of coils is placed external to the neck of the tube, and the current in them sets up the magnetic field. A diagrammatic representation of a magnetic-deflection system is shown in Fig. 1-12. To avoid cluttering the diagram, the coils are not shown there. Assume that the coils set up a magnetic field which exists only in the deflection region, is uniform there, and is perpendicular to the paper and points out of it.

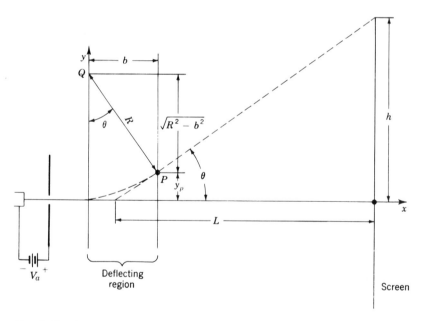

Fig. 1-12 A representation of a magnetostatic deflection system.

The electrons are accelerated by the electron gun, and as they enter the deflection region their velocity is [see Eq. (1-67)]

$$v_x = \sqrt{\frac{2V_a e}{m}} \qquad (1\text{-}76)$$

Thus [see Eq. (1-34)], in the deflection region, the electron will move in a circular arc of radius

$$R = \frac{mv_x}{\mathscr{B}e} = \frac{1}{\mathscr{B}} \sqrt{\frac{2V_a m}{e}} \qquad (1\text{-}77)$$

The electron leaves the deflecting region at point p at an angle θ with the horizontal. Thus, the deflection h is given by

$$h = y_P + \left(L - \frac{b}{2}\right) \tan \theta \qquad (1\text{-}78)$$

The line QP, which is the radius of the circular arc, makes a right angle with the straight-line path tangent to the circle. Thus, both angles marked θ are equal. Hence,

$$\tan \theta = \frac{b}{\sqrt{R^2 - b^2}} \qquad (1\text{-}79)$$

In addition,

$$y_P = R - \sqrt{R^2 - b^2}$$

Thus, the deflection becomes

$$h = R - \sqrt{R^2 - b^2} + \left(L - \frac{b}{2}\right) \frac{b}{\sqrt{R^2 - b^2}} \qquad (1\text{-}80)$$

Let us determine if h varies linearly with the magnetic field $\mathscr{B}$. Comparison of Eqs. (1-77) and (1-80) shows that this is not, in general, true. However, in some specific instances, it will be approximately true. Often, the radius of curvature R is very much larger than b,

$$R \gg b \qquad (1\text{-}81)$$

In this case, we often have

$$R - \sqrt{R^2 - b^2} \ll \left(L - \frac{b}{2}\right) \frac{b}{\sqrt{R^2 - b^2}} \qquad (1\text{-}82)$$

Thus, we can write

$$h \approx \left(L - \frac{b}{2}\right) \frac{b}{\sqrt{R^2 - b^2}} \qquad (1\text{-}83)$$

In addition, if relation (1-81) is true,

$$\sqrt{R^2 - b^2} \approx R$$

Hence, under these conditions

$$h \approx \frac{(L - b/2)b}{R} \tag{1-84}$$

Substituting Eq. (1-77), we have

$$h \approx \left(L - \frac{b}{2}\right)b\sqrt{\frac{e}{m}\frac{1}{2V_a}}\mathscr{B} \tag{1-85}$$

Thus, the deflection will essentially vary linearly with $\mathscr{B}$. Since $\mathscr{B}$ is proportional to the current through the coils, the deflection will be essentially proportional to the signal current.

The *magnetic-deflection sensitivity* is defined as

$$S_m = \frac{h}{\mathscr{B}} \tag{1-86}$$

Thus,

$$S_m = \left(L - \frac{b}{2}\right)b\sqrt{\frac{e}{m}}\sqrt{\frac{1}{2V_a}} \tag{1-87}$$

Note that this varies as $1/\sqrt{V_a}$, while the electrostatic-deflection sensitivity varies as $1/V_a$. In television receivers large accelerating potentials are used to obtain bright pictures. Magnetic-deflection systems are usually used there since the large values of V_a do not reduce the deflection sensitivity too much. Another reason for using magnetic-deflection systems in television receivers is that they can produce greater deflection angles than electrostatic ones. Thus shorter cathode-ray tubes can be used. However, in these cases, relation (1-81) will no longer be valid. To obtain the desired deflection, special circuits are used which cause the deflecting current to be appropriately different from the desired signal so that the deflection has the shape of the desired waveform.

The vacuum in a cathode-ray tube is high, but it is not perfect. There are always molecules of gas present. Some of them will collide with electrons and acquire a negative charge; i.e., they become negative ions. They can be accelerated by the electron gun. The magnetic-deflection sensitivity depends on the ratio of charge to mass [see Eq. (1-87)]. Hence, these ions, whose mass is many thousands of times greater that that of the electrons, will hardly be deflected. Thus, the center of the screen will constantly be bombarded by ions. In a relatively short time this bombardment will destroy the phosphor in the center of the screen.   To prevent this, the entire electron gun is tilted from the axis of the tube so that an undeflected particle will not strike the screen but will strike the side of the tube.   A permanent magnet placed on the neck of the tube sets up a constant field which causes the electron beam to return to its proper position.   However, the heavier ions are essentially undeflected by this magnetic field.   Thus, they do not strike the screen.   The tilted electron gun and permanent magnet are called an *ion trap*.

1-10 FOCUSING OF ELECTRON BEAMS

The function of the electron gun in a cathode-ray tube is to supply a continuous source of electrons in a very narrow beam.   In actual practice, if electrons are just passed through a hole in a plate of the electron gun, as diagrammatically indicated in Fig. 1-11, the electron beam will not remain narrow but will diverge.   The electron beam must impinge upon the face of the cathode-ray tube in a small spot.   Thus, some form of focusing must be used.   Other devices, such as electron microscopes, also require focused electron beams.   We shall discuss two focusing procedures here.

Magnetic focusing   Consider an electron gun of the type shown in Fig. 1-13.   The electrons are emitted by the cathode and are accelerated toward the right electrode.   The only electrons leaving the electron gun are those which pass through the *small* hole in the front electrode.   At this point the electron beam is very narrow.   However, the electrons have small components of velocity perpendicular to the x direction, which vary randomly from electron to electron.   Thus, the beam diverges as it leaves the electron gun. By the time the electrons reach the screen, the narrow beam will have diverged into a broad one.

We shall now demonstrate that the addition of a magnetic field $\mathscr{B}$, which lies in the x direction and has the correct magnitude, can cause the

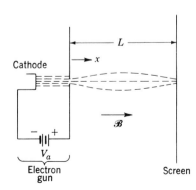

Fig. 1-13 Magnetic focusing of an electron beam.

electron beam to converge so that it strikes the screen in a spot no larger than the hole at the end of the electron gun.

All the electrons will have essentially the same x component of velocity given by [see Eq. (1-67)]

$$v_x = \sqrt{\frac{2eV_a}{m}} \tag{1-88}$$

However, they have varying components of velocity perpendicular to the x direction v_{0P}. The force set up by this perpendicular component of velocity and the magnetic field $\mathscr{B}_x$ causes the electrons to move in a helix. That is, they move with constant velocity v_x in the x direction and their projection on the yz plane is a circle. The time required for an electron to make one complete circular revolution is [see Eq. (1-35)]

$$T = \frac{2\pi m}{\mathscr{B}_x e} \tag{1-89}$$

Note that this is independent of v_{0P}. Thus, in time T or in any integral multiple of it, the projection of the electrons on the yz plane will fall on the hole in the electron gun. Thus, after the electron beam has traveled for KT sec, where K is an integer, it will again be only as wide as the hole in the electron gun. If the time KT corresponds to the time it takes an electron to travel from the electron gun to the screen, the electron beam will be focused. Thus, if

$$\frac{2\pi m K}{\mathscr{B}_x e} = \frac{L}{v_x} \quad K = 1, 2, 3, \ldots \tag{1-90}$$

the electron beam will be focused. Hence, if the electron beam is to be focused, a magnetic flux

$$\mathscr{B}_x = \frac{2\pi m v_x K}{eL} \quad K = 1, 2, 3, \ldots \tag{1-91}$$

must be used. Usually $K = 1$ is used since this results in the smallest magnetic field.

Note that this magnetic focusing procedure can be used to establish the value of e/m. That is, a cathode-ray tube is set up whose dimensions, accelerating potential, and $\mathscr{B}_x$ are known very accurately. The device is focused using the smallest value of $\mathscr{B}_x$. Equation (1-91) can then be solved for e/m.

We have assumed that the magnetic focusing field exists throughout the entire space. In practical cases involving cathode-ray tubes, the magnetic field is set up only over a small region in the neck of the tube. However, the effect is similar to the one we have discussed. The electrons move over a circular arc while they are in the field. By adjusting the field properly, the

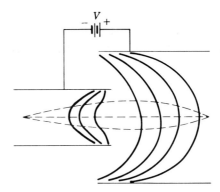

Fig. 1-14 A simple electrostatic lens
and accelerating system.

electrons can be made to leave the magnetic field region in such a way that
they impinge upon the screen in a small spot.

Electrostatic focusing In electrostatic focusing, electrodes at different
potentials are positioned so that the fields set up by them cause a diverging
electron beam to be focused. The analysis is far more complex than that for
simple magnetic focusing and will not be performed here. A simple electrostatic focusing system is shown in Fig. 1-14. The electron beam passes
through two coaxial right-circular cylinders of different radii. They are
maintained at a difference of potential V. In Fig. 1-14 equipotential lines
are drawn for this system. The electric field is normal to these lines (see
Sec. 1-2). Thus, this device acts analogously to an optical lens.

Note that the potentials are such that the configuration of Fig. 1-14
will accelerate the electron beam as well as focus it.

1-11 BASIC ATOMIC STRUCTURE—THE BOHR ATOM

Newtonian mechanics can often be used to explain the behavior of particles
moving in free space. However, we have seen that at high velocities this
theory must be modified and relativistic effects must be considered. When
basic atomic studies are made, it is found that these theories must be modified
still further to obtain proper results. These modified theories must also be
used when the motion of charges in conductors and semiconductors is
studied.

Let us start our discussion of the atom on a classical basis. We shall
then see that modifications must be made. The structure of the atom
proposed by Rutherford consists of protons and neutrons in a nucleus with
electrons traveling in orbits about it. The mass of the nucleus is very much
greater than that of an electron, so that the motion of the nucleus is often
negligible in comparison to that of the electrons. The electrons have a negative

charge, while the nucleus has a positive one.   Thus, there is an attraction between the electrons and the nucleus.   This should make the electrons "fall into" the nucleus.   However, the force due to the electrons' rotation balances the force of attraction, and a stable situation is apparently set up. The energy of the electron and its radial distance from the nucleus depend upon its velocity.   The electron's energy is called the *state of the electron.* The set of the states of all the electrons is called the *state of the atom.*

This type of rotary motion appears to be completely analogous to planets rotating about the sun, with the force of gravity replacing the electrostatic force.   However, one important difference causes the classical description to become invalid for the atom.   When an electron is accelerated, it radiates energy in the form of electromagnetic waves.   According to classical theory, electrons rotating in a circular orbit with a frequency f would radiate energy of the same frequency.   (An electron rotating in an orbit must have angular acceleration, since it does not travel in a straight line.)   Thus, the rotating electrons of the atom should result in the radiation of energy.   If this is so, the electrons must lose kinetic energy, otherwise the law of conservation of energy would be violated.   This loss in kinetic energy would result in the electrons' slowing down.   Thus, all the electrons should eventually fall into the nucleus.   However, this does not occur. Therefore, the classical theory must be modified.

Other phenomena remain unexplained by classical theory.   When atoms are excited, as they are in a mercury-vapor lamp, they *do* radiate energy, but only at certain fixed discrete frequencies.   These frequencies vary from material to material.   However, all atoms of the same type radiate the same set of discrete frequencies.   For instance, a mercury-vapor lamp produces only certain lines on a spectrograph.   According to classical theory, the radiation from the atom is at the frequency of rotation of the electrons.   Since, according to classical theory, they can rotate at any frequency, all atoms could radiate at all frequencies.   Thus, again, the classical theory does not yield results compatible with observation.

Bohr postulated fundamental laws which modified the classical description of a single isolated atom and eliminated the aforementioned differences between observed results and theory.   These laws are as follows:

1. The electrons in the atom *cannot* exist at all energy states but only at certain discrete ones, called *allowable states* or *allowable energy levels.* An atom possesses a set of these states, and the electrons of the atom can have only energies corresponding to this set.   (Atoms of different types of materials have different allowable states.)   When the energy of the electron corresponds to one of the allowed states, it does *not* radiate energy.   This is called a *stationary* or *nonradiating state.*   In such a state, the electron's orbit is stable, and the electron does not

slow down and fall into the nucleus. Thus, one of the objections to the classical theory is removed.

Allowable energy levels differ from material to material, but *all* allowable energy levels are characterized by the following: The angular momentum of the electron must be an integral multiple of $h/2\pi$, where h is *Planck's constant*, or 6.62×10^{-34} joule/sec. Note that this is an extremely small number. The energy levels are said to be *quantized* since only discrete levels can exist. The angular momentum of a particle rotating in a circular orbit of radius r with velocity v is mvr. Thus,

$$mvr = \frac{nh}{2\pi} \qquad n = 1, 2, 3, \ldots \tag{1-92}$$

In general, for any particular type of atom, not all integral values of n are possible. That is, only some of the $nh/2\pi$ levels are allowed.

2. An electron can change its state. That is, it can fall from one *allowable* state to another. In addition, it can be excited (by application of external energy) and can rise from one *allowable* state to another. When an electron changes to a lower state and loses energy, it radiates (electromagnetic) energy. The frequency of this energy is given by

$$f = \frac{W_2 - W_1}{h} \tag{1-93}$$

where W_2 = original energy, joules
$\qquad W_1$ = new energy, joules
$\qquad h$ = Planck's constant

Thus, an atom can radiate only discrete frequencies which correspond to its allowed energy levels. Thus, another observed result which could not be explained by classical theory is explained by the Bohr atom.

Equation (1-93) is often expressed in terms of the wavelength of the energy rather than the frequency. Using the relation

$$c = f\lambda \tag{1-94}$$

where λ is the wavelength of the radiation and c is the velocity of light, and Eq. (1-93), we obtain

$$\lambda = \frac{ch}{W_1 - W_2} \tag{1-95}$$

Substitution of the constants yields

$$\lambda = \frac{12,400}{W_1 - W_2} \tag{1-96}$$

where λ is now expressed in angstrom units ($1 \text{ Å} = 10^{-10}$ meter).

The Bohr model of the atom enables many calculations concerning the atom to be verified by experiment. However, as we shall subsequently discuss, there are times when further modifications must be made to explain observed results.

1-12 ALLOWABLE ENERGY STATES IN THE SINGLE ATOM—EXCITATION AND IONIZATION

Each atom has only certain allowable energy levels for its electrons, which are often indicated by an *energy-level diagram*. For instance such a diagram is shown in Fig. 1-15 for the mercury atom. The various allowed energy levels can be determined by spectroscopic studies of the frequencies of the emitted radiation. That is, the atom is excited, and then the frequency of the resultant radiation is observed. After many such measurements are made, the differences between allowed energy levels can be obtained by applying Eq. (1-93) or (1-96). Electrons of the atom can be raised to a higher allowable energy level by the application of external energy. Let us consider some procedures whereby this can be done.

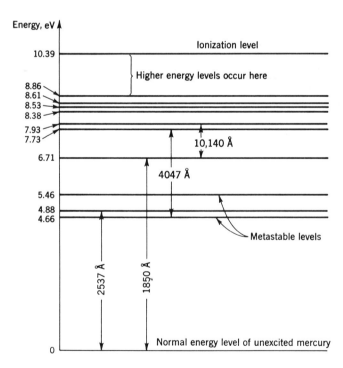

Fig. 1-15 Allowable energy levels of the mercury atom, showing some of the possible radiated wavelengths.

Excitation by electron collision If an external electron is accelerated toward an atom, it may impart some of its energy to the atom. Such an interaction is termed a *collision* of the electron with the atom. Two types of collision result, *elastic* and *inelastic*. In an elastic collision, a slowly moving electron interacts with an atom. If the kinetic energy of the impinging electron is not sufficient to raise any of the electrons of the atom into a higher allowable energy level, the impinging electron *cannot* impart *any* of its energy to the atom. In this case, the interaction behaves as though two ideal elastic particles had collided. Since the atom's mass is very much greater than that of the electron, the atom hardly moves at all while the direction of the electron is changed but the magnitude of its velocity remains essentially constant.

Now let us assume that the impinging electron has sufficient kinetic energy to raise the electrons of the atom into a higher state; i.e., it has sufficient kinetic energy to increase the energy of one of the atom's electrons to a higher allowance energy level. In this case, the atom can absorb energy from the incident electron. Thus, after the collision, not only will the impinging electron be deflected, but the magnitude of its velocity will also be reduced. It is important to note that the kinetic energy of the impinging electron must at least be equal to the minimum difference between allowable levels if the inelastic type of collision is to take place.

Excitation by photon collision When an electron in one allowable state falls back into a lower one, electromagnetic energy is radiated. The frequency of the radiation is given by Eq. (1-93). Usually, this frequency corresponds to visible, infrared, or ultraviolet light. Actually, this radiation does not consist of waves of light continuously emitted in all directions but of a "packet" of light energy, called a *photon*. Light has a dual wave-particle behavior. The energy in a single photon of frequency f is hf [see Eq. (1-93)]. In ordinary luminescent devices, such as mercury-vapor lamps, light appears to be emitted continuously, because there is an extremely large number of atoms, all emitting photons. Thus, even though each individual atom is emitting discrete photons, the sum of all the emitted photons appears to be a continuous source of light.

If a photon impinges on an atom, e.g., a beam of light shines on it, the atom may absorb energy from the photon and one or more of its electrons may be raised into a higher allowable energy state. This is similar to excitation by electron collision, but there is one important difference. If an electron has more than enough energy to excite an atom, excitation *can* take place and the exciting electron is left with the excess energy in the form of kinetic energy. However, the photon is the smallest unit of electromagnetic energy that can exist at its particular frequency. It must be *totally* absorbed. Thus, if the energy of the photon hf does not *exactly* correspond to the difference between two allowed energy levels, it will *not* be absorbed by the atom. This effect is verified by passing monochromatic light of various frequencies through gases. The light will be absorbed only at those frequencies which correspond to differences between allowable energy states.

An atom usually has many allowable energy levels. Emission or absorption of photons can take place at a frequency corresponding to a difference between any of these levels. It is possible for a photon to excite an electron so that it rises several levels. For instance, in Fig. 1-15, a photon might impart 7.73 eV to an electron of the atom. This electron will remain in the excited state for only a very short time. The average *lifetime* of such an excited state ranges between 10^{-7} and 10^{-10} sec. The electron then drops down to a lower state and radiates electromagnetic energy. For the example we have just considered, the electron could lose 7.73 eV. In this case, the electron radiates a photon whose frequency is the same as that of the photon that excited it. On the other hand, the excited electron could lose just enough energy to fall to another allowable state, e.g., to the 6.71-eV level. In this case, it would emit a photon of frequency which corresponds to $7.73 - 6.71 = 1.02$ eV. At a later time the 6.71-eV electron could fall to the normal state and emit another photon. This last discussion also applies to an atom excited by collision with an electron. That is, the excited electron may fall back to the unexcited state in one step, or it may take several steps.

Metastable states In some atoms, some *particular* allowable energy levels behave differently from those we have discussed. These levels have the following properties. An electron *cannot* be raised to these levels by means of the absorption of a photon. It can be raised by absorbing the kinetic energy of an impinging electron. In addition, the electron cannot fall from this state by the emission of a photon. This *special* energy level is called a *metastable level* or *metastable state*. In the diagram of Fig. 1-15, the 4.66- and 5.46-eV levels are metastable states.

Although it may appear as though an electron could not leave a metastable state since it cannot emit a photon to do so, there are several ways it can leave the level. An electron in the metastable state can absorb energy from an impinging electron which raises it to a higher allowable state. If this is not a metastable state, the electron can then lose energy by the emission of a photon. If the entire atom collides with another atom, it can impart energy to it. Some of this energy can come from the electron in the metastable state which then can fall to a lower allowed state. If the atoms are in a vapor lamp, such as a mercury-vapor lamp, some of them can diffuse to the walls of the lamp and collide with them. This often results in the walls being heated. Some of this energy can come from metastable electrons, which then fall to a lower state.

The average life of a metastable-state electron is much longer than that of an ordinary excited electron. It varies from 10^{-4} to 10^{-2} sec.

Ionization If sufficient energy is imparted to an electron, it may be able to break away from the nucleus and leave the atom. In this case, it becomes a *free electron* and the remaining atom is said to be *ionized*. For instance, in the mercury atom of Fig. 1-15, if an electron is in the highest unexcited state and 10.39 eV or more energy is imparted to it, it will become a free electron. The 10.39-eV level in mercury is termed its *ionization level*. Note that once an electron becomes a free electron, it can possess *any* kinetic energy. Thus, any energy which can raise the electron's energy to or over the ionization level can cause ionization.

Atoms can be ionized in steps. For instance, consider the mercury atom of Fig. 1-15. A photon of energy 6.71 eV can excite the atom, and then any source of excitation which supplies $10.39 - 6.71 = 3.68$ eV can ionize the atom.

1-13 PROBABILITY DISTRIBUTIONS

Modern physical descriptions of the behavior of solids do not involve quantitative expressions for the behavior of the individual particles. For instance, the location of the individual electrons in their orbits cannot be exactly specified. However, the *probability* that an electron is in a certain position can be specified. The microscopic behavior of matter is always expressed in terms of such probabilities. Let us now consider the expression of probability on a purely mathematical basis. In subsequent sections, we shall use probabilities to discuss physical principles.

In order to express probabilities, a function called a *probability distribution* is used. Let us define it with an example. Suppose we express the x-axis coordinates of a particle on the basis of the probability distribution $\rho(x)$. Then the probability that the particle lies between two points x_0 and x_1, where $x_0 < x_1$, is given by

$$P_{x_0, x_1} = \int_{x_0}^{x_1} \rho(x)\, dx \tag{1-97}$$

That is, the probability that the particle lies in the region between two points is given by the area under the probability-distribution curve between the two points. Since the particle must always have some x coordinate, the probability that the particle lies at some point on the x axis is 1. Thus, $\rho(x)$ must be such that

$$\int_{-\infty}^{\infty} \rho(x)\, dx = 1 \tag{1-98}$$

Let us consider an example.   Suppose

$$\rho(x) = \begin{cases} \epsilon^{-x} & x \geq 0 \\ 0 & x < 0 \end{cases} \tag{1-99}$$

Then the probability distribution has the form shown in Fig. 1-16.   Note that

$$\int_{-\infty}^{\infty} \rho(x)\, dx = \int_{0}^{\infty} \epsilon^{-x}\, dx = 1$$

The probability distribution is zero for $x < 0$.   Thus, there is zero probability of finding the particle on the negative axis.

Let us determine the probability of finding the particle in the range $0 < x < 1$

$$P_{0,1} = \int_{0}^{1} \epsilon^{-x}\, dx = 1 - \epsilon^{-1} = 0.632$$

Thus, the probability is 0.632 that the particle will be in the interval $0 \leq x \leq 1$.   Now let us consider the range $0 < x < 10$

$$P_{0,10} = \int_{0}^{10} \epsilon^{-x}\, dx = 1 - \epsilon^{-10} = 0.99996$$

Thus, we are virtually certain of finding the particle between $x = 0$ and $x = 10$.

The variable need not be position.   For instance, in the previous example, x might represent energy.   Then, $P_{a,b}$ would represent the probability that the particle has an energy which lies between a and b.   *Energy probability-distribution functions* are of fundamental importance in the study of the physics of particles.

The probability distribution can be a function of more than one variable. For instance, suppose we wish to express the location of a particle in (three-dimensional) space on the basis of a probability distribution.   In this case, $P_{x_1,x_2;y_1,y_2;z_1,z_2}$ gives the probability that it lies in the region

$$x_1 \leq x \leq x_2$$
$$y_1 \leq y \leq y_2$$
$$z_1 \leq z \leq z_2$$

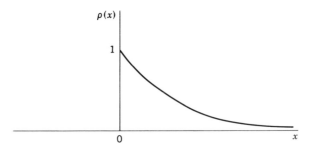

Fig. 1-16   A probability-distribution function.

This is then given by the volume integral

$$P_{x_1,x_2;y_1,y_2;z_1,z_2} = \int_{x_1}^{x_2} \int_{y_1}^{y_2} \int_{z_1}^{z_2} \rho(x,y,z)\, dx\, dy\, dz \qquad (1\text{-}100)$$

Again, the probability distribution must be such that

$$\iiint\limits_{-\infty}^{\infty} \rho(x,y,z)\, dx\, dy\, dz = 1 \qquad (1\text{-}101)$$

Note that now the probability-distribution function is a function of three variables.

1-14 THE SCHRÖDINGER EQUATION—WAVE MECHANICS AND QUANTUM MECHANICS—PAULI EXCLUSION PRINCIPLE AND HEISENBERG UNCERTAINTY PRINCIPLE

We have considered the Bohr atom. When we have discussed atomic structure still further, we shall be in a position to study conduction processes in solids and solid-state devices. Electrons at times behave as particles, but at other times they act as waves. For instance, an electron beam will be diffracted in the same way as light is if the proper diffraction grating is used. Light also has the dual wave-particle character.

The dual wave-particle nature of light and electrons was generalized by de Broglie, who proposed that all matter, not only electrons and light, exhibits a dual wave-particle behavior. The wavelength λ of an object of mass m traveling with velocity v was postulated to be

$$\lambda = \frac{h}{mv} = \frac{h}{p} \qquad (1\text{-}102)$$

where $p = mv$ is the momentum of the particle. This wavelength is called the *de Broglie wavelength*.

It may appear strange to think of a large solid object as having wave properties. However, this is a matter of experience. Until diffraction experiments were performed with electrons, it was just as strange to think of them as having wave properties. The de Broglie wavelength has been verified for electrons by many different experiments.

We can use the de Broglie wavelength to obtain some physical feel for the allowed energy levels (nonradiating states) of the electrons in an atom. These levels are characterized by Eq. (1-92). Manipulating this equation, we have the circumference of the orbit given by

$$2\pi r = \frac{nh}{mv} \qquad n = 1, 2, 3, \ldots$$

Substituting Eq. (1-102), we obtain

$$2\pi r = n\lambda \qquad n = 1, 2, 3, \ldots \qquad (1\text{-}103)$$

Thus, for an allowed state, the circumference of the orbit is equal to an integral multiple of de Broglie's wavelength.

A physical interpretation of the dual wave-particle behavior can be explained by discussing the following experiment. Consider that a beam of electrons is passed through a slit and then impinges upon a fluorescent screen. A diffraction pattern will appear on the screen. If the experiment is repeated, the same diffraction pattern will appear. Now let us repeat the experiment but pass only a *single* electron through the slit. Now, no diffraction pattern appears on the screen. Instead, the electron strikes the screen in a small spot. Thus it acts as a particle. Now, repeat this experiment. The single electron will again strike the screen in a single spot, but it will (probably) be a different spot from the first one. If this single-electron experiment is repeated a great many times, the electrons will strike the screen at single points which lie at all points in the original diffraction pattern. Thus, it will not be possible to predict where any single electron will strike the screen. However, one fact can be ascertained by repeating the single-electron experiment a great many times. The probability that an electron will strike the screen at any given point is directly proportional to the intensity of the diffraction pattern there. That is, the probability of an electron's striking the screen at a point will be high if the diffraction pattern is intense there. Thus, we can determine the location of any one electron only on a probability basis. (Note that the individual electrons appear as particles but their overall behavior is on a wave basis.)

When we work with solids which have extremely large numbers of atoms (and electrons), again we determine only the average behavior of the particles. Thus, the location of a particle is not expressed exactly but in terms of a probability distribution. In this way, the probability of determining the location of a particle within any range is specified (see Sec. 1-13). The fundamental equation used to determine these probability distributions was proposed by Schrödinger. Since all matter possesses a wavelike behavior, he postulated that the equation which characterized the probability distribution would have a wavelike solution. After considerable study, he hypothesized an equation, one form of which is

$$-\frac{h^2}{8\pi^2 m}\left(\frac{\partial^2 \Psi}{\partial x^2} + \frac{\partial^2 \Psi}{\partial y^2} + \frac{\partial^2 \Psi}{\partial z^2}\right) + V\Psi = W\Psi = +\frac{jh}{2\pi}\frac{\partial \Psi}{\partial t} \qquad (1\text{-}104)$$

where m is the particle's mass and $\Psi = \Psi(x,y,z,t)$ is a function of dimensions and of time which will be related to the desired probability distribution. $V = V(x,y,z)$ is the potential energy (in joules) for a particle in the system under consideration, and W is the total energy of the particle, i.e., the sum of the potential and kinetic energies. In general, this sum of potential and kinetic energies is a constant

$$\tfrac{1}{2}mv^2 + V(x,y,z) = W \tag{1-105}$$

In any energy system, the potential energy of a particle can be written as a function of position $V(x,y,z)$. In general, such potential distributions are used only to relate differences of potential between two points. Thus, a constant can always be added to V without causing it to become invalid. In this case, choose the constant so that at a point (x_1,y_1,z_1), where the kinetic energy of the particle is zero,

$$V(x_1,y_1,z_1) = W \tag{1-106}$$

One may ask how an equation which is fundamental to all physical behavior can be postulated. They may be lucky guesses, usually they are made after long studies. However, if the results predicted by them agree with all experimental measurements, the postulate is substantiated. Solutions to the Schrödinger equation have been shown to agree with actual experiments.

Equation (1-104) can be solved by assuming that $\Psi(x,y,z,t)$ is the product of two functions, one depending only upon position and the other depending only upon time

$$\Psi(x,y,z,t) = \psi(x,y,z)\phi(t) \tag{1-107}$$

If techniques for the solution of partial differential equations, which we shall not consider here, are now applied to Eq. (1-104), the solution for $\phi(t)$ becomes

$$\phi(t) = A\epsilon^{-j2\pi Wt/h} \tag{1-108}$$

where A is a constant. Thus, the time variation of $\phi(t)$ is similar to that of a phasor in sinusoidal steady-state electric-circuit theory.

The equation which characterizes $\psi(x,y,z)$ can be found by using techniques for solving partial differential equations. If these techniques are applied, the following equation results

$$\frac{h^2}{8\pi^2 m}\left(\frac{\partial^2\psi}{\partial x^2} + \frac{\partial^2\psi}{\partial y^2} + \frac{\partial^2\psi}{\partial z^2}\right) + (W - V)\psi = 0 \tag{1-109a}$$

This equation is often written in abbreviated form as

$$\frac{h^2}{8\pi^2 m}\nabla^2\psi + (W - V)\psi = 0 \tag{1-109b}$$

where ∇^2 is a differential operator, called the *Laplacian operator*, which is given by

$$\nabla^2 = \frac{\partial^2}{\partial x^2} + \frac{\partial^2}{\partial y^2} + \frac{\partial^2}{\partial z^2} \tag{1-110}$$

The quantity $\psi(x,y,z)$ is called the *wave function*. We shall relate it to a probability distribution of the position of the particle.

In general, V is a function of position. For example, a single electron traveling about a single positive charge, as it does in the hydrogen atom, will have a potential function V which varies as $1/r$, where r is the radial distance from the nucleus. The solution to Eq. (1-110) will contain an infinite number of solutions corresponding to an infinite set of values of W. That is, there will be a different solution for each total energy. However, physical conditions will enable us to specify ψ at some points in space. That is, *boundary conditions* will be specified because of the physical problem. In general, all of the infinite number of solutions of Eq. (1-109) will not satisfy the boundary conditions. We shall show that only certain values of W will yield solutions which satisfy the boundary conditions. Thus, only these W are allowed energy levels for the particle in question.

The ψ in Eq. (1-110) is not the actual probability distribution for the position of the particle. In fact, at times, ψ is not a real number but a complex one. If ψ is multiplied by its conjugate ψ^*, a real number will result. This product $\psi\psi^*$ is the probability distribution of the position of the particle.

To illustrate the use of Schrödinger's equation, let us consider a very simple example. To simplify our analysis, assume that we are dealing with a one-dimensional problem. Assume that an electron is constrained to lie along a line of length L, as shown in Fig. 1-17, and assume that the potential distribution is $V = 0$ there. (Consider that V is very large just outside of this region between 0 and L. This potential is what constrains the electron between 0 and L.) If we consider motion in only one dimension and $V = 0$, then in the range $0 \leq x \leq L$ Eq. (1-109) becomes

$$\frac{d^2\psi}{dx^2} + \frac{8\pi^2 m W}{h^2}\psi = 0 \tag{1-111}$$

Solving this differential equation, we obtain

$$\psi(x) = A_1 \cos x \sqrt{\frac{8\pi^2 m W}{h^2}} + A_2 \sin x \sqrt{\frac{8\pi^2 m W}{h^2}} \tag{1-112}$$

where A_1 and A_2 are arbitrary constants. The boundary conditions we use are

$$\psi(0) = 0 \tag{1-113a}$$

$$\psi(L) = 0 \tag{1-113b}$$

Fig. 1-17 Constraints on the location of an electron.

That is, we assume that there is no probability of finding an electron at either extremity.   From Eq. (1-113a), we have, at $x = 0$,

$$A_1 = \psi(0) = 0$$

Thus,

$$\psi(x) = A_2 \sin x \sqrt{\frac{8\pi^2 mW}{h^2}} \tag{1-114}$$

In order to satisfy Eq. (1-113b) without setting $A_2 = 0$, which is not allowable since then $\psi(x) = 0$ everywhere, we require that

$$L \sqrt{\frac{8\pi^2 mW}{h^2}} = n_x \pi \qquad n_x = 0, \pm 1, \pm 2, \ldots \tag{1-115}$$

Thus, the sinusoid will be zero at $x = L$.   The only term on the left-hand side of Eq. (1-115) that can be varied is W.   It can take on only those values which satisfy the left side of Eq. (1-115).   Let us call them W_n, corresponding to each value of n.   Thus, these allowable values of W_n, which are the allowable energy levels for the problem we are considering, are

$$W_n = \frac{h^2}{8mL^2} n_x^2 \qquad n_x = 0, \pm 1, \pm 2, \ldots \tag{1-116}$$

Thus, the allowable energy levels for this problem vary as the square of integers.

The n_x are called the *quantum numbers* for this problem.

Substituting Eq. (1-116) into Eq. (1-114) yields

$$\psi(x) = A_2 \sin \frac{n_x \pi x}{L} \tag{1-117}$$

Since this is real, $\psi^*(x) = \psi(x)$.   The probability distribution for the position of the electron is

$$\psi(x)\psi^*(x) = A_2^2 \sin^2 \frac{n_x \pi x}{L} \tag{1-118}$$

The electron must lie somewhere along the line $0 < x < 1$.   Thus,

$$\int_0^L \psi(x)\psi^*(x)\, dx = 1 \tag{1-119}$$

Hence,

$$\int_0^L A_2^2 \sin^2 \frac{n_x \pi x}{L}\, dx = \frac{LA_2^2}{2} = 1$$

Thus,

$$A_2 = \sqrt{\frac{2}{L}}$$

or $\psi(x) = \sqrt{\frac{2}{L}} \sin \frac{n_x \pi x}{L}$ (1-120)

Let us extend the problem we have just considered to a three-dimensional one. In other words, we assume that the electron is constrained to be in a three-dimensional cube, that is, $0 \le x \le L$, $0 \le y \le L$, $0 \le z \le L$. Without considering the details of the solution of the partial differential equation or the substitution of the boundary conditions but just stating the solution, we obtain

$$\psi(x,y,z) = A \sin n_x \frac{\pi x}{L} \sin n_y \frac{\pi y}{L} \sin n_z \frac{\pi z}{L} \qquad \begin{matrix} n_x = 0, \pm 1, \pm 2, \ldots \\ n_y = 0, \pm 1, \pm 2, \ldots \\ n_z = 0, \pm 1, \pm 2, \ldots \end{matrix}$$

(1-121)

Note that this satisfies the specified boundary conditions. To determine the constant A, we evaluate

$$\int\!\!\!\int\!\!\!\int_0^L \psi^2 \, dx \, dy \, dz = 1$$ (1-122)

since the particle must exist at some point in the cube. Doing this yields

$$A = \sqrt{\frac{8}{L^3}}$$ (1-123)

In general, for any problem, a particle must exist at some point in space. Thus, the constant multiplier of ψ must always be adjusted so that

$$\int\!\!\!\int\!\!\!\int_{-\infty}^{\infty} \psi\psi^* \, dx \, dy \, dz = 1$$ (1-124)

Note that in our example, $\psi = 0$ outside of the cube. Thus, the limits of integration of Eq. (1-122) differ from those of Eq. (1-124). The complete solution for ψ in terms of the energy is

$$\psi = A \sin x \sqrt{\frac{8\pi^2 m W_x}{h^2}} \sin y \sqrt{\frac{8\pi^2 m W_y}{h^2}} \sin z \sqrt{\frac{8\pi^2 m W_z}{h^2}}$$ (1-125)

where [see Eq. (1-116)]

$$W_x = \frac{h^2}{8mL^2} n_x^2 \qquad n_x = 0, \pm 1, \pm 2, \ldots \qquad (1\text{-}126a)$$

$$W_y = \frac{h^2}{8mL^2} n_y^2 \qquad n_y = 0, \pm 1, \pm 2, \ldots \qquad (1\text{-}126b)$$

$$W_z = \frac{h^2}{8mL^2} n_z^2 \qquad n_z = 0, \pm 1, \pm 2, \ldots \qquad (1\text{-}126c)$$

and the total energy is

$$W_n = W_x + W_y + W_z \qquad \begin{aligned} n_x &= 0, \pm 1, \pm 2, \ldots \\ n_y &= 0, \pm 1, \pm 2, \ldots \\ n_z &= 0, \pm 1, \pm 2, \ldots \end{aligned} \qquad (1\text{-}127)$$

The allowable energy levels W_n are given by all possible allowable values of n_x, n_y, and n_z. These are the *quantum numbers* for this system.

The energy of any electron is characterized by its quantum number. For instance, in the previous example, a knowledge of n_x, n_y, and n_z yields the energy. However, there is one other quantum number that is needed to completely characterize the electron's energy. Consider the electron as a particle which can spin on its own axis. (This constitutes a current.) If a magnetic field is applied, the spinning will cause the electron to interact with it. The electron will align its axis of spin to one of two stable positions, either parallel or antiparallel to the magnetic field. A quantum number n_s is assigned to indicate these two possible positions. n_s takes on the value $\pm \frac{1}{2}$ only.

Pauli exclusion principle   The quantum number n of an electron represents the set of its four quantum numbers. For instance, in the previous examples,

$$n = (n_x, n_y, n_z, n_s) \qquad (1\text{-}128)$$

Now let us consider the three-dimensional cube again. Assume that there are a great many electrons in the system. Experimental observations indicate that all the electrons cannot take on all the allowable sets of quantum numbers given by Eq. (1-128). According to an experimentally verified principle, stated by Pauli, *no two electrons in a system can have the same set of quantum numbers.* That is, no two electrons can have all the same n_x, n_y, n_z, and n_s. (Note that three or fewer of these numbers *can* be equal.)   For the problem we have considered, the set (n_x, n_y, n_z, n_s) is called the *quantum state* of the system. Thus, *no two electrons in a system can occupy the same quantum state.* The actual meaning of a system will be discussed in Sec. 1-16.

We have solved the Schrödinger equation for a very simple problem with very simple boundary conditions. Actually, in all but the simplest of cases, it is extremely difficult to obtain solutions for the Schrödinger equation.

Heisenberg uncertainty principle Earlier in this section we discussed the fact that the location of a single electron cannot be exactly specified. There is some uncertainty about its position. For instance, in the one-dimensional example considered, the electron could lie anywhere between $x = 0$ and $x = L$. Thus, its uncertainty can be written as

$$\Delta x = L \tag{1-129}$$

In a similar way, the knowledge of the momentum of a particle has an uncertainty associated with it. Heisenberg postulated that these two uncertainties are related. The postulate, which is verified by measurements, states that the product of the uncertainty in position and the uncertainty in momentum is of the order of magnitude of h. At times, this postulate is stated in different but equivalent terms. For instance, velocity replaces momentum.

1-15   RELATION OF QUANTUM MECHANICS
TO ALLOWED ENERGY LEVELS IN THE ATOM

In the last section we applied Schrödinger's equation (1-109) to the problem of a single electron constrained to be within a cube. We determined there that the electron's state was characterized by four quantum numbers. Three of these were related to the boundary conditions in the x, y, and z directions, while the fourth was a function of the electron's spin.

In principle, the solution of Eq. (1-109) for the atom is similar to the example of the last section. However, the details of the solution are much more complex. We shall not solve Schrödinger's equation here but just state the results.

As in the case of the cube, the allowable states of the electrons of an atom are characterized by four quantum numbers. In the simple cube problem, the boundary conditions were simply expressed in terms of the rectangular coordinates x, y, z, and thus three of the quantum numbers were associated with x, y, and z. In an atom, it is convenient to express the boundary conditions in terms of spherical coordinates. The quantum numbers are then associated with these spherical coordinates (r, θ, and ϕ). Let us discuss each of these quantum numbers in turn.

1. *The principal quantum number n.* This essentially determines the orbit of the electron. In Sec. 1-12 we discussed allowable orbits. The principal quantum numbers characterize the energy (size) of the allow-

able orbits. Thus, this quantum number is related to the total energy associated with a particular state. n can take on the values 0, 1, 2, ...

2. *The azimuthal quantum number l.* The shape and position of the orbit can vary, and a quantum number is associated with this variation. Actually, this quantum number is related to the orbital angular momentum of the electron, which is defined as

$$\mathcal{M} = m\imath v \sin \theta \qquad (1\text{-}130)$$

where $\imath$ = radius of orbit
v = velocity of electron
θ = angle between them

The angular momentum is a vector. Its direction is perpendicular to the plane of $\imath$ and v and is in the direction that a right-handed screw would move if turned from r to v through the smallest angle between them. It can be shown that, on the average, over the orbit, the magnitude of the angular momentum of the electrons will be

$$\mathcal{M} = \frac{\sqrt{l(l+1)}h}{2\pi} \qquad (1\text{-}131)$$

The allowed values of l for an electron are limited by the value of the principal quantum number n for that electron. In particular l can take on the values

$$l = 0, 1, 2, \ldots, n - 1 \qquad (1\text{-}132)$$

3. *The magnetic quantum number m_l.* This quantum number is similar to the preceding one except that now it gives the angular momentum only in the z direction. In this case,

$$\mathcal{M}_z = \frac{m_l h}{2\pi} \qquad (1\text{-}133)$$

The allowable values of m_l are

$$m_l = 0, \pm 1, \pm 2, \ldots, \pm l \qquad (1\text{-}134)$$

The quantum numbers m_l and l are related to the magnetic properties of the material. The three quantum numbers n, l, and m_l are related to the coordinates.

4. *The spin quantum number m_s.* As discussed in Sec. 1-14, an electron can rotate on its own axis. The angular momentum associated with this is called *electron spin.* This angular momentum has a magnitude

$$\mathcal{M}_s = \frac{m_s h}{2\pi} \qquad (1\text{-}135)$$

The spin quantum number m_s can take on only the values

$$m_s = \pm \tfrac{1}{2} \qquad (1\text{-}136)$$

Atomic structure   The structure of the atom can be determined by a study of the quantum numbers.   The principal quantum number essentially determines the location of the orbit of the electron.   All electrons with the same principal quantum number are said to lie in the same *electron shell*. Note that the Pauli exclusion principle is applicable to all systems.   Thus, no two electrons can have the same *four* quantum numbers.

It is common to describe the quantum shells by letters.   For instance, corresponding to $n = 1, 2, 3, 4, 5, 6, 7$, we shall use K, L, M, N, O, P, Q. Thus, we can speak of the K shell, etc.

The K shell can have two electrons.   Both electrons have $l = m_l = 0$ [see Eqs. (1-132) and (1-134)].   Their spin quantum numbers are $+\frac{1}{2}$ and $-\frac{1}{2}$, respectively.   There are eight electrons which can be in the L shell. Let us demonstrate this.   If $n = 2$, then l can take on the values 0 and 1. Corresponding to $l = 0$, we have $m_l = 0$, $m_s = \pm\frac{1}{2}$, or two allowable states. Corresponding to $l = 1$, we have $m_l = 0$, ± 1, $m_s = \pm\frac{1}{2}$.   Taking all possible combinations of these, we have six possible allowable states.   Thus, the total number of allowable states in the L shell is eight.   Similarly, the M shell has eighteen allowable states and the N shell has 32.   Note that all the allowable states of a shell need not have electrons with energies corresponding to them.   If all the states of any shell are occupied by electrons, the shell is said to be *filled*.

It is also common to designate the azimuthal quantum number by a letter.   For instance, corresponding to $l = 0, 1, 2, 3, 4, 5, 6$ we have $s, p, d,$ f, g, h, i.

A shorthand notation is used to indicate the n and l quantum numbers for the electron of an atom in its lowest energy state.   A number is used to indicate the shell, i.e., the principal quantum number n.   A letter follows this to indicate the azimuthal quantum number l.   A superscript is appended to this to indicate the number of electrons in the shell that have the same l quantum number.   For instance, an atom with one shell and two electrons is characterized by $1s^2$.   If the atom has two filled shells, it is written as

$$1s^2 2s^2 2p^6$$

Thus, it has $2s$ electrons in the first shell and $2s$ electrons and $6p$ electrons in the second shell.   The outermost shell need not be filled.   For instance, we could have an atom with

$$1s^2 2s^2 2p^5$$

The principal quantum number specifies the shells.   The l quantum numbers are said to specify *subshells*.   If an atom has only completely filled shells or subshells, it is chemically very stable.   A subshell is said to be filled if all the allowed energy states associated with it are occupied by electrons.

The electrons in the outermost shell are those with the highest energies.

The inner-shell electrons have lower energies and are tightly bound to the nucleus.

Quantum-mechanical considerations lead to an atomic structure somewhat more complicated than that of the Bohr atom, and the spectroscopic properties of actual atoms are more complex than can be predicted by the Bohr atom. Quantum-mechanical considerations can be used to explain some fine details of the spectrum emitted by excited atoms that could not previously be explained.

1-16 CRYSTAL STRUCTURE

Thus far we have discussed isolated atoms. In electronic devices, we are often concerned with processes that take place in solids with crystalline structure. That is, the atoms, or at least their nuclei, are arranged in regular geometric patterns. For instance, a simple cubic atomic structure is shown in Fig. 1-18. The atoms in a crystal are of the order of angstrom units apart. When atoms are this close, they interact with each other, causing a modification of some of the results discussed in Sec. 1-15.

The Pauli exclusion principle states that no two electrons of any *one system* can have the same quantum numbers. Now let us assume that we have two atoms, of the same material, which are very far apart. These atoms do not interact with each other. Hence, they are not part of the same system. Thus, corresponding electrons in each atom *can* have the same set of quantum numbers. Now assume that these two atoms are brought closer together. Eventually, they will interact with each other; e.g., their fields affect each other. This occurs when the spacing between them is of the order of magnitude of 10 crystalline atomic distances. In this case, the two atoms form a single system, and no two electrons can have the same quantum numbers. A solution of the Schrödinger equation (which can be found for only very simple crystals) indicates that the following occurs in these cases. Each allowable energy level becomes two closely spaced levels. It is common to say that the level "*splits*." That is, in place of any one level in each of the two atoms, the two-atom system has two levels, which will be very close to the

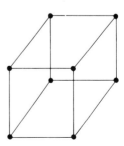

Fig. 1-18 Arrangement of atoms in a cubic crystal.

original one. This splitting occurs for each energy level. Note that this follows the Pauli exclusion principle (see Sec. 1-14). That is, two electrons in a system cannot occupy the same quantum state. Thus each level splits and becomes two levels.

If a third atom is brought into the system, the levels will split so that there are three levels for each original one. The energy levels split each time a new electron is brought into the system. Consider a solid where the density of atoms may be 10^{29} atoms per cubic meter. Each energy level splits an exceedingly large number of times. The system will have sets of levels, and each set will be closely spaced about the original single energy level of the atom. In any set of levels, the individual levels will be extremely close together. In most cases, problems can be analyzed by considering these sets of very closely spaced levels as a single continuous band of allowed energy. These bands will lie about the original allowed energy levels of the atom. The bands are usually several electron volts in width. (Note that the individual levels in a band are very closely spaced but that there are very many individual levels.)

In a single atom, there are discrete allowed energy levels, which are separated by regions of forbidden energy levels. If two atoms are brought together, each allowed energy level splits into two. Thus, in place of the energy levels of the single atom, there will now be groups of two closely spaced levels. These groups will be separated by regions of forbidden energy. Each forbidden region is called a *forbidden energy band*. When many atoms are brought together, the allowed energy levels split further. This results in regions where the allowed energy levels are extremely close together. These are called the *allowed energy bands*. However, there still will be forbidden energy bands between the allowed energy bands. A simple picture of this is that the original single energy levels split so that there is a region about them where the energy levels are extremely close together, i.e., energy bands. However, these bands do not completely fill the forbidden bands. Thus, in a crystal, bands of allowed and prohibited energy levels separate each other.

The preceding discussion is applicable to the outer energy shells of the atom. However, when the inner energy shells are considered, there is far less interaction because the inner-shell electrons of one atom are comparatively further from the inner-shell electrons of the other atom. The inner-shell electrons are also shielded by the electrons in the outer shell.

Let us be somewhat more specific now and consider a crystal of silicon atoms. Silicon has 14 electrons, and its atom is characterized by the configuration $1s^2 2s^2 2p^6 3s^2 3p^2$. *We shall confine our discussion to the outer shell.* This is the one which is of greatest interest when we consider conductors, semiconductors, and insulators. The third shell of an atom can have at most two s electrons, six p electrons and ten d electrons. Since, in the silicon atom, there are no d electrons present, we shall confine our discussion to the *s* and *p* electrons.   The *s* subshell is filled, but there are only two electrons in the *p* shell and thus there are four vacant positions in that subshell that can be filled.

Now let us consider a hypothetical experiment in which *N* isolated atoms of silicon are in some way brought together to form a single crystal.   Before they are brought together, the atoms are isolated and there are 2*N* *s* electrons completely filling the 2*N* available *s* subshells and 2*N* *p* electrons incompletely filling 6*N* available *p* subshells.

Now let us consider that the isolated atoms are brought together.   At even great (atomic) distances, there can be some slight interaction.   The discrete levels split into bands, but they are very narrow.   This is illustrated in Fig. 1-19 at spacing d_2.   Note that, at the start, there is a region of energy between the *s* states and *p* states which is forbidden.   This is spoken of as an *energy gap*.   That is, if an electron in one of the *s* states is to be excited into the *p* state, it must receive an amount of energy at least equal to the energy gap.   As the spacing between atoms is reduced, this gap becomes smaller and smaller and finally disappears when the interatomic spacing becomes d_1 (see Fig. 1-19).   At this point the *s* and *p* bands have merged, and there is no

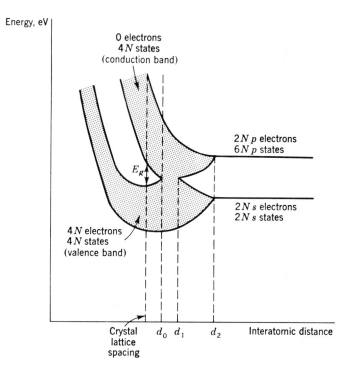

Fig. 1-19   Splitting of states in the *M* shell as silicon atoms are brought together.   It is assumed that $T = 0°K$.

longer any distinction between them. The electrons can no longer be considered as p or s electrons of a single atom but can interchange nuclei. That is, one electron can travel first about one nucleus and then about another. (Remember that we are discussing only the electrons in the outermost shell.)

If the atomic spacing is reduced still further, the (merged) allowable bands broaden even more. However, when the atomic distances decrease below d_0, the merged bands split again but in a somewhat different way. As noted before, we can no longer speak of p or s electrons. Each band will now consist of $4N$ extremely closely spaced states. In silicon, at a temperature of absolute zero ($0°K$) all the $4N$ electrons will be in the lower band, which is called the *valence band*. This band will be completely filled. The upper band, called the *conduction band*, will be empty. Note (see Fig. 1-19) that this behavior occurs when the atoms are at a spacing corresponding to that in an actual crystal.

If the crystal is heated to temperatures above $0°K$, the electron can be excited by photons. (Note that heat and light are both electromagnetic energy.) These can excite electrons from the valence band into the conduction band. The energy gap E_g that exists between the valence band and the conduction band determines the average number of electrons that can be excited into the conduction band at any given temperature.

We shall see that not all materials have valence bands empty of electrons at absolute zero. The electrical properties of materials differ greatly depending upon the energy gap E_g between the valence and conduction bands. In some materials, this gap is zero.

1-17 CONDUCTORS, SEMICONDUCTORS, AND INSULATORS

An electric current consists of a flow of electrons. In general, if a difference of potential is applied to any material (by means of a battery or generator), an electric current will result. If only relatively small amounts of voltage are required to produce large currents, the material is called a *conductor*. If large voltages result in only very small currents, the material is called an *insulator*. A *semiconductor* is between these two extremes.

We shall use the discussion of the previous sections to ascertain the differences in atomic structure which cause a material to be a conductor, semiconductor, or an insulator.

When a voltage is applied to a material by a battery or generator, an electric field is set up within the material. This field *tends* to accelerate the electrons. If it actually does, a current will result. Let us now discuss this on the basis of energy-band theory. Figure 1-20 represents the conduction and valence bands in an insulator. These bands are separated by an energy gap of at least several electron volts, for example, 5 eV (see Sec. 1-16 for a discussion of the energy gap). In Fig. 1-20, the x axis represents position in

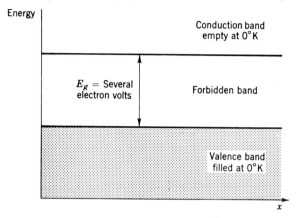

Fig. 1-20 The conduction and valence bands in an insulator. The shaded area indicates electron density at 0°K.

the crystal. (Note that the interatomic spacing is assumed to be fixed in the crystal.) The diagram indicates that at all points in the crystal, i.e., from atom to atom, the conduction band is empty and the valence band is filled. We assume, for the time being, that the temperature is 0°K.

When an electric field is applied, it tends to accelerate the electrons. If an electron is accelerated, it must gain energy. However, the valence band and all bands below it are filled. Electrons cannot have energies in the forbidden band. The only band with vacant states is the conduction band. Thus, if an electron is to be accelerated, it must gain an energy equal to E_g, the energy gap, so that it can be excited into the conduction band. It may appear as though only a small voltage need be applied, since this gap is only several electron volts wide, for example, 5 eV. However, the voltage must be applied over a space which corresponds to interatomic distances. This roughly corresponds to applying 1 volt for each angstrom unit of thickness of the material. Thus, a conductor 1 cm long would require a voltage of 100 million volts to accelerate any electrons. Thus, in all practical situations, no current would result.

If the temperature is increased above absolute zero, to room temperature, some of the electrons will be thermally excited to the conduction band from the valence band. In the conduction band, there is only an *extremely* small difference between levels; i.e., the band is almost continuous. Therefore, those electrons which have been excited into the conduction band can be accelerated by small applied voltages, and a current results.

If the energy gap is several electron volts, the number of electrons that are excited into the conduction band at room temperature is very small. Thus, a very small current results when a voltage is applied to an insulator.

Let us now discuss a conductor. Its band structure could be very similar to the atomic spacing between d_0 and d_1 in Fig. 1-19.   Thus, there is *no* gap between the conduction and valence bands.   Such a situation is illustrated in Fig. 1-21.   The valence band and conduction band have merged.   That is, the highest band is not filled.   Thus, even at $0°K$, small applied voltages can accelerate electrons, and a current results.   There is an extremely large number of electrons in the conduction band; e.g., in Sec. 1 16 there were $4N$ electrons in the valence band when N was the number of atoms in the crystal; that is about 10^{29} atoms per cubic meter.   Thus, there is an extremely large number of electrons available for conduction.   Hence, even small applied potentials can result in large currents.   Different conductors have different electrical resistances.   We shall discuss this in the next section.

The energy-band diagram for a semiconductor is shown in Fig. 1-22. Note that it is very similar to that for an insulator.   The only difference is that the forbidden band between the conduction and valence band has only a small energy gap of about 1 eV.   At a temperature of $0°K$, the semiconductor will act as an insulator.   The discussion of the insulator is completely applicable here.   However, if a semiconductor is heated to room temperature, many more electrons will be excited into the conduction band because the energy gap is smaller in a semiconductor than in an insulator.   The number of electrons that can be excited across the gap is an exponential function of the gap width.   Thus, comparatively small changes in E_g can produce very large changes in the number of electrons thermally excited into the conduction band.   If a voltage is applied to a semiconductor at room temperature, moderate currents will result.

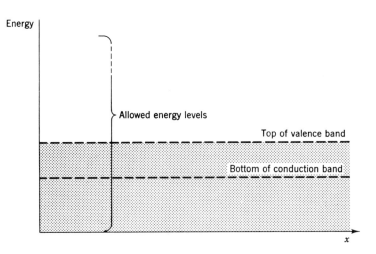

Fig. 1-21   The conduction and valence bands in a conductor.   The shaded area indicates electron density at $0°K$.

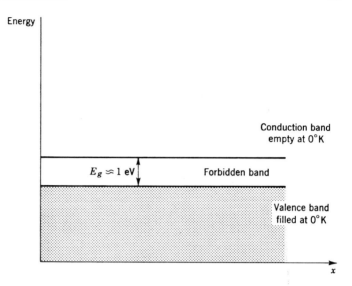

Fig. 1-22 The conduction and valence bands in a semiconductor. The shaded area indicates electron density at 0°K.

Note that increasing the temperature of a semiconductor or an insulator reduces the electrical resistance. That is, for a given applied voltage, more current will result if the temperature is raised. This is because many more electrons are made available for conduction. In a conductor, the resistance increases as temperature is raised. One factor which leads to electrical resistance is the collisions between the electrons which make up the current and the atoms of the crystal. If the material is heated, the probability of such collisions is increased. Thus, the resistance is increased. This effect also occurs in semiconductors and insulators. However, up to temperatures well above room temperature, it is more than offset by the fact that increasing the temperature supplies many more electrons to the conduction band. Thus, in general, the resistance of a semiconductor or an insulator will decrease with an increase in temperature.

1-18 ELECTRICAL CONDUCTIVITY

When a voltage is applied to a conductor, an electric field is set up which accelerates the electrons in the conduction band. Thus, a current results. The electrons in the conduction band are called *free electrons* since they can leave an individual nucleus and move throughout the material. On the other hand, electrons which are not in the conduction band are called *bound electrons* since they must receive an amount of energy at least equal to an energy gap if they are to be accelerated and leave their nuclei.

The motion of the free electrons constitutes a current in a conductor. Let us consider this motion in some detail. Under the influence of an applied electric field, an electron *in a vacuum* will accelerate continuously. *This is not the case for the free electrons in a conductor.* An applied electric field there will accelerate an electron. However, the electron will not continue to accelerate indefinitely because it will *collide* with one of the atoms of the crystal. This collision, which may be elastic or inelastic, will alter the magnitude and direction of the electron's velocity. On the average, the magnitude of the velocity in the direction of acceleration will be reduced. The net effect of the collisions is that, on the average, the magnitude of the electron's velocity in the direction of acceleration will not increase continuously but will oscillate about an average value, called the *drift velocity* v_d.

To clarify this, let us consider a simple model which behaves in a fashion similar to the actual one. In all instances, we shall consider the average behavior of electrons. Consider that the electron is accelerated from rest in the x direction and that it accelerates continuously for a time τ, when it collides with an atom. Such a collision is called *scattering*. After a scattering its velocity will be reduced to a velocity which we shall call v_0. Then the electron is accelerated for another τ_s sec, after which it is scattered again and its velocity again falls to v_0. This process will repeat itself continuously. Note that in an actual atom the time between scatterings τ_s will vary from scattering to scattering. However, we assume it to be constant at its average value τ_s. For this reason, τ_s is called the *mean time between scatterings*. Figure 1-23 illustrates this motion. We have somewhat oversimplified this procedure. After being accelerated from rest, it may take several scatterings of the electron before, on the average, the electron's

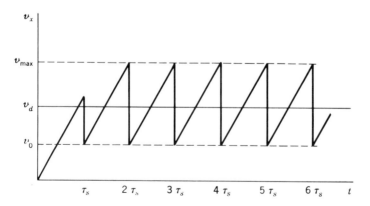

Fig. 1-23 A very simplified average representation of the velocity of an electron in a solid.

velocity will alternate between v_0 and v_{max}; that is, the first scattering will reduce its velocity to less than v_0. However, the first few scatterings are only a very small fraction of the total number of scatterings and will be neglected.

Now let us assume that the electric field within the solid is $\mathscr{E}_x$. Thus, the acceleration in the x direction is

$$a_x = -\frac{e\mathscr{E}_x}{m} \qquad (1\text{-}137)$$

If the electron starts from a velocity v_0 and accelerates for τ_s sec (see Fig. 1-23), its final velocity will have a magnitude

$$v_{max} = v_0 + \frac{e\mathscr{E}_x}{m}\tau_s \qquad (1\text{-}138)$$

The magnitude of the drift velocity is the average of v_0 and v_{max}. Thus,

$$v_d = v_0 + \frac{1}{2}\frac{e\mathscr{E}_x}{m}\tau_s \qquad (1\text{-}139)$$

Detailed studies indicate that if we use $v_0 = \frac{1}{2}e\mathscr{E}_x\tau_s/m$, the correct drift velocity will result. Thus,

$$v_d = \frac{e\mathscr{E}_x}{m}\tau_s \qquad (1\text{-}140)$$

Now, let us assume that there are n electrons per cubic meter in the valence band and that they are all traveling with the drift velocity v_d. The current density, i.e., the current per square meter of cross-sectional area, is

$$\mathscr{J}_x = -nev_d \qquad (1\text{-}141)$$

Note that this is the number of coulombs that pass a given point in 1 sec. (Also note that v_d is negative for positive $\mathscr{E}_x$.) Substituting Eq. (1-140), we obtain

$$\mathscr{J}_x = \frac{ne^2\mathscr{E}_x}{m}\tau_s \qquad (1\text{-}142)$$

The conductivity σ is defined as the magnitude or current density produced by a unit electric field. Thus,

$$\sigma = \frac{ne^2}{m}\tau_s \qquad (1\text{-}143)$$

The resistivity ρ is defined as the reciprocal of the conductivity. The resistance of a sample L meters long and of cross-sectional area A is

$$R = \frac{\rho L}{A} = \frac{L}{\sigma A} \qquad (1\text{-}144)$$

Thus, for a given sample, the greater its conductivity, the less will be its resistance. Note that the conductivity is directly proportional to n, the density of the electrons in the valence band. In a conductor, n will be very large, while in an insulator, it will be very small (see Sec. 1-17). Thus, Eq. (1-143) agrees with the discussion of Sec. 1-17.

The conductivity is proportional to τ_s. Let us discuss the factors which affect it. In a *perfect* crystal, the free electrons would not be scattered but would accelerate continuously. In an actual crystal, however, not all the atoms of the crystal are in their proper position. This is termed a *defect*. Such defects lead to scattering. In addition, since the crystal is not at a temperature of $0°K$, its atoms will be thermally excited. This will lead to a vibration of the atoms within the crystal lattice. This displacement of the atoms also leads to scattering, which reduces τ_s. Thermal excitation causes the electrons to acquire a random component of velocity which also results in scattering. In addition, the presence of impurities within the crystal structure also reduces τ_s.

If a conductor is heated, τ_s will be reduced because of the effects discussed above. However, n will not be substantially changed. Thus, the resistance of conductors increases as their temperature is increased. In insulators or semiconductors, the situation is more complex than in conductors. We shall discuss it in greater detail in Secs. 1-25 to 1-32. However, in a simple sense, increasing the temperature greatly increases n (see Sec. 1-17). This increase in n more than offsets the thermal reduction in τ_s. Thus, in general, the resistance of insulators and semiconductors falls off as the temperature is increased up to temperatures well above room temperatures.

In general v_d, the drift velocity in a conductor, is usually *not* a very large number. A typical value for it is just a small fraction of a meter per second.

Another parameter related to the mean time between scatterings which is often used is called the *mean free path* L_m. It is defined as the average distance that an electron travels before it is scattered. Thus, L_m can be obtained by multiplying τ_s by the magnitude of the velocity of the electron. It may appear as though v_d should be used here. However, at any temperature above $0°K$ the electron has another component of velocity which is due to thermal excitation of the electrons. This manifests itself in a random motion of the electrons. Let us call the average magnitude of this random velocity v_r. In general, the average velocity of the electron is $v_r + v_d$. However, at room temperature, v_r is usually very much greater than v_d. Thus, in computing L_m, we can consider that the electrons' velocity is v_r. Hence,

$$L_m = v_r \tau_s \tag{1-145}$$

Substituting in Eq. (1-143), we obtain

$$\sigma = \frac{ne^2}{mv_r} L_m \qquad (1\text{-}146)$$

Expressions of this type, using the mean free path, are commonly used.

Conductivity in thin films In general, the *conductivity is independent of the dimensions* of the sample. However, if we work with *very thin films*, such as those encountered in integrated circuits, we find that the conductivity of the sample decreases as its thickness increases. In all materials, the mean free path is smaller at the surface than it is in the remaining bulk of the material because there are many more crystal defects near the surface. In thick specimens, then, there is a large region of relatively high conductivity "in parallel" with small regions of low conductivity. We have what amounts to a low resistance in parallel with a high one, and the large resistance will have very little effect on the total resistance. Thus, the surface regions of low conductivity have very little influence on the total conductivity. That is, the mean free path averaged over the entire sample is essentially the same as the value far removed from the surface. However, in a thin film, there is no longer a very large region that is far from the surface. Thus, the conductivity of the surface regions becomes important. The average mean free path will approach that of the surface regions as the film is made thinner. Thus, for a thin film, we must use a smaller mean free path than for a bulk sample. Hence, the conductivity is lower.

1-19 ENERGY DISTRIBUTION OF ELECTRONS—FERMI-DIRAC FUNCTION

The electrons of a single atom can occupy only certain energy levels or, in the case of a solid, lie in allowed energy bands. The probability of a certain level's being filled depends upon the temperature of the atom. That is, an electron can be excited by a photon. If many photons impinge on the atom, the probability that the higher levels will be occupied increases. The electron can be excited in other ways (see Sec. 1-12), but in the present section, we shall just consider thermal excitation.

A relation can be derived which relates the probability of a state's being occupied to its energy and temperature. Instead of carrying out this derivation here we simply state the relation called the *Fermi-Dirac function*

$$f(E) = \frac{1}{1 + \epsilon^{(E - E_f)/kT}} \qquad (1\text{-}147)$$

where $f(E)$ is the probability that an allowed state of energy E is occupied, E_f is a parameter of the material called the Fermi level, both E and E_f are expressed in electron volts, k is Boltzmann's constant, 8.61×10^{-5} eV/°K (note that the magnitude and dimensions of k are such that the energies are expressed in electron volts), and T is the temperature in degrees Kelvin. Note that for $T > 0$ Eq. (1-147) has nonzero values for all values of energy. This does not mean that all energies are allowable. *Only allowable values of E should be substituted into Eq. (1-147) to find their probabilities.*

Let us now consider the shape of $f(E)$ at various temperatures. Such curves are shown in Fig. 1-24. Note that as T approaches 0°K, the magnitude of the exponent $(E - E_f)/kT$ approaches infinity. If $E > E_f$, the exponent is positive, while if $E < E_f$, the exponent is negative. Thus, if $T = 0$°K,

$$\epsilon^{(E-E_f)/kT} \rightarrow \begin{cases} \infty & \text{if } E > E_f \\ 0 & \text{if } E < E_f \end{cases}$$

Hence, at $T = 0$°K

$$f(E) = \begin{cases} 1 & E < E_f \\ 0 & E > E_f \end{cases} \tag{1-148}$$

This gives some physical meaning to E_f. At $T = 0$°K, those states whose allowable energies are less than E_f will have a probability of 1 of being filled, while those states whose allowable energies are greater than E_f will have zero probability of being filled. That is, at 0°K, all the allowable states below E_f will be filled while those above it will be empty.

At temperatures above 0°K, the distribution becomes as shown in Fig. 1-24. Thus, all energy states have some probability of being filled. However, even at high temperatures (T_2 could typically represent $T = 2500$°K) most of the energy states below E_f will be filled while few of the high-energy states will be occupied.

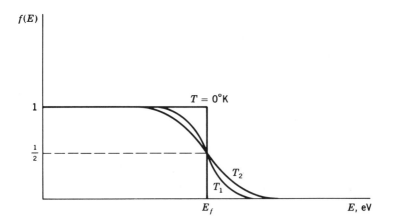

Fig. 1-24 The Fermi-Dirac distribution. $0 < T_1 < T_2$.

Note that independent of temperature

$$f(E_f) = \tfrac{1}{2} \tag{1-149}$$

That is, if an allowable energy level happens to fall at E_f, it always has a probability of $\tfrac{1}{2}$ of being filled. In many instances, E_f falls in the middle of a forbidden band. Remember that only the allowed values of E have meaning when substituted into Eq. (1-147).

Density of states Let us now consider the average number of free electrons that have energies between any two chosen values. To do this, we must know the number of allowable states for the free electrons per unit volume. That is, we must obtain a state density $d_s(E)$ such that the number of states per unit volume with energies lying between E_1 and E_2 is

$$D_{E_1, E_2} = \int_{E_1}^{E_2} d_s(E) \, dE \tag{1-150}$$

Note that this is very similar in form to a probability distribution (see Sec. 1-13). Note too that Eq. (1-150) is not a probability. However, we can work in a similar way with distribution functions other than probability-distribution functions.

A detailed analysis shows that

$$d_s(E) = \frac{4\pi}{h^3} (2m)^{\frac{3}{2}} e^{\frac{3}{2}} E^{\frac{1}{2}} \tag{1-151}$$

where E is the energy in electron volts. Thus, we can write

$$d_s(E) = \gamma E^{\frac{1}{2}} \tag{1-152}$$

where the constant γ is given by

$$\gamma = \frac{4\pi}{h^3} (2m)^{\frac{3}{2}} e^{\frac{3}{2}} \tag{1-153}$$

Note that $d_s(E)$ is a continuous function, while the energy levels are discrete. The interpretation of this is that on the average, Eq. (1-150) will give the number of states per unit volume that have energies between E_1 and E_2, even if E_1 and E_2 are not allowable energy levels. (Note that some error can result if nonallowable levels are used for E_1 and E_2. Usually this will be small.)

If we are to determine the number of free electrons with energies lying between E_1 and E_2, we must multiply the density of allowable energy states by the probability that a state is filled. Hence, the electron density per unit volume $\rho_e(E)$ is given by the product of Eqs. (1-152) and (1-147). Thus,

$$\rho_e(E) = \frac{\gamma E^{\frac{1}{2}}}{1 + \epsilon^{(E - E_f)/kT}} \tag{1-154}$$

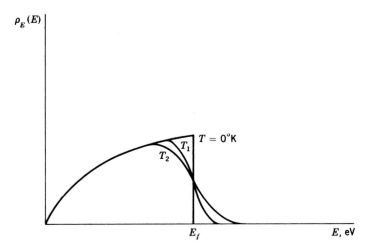

Fig. 1-25 The density of electrons (per unit volume) per electron volt. $0 < T_1 < T_2$.

This curve is plotted in Fig. 1-25. Then, on the average, the number of electrons having energies that lie between E_1 and E_2 is

$$n_{E_1,E_2} = \int_{E_1}^{E_2} \frac{\gamma E^{\frac{1}{2}}}{1 + \epsilon^{(E - E_f)/kT}} \, dE \qquad (1\text{-}155)$$

As an example, let us determine the *total* number of free electrons per unit volume. Thus we must consider all energies from zero to infinity. This is given by

$$n = \int_0^\infty \frac{\gamma E^{\frac{1}{2}}}{1 + \epsilon^{(E - E_f)/kT}} \, dE$$

It is simplest to integrate this when $T = 0$. Then, we have (see Figs. 1-24 and 1-25)

$$n = \int_0^{E_f} \gamma E^{\frac{1}{2}} \, dE$$
$$n = \tfrac{2}{3}\gamma E_f^{\frac{3}{2}} \qquad (1\text{-}156)$$

1-20 THERMONIC EMISSION—ENERGY BARRIERS

In Sec. 1-9 we discussed the cathode of an electron gun and stated that it acts as a source of electrons. That is, the cathode emits electrons into the vacuum of the cathode-ray tube. In general, most vacuum tubes have such a source of electrons. Before we consider how electrons can be emitted from a metal, we digress for a moment and study energy barriers.

Energy barriers Let us discuss Fig. 1-26, where we have drawn a ball of mass m rolling on the contour shown. The vertical axis is plotted in units of energy. That is, the potential energy of the mass at each point on the contour is given by the scale of the vertical axis. We have adjusted the scale so that the lowest point has zero potential energy.

Now consider that the mass has a total energy W_1. Thus, it is constrained to lie between x_2 and x_3, since at either of these points its total energy is equal to the potential energy. Thus, the kinetic energy and, hence, the velocity, is zero at x_2 and x_3. Therefore, the particle can travel between x_2 and x_3 but cannot leave the region $x_2 \leq x \leq x_3$. It is sometimes said that the mass *collides with a potential-energy barrier* at those points.

Suppose we wish the mass not to be restricted to any region but able to move to any point on the x axis. If its total energy is greater than W_b but less than W_a, for instance W_2, then it will not collide with an energy barrier to its right and can move unconstrained in this direction. However, there is an energy barrier to its left. The particle can go no farther to its left than x_1. If the total energy of the mass is made greater than W_a, for instance W_3, then it never collides with an energy barrier and can move unconstrained along the entire x axis.

Thermonic emission If an electron is to be emitted from a conductor, it must surmount a potential barrier which is similar to that of Fig. 1-26. Consider an electrically neutral conductor. If an electron is emitted from the conductor, the conductor is left with a net positive charge of e. The negative charge of the electron $-e$ and the positive charge of the conductor

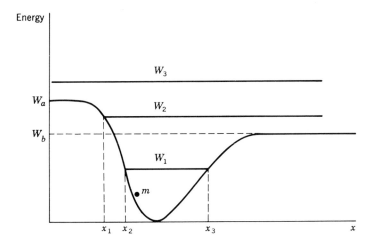

Fig. 1-26 A mass moving on a contour. The ordinate is plotted in units of energy.

attract each other. Thus, work must be done in removing the charge from the conductor. In general, for distances greater than several atomic distances, the force on the electron falls off as x^2, its distance from the conductor. The potential energy, i.e., the work done in removing the charge from the conductor, will be of the form shown in the right-hand curve of Fig. 1-27. The maximum energy here is E_B. If an electron is to be emitted from the conductor, it must have an energy equal to or greater than E_B.

Now let us determine the number of electrons which have energies in excess of E_B. The expression for the free-electron density is $\rho_E(E)$ [see Eq. (1-154)]. This curve is plotted as the left-hand curve of Fig. 1-27. (Note that this is the same as Fig. 1-25 but is turned 90°.) At a temperature of 0°K the maximum energy of the free electrons is E_F. Thus, an amount of energy at least equal to

$$E_W = E_B - E_F \tag{1-157}$$

must be added if an electron is to be emitted. E_W is called the *work function* of the material. The total number of electrons available for emission is thus given by [see Eq. (1-155)]

$$n_{EB,\infty} = \int_{E_B}^{\infty} \frac{\gamma E^{\frac{1}{2}}}{1 + \epsilon^{(E-E_F)/kT}} \, dE \tag{1-158}$$

Equation (1-158) does not give the number of electrons that will be emitted. If an electron is to be emitted, it must have a velocity which is directed toward the surface of the metal. In addition, to be emitted an electron must be at or near the surface of the conductor. Taking these factors into account, an

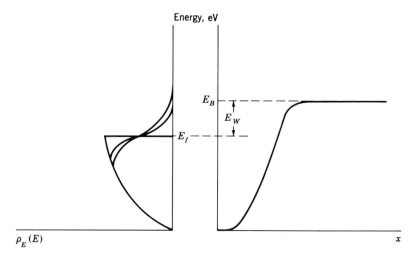

Fig. 1-27   The free-electron energy density and the energy barrier in a metal.

equation for the maximum current from an emitter can be obtained. This equation is called the *Richardson-Dushman* equation, and it gives the current that can be emitted from a cathode of area S

$$I = SaT^2\epsilon^{-E_w/kT} \tag{1-159}$$

where S = area, meters^2
T = temperature, °K
E_W = work function, eV
k = Boltzmann's constant = 8.61×10^{-5} eV/°K
(Note that this is expressed in electron volts per degree Kelvin and not in joules per degree Kelvin, as it sometimes is.) a is a constant which is a function of the material. For most cathode materials $a = 60.2$. The work functions for some common emitters are tungsten 4.52 eV, thorium 3.55 eV, and alkali-metal oxides approximately 1 eV. The emission current increases very rapidly as the temperature increases and/or the work function decreases.

Equation (1-159) is derived under the assumption that all the emitted electrons are removed from the cathode by an electric field and then are returned to the cathode. For instance, in the cathode-ray tube (see Fig. 1-10) the emitted electrons are removed from the cathode and directed to the screen by the electrodes of the electron gun. Once they strike the screen, they are conducted back to the cathode through the conductive coating and the external circuit. The current given by Eq. (1-159) is called the *saturation current*.

Energies of emitted electrons Note (see Fig. 1-27) that there are emitted electrons which have energies in excess of that required to surmount the potential barrier. These electrons will be emitted with a nonzero velocity, which varies from electron to electron. These random velocities can affect the characteristics of electronic devices.

Practical cathodes A practical cathode often consists of a ribbon of emitting material, which is heated by passing a current through it. The higher the temperature of the cathode, the greater the emission. However, the temperature of operation must be considerably below the melting point of the wire. The atoms of the cathode are actually evaporated from it, and this eventually causes the cathode to rupture. The rate of evaporation increases greatly as the temperature approaches the melting point.

Another factor must be considered. In most vacuum devices, the electrons emitted from the cathode are accelerated by applied electric fields. Since no vacuum is perfect, some gas molecules will be present and some of them will be ionized by collision with the accelerated electrons. Positive ions can be formed by the process; i.e., as a result of the collisions, one or more of an atom's electrons can receive energy greater than the ionization potential. The fields within the device will accelerate these heavy positive ions to the cathode. This can result in damage to it especially if very large electric fields are present.

Let us now consider three commonly used emitting materials.

Tungsten A material with a fairly high work function is tungsten. However, its melting point is also high. Thus, it can be operated at high temperatures which offset the disadvantage of the high work function. Positive-ion bombardment does not adversely affect tungsten. Thus, it is used as the cathode material in very high voltage devices such as x-ray tubes and large radio transmitting tubes. Tungsten cathodes are usually operated white hot.

Thoriated tungsten Thorium has a lower work function than tungsten and thus appears to be a better emitter of electrons. However, its melting point is considerably lower than that of tungsten. Thus, it must be operated at much lower temperatures than tungsten.

If a small amount of thorium is combined with tungsten before the filament is fabricated, the thoriated tungsten filament which results has the advantages of both materials. The tungsten, which makes up most of the material, provides the high melting point. However, at the usual operating temperatures, a thin monatomic layer of thorium continuously diffuses to the surface (some of it also evaporates continuously). Emission takes place from the thorium layer. It is found that the work function of this type of cathode (2.6 eV) is less than that of either thorium or tungsten alone. Thus, thoriated tungsten cathodes can be operated at lower temperatures than pure tungsten and still produce the same electron emission.

Thoriated tungsten can withstand positive-ion bombardment fairly well, but it is not as resistant as pure tungsten. Thoriated tungsten is used as a cathode material in devices where voltages do not exceed 15,000 volts.

Alkali-metal oxides The oxides of barium, strontium, and calcium, when coated on metals which serve as structural bases, have very low work functions, of the order of 1 eV. They can be operated at low temperatures (dull red hot) and still produce very substantial emission. For this reason, they are used in many vacuum tubes.

Oxide-coated cathodes do not withstand positive-ion bombardment well. They are used in devices where the voltages are relatively low, for example, 500 volts.

Because of the relatively low operating temperatures required, oxide cathodes are often made in the following way. The oxides are coated on a cylinder. A separate *heater* is spiraled inside the cylinder but electrically insulated from it. In this way, the cathode and heater are electrically

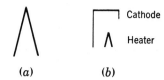

Fig. 1-28 The symbol for (*a*) a directly heated and (*b*) an indirectly heated cathode.

(*a*)   (*b*)

isolated from each other. Thus, the heater circuit can be made electrically independent of the cathode circuit. This is an advantage in most electronic devices. This type of cathode is called an *indirectly heated cathode*.

Symbols The symbols for a directly heated and an indirectly heated cathode are shown in Fig. 1-28.

Voltage-current characteristics Equation (1-159) represents the maximum current that can be obtained from an emitting cathode. Let us study the current that actually leaves the cathode in a simple vacuum tube. To do this, we shall use the device shown in Fig. 1-29, which is called a *vacuum-tube diode*. An indirectly heated cathode and a simple metallic element, called a *plate* or *anode*, are enclosed in an evacuated envelope. Actually these elements are usually concentric right cylinders; e.g., the cathode is a small right-circular cylinder surrounded by a larger cylinder which is the plate. A potential V_{bb} is connected between the cathode and the plate. Now let us consider a plot of I_b, the current that results, as a function of the applied voltage V_{bb}. Such a plot is shown in Fig. 1-30. The electric field at the cathode does not depend solely upon V_{bb}. When V_{bb} is zero, there will actually be a field at the cathode (in addition to the potential barrier), which tends to drive electrons back to it. This occurs because the cathode and plate are usually made of different materials. The diode acts as though there were a voltage $-V_0$ in series with V_{bb}. V_0 is of the order of 1 volt. The cause of this voltage is discussed in Sec. 1-24. Thus, when $V_{bb} = 0$, there will be a retarding field at the cathode. Only a very few of the emitted electrons will have sufficient kinetic energy to overcome this field and reach

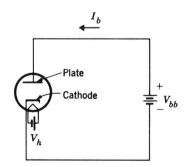

Fig. 1-29 A simple diode circuit.

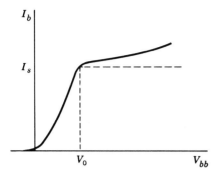

Fig. 1-30   The current in an actual diode.

the plate.   These electrons account for the very small current shown at $V_{bb} = 0$.   As V_{bb} is increased, the effect of the retarding field is reduced, more and more of the emitted electrons will be able to reach the plate, and the current will increase.   When $V_{bb} = V_0$, the effect of the retarding field is canceled and all the emitted electrons will reach the plate.   Let us assume that Eq. (1-159) predicts an emission current of I_s from the cathode.   When $V_{bb} = V_0$, all electrons that are emitted should reach the plate and the current will be $I_b = I_s$.   In theory, if V_{bb} is increased further, the current should not increase because the cathode cannot emit electrons at a faster rate.   Thus, for $V_{bb} \geq V_0$ the curve should have the form of the dashed line of Fig. 1-30.

However, as V_{bb} is increased above V_0, it is found that the current does increase.   This increase in current is due to the fact that the electric field set up by V_{bb} actually lowers the potential barrier of the cathode.   Thus, E_W in Eq. (1-159) is effectively reduced.   Hence, as V_{bb} is increased, I_b will increase.   This increase in emission current is called the *Schottky effect*.

1-21   SECONDARY EMISSION

Electrons impinging on a surface can impart energy to the free electrons of the metal.   If this imparted energy is sufficiently large, some of these free electrons can then be emitted.   The impinging electron is called a *primary electron*.   The emitted electron is called a *secondary electron*.   If there is to be secondary emission, the primary electron's energy must be equal to or greater than the difference between the initial energy of the excited electron and the potential barrier.   If the primary electron's energy is sufficiently high, it can excite more than one secondary electron.

The ratio of the number of secondary electrons emitted to the number of primary electrons impinging on the surface is called the *secondary-emission ratio*.   As the energy of the primary electrons is increased, the secondary-emission ratio increases up to a point and then decreases because very high energy electrons tend not to interact with electrons near the surface but to excite electrons well within the metal. Such electrons will probably not be emitted but will dissipate their excess energy within the metal.

1-22 PHOTOELECTRIC EMISSION

In Sec. 1-20 we considered electrons which were excited by thermal energy and were thus emitted. In essentially the same way, electrons can be excited by photons (of light frequency) and be emitted. The energy of a single photon is [see Eq. (1-93)]

$$W = hf \tag{1-160}$$

This energy must be sufficient to raise the electron's energy above the energy barrier. (Recall that W represents energy in joules and E represents energy in electron volts.)

Usually, photoemission devices are operated with their emitter at room temperature. We shall assume that the electron density $\rho_E(E)$ [see Eq. (1-154)] is essentially that for $T = 0°\text{K}$. (Actually, at room temperature, there are very few electrons with energy in excess of E_f, and this assumption is fairly accurate.) Thus (see Fig. 1-27) if an electron is to be emitted, it must receive an energy of at least $E_B - E_f = E_W$. If an electron receives more than enough energy to be emitted, it will have a nonzero velocity after it is emitted. The kinetic energy corresponding to this velocity is equal to the difference between the *excited* electron's energy before emission and the barrier potential. Thus, since eE_W is the *minimum* energy (in joules) that an electron within the metal must receive if is to be emitted, the kinetic energy (in joules) will be equal to or less than $hf - eE_W$

$$\tfrac{1}{2}mv^2 \leq hf - eE_W \tag{1-161}$$

This is called the *Einstein equation*.

Let us assume that a beam of monochromatic light falls on an emitter. There is a minimum frequency of the light below which no emission can take place. If hf is not at least equal to eE_W, the electrons will not obtain sufficient energy to surmount the barrier. Thus, the *minimum*, or *threshold*, frequency f_c that will produce emission is

$$f_c = \frac{eE_W}{h} \tag{1-162}$$

This is often expressed in terms of the wavelength and is called the *critical wavelength*. Using the relation between frequency and wavelength of light [see Eq. (1-94)], we obtain

$$\lambda_c = \frac{ch}{eE_W} \tag{1-163}$$

where c is the velocity of light.

Note that if the intensity of the monochromatic light beam is increased, more photons per second will strike the cathode. However, the energy of any individual photon will be unchanged. Increasing the intensity of the beam increases the number of emitted electrons (if $f > f_c$) since more photons will arrive at the emitter. Thus, more electrons can be excited. However, increasing the intensity of the monochromatic light will not change the threshold frequency.

1-23   HIGH-FIELD EMISSION

If a strong enough electric field, which tends to remove electrons from the surface, is applied to an emitter, substantial amounts of emission can take place even at room temperature. The potential barrier is reduced as in the case of the Schottky effect. In addition, the barrier also becomes thinner. Quantum-mechanical considerations indicate that if the barrier is thin enough, substantial numbers of electrons can pass through the barrier even though they do not have sufficient energy to surmount it. (This is a function of the wave nature of the electron and is not predicted classically.) This phenomenon is called *tunneling* (see Sec. 3-10). If the electric field is sufficiently high for the barrier to be thin enough to allow substantial emission at room temperature, the emission that results is called *high-field emission*.

1-24   CONTACT POTENTIAL

We now consider the effect of placing two dissimilar metals in contact, as shown in Fig. 1-31a. Because of thermal excitation, the free electrons move randomly in the metals. Thus, some electrons from metal 1 will move into metal 2 and vice versa. An electron leaving either metal must surmount the metals' potential barrier. Let us consider that metal 1 has a work function E_{W1} while metal 2 has a work function E_{W2}, where $E_{W1} < E_{W2}$. Now assume that the two metals are brought into contact. At the first instant of contact, more electrons will leave metal 1 and enter metal 2 than will leave metal 2 and enter metal 1 because of the difference in work functions. Thus, metal 2 will acquire a negative charge with respect to 1. This negative charge will tend to retard electrons from leaving metal 1 and entering metal 2. Thus, the barrier viewed by electrons going from metal 1 to 2 will be raised. This reduces the number of electrons that can leave metal 1. Eventually, an equilibrium will be set up so that as many electrons leave metal 1 and enter metal 2 as go the other way. Once this equilibrium has been established, metal 2 will have a constant negative potential with respect to metal 1. Thus a voltage V will exist between the two metals, as shown in Fig. 1-31a.

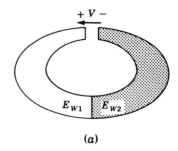

(a)

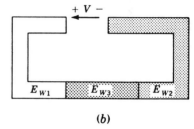

Fig. 1-31 (a) Two dissimilar metals in contact and (b) three dissimilar metals in contact.

(b)

This voltage, called the *contact potential*, equals the difference between the work functions of the metals

$$V = E_{W2} - E_{W1} \tag{1-164}$$

where E_{W1} and E_{W2} are expressed in electron volts.

Now let us assume that a third metal with work function E_{W3} is placed between the two (see Fig. 1-31b). The value of V is unchanged. Let us see why this is so. The contact potential between metal 1 and metal 3 is

$$V_{13} = E_{W3} - E_{W1}$$

while that between metals 3 and 2 is

$$V_{32} = E_{W2} - E_{W3}$$

Applying Kirchhoff's voltage law, we obtain

$$V = V_{13} + V_{32} = E_{W2} - E_{W3} + E_{W3} - E_{W1} = E_{W2} - E_{W1} \tag{1-165}$$

Thus, the effect of E_{W3} is canceled.

Contact potential produces the voltage V_0 discussed in Sec. 1-20 in conjunction with Fig. 1-29. There, the contact potential is the difference between the work functions of the cathode and plate. (Note that there is an external connection between the cathode and the plate.) Since the cathode's work function is usually lower than that of the plate, the contact potential sets up a field which retards the emission of electrons.

1-25 FREE ELECTRONS AND HOLES IN A PURE SEMICONDUCTOR

We now turn to conductive processes in semiconductors.   In this section, we shall discuss the behavior of charge carriers in pure semiconductor crystals. Typical semiconductor materials are germanium and silicon.   For purposes of discussion we shall consider a silicon crystal, although the results for germanium are essentially the same.   We shall repeat a few of the salient points of the discussion of silicon crystals in Sec. 1-16.   (It is assumed that the reader is familiar with the entire discussion.)   The outer shell of a silicon atom which is in a crystal lattice has eight available states only four of which are filled by electrons.   At a temperature of 0°K, all the electrons are in the valence band, and the conduction band is empty.   In a silicon crystal, the valence electrons of each atom are actually shared in the crystal structure. That is, each atom has four (valence) electrons which are shared by the four adjacent atoms.   In this way, each pair of adjacent atoms has two electrons which they share in common.   This is called a *covalent bond*, and it contributes to the binding force of the crystal.   It is conventional to represent the three-dimensional crystal structure and the covalent bonds by a two-dimensional diagram of the type shown in Fig. 1-32.

At a temperature of 0°K, all the outer-shell electrons are in the valence band.   Physically, this means that each of the outer-shell electrons is shared

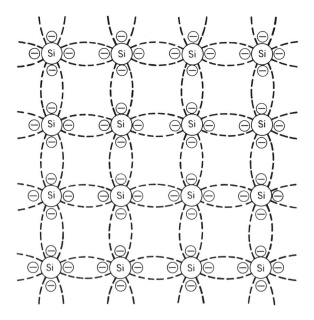

Fig. 1-32 A symbolic representation of the silicon crystal showing covalent bonds.

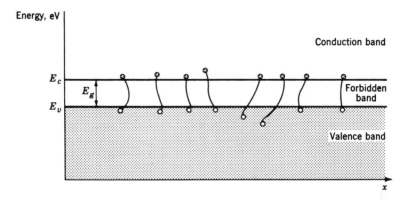

Fig. 1-33   The conduction and valence bands in a semiconductor at a temperature above 0°K.   The shaded area represents electron density.

by two atoms in a covalent bond.   An energy-level diagram for this condition is shown in Fig. 1-22.   Thus (see Sec. 1-17) at $T = 0°K$, the semiconductor acts as an insulator.

Now let us assume that the temperature of the semiconductor is increased above absolute zero.   Since the energy gap E_g between the valence and conduction bands is not too large, many valence electrons will be excited into the conduction band, where they can act as charge carriers.   An energy-level diagram illustrating this is shown in Fig. 1-33.   The thermally excited electrons in the conduction band are no longer constrained to remain in a covalent bond but can now move throughout the crystal.   These electrons are called *free electrons*.   In general, because of thermal excitation, the free electrons wander randomly throughout the crystal.   It is said that the free electrons have broken their covalent bonds.

If a voltage is applied to a semiconductor, an electric field is set up in it which accelerates the free electrons just as in a conductor.   The accelerations and scatterings discussed in Sec. 1-18 then take place.   This process is similar to that in a conductor, but there are some important differences.   In a conductor, there is no energy gap between the conduction and valence bands, and electrons do not have to be thermally excited to obtain conduction.   In a semiconductor, this is not true.   Electrons must be excited into the conduction band.   To consider all the ramifications, let us review one fact discussed in Sec. 1-17.   In an insulator (or semiconductor) at 0°K, conduction does not take place because an electron must gain energy to be accelerated by an electric field.   If the conduction band is empty and the valence band is full, an electron cannot gain energy unless it receives an amount of energy at least equal to the gap energy E_g.   This requires the application of very large voltages (see Sec. 1-17).   Thus, a full valence band

and an empty conduction band result in no current, i.e., an infinite resistance.

When an electron is thermally excited into the conduction band, it becomes a free electron and can be accelerated by an applied electric field (see Sec. 1-17). In addition, another important effect occurs. When an electron is excited from the valence band to the conduction band, *it leaves a vacant state in the valence band.* An electron in the valence band, at an energy level extremely close to the vacant one, can gain energy and move into the vacant level. Thus, it now can be accelerated. The accelerated electron occupies the vacant level. However, the energy level it occupied originally will now be vacant, and another electron can gain energy and enter that vacancy. Thus, this process can be repeated. (Remember that these levels are so close together that they can almost be considered a continuous distribution.)

The motion of valence electrons constitutes an electric current. The mechanism is somewhat different from the current due to free electrons. A single free electron moves continuously under the influence of an applied electric field. In valence-band conduction, the following occurs. A valence electron is excited into the conduction band. Thus, a covalent bond is broken. An electron from an adjacent covalent bond then moves into this vacancy, leaving a vacancy in the adjacent covalent bond which another valence electron can now enter. This process can continue. Thus, *the vacancy in the covalent bond moves throughout the crystal.* Such a vacancy is called a *hole.* We say that a hole can move throughout the crystal. The motion of a hole is really the motion of many electrons, but studies indicate that correct results will be obtained if we treat the hole as a positive charge, equal in magnitude to the charge of an electron. The dynamics of the motion of a hole can be considered to be essentially the same as that of a free electron. For instance, free electrons and holes move with an average drift velocity under the influence of an applied electric field. They move, however, in opposite directions. Thermal energy causes both free electrons and holes to move randomly throughout the material. The mass of the hole is usually considered to be somewhat different from that of the electron. The effective mass is generally used in equations of motion of holes. The magnitude of this mass is adjusted to account for approximations made in the derivations of the equations.

If a semiconductor contains no impurities, then whenever a free electron is formed, a vacancy in a covalent bond, and thus a hole, is also formed. Thus, in a pure semiconductor, the number of free electrons equals the number of holes. Pure semiconductors are called *intrinsic semiconductors.* A subscript i is often added to indicate that pure semiconductors are being considered. If the electrical behavior of an impure semiconductor approaches that of a pure one, the subscript i may also be used there.

If a free electron moving through the semiconductor encounters a hole, both will be destroyed. That is, the free electron can lose energy, fall back into the valence band, and eliminate the vacancy in the covalent bond. This is called *recombination*. In general, free electrons and holes have a finite lifetime because of recombination. At room temperatures, valence electrons are continuously excited into the conduction band. Thus, *free-electron–hole pairs* are continuously formed. The probability of a free electron and hole meeting and destroying each other grows as their numbers increase. Therefore, at any temperature, on the average, an equilibrium will be established. Thus, there is an equilibrium density of free electrons n, that is, the number of free electrons per cubic meter, and an equilibrium density of holes p. In an intrinsic semiconductor, since the number of free electrons equals the number of holes,

$$n_i = p_i \qquad\qquad (1\text{-}166)$$

1-26 IMPURE SEMICONDUCTORS

Free electrons and holes are thermally generated in a semiconductor. However, very many more charge carriers can be created if impurities of the proper type are included in the crystal. Only very small quantities of these impurities need be introduced: the concentration of the impurities are usually measured in fractions of 1 part per million (ppm). The impurity atoms are incorporated in such a way that they take the place of some of the semiconductor atoms in the lattice structure. The usual impurities have either three or five valence electrons.

Donors Let us now consider a crystal of silicon into which an impurity atom which has *five valence electrons* has been introduced. Such a situation is diagrammatically illustrated in Fig. 1-34, where the impurity is arsenic. Four of the valence electrons of the arsenic atom enter into covalent bonds with its neighboring atoms. The fifth valence electron has no atom with which it can enter into a covalent bond. Thus, this electron will be *very* loosely bound to its atom. Hence, only very small amounts of thermal energy are needed to excite this electron so that it breaks its bond and becomes a free electron. Note that a hole is not created when this occurs. However, a positively ionized arsenic atom does result. This atom is fixed in the lattice structure and does not contribute to conduction. An impurity with five valence electrons is called a *donor* since it gives up one of its electrons to become a free electron.

Let us consider the energy-band diagram of a semiconductor with a donor impurity. Such a diagram is shown in Fig. 1-35. The donor atom introduces one additional energy state. If many donor atoms are incorporated, this state becomes an energy band. Actually, the concentration of the

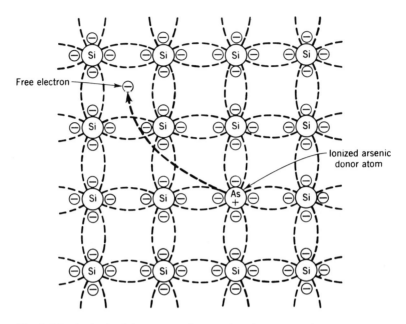

Fig. 1-34 An ionized donor atom in a semiconductor crystal.

donor atoms is kept very small.   Thus, the spacing between donor atoms is large, so that there is very little interaction between them.   Hence, the donor energy band is very narrow (it actually exists only near a donor atom) and often can be treated as a single level that exists at discrete points in the crystal. (Note that there are many such points—even though the percentage of

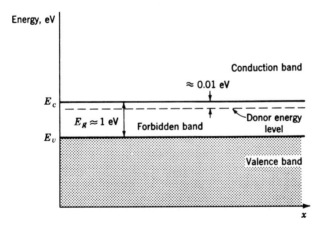

Fig. 1-35 The conduction and valence bands and the donor energy level in a semiconductor with a donor impurity.

donors is very low—since there is an extremely large number of atoms in the crystal.)

The energy gap between the donor level and the conduction band is very small (about 0.01 to 0.06 eV). Thus, at room temperature, essentially all the donor atoms contribute a free electron. Usually, donor concentrations are such that at room temperature the density of the donor atoms (atoms per cubic meter) is much greater than the density of free-electron–hole pairs generated in the intrinsic semiconductor. Thus, the number of free electrons in a crystal with donor impurities (in usual concentrations) is very much greater than in a pure semiconductor.

If a donor impurity is added to a semiconductor, the number of holes is actually reduced. If the number of free electrons is increased, the probability of a free electron and a hole meeting and destroying each other is greatly increased. Thus, increasing the number of free electrons reduces the number of holes. A free electron is eliminated each time a hole is. However, if there are very many more free electrons than holes, the percentage change in the number of holes will be very much greater than the percentage change in the number of free electrons.

Since, in the usual semiconductor with a donor impurity, the free-electron density n is very much greater than the hole density p, such semiconductors are called *n type*. The free electrons in n-type materials are called the *majority carriers*, while the holes are called the *minority carriers*.

Acceptors If an atom with only three valence electrons is incorporated into a semiconductor crystal, one of its covalent bonds will be missing an electron. An electron from an adjacent covalent bond need only gain very little energy in order to leave its covalent bond and enter the vacancy in the impurity's covalent bond. Thus, a *hole* is created without a free electron. The impurity atom now becomes a negative ion which is fixed in position. Since impurities with only three valence electrons can accept a fourth electron, such impurities are called *acceptors*.

An energy-level diagram for a semiconductor with acceptor impurities is shown in Fig. 1-36. The addition of the acceptor causes an energy level to exist very close to the valence band. Actually (see the discussion of donors) this is a very narrow band. Since the gap between the valence band and the acceptor level is very small, essentially all the acceptor-level states are filled at room temperature.

By analogy to the case of donors, the addition of acceptors greatly increases the density of the holes and greatly reduces the free-electron density. For this reason, materials with acceptor impurities are called *p type*. In *p*-type materials, holes are called the *majority carriers*, while free electrons are called the *minority carriers*.

The addition of impurities to a semiconductor is called *doping*. Doping

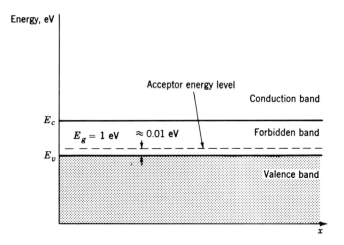

Fig. 1-36 The conduction and valence bands and the acceptor energy level in a semiconductor with an acceptor impurity.

semiconductors can greatly increase the number of available charge carriers and thus increase the conductivity of the material. (Addition of impurities of the order of 1 part in 10^8 can increase the conductivity by a factor of 10.) It can also make one type of charge carrier predominate over another. This is very important in the fabrication of semiconductor devices.

Pure semiconductors are called intrinsic semiconductors. Conversely, impure semiconductors are called *extrinsic semiconductors.*

1-27   CHARGE-CARRIER CONCENTRATIONS IN SEMICONDUCTORS

In Secs. 1-25 and 1-26 we discussed the density of the free electrons and holes on a qualitative basis. Now let us determine these densities quantitatively. In order to obtain the free-electron density, we must know the density of allowed energy states in the conduction band. The density of these states for free electrons in a conductor is given by Eq. (1-151). Note that there the energy E can vary from zero to infinity. Equation (1-151) is derived by assuming that the *potential energy* at the bottom of the conduction band of the conductor is zero. This is a valid assumption in a conductor, where the conduction and valence bands are a single band. However, in a semiconductor, where this is not true, the *density of states* becomes zero at the bottom of the conduction band. Thus, Eq. (1-151) must be modified to give this result. To do this we replace E by $E - E_c$ in Eq. (1-151). Then the density of states in the conduction band is

$$d_{sc}(E) = \frac{4\pi}{h^3}(2me)^{\frac{3}{2}}(E - E_c)^{\frac{1}{2}} \tag{1-167}$$

where E_c is the energy in electron volts, at the base of the conduction band. Then (see Sec. 1-19) to obtain $\rho_e(E)$, the electron density, per unit meter, we must multiply Eq. (1-167) by the Fermi-Dirac distribution [Eq. (1-147)]. Doing this, we obtain

$$\rho_{ec}(E) = \frac{4\pi}{h^3}(2me)^{\frac{3}{2}} \frac{(E - E_c)^{\frac{1}{2}}}{1 - \epsilon^{(E - E_f)/kT}} \tag{1-168}$$

Note that the Fermi-Dirac distribution (1-147) gives the probability of *any* state's being filled. Thus, it does not have to be modified as Eq. (1-167) was. The density of the electrons in the conduction band is found by integrating Eq. (1-168) from the bottom of the conduction band to infinity. Thus,

$$n = \frac{4\pi}{h^3}(2me)^{\frac{3}{2}} \int_{E_c}^{\infty} \frac{(E - E_c)^{\frac{1}{2}}}{1 + \epsilon^{(E - E_f)/kT}} dE \tag{1-169}$$

This integration can be simplified if we note the following. For typical semiconductors at usual operating temperatures

$$\frac{E_c - E_f}{kT} \gg 1$$

Note that kT is a very small number and, in general, $E_c > E_f$. We shall verify this in the next section. Thus, over the entire range of integration, that is, $E \geq E_c$,

$$1 + \epsilon^{(E - E_f)/kT} \approx \epsilon^{(E - E_f)/kT} \tag{1-170}$$

Thus, Eq. (1-169) becomes

$$n = \frac{4\pi(2me)^{\frac{3}{2}}}{h^3} \int_{E_c}^{\infty} (E - E_c)^{\frac{1}{2}} \epsilon^{-(E - E_f)/kT} dE \tag{1-171}$$

To integrate this we make use of the relation

$$\int_0^{\infty} x^{\frac{1}{2}} \epsilon^{-nx} dx = \frac{1}{2n}\sqrt{\frac{\pi}{n}} \tag{1-172}$$

Then, substituting $x = E - E_c$ into Eq. (1-172) and integrating, we obtain

$$n = 2\left(\frac{2\pi mekT}{h^2}\right)^{\frac{3}{2}} \epsilon^{-(E_c - E_f)/kT} \tag{1-173}$$

Note that k is expressed in electron volts per degree Kelvin rather than in joules per degree Kelvin since E_c and E_f are in electron volts.

It is found that Eq. (1-173) is slightly in error. To correct this, m (the mass of the electron) is usually replaced by a slightly different value m_n, which is called the *effective mass of the electron*. If this slight modification is made, it is found that Eq. (1-173) is very accurate. Thus, Eq. (1-173) is often written as

$$n = N_c \epsilon^{-(E_c - E_f)/kT} \tag{1-174}$$

where

$$N_c = 2 \left(\frac{2\pi m_n e k T}{h^2} \right)^{\frac{3}{2}} \tag{1-175}$$

Let us now determine the concentration of holes. The density of (allowed energy) states in the valence band can similarly be found to be

$$d_{sv}(E) = \frac{4\pi}{h^3} (2m_p e)^{\frac{3}{2}} (E_v - E)^{\frac{1}{2}} \tag{1-176}$$

where m_p is the effective mass of a hole. A hole represents an *unoccupied* allowed energy state in the valence band. The probability that a state is unoccupied is 1 minus the probability that it is occupied. Thus, the probability that a state is unoccupied is 1 minus the Fermi-Dirac distribution. Multiplying Eq. (1-176) by this, we obtain

$$\rho_{hv}(E) = \frac{4\pi}{h^3} (2m_p e)^{\frac{3}{2}} (E_v - E)^{\frac{1}{2}} \left(1 - \frac{1}{1 + \epsilon^{(E - E_f)/kT}} \right) \tag{1-177}$$

Then, to obtain the number of holes in the valence band, we integrate from $-\infty$, the lowest possible energy, to the top of the valence band. Thus p, the hole density, is

$$p = \frac{4\pi}{h^3} (2m_p e)^{\frac{3}{2}} \int_{-\infty}^{E_v} (E_v - E)^{\frac{1}{2}} \frac{\epsilon^{(E - E_f)/kT}}{1 + \epsilon^{(E - E_f)/kT}} \, dE \tag{1-178}$$

At usual operating temperatures kT is a very small number, so that

$$\frac{E_f - E_v}{kT} \gg 1 \tag{1-179}$$

(We shall show in the next section that, in general, $E_f > E_v$.) Thus, over the range of integration

$$1 + \epsilon^{(E - E_f)/kT} \approx 1 \tag{1-180}$$

(Note that in the valence band the exponent is negative.) Hence, Eq. (1-178) becomes

$$p = \frac{4\pi}{h^3} (2m_p e)^{\frac{3}{2}} \int_{-\infty}^{E_v} (E_v - E)^{\frac{1}{2}} \epsilon^{(E - E_f)/kT} \, dE$$

Now substitute $x = E_v - E$. This yields

$$p = \frac{4\pi}{h^3} (2m_p e)^{\frac{3}{2}} \epsilon^{(E_v - E_f)/kT} \int_0^\infty x^{\frac{1}{2}} \epsilon^{-x/kT} \, dx \qquad (1\text{-}181)$$

The integral can be evaluated using Eq. (1-172). This yields

$$p = 2\left(\frac{2\pi m_p ekT}{h^2}\right)^{\frac{3}{2}} \epsilon^{-(E_f - E_v)/kT} \qquad (1\text{-}182a)$$

which is often written as

$$p = N_v \epsilon^{-(E_f - E_v)/kT} \qquad (1\text{-}182b)$$

where

$$N_v = 2\left(\frac{2\pi m_p ekT}{h^2}\right)^{\frac{3}{2}} \qquad (1\text{-}183)$$

Note that m_p is the effective mass of a hole.

Equations (1-174) and (1-182) give the carrier concentrations in a semiconductor. At a fixed temperature the only variable in these expressions is the Fermi level E_f. The carrier concentrations are functions of the doping of a semiconductor. Thus, the effect of the doping must manifest itself in a change in E_f.

Now let us consider the product of the free-electron and hole concentrations. Multiplying Eqs. (1-174) and (1-182), we obtain

$$np = N_c N_v \epsilon^{-(E_c - E_v)/kT} \qquad (1\text{-}184)$$

This product is independent of the Fermi level and thus is independent of the impurities. Equation (1-184) illustrates the fact that an increase in the free-electron density due to the addition of impurities decreases the hole density and vice versa (see Sec. 1-26).

Note that $E_c - E_v$ in Eq. (1-184) represents the difference between the energy levels at the bottom of the conduction band and the top of the valence band. That is, it is the energy gap

$$E_g = E_c - E_v \qquad (1\text{-}185)$$

Thus, the product np will be a function of the energy gap and the temperature but not of the impurity concentration. (For silicon the energy gap is 1.11 eV, while it is 0.67 eV for germanium.)

The exponents in Eqs. (1-174) and (1-182) are both negative. Thus, the concentrations of free electrons and holes will both increase if the temperature is increased. In the next section, we shall demonstrate that in a pure semiconductor the Fermi level lies essentially midway between the valence and conduction bands. Thus, $E_c - E_f$ and $E_f - E_v$, in the intrinsic semiconductor, represent essentially $\frac{1}{2}E_g$ (one-half the energy gap). Thus, if the energy gap is reduced, the number of free electrons and holes in an intrinsic semiconductor will increase.

1-28 THE FERMI LEVEL IN A SEMICONDUCTOR

We can use the results of Sec. 1-27 to determine the location of the Fermi level in a semiconductor. Let us first consider an intrinsic semiconductor and then extend our results to impure ones.

From Eqs. (1-174) and (1-182) we have

$$n_i = N_c \epsilon^{-(E_c - E_{fi})/kT} \tag{1-186}$$

$$p_i = N_v \epsilon^{-(E_{fi} - E_v)/kT} \tag{1-187}$$

The subscript i indicates that the material is intrinsic. In an intrinsic semiconductor, the free-electron and hole densities are equal [see Eq. (1-166)]. Thus, we can equate Eqs. (1-186) and (1-187). Doing this, taking the natural logarithms of both sides of the equations, and solving for E_{fi}, we obtain

$$E_{fi} = \tfrac{1}{2}(E_v + E_c) + \tfrac{1}{2}kT \ln \frac{N_v}{N_c} \tag{1-188}$$

Substituting Eqs. (1-175) and (1-183), we have

$$E_{fi} = \frac{1}{2}(E_v + E_c) + \frac{3}{4} kT \ln \frac{m_p}{m_n} \tag{1-189}$$

The quantity kT is usually very small. In addition, the effective mass of a hole m_p is approximately equal to the effective mass of the free electron m_n. Thus, $kT \ln (m_p/m_n)$ will be very small, and we can approximately write

$$E_{fi} \approx \tfrac{1}{2}(E_v + E_c) \tag{1-190}$$

Thus, in an intrinsic semiconductor, the Fermi level is the average of the energies at the top of the valence band and the bottom of the conduction band. That is, *the Fermi level lies midway between the valence and conduction bands in the forbidden band.*

Impure semiconductors Let us determine the effect of doping on the location of the Fermi level. At the start, we shall work with an n-type semiconductor. Let us call the concentration of donor atoms N_D atoms per cubic meter, and at room temperature we shall assume that all the donor atoms are ionized. Thus, the density of free electrons is equal to N_D plus those free electrons which are generated as they would be in an intrinsic semiconductor. Thus, we can write

$$n = N_D + n_i \tag{1-191}$$

For the usual doping concentration and operative temperatures

$$N_D \gg n_i \tag{1-192}$$

Hence, we have

$$n \approx N_D \tag{1-193}$$

Substituting this into Eq. (1-174) and manipulating, we obtain

$$E_f = E_c - kT \ln \frac{N_c}{N_D} \tag{1-194}$$

In general, N_c will be a large number which is greater than N_D. Thus, E_f will lie below the conduction band. If numerical values are substituted into Eq. (1-194), it is found that as donor impurities are added, the Fermi level shifts from a point midway between the valence and conduction bands toward the conduction band. Usually, the Fermi level lies below the donor level.

To obtain the hole density in n-type material, we can substitute Eq. (1-193) into Eq. (1-182). This yields

$$p = \frac{N_v N_c}{N_D} \epsilon^{-(E_c - E_v)/kT} \tag{1-195}$$

[Note that this result could also be obtained by substituting Eq. (1-192) into Eq. (1-184).] This again demonstrates that the product np is independent of impurity concentrations.

Now let us consider that we have a p-type semiconductor with an acceptor concentration N_A. Proceeding as in the case of n-type material, we have for the hole density

$$p \approx N_A \tag{1-196}$$

Then, substituting into Eq. (1-182) and manipulating, we obtain

$$E_f = E_v + kT \ln \frac{N_v}{N_A} \tag{1-197}$$

As acceptor atoms are added, the Fermi level shifts from a point in the middle of the forbidden band toward the valence band. In general, the Fermi level lies above the acceptor energy level.

To obtain the free-electron density in the p-type material, we can either substitute Eq. (1-196) into (1-184) or substitute Eq. (1-197) into (1-174). Either of these yields

$$n = \frac{N_c N_v}{N_A} \epsilon^{-(E_c - E_v)/kT} \tag{1-198}$$

Both Eqs. (1-195) and (1-198) demonstrate that the minority-carrier density in a doped semiconductor increases with increasing temperature and decreasing energy gap. The minority-carrier density decreases as the doping or, equivalently, the majority-carrier density is increased.

1-29 DEFECTS IN THE CRYSTAL LATTICE

Ideally the nuclei of all the atoms in a crystal are arranged in a regular geometric pattern called the *crystal lattice*. In practice not all the nuclei lie in their proper positions in the lattice. Some can be displaced by pressure or shocks. In addition thermal energy can cause some nuclei to become displaced. In the usual semiconductor crystal, only a small fraction of the atoms will be displaced in this way. These displacements in the crystal structure are called *defects*.

At times, defects cause an additional energy level or levels to form in the forbidden band. Electrons in the valence band then can be excited to the conduction band in several steps. For instance, an electron at the top of the valence band ordinarily cannot absorb an energy less than E_g, since then its energy would lie in the forbidden band. However, because of the defect energy levels, valence electrons can receive an amount of energy less than E_g as long as the electron is excited to one of the new levels. The electron can subsequently be excited, by an amount of energy which again may be less than E_g, to the conduction band. This process also produces a hole. Thus, these imperfections increase the rate of generation of free-electron–hole pairs.

The probability that a free electron will lose its energy and recombine with a hole is also increased by the new energy levels. Crystal defects thus increase the rate of generation and recombination of free-electron–hole pairs, and for this reason they are called *recombination centers*.

There are other types of defects which behave similarly to the recombination centers except that the free electrons are held in them for comparatively long times.

1-30 DRIFT OF FREE ELECTRONS AND HOLES

When a voltage generator is applied to a semiconductor, an electric field is established in it and the free electrons and holes are accelerated by the field. Thus, a current results. The discussion of Sec. 1-18 for conduction in metals is applicable, in part, to semiconductors. That is, the free electrons and holes will be accelerated by the electric field and then be scattered. Thus, the charge carriers will move at an average drift velocity which may differ for the free electrons and for the holes. We shall use the values v_{dn} and v_{dp} for the drift velocities of the free electrons and holes, respectively. The drift velocity will be proportional to the electric field and thus to the applied voltage [see Eq. (1-140)]. We can therefore write

$$v_{dn} = -\mu_n \mathscr{E} \tag{1-199a}$$

$$v_{dp} = \mu_p \mathscr{E} \tag{1-199b}$$

The quantities μ_n and μ_p are constants of proportionality called the *mobility of the free electrons and holes,* respectively.   The dimensions of mobility are square meters per volt-second.   Typical values[1†] for μ_n and μ_p at 300°K are $\mu_n = 0.13$ for silicon and 0.38 for germanium, $\mu_p = 0.05$ for silicon and 0.18 for germanium.   If we assume that the electric field lies only in the x direction, then the current density will be in this direction and is [see Eq. (1-141)]

$$\mathscr{J}_{nx} = ne\mu_n\mathscr{E}_x \tag{1-200a}$$

$$\mathscr{J}_{px} = pe\mu_p\mathscr{E}_x \tag{1-200b}$$

where $\mathscr{J}_{nx}$ is the current density in the x direction due to free electrons and $\mathscr{J}_{px}$ is the current density in the x direction due to holes.   Note that Eq. (1-200a) does not have a minus sign since an electric field in the positive x direction will move an electron in the negative x direction.   An electron moving in the negative x direction produces a positive current in the positive x direction.

The total current density is the sum of the current densities due to free electrons and holes.   Thus,

$$\mathscr{J}_x = e(n\mu_n + p\mu_p)\mathscr{E}_x \tag{1-201}$$

The conductivity is defined as the current density produced by a unit electric field (see Sec. 1-18).   Thus,

$$\sigma = e(n\mu_n + p\mu_p) \tag{1-202}$$

If the material is n type, the concentration of the free electrons n will be very much greater than that of the holes p.   In general, μ_n and μ_p will be of the same order of magnitude.   Thus, in n-type material, we can approximate σ by

$$\sigma \approx en\mu_n \tag{1-203}$$

Analogously, in p-type material, the conductivity can be approximated by

$$\sigma \approx ep\mu_p \tag{1-204}$$

In a conductor, σ is given by Eq. (1-203), where n is the free-electron concentration and μ_p is the mobility.

Conductivity in semiconductors is somewhat more complicated than in conductors.   In semiconductors there are two types of charge carriers, free electrons and holes, and they have finite lifetimes.   The minority carriers, at usual concentrations, have lifetimes which lie between 50 and 1000 microseconds (μsec).[1]   The lifetimes of the free electrons and holes are written as τ_n and τ_p, respectively.   In a conductor, the charge carriers are only free electrons which do not recombine with holes.   For this reason, we cannot use all the relations of Sec. 1-18 in the discussion of semiconductor conductivity.

† Numbered references will be found at the end of the chapter.

It may appear as though drift of charge carriers were the most important mechanism of conductivity in semiconductors. However, in the next section, we shall discuss another mechanism which is of prime importance to the operation of junction transistors.

1-31   DIFFUSION OF FREE ELECTRONS AND HOLES

Even if no electric field is applied to a semiconductor, the free electrons and holes do not remain motionless. Thermal excitation causes them to move in a random fashion, and during the course of this motion they can be scattered by collisions with atoms. This random motion of the free electrons and holes is termed *diffusion*.

Diffusion tends to keep the concentration of the free electrons and holes uniform throughout a semiconductor. For instance, suppose that in some way, we insert a number of free electrons, at one point, into a block of silicon. At the first instant, the free-electron density will be higher at the point of insertion than in the rest of the block. To simplify matters, assume that initially all this excess charge is enclosed in a spherical portion of the block. All the free electrons in the block will be diffusing *randomly*. Thus, some of the free electrons from inside the sphere will diffuse outside of it, while some of those outside the sphere will diffuse into it. However, the free-electron density is much higher inside the sphere. Thus, on the average, *more* electrons will leave the sphere than will enter it. Hence, the net effect of the diffusion will be, after some time, to establish a uniform distribution of free electrons. This discussion also applies to the diffusion of holes.

It may appear as though drift were involved in the previous example. That is, if there is a large concentration of electrons in a region, their own electric fields should repel them and cause them to leave the region. Thus, in the example of the last paragraph, drift as well as diffusion would occur. However, this is usually *not* the case. For the usual concentrations of free electrons or holes the lattice structure shields the charge carriers from each other's fields. That is, the field set up by a charge carrier alters the location of the nuclei of nearby atoms slightly. This changes their fields, which tends to cancel the effects of fields of the mobile charge carriers. Thus, the motion in the example of the last paragraph is due almost entirely to diffusion.

The diffusion of charge carriers will always (on the average) take place from a region of high density to a region of low density. At any point the average rate of diffusion is proportional to the variation in the densities of the charge carriers. The current density is proportional to this rate of diffusion. Thus, if we consider variations only in the x direction, we can write

$$\mathscr{J}_{nx} = eD_n \frac{\partial n}{\partial x} \tag{1-205a}$$

In a similar way, if the free-electron density varies in the y and z directions, we can write

$$\mathcal{I}_{ny} = eD_n \frac{\partial n}{\partial y} \tag{1-205b}$$

$$\mathcal{I}_{nz} = eD_n \frac{\partial n}{\partial z} \tag{1-205c}$$

where D_n is a constant of proportionality called the *free-electron diffusion constant*. Its units are square meters per second. Typical values[1] of D_n at $T = 300°K$ are 0.0034 meter²/sec for silicon and 0.0098 meter²/sec for germanium.

Note that current is in the positive x direction if $\partial n/\partial x$ is positive. In this case electrons move in the negative x direction. Thus, no minus sign is associated with Eqs. (1-205).

An analogous relation exists for the hole currents. Now a minus sign must be incorporated since a hole has a positive charge.

$$\mathcal{I}_{px} = -eD_p \frac{\partial p}{\partial x} \tag{1-206a}$$

$$\mathcal{I}_{py} = -eD_p \frac{\partial p}{\partial y} \tag{1-206b}$$

$$\mathcal{I}_{pz} = -eD_p \frac{\partial p}{\partial z} \tag{1-206c}$$

where D_p is the *hole diffusion constant*. Typical values of D_p at $T = 300°K$ are 0.0013 meter²/sec for silicon and 0.0046 meter²/sec for germanium.

Both drift and diffusion involve the motion of charge carriers. The parameters of these two mechanisms, the mobility and the diffusion constants, are related by the *Einstein diffusion equation*,[2] which states

$$D_n = kT\mu_n \tag{1-207a}$$

$$D_p = kT\mu_p \tag{1-207b}$$

Note that k is in units of electron volts per degree Kelvin.

In a subsequent discussion we shall see that diffusion of charge carriers is of prime importance to the operation of junction transistors.

1-32 CHARGE-CARRIER TRANSPORT—THE CONTINUITY EQUATION

The total current density in a semiconductor at any point is the sum of the drift and diffusion current densities. For the sake of simplicity, we shall assume that all the current is in the x direction and that there are no variations in the y and z directions. Then the total free-electron current density is given by the sum of Eqs. (1-200a) and (1-205a). Thus,

$$\mathscr{I}_{nx} = e\left(n\mu_n\mathscr{E}_x + D_n\frac{\partial n}{\partial x}\right) \qquad (1\text{-}208a)$$

In a similar way, we can write the y and z components of currents

$$\mathscr{I}_{ny} = e\left(n\mu_n\mathscr{E}_y + D_n\frac{\partial n}{\partial y}\right) \qquad (1\text{-}208b)$$

$$\mathscr{I}_{nz} = e\left(n\mu_n\mathscr{E}_z + D_n\frac{\partial n}{\partial z}\right) \qquad (1\text{-}208c)$$

However, as noted above, we shall not discuss the y and z components here. Similarly, the total hole current is

$$\mathscr{I}_{px} = e\left(p\mu_p\mathscr{E}_x - D_p\frac{\partial p}{\partial x}\right) \qquad (1\text{-}209)$$

The total current density, at a point, is the sum of the current densities due to free electrons and holes. Thus,

$$\mathscr{I}_x = e(n\mu_n + p\mu_p)\mathscr{E}_x + e\left(D_n\frac{\partial n}{\partial x} - D_p\frac{\partial p}{\partial x}\right) \qquad (1\text{-}210)$$

This then is the total current density at any point in a semiconductor.

Continuity equation   We shall now discuss a relation, called the *continuity equation*, which is very helpful in describing semiconductor behavior. To obtain this equation, we shall determine the rate of change of the free-electron and/or hole density in a small volume. Again, we shall work with a one-dimensional variation. Consider Fig. 1-37, where a cube whose sides are length Δx is shown. The current density is only in the x direction. The current entering the left-hand side of the cube is I and that leaving the right side is $I + \Delta I$. Thus, a charge of I coul/sec flows into the cube through the left-hand side while a charge of $I + \Delta I$ coul/sec leaves the cube through the right face. Thus, a net charge of $-\Delta I$ coul/sec is accumulated in the box.

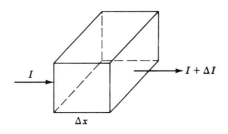

Fig. 1-37 A volume used to illustrate conservation of charge.

Now let us consider that the charge carriers are free electrons of charge $-e$. Then N, the number of free electrons accumulated in the box in time Δt, is

$$N = \frac{\Delta I}{e} \Delta t \tag{1-211}$$

Now let us assume that the box is small enough to permit the free-electron density to be considered approximately constant over the entire volume. The change in free-electron density in a time Δt is given by N divided by the volume of the box. Thus,

$$\Delta n \approx \frac{\Delta I \, \Delta t}{e(\Delta x)^3} \tag{1-212}$$

The current density $\mathscr{J}_x$ is given by I divided by the area of the face that the current enters. Then, manipulating Eq. (1-212), we obtain

$$\frac{\Delta n}{\Delta t} \approx \frac{\Delta \mathscr{J}_{nx}}{e \, \Delta x} \tag{1-213}$$

Now, let us take the limit so that these relations become exact. That is, let Δx and Δt become differentially small. Then,

$$\frac{dn}{dt} = \frac{1}{e} \frac{d\mathscr{J}_{nx}}{dx} \tag{1-214}$$

Note that dn/dt is the rate of change of the number of free electrons per unit volume with time. Equation (1-214) gives the rate of change of the electron density at a point as a function of the rate of change of current density with distance.

There are other factors that affect charge density. The free electrons are continuously being generated and recombining with holes within the semiconductor. Let us assume that in a unit volume g_n free electrons per second are created. g_n is called the *generation rate for free electrons*. In addition, free electrons are constantly recombining with holes. Let us assume that, per unit volume, r_n free electrons per second recombine with holes. r_n is called the *recombination rate for free electrons*. Thus, per unit volume, if we consider only generation and recombination

$$\frac{dn}{dt} = g_n - r_n \tag{1-215}$$

That is, the change in electron density per unit time is the difference between the rate of formation and recombination of free electrons. Equations (1-214) and (1-215) represent two independent effects on dn/dt. Thus, to obtain the complete expression for dn/dt, both effects should be included. Hence,

$$\frac{dn}{dt} = g_n - r_n + \frac{1}{e} \frac{d\mathscr{J}_{nx}}{dx} \tag{1-216}$$

This is one form of the *continuity equation for free electrons.* We can proceed in an analogous fashion and obtain the *continuity equation for holes*

$$\frac{dp}{dt} = g_p - r_p - \frac{1}{e}\frac{d\mathcal{J}_{px}}{dx} \tag{1-217}$$

Let us now manipulate these equations into some different forms. Substituting Eqs. (1-208) and (1-209) into Eqs. (1-216) and (1-217), we obtain

$$\frac{\partial n}{\partial t} = g_n - r_n + \mu_n \mathcal{E}_x \frac{\partial n}{\partial x} + \mu_n n \frac{\partial \mathcal{E}_x}{\partial x} + D_n \frac{\partial^2 n}{\partial x^2} \tag{1-218a}$$

$$\frac{\partial p}{\partial t} = g_p - r_p - \mu_p \mathcal{E}_x \frac{\partial p}{\partial x} - \mu_p p \frac{\partial \mathcal{E}_x}{\partial x} + D_p \frac{\partial^2 p}{\partial x^2} \tag{1-218b}$$

Note that we have used partial derivatives since n and p are functions of both x and t.

Now we shall express the quantities g_n, r_n, g_p, and r_p in a more useful form. First, some assumptions about these quantities must be made. The rate of recombination of free electrons depends upon their density n. We shall assume that r_n is proportional to n. That is,

$$r_n = k_n n \tag{1-219}$$

where k_n is a constant of proportionality. It is found that this assumption yields accurate results. At some value of n, which we shall call n_0, the rate of generation and rate of recombination of electrons will be equal. That is, if $n = n_0$, an equilibrium is established, and, on the average, n will remain constant. g_n is the rate of generation of free electrons. This depends only upon the temperature, impurities, and energy gap. Thus, in a given material at a fixed temperature g_n will be constant. Then, when $n = n_0$,

$$g_n = r_n|_{n=n_0} = k_n n_0 \tag{1-220}$$

Thus, we can write [see Eq. (1-211)]

$$g_n - r_n = k_n(n_0 - n) \tag{1-221}$$

Let us now evaluate k_n. Note that k_n is a constant. Thus, if we can establish its value for any one set of conditions, we have established it for all conditions. Let us consider the case where the current density $\mathcal{J}_{nx}$ is zero. Then [see Eqs. (1-216) and (1-221)]

$$\frac{dn}{dt} = k_n(n_0 - n) \tag{1-222}$$

Now suppose that the density of free electrons is such that

$$n = n_0 + 1$$

That is, there is one free electron per cubic meter in excess of the equilibrium value. Thus, at that instant of time,

$$\frac{dn}{dt} = k_n \tag{1-223}$$

The average lifetime of a free electron is τ_n (see Sec. 1-30). This is the average length of time that a free electron will exist before it recombines with a hole. Thus, if there is one free electron above the equilibrium value, it will, on the average, recombine in τ_n sec and the density will then become n_0 and remain at that value. Thus, when $n = n_0 + 1$, we have $dn/dt = 1/\tau_n$. Substituting this into Eq. (1-223), we obtain

$$k_n = \frac{1}{\tau_n} \tag{1-224}$$

Then, substituting Eqs. (1-221) and (1-224) into Eq. (1-218a), we have

$$\frac{dn}{dt} = -\frac{n - n_0}{\tau_n} + \mu_n \mathscr{E}_x \frac{\partial n}{\partial x} + \mu_n n \frac{\partial \mathscr{E}_x}{\partial x} + D_n \frac{\partial^2 n}{\partial x^2} \tag{1-225a}$$

In a similar way, we can write for holes,

$$\frac{dp}{dt} = -\frac{p - p_0}{\tau_p} - \mu_p \mathscr{E}_x \frac{\partial p}{\partial x} - \mu_p p \frac{\partial \mathscr{E}_x}{\partial x} + D_p \frac{\partial^2 p}{\partial x^2} \tag{1-225b}$$

Equations (1-225) are called the *continuity equations for free electrons and holes*, respectively. They hold in *n*-type, *p*-type, and intrinsic materials. Often we are interested in minority-carrier concentrations. In this case, if we are dealing with free electrons, a subscript *p* is added to indicate that the material is *p* type. Similarly, in *n*-type material, a subscript *n* is appended to the hole quantities. For instance, in *p*-type materials, Eq. (1-225a) would be

$$\frac{\partial n_p}{\partial t} = \frac{n_p - n_{0p}}{\tau_{np}} + \mu_n \mathscr{E}_x \frac{\partial n_p}{\partial x} + \mu_n n_p \frac{\partial \mathscr{E}_x}{\partial x} + D_n \frac{\partial^2 n_p}{\partial x^2} \tag{1-226}$$

The continuity equation can be extended to three dimensions by adding the appropriate derivatives with respect to *y* and *z*. For instance, Eq. (1-225a) becomes

$$\frac{\partial n}{\partial t} = -\frac{n - n_0}{\tau_n} + \mu_n \left(\mathscr{E}_x \frac{\partial n}{\partial x} + \mathscr{E}_y \frac{\partial n}{\partial y} + \mathscr{E}_z \frac{\partial n}{\partial z} \right)$$
$$+ \mu_n n \left(\frac{\partial \mathscr{E}_x}{\partial x} + \frac{\partial \mathscr{E}_y}{\partial y} + \frac{\partial \mathscr{E}_z}{\partial z} \right) + D_n \left(\frac{\partial^2 n}{\partial x^2} + \frac{\partial^2 n}{\partial y^2} + \frac{\partial^2 n}{\partial z^2} \right) \tag{1-227}$$

Similar results can be obtained for Eq. (1-225b).

Let us now consider some examples. Very often the only motion of the charge carriers is due to diffusion. Thus, the electric field will be zero.

We shall assume that $\mathscr{E}_x$ is zero in our examples. Hence, Eq. (1-225a) becomes, for the free electrons,

$$\frac{\partial n}{\partial t} = -\frac{n - n_0}{\tau_n} + D_n \frac{\partial^2 n}{\partial x^2} \tag{1-228}$$

Now, let us consider a specific problem. Suppose that we have a block of semiconductor that has been at a constant temperature for a long time. Then the free-electron density n will be uniform throughout the block and be equal to the equilibrium value n_0. Equation (1-228) states that

$$\frac{\partial n}{\partial t} = 0 \tag{1-229}$$

This is as expected since the block is at equilibrium.

Now assume that the block is further excited by shining a beam of light over all of it uniformly for a long time. An equilibrium density n_1 will be established. Now, remove the light beam. At the first instant the free-electron density will be n_1. However, the *equilibrium density* will be n_0, as before. Thus, Eq. (1-228) yields

$$\frac{\partial n}{\partial t} = -\frac{n - n_0}{\tau_n} \tag{1-230}$$

Since there is no variation with x, we can use total derivatives and write Eq. (1-230) as

$$\frac{d(n - n_0)}{dt} + \frac{n - n_0}{\tau_n} = 0 \tag{1-231}$$

Note that $d(n - n_0)/dt = dn/dt$ since n_0 is a constant. Solving Eq. (1-231), we obtain

$$n - n_0 = A\epsilon^{-t/\tau_n} \tag{1-232}$$

where A is a constant. At $t = 0$, $n = n_1$. Then, substituting in Eq. (1-232), we have

$$n = n_0 + (n_1 - n_0)\epsilon^{-t/\tau_n} \tag{1-233}$$

Thus, the density returns to the equilibrium value on an exponential basis. τ_n is the time constant of the exponential. Thus, in time $t = \tau_n$, the difference between the concentration and its equilibrium values falls off to $1/\epsilon$ of its initial value. Note that τ_n is also the average lifetime of a free electron.

Now let us consider another example. To simplify matters, let us establish a situation where n does not vary with time. Consider Fig. 1-38. A very long semiconductor crystal is shown there. Assume that, in some way, we continuously insert free electrons at the left-hand end of the semiconductor, i.e., at $x = 0$. This causes the density of the free electrons n to

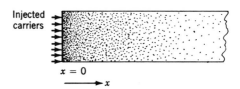

Injected carriers

Fig. 1-38 Free electrons injected into a long semiconductor crystal. The shading indicates free-electron density above the equilibrium value n_0.

$x = 0$

$\longrightarrow x$

be greater than the equilibrium value n_0 at $x = 0$. The inserted electrons diffuse into the material and, on the average, recombine in τ_n sec with holes. Thus, the excess free-electron density $n - n_0$ falls off to zero as the distance from the point of injection is increased. The value of n *is* a function of time; e.g., at the first instant all of the block for $x > 0$ will have a density n_0. However, after a sufficiently long time has elapsed, the density reaches an equilibrium value, so that it is a function of x but not of time. Let us solve Eq. (1-228) assuming that this equilibrium has been reached. Then $dn/dt = 0$, and we can write Eq. (1-228) as

$$0 = -\frac{n - n_0}{\tau_n} + D_n \frac{d^2(n - n_0)}{dx^2} \tag{1-234}$$

where we have made use of the fact that

$$\frac{d^2(n - n_0)}{dx^2} = \frac{d^2 n}{dx^2} \tag{1-235}$$

Then, solving Eq. (1-234), we have

$$n - n_0 = A_1 \epsilon^{-x/L_n} + A_2 \epsilon^{x/L_n} \tag{1-236}$$

where

$$L_n = \sqrt{D_n \tau_n} \tag{1-237}$$

We have assumed that the block is very long (ideally, infinite in length). Thus, the second exponential becomes very large for large x. It is unreasonable to assume that the distribution behaves in this way, e.g., approaches infinity for the infinite block. Thus,

$$A_2 = 0 \tag{1-238}$$

In addition, we shall assume that the free-electron density at $x = 0$ is known and that $n - n_0|_{x=0} = N(0)$. Then, substituting in Eq. (1-236), we have

$$n = n_0 + N(0)\epsilon^{-x/L_n} \tag{1-239}$$

Thus, the free-electron density falls off from its value $n_0 + N(0)$ to the equilibrium value n_0 exponentially with x. Note that the exponential term falls off by a factor of $1/\epsilon$ every L_n meters.

We shall now demonstrate that L_n is the average diffusion length for free electrons. That is, it is the length, on the average, that a free electron will diffuse before it recombines with a hole. This average length

$$L_{\mathrm{av}} = v_{\mathrm{av}}\tau_n \tag{1-240}$$

is the average velocity of the electron multiplied by its lifetime. The current density due to moving free electrons is given by [see Eq. (1-141)]

$$\mathscr{I}_e = -ev_{\mathrm{av}}n' \tag{1-241}$$

where, in this case, n' is the (average) free-electron density that contributes to diffusion. If the free-electron density is uniform, there is no diffusion current. Therefore, for the problem under consideration, n' should be only the free-electron density which differs from n_0, the equilibrium value. Thus,

$$n' = n - n_0 \tag{1-242}$$

Substituting this value [see Eq. (1-239)] into Eq. (1-241), we have

$$\mathscr{I}_e = -ev_{\mathrm{av}}N(0)\epsilon^{-x/L_n} \tag{1-243}$$

The diffusion current is also given by Eq. (1-205). Substituting Eq. (1-239) into this and manipulating, we have

$$\mathscr{I}_e = -\frac{eD_n}{L_n} N(0)\epsilon^{-x/L_n} \tag{1-244}$$

Equate Eqs. (1-243) and (1-244), solve for v_{av}, substitute this into Eq. (1-240) and, finally, compare this with Eq. (1-237). This yields

$$L_{\mathrm{av}} = L_n \tag{1-245}$$

Thus, we have determined that L_n is the average diffusion length of the free electrons.

As a final example, let us consider a time-varying distribution. We shall extend the previous example to one where the injected free electrons are such that n varies with time about the equilibrium value. That is, at $x = 0$

$$n - n_0 = N(0) \cos \omega t \tag{1-246}$$

In this case, the solution to the continuity equation will consist of two parts, one which falls off exponentially with time and another which varies sinusoidally. After a short time, the first part of the solution becomes negligible. Let us determine the second one. This is analogous to determining the sinusoidal steady-state solution in network analysis. To do this, we use phasors instead of sinusoids; i.e., we replace $A \sin(\omega t + \phi)$ by $Ae^{j(\omega t + \phi)}$. Thus,

$$n - n_0|_{\mathrm{phasor}} = \mathbf{N}(x)\epsilon^{j\omega t} \tag{1-247}$$

Note that $\mathbf{N}(x)$ is not a function of time. However, it generally will be a complex number. Its magnitude and phase angle are equal to the magnitude and phase angle of the sinusoid. In this book, we use boldface letters for complex quantities. Then, substituting Eq. (1-247) into Eq. (1-228), we obtain

$$j\omega\mathbf{N}(x)e^{j\omega t} = -\frac{\mathbf{N}(x)e^{j\omega t}}{\tau_n} + D_n\epsilon^{j\omega t}\frac{d^2\mathbf{N}(x)}{dx^2} \tag{1-248}$$

Manipulating, and substituting Eq. (1-237), we have

$$0 = -\mathbf{N}(x)\frac{1 + j\omega\tau_n}{L_n{}^2} + \frac{d^2\mathbf{N}(x)}{dx^2} \tag{1-249}$$

Now let us compare this with the time-invariant case. Substitute Eqs. (1-237) and (1-247) into Eq. (1-234) and manipulate. This yields

$$0 = -\frac{\mathbf{N}(x)}{L_n{}^2} - \frac{d^2\mathbf{N}(x)}{dx^2} \tag{1-250}$$

where, in this case,

$$\mathbf{N}(x) = n - n_0 \tag{1-251}$$

Note that this is compatible with Eq. (1-247) since $\omega = 0$ in the non-time-varying case.

Equations (1-249) and (1-251) are the same except that L_n has been replaced by $L_n/\sqrt{1 + j\omega\tau_n}$. Note that when $\omega = 0$, they are identical. Thus, the solution of Eq. (1-249) will essentially be the same as that for Eq. (1-239) except that L_n must be replaced by $L_n/\sqrt{1 + j\omega\tau_n}$.

All the examples were in terms of free electrons, but they could have just as well been in terms of holes, in which case we would have worked with Eq. (1-225b) instead of with Eq. (1-225a).

1-33 THE HALL EFFECT

Let us consider that a block of n-type semiconductor carrying a current I is placed in a magnetic field, which is perpendicular to the current, as illustrated in Fig. 1-39. The current I is in the x direction while the magnetic field $\mathscr{B}_z$ lies in the z direction. Points a and b are in the upper and lower faces of the block, respectively. The charge carriers are free electrons. Because of the magnetic field, they experience a force in the negative y direction (see Sec. 1-5). This forces some free electrons down to the lower surface of the block, which causes a deficiency of electrons at the top of the block. Thus, there will be a net positive charge there. The positive charges at the top of the block and the negative charges at the bottom of the block set up an electric field. Let us assume that this field $-\mathscr{E}_y$ is uniform throughout the

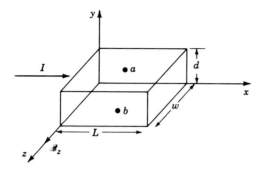

Fig. 1-39 A block used to illustrate the Hall effect. Points a and b are in the upper and lower faces, respectively.

block. The electric field exerts an upward force on electrons that is opposite to the magnetic force. Eventually, an equilibrium will be established wherein the magnetic and electric forces cancel each other. This occurs when

$$e\mathscr{B}_z v_d = \mathscr{E}_y e \tag{1-252}$$

where v_d is the magnitude of the average drift velocity of the electrons. Since the electric field is uniform, the voltage drop V_{ab} is given by [see Eq. (1-5)]

$$V_{ab} = \mathscr{E}_y d \tag{1-253}$$

Then, substituting Eq. (1-252), we obtain

$$V_{ab} = \mathscr{B}_z v_d d \tag{1-254}$$

Substituting Eq. (1-141), which holds for free electrons in a semiconductor as well as in a conductor, we have

$$V_{ab} = \frac{\mathscr{B}_z d}{ne} \mathscr{J}_x \tag{1-255}$$

(note that v_d actually is negative). The current density is equal to the current I divided by the cross-sectional area dw. Hence,

$$V_{ab} = \frac{\mathscr{B}_z}{new} I \tag{1-256}$$

This voltage is called the *Hall effect voltage*. The entire process is called the *Hall effect*.

A quantity called the *Hall coefficient* is often defined as

$$R_H = \frac{1}{ne} \tag{1-257}$$

Substituting this into Eq. (1-256) and manipulating, we obtain

$$R_H = \frac{V_{ab}w}{\mathscr{B}_z I} \tag{1-258}$$

The quantities V_{ab}, w, $\mathscr{B}_z$, and I can easily be measured experimentally. Thus, R_H can be determined. Since e is known, the free-electron density n can easily be measured using the Hall effect.

From Eq. (1-203) we have the conductivity of n-type material as

$$\sigma = en\mu_n$$

Manipulating this and substituting Eq. (1-257), we have

$$\mu_n = \sigma R_H \tag{1-259}$$

Conductivity also can be easily measured. Thus, the mobility of the free electrons can also be obtained from Hall effect measurements.

In this discussion we have considered free electrons in a semiconductor. The same discussion would also apply to free electrons in a conductor. In addition, a very similar discussion would apply to holes in a p-type material. The polarity of the Hall effect voltage is reversed in this case. Thus, Hall effect measurements can be used to determine whether a material is n type or p type.

REFERENCES

1. Middlebrook, R. D.: "An Introduction to Junction Transistor Theory," app. B, John Wiley & Sons, Inc., New York, 1957.
2. Einstein, A.: Über die von der molekularkinetischen Theorie der Wärme gefordete Bewegung von in ruhenden Flüssigkeiten suspendierten Teilchen, *Ann. Physik*, vol. 17, pp. 549–560, 1905.

BIBLIOGRAPHY

Alley, C. L., and K. W. Atwood: "Electrical Engineering," 2d ed., chaps. 1 and 2, John Wiley & Sons, Inc., New York, 1962.
Beam, W. R.: "Electronics of Solids," chaps. 1–4, McGraw-Hill Book Company, New York, 1965.
Chirlian, P. M., and A. H. Zemanian: "Electronics," chaps. 1, 2, and 4, McGraw-Hill Book Company, New York, 1961.
Millman, J., and C. C. Halkias: "Electronic Devices and Circuits," chaps. 1, 2, 3, and 5, McGraw-Hill Book Company, New York, 1967.
van der Ziel, A.: "Solid State Physical Electronics," 2d ed., chaps. 1–10, Prentice-Hall, Inc., Englewood Cliffs, N.J., 1968.
Wang, S.: "Solid-state Electronics," chaps. 1–5, McGraw-Hill Book Company, New York, 1966.

PROBLEMS

1-1. Find the force on a 1-coul charge placed 1 meter from another 1-coul charge in a vacuum.

1-2. Find the force on a 1-coul charge placed at point P of Fig. 1-40.

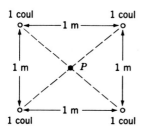

Fig. 1-40

1-3. Find the electric field as a function of distance about a point charge Q.

1-4. Find the electric field at point P of Fig. 1-40.

1-5. Find the voltage drop V_{ab} in Fig. 1-41.

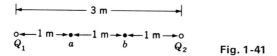

Fig. 1-41

1-6. The potential in a certain region, i.e., the potential difference between point (x,y,z) in the region and a fixed point, is

$$V = 100ze^x \cos y$$

Compute the x, y, and z components of the electric field in the region.

1-7. An electron is accelerated from rest in a region where the electric field is uniform and equal to 100 volts/meter. Compute the electron's velocity, kinetic energy, and displacement after 1 nanosecond, (i.e., 10^{-9} sec).

1-8. An electron is injected into the parallel-plate capacitor of Fig. 1-5 at point P with an initial velocity v_0 which is perpendicular to the plates. The polarity of the battery is opposite to that of Fig. 1-5. What is the minimum value of V if the electron is not to strike the right-hand plate?

1-9. In Fig. 1-42, $V = 200$ volts. An electron which has been accelerated through 100 volts is injected into the left-hand hole at an angle $\theta = 60°$. The electron is to leave the right-hand hole. Determine the value of b.

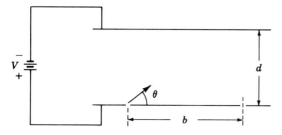

Fig. 1-42

1-10. Repeat Prob. 1-9 but now adjust θ so that b has its maximum value.

1-11. What is the velocity of an electron which has been accelerated through 300 volts?

1-12. An electron is injected at right angles to a uniform magnetic field of 0.1 weber/meter^2 at a velocity of 3×10^5 meters/sec. What is the radius of the circle that the electron traces? How long does it take for the electron to traverse a semicircle?

1-13. An electron which has been accelerated through a difference of potential of 500 volts is injected into a region where the magnetic field is 1 weber/meter^2. The initial velocity of the electron is perpendicular to the magnetic field. What is the radius of the path of the electron?

1-14. A particle whose charge is equal to that of the electron but whose mass is unknown is accelerated through a potential difference of V and injected into a magnetic field B. The initial velocity of the particle is perpendicular to the magnetic field. The particle moves in a circle of radius R. Determine the mass of the particle in terms of B, V, e, and R.

1-15. In a certain region the electric and magnetic fields are parallel to each other and lie in the positive x direction. The electric field intensity is 100 volts/meter, and the magnetic flux density is 0.1 weber/meter^2. An electron is accelerated through 100 volts and then is injected into the region at $x = 0$, at an angle of 30° with the positive x axis. The z component of the initial velocity is 0. After the projection of the electron on the yz plane has gone through one complete revolution, what is the x coordinate of the electron?

1-16. In a certain region, the electric field $\mathscr{E}$ and the magnetic flux density $\mathscr{B}$ are in the positive x direction. An electron whose initial velocity is v_0 at an angle of 45° with the axis is injected into this region at the origin. Determine the relation among the fields and v_0 such that the electron is returned to the origin.

1-17. An electron is placed midway between the parallel plates of Fig. 1-42, where $V = 100$ volts and $d = 0.1$ meter. A magnetic field $\mathscr{B}$ is to be set up perpendicular to the paper such that the electron does not strike either plate. Determine the minimum value that $\mathscr{B}$ can have.

1-18. Use the same configuration as in Prob. 1-17 but now assume that an electron is injected with an initial velocity v_{0x} which is parallel to the plates. The electron's velocity is to remain constant at v_{0x}. Determine the direction and magnitude of a magnetic field which can accomplish this.

1-19. An electron is accelerated from rest through a potential of 100,000 volts. What is its final velocity? Do not ignore relativistic effects.

1-20. An electron is to be accelerated from rest to a velocity of $0.99996c$. What accelerating potential must be used? Compute the potential in two ways, one considering relativistic effects and the other ignoring them.

1-21. In the cathode-ray tube of Fig. 1-11, $b = 1$ cm, $d = 0.5$ cm, and $V_a = 5000$ volts. If a deflection voltage of 100 volts is to produce a 1.0-cm deflection h, what must the value of L be?

1-22. The deflection voltage in the cathode-ray tube of Prob. 1-21 is $V_d \cos 2\pi f_0 t$, where $f_0 = 100 \times 10^6$ Hz. If any one electron is to remain in the region between the deflection plates for no more than 0.1 cycle, what is the minimum value of V_a that can be used?

1-23. For the magnetic-deflection cathode-ray tube of Fig. 1-12, $L = 100$ cm, $b = 1$ cm, and $V_a = 2000$ volts. Compute the value of $\mathscr{B}$ necessary to produce a deflection h of 5 cm.

1-24. Repeat Prob. 1-23 but now use $V_a = 4000$ volts.

1-25. Electrons are accelerated through a potential of 4000 volts in an electron gun. They are to be focused by the arrangement of Fig. 1-13. Compute all values of $\mathscr{B}$ which will accomplish this.

1-26. Discuss the experimental evidence that led to the postulation of the Bohr atom.

1-27. An atom, when excited, emits light at wavelengths of 6000 and 5500 Å. Using zero as a reference level, i.e., for the unexcited atom, compute the allowed energy levels of the atom.

1-28. Determine four different frequencies that can be radiated by the mercury atom.

1-29. Can radiation of 2656 Å take place from the mercury atom? Explain your answer.

1-30. The probability distribution that a particle lies at some point on the x axis is

$$p(x) = \tfrac{1}{2}\epsilon^{-|x|}$$

Compute the probability that the particle lies between $-1 \leq x \leq \tfrac{1}{2}$.

1-31. What is the probability that the particle of Prob. 1-30 lies outside the range $-1 \leq x \leq 1$?

1-32. What is the de Broglie wavelength of an electron which has been accelerated through 1000 volts?

1-33. Repeat Prob. 1-32 but now assume that the accelerating potential is 10^6 volts. Do not neglect relativistic effects.

1-34. An electron moves along the x axis. It is constrained to lie in the region $0 \leq x \leq 10^{-8}$ meter. The potential distribution is zero within the region. Compute the allowed energy levels of the electron and the probability distribution of finding it at a point in the range $0 \leq x \leq 10^{-8}$.

1-35. Discuss the Pauli exclusion principle.

1-36. Determine the number of electrons which can be in each of the $K, L, M, N, O, P,$ and Q shells.

1-37. Use the technique of Sec. 1-15 to characterize seven atoms each of whose outer shell is filled.

1-38. Discuss energy bands in a crystal in terms of Fig. 1-19.

1-39. Assume that the interatomic distance of the crystal characterized in Fig. 1-19 could be varied at will. Determine the interatomic distances that will result in the crystal's being a conductor, semiconductor, or insulator.

1-40. The energy gap in a certain insulator is 5 volts, and its interatomic spacing is 5 Å. The insulator is 10 cm long. At a temperature of 0°K, how much voltage must be applied to the insulator if a current is to result?

1-41. A certain conductor has a free-electron density which is 10^{25} electrons per cubic meter. It has a current whose density is 10^6 amp/meter^2. Compute the drift velocity of the free electrons.

1-42. Why is the mean free path of the free electrons in a conductor at room temperature essentially independent of the drift velocity?

1-43. Compute the density of the free electrons in a conductor which have energies greater than $2E_f$ at a temperature of $T = 2000°K$. Assume that the energies between $2E_f$ and ∞ all lie in an allowed energy band. Make the approximation

$$\frac{1}{1 + \epsilon^{(E-E_f)/kT}} = \frac{1}{\epsilon^{(E-E_f)/kT}}$$

in the range of integration.

1-44. A right-circular cylindrical emitter has a diameter of 1 mm and a length of 1 cm. Its temperature is 1000°K. Neglecting Schottky effects, compute the maximum current that can be drawn from the emitter if it is made of tungsten, thoriated tungsten, and barium oxide.

1-45. Emitters of the same dimensions are to be made of tungsten, thoriated tungsten, and barium oxide. The oxide cathode is to be operated at $T = 1000°K$. If the other two cathodes are to produce the same emission current, at what temperatures must they be operated?

1-46. Assume that the cathode of diode of Fig. 1-29 is excited photoelectrically rather than thermionically. The work function of the cathode is 1 eV. If V_{bb} is adjusted so that there is no external potential barrier between the cathode and the plate, what is the minimum frequency of light that will produce a nonzero I_b?

1-47. Repeat Prob. 1-46 but now assume that V_{bb} is adjusted so that an electron traveling from the cathode to the plate must surmount an external potential barrier of 1 volt.

1-48. If, in Fig. 1-29, the work function of the cathode is 1 eV, while that of the plate is 5 eV, and if $V_{bb} = 0$, what minimum kinetic energy must an emitted electron have if it is to reach the plate?

1-49. Describe the mechanism of conduction by holes.

1-50. Describe why doping a semiconductor with an acceptor impurity reduces the number of free electrons.

1-51. A pure semiconductor operating at $T = 3000°K$ has a free-electron density of $n = 3 \times 10^{19}$ electrons per cubic meter. Assume that m_n and m_p are both approximately equal to the mass of an electron. Find the energy gap between the conduction and valence bands for this semiconductor.

1-52. A pure semiconductor has an energy gap of 1 eV. Plot $np/N_c N_v$ versus temperature for this material.

1-53. A pure semiconductor has an energy gap of 1 eV. Plot a curve of $n_i = p_i$ versus temperature for this material. Assume that $m_n \approx m$, the mass of the electron.

1-54. A pure semiconductor has an energy gap of 1.2 eV. If $N_c = N_v = 2 \times 10^{26}$, compute the free-electron density and hole density at a temperature of 300°K.

1-55. Repeat Prob. 1-5 but now assume that the Fermi level has been shifted by 0.3 eV toward the conduction band. Have donor or acceptor impurities been added?

1-56. Derive an expression for the location of the Fermi level in a semiconductor with donor impurities but do not assume that relation (1-192) is valid.

1-57. Derive an expression for the location of the Fermi level in a semiconductor containing both donor and acceptor impurities.

1-58. A voltage of 10 volts is applied to a pure silicon rod 0.1 meter long. The density of the free electrons is $n = 25 \times 10^{19}$ electrons per cubic meter. What are the drift velocities of the free electrons and holes?

1-59. A pure silicon rod has been excited so that the free-electron density varies linearly from 10^{25} to 10^5 electrons per cubic meter over a distance of 1 cm. The free-electron density is constant outside the region (at 10^{25} electrons per cubic meter to the left of the region and at 10^5 electrons per cubic meter to the right of the region). Plot the current density through the rod at the first instant of time. The temperature is 300°K.

1-60. Repeat Prob. 1-59 for a germanium rod.

1-61. The equilibrium density of free electrons in a certain n-type germanium rod is

10^{25} electrons per cubic meter. The lifetime of the free electrons is $\tau_n = 150 \times 10^{-6}$ sec. The rod is excited so that $n = 10^{34}$ electrons per cubic meter throughout it, and then the excitation is removed. Determine an expression for n as a function of time.

1-62. Repeat Prob. 1-61 but assume that the charge carriers are holes, i.e., the material is p type.

1-63. The semiconductor crystal of Fig. 1-38 is at equilibrium. At $t = 0$, free electrons are injected into the rod at the end $x = 0$, such that

$$n - n_0|_{x=0} = N(0)\epsilon^{-at}$$

Determine $n - n_0$ as a function of time and position. (This involves solving a partial differential equation.)

1-64. Repeat Prob. 1-63 but assume that holes are injected.

1-65. The semiconductor rod of Fig. 1-38 has an equilibrium hole density of $p_0 = 10^{25}$ holes per cubic meter. Holes are injected so that, at $x = 0$, $p(0) = 10^{30}$ holes per cubic meter. Assume that this is done for a long time so that an equilibrium is established. For the rod $L_p = 0.5 \times 10^{-3}$ meter. Plot a curve of the hole density versus x.

1-66. A p-type semiconductor L meters long has a current I passed through it and is placed in a magnetic field $\mathscr{B}_z$, as shown in Fig. 1-39. The voltage V_{ab} is measured. Then the magnetic field is removed, and it is found that the voltage between the faces at $x = 0$ and $x = L$ is V volts. Determine the mobility of the holes in terms of the dimensions of the sample, V_{ab}, I, V, and $\mathscr{B}_z$.

1-67. Describe the differences in the Hall effect if the charge carriers are free electrons or holes. Use the diagram of Fig. 1-39 for your discussion.

2
Vacuum-tube Principles
and Characteristics

In this chapter we discuss the principles and characteristics of the most commonly used vacuum tubes. At one time vacuum tubes were the basic elements of all electronic devices. They have been supplanted in many cases by solid-state elements, e.g., transistors. However, there are applications, such as cathode-ray tubes, microwave tubes, and phototubes, where the vacuum tube is regularly used. The detailed discussion of this chapter will consider only current in vacuum devices. This is pertinent to all such devices. The discussion of receiving tubes will be a brief one.

2-1 THE VACUUM-TUBE DIODE

The simplest vacuum tube is the *diode*, which consists of two electrodes enclosed in an evacuated envelope (see Sec. 1-20). One of the electrodes is a heated cathode, which emits electrons. The other is a conductor; it is neither heated nor chosen to have a low work function. Thus, for all practical purposes, only the cathode emits electrons.   A vacuum-tube diode is shown schematically in the circuit of Fig. 2-1.

The usual construction of vacuum tubes consists of concentric right cylinders.   That is, the cathode is a small cylinder, having a heater within it, or a thin ribbon (see Sec. 1-20).   The plate is a large cylinder enclosing the cathode.

In Sec. 1-20 we considered a plot of the plate current I_b versus the plate voltage V_b.   (In a vacuum tube, it is conventional to refer all voltages to the cathode.   Thus, the plate-to-cathode voltage is called the plate voltage.) Such a plot is shown in Fig. 1-30.   If we neglect the Schottky effect, the current cannot become greater than I_s.   In this case, all the current the cathode is capable of supplying is being taken from it.   The temperature of the cathode must be raised if the current is to be increased.   In this case, the current is said to be *temperature-limited*.

Now let us keep the voltage V_b constant but vary the temperature of the cathode and determine the current.   Figure 2-2 illustrates the results of such an experiment.   As the temperature is increased, the plate current increases up to a point and then becomes essentially constant.   If the plate voltage is increased, the curve has essentially the same shape but tends to level off at a higher value of current.

The shape of this curve is due to the following factors.   At low temperatures, all the emitted electrons are immediately attracted to the plate. As the temperature of the cathode is increased, the current it can emit is also increased, and thus the plate current increases.   However, at sufficiently high temperatures, the cathode emits electrons at a faster rate than they are drawn away to the plate.   Then, a "cloud" of electrons called a *space charge* forms about the cathode.   The space charge sets up a field which tends to repel electrons back to the cathode.   This effectively increases the potential barrier, which reduces the number of electrons that can reach the space-charge cloud; i.e., some electrons will be repelled back to the cathode. Thus, an equilibrium is set up whereby as many electrons leave the cathode and enter the space charge as are drawn off from the space charge to the plate.   If the cathode temperature is increased further, the cathode emits electrons at a still faster rate.   However, if V_b remains fixed, the electrons

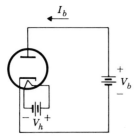

Fig. 2-1   A simple vacuum-tube-diode circuit.

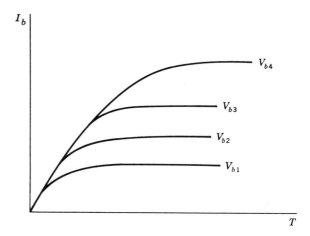

Fig. 2-2 Plate current versus temperature in a vacuum-tube diode. The plate voltage V_b is a parameter. $V_{b1} < V_{b2} < V_{b3} < V_{b4}$.

will leave the space charge at almost the same rate as before. Thus, the size of the space charge increases. This increases the potential barrier, and an equilibrium is again established. Thus, I_b does not increase to any extent. If the temperature is large enough to ensure that all the emitted electrons are not immediately drawn to the plate, then the plate current is almost independent of temperature. Vacuum tubes operated in such a way are said to be *space-charge-limited*. In the next section we shall see that the current in space-charge-limited devices is *slightly* dependent on the cathode temperature.

In general, vacuum tubes are operated so that they are space-charge-limited. In this case, the plate current is a function of the plate voltage but essentially not a function of the cathode temperature. In general, we wish the plate current to be a function of some signal voltage. The plate voltage is used for this here. The reader may ask why I_b is not made a function of the heater voltage V_h. That is, why not operate in the temperature-limited region so that a variation in V_h varies T which can vary I_b? Because of thermal inertia, the cathode temperature will follow changes in V_h very slowly. In general, we wish I_b to respond rapidly to changes in voltage. Thus, it is not suitable to vary V_h for this purpose.

2-2 CURRENT IN A VACUUM-TUBE DIODE—
THE CHILD-LANGMUIR EQUATION

Almost all vacuum tubes are operated in a space-charge-limited fashion. For this case let us now quantitatively determine the variation of I_b with V_b in the vacuum-tube diode. At first, to simplify the derivation, we shall assume that the cathode and plate of the vacuum tube are parallel planes, as illustrated in Fig. 2-3. In order to determine the current, we must know the potential distribution within the diode, i.e., the potential at any point with respect to a fixed point, in this case, the cathode (see Sec. 1-2). The potential at any point must obey *Poisson's equation*, which states

$$\frac{\partial^2 V}{\partial x^2} + \frac{\partial^2 V}{\partial y^2} + \frac{\partial^2 V}{\partial z^2} = -\frac{\rho}{\epsilon} \tag{2-1}$$

where V = potential, volts

ρ = charge density, coul/meter

ϵ = permittivity, farads/meter

In Fig. 2-3 we shall assume that the spacing d between the plates is small in comparison with the dimensions of the plates. Thus, in most of the region between the plates, the potential will be independent of y and z. [This is analogous to the fields in a parallel-plate capacitor (see Sec. 1-2).] Thus, Eq. (2-1) becomes

$$\frac{d^2 V}{dx^2} = -\frac{\rho}{\epsilon} \tag{2-2}$$

We have used total derivatives here since there is now only one variable.

Before considering the solution of this equation, let us discuss the potential on a physical basis. (It is necessary to do so to determine the boundary conditions.) If $\rho = 0$, that is, there is no charge between the plates, then $d^2V/dx^2 = 0$ and $dV/dx = K$, a constant. Thus, V will vary linearly with x. (This is just the case of a parallel-plate capacitor.) Since the cathode is taken as a reference, its potential is zero. The plate is maintained at a potential of V_b (with respect to the cathode) by the battery. Thus, the potential distribution will have the form shown in Fig. 2-4 for $T = 0$.

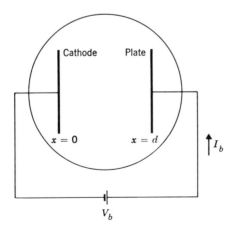

Fig. 2-3 A parallel-plane diode.

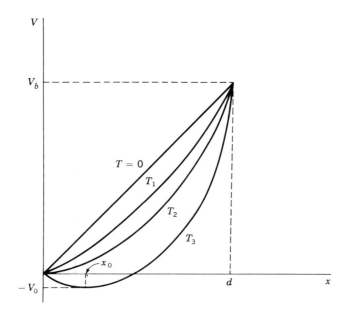

Fig. 2-4 The potential variation in a parallel-plane vacuum-tube diode. Temperature is a parameter. $T_3 > T_2 > T_1 > 0$.

Now assume that the temperature is increased to T_1. The cathode now emits electrons into the region between the electrodes. Since the electrons are negative charges, they will depress the potential distribution, as shown in Fig. 2-4. Note that the battery fixes the potential at point d at V_b. If the temperature is further increased, the curve is further depressed. At temperature T_2 it becomes tangent to the abscissa at $x = 0$. This is the point where the space-charge cloud is established. Further increases in temperature result in curves of the form shown for T_3.

Now let us use Eq. (2-2) to obtain an expression for the space-charge-limited current. We shall assume that the diode has been operating sufficiently long for an equilibrium to have been established. That is, on the average, the current density at any point is independent of time. Then [see Eq. (1-141)] the current density at any point within the diode is

$$\mathcal{J}_x = -ne v_x \tag{2-3}$$

This current density must be independent of x. Otherwise, the charge density at any point would vary with time. This violates the assumption of an equilibrium. Thus, v_x varies, then n must also vary in such a way that $\mathcal{J}_x$ remains constant.

The charge density ρ is given by

$$\rho = -ne \tag{2-4}$$

This value should be substituted into Eq. (2-2). We shall assume that the electrons are emitted from the cathode with zero initial velocity. Thus, at any point, the velocity of the electrons will be [see Eq. (1-27a)]

$$v_x = \sqrt{\frac{2e}{m}} \, V \tag{2-5}$$

Substitute Eq. (2-5) into Eq. (2-3), solve the resulting equation for $-ne = \rho$, and substitute it into Eq. (2-2). This yields

$$\frac{d^2V}{dx^2} = \frac{\mathscr{J}_x}{\epsilon} \sqrt{\frac{m}{2e}} \, V^{-\frac{1}{2}} \tag{2-6}$$

We can write this as

$$\frac{d^2V}{dx^2} = kV^{-\frac{1}{2}} \tag{2-7}$$

where k is a constant which is independent of x and is given by

$$k = \frac{\mathscr{J}_x}{\epsilon} \sqrt{\frac{m}{2e}} \tag{2-8}$$

To solve Eq. (2-7), multiply both sides by $(dV/dx) \, dx$ and integrate. Thus,

$$\int \frac{dV}{dx} \frac{d^2V}{dx^2} \, dx = \int kV^{-\frac{1}{2}} \frac{dV}{dx} \, dx = \int kV^{-\frac{1}{2}} \, dV$$

Note that

$$\frac{dV}{dx} \frac{d^2V}{dx^2} = \frac{1}{2} \frac{d}{dx} \left(\frac{dV}{dx}\right)^2 \tag{2-9}$$

Substituting this into Eq. (2-7) and integrating yields

$$\frac{1}{2}\left(\frac{dV}{dx}\right)^2 = 2kV^{\frac{1}{2}} + c \tag{2-10}$$

where c is a constant whose value must be established. We shall assume that (see Fig. 2-4) $T = T_2$. That is, the temperature is the minimum that will establish the space charge. Then

$$\left.\frac{dV}{dx}\right|_{x=0} = 0 \tag{2-11}$$

Hence,

$$c = 0$$

Substituting this into Eq. (2-10) and taking the square root of both sides of the equation yields

$$V^{-\frac{1}{4}} \, dV = 2\sqrt{k} \, dx$$

Integrating, we obtain

$$V = (\tfrac{3}{2}k^{\frac{1}{2}}x)^{\frac{4}{3}} + c_1 \tag{2-12}$$

We evaluate the constant c_1 by noting that $V = 0$ at $x = 0$. Thus, $c_1 = 0$. The constant k is given by Eq. (2-8). It contains the unknown $\mathscr{J}_x$. There is one other boundary condition we must satisfy. Because of the battery, when $x = d$, $V = V_b$. Thus, the value of k must be such that this is so. Hence,

$$k = \frac{4V_b^{\frac{3}{2}}}{9d^2} \tag{2-13}$$

Substituting into Eq. (2-12), we obtain

$$V = V_b\left(\frac{x}{d}\right)^{\frac{4}{3}} \tag{2-14}$$

Thus, the potential varies as the four-thirds power of x.

To obtain the current density, equate Eq. (2-13) to Eq. (2-8) and manipulate. This yields

$$\mathscr{J}_x = \frac{4\epsilon}{9d^2}\sqrt{\frac{2e}{m}}\,V_b^{\frac{3}{2}} \tag{2-15}$$

Thus, the current varies as the three-halves power of the applied voltage. This relation is known as the *Child-Langmuir law*. The total current can be found by multiplying the current density by the cross-sectional area of one of the plates.

In general, vacuum tubes are built not with parallel plates but with concentric cylinders. A theoretical analysis for such structures yields

$$J = KV_b^{\frac{3}{2}} \tag{2-16}$$

where K is a function of the dimensions but not of the applied voltage. That is, the current is still a function of $V_b^{\frac{3}{2}}$.

Equation (2-15) or (2-16) is only approximately correct. In general, the cathode temperature will be above the minimum temperature which produces a space charge. Thus, in Fig. 2-4, the potential will correspond to T_3 rather than to T_2. In this case, $dV/dx \neq 0$ at $x = 0$. However, Eq. (2-15) can still be accurate if we adjust it so that the boundary conditions used in deriving it are still satisfied. To do this, d is not considered to be the spacing between the electrodes but is replaced by the distance between the point x_0, where dv/dx actually is equal to zero, and d. In addition, V_b is replaced in Eq. (2-15) by $V_b + V_0$, where $-V_0$ is the negative potential of the point x_0. In this case, we can consider that the diode acts as though its cathode were at the point x_0. It is said that a *virtual cathode* exists at $x = x_0$.

In general, as T is varied, both $d - x_0$ and $V_b + V_0$ will vary. For this reason, the diode current is slightly dependent on cathode temperature. However, this dependence is usually small.

The analysis also assumed that the electrons were emitted with zero initial velocity. This is not so. For both of the reasons discussed above, the diode current will be slightly more than that predicted by Eq. (2-15) or (2-16).

Note that Eqs. (2-15) and (2-16) yield the current density when V_b is positive. Let us now consider negative values of V_b. (To simplify the discussion, we shall ignore the contact potential.) If the electrons are all emitted with zero initial velocity, then when V_b is negative, all the electrons will be repelled to the cathode and $\mathscr{J}_x$ will be zero. Note that the plate, with its high work function and low temperature, essentially emits no electrons, so that the electrons cannot leave the plate and be accelerated to the cathode. Even in actual diodes where the electrons are emitted from the cathode with nonzero initial velocity, the plate currents are *extremely* small when the applied voltage is more negative than a fraction of a volt.

Since they only conduct in one direction, vacuum-tube diodes are often used as *rectifiers*, i.e., circuits that convert alternating current to direct current.

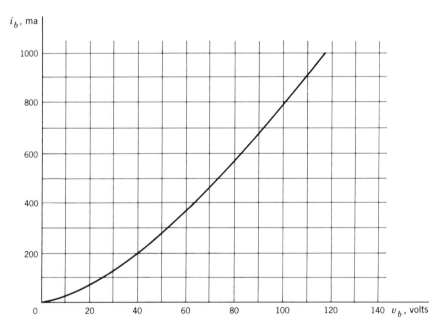

Fig. 2-5 The plate characteristics of the 5U4–GB vacuum-tube diode. (*General Electric Company.*)

2-3 ACTUAL VACUUM-TUBE-DIODE CHARACTERISTICS

The three-halves-power law of Eq. (2-15) or (2-16) is only approximately correct. To obtain an accurate relation, the characteristic of a diode is often experimentally measured. A plot of a typical measurement is given in Fig. 2-5. Such a plot of plate current versus plate voltage is called a *plate characteristic* (or at times a *static plate characteristic*). Analyses using these characteristics will be presented subsequently (see Sec. 3-5).

The slope of the static characteristic at an operating point is often of interest (see Sec. 3-5). Actually, we usually work with the reciprocal of the slope

$$r_p = \frac{dv_b}{di_{b_2}}\bigg|_{v_b = V_{bQ}} \tag{2-17}$$

This has the dimensions of a resistance and is called the *dynamic plate resistance* or simply the *plate resistance*. The reciprocal of r_p is designated g_p and is called the *dynamic plate conductance* or *plate conductance*. That is,

$$g_p = \frac{1}{r_p} \tag{2-18}$$

2-4 THE VACUUM-TUBE TRIODE

One of the principal functions of electronic devices is to provide *amplification*. In such circuits, a small low-power input signal controls the device so that a large high-power output signal, which is a faithful reproduction of the input signal, results. For instance, in a high fidelity phonograph amplifier, the phonograph pickup often supplies a signal which is less than 10^{-9} watt. However, this signal controls the amplifier, which then can deliver a 100-watt signal to the loudspeaker. The output signal has essentially the same waveform as the input.

A device which can provide amplification is the vacuum-tube triode. It is similar in construction to the vacuum-tube diode except that a third electrode, called a *control grid* or simply a *grid*, is placed between the cathode and the plate. A simple vacuum-tube triode is shown in Fig. 2-6a. The grid is usually a helix of wire, but at times it is made with crossed wires (like a window screen) hence, the name, grid. The electrons pass through the spaces between the grid wires as they travel from cathode to plate.

The symbol for the vacuum-tube triode is shown in Fig. 2-6b.

A simple vacuum-tube-triode amplifier is shown in Fig. 2-7. Usually the direct power supplies are such that v_b is positive and the grid is at a negative potential with respect to the cathode. Because of this, almost none of the emitted electrons reach the grid and the grid current is zero. Thus, the signal source which is connected to the grid will not supply any power.

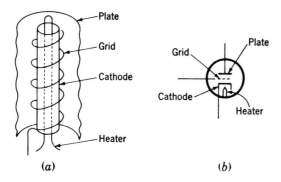

(a)   (b)

Fig. 2-6 (a) The structure of a typical vacuum-tube triode and (b) its symbol.

   Voltages in vacuum tubes are almost always measured with respect to the cathode. Thus, double-subscript notation need not be used. The grid-to-cathode voltage is usually designated v_c, while the plate-to-cathode voltage is called v_b.

   Since the grid current is usually zero, the current leaving the cathode is equal to the plate current i_b. In theory, the cathode current in a vacuum-tube triode varies with the electric field at the cathode in the same way as it does in a vacuum-tube diode. Thus, a relation similar to the Child-Langmuir law can be used to obtain i_b. However, this relation must now take into account the fact that both v_b and v_c affect the electric field at the cathode and that the grid-to-cathode distance is less than the plate-to-cathode distance. Thus, the relation is

$$i_b = \begin{cases} K(v_b + \mu v_c)^{\frac{3}{2}} & v_b + \mu v_c \geq 0 \\ 0 & v_b + \mu v_c < 0 \end{cases} \qquad (2\text{-}19)$$

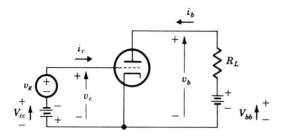

Fig. 2-7 A simple vacuum-tube-triode amplifier. The heater and its circuit are omitted from the diagram. Note that V_{cc} is defined as a negative number.

Note that the plate current cannot become negative since the plate emits no electrons (for all practical purposes). Equation (2-19) is only approximate. This is analogous to the case of the vacuum-tube diode.

2-5 STATIC CHARACTERISTICS OF THE VACUUM-TUBE TRIODE

Equation (2-19) is only approximately correct. Experimentally measured curves are often used to express the relation among i_b, v_b, and v_c accurately. Since there are three variables, i_b, v_b, and v_c, a three-dimensional plot is required. Since this is inconvenient, the information is usually represented by a family of curves on a two-dimensional plot. For instance, consider the curves of Fig. 2-8. There are a number of curves. Each one is a plot of i_b versus v_b for a fixed value of v_c. This family of curves is called the *static plate characteristic* or simply the *plate characteristic*. At times, the grid is operated at a positive potential. Thus, a characteristic is shown for $v_c = +5$ volts.

When v_c is positive, grid current results. The dashed curves are a plot of i_c versus v_b.

An analysis of the simple vacuum-tube-triode amplifier of Fig. 2-7 will not be considered at this time. The analysis of Sec. 3-22 can be applied to this circuit. After the material of Chaps. 3, 5, and 6 has been studied, the reader will be in a position to note that much of the analysis of the field-effect transistor can be used for the vacuum tube if *gate* is replaced by *grid*, *source* by *cathode*, and *drain* by *plate*. We shall rely upon this in much of this book.

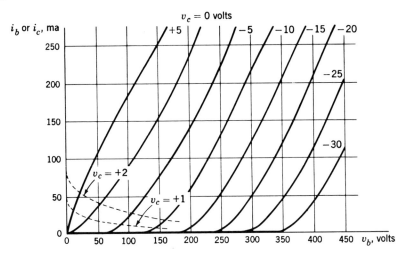

Fig. 2-8 Typical plate characteristic of a vacuum-tube triode. Grid current i_c is plotted as the dashed curve.

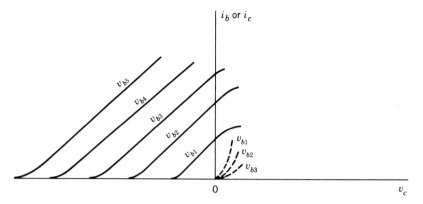

Fig. 2-9 Typical transfer-current characteristic for a vacuum-tube triode. The grid current is plotted as the dashed curves. $v_{b1} < v_{b2} < v_{b3} < v_{b4} < v_{b5}$.

There are other forms of characteristics that can be used. Since we are working with a relation among v_c, v_b, and i_b, a family of curves can be obtained by plotting any two of these with the third as a parameter. The plot of i_b versus v_c with v_b as a parameter is called the *static transfer characteristic* or simply the *transfer characteristic*. A typical one is shown in Fig. 2-9.

The set of plots of v_c versus v_b with i_b as a parameter is called the *constant-current characteristic*. Such a family of curves is shown in Fig. 2-10.

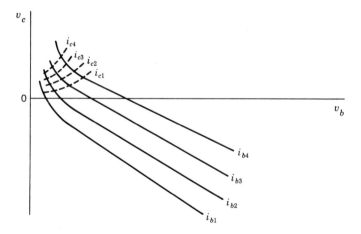

Fig. 2-10 Typical constant-current characteristic for a vacuum-tube triode. The grid current is plotted as the dashed curves. $i_{b1} < i_{b2} < i_{b3} < i_{b4}$ and $i_{c1} < i_{c2} < i_{c3} < i_{c4}$.

2-6 THE DYNAMIC PARAMETERS OF THE VACUUM-TUBE TRIODE

Often (see Sec. 3-22) the slopes of the static characteristic are of interest. Since there are three sets of these characteristics, three slopes, called the *dynamic parameters*, are commonly used.

Amplification factor μ The amplification factor is defined as

$$\mu = -\frac{dv_b}{dv_c}\bigg|_{i_b = \text{const}} = -\frac{\partial v_b}{\partial v_c} \tag{2-20}$$

Then μ is defined as the negative of the slope of the constant-current characteristic at the operating point. It is dimensionless. Typical values for vacuum-tube triodes lie between 2 and 100. The definition of μ is compatible with the μ of Eq. (2-19), as can be seen by solving Eq. (2-19) for $-\partial v_b/\partial v_c$.

Dynamic plate resistance or plate resistance r_p This parameter is defined as

$$r_p = \frac{dv_b}{di_b}\bigg|_{v_c = \text{const}} = \frac{\partial v_b}{\partial i_b} \tag{2-21}$$

Thus, r_p is the reciprocal of the slope of the plate characteristic at a given operating point. The units of r_p are ohms. Typical values for vacuum-tube triodes lie between 50 and 100,000 ohms.

Transconductance or mutual conductance g_m This parameter is defined as the slope of the transfer characteristic at a given operating point. Thus,

$$g_m = \frac{di_b}{dv_c}\bigg|_{v_b = \text{const}} = \frac{\partial i_b}{\partial v_c} \tag{2-22}$$

The units of g_m are mhos. Since the transconductance is usually only a small fraction of a mho, it is usually expressed in micromhos (μmhos). Typical values of g_m lie between 500 and 30,000 μmhos.

The three dynamic parameters are related by the equation

$$\mu = g_m r_p \tag{2-23}$$

which is derived in Sec. 3-22.

2-7 INTERELECTRODE CAPACITANCE OF THE VACUUM-TUBE TRIODE

Any two conductors in space have a capacitance between them. Thus, a capacitance exists between each pair of electrodes in a vacuum tube. These are called *interelectrode capacitances*. Since they are not placed there

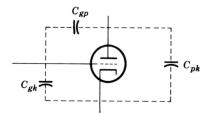

Fig. 2-11   The interelectrode capacitances of a vacuum-tube triode.

deliberately and are usually not desirable, they are also called *stray capacitances* or *parasitic capacitances*.   There are three such capacitances in the vacuum-tube triode, the *grid-to-plate capacitance* C_{gp}, the *grid-to-cathode capacitance* C_{gk}, and the *plate-to-cathode capacitance* C_{pk}.   They are diagrammatically represented in Fig. 2-11.

We shall see that all these capacitances produce undesirable effects when vacuum tubes are operated with high-frequency signals.   However, C_{gp} is particularly undesirable because it couples the relatively large signal in the plate circuit back into the grid circuit (see Sec. 3-27).   To reduce this effect, other types of vacuum tubes have been developed.   It should be noted that in many circuits the vacuum-tube triode performs satisfactorily.

2-8   THE VACUUM-TUBE TETRODE

The relatively large grid-to-plate capacitance is a disadvantage of the vacuum-tube triode.   This capacitance can be reduced by a factor of 1000 or more by the addition of another grid that shields the original grid from the plate. That is, a second grid is placed between the first grid and the plate.   The second grid acts as an electrostatic shield which essentially eliminates the electric field set up by the plate from the region of the first grid.   Thus, variations in the plate voltage do not affect the original grid circuit.   Since C_{gp} is the mechanism by which these variations in v_p are coupled to the grid circuit, C_{gp} will be effectively reduced.

In order to avoid confusion, let us introduce some terminology.   The original grid is called the *control grid* since its purpose is to provide a means for controlling the plate current.   The new grid is called the *screen grid* or *shield grid* or *grid 2*.   Since this vacuum tube has four electrodes, it is called a *vacuum-tube tetrode*.

A simple circuit using a vacuum-tube tetrode is shown in Fig. 2-12. The screen grid is to shield the control grid from variations in plate voltage. Thus, the screen-grid potential must not vary with the plate voltage.   One way to accomplish this would be to connect the screen grid directly to the cathode.   However, this cannot be done since the screen grid will not only shield the control grid from the effects of the plate but also shield the cathode

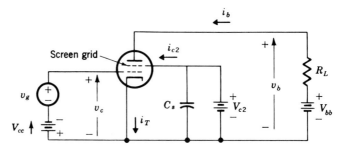

Fig. 2-12 A simple vacuum-tube-tetrode circuit. Note that V_{cc} is negative.

from the plate. Thus, the field which accelerates the electrons from the cathode (to the plate) will not be present. To reestablish such a field, the screen grid is connected to a positive potential, as shown in Fig. 2-12. In addition, a large capacitance is connected between the screen grid and the cathode. This capacitance should be large enough so that, at all signal frequencies, it acts as a short circuit. Thus, as far as signal components are concerned, the screen grid is connected directly to the cathode, and it acts as a shield for the control grid.

Let us consider the plate characteristics of the vacuum-tube tetrode. A typical set is shown in Fig. 2-13. The dip in each of the characteristics is due to secondary emission of electrons from the plate (see Sec. 1-21). At low values of v_b there is negligible secondary emission. As v_b is increased, the secondary emission also increases. If $v_b < v_{c2}$, all the secondary electrons will be attracted to the screen grid. Thus, the dip in the characteristic occurs because an increase in v_b causes the secondary emission to increase at a faster rate than the number of primary electrons arriving at the plate.

If $v_b > v_{c2}$, the electric field between the screen grid and plate tends to attract the secondary electrons back to the plate. Thus, further increases in v_b reduce the effect of the secondary emission, and i_b will increase. In addition, large values of v_b cause primary electrons near the screen grid to be attracted to the plate. Hence, at large values of v_b, i_{c2} falls off to very small values. Thus, i_b becomes almost equal to the total current leaving the cathode. Note that this cathode current is essentially independent of v_b because of the shielding effect of the screen grid.

The characteristics of Fig. 2-13 are very nonlinear to the left of the vertical line AB. For this reason, if the vacuum-tube tetrode is to function as a linear amplifier, its operation is restricted to the right of line AB. This is a serious limitation and has led to the development of the vacuum-tube pentode and the beam power tube. In almost all instances, these tubes have supplanted the vacuum-tube tetrode.

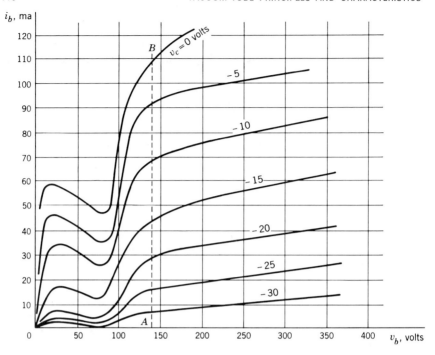

Fig. 2-13 Typical static plate characteristics for a vacuum-tube tetrode. V_{c2} is constant.

2-9 THE VACUUM-TUBE PENTODE

Secondary emission produces large undesirable nonlinear regions in the plate characteristics of the vacuum-tube tetrode. A vacuum tube called a *vacuum-tube pentode* with a third grid placed between the screen grid and the plate can eliminate this effect. This grid is called a *suppressor grid* or *grid 3*.

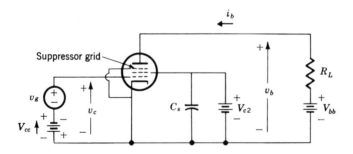

Fig. 2.14 A simple vacuum-tube-pentode amplifier. Note that V_{cc} is a negative number.

It is usually connected directly to the cathode. A simple vacuum-tube-pentode amplifier circuit is shown in Fig. 2-14. The suppressor grid is at the potential of the cathode. Thus, for positive values of v_b, the electric field between the suppressor grid and the plate tends to repel the secondary electrons back to the plate, thus eliminating the effect of secondary emission.

It may appear as though the suppressor grid would repel all the primary electrons back to the screen grid causing i_b to be zero. However, this is not the case since the potential near the suppressor grid falls completely to zero only at the grid wires and not in the space between the wires and, in addition, the electrons are emitted from the cathode with nonzero initial velocities. Thus, the primary electrons can surmount the potential minimum between the screen grid and the plate.

A typical set of static characteristics is shown in Fig. 2-15. Note that the very nonlinear region of the vacuum-tube tetrode has been eliminated. Note also that, as in the case of the tetrode, v_b has almost no effect on the total cathode current. Thus, as for the vacuum-tube tetrode, the curves become almost constant for large enough v_b.

Dynamic parameters   For most conditions of operation, the screen and suppressor grids are maintained at a constant potential. Thus, the only

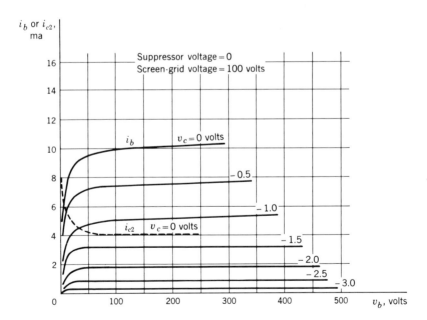

Fig. 2-15 Static plate characteristic of a 6AU6 vacuum-tube pentode. The screen-grid current is indicated by the dashed curve. (*Westinghouse Electric Corp.*)

variable voltages that affect i_b are v_b and v_c. Hence, the pentode can be characterized by the same static characteristics that were used to characterize the triode. The dynamic parameters are defined as the *control-grid-to-plate amplification factor* μ

$$\mu = -\frac{dv_b}{dv_c}\bigg|_{i_b, v_{c2}, v_{c3} = \text{const}} = -\frac{\partial v_b}{\partial v_c} \tag{2-24}$$

the *dynamic plate resistance* r_p

$$r_p = \frac{dv_b}{di_b}\bigg|_{v_c, v_{c2}, v_{c3} = \text{const}} = \frac{\partial v_b}{\partial i_b} \tag{2-25}$$

and the *control-grid-to-plate transconductance* g_m

$$g_m = \frac{di_b}{dv_c}\bigg|_{v_b, v_{c2}, v_{c3} = \text{const}} = \frac{\partial i_b}{\partial v_c} \tag{2-26}$$

where v_{c2} and v_{c3} are the screen-grid and suppressor-grid voltages, respectively. In addition Eq. (2-23) is also valid. Over most of the region of operation, the static plate characteristics are almost independent of v_b. Thus, r_p will be very large. In a vacuum-tube pentode, r_p usually lies in the range from 50,000 to greater than 2×10^6 ohms. [In the triode, r_p rarely exceeds 10^4 ohms (see Sec. 2-6).] The transconductance of vacuum-tube pentodes and triodes is of the same order, i.e., between 500 and 30,000 μmhos. Thus, the amplification factor of vacuum-tube pentodes will generally be very much greater than that of the vacuum-tube triode. Typical values of μ for vacuum-tube pentodes lie between 100 and 20,000.

At times the potentials of all the grids of the vacuum-tube pentode are allowed to vary. In such cases, we define other dynamic parameters in addition to those of Eqs. (2-24) to (2-26). For instance, the *screen-grid-to-plate transconductance* g_{ps}

$$g_{ps} = \frac{di_b}{dv_{c2}}\bigg|_{v_c, v_{c3}, v_b = \text{const}} = \frac{\partial i_b}{\partial v_{c2}} \tag{2-27}$$

the *screen-grid-to-plate amplification factor* μ_{ps}

$$\mu_{ps} = -\frac{dv_b}{dv_{c2}}\bigg|_{v_c, v_{c3}, i_b = \text{const}} = -\frac{\partial v_b}{\partial v_{c2}} \tag{2-28}$$

and the *dynamic screen-grid resistance* r_s

$$r_s = \frac{dv_{c2}}{di_{c2}}\bigg|_{v_c, v_{c3}, v_b = \text{const}} = \frac{\partial v_{c2}}{\partial i_{c2}} \tag{2-29}$$

In a similar way, a transconductance and amplification factor can be defined for any two pairs of electrodes except the reference (in general, the cathode). Also, a dynamic resistance can be defined for any electrode except the reference. This will be discussed further in Sec. 6-22.

2-10 INTERELECTRODE CAPACITANCE OF THE VACUUM-TUBE PENTODE

Just as in the case of the vacuum-tube triode (see Sec. 2-7) there will be a capacitance between each of the electrodes of the vacuum-tube pentode. This is illustrated in Fig. 2-16. In general, these capacitances become important only at high frequencies.

In actual circuits, the suppressor grid is usually directly connected to the cathode. The screen grid is usually connected to the cathode by means of a large capacitor which can be considered a short circuit at high frequencies. Therefore, at high frequencies, the cathode, the screen grid, and the suppressor grid can be considered to be a single electrode. Thus, in computing capacitance, only three "electrodes" are considered, the plate, the control grid, and the combined cathode, screen grid, and suppressor grid. Vacuum-tube manuals usually take this into account and list only three capacitances. These are analogous to C_{gp}, C_{gk}, and C_{pk} for the vacuum-tube triode. They are, respectively,

$$C_{gp}$$
$$C_{in} = C_{gk} + C_{gg2} + C_{gg3} \tag{2-30}$$

and

$$C_{out} = C_{pk} + C_{pg2} + C_{pg3} \tag{2-31}$$

Note that in a vacuum-tube pentode, C_{in} and C_{out}, all other things being equal, will be larger than C_{gk} and C_{pk} for a vacuum-tube triode. However, this is completely offset by the fact that C_{gp} for a vacuum-tube pentode may be 1000 or more times less than it is for a vacuum-tube triode.

2-11 THE BEAM POWER TUBE

The characteristics of vacuum-tube pentodes are fairly linear except in the region of low plate voltage, where they have fairly broad *knee*, i.e., bending of the curves. For most applications, the linear region is large enough so that the knee does not prove troublesome. However, when high signal

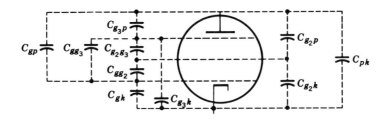

Fig. 2-16 The interelectrode capacitances of a vacuum-tube pentode.

power is to be supplied to a load, it is desirable to make the output signal voltage and current as large as possible.   In such cases, larger voltage and current swings can be obtained if the knees of the curve are small.

The knees of the plate characteristic are much smaller in a vacuum tube called the *beam power tube*.   Here, the suppressor grid is replaced by a pair of plates which cause the electrons to flow in a dense beam.   Their field is similar to that set up by the suppressor grid.   These plates are often omitted from the schematic diagram.

2-12   RATINGS OF VACUUM TUBES

To ensure reasonable vacuum-tube life, the maximum values of the voltage, current, and power are limited.   These limitations are called *ratings*.   Let us consider the various vacuum-tube ratings in turn.

Plate dissipation   When the electrons strike the plate of a vacuum tube, their kinetic energy is, in general, converted to thermal energy.   This heats the plate.   The temperature of the plate must be limited.   If it becomes hot enough, structural damage may occur; e.g., welds in the vacuum tube may break, or the envelope may rupture.   In addition, all material traps gas molecules within it.   In a vacuum, this gas slowly escapes.   This is called *outgassing* and will eventually contaminate the vacuum.   The vacuum tube will no longer function properly.   Increasing the temperature of a material increases the rate of outgassing.   Thus, the plate temperature must be limited.

The temperature of the plate depends upon the power dissipated there, i.e., the rate at which energy is supplied to it, and the ability of the plate to dissipate heat.   In general, vacuum-tube plates are blackened to increase their thermal radiation.   Ordinary, low-power vacuum tubes have metal plates.   Vacuum tubes designed to operate at moderately high power levels often have plates which are made of graphite.   They can operate properly at a relatively high temperature (dull cherry-red hot).   At still higher power levels, the plate is made part of the outer jacket of the tube, which has radiating fins connected to it.   At times, to increase cooling, air is forced over these fins.   At very high power levels, water cooling is used.

Any vacuum tube has a rated plate dissipation.   If the (average) power dissipated by the plate exceeds this value, the life of the tube will be shortened.

Let us now compute the actual plate dissipation.   An electron accelerated (from rest) from the cathode to the plate, whose voltage is v_b, gains an energy of v_b eV, or ev_b joules.   Thus, if N electrons per second strike the plate, they supply a power of

$$p = Nev_b \qquad\qquad (2\text{-}32)$$

The plate current is given by

$$i_b = Ne \tag{2-33}$$

Thus,

$$p_b = v_b i_b \tag{2-34}$$

This power is called the *plate dissipation*. In general, v_b and i_b, and thus p_b, are functions of time. The average value of p_b determines the temperature of the plate. (This assumes that the time of one cycle is short in comparison with the time it takes for the plate to reach its equilibrium temperature.) In vacuum-tube handbooks, the allowed average plate dissipation is usually specified. It is called the *rated plate dissipation*.

Grid dissipation If any grid draws current, the power dissipated in it will instantaneously be equal to the product of its voltage and current. Grids which normally draw current have a *rated grid dissipation* specified in tube manuals.

Voltage ratings If the voltage between any pair of electrodes becomes too large, an arc may result. (This arc often occurs at the leads which pass through the envelope of the tube.) Such arcs result in improper operation of the vacuum tube, since the electrodes in question are effectively short-circuited. In addition, they can actually destroy the vacuum tube if they persist.

A special voltage rating is specified for vacuum-tube diodes used as rectifiers. In this case, the maximum voltage across the diode occurs when the plate voltage is negative. This is called an *inverse voltage*. Thus, a *peak-inverse-voltage* rating is specified for rectifier diodes.

Current ratings Since there is a maximum current that can be drawn from the thermonic cathode, a maximum-current rating is specified.

Filament-heater voltage The operating voltage of the filament heater is specified. If this voltage is exceeded, the cathode temperature, and hence the maximum plate current, is increased. However, the life of the heater can be greatly reduced if the heater is operated at voltages which are only slightly above the rated value.

BIBLIOGRAPHY

Beck, A. H. W.: "Thermionic Values," chaps. 6, 9, and 10, Cambridge University Press, London, 1953.
Chirlian, P. M., and A. H. Zemanian: "Electronics," chaps. 3, 7, and 8, McGraw-Hill Book Company, New York, 1961.

Millman, J., and C. C. Halkias: "Electronic Devices and Circuits," chaps. 4 and 7, McGraw-Hill Book Company, New York, 1967.

Spangenberg, K. R.: "Vacuum Tubes," chaps. 2 and 7–11, McGraw-Hill Book Company, New York, 1948.

———: "Fundamentals of Electronic Devices," chaps. 8–10, McGraw-Hill Book Company, New York, 1957.

PROBLEMS

2-1. A single electron is emitted from the cathode of the parallel-plane diode of Fig. 2-3 at $t = 0$. It is accelerated toward the plate. Write an expression for the plate current as a function of time.

2-2. An ideal parallel-plane diode has a plate voltage of V_b. The spacing between the plates is d meters. Assume that the charge density throughout the diode is constant at ρ coul/meter^3. Determine the potential distribution within the diode.

2-3. According to Eq. (2-3), if electrons are emitted from the cathode with zero initial velocity, their density there must be infinite. Why is the charge density at the cathode finite in an actual diode?

2-4. An ideal parallel-plane diode operated in the space-charge-limited region has a spacing between its plate and cathode of 1 cm. The area of the cathode is 2 cm^2. What current results if the plate voltage is 50 volts?

2-5. In an ideal cylindrical diode operated in the space-charge-limited region, a current of 50 ma results when the plate voltage V_b is 50 volts. What will be the plate current when $V_b = 100$ volts?

2-6. Determine a relation for the electric field within an ideal parallel-plane diode which is operating under space-charge-limited conditions. Assume that the electrons are emitted with zero initial velocity and that $dV/dx = 0$ at $x = 0$ (see Fig. 2-3).

2-7. Repeat Prob. 2-6 but now obtain an expression for the velocity of the electrons as a function of position.

2-8. Compute the time it takes for an electron emitted with zero initial velocity to travel from the cathode to the plate in an ideal space-charge-limited diode.

2-9. Repeat Prob. 2-8 but now assume that there is no space charge.

2-10. Determine the dynamic plate resistance of the 5U4-GB vacuum-tube diode at the operating point $V_b = 43$ volts (see Fig. 2-5).

2-11. Plot a curve of dynamic plate resistance versus V_b for the 5U4-GB vacuum-tube diode.

2-12. A certain vacuum-tube triode is characterized by Eq. (2-19). The following data are measured for it. When $v_c = -5$ volts and $v_b = 200$ volts, $i_b = 125$ ma, and when $v_c = -10$ volts and $v_b = 200$ volts, $i_b = 50$ ma. Compute μ for the triode.

2-13. Determine the values of μ, g_m, and r_p for the triode whose plate characteristics are given in Fig. 2-8. Use the operating point $V_b = 250$ volts, $V_c = -10$ volts. Note that μ and g_m can be obtained from Fig. 2-8 without drawing the constant-current and transfer characteristics, e.g.,

$$\mu \approx \frac{\Delta v_b}{\Delta v_c}\bigg|_{i_b=\text{const}}$$

2-14. Draw the transfer characteristics and the constant-current characteristics for the vacuum-tube triode whose characteristics are given in Fig. 2-8.

2-15. Determine the dynamic parameters μ, g_m, and r_p for the vacuum-tube tetrode of Fig. 2-13 at an operating point $V_{bQ} = 250$ volts, $V_{cQ} = -15$ volts.

2-16. Repeat Prob. 2-15 but now assume that $V_{bQ} = 100$ volts.

2-17. For the 6AU6 vacuum-tube pentode, determine μ, g_m, and r_p at the operating point $V_{bb} = 300$ volts, $V_{CQ} = -1$ volt (see Fig. 2-15).

2-18. Repeat Prob. 2-17 but now use $V_{CQ} = -2.5$ volts.

2-19. The plate voltage of a vacuum tube is 300 volts. Compute the kinetic energy imparted to the plate by an electron which is emitted from the cathode with zero velocity.

2-20. The vacuum-tube triode whose plate characteristics are given in Fig. 2-8 has a rated plate dissipation of 45 watts. Draw a curve which shows the maximum values that v_b and i_b can have if this dissipation is not to be exceeded.

3

Principles and Characteristics of Solid-state Devices—Diodes— Junction Transistors and Field-effect Transistors

In this chapter we shall study the basic solid-state elements used in electronic devices. These devices find wide application in almost all electronic equipment.

3-1 THE p-n JUNCTION

Most semiconductor devices do not consist of a homogeneously doped semi-conductor crystal. Rather, the doping varies as a function of position. This variation produces the desired electrical characteristics. A fundamental configuration which is common to many devices consists of the junction of p-type material and n-type material. This is called a *p-n junction*. It is not formed by simply placing p-type material in contact with n-type material but occurs in a single crystal. A p-type semiconductor crystal can be grown. If it is placed in a hot atmosphere containing gaseous donor impurities, they will diffuse into the crystal. The concentration of the diffused impurities falls off as the distance from the surface increases.   If, near the surface, the donor concentration is high enough, the net impurity concentration will be *n* type there.   However, within the bulk of the material, it will still be *p* type. Thus, a *p-n* junction results.   This is called a *diffused junction.*

Other procedures can be used to fabricate a *p-n* junction.   A piece of donor impurity is placed on a *p*-type semiconductor crystal and then heated. The impurity melts and alloys into the semiconductor, resulting in a *p-n* junction.   This is called an *alloyed junction.*

Semiconductor crystals are grown by slowly removing crystals from a molten mass (or *melt*) of silicon or germanium which contains impurities.   If the melt contains donor impurities, an *n*-type crystal results.   If, after the crystal is partially withdrawn, acceptor impurities are added to the melt and their concentration is higher than the donor impurities, the remainder of the crystal will be *p* type.   This *p-n* junction is called a *grown junction.*   We shall discuss the fabrication of semiconductor crystals in Sec. 4-1.

Let us now qualitatively consider the behavior of the *p-n* junction diagrammatically represented in Fig. 3-1*a*.   Figure 3-1*b* and *c* represents the donor and acceptor concentration, respectively.

To explain some of its electrical characteristics, let us assume that the *p-n* junction is formed by joining *n*-type and *p*-type semiconductors.   At the first instant, in the *n*-type region, the free-electron density will be much higher than the hole density.   The reverse will be true in the *p*-type region.   All the free electrons and holes will *diffuse* randomly throughout the material.   Thus, both free electrons and holes from the *n*-type region will diffuse into the *p*-type region.   Similarly, both free electrons and holes from the *p*-type region will diffuse into the *n*-type region.   However, there are many more free electrons than holes in the *n*-type region and many more holes than free electrons in the *p*-type region.   Thus, there will be more free electrons diffusing into the *p*-type region from the *n*-type region and more holes diffusing into the *n*-type region from the *p*-type region than there will be charge carriers diffusing in the opposite direction.

Free electrons traveling from the *n*-type region to the *p*-type region and holes traveling from the *p*-type region to the *n*-type region are said to constitute a *forward current* I_f.   Free electrons and holes diffusing in the opposite direction, (e.g., free electrons from the *p*-type region to the *n*-type region) are said to constitute a *reverse current* I_r.

At the first instant that the junction is formed, the forward current is greater than the reverse current.   Before the *n*-type and *p*-type materials were joined, they were electrically neutral.   (Note that when a free electron or hole is formed, the *total* number of positive and negative charges within the material does not change.)   The forward current tends to produce a *net* positive charge in the *n*-type region and a *net* negative charge in the *p*-type region.   The reverse current does the opposite.   However, initially, the

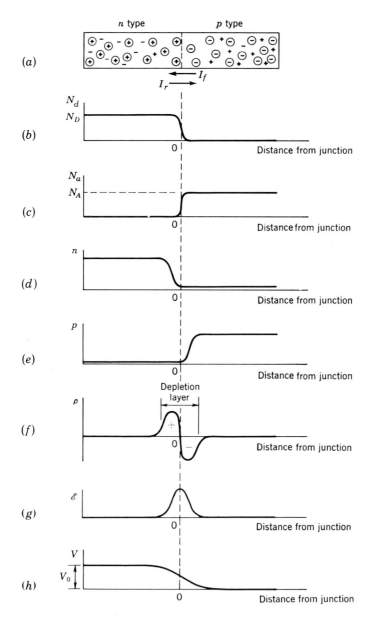

Fig. 3-1 Diagrammatic representation of a *p-n* junction: (*a*) the *p-n* junction; (*b*) donor density; (*c*) acceptor density; (*d*) free-electron density; (*e*) hole density; (*f*) net charge density; (*g*) electric field; (*h*) potential distribution.

forward current is very much greater than the reverse current. Thus, the *n*-type region becomes positively charged while the *p*-type region becomes negatively charged. We shall see that the regions of charge unbalance are near the junction. Thus, the net charge densities will have the form of Fig. 3-1*f*. (Note that this is *not* a free-electron or hole density. It represents only unbalanced charges.)

If the *n*-type material is positively charged while the *p*-type is negatively charged, there will be an electric field which points from the *n*-type material to the *p*-type material (see Fig. 3-1*g*). Hence, the *n*-type region will be at a positive potential with respect to the *p*-type region (see Sec. 1-2). This potential is shown in Fig. 3-1*h*. The difference of potential between the *p*-type and *n*-type regions is V_0. This potential tends to retard the flow of free electrons into the *p*-type region and of holes into the *n*-type region. That is, it tends to retard I_f. As long as I_f is in excess of I_r, the potential V_0 will increase. This further retards I_f. Eventually, an equilibrium is established where

$$I_f = I_r \tag{3-1}$$

Free electrons and holes are constantly recombining and being generated. The free electrons in the *p*-type region and the holes in the *n*-type region are minority carriers (see Sec. 1-26). The free-electron and hole densities are shown in Fig. 3-1*d* and *e*.

The electric field set up by the charge unbalance will tend to drive free electrons in the *n*-type region and holes in the *p*-type region away from the junction. Thus, there will be very few mobile charge carriers there. However, there are impurity atoms throughout the material. The ionized donor and acceptor ions are fixed in position. Thus, there is a small region about the junction which is free (or depleted) of mobile charge carriers but which contains fixed ions. These are fixed positive charges in the *n*-type material and fixed negative charges in the *p*-type material. This region is called the *depletion layer* or *depletion region*.

The bulk of the semiconductor material, removed from the depletion layer, contains many free charge carriers. Thus, the electric field will be zero there. (If there is an electric field in a region containing free charge carriers, the charge carriers will move so as to cancel the field within the region.) Thus, the electric field which sets up the potential difference between the *p*-type and *n*-type regions lies in the depletion layer. It can be considered to be set up by the ionized donor and acceptor atoms.

The electric field is essentially zero outside the depletion region. Thus, in this region there must be as many positive charges (donor atoms) on one side of the junction as negative charges (acceptor atoms) on the other. The number of charges depends upon the donor (or acceptor) density and the width of the depletion layer. If $N_d = N_a$ (the donor and acceptor densities are equal), the width of the depletion layer will be the same on either side of the junction. If the impurity concentrations are unequal, the depletion-layer width will be less on the side with the large impurity concentration. A typical width for a depletion layer is 10^{-6} meter.

We have thus far considered an open-circuited *p-n* junction. It may appear as though a current would result in a short-circuited *p-n* junction (see Fig. 3-2) because of the potential V_0. However, this is not the case. V_0 can be considered to be a contact potential (see Sec. 1-24). In addition to V_0, there will be contact potential at the points where the conductor is connected to the semiconductor. These potentials are V_1 and V_2. The net sum of the potentials around the closed loop, $V_0 + V_1 - V_2$, is zero as can be seen by computing the sum of the contact potentials of any three arbitrary materials connected in a closed loop, using the procedures of Sec. 1-24. Thus, there will be no current in the short circuit.

3-2 THE *p-n*-JUNCTION DIODE

Let us now qualitatively discuss the electrical characteristics of a *p-n* junction. When it is used as a circuit element it is called a *p-n-junction diode*. The current in this device depends upon the polarity of the applied voltage. Such an applied direct voltage is called a *bias*.

The forward-biased *p-n* junction   We shall start our discussion by considering a *p-n*-junction diode with an applied potential, as shown in Fig. 3-3a. This circuit is symbolically represented in Fig. 3-3b. When a potential of this polarity is applied, the junction is said to be *foward-biased*. The voltages V_1 and V_2, due to contact potential (see Fig. 3-2), are such that under open-circuit conditions $V_1 - V_2 + V_0 = 0$. For any closed loop, the sum of the voltage drop around the loop must be zero. In addition, V_1 and V_2 are unchanged by the application of V_b. Thus, the potential across the semiconductor crystal must be $V_0 - V_b$. This can be divided into two components. One is due to the scattering of charge carriers at the contacts and in the bulk of the semiconductor. It is called an *ohmic resistance* and acts as an ordinary resistance; i.e., the current is proportional to the voltage. The other component of voltage drop appears across the depletion layer. At the start, let us assume that the ohmic voltage drop is negligible.

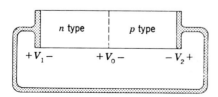

Fig. 3-2   A short-circuited *p-n* junction. The shaded area represents a conductor.

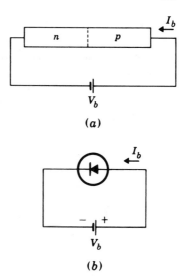

Fig. 3-3 (a) Forward-biased p-n junction and (b) symbolic representation of the diode.

The potential across the depletion layer is then $V_0 - V_b$. Assume for the present that V_b is small, so that $V_0 - V_b > 0$. Then (see Fig. 3-1) the potential barrier of the depletion layer is reduced from V_0 to $V_0 - V_b$. This potential barrier is due to the fields set up by the exposed donor and acceptor atoms. If the barrier is reduced, the number of such charges must be reduced. Thus, *the width of the depletion region is reduced*.

The free electrons and holes that make up the forward current diffuse randomly throughout the material. Only those which have sufficient energy to surmount the potential barrier at the depletion layer can diffuse across it. The application of a forward bias reduces the potential barrier. Thus, a forward bias increases the forward current.

The free electrons and holes that constitute the reverse current diffuse to the potential barrier and *fall* across it. The reverse current I_r depends upon the number of free electrons in the p-type region and holes in the n-type region that diffuse to the barrier, but it is essentially independent of the barrier height. I_r depends mainly upon the temperature of the material and the concentrations of the impurities (see Sec. 1-27).

The applied forward bias increases I_f but leaves I_r unchanged. In general (see Fig. 3-1a) the total current is given by

$$I_b = I_f - I_r \qquad (3-2)$$

Thus, an increase in V_b increases I_b. Actually, the majority-carrier densities are usually very high, and their energy distributions are such that I_b increases very rapidly with increases in V_b. The forward current can become very much greater than the reverse current.

It may appear as though a value of V_b greater than V_0 would cause the barrier potential to reverse. Actually, this is not the case. In the preceding discussion we neglected the ohmic drop. However, as $V_0 - V_b$ becomes small, I_b becomes so large that this drop cannot be ignored. In fact, in such cases, the ohmic drops become larger than the potential across the junction, $V_0 - V$. In general, the ohmic drops are such that $V_0 - V$ will always be positive. Note that the potential across the junction is no longer $V_0 - V_b$ because of the ohmic drops ($V = V_b -$ ohmic drops).

The reverse-biased p-n junction   Let us now assume that the polarity of the voltage source of Fig. 3-3 is reversed. That is, let us now consider that in Fig. 3-3 V_b is negative. Then the applied voltage increases the potential barrier at the depletion layer to $V_0 + V_b$. This *increases the width of the depletion layer*.

If the barrier height is increased, fewer free electrons and holes that constitute the forward current will have sufficient energy to surmount it and I_f will be reduced.

As in the case of the forward-biased junction, the reverse current is essentially unaffected by the height of the potential barrier. Thus, I_r is independent of V_b. Then [see Eq. (3-2)] when V_b is negative and its magnitude is increased from zero, I_b will be negative and vary from 0 to $-I_r$. In general, the doping of p-n-junction diodes is such that the minority-carrier densities are small. Thus, I_r will be very small. An ideal current-voltage characteristic for a p-n-junction diode is shown in Fig. 3-4. The current for reverse bias has a maximum magnitude of I_s, where $I_s = -I_r$. I_s is called the *reverse saturation current*.

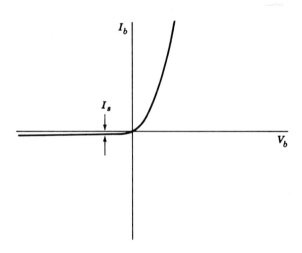

Fig. 3-4 Current-voltage characteristic of an ideal p-n-junction diode.

Note that the current in the forward direction is very much greater than that in the reverse direction.   Often, I_s is of the order of microamperes while the current in the forward direction is thousands of times greater even if V_b is only a fraction of a volt.

Ohmic contacts   The wires of Fig. 3-3 are assumed to be connected to the semiconductor with low-resistance ohmic contacts.   The charge carriers are only free electrons in the wire.   At the junction between the wire and the n-type material, the free electrons flow across the boundary between the metal and the semiconductor.

The charge carriers in the p-type material are predominantly holes. However, the motion of a hole actually consists of the motion of many electrons.   Thus, a hole in the semiconductor moving away from the metal-semiconductor junction is equivalent to a free electron moving away from the junction in the metal.   For example, a valence electron can break its bond and leave the semiconductor and enter the metal.   This forms a hole in the semiconductor which moves away from the junction.

We shall discuss metal-semiconductor junctions in more detail subsequently.

3-3   BAND STRUCTURE OF p-n-JUNCTION DIODES: QUANTITATIVE THEORY

Let us now consider p-n junctions on a quantitative basis.   In Sec. 3-1 we discussed how under equilibrium conditions an open-circuited p-n junction has a potential V_0 across it.   Let us now determine V_0.

When two materials are placed in a junction, it is an experimentally determined fact that equilibrium results when the Fermi levels are aligned. That is, an energy-band diagram (see Figs. 1-35 and 1-36) can be drawn for each material.   The levels of the diagram represent energies.   When a difference of potential occurs between the materials, the band diagrams are displaced from each other by this difference in potential energy.   The energy-band diagrams for n-type and p-type semiconductors are shown in Figs. 1-35 and 1-36, respectively.   Let us redraw them adjacent to each other but displace one diagram by a potential V_0.   (Note that we shall use the letter V to indicate voltage while the letter E will indicate energy in electron volts.) Thus, the energy diagram will be displaced by E_0 electron volts, where E_0 is numerically equal to V_0.   This energy-band diagram is shown in Fig. 3-5. Potential energy for electrons is represented here.   They must surmount the barrier of E_0 eV in traveling from the n-type region to the p-type region.   To obtain a potential-energy diagram for holes, the negative of this diagram must be plotted.

The value of E_0 must be such that the Fermi levels of the p-type and

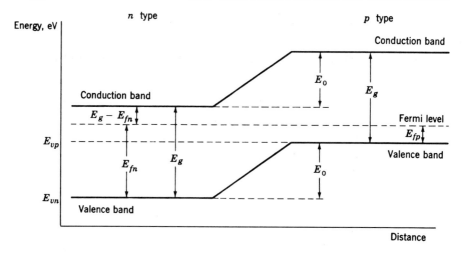

Fig. 3-5 Band diagram for an open-circuited p-n junction at equilibrium. The energy levels for the top of the valence band and the bottom of the conduction band are shown.

n-type materials are aligned. This displaces both the valence and the conduction bands by an amount E_0. It is assumed that, except for impurities, the semiconductor materials are the same on each side of the junction. Thus, each material has the same energy gap. Then, from Fig. 3-5, we have

$$E_g = E_0 + (E_g - E_{fn}) + E_{fp} \tag{3-3}$$

Note that the subscripts n and p have been added to indicate whether the material is n type or p type. Solve Eq. (3-3) for E_0 and substitute Eqs. (1-194) and (1-197) for E_{fn} and E_{fp}, respectively. This yields

$$E_0 = E_g + kT \ln \frac{N_A N_D}{N_c N_v} \tag{3-4}$$

where $E_g = E_c - E_v$. This can be written in a somewhat different form by noting that the energy gap can be expressed in terms of the carrier concentration in *intrinsic* materials, i.e., the charge density that would result if there were no impurities. From Eqs. (1-186) and (1-187), we have, respectively,

$$E_{fi} - E_c = kT \ln \frac{n_i}{N_c} \tag{3-5}$$

and

$$E_v - E_{fi} = kT \ln \frac{p_i}{N_v} \tag{3-6}$$

In intrinsic materials

$$E_g = -2(E_c - E_{fi}) = 2(E_{fi} - E_v) \tag{3-7}$$

[see Eq. (1-190)]. In addition, $n_i = p_i$ [see Eq. (1-166)]. Add Eqs. (3-5) and (3-6) and substitute $n_i = p_i$. Then, substituting this into Eq. (3-4) and manipulating, we obtain

$$E_0 = kT \ln \frac{N_A N_D}{n_i^2} \tag{3-8}$$

Note that k is expressed in electron volts per degree Kelvin. The potential across the junction is numerically equal to Eq. (3-8). Thus,

$$V_0 = kT \ln \frac{N_A N_D}{n_i^2} \tag{3-9}$$

Hence, we can use Eq. (3-9) or (3-4) to determine V_0 in terms of the donor and acceptor concentrations N_D and N_A and n_i or E_g, all of which are known for semiconductor materials.

Now let us manipulate this expression into a form to be used in the next section to compute the p-n-junction diode voltage-current characteristic. We assume that all the donor and acceptor atoms are ionized. Thus, we can approximately state, for regions not in the depletion layer, [see Eqs. (1-193) and (1-196)]

$$n_n = N_D \tag{3-10}$$

and

$$p_p = N_A \tag{3-11}$$

where n_n and p_p are the free-electron and hole densities in the n-type and p-type regions, respectively, and N_A and N_D are the constant acceptor and donor densities in the p-type and n-type regions, respectively. Note that Eqs. (3-10) and (3-11) are not true in the depletion layer, which is almost free of mobile charge carriers.

The product np is constant, independent of the doping [see Eq. (1-184) and the discussion following it]. In intrinsic materials, $n_i = p_i$. Thus,

$$np = n_i^2 \tag{3-12}$$

Thus, in p-type and n-type materials, respectively,

$$n_{p0} = \frac{n_i^2}{p_p} \tag{3-13}$$

and

$$p_{n0} = \frac{n_i^2}{n_n} \tag{3-14}$$

where we have added the subscript 0 to indicate that these are for conditions of thermal equilibrium and that there is zero applied bias.   Again note that these equations do not apply for the depletion region.   Substituting Eqs. (3-10), (3-11), (3-13), and (3-14) into Eq. (3-9), we have

$$V_0 = kT \ln \frac{n_n}{n_{p0}} \tag{3-15a}$$

$$V_0 = kT \ln \frac{p_p}{p_{n0}} \tag{3-15b}$$

Now, solving Eqs. (3-15) for n_{p0} and p_{n0}, we have

$$n_{p0} = n_n \epsilon^{-V_0/kT} = N_D \epsilon^{-V_0/kT} \tag{3-16a}$$

$$p_{n0} = p_p \epsilon^{-V_0/kT} = N_A \epsilon^{-V_0/kT} \tag{3-16b}$$

Thus, the minority-carrier density far from the depletion region varies exponentially with V_0/kT.

3-4   THE CURRENT-VOLTAGE CHARACTERISTIC OF A p-n-JUNCTION DIODE

When a p-n junction is forward-biased, the potential barrier between the n-type and p-type regions is reduced to $V_0 - V_b$ (see Sec. 3-2).   Thus, more free electrons from the n-type region diffuse across the barrier into the p-type region.   Similarly, more holes from the p-type region diffuse into the n-type region.   Once these free electrons and holes diffuse across the junction, they become minority carriers.   This process is called the *injection* of minority carriers.   Note that this actually consists of the *diffusion* of charge carriers across a barrier of reduced height.

The equilibrium density of the minority carriers with no applied bias is n_{p0} and p_{n0} (see Sec. 3-3).   When a forward bias is applied, the concentration of free electrons in the p-type region and holes in the n-type region *just outside the depletion layer* will be increased above the equilibrium value.   However, as the distance from the junction increases, the minority-carrier densities will fall back to their equilibrium values.   This situation was studied in one of the examples of Sec. 1-32.   Thus, we have [see Eq. (1-239)]

$$n_p = n_{p0} + N(0)\epsilon^{x/L_{np}} \tag{3-17a}$$

where n_p is the free-electron density in the p-type region as a function of x, the distance from the junction. $N(0)$ is the *increase* in free-electron density near the junction due to injection of minority carriers, and L_{np} is the diffusion length for free electrons in the p-type material.   Note that, in the p-type region, x is defined as negative.   Thus the positive direction of current as defined in Fig. 3-3 is in the positive direction.   Thus, the exponent of Eq.

(3-17a) is negative, and its magnitude increases as distance from the junction increases. We can proceed in a similar way and write the hole density in the n-type region as

$$p_n = p_{no} + P(0)\epsilon^{-x/L_{pn}} \qquad (3\text{-}17b)$$

where, in this case, x is the distance measured from the junction in the n-type region and is a positive quantity.

Now let us compute the current density due to free electrons and then that due to holes. When a bias is applied to a semiconductor, as shown in Fig. 3-3a, the charge carriers with sufficient energy can surmount the barrier and diffuse across the junction. At the junction, almost all the current is due to diffusion. However, in the bulk of the semiconductor material [see Eqs. (3-17)] the charge densities fall off, and thus so does the diffusion current density. However, the total current density must be independent of distance from the junction if charge is not to "pile up" at a point. In the bulk of the semiconductor, drift currents are set up by the field due to the applied voltage V_b. The drift currents increase as the diffusion currents decrease in such a way that the total current density is independent of position.

If we are near the junction, $x \approx 0$. The current can be considered to be due only to diffusion. Then, applying Eqs. (1-205), (1-206), and (3-17), we have

$$J_{nx} = \frac{eD_nN(0)}{L_{np}} \epsilon^{x/L_{np}}\bigg|_{x=0}$$

$$J_{nx} = \frac{eD_nN(0)}{L_{np}} \qquad (3\text{-}18a)$$

Similarly,

$$J_{px} = \frac{eD_pP(0)}{L_{pn}} \qquad (3\text{-}18b)$$

To determine the current as a function of the applied voltage V_b, we must determine $N(0)$ and $P(0)$ as functions of V_b. In Eqs. (3-16) the equilibrium minority-carrier density is expressed in terms of the barrier potential V_0. If the barrier potential is changed by the application of an external voltage, the minority-carrier densities throughout the material will *not* be changed to a new equilibrium value [see Eqs. (3-17)]. This is due to the fact that the injected minority carriers recombine with the majority carriers in the bulk of the semiconductor. However, just at the edge of the depletion layer, that is, $|x| \approx 0$, very little of this recombination takes place. Thus, we shall assume that Eqs. (3-16) can be used to give the minority-carrier density very close to the edge of the depletion layer if V_0 is replaced by the barrier height $V_0 - V_b$. We shall assume that $x \approx 0$ at the edge of the depletion layer.

Then [see Eqs. (3-17) and (3-16)] at $x = 0$

$$n_p(0) = n_{p0} + N(0) = n_n \epsilon^{-(V_0 - V_b)/kT} \tag{3-19a}$$

$$p_n(0) = p_{n0} + P(0) = p_p \epsilon^{-(V_0 - V_b)/kT} \tag{3-19b}$$

Substituting Eqs. (3-16) for n_{p0} and p_{n0}, respectively, we obtain

$$N(0) = n_{p0}(\epsilon^{V_b/kT} - 1) \tag{3-20a}$$

$$P(0) = p_{n0}(\epsilon^{V_b/kT} - 1) \tag{3-20b}$$

Substituting in Eqs. (3-18), we have

$$\mathscr{I}_{nx} = \frac{eD_n n_{p0}}{L_{np}} (\epsilon^{V_b/kT} - 1) \tag{3-21a}$$

$$\mathscr{I}_{px} = \frac{eD_p p_{n0}}{L_{pn}} (\epsilon^{V_b/kT} - 1) \tag{3-21b}$$

The total current density is equal to the sum of Eqs. (3-21a) and (3-21b). Thus,

$$\mathscr{I}_x = \left(\frac{eD_n n_{p0}}{L_{np}} + \frac{eD_p p_{n0}}{L_{pn}}\right)(\epsilon^{V_b/kT} - 1) \tag{3-22}$$

The total current is equal to $\mathscr{I}_x$ multiplied by the cross-sectional area A. Hence,

$$I_b = I_s(\epsilon^{V_b/kT} - 1) \tag{3-23}$$

where

$$I_s = Ae\left(\frac{D_n n_{p0}}{L_{np}} + \frac{D_p p_{n0}}{L_{pn}}\right) \tag{3-24}$$

This equation is valid for both forward and reverse biases. For forward bias, V_b is positive. Then I_b increases very rapidly with increases in V_b. In the reverse-biased case, V_b is negative, and I_b has a maximum negative value of $-I_s$. Note that I_s is the reverse saturation current (see Sec. 3-2). The voltage-current characteristic is of the form of Fig. 3-4.

An ideal diode acts as a short circuit when it is forward-biased but as an open circuit when it is reverse-biased. The actual diode approximates this characteristic.

The current relation [see Eq. (3-23)] contains I_s as a multiplier. The value of I_s is thus an important one. Unfortunately, it is very temperature-dependent. Thus, a variation in temperature will change the diode characteristics. Let us determine this temperature dependence. Substituting Eqs. (3-10), (3-11), (3-13), and (3-14) into Eq. (3-24), we obtain

$$I_s = Ae\left(\frac{D_n}{L_{np}N_A} + \frac{D_p}{L_{pn}N_D}\right)n_i^2 \tag{3-25}$$

Then, substituting Eqs. (1-184), (1-183), and (1-175) and noting that $np = n_i^2$, we have

$$I_s = 4Ae\left(\frac{D_n}{L_{np}N_A} + \frac{D_p}{L_{pn}N_D}\right)(m_p m_n)^{\frac{3}{2}}\left(\frac{2\pi e k T}{h^2}\right)^3 \epsilon^{-E_g/kT} \tag{3-26}$$

The mean free path of the electron in the semiconductor does not vary rapidly with temperature. However, D_n and D_p are approximately inversely proportional to temperature. Thus, we can write

$$D_n \approx \frac{K_n}{T} \tag{3-27a}$$

$$D_p \approx \frac{K_p}{T} \tag{3-27b}$$

where K_n and K_p are constants of proportionality. Hence,

$$I_s = K_s T^2 \epsilon^{-E_g/kT} \tag{3-28}$$

where K_s is a constant of proportionality which can be obtained by substituting Eqs. (3-27) into Eq. (3-26). The marked dependence of I_s upon temperature is shown by Eq. (3-28).

The values of E_g that should be used in Eq. (3-28) at 300°K are 0.67 eV for germanium and 1.11 eV for silicon. Substitution in Eq. (3-28) indicates that at usual operating temperatures I_s approximately doubles for each 10°C increase in temperature. Thus, I_s increases very rapidly with increases in temperature.

The preceding derivation assumed that the free electrons and holes did not recombine in the depletion layer. Since recombination can take place there, Eqs. (3-23) and (3-28) are slightly in error. It is experimentally found that Eq. (3-23) can be slightly modified[1] to obtain more accurate results. This modified form is

$$I_b = I_s(\epsilon^{V_b/\eta kT} - 1) \tag{3-29}$$

where η is a correction factor. In the case of germanium diodes, $\eta = 1$; that is, Eq. (3-23) is accurate. For the case of silicon at usual operating currents, $\eta = 2$ should be used.

The reverse saturation current in modified form can be written as

$$I_s = K_s T^{2\delta} \epsilon^{-E_g/\eta kT} \tag{3-30}$$

For germanium, again the results are accurate, and $\delta = 1$. For silicon, a correction factor must be used, and $\delta = 0.75$. The same value of η should be used here as in Eq. (3-29).

Even with the correction factors, Eqs. (3-29) and (3-30) have almost the same shape as that predicted by Eqs. (3-23) and (3-28). Thus, the diode characteristics will be almost as predicted.

3-5 ACTUAL CURRENT-VOLTAGE CHARACTERISTICS
OF A *p-n*-JUNCTION DIODE—LOAD LINES

Equations (3-29) and (3-30) are only approximately correct, and diode characteristics are often presented graphically using experimentally measured information.   A typical plot of v_b versus i_b for a *p-n*-junction diode is shown in Fig. 3-6, which is called the *static characteristic* of the diode.   Let us use this characteristic to determine the current I_b and the voltage V_b in the simple diode circuit of Fig. 3-7.   The static characteristic is, in effect, one equation which relates the two unknowns V_b and I_b.   Another equation can be obtained by applying Kirchhoff's law to the external circuit.   This gives

$$V_b = V_{bb} - I_b R_L \tag{3-31}$$

The plot of this curve on a v_b versus i_b axis is a straight line of slope $-1/R_1$. The intercepts are V_{bb}/R_L and V_{bb}.   This curve is called a *load line*.   In Fig. 3-7, let $V_{bb} = 3$ volts and $R_L = 50$ ohms.   This results in the load line shown in Fig. 3-6.   The intersection of the load line with the static characteristic yields V_b and I_b.   In this case, $V_b = 0.9$ volt and $I_b = 43$ ma. V_b and I_b are called the *operating point* of the diode.

If V_{bb} is made negative, the load line will be in the third quadrant.   If $|V_{bb}|$ is less than 100 volts, for the diode of Fig. 3-6, the reverse current will be negative and have a magnitude no greater than 3 μa.   Note that both axes

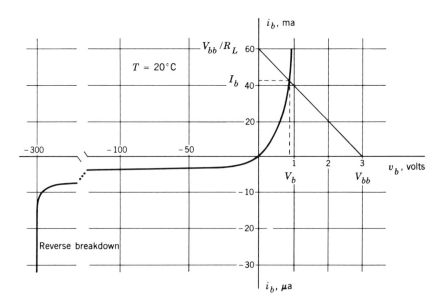

Fig. 3-6 A typical current-voltage characteristic for a *p-n*-junction diode at a fixed operating temperature.   (Note the scale changes on the axes.)

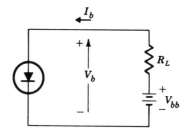

Fig. 3-7 A simple *p-n*-junction-diode circuit.

have different scales for positive and negative values.   Thus, for this diode, the reverse saturation current is 3 μa.

At large negative voltages, I_b abruptly rises.   This is called *reverse breakdown*.   It will be discussed in Sec. 3-9.   If the diode is to function as a rectifier, i.e., to act as a low resistance to current in one direction and as a high resistance to current in the other direction, then the negative value of v_b should not exceed the breakdown voltage.   However, there are times when the reverse breakdown is a useful characteristic.

In many semiconductor diode circuits, we are interested in small changes which are functions of time about an average value.   For instance, suppose that V_{bb} changes its value by an amount ΔV_{bb}, which varies with time.   In this case, the slope of the load line does not change, but the load line shifts parallel to itself.   The shifted load line is used to compute the change in v_b and i_b.   The values of v_b and i_b that result when $\Delta V_{bb} = 0$ are called the *quiescent values* and are written as V_{bQ} and I_{bQ}.   The point (V_{bQ}, I_{bQ}) is called the *quiescent operating point*.   The instantaneous values of v_b and i_b define the *operating point* (v_b, i_b).   Note that lowercase letters are used for time-varying quantities.

For small changes in V_{bb}, the change in v_b and i_b is a function of the slope of the static characteristic at the quiescent operating point.   It is useful to define a parameter which is the reciprocal of this slope

$$r_d = \left.\frac{dv_b}{di_b}\right|_{v_b = V_{bQ}} \tag{3-32}$$

This has the dimensions of a resistance and is called the *dynamic junction resistance* or *junction resistance* of the *p-n*-junction diode.   The reciprocal of r_d, designated g_d, is called the *dynamic junction conductance* or *junction conductance*.   Note that r_d is a function of V_{bQ}.

Cut-in voltage   Let us consider the current-voltage characteristic for very small voltages.   A typical graph of i_b versus v_b for small v_b is shown in Fig. 3-8.   Note that the current remains very small until $v_b = V_\gamma$.   Further increases in v_b result in rapid increases in i_b.   Actually, i_b increases continuously as v_b is increased from zero.   However, once i_b reaches a current

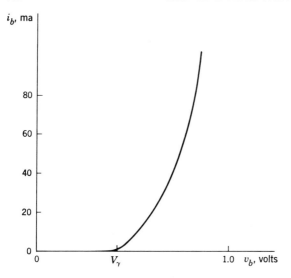

Fig. 3-8 An illustration of cut-in voltage.

which is in the range of 1 percent of the rated value, it then increases rapidly with increases in v_b. Let us call the value of v_b which corresponds to this value of i_b the *cut-in voltage*. It is designated in Fig. 3-8 as V_γ. This shape of the characteristic is due in part to the exponential nature of the v_b, i_b characteristic [see Eq. (3-29)]. For germanium *p-n*-junction diodes, $V_\gamma \approx 0.1$ volt while for silicon *p-n*-junction diodes, $V_\gamma \approx 0.5$ volt.

Thermal effects   Diode characteristics are very temperature-sensitive (see Sec. 3-4).   At times, manufacturers specify a set of static characteristics containing many curves of the type shown in Fig. 3-6.   Each curve is drawn for a single operating temperature.   If only one static characteristic curve is drawn, the operating temperature should be specified.   In such cases, the characteristics at other temperatures can be approximately determined in the following way.   From Eqs. (3-29) and (3-30) we have, for germanium,

$$I_b = I_s(\epsilon^{V_b/kT} - 1) \tag{3-33a}$$

$$I_s = K_s T^2 \epsilon^{-E_g/kT} \tag{3-33b}$$

and, for silicon,

$$I_b = I_s(\epsilon^{V_b/2kT} - 1) \tag{3-33c}$$

$$I_s = K_s T^{1.5} \epsilon^{-E_g/2kT} \tag{3-33d}$$

The value of K_s can be obtained from the static characteristic.   That is, a value of the reverse saturation current can be obtained from it.   The values of I_s, E_g, K, and T are then substituted into Eq. (3-33b) or (3-33d). Alternatively, a value of I_b can be ascertained for a chosen V_b. Substitution in Eqs. (3-33a) and (3-33c) then gives I_s. This is then substituted into Eq. (3-33b) or (3-33d) to determine K_s and curves of I_b versus V_b for various temperatures can be plotted. (Actually several values of K_s should be determined using different values of I_b and V_b. The average value of K_s should be the one used.)

3-6 SPACE-CHARGE, TRANSITION, OR BARRIER CAPACITANCE

When the potential V_b applied across a *p-n* junction varies, the width of the depletion region varies. Thus, as V_b increases, more charges will be exposed in the depletion layer. This is equivalent to a varying voltage varying the charge in the plates of an ordinary capacitor. Thus, a diode has an effective capacitance which acts as if it were in parallel with the diode. This capacitance affects the high-frequency and switching behavior of the diode.

The capacitance is a function of the variation of the impurity concentration in the depletion region. We shall consider two typical variations here.

Linear variation of impurity concentrations   At times, e.g., with grown junctions, the impurity density of the *p-n* junction has the form shown in Fig. 3-9. That is, the acceptor density is N_A atoms per cubic meter in the *p*-type region, and then it varies linearly to N_D donor atoms per cubic meter in the *n*-type region. The *net* exposed charge density in the depletion layer will be of the form of Fig. 3-9b. In order to simplify the problem, we shall approximate Fig. 3-9b by the distribution of Fig. 3-9c. In Fig. 3-9c, let the slope of the straight line segment at $x = 0$ be u. Since we assume that all the donor and acceptor atoms are ionized, the charge density in the idealized depletion region will be the same as the curve at $N_d - N_a$. Note that the depletion layer does not extend over the entire region where the density of the impurity atoms varies. Thus, the charge density is given by

$$\rho = \begin{cases} -uex & -\dfrac{d}{2} < x < \dfrac{d}{2} \\ 0 & |x| > \dfrac{d}{2} \end{cases} \tag{3-34}$$

We must determine d, the width of the depletion layer, as a function of the applied potential V_b. Note that the potential across the depletion layer is $V_0 - V_b$ (see Sec. 3-4). Poisson's equation gives the variation in potential as a function of position [see Eq. (2-1)]. Thus, for a one-dimensional variation

$$\frac{d^2 V}{dx^2} = -\frac{\rho}{\epsilon} = +\frac{uex}{\epsilon} \tag{3-35}$$

where ϵ is the permittivity of the medium.   Integrating, we have

$$\frac{dV}{dx} = \frac{uex^2}{2\epsilon} + C_1 \tag{3-36}$$

where C_1 is a constant.   At the edges of the depletion layer, the potential becomes constant, as shown in Fig. 3-9d.   Thus, $dV/dx = 0$ at $x = \pm d/2$.

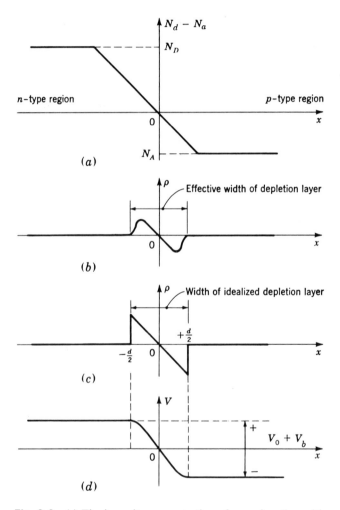

Fig. 3-9 (a) The impurity concentration of a p-n junction with a linear variation of impurity concentration; (b) net charge concentration; (c) idealized charge concentration; (d) potential distribution.

Substituting in Eq. (3-36), solving for C_1, and substituting this value back into Eq. (3-36), we have

$$\frac{dV}{dx} = \frac{ue}{2\epsilon}\left(x^2 - \frac{d^2}{4}\right) \tag{3-37}$$

Integrating, we obtain

$$V = \frac{uex}{2\epsilon}\left(\frac{x^2}{3} - \frac{d^2}{4}\right) + C_2 \qquad -\frac{d}{2} \leq x \leq \frac{d}{2} \tag{3-38}$$

Any point may be chosen as reference, i.e., where $V = 0$. Let us choose the reference at $x = 0$. Thus, $C_2 = 0$. The difference between the potential at $x = -d/2$ and the potential at $x = d/2$ is the barrier potential $V_0 - V_b$ (see Fig. 3-9c). The transition capacitance is of most importance when the diode is reverse-biased; i.e., it is then in shunt with large resistance. Hence, we can consider that the applied voltage V_b is negative. Then, solve Eq. (3-38) for $V|_{x=-d/2}$ and $V|_{x=d/2}$ and set the difference equal to $V_0 - V_b$. This yields

$$V_0 - V_b = \frac{ued^3}{12\epsilon} \tag{3-39}$$

or, equivalently, the width of the depletion layer is

$$d = \left[\frac{12\epsilon(V_0 - V_b)}{ue}\right]^{\frac{1}{3}} \tag{3-40}$$

The total charge per unit cross-sectional area can be found by integrating the charge density of Eq. (3-34) from $x = -d/2$ to $x = 0$. Doing this and multiplying by A, the area of the junction, we obtain the total charge on one side of the capacitor

$$Q = \frac{eud^2A}{8}$$

Substituting Eq. (3-40), we have

$$Q = A[\tfrac{9}{32}eu\epsilon^2(V_0 - V_b)^2]^{\frac{1}{3}} \tag{3-41}$$

The capacitance that is of importance is the *incremental capacitance*, defined as the ratio of a change of charge with respect to a change in voltage. (Note that charge on one side of the capacitor is positive while that on the other is negative. When a negative V_b is applied, the charge on the p-type side is negative, as it should be.) Then

$$C_T = \left|\frac{dQ}{dV_b}\right|_{V_b = V_{bQ}} \tag{3-42}$$

This is the effective capacitance of the diode for small variation of V_b around a quiescent operating point $V_b = V_{bQ}$. This capacitance is called the *space-charge, transition,* or *barrier capacitance.* Hence, the transition capacitance is

$$C_T = A(\tfrac{1}{12}eu\epsilon^2)^{\frac{1}{3}}(V_0 - V_b)^{-\frac{1}{3}}|_{V_b = V_{bQ}} \tag{3-43}$$

The capacitance of an ordinary parallel-plate capacitor one of whose plates is of area A with spacing d between the plates is $\epsilon A/d$. Substituting Eq. (3-39) into Eq. (3-43), we obtain

$$C_T = \frac{\epsilon A}{d} \tag{3-44}$$

Thus, the transition capacitance is exactly that which would be obtained for a parallel-plate capacitor whose permittivity was the same as that of the semiconductor, whose area was equal to the cross-sectional area of the junction, and whose spacing was equal to the width of the depletion layer.

Note that the transition capacitance is nonlinear; i.e., it is a function of the applied voltage.

Abrupt variation of impurity concentrations   Another type of impurity concentration, which occurs with alloyed junctions, is shown in Fig. 3-10a. Here we assume that the impurity concentration abruptly changes from N_D to N_A. We then proceed in essentially the same way as for the linear variation of impurity concentration. This yields

$$V_0 - V_b = \frac{e}{2\epsilon}(N_D d_1{}^2 + N_A d_2{}^2) \tag{3-45}$$

The magnitude of the total exposed charge on one side of the junction must equal the magnitude of the total exposed charge on the other side. Thus,

$$N_D d_1 = N_A d_2 \tag{3-46}$$

Substituting into Eq. (3-45) and solving for d_1, we obtain

$$d_1 = \sqrt{\frac{2\epsilon(V_0 - V_b)}{eN_D(N_D/N_A + 1)}} \tag{3-47}$$

The total exposed charge on one side of the junction is

$$Q = eN_D d_1 A \tag{3-48}$$

where A is the cross-sectional area of the junction. Substituting Eq. (3-47) into Eq. (3-48) and differentiating as in Eq. (3-42), we have

$$C_T = A\sqrt{\frac{\epsilon e}{2(V_0 - V_b)(1/N_D + 1/N_A)}} \tag{3-49}$$

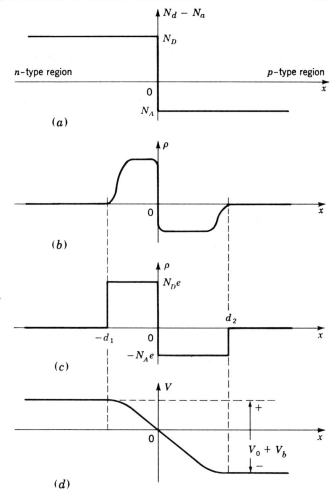

Fig. 3-10 (*a*) The impurity concentration of a *p-n* junction with an abrupt variation of impurity concentration; (*b*) net charge concentration; (*c*) idealized charge concentration; (*d*) potential distribution.

Substituting Eqs. (3-47) and (3-46), we obtain

$$C_T = \frac{\epsilon A}{d_1 + d_2} \tag{3-50}$$

Again, the transition capacitance is the same as that which would be obtained by a parallel-plate capacitor of the same cross-sectional area as the junction whose dielectric constant is the same as that of the semiconductor and whose spacing between the plates is equal to the total width of the depletion region.

Note that in both cases considered the transition capacitance varied as $1/(V_0 - V_b)$ to either the one-half or the one-third power. Thus, as the reverse bias is increased, this capacitance is decreased.

Varactor diodes   The transition capacitances are functions of the applied voltage V_b. At times, it is desirable to have a capacitor whose capacitance can be varied in accordance with an applied signal. To accomplish this, reverse-biased p-n-junction diodes are often used. In such cases, the diodes are called *Varactor diodes* or *Varicaps* or *Voltacaps*.

3-7 DIFFUSION CAPACITANCE—CHARGE CONTROL

In deriving the transition capacitance (see Sec. 3-6) we assumed that all the "charge" of the capacitor was due to the exposed donor and acceptor atoms in the depletion layer. This is a valid assumption when the p-n junction is reverse-biased. However, in the forward-biased case, an additional effect must be considered. When the junction is forward-biased, minority carriers are injected across the barrier. The charge density has the form of Eqs. (3-17). The charge n_p or p_n which is in excess of the equilibrium value n_{p0} or p_{n0} acts as though it were charge stored on the plates of a capacitor. That is, an increase in the forward bias increases the charge in excess of equilibrium values. Thus, this charge can be considered to be stored in the semiconductor.

For the moment, let us consider only holes. If the semiconductor is of overall length L_T, the total charge, in excess of equilibrium, stored is [see Eq. (3-17b)]

$$Q_p = AeP(0) \int_0^{L_T} \epsilon^{-x/L_{pn}} \, dx \qquad (3-51)$$

where A is the cross-sectional area. [Actually Eq. (3-17b) is valid only for an infinite slab. However if $L_T \gg L_{pn}$ it will be accurate.] Integrating, we obtain

$$Q_p = AeP(0)L_{pn}(1 - \epsilon^{-L_T/L_{pn}})$$

In general, $L_T \gg L_{pn}$. Thus, $\epsilon^{-L_T/L_{pn}} \ll 1$. Hence,

$$Q_p = AeP(0)L_{pn} \qquad (3-52)$$

Then, substituting Eqs. (3-20b) and (3-21b), we have

$$Q_p = \frac{A \mathscr{J}_{px}}{D_p} L_{pn}{}^2 \qquad (3-53)$$

but $A \mathscr{J}_{px} = I_p$, the total junction current due to holes. Thus,

$$Q_p = \frac{L_{pn}{}^2 I_p}{D_p} \qquad (3-54)$$

The incremental capacitance is given by Eq. (3-42). Hence,

$$C_{Dp} = \frac{dQ_p}{dV_b}\bigg|_{V_b = V_{bQ}} = \frac{L_{pn}^2}{D_p}\frac{dI_p}{dV_b}\bigg|_{V_b = V_{bQ}} \tag{3-55}$$

Note that the derivative is taken about the operating point of the diode. From Eqs. (1-240) to (1-245), written for holes instead of for free electrons, we have, after some manipulation,

$$L_{pn}^2 = \tau_{pn}D_p \tag{3-56}$$

where τ_{pn} is the lifetime of the holes in the n-type region. Thus,

$$C_{Dp} = \tau_{pn}\frac{dI_p}{dV_b}\bigg|_{V_b = V_{bQ}} \tag{3-57}$$

In Sec. 3-5 we defined a dynamic conductance of the diode

$$g_d = \frac{dI_b}{dV_b}\bigg|_{V_b = V_{bQ}}$$

Here we are considering only the component of current due to holes. Let us call this g_{dp}

$$g_{dp} = \frac{dI_p}{dV_b}\bigg|_{V_b = V_{bQ}} \tag{3-58}$$

$$C_{Dp} = \tau_{pn}g_{dp} \tag{3-59}$$

This capacitance is called the *diffusion capacitance due to holes* since it is caused by holes diffusing across the potential barrier.

We can proceed in a similar way and determine the *diffusion capacitance due to free electrons*. This is

$$C_{Dn} = \tau_{np}g_{dn} \tag{3-60}$$

where τ_{np} is the lifetime of the free electrons in the p-type regions, and

$$g_{dn} = \frac{dI_n}{dV_b}\bigg|_{V_b = V_{bQ}} \tag{3-61}$$

where I_n is the current due to free electrons. The total *diffusion capacitance* is the sum of that due to free electrons and holes. Thus,

$$C_D = \tau_{pn}g_{dp} + \tau_{np}g_{dn} \tag{3-62}$$

In general, the dynamic conductance of a forward-biased diode can be 10^6 or more times that of a reverse-biased diode. Thus, in the forward-bias case, the diffusion capacitance will usually be very much greater than the transition capacitance, and the transition capacitance can be neglected. For reverse-biased junctions, the transition capacitance is usually much larger than the diffusion capacitance, and the diffusion capacitance can be neglected.

The diffusion capacitance for a forward-biased junction is usually large, for example, 20 μf. However, it is shunted by the forward-biased resistance of the diode, which is very low. In many applications, this capacitance can be neglected.

Charge control of a diode   The excess charge above the equilibrium value that we have discussed in this section in Eqs. (3-51) to (3-54) is a useful parameter in describing the operation of the diode. For instance, substituting Eq. (3-56) into Eq. (3-54) and manipulating, we obtain

$$I_p = \frac{Q_p}{\tau_{pn}} \tag{3-63}$$

That is, the hole current is proportional to the stored excess minority carriers in the n-type region. Note that I_p varies directly with this stored charge but varies exponentially with voltage [see Eq. (3-23)]. Thus, it is sometimes more convenient to work with charge than it is to work with voltage. We can write an equation similar to Eq. (3-62) for the current due to free electrons. This is

$$I_n = \frac{Q_n}{\tau_{np}} \tag{3-64}$$

Since τ is the lifetime of the minority carriers, Q/τ, on the average, is the rate of change of charge due to recombination. Equations (3-63) and (3-64) state that the hole current or free-electron current diffusing across the junction replaces the charge carriers lost by recombination. That is, charge carriers are replaced at the proper rate to maintain the charge density.

Since, in this description, the current is a function of the stored charge, it is called a *charge-control description*. It is often a useful procedure for describing *p-n*-junction behavior and will be considered in greater detail in Sec. 15-2.

3-8   METAL-SEMICONDUCTOR JUNCTIONS

Metallic contacts must be placed on semiconductors so that they can be connected to wires or other parts of the circuit. Such contacts form a *metal-semiconductor junction*. Some of these junctions act as an ordinary small resistance, but other metal-semiconductor junctions have characteristics which are similar to those of the *p-n*-junction diode; i.e., they act as a rectifier. If the purpose of the metal-semiconductor junction is simply to provide a connection, the junction should be nonrectifying. However, at times, rectifier diodes are deliberately fabricated using metal-semiconductor junctions.

Rectifying junctions   When two materials are placed in contact, their Fermi levels align and a contact potential appears between them.   If one of the materials is a metal and the other a semiconductor and the contact potential has the proper polarity, a rectifier will result.   Contact potential is established by a charge redistribution within the materials; e.g., in a *p-n* junction, it is set up by the ionized atoms of the depletion layer.

In a rectifying junction between a metal and an *n*-type semiconductor the Fermi levels are such that metal acquires a negative charge with respect to the semiconductor.   Thus, prior to equilibrium, there is a net flow of free electrons from the semiconductor to the metal.   Since the metal is a conductor, almost all the excess charge will reside on the surface of the metal adjacent to the semiconductor.   These charges set up a field which drives the free electrons in the semiconductor away from the junction and forms a depletion layer.   Thus, a layer of fixed positive charges results.   A potential barrier against free electrons traveling from the semiconductor to the metal is set up by the positive charges and surface free electrons.   This is analogous to the barrier for forward current in a *p-n* junction.   On the other hand, free electrons traveling from the interior of the metal to the junction must *also* surmount a potential barrier, which is set up by the negative surface charges. (Note that the positive charges in the depletion region are relatively far from the interior of the metal and thus do not neutralize the field of the surface charges.)   At equilibrium, with zero applied voltage, the barriers are such that flow of free electrons in each direction is equal.

The application of a forward bias reduces the potential barrier for free electrons leaving the semiconductor   The forward bias reduces the width of the depletion layer.   The forward free-electron current increases rapidly with forward bias.   This is similar to forward current in a *p-n*-junction diode.

When a reverse bias is applied, the width of the depletion layer increases, increasing the resulting potential barrier and reducing the forward current.

The potential barrier for free electrons leaving the metal, i.e., the reverse current, is essentially established by the surface-charge layer.   This is almost independent of the applied bias.   Then the reverse free-electron current from the metal to the semiconductor is essentially independent of the applied potential.   Hence, as the magnitude of the reverse bias is increased, the total current approaches a saturation value.   Therefore, the metal-to-semiconductor junction has a rectifying characteristic which is similar to that of a *p-n* junction.

Metal-semiconductor rectifying junctions can be formed using *p*-type materials.   However, the theory of their operation is not completely understood.

Point-contact diodes   One metal-to-semiconductor diode, a form of which has been in use since the earliest days of radio, consists of a thin stiff metal wire called a *cat's whisker*, which is pressed onto a semiconductor. Called a *point-contact diode*, it has been replaced in most applications by the *p-n*-junction diode. However, the effective area of a point contact can be made very small. This limits the junction capacitance. At times, point-contact diodes are used for very high frequency applications.

Nonrectifying contacts   In ordinary semiconductor devices, for example, *p-n*-junction diodes, it is necessary to connect metallic leads to the semiconductor. These contacts should *not* act as rectifiers. If the area directly under the surface of a semiconductor is such that very many charge carriers are being generated, then the depletion region in the semiconductor would not be formed. For instance, in an *n*-type material, if free electrons are continuously generated near the surface, this region would not become depleted of free electrons. Thus, a potential barrier of the type discussed would not be established, and the metal-to-semiconductor contact would not act as a rectifier.

In order to have a region where majority carriers are generated at a high rate, the area where the metal contact is to be made can be very highly doped. Alternatively, it is mechanically abraded. This produces allowable energy levels in the forbidden band and increases the generation of free-electron–hole pairs (see Sec. 1-29). Besides, these procedures reduce the resistance of the contact, which is also desirable.

The formation of a rectifying junction between a metal and an *n*-type semiconductor requires that the polarity of the metal be negative with respect to the semiconductor. Thus, the work function of the metal must be greater than that of the semiconductor. If this is not the case, the metal will not acquire the negative surface charge and a rectifying junction will not be formed. This is an alternative procedure for obtaining a nonrectifying junction. However, it is not too practical a procedure since then the only metals which can be used for contacts are those whose work functions are greater than that of the semiconductor. This often limits the choice of metals to ones with undesirable properties, e.g., ones which corrode readily.

3-9   BREAKDOWN EFFECTS IN *p-n* JUNCTIONS

Figure 3-6 indicates that the reverse current increases suddenly if the reverse voltage is made sufficiently large. This is called *reverse breakdown*. It can be caused by two different effects.

If the applied reverse voltage, and hence the electric field in the depletion layer, is made sufficiently large, the charge carriers, which constitute the reverse current, will acquire a great deal of energy while moving through the depletion region. If this energy is sufficient, the charge carriers will ionize atoms in the depletion region by collision. This will liberate valence electrons in the depletion region and increase the number of charge carriers. These in turn will be accelerated by the fields and can ionize other atoms. Thus, the process can be a cumulative one.   Hence, the reverse current can increase very sharply once the reverse voltage becomes large enough.   This process is called *avalanche breakdown.*

Fixed atoms in the depletion layer can also become ionized if there is a strong enough electric field even if there is no ionization by collision.   In this case, the electric field is sufficient to allow the valence electrons to surmount the energy gap and become free electrons.   This too can result in a large increase in reverse current.   This effect is called *zener breakdown.*

When breakdown occurs, the static characteristics of the diode are such that the voltage is almost independent of current (see Fig. 3-6).   At times, special diodes are built which are designed to be operated in this constant-voltage region and are used as voltage-regulating devices.   They are called *zener diodes*, even though, at times, the mechanism is an avalanche break-down.   Thus the name is an improper one.

In general, it should be noted that neither avalanche nor zener break-down results in damage to the diode if the external circuit limits the current so that it does not become excessive.   Of course, if the reverse current is allowed to become large enough, the resultant heating can cause damage.

3-10   THE TUNNEL DIODE

We have thus far considered that an electron cannot pass beyond a potential barrier unless it has an energy greater than the height of the potential barrier. However, this is not completely true.   Consider a potential barrier of the form of Fig. 3-11a whose height is E_0 and an electron to the left of the origin. If Schrödinger's equation (1-109) is solved, the probability distribution that an electron whose total energy is E, which is less than E_0, lies at some point to the right of the origin is not zero but is given by

$$\psi\psi^* = K\epsilon^{-x/d_0} \qquad x > 0 \tag{3-65}$$

where K is a constant and

$$d_0(E) = \frac{h}{4\pi} \sqrt{\frac{1}{2me(E_0 - E)}} \qquad E < E_0 \tag{3-66}$$

Equation (3-65) indicates that there is a *finite probability of finding an electron to the right of the origin.*   This probability falls off rapidly (exponentially) with distance.   When $x = d_0$, the probability has fallen off to $1/\epsilon$ of the value at the origin.   Note that as E, the electron's energy, approaches E_0, the value of d_0 increases.   This increases the probability of finding the electron at some distance to the right of the origin.

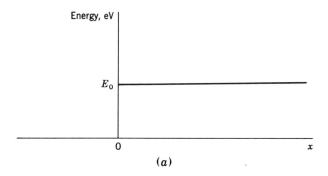

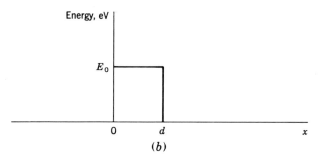

Fig. 3-11 (*a*) A potential-energy step of height E_0; (*b*) a potential-energy barrier of height E_0 and width d.

Now consider the potential barrier of Fig. 3-11*b*. The solution of Schrödinger's equation is somewhat more complex for this barrier, but the ideas of the last paragraph are still valid. That is, the probability that the electron can pass through the barrier is nonzero. If d is much less than d_0 [see Eq. (3-66)], this probability will become large. Thus, it is possible for an electron whose total energy is less than E_0 to pass *through* the barrier. This process is called *tunneling*.

We have ignored one effect in the preceding discussion. An electron can tunnel through a barrier only if an energy state corresponding to its energy is vacant on the other side of the barrier. Note that the electron's energy is not changed by the process of tunneling.

We have restricted this discussion to the tunneling of electrons, but in theory other particles can tunnel as well.

An electronic device that utilizes tunneling is called a *tunnel diode* or an *Esaki diode*. It consists of an ordinary *p-n*-junction diode except that the doping densities are made very large, for example, 1000 to 10^4 times as great as in the usual *p-n*-junction diode. The width of the depletion layer will be very small in such cases. For instance [see Eq. (3-47)] in an abrupt junction, the width of the depletion layer varies essentially as the reciprocal of the square root of the impurity concentration. The impurity concentration is made large enough to ensure that the depletion layer becomes narrow enough to make appreciable tunneling possible.

In a very heavily doped semiconductor, the Fermi level does not lie in the forbidden region but in the conduction band for n-type material and in the valence band for p-type material. This can be seen from Eqs. (1-194) and (1-197). For instance, in ordinary n-type semiconductors, $N_D < N_c$, and the Fermi level predicted by Eq. (1-194) lies below the bottom of the conduction band. However, when N_D becomes greater than N_c, as it does in the tunnel diode, the Fermi level lies above the bottom of the conduction band. In these cases the material is called a *degenerate semiconductor*.

A typical energy-band diagram for a tunnel diode is shown in Fig. 3-12a. The shaded areas represent electrons occupying available energy levels. In Fig. 3-12a, tunneling can occur across the depletion layer. However, the probability of an electron's tunneling one way is equal to the probability of another electron's tunneling the other way. Thus, the net current due to tunneling is zero when there is no applied bias.

Now let us assume that a small forward bias is applied. Application of a forward-bias voltage decreases the potential barrier of the junction by an amount equal to the potential of the bias voltage. (This assumes that there are no ohmic drops and the full bias potential appears across the junction.) Thus, the application of a bias causes the energy diagram on one side of the junction to be displaced with respect to the other side by an amount equal to the bias voltage. Hence, the energy diagram becomes that of Fig. 3-12b. In general, the free-electron density in the conduction band of the n-type material falls off as energy increases. Thus, the density is higher at the bottom of the valence band than at the top. Similarly, there are more available states at the top of the valence band of the p-type material than at the bottom. Thus, applying a small forward bias brings more of the free electrons of the n-type material opposite more available allowable energy states in the p-type material. Therefore, the number of free electrons tunneling from the n-type material to the p-type material increases. The opposite effect occurs for electrons tunneling in the reverse direction. That is, the number of available states opposite the electrons of the p-type region is decreased. Thus, there will be a net current due to free electrons tunneling from the n-type region to the p-type region.

If the bias is increased further, so that the energy level is as shown in Fig. 3-12c, the *tunneling will decrease*. This is because most of the free electrons in the n-type region will be opposite the forbidden band and cannot tunnel. The electrons in the p-type region will be opposite either filled energy levels or the forbidden energy band. Thus, again, there will be no tunneling.

The current due to tunneling, as a function of the forward bias V_b, has

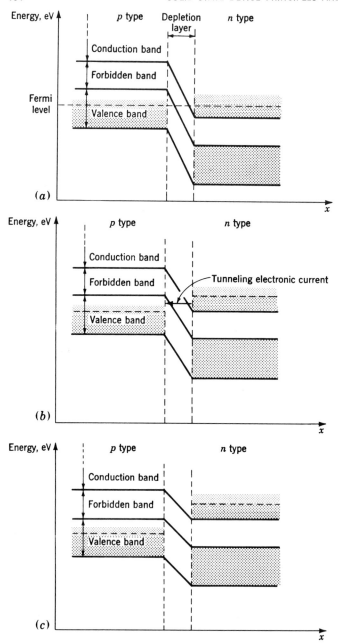

Fig. 3-12 Energy levels in a tunnel diode: (*a*) with zero bias; (*b*) for a small forward bias; (*c*) for a larger forward bias. The shaded areas represent electron densities in allowed energy levels at room temperature.

the form shown in the solid curve of Fig. 3-13a. The tunneling current rises to a maximum and then falls to zero as V_b is increased. In addition to the tunneling component of current, there is also a component due to the normal p-n-junction-diode current, shown by the dashed curve of Fig. 3-13a. The total current of the diode is the sum of these two components and is shown in Fig. 3-13b.

The dynamic resistance (see Sec. 3-5) of the tunnel diode will be *negative* for values of V_b between V_P and V_V. This negative dynamic-resistance region allows the tunnel diode to be used in certain computer applications and microwave oscillators. The currents I_P and I_V and the voltages V_P, V_V, and V_{PP} are used to establish the characteristics of the tunnel diode. They are listed in semiconductor manuals. In general, I_P/I_V, V_P, and

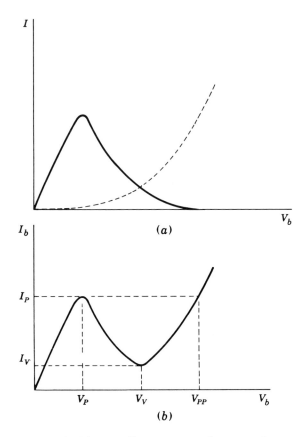

Fig. 3-13 (*a*) Tunneling current and current due to ordinary p-n-junction current (shown dashed) and (*b*) total current in a tunnel diode.

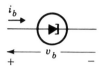

i_b

v_b

+   −   **Fig. 3-14** Symbol for the tunnel diode.

V_V are functions of the semiconductor used in fabricating the tunnel diode. Typically V_P is of the order of 0.1 volt.

The symbol for the tunnel diode is shown in Fig. 3-14.

3-11 THE JUNCTION TRANSISTOR

One of the principal functions of electronic devices is *amplification*. That is, they provide a circuit which is controlled by a small low-power input signal so that a large high-power output signal which is a faithful reproduction of the input signal results. For instance, the signal supplied by the pickup of a high-fidelity phonograph may be less than 10^{-9} watt. However, this signal controls the amplifier so that a 100-watt signal is supplied to the loudspeaker. The output signal has essentially the same waveform as the input.

The *junction transistor* is a solid-state device which can provide amplification. In a great many applications it has completely supplanted the vacuum tube. The transistor requires no heater, so that it has no warm-up time. The transistor is also smaller, lighter, more rugged, and free from microphonic noise. The life of a vacuum tube is limited by the finite life of the cathode heater. The transistor suffers from no such limitations. In fact, the lifetime of the transistor may be extremely long. Lower power-supply voltages can be used with the transistor, and its efficiency is higher. One of the most important advantages of the transistor is that it can readily be incorporated into extremely small integrated circuits. Although the transistor has replaced the vacuum tube in very many applications, there still are occasions when it is desirable to use the vacuum tube. Under certain conditions, it has lower noise and can be operated at much higher power levels than the transistor.

A commonly encountered form of transistor is called the *junction transistor*, diagrammatically represented in Fig. 3-15a and c. The transistor can be considered to be two *p-n* junctions in series. These junctions are not simply placed in series but are fabricated in the same semiconductor crystal, as in the case of the *p-n*-junction diode (see Sec. 3-1). Two types of junction transistors exist. One, called the *p-n-p transistor*, consists of a semiconductor crystal with a *p*-type, then an *n*-type, and finally a *p*-type region. The other, called an *n-p-n transistor*, consists of an *n*-type region, then a *p*-type region, and finally another *n*-type region. In Fig. 3-15a and c, the right-hand region of either junction transistor is called the *emitter*, the middle region is called

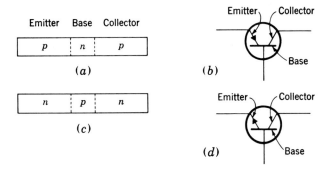

Fig. 3-15 The junction transistor: (*a*) diagrammatic representation of the *p-n-p* transistor; (*b*) its symbol; (*c*) diagrammatic representation of the *n-p-n* transistor; (*d*) its symbol.

the *base*, and the left-hand region is called the *collector*. Parts *a* and *c* of Fig. 3-15 are not drawn to scale. The base is a very narrow region. Actually, its width must be less than the diffusion length of the minority carriers there. We shall discuss the operation of the transistor in the next section.

The symbols for the *p-n-p* and *n-p-n* transistors are shown in Fig. 3-15*b* and *d*, respectively.

In Sec. 4-1, we shall discuss fabrication procedures for transistors.

3-12 CURRENT AND POTENTIAL DISTRIBUTION IN A JUNCTION TRANSISTOR

In order to discuss the operation of the junction transistor, we shall consider the potential distribution within it. For purposes of discussion, we shall work with a *p-n-p* transistor. The results are very similar if an *n-p-n* transistor is used, except that the current directions and the polarities of the voltages are reversed.

Let us consider the potential distribution in an open-circuited transistor. The transistor can be considered to be two *p-n* junctions in series. Thus, as in the case of the *p-n*-junction diode (see Sec. 3-1), an equilibrium will be established wherein the *n*-type region is at a positive potential with respect to the *p*-type regions. This is illustrated in Fig. 3-16*a*. The potential difference across the emitter-base *p-n* junction is V_{01} while that across the collector-base *p-n* junction is V_{02}. There are depletion layers at each junction whose exposed charges set up electric fields. These fields establish the potential differences, just as in the case of the *p-n*-junction diode.

If the transistor were symmetrical, V_{01} would be equal to V_{02}. However, this is usually not the case. The cross-sectional area of the collector-base junction is often made larger than that of the emitter-base junction. In

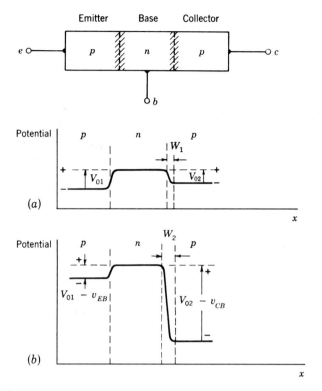

Fig. 3-16 Potential distribution in (a) an open-circuited transistor and (b) a conventionally biased transistor. Note that v_{CB} is a negative number.

addition, the doping in the emitter region is usually very much larger than the doping in the collector region. In general, V_{01} is greater than V_{02}.

Now let us consider a transistor which is biased in the usual way. A simple transistor amplifier circuit is shown in Fig. 3-17. For the time being, assume that $v_{eb} = 0$. Then, the battery V_{EE} forward-biases the emitter-base junction while the battery $-V_{CC}$ reverse-biases the collector-base junction. Note that the polarity of V_{CC} is chosen so that it is a negative quantity.

In the notation we have used here lowercase letters with capital subscripts refer to total quantities, while lowercase letters with lowercase subscripts refer to signal (alternating) quantities. For example, v_{EB} is the total emitter-base voltage, while v_{eb} is the signal component of v_{EB}.

Consider for a moment that the emitter lead is open-circuited. The magnitude of V_{CC} is usually large enough so that the forward component of junction current (see Sec. 3-1) is essentially zero. Thus, the current i_C will be

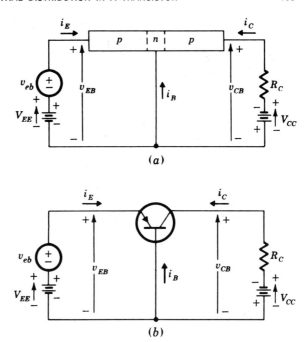

Fig. 3-17 (*a*) A simple transistor amplifier and (*b*) its schematic representation. Note that v_{CB} and V_{cc} are negative.

the reverse saturation current of the junction.   In the transistor this is called the *collector cutoff current* and is written I_{CO}.   In this case,

$$i_C = I_{CO} \tag{3-67}$$

Note that for the *p-n-p* transistor, I_{CO} is a negative quantity.

Now assume that a voltage V_{EE} is connected to the emitter-base leads, as shown in Fig. 3-17.   This forward-biases the emitter-base junction and causes its forward current to become very much greater than the reverse current (see Sec. 3-1).   The forward current consists of holes flowing from the emitter to the base and free electrons flowing in the opposite direction. In general, in a transistor, the doping in the emitter is made much greater than the doping in the base.   Thus, the hole component of forward current will be much greater than the free-electron component of forward current for the *p-n-p* transistor.   The free-electron component of forward current acts essentially as it does in a diode.   That is, it contributes to the base and emitter currents.   (Note that the assumed direction of base current is such that i_B is negative.)

The hole component of the emitter current is the important one in a *p-n-p* transistor.   In an ordinary *p-n*-junction diode, the holes injected into the *n*-type region diffuse into it and recombine with free electrons there. These contribute to the diode current.   In the transistor, some of the holes injected into the base do recombine with the free electrons and contribute to the base current; i.e., these electrons are replenished by i_B.   However, most of the injected holes do not recombine.   The transistor is constructed so that the *width of the base is made very much less than the diffusion length of the holes there*.   Thus, most of the holes diffuse to the depletion layer at the collector-base junction before they can recombine with free electrons.   Once the holes reach this depletion layer, the electric field there sweeps them into the collector.   This results in a net current into the collector.   Thus, the magnitude of the collector current will increase from I_{C0} to a larger (negative) value.   (Note that the negative values are due to the assumed direction of i_C.)

Let us consider this again since it is of fundamental importance to transistor operation.   If the emitter lead is open-circuited ($i_E = 0$) and the collector-base junction is strongly reverse-biased, then $i_C = I_{C0}$, which is a very small (negative) current.   If a forward bias is applied to the emitter-base junction, then $i_E > 0$.   This current is due to free electrons flowing from the base to the emitter and holes flowing from the emitter to the base.   The free-electron component contributes to the base current i_B.   The holes which diffuse across the emitter-base junction can do one of three things: (1) they can diffuse back to the base, in which case their effect is nullified; (2) they can recombine with free electrons in the base, in which case they contribute to base current; or (3) they can diffuse to the collector-base depletion layer and be swept into the collector, in which case they contribute to the collector current.   The third effect is by far the largest one since the base width is very much less than the diffusion length of the holes there.

Thus, the collector current will have a component of current which is nearly proportional to the emitter current.   We can write

$$i_C = -\alpha_L i_E + I_{C0} \tag{3-68}$$

where α_L is the constant of proportionality.   Note that I_{C0} is a negative quantity and the minus sign appears in the equation because of the assumed direction of i_C.   In general, for the reasons discussed in the last paragraph, α_L is slightly less than unity.   It should be noted that Eq. (3-68) is only approximately correct.   That is, i_C does not vary exactly linearly with i_E. However, for the purpose of our present discussion, we shall assume that it is accurate.

Equation (3-68) can be used to explain the amplifying ability of the transistor.   Consider Fig. 3-17 and assume that v_{eb} is a small signal voltage. As v_{eb} varies, i_E will also vary.   Let us write

$$i_E = i_e + I_{EE} \tag{3-69}$$

where i_e is the signal (time-varying) component of i_E.   Then i_C can be written as

$$i_C = -\alpha_L i_e - \alpha_L I_{EE} + I_{C0} \qquad (3\text{-}70)$$

Thus, the varying component of the collector current will be slightly less than the varying component of emitter current.   Note that the signal voltage v_{eb} is approximately equal to i_e times the resistance of the forward-biased emitter-base junction.   The collector-base junction is reverse-biased.   The magnitude of v_{CB} can be very much larger than v_{EB}.   The resistance R_C can be made such that the voltage drop across it is much less than v_{CB} but is still much greater than v_{EB}.   In this case, R_C will be a much larger resistance than that of the forward-biased emitter-base junction.   Since the signal components of i_E and i_C are almost equal, the signal voltage across R_C ($\alpha_L i_e R_C$) will be very much greater than v_{eb}.   Thus, the output signal voltage will be greater than the input signal voltage, and amplification results.

In addition, the power supplied by the input signal generator is $v_{eb} i_e$. The signal power delivered to the load is αi_e times the signal voltage across the load.   Thus, the output signal power will be greater than the input signal power.

The actual relation between collector and emitter current is not exactly a linear one, as indicated in Eq. (3-68).   Usually, we are interested in the signal components of current.   Often, this is a relatively small change in collector current in response to a small change in emitter current.   For very small changes, the ratio of these changes becomes the slope of the i_C-versus-i_E curve.   Let us define a parameter which is equal to this slope.   It is called the *common-base short-circuit forward-current gain*

$$\alpha = -\frac{di_C}{di_E}\bigg|_{v_{CB}\,=\,\text{const}} = -\frac{\partial i_C}{\partial i_E} \qquad (3\text{-}71)$$

Note that α is dimensionless.   The minus sign is included to make α positive. Note that if Eq. (3-68) is valid, then $\alpha = \alpha_L$.

Ideally, the value of α should be unity since this would mean that all the holes injected into the base would reach the collector.   It is usually slightly less than this.   Let us consider the factors which affect α.

Not all the holes injected across the emitter-base junction diffuse across to the collector-base junction.   Some recombine in the base and contribute to base current.   The ratio of the hole current across the emitter-base junction to the hole current reaching the collector-base junction is called the *transport factor* β_t.   Usually, this is slightly less than 1.

The emitter current is not composed entirely of holes but has a component due to free electrons.   These do not contribute to the collector current.   The *emitter efficiency* γ is defined as the ratio of emitter current due to holes to the total emitter current.   Since the doping of the emitter is made much greater than the doping of the base, γ is usually only slightly less than unity.

Finally, the holes gain energy while drifting across the collector-base depletion region. Some may gain enough energy to ionize atoms in the depletion layer. This increases the collector current. The *collector efficiency* δ is defined as the magnitude of the ratio of the total collector current minus I_{C0} to the collector current due to holes arriving at the collector-base junction. The value of δ is usually greater than unity by an extremely small amount.

The short-circuit forward-current amplification factor is the product of the three effects we have discussed

$$\alpha = \beta_t \gamma \delta \qquad (3\text{-}72)$$

One other fact should be noted about the operation of the transistor. As the potential across a *p-n* junction varies, the width of the depletion layer also varies. There are two junctions in the transistor. The emitter-base junction is forward-biased, and therefore its depletion layer is narrow, while the reverse-biased collector-base junction has a relatively wide depletion layer. If varying signals are present, the width of these depletion layers will vary. The base can actually be considered to be the region *between* the two depletion layers. Thus, the width of the base will vary if the voltages and currents vary. This is called the *Early effect*. The width of the collector-base depletion layer has more effect on the width of the base than the emitter-base depletion layer does because it is wider.

Note that as the collector-base voltage is increased in magnitude, the width of the collector-base depletion layer increases. Thus, the base width decreases. This increases α [see Eq. (3-72)] since β_t and δ are increased. β_t is increased because the base width is decreased and fewer holes will recombine in it. δ increases since the increased potential across the depletion layer results in increased ionization.

3-13 CURRENT IN A JUNCTION TRANSISTOR AND TRANSISTOR PARAMETERS: QUANTITATIVE DISCUSSION

Let us now determine the relations among the currents and voltages in a junction transistor. We shall again work with a *p-n-p* transistor. The results are similar for an *n-p-n* transistor. Let us consider a transistor such as that of Fig. 3-17 and determine relations among i_E, i_C, i_B, v_{EB}, and v_{CB}. The emitter current is equal to the current across the emitter-base junction, and the collector current is the current across the collector-base junction.

We shall use the diagrammatic representation of Fig. 3-18 to help clarify our discussion. Usually, the emitter-base junction is forward-biased. i_E consists of two components, free electrons flowing from emitter to base and holes flowing from base to emitter. The flow of these free electrons is

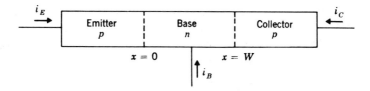

Fig. 3-18 Diagrammatic representation of a *p-n-p* transistor.

analogous to their flow in the diode. Thus, Eq. (3-21a) can be used to obtain the component of emitter current due to free electrons. Multiplying Eq. (3-21a) by A_E, the area of the emitter junction, we obtain

$$i_{En} = \frac{A_E e D_n n_{E0}}{L_{nE}} (\epsilon^{v_{EB}/kT} - 1) \qquad (3\text{-}73)$$

where we have changed the notation somewhat. n_{E0} is the thermal equilibrium value of the electron density in the *p*-type emitter region far removed from the junction. (Note that we have not called this n_{p0} here since there are two *p*-type regions.) Similarly, L_{nE} is the diffusion length of the free electrons in the emitter region. D_n is the free-electron diffusion constant.

It may appear as though we could proceed in an analogous fashion and determine the hole component of emitter current from Eq. (3-21b). However, Eqs. (3-21) are derived assuming that there is a region far removed from the junction where the minority-carrier density becomes essentially equal to the equilibrium value. This is true for the free-electron component of emitter current since the emitter region is usually large in comparison with the diffusion length of the free electrons there. However, the holes are minority carriers in the base. The base has two *p-n* junctions, one at each end. In addition, the base is constructed so that it is much shorter than the diffusion length of the holes there. Thus, the hole density at any point in the base will be a function of the conditions at both *p-n* junctions. To determine the current due to holes we shall first determine the hole density in the base p_B. Solving the continuity equation for a slab of semiconductor of uniform cross-sectional area, we obtain [see Eqs. (1-234) to (1-237)]

$$p_B(x) = p_{B0} = A_1 \epsilon^{-x/L_{pB}} + A_2 \epsilon^{x/L_{pB}} \qquad (3\text{-}74)$$

where L_{pB} = diffusion length of holes in base
$p_B(x)$ = density of holes in base as function of x
p_{B0} = thermal-equilibrium hole density in base
A_1, A_2 = constants
Note that the hole density will, in general, not be equal to p_{B0} at any point in the base. To evaluate these constants, we shall determine the value of p_B at both ends of the base and assume that the base region lies between the

depletion layers, i.e., between $x = 0$ and $x = W$, as shown in Fig. 3-18. The hole densities immediately adjacent to each depletion layer will be assumed to be the same as in an ordinary p-n junction. Thus, using Eqs. (3-19b) and (3-20b), at the emitter-base and collector-base junctions, respectively,

$$p_B(0) - p_{B0} = p_{B0}(\epsilon^{v_{EB}/kt} - 1) \tag{3-75}$$

$$p_B(W) - p_{B0} = p_{B0}(\epsilon^{v_{CB}/kT} - 1) \tag{3-76}$$

where the potentials are positive when the respective junctions are forward-biased. Substituting into Eq. (3-74) and solving for A_1 and A_2, we obtain

$$A_1 = p_{B0} \frac{\epsilon^{W/L_{pB}}(\epsilon^{v_{EB}/kT} - 1) - (\epsilon^{v_{CB}/kT} - 1)}{\epsilon^{W/L_{pB}} - \epsilon^{-W/L_{pB}}} \tag{3-77a}$$

$$A_2 = -p_{B0} \frac{\epsilon^{-W/L_{pB}}(\epsilon^{v_{EB}/kT} - 1) - (\epsilon^{v_{CB}/kT} - 1)}{\epsilon^{W/L_{pB}} - \epsilon^{-W/L_{pB}}} \tag{3-77b}$$

The hole current in the base is almost entirely due to diffusion. Thus [see Eq. (1-206)]

$$i_{Bp} = -eD_p \frac{\partial p}{\partial x} A \tag{3-78}$$

where A is the cross-sectional area at the point in question. At the emitter-base junction ($x = 0$)

$$i_{Bp} = i_{Ep} \tag{3-79}$$

Thus, substituting Eq. (3-74) into Eq. (3-78) and evaluating the result at $x = 0$, we have

$$i_{Ep} = -eD_p \left(-\frac{A_1}{L_{pB}} + \frac{A_2}{L_{pB}} \right) A_E \tag{3-80}$$

Substituting Eqs. (3-77), we obtain

$$i_{Ep} = \frac{A_E e D_p p_{B0}}{L_{pB}} \frac{(\epsilon^{v_{EB}/kT} - 1)(\epsilon^{-W/L_{pB}} + \epsilon^{W/L_{pB}}) - 2(\epsilon^{v_{CB}/kT} - 1)}{\epsilon^{W/L_{pB}} - \epsilon^{-W/L_{pB}}}$$

Noting that

$$\sinh x = \frac{1}{\operatorname{csch} x} = \frac{\epsilon^x - \epsilon^{-x}}{2} \tag{3-81a}$$

$$\cosh x = \frac{1}{\operatorname{sech} x} = \frac{\epsilon^x + \epsilon^{-x}}{2} \tag{3-81b}$$

and

$$\coth x = \frac{1}{\tanh x} = \frac{\cosh x}{\sinh x} \tag{3-81c}$$

we have

$$i_{Ep} = \frac{A_E e D_p p_{B0}}{L_{pB}} \left[\coth \frac{W}{L_{pB}} (\epsilon^{v_{EB}/kT} - 1) - \operatorname{csch} \frac{W}{L_{pB}} (\epsilon^{v_{CB}/kT} - 1) \right]$$

$$(3\text{-}82)$$

The total emitter current is the sum of the current due to holes and that due to free electrons

$$i_E = i_{En} + i_{Ep} \tag{3-83}$$

Then, adding Eqs. (3-73) and (3-82), we have

$$i_E = A_E e \left(\frac{D_n n_{E0}}{L_{nE}} + \frac{D_p p_{B0}}{L_{pB}} \coth \frac{W}{L_{pB}} \right) (\epsilon^{v_{EB}/kT} - 1)$$
$$- \frac{A e D_p p_{B0}}{L_{pB}} \operatorname{csch} \frac{W}{L_{pB}} (\epsilon^{v_{CB}/kT} - 1) \quad (3\text{-}84)$$

In a similar way, we can compute the collector current. Analogous to Eq. (3-73), the collector current due to free electrons is

$$i_{Cn} = \frac{A_C e D_n n_{C0}}{L_{nC}} (\epsilon^{v_{CB}/kT} - 1) \tag{3-85}$$

The collector current due to holes is the negative of i_{Bp} evaluated at $x = W$. Thus, substituting Eq. (3-74) into Eq. (3-78) and evaluating it at $x = W$, we have

$$i_{Cp} = A_C e D_p \left(-\frac{A_1}{L_{pB}} \epsilon^{-W/L_{pB}} + \frac{A_2}{L_{pB}} \epsilon^{W/L_{pB}} \right) \tag{3-86}$$

Substituting Eqs. (3-77), we obtain

$$i_{Cp} = \frac{A_C e D_p p_{B0}}{L_{pB}} \left[-\operatorname{csch} \frac{W}{L_{pb}} (\epsilon^{v_{EB}/kT} - 1) + \coth \frac{W}{L_{pB}} (\epsilon^{v_{CB}/kT} - 1) \right]$$

$$(3\text{-}87)$$

The total collector current is

$$i_C = i_{Cp} + i_{Cn} \tag{3-88}$$

Then, adding Eqs. (3-85) and (3-88), we have

$$i_C = -A_C e \frac{D_p p_{B0}}{L_{pB}} \operatorname{csch} \frac{W}{L_{pB}} (\epsilon^{v_{EB}/kT} - 1)$$
$$+ A_C e \left(\frac{D_n n_{C0}}{L_{nC}} + \frac{D_p p_{B0}}{L_{pB}} \coth \frac{W}{L_{pB}} \right) (\epsilon^{v_{CB}/kT} - 1) \quad (3\text{-}89)$$

In general, Eq. (3-74) is valid only for a slab of uniform cross section. Thus, the cross-sectional area of the emitter and collector junctions should be

equal.   That is, this development is exact only for a transistor where this is
so.   Thus, we shall set

$$A_E = A_C = A \tag{3-90}$$

The base current can be obtained by applying Kirchhoff's current law
to the entire transistor.   Thus,

$$i_B = -(i_E + i_C) \tag{3-91}$$

Equations (3-84), (3-89), and (3-91) relate all the voltages and currents of the
transistor.   They are called *Ebers-Moll* equations.[2]   At times, these equations are written as

$$i_E = c_{11}(\epsilon^{v_{EB}/kT} - 1) + c_{12}(\epsilon^{v_{CB}/kT} - 1) \tag{3-92a}$$

$$i_C = c_{21}(\epsilon^{v_{EB}/kT} - 1) + c_{22}(\epsilon^{v_{CB}/kT} - 1) \tag{3-92b}$$

where [see Eqs. (3-84), (3-89), and (3-90)]

$$c_{11} = Ae\left(\frac{D_n n_{E0}}{L_{nE}} + \frac{D_p p_{B0}}{L_{pB}} \coth \frac{W}{L_{pB}}\right) \tag{3-93a}$$

$$c_{21} = c_{12} = -\frac{Ae D_p p_{B0}}{L_{pB}} \operatorname{csch} \frac{W}{L_{pB}} \tag{3-93b}$$

$$c_{22} = Ae\left(\frac{D_n n_{C0}}{L_{nC}} + \frac{D_p p_{B0}}{L_{pB}} \coth \frac{W}{L_{pB}}\right) \tag{3-93c}$$

At times it is desirable to express the collector current in terms of the emitter
current and the collector-base voltage.   Solving Eq. (3-92a) for $\epsilon^{v_{CB}/kT} - 1$
and substituting in Eq. (3-93b), we obtain

$$i_C = \frac{c_{21}}{c_{11}} i_E + \frac{c_{11}c_{22} - c_{21}c_{12}}{c_{11}} (\epsilon^{v_{CB}/kT} - 1) \tag{3-94}$$

It should be noted that Eqs. (3-84), (3-89), (3-92), and (3-94) are valid
for both positive and negative values of v_{EB} and v_{CB}.

In the usual transistor, the base width is made very much less than L_{pB},
the diffusion length of the minority carriers there.   Thus, $W/L_{pB} \ll 1$.   In
this case, we can make the following approximations:

$$\frac{1}{\operatorname{csch}(W/L_{pB})} = \sinh \frac{W}{L_{pB}} \approx \frac{W}{L_{pB}} \tag{3-95a}$$

$$\cosh \frac{W}{L_{pB}} = \frac{1}{\operatorname{sech}(W/L_{pB})} \approx 1 + \frac{1}{2}\left(\frac{W}{L_{pB}}\right)^2 \tag{3-95b}$$

$$\frac{1}{\tanh(W/L_{pB})} = \coth \frac{W}{L_{pB}} \approx \frac{1 + \frac{1}{2}(W/L_{pB})^2}{W/L_{pB}} \approx \left(\frac{W}{L_{pB}}\right)^{-1} \tag{3-95c}$$

If $W/L_{pB} \ll 1$, these relations can be substituted into Eqs. (3-84), (3-89), and
(3-93), simplifying the results somewhat.

3-14 TRANSISTOR α AND COLLECTOR CUTOFF CURRENT: QUANTITATIVE DISCUSSION

The parameter α of a transistor is very important. In subsequent chapters, we shall relate it to the amplifying ability of the transistor and show that it should be as close to unity as is possible. From Eqs. (3-71) and (3-94), we have

$$\alpha = -\frac{c_{21}}{c_{11}} \tag{3-96}$$

Substituting Eqs. (3-93), we obtain

$$\alpha = \frac{\text{sech}\,(W/L_{pB})}{1 + \dfrac{D_n}{D_p} \dfrac{n_{E0}}{p_{B0}} \dfrac{L_{pB}}{L_{nE}} \tanh \dfrac{W}{L_{pB}}} \tag{3-97}$$

Often, in a transistor, $W/L_{pB} \ll 1$. In this case, the approximations of Eqs. (3-95) can be used. Substituting these into Eq. (3-97) yields

$$\alpha \approx \frac{1}{1 + \dfrac{1}{2}\left(\dfrac{W}{L_{pB}}\right)^2 + \dfrac{D_n}{D_p} \dfrac{n_{E0}}{p_{B0}} \dfrac{W}{L_{nE}}} \tag{3-98}$$

In general, the denominator will be approximately unity. Thus, Eq. (3-98) can be approximated by the binomial expansion

$$\alpha \approx 1 - \frac{1}{2}\left(\frac{W}{L_{pB}}\right)^2 - \frac{D_n}{D_p} \frac{n_{E0}}{p_{B0}} \frac{W}{L_{nE}} \tag{3-99}$$

Equations (3-97) and (3-99) can be written in a somewhat different form. Combining Eqs. (1-203), (1-204), and (1-207a) and noting that np is constant independent of the doping [see Eq. (1-184)], we have

$$\frac{D_n n_{E0}}{D_p p_{B0}} = \frac{\sigma_B}{\sigma_E} \tag{3-100}$$

where we have assumed that the conductivity of a region is due entirely to the majority-carrier density there. Note that σ_E and σ_B refer to the conductivity of two bulk semiconductor crystals, one with doping the same as that of the emitter and the other with doping the same as that of the base. Substitution in Eqs. (3-97) and (3-99) yields

$$\alpha = \frac{\text{sech}\,(W/L_{pB})}{1 + \dfrac{\sigma_B}{\sigma_E} \dfrac{L_{pB}}{L_{nE}} \tanh \dfrac{W}{L_{pB}}} \tag{3-101}$$

$$\alpha = 1 - \frac{1}{2}\left(\frac{W}{L_{pB}}\right)^2 - \frac{\sigma_B}{\sigma_E} \frac{W}{L_{nE}} \tag{3-102}$$

The transistor is constructed so that $W/L_{pB} \ll 1$. In general, the emitter is more highly doped than the base, so that $L_{nE} < L_{pB}$. However, W is usually small enough so that $W/L_{nE} \ll 1$. Because of the doping, $\sigma_E > \sigma_B$. If W is kept small enough, then $\sigma_E W/\sigma_B L_{nE} \ll 1$. In this case, $\alpha \approx 1$. Since it is desirable to make α as close to unity as possible, the importance of keeping the base width small can be seen. We shall also discuss (see Sec. 3-18) that a narrow base aids in improving the high-frequency response of the transistor.

The collector cutoff current is defined as the collector current that results when $i_E = 0$ and v_{CE} is a large negative number. Thus, from Eq. (3-94), we have

$$I_{C0} = -\frac{c_{11}c_{22} - c_{12}c_{21}}{c_{11}} \tag{3-103}$$

To relate this to the semiconductor parameters, substitute Eqs. (3-93) into Eq. (3-103). The details will be left to the reader.

3-15   COMMON-BASE TRANSISTOR CHARACTERISTICS

The equations derived in Sec. 3-13 relate the transistor's voltages and currents. However these equations are only approximate (although they are, at times, fairly accurate). To characterize the transistor accurately, experimentally measured graphical characteristics are often used. In general, these are three voltages existing between the three terminals of the transistor. There are also three terminal currents. Any two of these voltages or currents uniquely determine the third, using Kirchhoff's laws. One of the leads of the transistor is always chosen as the reference. This choice is usually made on the basis of convenience. For instance, in Fig. 3-17, the base is taken as the reference. The variables that are then used are v_{EB}, v_{CB}, i_E, and i_C. In general, we can use a set of equations of the type of Eqs. (3-92) to express two of these variables in terms of the other two. A graphical representation of all these variables would require a four-dimensional plot. To avoid this, two separate families of plots are used. One consists of i_C versus v_{CB} with the emitter current i_E as a parameter, and the second consists of a plot of i_E versus v_{EB} with the collector voltage v_{CB} as a parameter. A typical set of such characteristics is shown in Fig. 3-19. The plot of i_C versus v_{CB} is called the *output characteristic*, and that of i_E versus v_{EB} is called the *input characteristic*. Note that for a *p-n-p* transistor, both i_C and v_{CB} are negative over most of the characteristic. It is conventional to draw the axes as shown. That is, when appropriate, the curves are drawn in the first quadrant with the axes scaled in negative numbers.

The output characteristics are divided into three regions, the active region, the saturation region, and the cutoff region. We shall discuss each of these in turn.

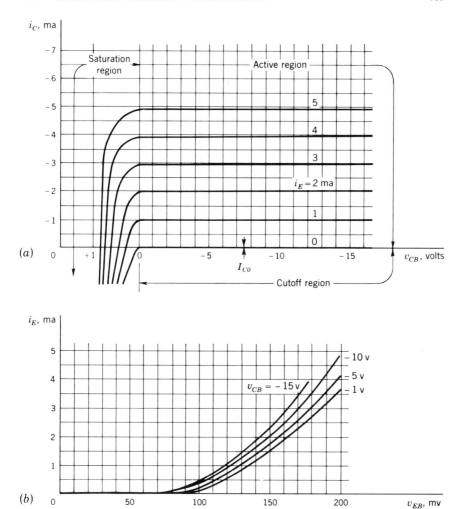

Fig. 3-19 Common-base characteristic of a typical *p-n-p*-junction transistor: (*a*) output characteristic; (*b*) input characteristic. (*Adapted from D. DeWitt and A. L. Rossoff,* "*Transistor Electronics.*" *Copyright* 1957. *McGraw-Hill Book Company. Used by permission.*)

The active region   When the transistor functions as a normal amplifier, it operates entirely in the active region.   Here the emitter-base junction is forward-biased, while the collector-base junction is reverse-biased.   This region comprises most of Fig. 3-19*a*.   Note that the collector current is almost equal in magnitude to the emitter current over most of the active region.   When $i_E = 0$, the collector current is not exactly zero but is equal to the collector cutoff current I_{C0}.   This is often so small that it appears to be zero on the graph.

The saturation region   If v_{CB} is made positive, the collector-base junction will be forward-biased.   This results in a very large increase in its forward current, i.e., holes flowing from collector to the base and free electrons flowing from the base to the collector.   If v_{CB} is made more than a fraction of a volt positive, the collector current will usually reverse and become positive. This is shown in Fig. 3-19a.   Note that the voltage axis is drawn to different scales in the saturation and active regions.

The cutoff region   If the emitter-base junction is reverse-biased, minority carriers will not be injected into the base region.   Then if v_{CB} is negative, the collector current will essentially be the small value of I_{C0}.   This region where $v_{EB} \leq 0$ and $v_{CB} < 0$ is called the cutoff region because the current i_C is almost zero.   Note that this region lies in between the $i_E = 0$ curve and the v_{CB} axis; i.e., it is a very narrow region.

The input characteristics of the transistor are shown in Fig. 3-19b. They are similar to those of a forward-biased p-n junction.   Note that the emitter current is affected slightly by the collector current or voltage.   This is also shown by Eq. (3-92) and is due to the reasons discussed in Sec. 3-13.

Just as in the case of a p-n-junction diode, the emitter current remains very small until v_{EB} reaches a value called the *cut-in voltage* (see Sec. 3-5). For germanium, this is about 0.1 volt, while it is about 0.5 volt for silicon.

Note that the base-emitter voltage is very small in comparison with the collector-emitter voltage.   The base-emitter voltage is usually of the order of millivolts while the collector-emitter voltage is of the order of volts.

If the emitter-base junction is reverse-biased and then the collector-base junction is forward-biased, the emitter current will increase in magnitude because the transistor is operated backwards; i.e., the collector tends to act as an emitter and vice versa.   The transistor is usually not operated this way.

Determination of α The value of α can be obtained from the characteristics of Fig. 3-19.   From Eq. (3-71), we can approximate α by

$$\alpha \approx -\frac{\Delta i_C}{\Delta i_E}\bigg|_{v_{CB}=\text{const}} \tag{3-104}$$

Then, at a constant value of v_{CB}, that is, the value at which the transistor is to be operated, we determine two values of i_C which correspond to two values of i_E.   (These values should be in the vicinity of the values where the transistor is to be operated.)   The difference between each pair of values gives Δi_C and Δi_E, which are then substituted into Eq. (3-104) to determine α.   The smaller Δi_E is, the more accurately will Eq. (3-104) approximate α.   Usually

Δi_E is taken as the difference between the values of i_E for two characteristic curves of the output characteristics.

We shall analyze a simple transistor amplifier graphically in the next section.

3-16 COMMON-EMITTER TRANSISTOR AMPLIFIER AND CHARACTERISTICS

The most commonly used type of transistor amplifier is not the common-base configuration we have studied but one where the emitter lead is taken in common. A simple *common-emitter amplifier* is shown in Fig. 3-20. The base current of a transistor is given by

$$i_B = -(i_E + i_C) \tag{3-105}$$

Since the collector and emitter currents are of opposite sign and almost equal in magnitude, i_B will be very small. Hence, the collector current will, in general, be much greater than the base current. We shall demonstrate that the common-emitter amplifier can have a current gain which is much greater than unity.

When a common-emitter transistor circuit is analyzed, it is convenient to use the variables i_B, i_C, v_{BE}, and v_{CE}. These are presented on two families of curves. The *output characteristic* consists of i_C versus v_{CE} with i_B as a parameter. The *input characteristic* consists of i_B versus v_{BE} with v_{CE} as a parameter. A typical set of characteristics is shown in Fig. 3-21. Note that all the voltages and currents are negative for the *p-n-p* transistor.

The voltage-current characteristics of Figs. 3-19 and 3-21 *each* provide a complete set of data about the transistor. However, it is often more convenient to use one set than the other.

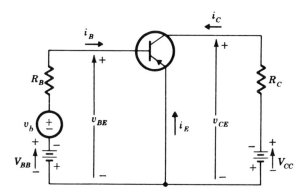

Fig. 3-20 A simple common-emitter transistor amplifier. Note that V_{BB} and V_{CC} are defined as negative numbers.

Let us now consider the active, saturation, and cutoff regions for the transistor of Fig. 3-21. They are equivalent to the corresponding regions of Fig. 3-19.

Cutoff region   In this region, the collector current i_C is essentially equal to I_{C0}, the collector cutoff current (see Sec. 3-15). Cutoff occurs when the emitter-base junction (as well as the collector-base junction) is reverse-biased. Thus, the emitter current is essentially zero. Hence [see Eq. (3-105)]

$$i_B = -I_{C0} \tag{3-106}$$

If the base current is made more *positive* than the value which just produces this i_B (note that the emitter-base junction is reverse-biased in the cutoff region), the collector current will remain essentially I_{C0}. Hence, the cutoff region lies between the $i_B = -I_{C0}$ curve and the v_{CE} axis. (Thus, this region lies very close to the v_{CE} axis.)

Saturation region   In the saturation region v_{CE} ranges from a very small negative number to a positive value. [The collector-base voltage v_{CB} is positive in this region (see Fig. 3-19).] In Fig. 3-21 the saturation region occurs when all the curves come together near the i_C axis. If v_{CE} is made positive, i_C will become positive and increase rapidly. This is also part of the saturation region. However, usually the transistor is not operated in this ($v_{CE} > 0$) region. In the saturation region, v_{CE} usually has a very small magnitude. If this region is of interest, the active characteristics are often plotted showing this region expanded; e.g., for the transistor of Fig. 3-21, the entire v_{CE} axis would be from 0 to 0.5 volt.

Active region   As is true of the common-base amplifier, usual transistor amplifiers are operated in the active region. In this region, a variation in input (base) current produces a marked variation in output (collector) current. The active region lies between the saturation and cutoff regions. That is, it consists of almost all the characteristics of Fig. 3-21a.

Input characteristics   The input characteristic consists of a plot of i_B versus v_{BE}. This essentially has the character of a forward-biased emitter-base junction. However, this current is also affected by v_{CE}, which is to be expected since i_E is a function of v_{CB} (see Sec. 3-16). Note that v_{BE} is expressed in millivolts.

The common-base and common-emitter characteristic provide the same information, but more accuracy can sometimes be obtained from the common-emitter characteristic. For instance, i_B can be obtained from the common-base characteristic and Eq. (3-105). However, $i_E + i_C$ involves the subtraction (i_C is negative) of two nearly equal numbers. (Thus, a small error in either of these can result in a large error in i_B.) However, the

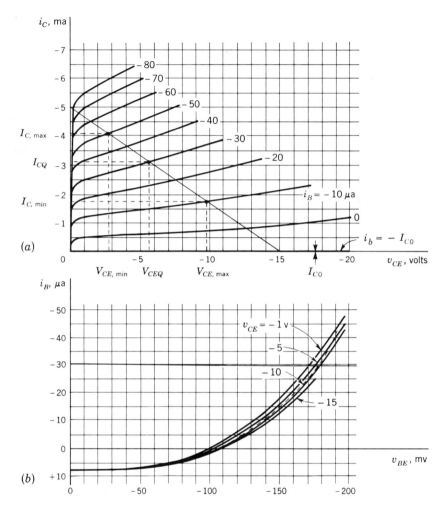

Fig. 3-21 Common-emitter characteristics of a typical *p-n-p*-junction transistor: (*a*) output characteristic; (*b*) input characteristic. Load lines are drawn. The dynamic input characteristic is shown dashed. (*Adapted from D. DeWitt and A. L. Rossoff, "Transistor Electronics." Copyright 1957. McGraw-Hill Book Company. Used by permission.*)

common-emitter characteristics give i_B directly. If the common-emitter characteristics are used to determine i_E, from Eq. (3-105), no such inaccuracy results, since two nearly equal numbers are not subtracted.

Analysis of a simple amplifier Let us use the graphical characteristics of Fig. 3-21 to analyze the simple common-emitter amplifier of Fig. 3-20. We assume that v_b, V_{BB}, V_{CC}, R_C, and R_L are known. There are then four unknowns, i_B, i_C, v_{BE}, and v_{CE}. The characteristics of Fig. 3-21 provide two "equations" for determining these unknowns. Two more equations must be provided from the external circuit.

Applying Kirchhoff's voltage law to the output circuit of Fig. 3-20, we obtain

$$v_{CE} = V_{CC} - i_C R_C \tag{3-107}$$

This is the equation of a straight line. Its slope is $-1/R_C$, and its v_{CE} and i_C axes intercepts are V_{CC} and V_{CC}/R_C, respectively. This straight line is called the *load line for the output circuit.*

In a similar way, we can write, by applying Kirchhoff's law to the input circuit,

$$v_{BE} = V_{BB} - i_B R_B \tag{3-108}$$

This is the *load line for the input circuit.* It is a straight line of slope $-1/R_B$ with v_{BE} and i_B intercepts of V_{BB} and V_{BB}/R_B, respectively.

Load lines are drawn in Fig. 3-21. We have assumed here that $V_{CC} = -15$ volts, $R_C = 3000$ ohms, $V_{BB} = -15$ volts, $R_B = 500,000$ ohms, and $v_b = 0$. Note that the load line on the input characteristic always appears to be almost horizontal. This is due to the scale of the v_{BE} axis.

To determine the operating point of the transistor we must know which curve in the family to read. However, we cannot determine i_B unless v_{CE} is known and vice versa. Actually, the curves on the input characteristic are so close together and the load line so nearly horizontal, that we can approximate $i_B \approx 30$ μa no matter which curve is used. However, for the sake of explanation, let us assume that this is not so. We would then draw a curve called the *dynamic input characteristic.* That is, using the output characteristic *and* load line, we can plot a curve of i_B versus v_{CE}. This is obtained by plotting the value of v_{CE} at the intersection of the load line and the output characteristic corresponding to the i_B in question. For example, when $i_B = 0$, $v_{CE} = -12.5$ volts, and when $i_B = -10$ μa, $v_{CE} = -9.8$ volts. This curve is plotted on the input characteristic and is shown dashed. The intersection of the input-circuit load line and the dynamic characteristic gives i_B and v_{BE}. In this case, $i_B = -30$ μa and $v_{BE} = -175$ mv. Now, in Fig. 3-21a, we use the curve corresponding to $i_B = -30$ μa. The intersection of this curve with the load line yields $v_{CB} = -5.5$ volts and $I_C = 3.2$ ma.

Very often i_B is almost independent of the transistor. This was true in the example just considered. Let us demonstrate this by solving Eq. (3-108) for i_B. This yields

$$i_B = \frac{V_{BB} - v_{BE}}{R_B} \tag{3-109}$$

If

$$|V_{BB}| \gg |v_{BE}| \tag{3-110}$$

then Eq. (3-109) becomes

$$i_B \approx \frac{V_{BB}}{R_B} \tag{3-111}$$

This is independent of v_{BE}. In this case, the input characteristics are not needed to determine the input current or the output current and voltage.

In the last example, we assumed that $v_b = 0$. Now let us assume that it represents a time-varying signal voltage

$$v_b = 10 \sin \omega t \quad \text{volts} \tag{3-112}$$

Then we can write

$$i_B = \frac{V_{BB} + v_b - v_{BE}}{R_B} \tag{3-113}$$

If

$$|V_{BB} + v_b| \gg |v_{BE}| \tag{3-114}$$

then

$$i_B = \frac{V_{BB} + v_B}{R_B} \tag{3-115}$$

Relation (3-114) will be satisfied for all time for the circuit in question. Then, substituting the known values, we have

$$i_B = -30 + 20 \sin \omega t \quad \mu\text{a} \tag{3-116}$$

Note that if relation (3-114) is not true, a series of input load lines must be drawn, one for each value of $V_{bb} + v_b$. These will all be parallel. The intersections of the load lines with the dynamic input characteristics yield the instantaneous values of i_B.

When $v_b = 0$, the circuit is said to be operating under *quiescent conditions*. A subscript Q is appended to the voltages and currents to indicate this. Thus, $I_{BQ} = -30 \ \mu\text{a}$, $V_{BE} = -175 \text{ mv}$, $I_{CQ} = -3.2 \text{ ma}$, and $V_{CBQ} = -5.5$ volts. These four values characterize the location of the *quiescent operating point*.

When $v_b \neq 0$, the values of i_B, v_{CE}, i_C, and v_{CB} will vary. At any instant they determine the location of the *instantaneous operating point* or simply the *operating point*. The output voltage and current are determined from the intersection of the load line with the output characteristic which corresponds to i_B at *the instant of operation*. The value of i_B given in Eq.

(3-116) varies from -50 to -10 μa. These points and the corresponding values of i_C and v_{CE} are marked on Fig. 3-21. Note that i_C varies from -4.2 to -1.8 ma while i_B varies from -50 to -10 μa. Thus, a change of 40 μa in the input signal current produces a variation of 2.4 ma in the output current. Hence, this circuit provides a *current amplification*, or *current gain*, of

$$A_i = \frac{2.4 \times 10^{-3}}{40 \times 10^{-6}} = 60$$

That is, if there were no distortion, the output signal current would be 60 times as large as the input signal current. If there is no distortion, the output current would be

$$i_C = -\left(3.2 + \frac{2.4}{2}\sin \omega t\right) = -(3.2 + 1.2 \sin \omega t) \qquad \text{ma}$$

Thus, a 20 μa signal produces a 1.2 ma output. Note that the actual output current will not be exactly sinusoidal since the transistor characteristics are not exactly linear. However, the output current can be made to approximate the input current closely. Any deviation of the output waveform from the input waveform due to nonlinearities is termed *nonlinear distortion*. It will be discussed in Secs. 5-10 and 5-11.

The α of a transistor relates changes in input current to changes in output current for a common-base configuration [see Eq. (3-71)]. This is related to the amplifying ability of the common-base circuit. When the common-emitter configuration is used, it is convenient to define a similar parameter called β, which again is the ratio of a change in output current to a (differentially small) change in input current and is called the *common-emitter short-circuit forward-current gain*. Note that in this case the input current is i_B, not i_E. Here we define

$$\beta = \left.\frac{di_C}{di_B}\right|_{v_{CE}=\text{const}} = \frac{\partial i_C}{\partial i_B} \qquad (3\text{-}117)$$

Let us relate this to α. Using Eq. (3-105), we have

$$\frac{1}{\beta} = -\left.\frac{di_E}{di_C}\right|_{v_{CE}=\text{const}} - \left.\frac{di_C}{di_C}\right|_{v_{CE}=\text{const}} \qquad (3\text{-}118)$$

This can be written

$$\frac{1}{\beta} = -\left.\frac{di_E}{di_C}\right|_{v_{CE}=\text{const}} - 1 \qquad (3\text{-}119)$$

The first term on the right-hand side appears to be the reciprocal of α [see Eq. (3-71)]. However, it is not, because α is defined with v_{CB} and not v_{CE}

held constant. However, applying Kirchhoff's voltage law to any transistor, we have

$$v_{CB} = v_{CE} + v_{EB} \tag{3-120}$$

The magnitude of v_{EB} is usually very small in comparison with the magnitude of v_{CB} or v_{CE} (see Figs. 3-19 and 3-21). Thus, we can write

$$v_{CB} \approx v_{CE} \tag{3-121}$$

Hence, if v_{CB} is held constant, v_{CE} will also be held essentially constant and vice versa. Thus, Eq. (3-119) can be rewritten as

$$\frac{1}{\beta} \approx -\frac{di_E}{di_C}\bigg|_{v_{CB} = \text{const}} - 1 \tag{3-122}$$

Substituting Eq. (3-71) and manipulating, we obtain

$$\beta = \frac{\alpha}{1 - \alpha} \tag{3-123}$$

If α is a number only slightly less than 1, then β will be very much greater than 1; for example, if $\alpha = 0.99$, then $\beta = 99$. We shall demonstrate (see Chap. 6) that this indicates that the current gain of a common-emitter amplifier can be very much greater than that of a common-base amplifier.

β can be determined from the common-emitter output characteristics by noting that Eq. (3-117) can be approximately written as

$$\beta \approx \frac{\Delta i_C}{\Delta i_B}\bigg|_{v_{CE} = \text{const}} \tag{3-124}$$

A change in i_C corresponding to a change in i_B, determined at constant v_{CE}, can then be read from the output characteristic and substituted into Eq. (3-124).

The common-emitter output characteristics can be accurately used to determine α. One way is to determine β and then substitute in Eq. (3-123) to determine α. Solving Eq. (3-123) for α yields

$$\alpha = \frac{\beta}{\beta + 1} \tag{3-125}$$

3-17 COMMON-COLLECTOR TRANSISTOR AMPLIFIER

We have thus far considered two simple transistor amplifiers, one where the base has been the common lead and the other where the emitter has been the common lead. Another simple amplifier, called the *common-collector amplifier*, is shown in Fig. 3-22. Note that this is similar to the common-emitter amplifier except that the emitter and collector leads have been interchanged.

It is not conventional to draw common-collector characteristics. We shall analyze the common-collector amplifier in subsequent chapters.

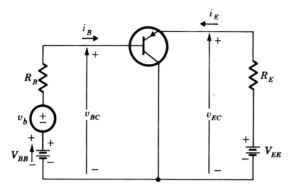

Fig. 3-22 A simplified form of a common-collector amplifier.

3-18   HIGH-FREQUENCY EFFECTS IN THE JUNCTION TRANSISTOR

The analysis of the transistor in Secs. 3-13 and 3-14 considered that the voltage and currents do not vary with time (or vary very slowly). If this is not the case, some of the results must be modified. The transistor currents derived in those sections were based on Eq. (3-74), which gives the minority-carrier density in the base. This equation was obtained from Eqs. (1-234) to (1-237) and gives the carrier density assuming that carriers are injected into a semiconductor at a constant rate. In Eqs. (1-247) to (1-251) a similar set of equations is derived except that now the injected-carrier density is assumed to vary sinusoidally with a frequency ω. It is demonstrated [see Eqs. (1-247) to (1-251) and the discussion following] that the solution to these equations on a *phasor* basis will have the same form as Eq. (3-74) except that L_{pB} must be replaced by $L_{pB}/\sqrt{1 + j\omega\tau_{pB}}$, where τ_{pB} is the lifetime of the minority carriers (holes) in the base. (We shall again use a *p-n-p* transistor in our discussions.) Thus, we can replace L_{pB} by $L_{pB}/\sqrt{1 + j\omega\tau_{pB}}$ in the equations of Secs. 3-13 and 3-14.

One of the most important parameters to be considered when we analyze the high-frequency behavior of transistors is α. Note that it relates the variations in output current to variations in input current in a common-base amplifier. Hence, it is a measure of the gain. Let us now consider α's variation with frequency.

The expression for α is given by Eq. (3-97). Replacing L_{pB} by $L_{pB}/\sqrt{1 + j\omega\tau_{pB}}$ in this expression, we obtain

$$\alpha = \frac{\operatorname{sech}\left[(W/L_{pB})\sqrt{1 + j\omega\tau_{pB}}\right]}{1 + \dfrac{D_n}{D_p}\dfrac{n_{E0}}{p_{B0}}\dfrac{L_{pB}}{L_{nE}\sqrt{1 + j\omega\tau_{pB}}}\tanh\left(\dfrac{W}{L_{pB}}\sqrt{1 + j\omega\tau_{pB}}\right)} \tag{3-126}$$

A boldface letter is now used for $\boldsymbol{\alpha}$ since it is a complex number. When $\omega = 0$, this reduces to Eq. (3-97), as it should. Let us define α_0 as the value of $\boldsymbol{\alpha}$ when $\omega = 0$.

$$\alpha_0 = \frac{\operatorname{sech}(W/L_{pB})}{1 + \dfrac{D_n}{D_p}\dfrac{n_{E0}}{p_{B0}}\dfrac{L_{pB}}{L_{nE}}\tanh\dfrac{W}{L_{pB}}} \tag{3-127}$$

The expression for $\boldsymbol{\alpha}$ given by Eq. (3-126) is often too cumbersome for practical use. Fortunately, we can usually make some simplifying approximations. For most transistors operated over their usual frequency ranges

$$\left|\frac{W}{L_{pB}}\sqrt{1 + j\omega\tau_{pB}}\right| \ll 1 \tag{3-128}$$

In this case [see Eq. (3-95)] we can make the following approximations

$$\operatorname{sech}\frac{W}{L_{pB}}\sqrt{1 + j\omega\tau_{pB}} \approx \frac{1}{1 + \tfrac{1}{2}(W/L_{pB})^2(1 + j\omega\tau_{pB})} \tag{3-129a}$$

$$\tanh\frac{W}{L_{pB}}\sqrt{1 + j\omega\tau_{pB}} \approx \frac{(W/L_{pB})\sqrt{1 + j\omega\tau_{pB}}}{1 + \tfrac{1}{2}(W/L_{pB})^2(1 + j\omega\tau_{pB})} \tag{3-129b}$$

Substituting Eqs. (3-129) into Eq. (3-126), we have

$$\boldsymbol{\alpha} = \frac{\dfrac{1}{1 + \tfrac{1}{2}(W/L_{pB})^2(1 + j\omega\tau_{pB})}}{1 + \dfrac{D_n}{D_p}\dfrac{n_{E0}}{p_{B0}}\dfrac{W/L_{nE}}{1 + \tfrac{1}{2}(W/L_{pB})^2(1 + j\omega\tau_{pB})}} \tag{3-130}$$

When $\omega = 0$,

$$\alpha_0 = \frac{1}{1 + \dfrac{1}{2}\left(\dfrac{W}{L_{pB}}\right)^2 + \dfrac{D_n}{D_p}\dfrac{n_{E0}}{p_{B0}}\dfrac{W}{L_{nE}}} \tag{3-131}$$

Equation (3-130) can be written as

$$\boldsymbol{\alpha} = \frac{\alpha_0}{1 + j\omega/\omega_\alpha} \tag{3-132}$$

where

$$\omega_\alpha = \frac{1 + 2\left(\dfrac{L_{pB}}{W}\right)^2\left(1 + \dfrac{D_n}{D_p}\dfrac{n_{E0}}{p_{B0}}\dfrac{W}{L_{nE}}\right)}{\tau_{pB}} \tag{3-133}$$

Let us consider the physical significance of Eq. (3-132), which we rewrite as

$$\boldsymbol{\alpha} = \frac{\alpha_0}{\sqrt{1 + (\omega/\omega_\alpha)^2}}\ \underline{/-\tan^{-1}\omega/\omega_\alpha} \tag{3-134}$$

Thus, as ω increases from zero, the magnitude of α, which we write as α, falls off from α_0. When $\omega = \omega_\alpha$, then $\alpha = (1/\sqrt{2})\alpha_0 = 0.707\alpha_0$. If the transistor is to produce amplification at high frequencies, then α should remain close to unity (see Sec. 6-13). Thus, it is desirable for ω_α to be as large as possible. Let us consider Eq. (3-133) to see what can be done to accomplish this. For most transistors, $W/L_{pB} \ll 1$. Thus, we can approximate Eq. (3-133) by

$$\omega_\alpha \approx \frac{2}{\tau_{pB}} \left(\frac{L_{pB}}{W}\right)^2 \left(1 + \frac{D_n}{D_p} \frac{n_{E0}}{p_{B0}} \frac{W}{L_{nE}}\right) \tag{3-135a}$$

The second term in the last parenthesis is usually very much less than 1. Thus,

$$\omega_\alpha \approx \frac{2}{\tau_{pB}} \left(\frac{L_{pB}}{W}\right)^2 \tag{3-135b}$$

If the base width is made smaller, the value of ω_α increases. Another reason for keeping the ratio L_{pB}/W small is thus indicated.

Approximations were made in the derivation of Eq. (3-132). Usually the results of this equation are accurate enough for most calculations, but at times more accuracy is required. It is usually found that the expression for the magnitude of α is close enough, but sometimes the phase angle must be corrected. It is experimentally found that a more accurate expression for α is

$$\alpha = \frac{\alpha_0 \epsilon^{-jk\omega/\omega_\alpha}}{1 + j\omega/\omega_\alpha} \tag{3-136}$$

where k is a constant which is determined experimentally, a typical value being 0.2. Usually, Eq. (3-132) is accurate enough, and the modification given by Eq. (3-136) is not required.

Let us now see how β, the common-emitter short-circuit current gain, varies with frequency. Substituting Eq. (3-132) into Eq. (3-123), we obtain

$$\beta = \frac{\beta_0}{1 + j\omega/\omega_\beta} \tag{3-137}$$

where

$$\beta_0 = \frac{\alpha_0}{1 - \alpha_0} \tag{3-138}$$

$$\omega_\beta = \omega_\alpha(1 - \alpha_0) \tag{3-139}$$

Note that β_0 will generally be much greater than α_0. However, ω_β will be much less than ω_α. The frequency ω_β has the same significance for β that ω_α has for α.

Let us now consider why α falls off as the frequency of the signal increases. The charge carriers which contribute to collector current diffuse across the base region from the emitter-base junction to the collector-base junction. Diffusion is a random process. Consider that the signal and hence the injected minority carriers (holes) at the emitter-base junction vary in accordance with the pulses of Fig. 3-23a. Square pulses rather than sinusoidal ones are used here since the diagrams are more understandable, but the ideas are the same. As the carriers diffuse across the base, the randomness of the motion causes the corners of the pulse to be rounded off. Thus, the hole current density reaching the collector-base junction will have the form of Fig. 3-23b. The pulses still have essentially the same height. They have been rounded slightly. Now let us increase the frequency of the pulses to that of Fig. 3-23c. The same rounding off occurs in the collector component of hole current, but now the duration of the pulses is so short that the rounding off causes their height to be much less than before. The shape of the pulses is also very distorted.

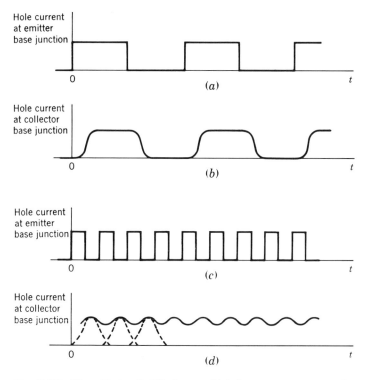

Fig. 3-23 The effects of diffusion on high-frequency response of a *p-n-p*-junction transistor: (*a*) hole current at the emitter-base junction; (*b*) resultant hole current at the collector-base junction; (*c*) hole current of a higher frequency than in (*a*) at the emitter-base junction; (*d*) resultant hole current at the collector-base junction.

If the time it takes for the holes to diffuse across the base is reduced, the rounding off will also be reduced, thus improving the high-frequency response. If the base width is made narrower, the diffusion time is reduced and the frequency response is increased.

Junction capacitance   In Secs. 3-6 and 3-7 we discussed the capacitance that appears across the junction of a *p-n*-junction diode.   Capacitance of this type appears across each *p-n* junction of a junction transistor.   The emitter-base junction is usually forward-biased.   In this case, the diffusion capacitance predominates (see Sec. 3-7).   The collector-base junction is usually reverse-biased.   Thus, the transition capacitance predominates (see Sec. 3-6).

These capacitances affect the high-frequency response of the transistor, as we shall discuss in Chap. 6, where the linear models of the transistor will be studied.

3-19   OTHER TRANSISTOR TYPES

In this section we shall consider some of the modifications which can be made in the basic junction-transistor structure to improve high-frequency response.

The drift transistor   The high-frequency response of a transistor is improved by reducing the base width, since this reduces the time it takes for the charge carriers to diffuse across the base (see Sec. 3-18).   Because of fabrication difficulties, the minimum base width is limited.   However, the time it takes for minority carriers to move across the base can be reduced in another way.   We shall again use a *p-n-p* transistor in our discussion.   The results are similar for an *n-p-n* transistor.

The transistor we shall discuss is called the *drift transistor*.   When it is fabricated, the impurity concentration in the base is not uniform but is made to vary in such a way that the donor density is higher at the emitter-base junction than it is at the collector-base junction.   This is diagrammatically illustrated in Fig. 3-24a.   Let us consider the base region.   The ionized donors are fixed positive charges.   Random motion causes the free-electron (majority-carrier) density to be uniform in the base.   Thus, there will be a net positive charge on the emitter side of the base and a net negative charge on the collector side of the base (see Fig. 3-24a).   This charge imbalance sets up an electric field in the base which modifies the potential distribution of Fig. 3-16.   The potential distribution for the drift transistor is shown in Fig. 3-24b.

The electric field set up by the charge imbalance causes holes to *drift* from the emitter-base junction to the collector-base junction.   Therefore, holes move by drift as well as by diffusion in the base.   This motion due to drift reduces the time required for the minority carriers (holes) to move

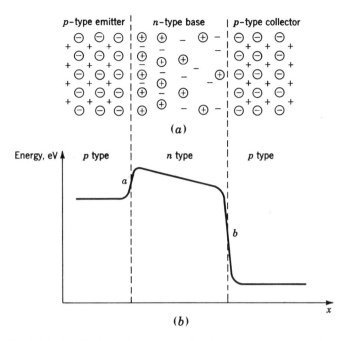

Fig. 3-24 (*a*) The impurity concentration in a drift transistor. The circles represent impurity ions. The plus and minus signs represent free charge carriers. (*b*) The potential distribution.

across the base. Hence, its effect is similar to reducing the base width. Thus, the high-frequency response is improved.

The junction capacitance (see Sec. 3-18) limits the high-frequency response of the transistor. Thus, it is desirable that this capacitance be as small as possible. Since the collector-base junction is reverse-biased, the transition capacitance predominates there (see Sec. 3-6). This capacitance can be given by [see Eqs. (3-44) and (3-50)]

$$C = \frac{\epsilon A}{d} \tag{3-140}$$

where ϵ = permittivity of semiconductor

A = cross-sectional area of junction

d = total width of depletion layer

If d is increased, the capacitance will be reduced. For a given voltage across the depletion layer, the width d varies inversely with the impurity concentration. In the drift transistor, the impurity density is low at the collector-base junction. Thus, d is greater than it would be if the impurity density had been constant at the value at the emitter-base junction or at the average impurity density. Hence, the junction capacitance is reduced.

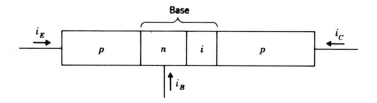

Fig. 3-25 Diagrammatic representation of a *p-n-i-p* transistor.

The *p-n-i-p* or *n-p-i-n* transistor   At times a junction transistor is fabricated such that a region of intrinsic material exists between the base and the collector.   This is shown diagrammatically in Fig. 3-25 for a *p-n-p* transistor. This is called a *p-n-i-p transistor*.   The impurity concentration in the base near the collector is essentially zero.   Thus (see the discussion of the last paragraph) the transition capacitance will be low.

If the impurity density from the *n*-type region to the *i*-type region varies gradually, it will be similar to that of a drift transistor.   This will also improve the high-frequency response.

The surface-barrier transistor   The performance of a transistor is improved as the base width is made narrower.   It is more difficult to construct transistors with very thin bases.   An early type of transistor constructed with a very thin base was the *surface-barrier transistor*, fabricated by etching a single doped crystal electrochemically.   Two jets of metallic salt are directed onto the doped crystal and maintained at a fixed electric potential with respect to it.   This produces the electrochemical etching.   When the crystal is etched to the desired thickness, the potential is reversed.   This plates metal contacts onto the crystal.

The collector and emitter junctions are metal-to-semiconductor junctions and occur at the surface of the semiconductor, accounting for the name surface-barrier transistor.

3-20   THE JUNCTION FIELD-EFFECT TRANSISTOR

We shall now consider another semiconductor device which can be used for amplification, called the *junction field-effect transistor*, the words field-effect transistor often being abbreviated FET.   The physical configuration and principles of operation of the FET are different from those of the junction transistor.   The FET has several advantages over the junction transistor, in that it has a *very high input resistance*, produces less noise, has better thermal stability, and is relatively unaffected by radiation.   However, the junction transistor has much better high-frequency response.

The junction FET is diagrammatically illustrated in Fig. 3-26. It consists of an *n*-type semiconductor bar with two *p*-type regions as shown. (The *p*- and *n*-type regions can be interchanged. The theory of operation will be the same. We shall describe the FET as shown in Fig. 3-26.) One side of the *n*-type crystal is called the *source*, the other the *drain*. The *n*-type region between the depletion regions of the *p-n* junctions, from the source to the drain, is called the *channel*. The main current is the drain current I_D, which is from the drain to the source through the channel. The two *p*-type regions are called *gates*. They are electrically connected externally. The doping in the *p*-type region is made very high.

There are two *p-n* junctions. They are between each gate and the *n*-type channel. Let us assume that both the gate-channel *p-n* junctions are reverse-biased by V_{GS}, as shown in Fig. 3-26. The depletion layer extends much farther into the *n* channel than into the *p* gates because the doping in the gates is very much higher than in the channel. The depletion region (shown shaded in Fig. 3-26) is wider near the drain because of the drain current. We shall discuss this subsequently.

The charge carriers are free electrons. Note that they are the *majority* carriers in the channel. There is only one type of charge carrier in the FET.

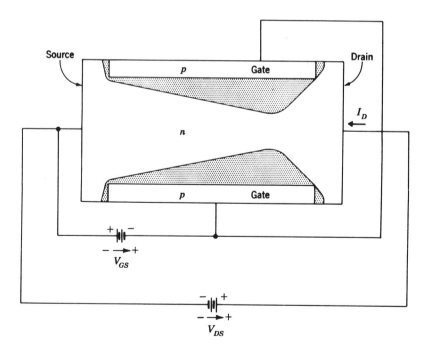

Fig. 3-26 A diagrammatic representation of a junction FET. The depletion regions are shown shaded. Note that V_{GS} is a negative number.

For this reason, it is called a *unipolar* device.   In contrast the junction transistor utilizes both free electrons and holes.   Thus, there are two types of charge carriers, and it is called a *bipolar* device.

The drain current I_D is a function of the applied voltage V_{DS} and the resistance from the drain to the source.   This resistance is a function of the conductivity of the semiconductor and of the cross-sectional area of the channel.   The depletion region is almost free of mobile charge carriers. Hence, it does not contribute to the area available for conduction.   Therefore, the conduction takes place in the channel between the depletion layers. If the reverse bias on the gate-channel *p-n* junctions is increased, the depletion-layer width will increase.   This decreases the width of the channel and increases the resistance from drain to source.

Now let us consider that a small potential V_{DS} is applied between drain and source, as shown in Fig. 3-26.   The gate is maintained at a constant potential V_{GS} with respect to the source.   Thus, the potential difference between gate and source is V_{GS}.   (Note that this is negative.)   However, the drain is at a potential of V_{DS} volts with respect to the source.   Hence, the gate-drain potential is $V_{DS} - V_{GS}$.   Therefore, the gate-channel potential will be higher near the drain than near the source.   This can be considered to come about in a different way.   Current in the channel results in a voltage drop there.   The potential between the gate and channel, as a function of position, is $-V_{GS}$ plus the voltage drop between the source and the point in question.   As the distance from the source increases, the voltage drop increases.   Thus, the potential between the gate and the channel increases.

Let us now consider the current-voltage characteristics of the FET. Assume that V_{GS} is fixed and V_{DS} is increased from zero.   When V_{DS} is zero, the depletion regions are symmetrical about the gates.   As V_{DS} is increased, some drain current results.   The voltage drop in the bulk of the channel causes the depletion-layer width to widen and become skewed, as shown in Fig. 3-26.   As V_{DS} is increased, the current I_D increases.   The resistance of the channel also increases, because the depletion-layer width increases.   This is illustrated in each of the curves of Fig. 3-27.   The slope of the I_D-versus-V_{DS} curve decreases as V_{DS} increases, indicating that the drain-to-source resistance increases as V_{DS} increases.

It might appear as though V_{DS} would be increased sufficiently to permit the depletion region to be extended across the entire channel and cut off the current.   Actually, this never completely occurs.   The increase in the width of the depletion region with increasing I_D occurs because of the voltage drop *due* to I_D.   If the depletion region completely closed off the channel, I_D would be zero.   As V_{DS} is increased, the channel width does become very narrow.   However, the current density also increases, so that I_D increases. In this case, the resistance of the channel becomes very high, as indicated by the almost horizontal portions of the curves of Fig. 3-27.   Ideally, the

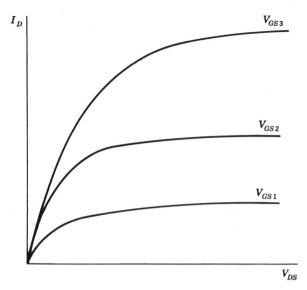

Fig. 3-27 Typical current-voltage characteristics for a junction FET. $V_{GS1} < V_{GS2} < V_{GS3}$. Note that these are negative voltages, i.e., V_{GS3} is a smaller magnitude than V_{GS1}.

channel width becomes infinitesimally narrow while the current density becomes infinite, but this cannot occur except in an ideal case.

The voltage where the channel width becomes very narrow is not exactly defined. However, the point where—in theory—the channel becomes differentially narrow or—in practice—the V_{DS}-versus-I_D curves become almost horizontal is called *pinch-off*. The voltage which produces it is called the *pinch-off voltage* (it is a function of V_{GS}).

In Fig. 3-27 we have plotted three different V_{DS}-versus-I_D curves for three different values of V_{GS}. If V_{GS} is made more negative, the depletion-layer width will increase. Thus, pinch-off occurs at lower voltages and, correspondingly, at lower values of I_D. Therefore, the curves will have the form shown in Fig. 3-27.

Note that the gate source voltage can be made positive. In this case, the gate-channel *p-n* junctions are forward-biased. However, there is still a depletion layer (see Sec. 3-2), and the operation proceeds as before. Of course, the currents will be larger with a positive V_{GS} than with a negative one. For instance, in Fig. 3-27, V_{GS3} could be a positive voltage.

If V_{DS} is increased sufficiently, I_D will suddenly increase very rapidly due to avalanche breakdown (see Sec. 3-9), which occurs in the depletion layer. Normally, the maximum value of V_{DS} is limited so that this breakdown does not occur.

Fig. 3-28 Symbols for the FET: (*a*) *n*-channel type and (*b*) *p*-channel type.

The symbols for the FET are shown in Fig. 3-28. One is for an *n*-channel FET, while the other is for a *p*-channel FET. Note that the symbols for the drain and source are the same. At times, the letter *D* is placed near the drain to clarify the drawing.

FETs of the kind shown in Fig. 3-26 are difficult to fabricate, a more practical form being that shown in Fig. 3-29. The drain is "surrounded" by the gate for the upper part of the structure. To pass from the source to the drain, the free electrons must pass under the gate, i.e., between the gate and the substrate. The substrate provides mechanical support but does not conduct charge carriers. A depletion layer at the gate–*n*-type junction narrows the channel which lies between the gate and the substrate. Thus, the operation of this device is essentially the same as that of the device of Fig. 3-26.

At times the substrate is made of *p*-type material. It is insulated from the channel by reverse-biasing the *p-n* junction between the channel and the substrate. This and the actual construction of the FET will be discussed in the next chapter.

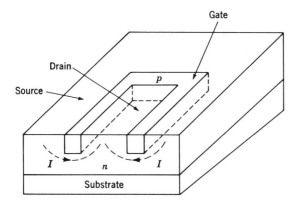

Fig. 3-29 Section of a more practical FET structure.

3-21 CURRENT IN THE JUNCTION FET: QUANTITATIVE DISCUSSION

Let us now obtain quantitative expressions for the current-voltage characteristics of a junction FET. At the start, we shall consider that the drain-to-source voltage v_{DS} is zero. The width of the channel as a function of v_{GS}, the gate-to-source voltage, will then be determined. If $v_{DS} = 0$, then i_D, the drain current, will be zero and the depletion region will be uniform for most of the channel, as illustrated in Fig. 3-30. Let us assume that the impurity concentration varies abruptly from N_A to N_D at the p-n junction. For most of the region of the FET, the depletion-layer width will be constant. We shall work in this constant region. Equation (3-47) gives the depletion-layer width for an abrupt p-n junction. It is

$$d = \sqrt{\frac{2\epsilon(V_0 - v_{GS})}{eN_D(N_D/N_A + 1)}} \tag{3-141}$$

where ϵ = permittivity

V_0 = potential across p-n junction when it is unbiased

e = magnitude of charge of electron

In the FET

$$\frac{N_D}{N_A} \ll 1 \tag{3-142}$$

Thus, after some manipulation, we have for the width of the channel (see Fig. 3-30)

$$w(x) = b - 2d = b - 2\sqrt{\frac{2\epsilon(V_0 - v_{GS})}{eN_D}} \tag{3-143}$$

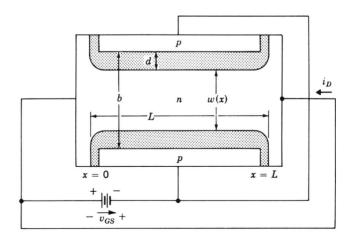

Fig. 3-30 A representation of a junction FET with $v_{DS} = 0$. Note that v_{GS} is negative.

Note that Eq. (3-143) is valid only for values of $w(x)$ greater than or equal to 0. That is, the channel width cannot be negative. Thus, values of v_{GS} which make $w(x)$ less than 0 *cannot* be used in Eq. (3-143).

Now let us determine the value of v_{GS} which produces pinch-off when $v_{DS} = 0$. At pinch-off $w(x)$ becomes zero. Hence, setting Eq. (3-143) equal to zero and solving for V_{GSP}, where the subscript P indicates pinch-off, we have

$$V_{GSP} = -\frac{b^2 e N_D}{8\epsilon} + V_0 \qquad (3\text{-}144)$$

Note that v_{GSP} is a negative quantity. In general,

$$\frac{b^2 e N_D}{8\epsilon} \gg V_0 \qquad (3\text{-}145)$$

Thus, we have

$$V_{GSP} = -\frac{b^2 e N_D}{8\epsilon} \qquad (3\text{-}146)$$

or

$$|V_{GSP}| = \frac{b^2 e N_D}{8\epsilon} \qquad (3\text{-}147)$$

Now let us assume that the short circuit between the drain and source is replaced by a voltage v_{DS}. This will result in a current i_D. It should be noted that if v_{GS} is at the pinch-off value V_{GSP}, the channel width will be essentially zero and i_D will also be zero. In general, under the condition that v_{GS} is negative and that $|v_{GS}| \geq |V_{GSP}|$, i_D will be very small, of the order of nanoamperes, that is, 10^{-9} amp.

If v_{DS} is very small, so that

$$v_{DS} \ll |v_{GS}| \qquad (3\text{-}148)$$

then the depletion layer will essentially be unchanged by the application of the drain-source voltage. The skewing and narrowing of the channel indicated in Fig. 3-26 becomes apparent only at larger drain-source voltages.

Let us consider that v_{DS} is such that relation (3-148) is satisfied. If the FET is a meters thick, i.e., into the paper, then the cross-sectional area of the channel is aw. If the effective length of the channel is L meters, then the resistance of the channel from drain to source is

$$R = \frac{L}{\sigma a w} \qquad (3\text{-}149)$$

where σ is the conductivity of the n-type semiconductor. Then, using Ohm's law and substituting Eq. (3-143), we have

$$i_D = v_{DS} \frac{\sigma a}{L} \left[b - \sqrt{\frac{8\epsilon(V_0 - v_{GS})}{e N_D}} \right] \qquad (3\text{-}150)$$

Manipulating Eq. (3-146), we obtain

$$b = \sqrt{-\frac{8\epsilon}{eN_D} V_{GSP}} \tag{3-151}$$

Substituting into Eq. (3-150) yields

$$i_D = \frac{\sigma a}{L} b \left[\left(1 - \sqrt{\frac{v_{GS} - V_0}{V_{GSP}}} \right) \right] v_{DS} \tag{3-152}$$

Now let us consider a current-voltage characteristic where we are not restricted to small values of v_{DS}. We shall work with the representation of the junction FET shown in Fig. 3-31. To simplify the analysis we shall assume that the difference of potential between the channel at $x = 0$ and the source is $-v_{GS}$; that is, the voltage drop in the channel between the source contact and $x = 0$ is zero. We shall assume that the voltage drop in the channel between $x = L$ and the source is essentially v_{DS}. Thus, the "applied" potential between the part of the gate at $x = L$ and the channel is $-v_{GS} + v_{DS}$. The potential difference between the gate and channel is $v(x) + V_0$. That is, $v(x)$ is the potential difference *not* due to contact potential. Thus, according to the assumption made at the beginning of this paragraph,

$$v(0) = -v_{GS} \tag{3-153}$$

$$v(L) = -v_{GS} + v_{DS} \tag{3-154}$$

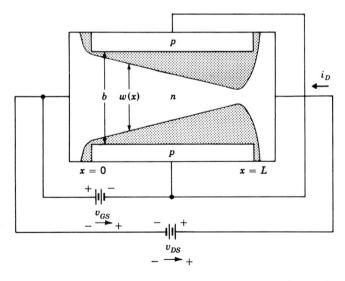

Fig. 3-31 Representation of a junction FET. Note that v_{GS} is negative.

Note that we have defined $v(x)$ to be a positive quantity.   Equation (3-143) will approximately give $w(x)$ at all points providing that $-v_{GS}$ is replaced by $v(x)$.   Hence,

$$w(x) = b - \sqrt{\frac{8\epsilon[V_0 + v(x)]}{eN_D}} \tag{3-155}$$

For a differentially small length, the resistance of the channel is [see Eq. (3-149)]

$$dR = \frac{dx}{a\sigma w(x)} \tag{3-156}$$

where dx is now the length of the piece in question.   The voltage drop across a differential length dx is equal to the product of the electric field intensity $\mathscr{E}_x$ and dx.   But [see Eq. (1-10)] the electric field is given by

$$\mathscr{E}_x = -\frac{dv(x)}{dx} \tag{3-157}$$

Thus the current through the channel at point x is found from Ohm's law and Eqs. (3-156) and (3-157) to be

$$i_D = -\frac{a\sigma w(x)}{dx}\left[\frac{dv(x)}{dx}\,dx\right] \tag{3-158}$$

Note that the current is constant throughout the channel at i_D, independent of x.   If this were not true, charge would pile up at a point.   Manipulating, we have

$$i_D\,dx = -a\sigma w(x)\,dv(x) \tag{3-159}$$

Substituting Eqs. (3-155) and (3-151), we obtain

$$i_D\,dx = -a\sigma\sqrt{\frac{8\epsilon}{eN_D}}\,[\sqrt{V_{GSP}} - \sqrt{V_0 + v(x)}]\,dv$$

Integrating from $x = 0$ to $x = L$ or, equivalently, from $v(x) = v(0)$ to $v(x) = v(L)$ yields

$$\int_0^L i_D\,dx = -a\sigma\sqrt{\frac{8\epsilon}{eN_D}}\left\{\int_{v(0)}^{v(L)} [\sqrt{-V_{GSP}} - \sqrt{V_0 + v(x)}]\right\}dv \tag{3-160}$$

Carrying out the integration, we have

$$i_D = -\frac{a\sigma}{L}\sqrt{\frac{8\epsilon}{eN_D}}\{\sqrt{-V_{GSP}}\,v_{DS} - \tfrac{2}{3}[(V_0 + v_{DS} - v_{GS})^{\frac{3}{2}} - (V_0 - v_{GS})^{\frac{3}{2}}]\} \tag{3-161}$$

Equation (3-143) and thus Eqs. (3-155) and (3-161) are valid only for values of v_{DS} and v_{GS} which result in nonnegative values of $w(x)$.   Thus, Eq. (3-155) is valid only up to that value of $v(x)$ which causes $w(x)$ to become zero.   This occurs when

$$v_{DS} - v_{GS} = -V_{GSP} \tag{3-162}$$

[see the derivation of Eq. (3-144)].   This determines the maximum value of i_D for which Eq. (3-161) is valid.   However, this corresponds to the i_D at pinch-off.   Above pinch-off, the curve of i_D versus v_{DS} becomes almost horizontal.   Thus, Eq. (3-162) can be used to predict these almost constant values.   Substituting Eq. (3-162) into Eq. (3-161), we obtain the current at the horizontal portion of Fig. 3-27.   This is

$$i_{D,\text{sat}} = \frac{a\sigma}{L} \sqrt{\frac{8\epsilon}{eN_D}} \{\sqrt{-v_{GSP}}(-v_{GSP} + v_{GS})$$
$$- \tfrac{2}{3}[(V_0 - V_{GSP})^{\frac{3}{2}} - (V_0 - v_{GS})^{\frac{3}{2}}]\} \tag{3-163}$$

Since i_D cannot become imaginary, this equation is valid only if v_{GS} is no more negative than V_{GSP}.   At this point $i_D = 0$.   FET amplifiers are usually operated in the region of this characteristic where the i_D-versus-v_{DS} curves are almost horizontal.   Thus, Eq. (3-163) can be used to predict these curves. Note that the variation of $i_{D,\text{sat}}$ with v_{GS} is not a linear one.

3-22   JUNCTION FET STATIC CHARACTERISTICS AND DYNAMIC PARAMETERS

The analysis of the last section is only approximate.   To obtain more accurate results, the FET is often characterized by experimentally measured graphical characteristics.   In general, there are three variables to be represented, i_D, v_{DS}, and v_{GS}.   Note that the source is usually the reference electrode.   To avoid using a three-dimensional plot, a family of curves is presented wherein a variable is plotted as a function of one of the others with the third held constant.   Each curve of the family is for a different constant value of the third variable.   Three such families of curves can be given.   We shall consider each of them in turn.

Output characteristics   The static output characteristics, or simply the output characteristics, are plots of i_D versus v_{DS} with v_{GS} as a parameter. These curves have the form of Fig. 3-27.   A typical set is given in Fig. 3-32. Note that these characteristics are very similar to those of a vacuum-tube pentode (see Fig. 2-21).

Let us use the output characteristics to analyze the simple FET amplifier shown in Fig. 3-33.   To do this we draw a load line on the output characteristic (see Secs. 3-5 and 3-16).   The equation for the load line is

$$v_{DS} = V_{DD} - i_D R_L \tag{3-164}$$

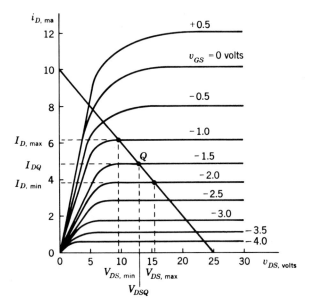

Fig. 3-32 Typical output characteristic of a junction FET. A load line is drawn.

This is the equation of a straight line of slope $-1/R_L$ and intercepts V_{DD} and V_{DD}/R_L.

Let us analyze the amplifier of Fig. 3-33 using the following element values: $V_{DD} = 25$ volts, $v_{GG} = -1.5$ volts, $R_L = 2500$ ohms and $v_{gs} = 0.5 \sin \omega t$ volt. The load line is drawn on Fig. 3-32. The quiescent operating point (see Secs. 3-5 and 3-16) is obtained by considering that the signal voltage is $v_{gs} = 0$. Thus, it is obtained from the intersection of the load line with the curve for $v_{GS} = -1.5$ volts. Hence, $I_{DQ} = 4.9$ ma and $V_{DSQ} = 12.5$ volts.

The signal voltage is v_{gs}. This causes the gate-to-source voltage v_{GS} to vary between -1.0 and -2.0 volts. The instantaneous operating point

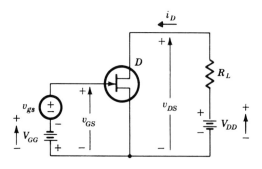

Fig. 3-33 A simple FET amplifier. Note that V_{GG} is negative. Often a D is added to distinguish the drain from the source.

moves between the two extremes marked on Fig. 3-32. The various wave-forms are as drawn in Fig. 3-34. Note that the output signal voltage is 180° out of phase with the input signal voltage. As v_{gs} becomes positive, v_{GS} becomes less negative and i_D increases. This increases the voltage drop in R_L and reduces v_{DS}. Thus, the 180° phase shift results.

The output signal varies between 9 and 16 volts while the input signal varies between −1 and −2 volts. Thus, a 1-volt input signal produces a 7-volt output signal. The voltage amplification of this circuit is

$$A_v = -\frac{16 - 9}{2 - 1} = -7 \tag{3-165}$$

The minus sign indicates the 180° phase shift. Actually the output voltage and current do not vary exactly sinusoidally because the characteristics are nonlinear.

Note that a characteristic curve is given for v_{GS} positive. When v_{GS} becomes positive, the gate-channel *p-n* junction becomes forward-biased and a gate current i_G results. This current can also be drawn on the output

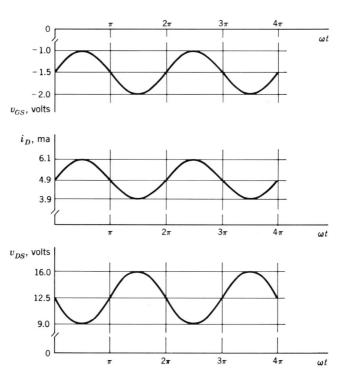

Fig. 3-34 Curves of v_{GS}, i_D, and v_{DS} for the amplifier of Fig. 3-33. The phase shift between v_{GS} and v_{DS} is illustrated.

characteristic. Junction FETs are usually not operated with the gate-channel junction forward-biased. The high input impedance of the FET is one of its advantages. If the gate-channel junction is forward-biased, this advantage is eliminated.

Transfer characteristics   Another set of static characteristics used to characterize the FET are the transfer characteristics. These are a plot of i_D versus v_{GS} with v_{DS} as a parameter. A typical set of transfer characteristics is shown in Fig. 3-35. Note that all the curves are close together, indicating that i_D is almost independent of v_{DS} for most values of v_{DS}.

Constant-current characteristics   The third set of static characteristics consists of a plot of v_{DS} versus v_{GS} with i_D as a parameter. A typical set of these characteristics is shown in Fig. 3-36. The characteristics are almost horizontal for most values of v_{DS}, again indicating that i_D is almost independent of v_{DS} over much of the range of operation.

Dynamic parameters   When amplifiers are considered, we are often interested in a small change in output voltage or current in response to a small change in input voltage. These small changes are the signal quantities. The slopes of the static characteristics at the quiescent operating point are

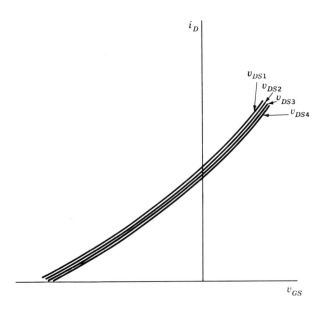

Fig. 3-35 Typical transfer characteristic for an FET. $v_{DS1} > v_{DS2} > v_{DS3} > v_{DS4}$.

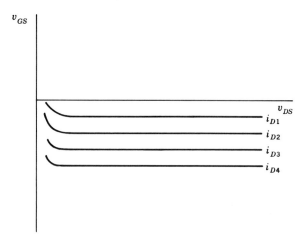

Fig. 3-36 Typical constant-current characteristic for an FET. $i_{D1} > i_{D2} > i_{D3} > i_{D4}$.

often used to characterize the signals. We shall discuss this in detail in Chap. 6. Let us now define the parameters we shall use.

Amplification factor μ The amplification factor is defined by

$$\mu = -\frac{dv_{DS}}{dv_{GS}}\bigg|_{i_D = \text{const}} = -\frac{\partial v_{DS}}{\partial v_{GS}} \tag{3-166}$$

Thus, μ is the reciprocal of the slope of the constant-current characteristic. It is a dimensionless quantity.

Transconductance g_m The transconductance is defined as

$$g_m = \frac{di_D}{dv_{GS}}\bigg|_{v_{DS} = \text{const}} = \frac{\partial i_D}{\partial v_{GS}} \tag{3-167}$$

This is the slope of the transfer characteristic at the operating point. The units of transconductance are mhos, that is, 1/ohm. Usually the mho is too large a unit, and the transconductance is expressed in micromhos (1 μmho $= 10^{-6}$ mho). Typical values of g_m range from 1000 to 10,000 μmhos.

Drain resistance, drain-source resistance r_d The drain resistance (or equivalently the dynamic drain-source resistance) is defined as

$$r_d = \frac{dv_{DS}}{di_D}\bigg|_{v_{GS} = \text{const}} = \frac{\partial v_{DS}}{\partial i_D} \tag{3-168}$$

which is the reciprocal of the slope of the output characteristic at the operating point. The units of r_d are ohms. At times, we work with the drain conductance g_d, where

$$g_d = \frac{1}{r_d} \tag{3-169}$$

Typical values of r_d range from 10^5 to 10^6 ohms for a junction FET.

Dynamic resistances between the gate and source and the gate and drain can also be determined. In general, for a reverse-biased gate-channel junction, these are very high, i.e., greater than 10^8 ohms.

We have defined the dynamic parameters as slopes of static characteristics. Actually, we can obtain all three parameters from only one set of characteristics. For instance, Eq. (3-167) can be approximated by

$$g_m \approx \frac{\Delta i_D}{\Delta v_{GS}}\bigg|_{v_{DS} = \text{const}} \tag{3-170}$$

The change in i_D corresponding to a change in v_{GS} at a constant value of v_{DS} can be obtained from the output characteristics and substituted into Eq. (3-170) to obtain g_m.

The three dynamic parameters are not independent. Let us determine the relation among them. If we consider differentially small changes in i_D, we can write

$$di_D = \frac{\partial i_D}{\partial v_{GS}} dv_{GS} + \frac{\partial i_D}{\partial v_{DS}} dv_{DS} \tag{3-171}$$

Thus, substituting Eqs. (3-167) and (3-168), we have

$$di_D = g_m \, dv_{GS} + \frac{1}{r_d} \, dv_{DS} \tag{3-172}$$

Now assume that v_{GS} and v_{DS} are varied in such a way that i_D remains constant. If this is done, $di_D = 0$ and Eq. (3-172) becomes, after manipulation,

$$g_m r_d = -\frac{dv_{DS}}{dv_{GS}}\bigg|_{i_d = \text{const}}$$

Then, substituting Eq. (3-166), we obtain

$$\mu = g_m r_d \tag{3-173}$$

and we have determined the relation among the dynamic parameters.

3-23 HIGH-FREQUENCY EFFECTS IN THE JUNCTION FET

The high-frequency behavior of the junction FET is affected predominantly by the capacitances of the device. The reverse-biased gate-channel p-n junction has a transition capacitance (see Sec. 3-6) associated with its entire

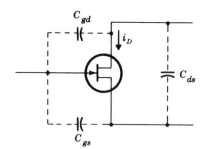

Fig. 3-37 The stray capacitance of the FET.

length. This is actually a distributed capacitance. That is, the capacitance and resistance of the channel exist simultaneously over the length of the channel. However, the effect of the capacitance can usually be represented by lumped capacitors. In addition, capacitance exists between the leads and contacts of the FET. All these effects can usually be accounted for accurately by considering that there are three lumped capacitors, one, C_{gs}, between the gate and the source, another, C_{gd}, between the gate and the drain, and the third, C_{ds}, between the source and the drain. These are illustrated in Fig. 3-37. These capacitances are called *stray capacitances* or *parasitic capacitances* since they are not placed there deliberately and they degrade the high-frequency response. The effects of these capacitances will be discussed in Sec. 6-14.

3-24 THE INSULATED-GATE FET—IGFET AND MOSFET

High input resistance is one of the advantages of the junction FET. In this section we shall discuss a form of FET whose input resistance is very much greater than the already high input resistance of the junction FET. In addition, a bias voltage need not be applied to establish this high resistance. The basic structure of one form of this FET is shown in Fig. 3-38. Two highly doped *n*-type regions are incorporated in a *p*-type substrate; one of these *n*-type regions is the source, and the other is the drain. The *p*-type region is lightly doped. An insulating layer is placed over the region between the source and drain, and a metallic conductor is placed on top of it. The conductor is the gate. This type of device is usually fabricated using integrated-device procedures (the fabrication will be discussed in the next chapter). In these procedures, the semiconductor is silicon, and the insulating layer is quartz, i.e., silicon dioxide, SiO_2. The gate, insulator, and substrate consist of layers of metal, oxide, and silicon, respectively, abbreviated MOS. Thus, the entire FET is abbreviated MOSFET. There are two types of MOSFET, which we discuss in turn.

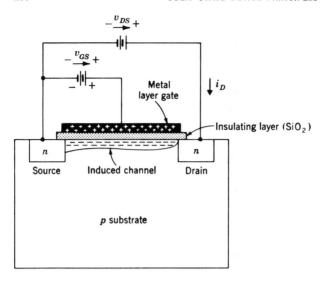

Fig. 3-38 An enhancement MOSFET.

The enhancement MOSFET We first consider the type of MOSFET illustrated in Fig. 3-38, called an *enhancement* MOSFET. The two *n*-type regions are very highly doped, while the *p*-type region is lightly doped. Now consider that a potential is applied between the drain and source. Very little drain current will result from the application of v_{DS} because of the low conductivity of the *p*-type region and because the *p-n* junction near the drain is reverse-biased. (Often the *p*-type substrate is externally connected to the source.)

Now consider that a positive voltage is applied to the gate, as shown in Fig. 3-38. The metal insulator (oxide) and substrate form a capacitor. The positive potential on the gate attracts negative charges to the region in the substrate under the gate; i.e., in any capacitor, the charge imbalance in *each* plate has a magnitude $q = vc$. Thus, free electrons are brought into the region between gate and drain. Because of the light doping, there are few holes in the *p*-type region; i.e., there are not very many more holes than free electrons. Thus, when many free electrons are attracted to this region, they outnumber the holes and it acts as an *n*-type region. This is called *enhancement operation* since the number of free electrons is enhanced. The addition of the charge carriers increases the conductivity of the region. In addition, there is now a continuous "*n*-type" channel between the source and the drain. Thus, a drain current will result from the application of v_{DS}. As v_{DS} is increased, the current increases. However, as the drain is made more positive, the voltage drop along the channel increases, i.e., becomes more positive with respect to the source. Thus, the potential difference between the gate and the channel decreases. Note that this gate-to-channel potential is a function of distance. It decreases from v_{GS} at the source end of the channel to $v_{GS} - v_{DS}$ at the drain end. If the gate-to-channel potential decreases, the enhancement operation will also decrease. Thus as i_D increases, the resistance of the channel also increases. Typical curves of i_D versus v_{DS} with v_{GS} as a parameter are shown in Fig. 3-39. The reduction in slope as v_{DS} is increased indicates that the resistance between source and drain is increased as v_{DS} increases.

As v_{GS} is made more positive, more charge is induced into the channel and the drain current increases, as shown in Fig. 3-39.

The characteristics of the MOSFET are very similar to those of the junction FET. We shall compare them in further detail subsequently.

The depletion MOSFET If the fabrication of MOSFET is changed so that there is an actual n-type region produced between the source and drain, the operation of the device is modified somewhat. Such a device is shown in Fig. 3-40. Because the doping in the source and drain is much higher than in the n-type channel, the source and drain are marked n^+. The substrate usually is a p-type region which is insulated from the n-type regions by the p-n junction.

Now let us consider the operation of the device. If no voltage is applied to the gate ($v_{GS} = 0$) and a voltage v_{DS} is applied between drain and

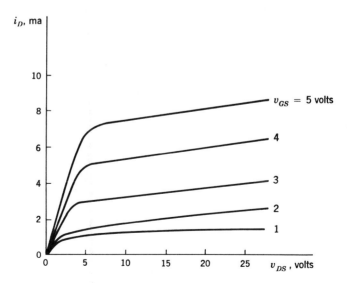

Fig. 3-39 Typical static output characteristic of an enhancement MOSFET.

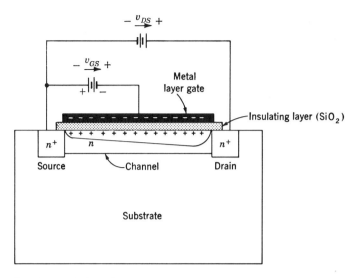

Fig. 3-40 A depletion MOSFET. Note that v_{GS} is negative.

source, a current will result in the channel.   Now suppose that a negative v_{GS} is applied, as shown in Fig. 3-40.   A capacitor is formed between the gate conductor and the n-type channel, just as in the enhancement type, but now the polarity of v_{GS} is reversed so that the positive charges are induced in the channel.   Note that actually free electrons are driven away; this exposes ionized donor atoms, which are the positive charges.   Thus, a depletion region is set up, as shown in Fig. 3-40, narrowing the channel and increasing its resistance.   Thus, the drain current is reduced.   This type of operation is called *depletion* since charge carriers are depleted from the channel.

Now let us consider that v_{DS} is increased from zero.   This increases i_D. As i_D becomes larger, the voltage drop in the channel increases, thus making the end of the channel near the drain more positive and increasing the width of the depletion layer.   Thus, the resistance increases as i_D increases.

If v_{GS} is made positive, additional free electrons will be brought into the channel.   This results in essentially the same type of operation as in the case of the enhancement MOSFET.   In fact, this is called enhancement operation.

The static output characteristics for a typical depletion type MOSFET are shown in Fig. 3-41.   Note that they are given for positive as well as negative v_{GS}; that is, this characteristic has regions of both depletion and enhancement operation.

The symbols for a MOSFET are shown in Fig. 3-42.   These are for an n-channel MOSFET, which is the type discussed in this section.   Note that, in Fig. 3-38, the channel is n type even though the substrate is p type.   A D

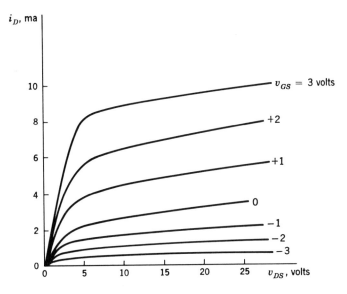

Fig. 3-41 Typical static characteristics of a depletion MOSFET. Operation for positive values of v_{GS} in an enhancement type.

is added to indicate the drain in two of the symbols of Fig. 3-42. If it is obvious which lead is the drain, the D can be omitted.

The n-type regions can be replaced by p-type ones, and vice versa, in the MOSFETs we have discussed in this section. In this case, the channel becomes p type, and the appropriate polarities of voltages and currents must be reversed. The arrowheads are reversed in the symbols of Fig. 3-42 for p-channel MOSFET.

The symbols of Fig. 3-42 have a fourth electrode connected to the substrate. At times, this lead is actually available, but it is often internally connected to the source. The symbols of Fig. 3-28 can be used to represent a MOSFET. In such cases, source and substrate must be internally connected.

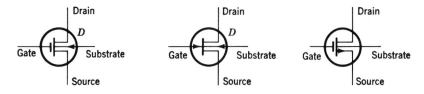

Fig. 3-42 Three symbols for an n-channel MOSFET. The directions of all the arrowheads are reversed for the p-channel MOSFET.

3-25 STATIC CHARACTERISTICS AND
DYNAMIC PARAMETERS OF THE MOSFET

The static characteristics of the MOSFET and the junction FET are very similar, and much of the discussion of Sec. 3-22 is applicable to the MOSFET. The static output characteristics of an enhancement and a depletion-enhancement MOSFET are given in Figs. 3-39 and 3-41, respectively, and are very similar to those of Fig. 3-32 for the junction FET.   The essential differences between these characteristics are the polarities of the gate-source voltage.   In the (n-channel) junction FET, v_{GS} is almost always negative, while in the MOSFET, it can be of either polarity.   Note that v_{GS} can be positive for the junction FET.   Then the gate-channel p-n junction becomes forward-biased, and the input impedance becomes small.   Thus, this mode of operation is rarely used.   However, the insulated-gate FETs rely on the insulating layer and not on a reverse-biased p-n junction to obtain their high input impedance.   Therefore, both positive and negative gate-source voltages can be used.

The static output characteristics of the junction FET have a region where the curves become almost horizontal, i.e., independent of v_{DS}.   In the case of the MOSFET there is also a region where the slope is small but not as small as in the case of the junction FET.

The transfer characteristics are very similar for the MOSFET and the junction FET.   However, the curves corresponding to different values of v_{DS} are not as close together for the MOSFET because i_D is somewhat more dependent on v_{DS} (see the discussion of the last paragraph).

For the same reason, the constant-current characteristics of the MOSFET are not as close to horizontal as they are for the junction FET. However, the curves for both devices are similar.

The same dynamic parameters are defined for the MOSFET and the junction FET, but there is some difference in the values of the parameters.   The transconductance g_m for the MOSFET varies from 1000 to 30,000 μmhos.   The upper limit is somewhat higher than for a junction FET. The dynamic drain resistance r_d for the MOSFET is less than that of the junction FET.   For the MOSFET, typical values of r_d range from 1000 to 100,000 ohms, while, for the junction FET, r_d varies from 100,000 to 10^6 ohms.

The resistance between the gate and drain or gate and source is higher for the MOSFET—in excess of 10^{14} ohms—while the resistance between gate and source is usually in excess of 10^{10} ohms.   In the junction FET, the values are typically in excess of 10^8 ohms.   All these resistances are extremely large and can usually be ignored, i.e., considered to be open circuits, when they are shunted by external circuit resistances.

3-26 HIGH-FREQUENCY EFFECTS IN THE MOSFET

The high-frequency behavior of the MOSFET is similar to that of the junction FET. In the MOSFET the capacitance between the gate and the channel is not the transition capacitance of the *p-n* junction but the capacitance of two conductors separated by an insulator. However, the capacitance has essentially the same effect for both devices. The representation of Fig. 3-37 is often used to account for the capacitance of a MOSFET.

3-27 THE DUAL-GATE MOSFET

The capacitance C_{gd} in an FET is a particularly troublesome one since it can couple a signal from the output (drain) back to the input (gate). We shall discuss (see Secs. 6-16 and 9-26) how large values of this capacitance can lead to poor high-frequency response and at times to unstable operation. To reduce these effects, the value of C_{gd} should be made small. The FET illustrated in Fig. 3-43 can accomplish this. The channel is divided into two regions, and there are two gates electrically insulated from each other. Usually, gate 2 is biased with a fixed positive potential. In this way, the resistance of channel 2 is kept small. The potential of gate 2 is not allowed

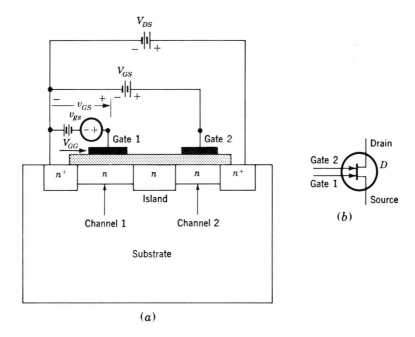

Fig. 3-43 (*a*) A dual-gate MOSFET and (*b*) its symbol.

to vary with the signals.   Thus, there is a conductor, i.e., gate 2 and channel 2, between gate 1 and the drain whose potential remains constant.   This acts as an electrostatic shield and greatly reduces the capacitance from gate 1 to drain.   Typical values of C_{gd} are from 0.005 to 0.02 pf.

The symbol for the dual-gate MOSFET is shown in Fig. 3-43b.

3-28 STRAY CAPACITANCE OF THE DUAL-GATE MOSFET

Just as in the case of the single-gate FET (see Sec. 3-23) there is stray capacitance between all the electrodes of the dual-gate MOSFET.   This is illustrated in Fig. 3-44.   In general, these capacitances become important only at high frequencies.   A large capacitance is usually externally connected between gate 2 and the source in most circuits (see Fig. 3-44).   This capacitor acts essentially as a short circuit at high frequencies.   Therefore, at high frequencies, the source and gate 2 can be considered to be a single electrode.   Thus, in computing capacitance, only three "electrodes" need be considered, the drain, gate 1, and the combined source-gate 2.   Transistor manuals usually take this into account and list only three capacitances, which are analogous to C_{gd}, C_{gs}, and C_{ds} for the single-gate FET.   These are, respectively,

$$C_{gd}$$
$$C_{\text{in}} = C_{gs} + C_{gg2} \tag{3-174a}$$

$$C_{\text{out}} = C_{ds} + C_{dg2} \tag{3-174b}$$

In a dual-gate FET, all other things being equal, C_{in} and C_{out} are larger than C_{gs} and C_{ds} for a single-gate FET.   However, this is completely offset by the fact that C_{gd}, for a dual-gate FET, may be very many times less than it is for a single-gate FET.

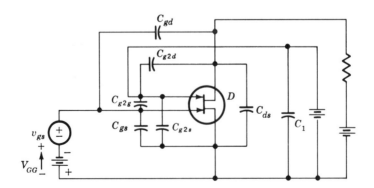

Fig. 3-44 A simple dual-gate-MOSFET amplifier.   The stray capacitances are illustrated.

3-29   RATINGS OF SEMICONDUCTOR DEVICES

To ensure that the device has a reasonable life and operates properly, limitations called *ratings* are imposed upon the voltages, currents, and powers of semiconductor devices.   We shall discuss the various ratings in turn.

Junction-diode ratings   If the temperature of a *p-n* junction becomes too large, the device may operate improperly because too many charge carriers are generated thermally.   Moreover, the excess temperature may actually destroy the device.   The temperature is a function of the power dissipated within a *p-n* junction.   The instantaneous power dissipated within the junction is equal to the product of the voltage across the junction and the current through it

$$p_d = v_b i_b \tag{3-175}$$

The temperature depends upon the average power.   If v_b and i_b vary periodically with period T, then the average power is

$$P_d = \frac{1}{T} \int_0^T v_b i_b \, dt \tag{3-176a}$$

Under quiescent conditions, the average power is given by

$$P_d = V_{bQ} I_{bQ} \tag{3-176b}$$

The maximum permitted average power is specified in semiconductor device manuals.

If Eq. (3-176a) is to be an accurate measure of the temperature, the period T must be short in comparison with the thermal-inertia effects of the junction.   In this case, the temperature of the junction will not fluctuate with the periodic fluctuations in voltages and currents.

The junction voltage can be expressed as a function of the current. Thus, the power can be determined if only the current is known.   For this reason, a maximum current is often specified.

The junction temperature depends not only upon the power dissipated within the junction but also on the means provided to remove the heat. Manufacturers usually specify appropriate means for removing this heat from high-power semiconductor devices.   These will be discussed in greater detail in Sec. 10-8.

If the reverse voltage exceeds the breakdown voltage (see Sec. 3-9), the diode will not function properly.   Thus, the maximum reverse voltage is also specified.   In a rectifier, this maximum reverse voltage is called the *peak inverse voltage*.   Of course, some diodes are designed to operate in the breakdown region.

The ratings for metal-to-semiconductor junction devices are essentially the same as for junction diodes.

Junction-transistor ratings   The power ratings for each p-n junction of a transistor are essentially the same as for a junction diode.   Note that, for usual operation, the emitter and collector currents are almost equal, while the magnitude of the collector-base voltage is very much greater than the emitter-base voltage.   Thus, the power dissipated in the collector-base junction will be very much greater than that dissipated in the emitter-base junction.   Often a rating for the maximum emitter-base-junction power dissipation is not given.

Relations of the form of Eqs. (3-175) and (3-176) can be used to compute the dissipation within the transistor when the appropriate junction current and voltage are used.

The collector-base junction is reverse-biased for normal transistor operation.   This junction voltage should not exceed the value which produces avalanche breakdown.

There is another effect which limits the collector-base voltage.   Increasing magnitude of v_{CB} increases the (reverse-bias) potential across the collector-base junction.   This increases the width of the depletion layer in the base.   If the magnitude of v_{CB} is made large enough, the depletion layer will touch the emitter-base junction's depletion layer.   This effect is called *punch-through* or *reach-through*.   Once punch-through occurs, normal transistor action stops, since the collector and emitter are effectively short-circuited. Thus, the magnitude of v_{CB} must be less than that producing punch-through. The maximum magnitude rating of v_{CB} is specified so that neither avalanche breakdown nor punch-through occurs.   The effect which occurs at the smallest voltage magnitude determines the rating.

The collector current cannot be directly related to the power dissipated within the collector-base junction since the collector voltage is also a function of the input current.   However, a maximum current is, at times, specified. If this is exceeded, then, for usual conditions of operation, the other ratings will be exceeded.

FET ratings   The average power dissipated within the channel of the FET is given by Eqs. (3-175) and (3-176), where the current now is i_D, the drain current, and the voltage is v_{DS}, the drain-to-source voltage.   This average power should be kept below rated values.

If v_{DS} is made too large, avalanche breakdown can occur in the depletion regions of the junction FET and the MOSFET.   This results in an abrupt rise in i_D and improper operation.   Thus, a maximum value of v_{DS} is specified.

If v_{GS} is made too large in a junction FET, avalanche breakdown can occur in the p-n junction between the gate and channel and the FET will no longer have high input impedance; nor will it function properly.   Thus, a maximum v_{GS} is specified.   A maximum v_{GS} is also specified for a MOSFET, since too high voltage will break down the oxide insulating layer.

REFERENCES

1. Sah, C. T., R. N. Noyce, and W. Schockley: Carrier Generation and Recombination in *P-N* Junctions and *P-N* Junction Characteristics, *Proc. IRE*, vol. 45, pp. 1228–1243, 1957.
2. Ebers, J. J., and J. L. Moll: Large-signal Behavior of Junction Transistors, *Proc. IRE*, vol. 42, pp. 1761–1772, 1954.

BIBLIOGRAPHY

Beam, W. R.: "Electronics of Solids," chap. 5, McGraw-Hill Book Company, New York, 1965.

Blatt, F. J.: "Physics of Electronic Conduction in Solids," chap. 9, McGraw-Hill Book Company, New York, 1968.

Chirlian, P. M., and A. H. Zemanian: "Electronics," chaps. 5 and 9, McGraw-Hill Book Company, New York, 1961.

Middlebrook, R. D.: "An Introduction to Junction Transistor Theory," chaps. 6–10, John Wiley & Sons, Inc., New York, 1957.

Millman, J., and C. C. Halkias: "Electronic Devices and Circuits," chaps. 6, 9, and 14, McGraw-Hill Book Company, New York, 1967.

Valdes, L. B.: "The Physical Theory of Transistors," chaps. 14 and 15, McGraw-Hill Book Company, New York, 1961.

van der Ziel, A.: "Solid State Physical Electronics," 2d ed., chaps. 14–16 and 18, Prentice-Hall, Inc., Englewood Cliffs, N.J., 1968.

Wang, S.: "Solid-state Electronics," chap. 6, McGraw-Hill Book Company, New York, 1966.

PROBLEMS

3-1. Discuss the reason for the existence of a depletion layer in a *p-n* junction. Relate it to the rectifying properties of a *p-n* junction.

3-2. In a *p-n* junction, $N_D = N_A = 10^{22}$ atoms per cubic meter, and the energy gap is 1 eV. Compute the value of V_0, the potential across the unbiased junction, at a temperature of 20°C. Assume that the effective mass of the holes and the free electrons is approximately equal to the rest mass of the free electron.

3-3. For an ideal *p-n* junction, a forward bias of 1 volt produces a current of 100 ma at a temperture of 300°K. What current will result if a forward bias of 2 volts is applied at the same temperature?

3-4. For the diode of Prob. 3-3, what is the reverse saturation current?

3-5. Compute the reverse saturation current of the diode of Prob. 3-3 if the temperature is increased to 350°K. Assume that the semiconductor is germanium.

3-6. Repeat Prob. 3-5 but now assume that the semiconductor is silicon.

3-7. The element values of the diode circuit of Fig. 3-7 are $V_{bb} = 2$ volts and $R_L = 100$ ohms. The diode is characterized by the curve of Fig. 3-6. Compute V_b and I_b.

3-8. Repeat Prob. 3-7 but now assume that $V_{bb} = -100$ volts.

3-9. Repeat Prob. 3-7 but now assume that $V_{bb} = -400$ volts.

3-10. Assume that the diode which is characterized by Fig. 3-6 uses germanium as a semiconductor. Draw a new set of characteristics valid for $T = 30°C$.

3-11. In a p-n junction, the difference between the donor and acceptor densities, as a function of position, is given by

$$N_D - N_A = -5 \times 10^{20}x \qquad \text{atoms per cubic meter}$$

When the junction is open-circuited, the potential across it is 0.1 volt. The permittivity of the semiconductor is 16 times that of a vacuum. The area of the junction is 1 mm². If a reverse bias of 5 volts is applied, what is the transition capacitance?

3-12. Determine the expression for the transition capacitance of a junction where the difference between the donor and acceptor densities is given by

$$N_D - N_A = -ux^3 \qquad -\frac{d_1}{2} \leq x \leq \frac{d_1}{2}$$

Assume that the applied potentials are such that the depletion layer lies between $-d_1/2$ and $d_1/2$.

3-13. A reverse-biased p-n junction has a capacitance of 3 pf ($\mu\mu f$). The area of the junction is 1 mm². The permittivity of the semiconductor is 16 times that of a vacuum. What is the total width of the depletion layer?

3-14. A p-n junction has a donor density of $N_D = 10^{18}$ atoms per cubic meter and an acceptor density of $N_A = 10^{19}$ atoms per cubic meter. A reverse bias of 3 volts is applied to the junction. The energy gap of the semiconductor is 1.1 eV. The area of the junction is 1 mm². Compute the transition capacitance and width of the depletion layer. The permittivity of the semiconductor is 16 times that of a vacuum. The temperature is 300°K.

3-15. Show that Eq. (3-49) can be expressed as

$$C_T = A\sqrt{\frac{\epsilon}{2(V_0 - V_b)(\mu_n/\sigma_n + \mu_p/\sigma_p)}}$$

where u_n, μ_p and σ_n, σ_p are the mobility and conductivity of the n-type and p-type regions, respectively.

3-16. Derive an expression for the transition capacitance of an abrupt p-n junction if the doping in the p-type region is much greater than the doping in the n-type region.

3-17. For the junction of Prob. 3-16, obtain an expression for the transition capacitance in terms of the depletion-layer width in the n-type material, the area of the junction, and the permittivity of the semiconductor.

3-18. In a forward-biased p-n junction it is found that at

$$\frac{di_b}{dv_b}\bigg|_{v_b = V_1} = 2 \text{ mhos}$$

the capacitance across the junction is 2 μf (when $V_b = V_1$). The doping of the n-type region is much greater than that of the p-type region. What is the lifetime of the free electrons in the p-type region?

3-19. Derive an expression for diffusion capacitance if $N_A \gg N_D$.

3-20. In a certain p-n junction, $N_A \gg N_D$. The junction is biased so that, in the n-type region,

$$p_n = p_{n0} + P(0)e^{-x/L_{pn}}$$

The average lifetime of the holes in the n-type region is τ_{pn}. The area of the junction is A meters². What is the current through the junction?

3-21. Describe the rectifying action of a metal-to-p-type semiconductor junction.

3-22. Describe the differences between rectifying and nonrectifying metal to semiconductor junctions.

3-23. What type of breakdown is utilized to produce voltage-regulating diodes?

3-24. The diode whose characteristic is given in Fig. 3-6 is to be used in a voltage-regulating circuit. Determine a circuit which will accomplish this.

3-25. An electron whose total energy is 1 eV is released to the left of the barrier of Fig. 3-11a. If $E_0 = 1.1$ eV, what is the probability that the electron can be 10^{-10} meter to the right of $x = 0$?

3-26. Repeat Prob. 3-25 for a distance of 10^{-6} meter.

3-27. Sketch a curve of dynamic resistance versus current for the tunnel diode whose characteristics are given in Fig. 3-13b.

3-28. The tunnel diode whose characteristics are given in Fig. 3-13b is to be used in the circuit of Fig. 3-45. If R_L is small, the operation will be stable; i.e., there is only one

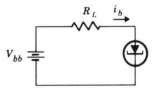

Fig. 3-45

possible solution for I_b for any value of V_{bb}. If R_L is large, this is not true. Demonstrate why this is so.

3-29. Discuss the operation of an n-p-n-junction transistor and draw the potential diagram for it.

3-30. Draw a diagram for a simple transistor amplifier which corresponds to Fig. 3-17 but uses an n-p-n transistor.

3-31. Describe in detail all the components of the hole current and the free-electron current in the base of an n-p-n transistor.

3-32. In a certain p-n-p transistor, when $i_E = 0$ and the collector is strongly reverse-biased, $i_C = -10$ ma. When the emitter current is increased from 0 to 100 μa, i_C becomes -100 μa. What is α for this transistor?

3-33. Obtain an expression for the ratio of the component of emitter current due to holes to the component of emitter current due to free electrons in a p-n-p transistor.

3-34. Express the ratio of Prob. 3-33 in terms of the doping of the base and emitter and any other terms necessary.

3-35. A p-n-p transistor is connected as shown in Fig. 3-17. When $v_{CB} = -10$ volts and $v_{EB} = 0.100$ volt, then $i_C = -2.95$ ma and $i_E = 3.0$ ma. When $v_{CB} = -10$ volts and $v_{EB} = 0.05$ volt, then $i_C = -0.95$ ma and $i_E = 1.0$ ma. Compute the constants c_{11}, c_{12}, c_{21}, and c_{22} of Eq. (3-92). The temperature is 300°K.

3-36. In a p-n-p transistor when v_{CB} is a large negative number and $i_E = 0$, then $i_C = -100$ μa. When v_{CB} is a large negative number and $i_E = 1$ ma, then $i_C = -0.99$ ma. What will i_C be if $v_{CB} = -10$ volts and $i_E = 2$ ma?

3-37. Assume that, in a certain transistor,

$$\frac{D_n}{D_p} \frac{n_{E0}}{p_{B0}} \frac{L_{pB}}{L_{nE}} = 0.01$$

Plot a curve of α versus W/L_{pB}.

3-38. The transistor in Fig. 3-17 is characterized by the curves of Fig. 3-19. If $V_{CC} = -15$ volts, $V_{EB} = 0.15$ volt, $v_{eb} = 0$, and $R_C = 3000$ ohms, find v_{CB} and i_C.

3-39. Determine α for the transistor whose characteristics are given in Fig. 3-19. Assume that α is to be evaluated about $v_{CB} = -10$ volts and $i_E = 3$ ma. Comment on the accuracy of this calculation.

3-40. The transistor of Fig. 3-21 is operated in the circuit of Fig. 3-20, where $V_{CC} = -20$ volts, $R_C = 5000$ ohms, $V_{BB} = -20$ volts and $R_B = 10^6$ ohms, and $v_b = 0$. Compute v_{CE}, i_E, v_{BE}, and i_B.

3-41. The transistor of Prob. 3-40 is now operated so that $v_b = 5 \sin \omega t$ volts. Draw curves of the i_E and v_{CE} as a function of time. What is the current amplification of this circuit, that is, $A_i = i_c/i_e$, where i_c and i_e are the signal components of i_C and i_E, respectively?

3-42. Repeat Prob. 3-40 but now use $V_{BB} = -0.150$ volt and $R_B = 5000$ ohms.

3-43. Determine β for the transistor of Fig. 3-21. Evaluate it about the operating point $V_{CE} = -10$ volts, $i_B = -20$ μa.

3-44. Determine α for the operating point and transistor of Prob. 3-43.

3-45. Why is it often more accurate to determine α using common-emitter characteristics than by using common-base characteristics?

3-46. Using the characteristics of Fig. 3-21, draw the common-collector static characteristics of the transistor.

3-47. Discuss the effect of W/L_{pB} on α_0 and ω_α for a p-n-p transistor.

3-48. Obtain an expression for β_0 and ω_β in terms of the parameters of the semiconductor and the base width.

3-49. If, for a certain transistor, $\alpha_0 = 0.99$ and $\omega_\alpha = 10^8$ Hz, what are β_0 and ω_β? Show that, in general, $\alpha_0\omega_\alpha = \beta_0\omega_\beta$.

3-50. Physically describe why increased base width reduces ω_α.

3-51. Discuss the operation of the n-p-n drift transistor.

3-52. Discuss the operation of the n-p-i-n transistor and sketch the potential distribution for it.

3-53. Describe the operation of the junction FET where the source and drain are n type and the channel is p type.

3-54. For the FET of Fig. 3-30, $b = 10^{-6}$ meter and $N_D = 10^{22}$ atoms per cubic meter. Find the pinch-off voltage v_{GSP}. Use $\epsilon = 1/(36\pi \times 10^9)$.

3-55. For a certain junction FET

$$\frac{a\sigma}{L}\sqrt{\frac{8\epsilon}{eN_D}} = 10^{-3}$$

$V_{GSP} = -10$ volts, and $V_0 = 0.1$ volt. Draw the static output characteristics for this device.

3-56. Explain why Eq. (3-161) is not valid if $V_{DS} - v_{GS} > -V_{GSP}$.

3-57. Discuss why the limitation of Prob. 3-56 does not affect the usefulness of Eq. (3-161) to any great extent.

3-58. The FET of Fig. 3-33 is characterized by the curves of Fig. 3-32. In Fig. 3-33, $V_{DD} = 30$ volts, $R_L = 3000$ ohms, $V_{GG} = -2$ volts, and $v_{gs} = 0.5 \sin \omega t$ volt. Find the quiescent operating point.

3-59. For the FET and circuit of Prob. 3-58, draw curves of i_D, v_{DS}, and v_{GS} versus time. What is the voltage amplification of this circuit?

3-60. Repeat Prob. 3-59 but now use $V_{dd} = 50$ volts, $R_L = 5000$ ohms.

3-61. Repeat Prob. 3-59 but now use $v_{gs} = 2 \sin \omega t$. Compare the distortion with that of Prob. 3-59.

3-62. Draw the transfer characteristics for the FET whose static output characteristics are given in Fig. 3-32.

3-63. Draw the constant-current characteristics for the FET whose static output characteristics are given in Fig. 3-32.

3-64. Find μ, g_m, and r_d for the FET of Fig. 3-32. Use an operating point of $v_{DS} = 20$ volts, $v_{GS} = -1.5$ volts.

3-65. Repeat Prob. 3-64 but now use $v_{GS} = -3.5$ volts.

3-66. Repeat Prob. 3-64 but use the characteristics obtained in Prob. 3-62.

3-67. Compare the operation of a depletion and an enhancement MOSFET.

3-68. Obtain an expression for power dissipation in a *p-n* junction as a function of the applied voltage.

3-69. Repeat Prob. 3-68 but now obtain the expression in terms of the current.

3-70. Compute the power dissipated by the diode of Prob. 3-7.

3-71. Repeat Prob. 3-70 for the diode of Prob. 3-8.

3-72. Compute the power dissipated in the emitter-base junction and in the collector-base junction for the transistor of Prob. 3-38.

3-73. Repeat Prob. 3-72 for the transistor of Prob. 3-40.

3-74. Compute the power dissipated within the FET of Prob. 3-58 if $v_{gs} = 0$.

3-75. Repeat Prob. 3-74 but now do not assume that $v_{gs} = 0$.

4

Integrated-device Principles and Fabrication of Semiconductor Devices

In this chapter we shall discuss the fabrication and principles of semiconductor integrated circuits. These are extremely small circuits that can contain many semiconductor devices and circuit elements. Integrated circuits are used for reducing large complex circuits to smaller sizes and making them much more reliable. They have already found extensive use in such devices as computers, high-fidelity radio receivers, and television receivers.

Many of the techniques for manufacturing integrated circuits resemble or utilize fabrication techniques for ordinary discrete semiconductor devices. These procedures will also be discussed here.

4-1 CRYSTAL GROWING—GROWN AND ALLOYED JUNCTIONS

Most semiconductor fabrications require extremely pure material. One means of achieving this purity is called *zone refining*. Consider that a rod of impure semiconductor material is to be refined. The rod is placed in a crucible, and then only a portion of the rod is heated by a small induction-heater coil. The coil is moved along the rod so that a molten region also moves along with it. It is a characteristic of many materials that the impurities tend to *remain* in the molten portion. Thus, as the molten region moves from one end of the rod to the other, the impurities are "swept" to that end of the rod.

The *ratio* of the concentration of impurities in the solid region to that in the molten region tends to be a constant which is independent of the concentration of the impurity in the solid. This ratio is called the *distribution coefficient* K_d

$$K_d = \frac{C_S}{C_L} \tag{4-1}$$

where C_S is the impurity concentration in the solid and C_L is the impurity concentration in the liquid. If K_d is less than 1, zone refining can be used, since more impurities enter the liquid than remain in the solid.

Often several uniformly spaced heaters are moved along the bar. Normally, repeated passes are made along the bar with the heaters. After each pass, the impurity concentration along most of the bar is reduced. Of course, the impurity concentration increases at the end. If enough repetitions are made, an extremely pure semiconductor results. The impure end of the bar is cut off and discarded.

The pure semiconductor bar is then melted. A single crystal is grown by inserting a small *seed* crystal into the molten mass and then slowly rotating and removing it. The molten material solidifies in such a way that a large single crystal results; i.e., the atoms are arranged in a regular geometric pattern.

If impurities are added before the crystal is *pulled* from the molten mass, which is called a *melt*, a doped semiconductor results.

A simple *p-n* junction can be formed by adding donor impurities to the melt and then pulling part of the crystal. An *n*-type semiconductor results. Before the remainder of the crystal is pulled, acceptor impurities are added in sufficient quantity to override the donors so that the remainder of the crystal will be *p*-type. This type of junction is called a *grown* junction. This procedure, which was formerly common, is no longer used to any great extent.

Similarly uncommon now is another procedure for forming a *p-n* junction based on the fact that the impurity density is at times a function of the rate at which the crystal is pulled from the melt. For instance, the concentration of antimony, which is a donor, increases as the rate of pulling increases. However, the concentration of the acceptor impurity, gallium, is almost independent of the pulling rate. Thus, if both these impurities are added to the melt and the crystal is pulled slowly at first and then faster, a *p-n* junction will result. This is called a *rate-grown p-n junction*.

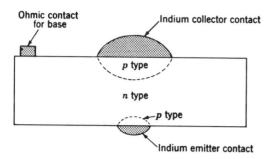

Fig. 4-1   An alloyed junction *p-n-p* transistor.

If these procedures are repeated in reverse order, two *p-n* junctions result.   Thus, a transistor is fabricated (after cutting the resulting *p-n-p* sandwich to the proper size and adding leads).

A crystal fabricated by either of these procedures is usually too large for a single transistor or diode and is cut to form many such devices.   Nonrectifying ohmic contacts are also added (see Sec. 3-8).

Another procedure for forming a *p-n* junction consists of placing a piece of molten impurity on a semimolten semiconductor.   On cooling an alloy is formed.   That is, when the semiconductor recrystallizes, impurity atoms replace some of the semiconductor atoms in the crystal lattice structure.   For instance, in Fig. 4-1, a *p-n-p* transistor is formed by placing molten indium, an acceptor, on an *n*-type semiconductor.   The alloying of the indium results in formation of a *p*-type region.   Doing this twice yields a *p-n-p* transistor.   The indium that remains on the surface is used for electrical contacts.

The techniques discussed here are useful for low-frequency devices.   The diffusion techniques discussed in the next section are used for making high-frequency transistors and integrated networks.

4-2   FABRICATION OF SEMICONDUCTOR DEVICES BY DIFFUSION AND EPITAXIAL GROWTH

A very important technique for doping a semiconductor crystal consists of placing it in a furnace at a high temperature (e.g., 1200°C) with a gaseous atmosphere of the desired impurity.   The impurity will then *diffuse* into the semiconductor.   The diffusion process is used in the fabrication of extremely small integrated circuits and high-frequency transistors with very thin base regions.

Diffusion fabrication usually takes place in an electric furnace whose temperature and atmosphere can be very precisely controlled.   Such a furnace is called a *diffusion furnace*.

The diffusion of atoms into a solid follows the same type of equation as the diffusion of charge carriers in a semiconductor. This resembles the continuity equation [see Eq. (1-218)], which can be simplified, since neither generation, recombination, nor drift occurs in atomic diffusion. Thus, eliminating these terms from Eq. (1-218), we have

$$\frac{\partial N}{\partial t} = D \frac{\partial^2 N}{\partial x^2} \tag{4-2}$$

where N = impurity concentration
  t = time
  x = distance from surface
D is called the *impurity diffusion coefficient*. It is independent of N and x but varies rapidly with temperature.

Equation (4-2) can be solved. We omit details of the solution and just state the results. The solution depends upon the boundary conditions. It is assumed that the concentration of impurity atoms at the surface is maintained at a constant value $N(0)$. Then, solution of Eq. (4-2) for the impurity concentration within the material yields

$$N(x,t) = N(0)\left(1 - \frac{2}{\sqrt{\pi}} \int_0^{x/2\sqrt{Dt}} e^{-y^2}\, dy\right) \tag{4-3}$$

The integral cannot be evaluated in closed form. However, numerical evaluation methods have been used, and the term in parentheses has been tabulated.[1] It is called the *complementary error function* and is written

$$\text{erfc } y = 1 - \frac{2}{\sqrt{\pi}} \int_0^y e^{-y^2}\, dy \tag{4-4}$$

Thus,

$$N(x,t) = N(0) \text{ erfc } \frac{x}{2\sqrt{Dt}} \tag{4-5}$$

A graph of this function is given in Fig. 4-2. Note that x is the distance, in meters, for the surface and t is the length of time the diffusion is allowed to take place. For a fixed t, the impurity density falls off rapidly as distance from the surface increases. Note that by varying $N(0)$ and t, the impurity density can be made any (reasonable) value. As t becomes very long, the impurity density throughout the material approaches $N(0)$.

One procedure for forming a *p-n* junction is to diffuse donor impurities into a *p*-type crystal (or to diffuse acceptor impurities into an *n*-type crystal). The bulk of the crystal will be *p* type. However, the region near the surface will be *n* type, resulting in the desired junction. For instance, consider that a crystal with an acceptor density N_A is placed in a diffusion furnace such that

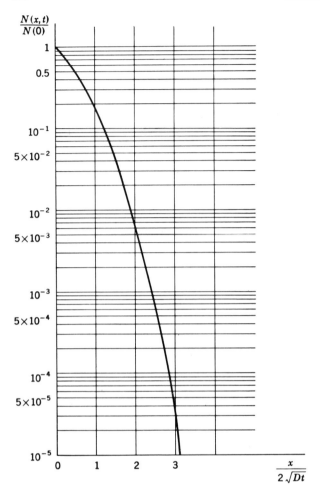

Fig. 4-2   A plot of $N(x,t)$ versus $x/2\sqrt{Dt}$.   Note the semilog axes.

the impurity density at the surface is $N_D(0)$.   After t sec, the net impurity concentration $N_D - N_A$ will have the form shown in Fig. 4-3.   Thus, a p-n junction is formed.   The junction can be said to occur at $x = x_j$ (see Fig. 4-3).

In the preceding discussion we have assumed that the semiconductor crystal is placed in an atmosphere containing the impurities.   The atmosphere is maintained constant, independent of time, and the distribution of Eq. (4-5) results.   This is called *constant-source* diffusion since the impurity concentration at the surface of the semiconductor is held constant.   In another diffusion procedure a fixed *number* of impurity atoms is deposited on

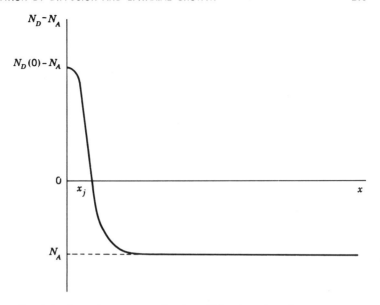

Fig. 4-3 Impurity concentration in a diffused *p-n* junction.

the semiconductor surface, and *then* it is placed in the diffusion furnace. This is called *limited-source* diffusion since the source of impurity atoms is limited to those initially deposited. In this case, the impurity concentration varies as a gaussian distribution. That is,

$$N(x,t) = \frac{N_T}{\sqrt{\pi Dt}} \epsilon^{-x^2/4Dt}$$

where N_T is the total number of impurity atoms per square meter originally deposited on the semiconductor surface.

The impurity diffusion constant D varies rapidly with temperature. Thus, to obtain precise results it is important that the temperature in the diffusion furnace be controlled very acurately.

If a tight-fitting mask with openings cut in it is placed over the semiconductor crystal before it is put in the diffusion furnace, diffusion will take place only through the openings. Thus, the location of the diffusion can be controlled. Actually, the masks are not just placed in contact with the semiconductor but are fabricated from the crystal itself. Silicon (but not all semiconductors) can be used for this, a fact which has led to the development of integrated circuits.

If there is a layer of silicon dioxide, SiO_2, over the silicon crystal, it will prevent the diffusion of certain gaseous impurities. Note that SiO_2 is quartz. If a silicon crystal is placed in an atmosphere containing oxygen and then heated, a layer of SiO_2 will form. The layer must be removed at the points where the diffusion is to take place. Hydrofluoric acid, HF, is used to etch the SiO_2 at the appropriate places. If very many small devices are to be produced in a small crystal, the etching must be very precisely controlled. This is done photographically. A photosensitive substance, such as Kodak *photoresist*, is painted on the SiO_2 layer. The photoresist has two important properties: (1) it is polymerized by exposure to ultraviolet light, and (2) it resists etching by hydrofluoric acid. A large drawing which is exactly to scale is made. The areas where diffusion is to take place are made white and the other areas are made black. A reduced-size negative is then made photographically. Then, using ultraviolet light, the negative image is projected onto the photoresist coating the crystal. Those areas where diffusion is to take place are not exposed to the ultraviolet light and hence not polymerized, while the others are. The photoresist is then washed in a solution which removes only the unpolymerized regions. The entire surface is then placed in hydrofluoric acid, which etches the SiO_2 from areas not protected by photoresist. The photoresist is then removed from the crystal, which is then placed in a diffusion furnace. Impurity diffusion takes place at the areas which are not covered by SiO_2. Finally, the SiO_2 layer is removed.

If it is necessary to diffuse other impurities into any parts of the crystal after the first diffusion has taken place, the crystal can again be placed in an oxygen atmosphere and a new SiO_2 layer formed. The entire process is then repeated.

Let us illustrate this procedure by fabricating a transistor (see Fig. 4-4). First an SiO_2 layer is formed and coated with photoresist. It is then exposed to ultraviolet light, except for a small region in the center. After development, the photoresist remains at all points except for the region in the center (see Fig. 4-4a). The resultant structure is then etched with hydrofluoric acid, which etches the SiO_2 only at the center. After etching, the photoresist layer is removed (see Fig. 4-4b). The crystal is then placed in a diffusion furnace, where donor impurities are diffused (see Fig. 4-4c). The SiO_2 layer is then removed, and a new SiO_2 layer is established. This is coated with photoresist, which is exposed to ultraviolet light except for a very small region at the center. The photoresist layer is then developed (see Fig. 4-4d). Finally, the SiO_2 is etched from this small region, acceptor impurities are diffused, and the SiO_2 is removed. The transistor structure of Fig. 4-4e results. The actual transistor is very thin. For instance, the total thickness of the base and emitter regions is about 4×10^{-6} meter. This transistor is called a *planar-diffused transistor* since all the diffusion takes place from a plane, i.e., the top surface of the transistor.

In order to become a practical transistor, the structure of Fig. 4-4e must have leads attached to it and be physically supported and placed in a case.

The planar-diffused transistor has very good high-frequency response for two reasons: (1) the base width can be made very narrow because of the

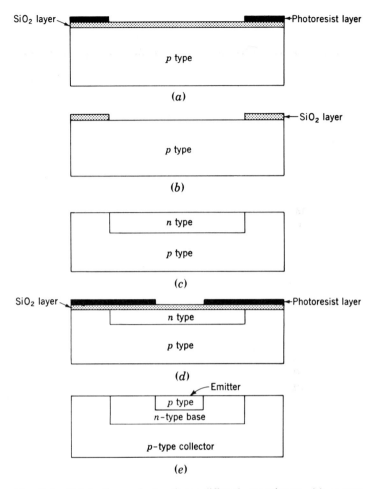

Fig. 4-4 Fabrication of a planar-diffused transistor: (*a*) *p*-type semiconductor with SiO₂ layer formed by oxidation and exposed and developed photoresist layer; (*b*) crystal after SiO₂ layer is etched by hydrofluoric acid and photoresist is removed; (*c*) semiconductor after diffusion of donor impurity and removal of oxide; (*d*) crystal after oxidation and application, exposure, and development of photoresist; (*e*) transistor after etching and final diffusion of acceptor.

precise nature of the diffusion process, and (2) (see Fig. 4-3) the impurity density falls off as distance from the surface increases. Thus, the impurity density in the base, which is produced by diffusion of donors, will be that of a drift transistor (see Sec. 3-19).

There is one drawback to the transistor of Fig. 4-4*e*. The transition capacitance of the collector-base junction is low (see Sec. 3-19) if the impurity density in the collector (as well as in the base) is kept low. However, the series resistance of the bulk of the collector is high if the impurity density is low. This reduces the gain of the transistor. It would be desirable (if the acceptor density near the collector-base *p-n* junction were low) to reduce the transition capacitance. However, the acceptor density should be high in the remainder of the collector to reduce its series resistance. Diffusion techniques cannot be used to accomplish this since impurity density falls off as distance from the surface increases, which is just the opposite of the desired effect.

Another type of fabrication, called *epitaxial growth*, can be used to obtained the desired impurity density. A single heated crystal is placed in a gaseous atmosphere of the element of the crystal itself. The atmosphere condenses on the cooler crystal, often in such a way that a single crystal results. This is called an epitaxially grown crystal. For silicon a somewhat more complex procedure is used. The single silicon crystal is placed in an atmosphere containing silicon tetrachloride, $SiCl_4$, and hydrogen, H_2. At a temperature of 1200°C the hydrogen reacts with the $SiCl_4$ to form pure silicon and hydrogen chloride, HCl. The silicon grows epitaxially on the original crystal.

If donor or acceptor impurities are incorporated into the atmosphere while epitaxial growth is taking place, the epitaxially grown portion of the crystal will be doped.

Let us illustrate a modification of the planar-diffused transistor utilizing epitaxial growth. The *p*-type region (see Fig. 4-4*a*) is formed in the following way. A very highly doped region, labeled p^+, is formed from a melt. Then, a thin, lightly doped region, labeled *p*, is epitaxially grown upon it. The operations of Fig. 4-4 are then performed, and the resultant transistor is shown in Fig. 4-5. Note that the acceptor density in the collector now has the desired structure.

FETs (see Chap. 3) are usually fabricated by diffusion techniques. For instance, the MOSFET diagrammatically illustrated in Fig. 3-40 would have the structure shown in Fig. 4-6. The gate, drain, and channel can be diffused into the substrate. Then further diffusion can be performed at the gate and drain only, forming the n^+ region. Subsequently a layer of SiO_2 is formed and removed only over the center of the source and drain. The remainder of the layer of SiO_2 is *not* removed. Finally, a film of aluminum

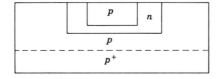

Fig. 4-5 A planar-diffused transistor with a epitaxially grown collector.

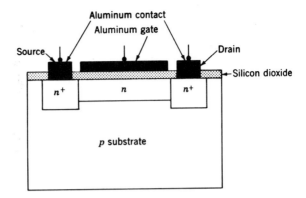

Fig. 4-6 A MOSFET fabricated by diffusion techniques.

is placed over the entire surface using vacuum evaporation (see Sec. 4-5). The aluminum surface is then coated with photoresist. The photoresist is exposed to ultraviolet light at those points where the gate and the contacts for the source and drain are wanted. The photoresist is developed, the aluminum is etched from the surface, and the remaining photoresist is removed. This then establishes the gate and the desired contacts.

In this section we have discussed the fabrication of transistors. Fabrication of diodes will be discussed in the next section.

4-3 MONOLITHIC CIRCUITS CONTAINING TRANSISTORS AND DIODES—ISOLATION TECHNIQUES

We shall now consider a procedure whereby many transistors, diodes [and circuit elements (see Sec. 4-4)] can be fabricated within a single silicon crystal *chip*. These are called *monolithic circuits.*

The procedures of Sec. 4-2 can be used to form many transistors in a single crystal chip, but one modification must be made. Some circuit element must be isolated from the others. Consider the transistor of Fig. 4-4 (or 4-5). The *p*-type region, which forms the collector, could actually be the bulk of the crystal chip. This region has relatively high conductivity. If it is used as the collector of each transistor (or an element of a diode), all the collectors will be effectively connected together. In almost all circuits, this results in improper operation. Thus, a procedure must be developed for isolating the elements in the same substrate.

A fundamental isolation procedure consists of the formation of an additional *p-n* junction, as illustrated in Fig. 4-7. There, two *p-n-p* transistors are incorporated into an *n*-type substrate. An extra *p-n* junction is between the collector and the substrate. The collectors are usually maintained at a large negative potential by an external power supply. Thus, the

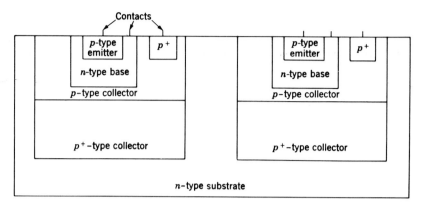

Fig. 4-7 Two transistors integrated in a single crystal. The collector-substrate *p-n* junctions are reverse-biased by an external power supply to provide isolation. Typical lengths for each transistor are 0.005 cm. The diagram is not to scale and is idealized since the actual diffused regions are not as well defined as shown. The collector is usually epitaxially grown.

collector-substrate junction will be reverse-biased. This reverse-biased *p-n* junction has a very high resistance. Thus, the transistors are electrically isolated from the substrate. This is especially true at low frequencies. Note that there is a p^+ region in the collector near the substrate. Called a *buried layer*, it reduces the series resistance of the collector (see Sec. 4-2). At times, this p^+ region is grown epitaxially, and the *p*-type region is epitaxially grown over it. The other p^+ regions are put in each collector to provide a low-resistance contact.

It might appear that a similar technique could be used for isolating diodes; i.e., diodes could be constructed by leaving out the emitters in Fig. 4-7. However, this presents a problem when isolation is considered. For isolation the *p*-type region of the diode must be maintained at a large negative potential with respect to the *n*-type substrate, but circuit requirements may necessitate the *p*-type region to be at a different potential. Thus, the isolation will not work. (Note that in the *p-n-p* transistor the collector is almost always at a negative potential with respect to the substrate, so that this problem does not arise.) A method used to produce diodes consists of fabricating a transistor and then connecting it in such a way that it acts as a diode. Five possible diode configurations are shown in Fig. 4-8. In Fig. 4-8*a*, the collector lead of the transistor is left open, and the emitter-base junction is utilized for the diode. If the "open" collector is connected to a large negative potential, both the collector-base and collector-substrate junctions will be open-circuited, and isolation will be achieved. In Fig. 4-8*b* the emitter is open-circuited, and the collector-base junction is utilized to form the diode. In this case, the collector must be maintained at a large

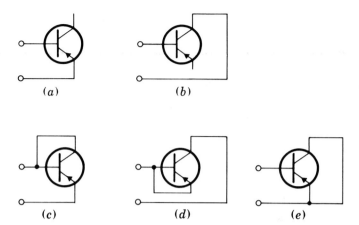

Fig. 4-8 Diodes fabricated from a transistor: (*a*) open collector; (*b*) open emitter; (*c*) collector connected to base; (*d*) emitter connected to base; (*e*) collector connected to emitter.

negative potential.   In Fig. 4-8*c*, the base is short-circuited to the collector, and the emitter-base junction is utilized as the diode.   This diode has lower forward conductance than the other two.   Its pulse response is also better. The circuits of Fig. 4-8*d* and *e* are also possible combinations.   If the circuits of Fig. 4-8*b* to *e* are to be used, the overall circuit requirements must allow the collector (one electrode of the diode) to be connected to a large negative potential.

It may appear costly to fabricate diodes from transistor structures. However, once the photomasks are made, it is no more expensive to diffuse many elements than it is to diffuse only one; e.g., the bases of all the transistors are diffused at one time.   Thus, standard transistor masks can be used to produce the diode.

EPIC isolation   The isolation provided by a reverse-biased *p-n*-junction isolation often is satisfactory, but it has two major drawbacks: (1) an extra power-supply voltage is required to reverse-bias the junction, which can introduce difficulties, and (2) the transition capacitance (see Sec. 3-6) of the junction is relatively high.   This latter effect is very important.   The transition capacitance effectively shunts the high impedance of the reverse-biased junction.   Thus, at high frequencies, the reverse-biased *p-n* junction will not provide good isolation.   To eliminate these disadvantages, another isolation procedure is often used.   Let us consider it and then discuss its production in the monolithic structure.

The isolation technique is shown in Fig. 4-9.   Each circuit element is surrounded by a layer of silicon dioxide.   Thus, in the crystal chip, there are

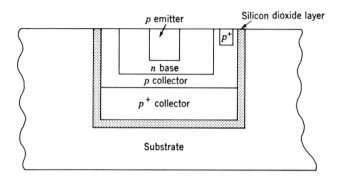

Fig. 4-9 The EPIC isolation procedure. A layer of SiO₂ is used to obtain isolation.

"islands" of single crystals of silicon with each island surrounded by silicon dioxide. Since this is an insulator, it requires no external bias to maintain its high resistance. More important, the capacitance in shunt with the resistance will be that of a capacitor with a SiO₂ dielectric. This will be very much less than the transition capacitance of a *p-n* junction. Thus, the SiO₂ isolation will be effective at high as well as at low frequencies. This isolation procedure, shown in Fig. 4-9, is called the EPIC (*epitaxial passivated isolated circuit*). It has been used extensively by the Motorola Semiconductor Products Corporation.

Let us now consider a procedure whereby many islands isolated by SiO₂ can be produced in a silicon crystal. For simplicity, we shall consider the islands to be *p* type. Actually, they can be the p^+-p type shown in Fig. 4-9.

The first step in the procedure consists of taking a *p* (or p^+-p) crystal and etching grooves in it (see Fig. 4-10*a*), two sets of grooves being etched at right angles to each other. Thus, the surface of the crystal appears like a checkerboard. The surface of the chip is then exposed to heated oxygen, producing the layer of SiO₂ shown. Silicon is now deposited epitaxially on the chip, as shown in Fig. 4-10*b*. This silicon is used only for mechanical support and will be electrically isolated from the circuit. Thus, it need not be a single crystal. Usually a polycrystalline silicon structure results. The resulting wafer is then placed in a lapping machine, which cuts the top off (see Fig. 4-10*c*), resulting in *p*-type islands surrounded by SiO₂, as desired. The lapping procedure must be very precise so that the *p*-type islands have the desired thickness. This is especially true if p^+-p structures are used.

In the example we assumed that all islands were squares of equal area. Actually, the grooves may be cut so that the shapes and sizes of the islands are different.

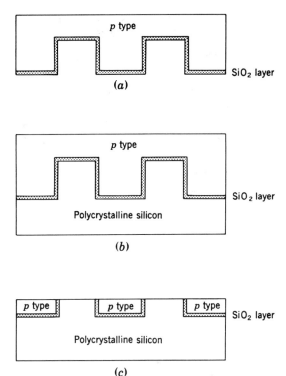

Fig. 4-10 Steps in the EPIC isolation procedure: (a) p-type crystal with etched grooves and SiO_2 layer; (b) polycrystalline substrate added; (c) isolated p-type islands produced by lapping.

Beam-lead isolation Another isolation technique developed by the Bell Telephone Laboratories is called beam-lead isolation. Here the individual elements are fabricated in a single crystal chip with no regard to isolation. The elements are interconnected with relatively heavy leads. The chip is turned over, and the regions between elements are completely etched away, leaving isolated regions which are supported only by the interconnecting leads. The insulating medium between the regions is air. Thus, the leakage resistance is very large and the stray capacitance small.

If the top of the chip has been attached to a glass substrate before etching, then after etching, the isolated islands will have somewhat greater mechanical support than if only the leads are used.

Both the EPIC and beam-lead-isolation procedures require extra steps. If the devices are not to be used at high frequencies, ordinary p-n-junction isolation is often used.

4-4 MONOLITHIC CIRCUITS CONTAINING RESISTANCE, CAPACITANCE, AND INDUCTANCE

Monolithic chips should contain a complete circuit if possible. Thus, besides transistors, FETs, and diodes we may have to add resistors, capacitors, and possibly inductances to the chip. Let us discuss each of these in turn.

Resistors A resistor often consists of a thin slab of doped silicon. It must be isolated from the other elements of the chip by one of the procedures discussed in Sec. 4-3.

Let us determine the resistance of a slab of resistive material such as that shown in Fig. 4-11. The resistance of any regular piece of material is given by

$$R = \frac{\rho L}{A} \tag{4-6}$$

where ρ = resistivity of sample, ohm-meters
L = length of sample, meters
A = cross-sectional area of sample, meters^2
Substituting the dimensions of the square slab of Fig. 4-11, we obtain

$$R = \frac{\rho}{T} \tag{4-7}$$

This is independent of the size of the square. Let us define

$$\rho_s = \frac{\rho}{T} \tag{4-8}$$

The quantity ρ_s is called the *sheet resistivity*. Although its units are ohms, the units are often called *ohms per square* to serve as a reminder of the square sample shape. ρ_s is useful in computing the resistance of resistors made from slabs of the same thickness and resistivity. For instance, if a slab of thickness T is of length l and width w, then

$$R = \frac{\rho_s l}{w} \tag{4-9}$$

Now let us consider the construction and isolation of the resistive

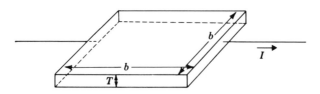

Fig. 4-11 A square slab of resistive material.

elements. A typical resistor is shown in Fig. 4-12. The *n*-type region is added for isolation. It might appear as though the resistor could consist of an *n*-type region in a *p*-type substrated (or vice versa). However, in order to obtain isolation, the potential of the resistor with respect to the substrate would have to be positive. This may require an additional power-supply voltage. Thus, resistors are fabricated in the form of Fig. 4-12. The *n*-type region is maintained at a high positive potential with respect to both the resistor and the substrate. Thus, both *p-n* junctions act as high resistance, and the desired isolation is obtained without restricting the potential of the resistor. Note that the transition capacitance of the junctions reduces the isolation at high frequencies (see Sec. 4-3).

Note that the *p-n-p* structure of Fig. 4-12 forms a transistor, with the substrate acting as the collector and the *n*-type region acting as the base. In a transistor, even if the collector-base junction is strongly reverse-biased, the collector current can be large because of transistor action. To prevent this from occurring, the "emitter-base junction" must also be reverse-biased. Both these junctions will be reverse-biased if the *n*-type region is connected to a large enough positive potential. (The α of this transistor will be low because the base width is large. This aids in keeping the "collector" current low.)

If the EPIC or beam-lead (see Sec. 4-3) isolation procedures are used, the high-frequency isolation will be improved. For instance, in the EPIC process, the resistor would be fabricated in an island isolated by SiO_2.

Resistances from 10 to 50,000 ohms can be obtained using this procedure.

Resistances obtained in this way often occupy much more surface area than transistors, FETs, or diodes; i.e., many more transistors can be included on the chip than resistors. For this reason, resistors are sometimes fabricated using junction transistors or FETs. For instance, the drain-to-source resistance of the FET can be used as a resistance. The resistor can be varied by varying the gate-to-source voltage.

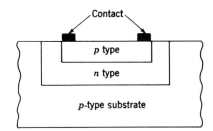

Fig. 4-12 A resistor integrated in a semiconductor chip.

Capacitors A simple capacitor can be fabricated using the transition capacitance of a reverse-biased *p-n* junction (see Fig. 4-13*a*). This is simple, but it has several disadvantages. The reverse bias must be maintained across the capacitor. This may interfere with the external circuitry. The transition capacitance is nonlinear (see Sec. 3-6); i.e., it varies with the applied voltage. Finally, reverse saturation current is through the junction. Thus, the effective shunt resistance of the capacitor, although high, is less than that of other capacitor types.

Any capacitor must be operated at potentials which are less than the dielectric breakdown voltage. In the case of a reverse-biased *p-n* junction, this will be avalanche breakdown.

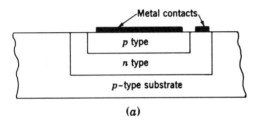

(a)

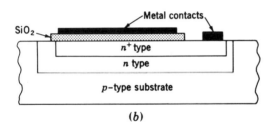

(b)

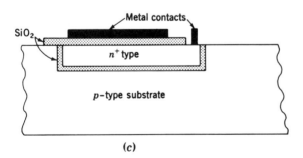

(c)

Fig. 4-13 Integrated capacitors: (*a*) *p-n*-junction type with *p-n*-junction isolation; (*b*) MOS type with *p-n*-junction isolation; (*c*) MOS type with EPIC isolation.

It is often desirable to obtain relatively large capacitance. The capacitance of the junction can be increased by increasing the impurity concentration. However, this also reduces the breakdown voltage. Capacitances on the order of 10^5 pf/cm² can be obtained with breakdown voltages of the order of 5 volts. If the impurity densities are reduced, the breakdown voltage is increased. However, the capacitance is reduced; e.g., an impurity density corresponding to 100 volts breakdown potential yields 1000 pf/cm².

The disadvantages of the *p-n*-junction capacitor are eliminated if the capacitor of Fig. 4-13*b* is used. Here, an n^+ region is produced to obtain a low-resistance slab. A layer of SiO_2 is produced above it, and a metal film is deposited on the SiO_2. The plates of the capacitor consist of the metal film and the n^+ region, and the dielectric is SiO_2. Thus, this is a metal-oxide-silicon (MOS) capacitor. This is a linear capacitor which requires no reverse bias voltage. If the SiO_2 layer is 2000 Å thick, a capacitor of 20,000 pf/cm² with a breakdown voltage of 100 volts is obtained. The capacitance is inversely proportional to the thickness of the SiO_2 layer, while the breakdown potential is directly proportional to this thickness.

The capacitor of Fig. 4-13*b* is isolated from the substrate by a reverse-biased *p-n* junction. Note that the n^+ region is separated from the substrate by a lightly doped *n*-type region to increase the depletion-layer width and reduce the transition capacitance between the capacitor and the substrate.

If very low coupling capacitance between the capacitor and the substrate is desired, the capacitor of Fig. 4-13*b* can be modified to use EPIC isolation, as shown in Fig. 4-13*c*.

Inductors No really satisfactory means for producing integrated inductors has been developed. If high Q inductors, larger than about 5 microhenrys (μh), are required, ordinary inductors are used and connected externally to the silicon chip. The physical size of these inductances is usually extremely large compared with the size of the chip.

The accuracy of fabrication of the integrated components is about 10 percent. However, relative ratios can be maintained between various components to about 3 percent. For instance, if two resistors are to be fabricated and the ratio of their resistances is to be 2 to 1, that ratio can be obtained to 3 percent accuracy while there may be a 10 percent error in the resistances themselves.

4-5 THIN-FILM FABRICATION

Another type of integrated circuit consists of thin films of conductors, insulators, or semiconductors deposited on a nonconducting substrate. In addition, the contacts and conductors required in monolithic silicon circuits, e.g., those which interconnect the transistors, FETs, resistors, and capacitors, are thin conducting films deposited on a layer of SiO_2 covering the substrate. In this section we shall consider procedures for depositing thin films and some circuit elements made from thin films.

Vacuum evaporation When materials are heated to a sufficiently high temperature, they vaporize. If this is done in a vacuum, the material cannot react with oxygen or any other components of the air. In addition, the evaporated molecules travel essentially in straight lines since there are no gas particles for them to collide with. If the pressure of the vacuum system is 10^{-6} torr (1 torr = 1 mm of mercury at standard temperature and pressure) the mean free path of the evaporated molecules will usually be far greater than the dimensions of the vacuum chamber. Thus, most of the evaporated molecules will travel in a straight line until they strike a solid object. A non-conducting plate, called a *substrate*, is placed in the vacuum system in such a way that many of the evaporated molecules strike it. If the substrate is cool enough, the impinging molecules will, on striking the substrate, lose much of their kinetic energy and condense, adhering to the substrate. Thus, a film is deposited. To aid this process the substrate is sometimes cooled with liquid nitrogen, at temperatures of 77°K.

If a *mask*, i.e., a sheet with holes etched in it, is placed between the source of the evaporant and the substrate (very close to the substrate), the deposited film can be made to take on any desired shape and position.

The evaporant is often heated by means of an electric resistance heater. For instance, the evaporant can be placed in a crucible which is heated by a resistance heater. Alternatively, the heater can be a tungsten ribbon where the evaporant is placed in a depression on it. Such a directly heated ribbon is called a *boat*.

Materials with very high boiling points or which would react chemically with the crucible or boat are often heated by bombarding them with a beam of electrons. The energy of the impinging electrons is imparted to the evaporant, which then evaporates.

The techniques of the last two paragraphs are used for evaporation of metallic elements, which may be very good conductors, such as aluminum, or may have relatively high resistances, such as nichrome. In addition, insulators may be evaporated, a typical one used in this process being silicon monoxide, SiO.

Semiconductors can also be evaporated. If the substrate is a single crystal, this procedure can be used for epitaxial growth. Actually, when silicon is deposited, a more complex process is used. Silicon compounds are evaporated. They decompose, and one of the products is pure silicon, which deposits on the substrate.

Cathode sputtering   To evaporate high-melting-point conductors, another technique is sometimes used.   The pressure in the vacuum system is increased to 0.05 to 0.1 torr by the introduction of an inert gas, e.g., argon, in the system.   A metallic electrode is placed in the vacuum system, and a high positive potential is maintained between it and the evaporant.   Thus, the evaporant is the cathode in the electrical system.   The high voltage ionizes the gas.   The positive ions bombard the evaporant and impart energy to it, and sputtering takes place (i.e., the molecules of the cathode leave it).

Gas plating   A heated vapor of a metallic halide often decomposes into the metal and another halogen compound when it strikes a substrate.   This results in the metal's plating on the substrate.

The evaporation procedures discussed in this section are usually used to deposit conductors for contacts of all elements in monolithic silicon devices, for gates of MOSFETs, and for plates of capacitors (see Secs. 4-3 and 4-4).   Conductors are also evaporated onto a SiO_2 layer on top of a monolithic silicon chip to act as interconnecting leads between the various elements.   This will be discussed in Sec. 4-6.

Evaporation is also used to produce or protect circuit elements.   For instance, a relatively high resistance metal such as nichrome can be deposited on a substrate to form a resistance.   In evaporation procedures, a layer of SiO or another insulator is evaporated over the conductors to protect them from oxidation and physical damage.

Capacitors can also be formed by evaporation.   In this case, a metal is evaporated.   Then a layer of SiO is evaporated as an insulator.   Finally, a second conductor is evaporated over the insulator.   If the SiO film is 10,000 Å thick, the capacitance will be about 5000 pf/cm^2.   The breakdown potential will be 0.2 volt for each angstrom of thickness.   At times, cerium fluoride is used as a dielectric since its permittivity is 33.3 times that of SiO.   Hence, the capacitance of a capacitor using cerium fluoride will be 33.3 times that of one of the same dimensions using SiO as an insulator.

If small inductors, i.e., no larger than 5 μh, with Q's no greater than 50 are required, a thin-film procedure can be used.   A special metallic film is deposited on the substrate.   The spiral is the inductor.

Thin-film circuit elements are about an order of magnitude larger than those using monolithic silicon circuits.

4-6   LAYOUT OF COMPLEX MONOLITHIC CIRCUITS

A single silicon chip can contain a great many transistors, diodes, resistors, and capacitors.   Their locations should be such that (1) the chip can be fabricated as conveniently as possible, (2) the various interconnections can be made conveniently, and (3) the electric characteristics are optimized.   Let us consider these effects.

As far as electrical characteristics are concerned, there are two important factors to be considered.   No interconnecting leads have zero impedance.   They all have some resistance and inductance.   The latter is especially important for high-frequency operation.   If there are parts of the circuit where low-impedance interconnections are especially important, they should be placed close together, so that the interconnecting leads can be kept short.

Any two circuit elements will always be coupled, to some degree, by stray capacitance.   If it is important for this coupling to be particularly low between two certain elements, these elements should *not* be placed close together.

The frequency of operation determines the type of isolation to be used between components.   For instance, if only low-frequency operation is required, then *p-n*-junction isolation may be used.   For higher-frequency operation, EPIC or beam-lead isolation (see Sec. 4-3) may have to be used.

Monolithic circuits are often enclosed in a metallic case which physically protects it and shields it from stray electric fields.   Leads are brought out through the case.   The monolithic circuit is connected to these leads.   Thus, it has points on it where external leads are connected.

As a final step in its fabrication, the monolithic chip is coated with a layer of SiO_2, which is then etched from the points on the transistor, FET, diode, and circuit elements where electrical contacts are to be made.   A mask is placed over the chip, and metallic conductors are deposited by evaporation techniques.   These metallic leads interconnect the various components and make connections to the points where the external leads enter.

One important fact should be noted.   There are times when the layout and circuit diagram is such that metallic conductors must cross over each other without being electrically connected.   This is called a *crossover*.   However, if metallic contacts are just deposited crossing each other, they will be connected electrically.   Thus, two parts of the circuit which should not be connected will be short-circuited.   Thus, crossovers must be made in such a way that the conductors are insulated from each other.   One procedure is to place a monolithic resistance at right angles to the place where a conductor is to be deposited.   The resistance of this resistor is made very low.   The resistor is then used as one conductor which crosses under the metallic one.   Since the resistor is under the SiO_2 layer that covers the chip, it is insulated from the conductor which crosses over it.   The area occupied by a resistor is relatively large.   Thus, the layout should minimize the number of crossovers required.

An alternative procedure for producing crossovers is the following.   The first layer of conductor is formed.   Next, SiO is evaporated onto the

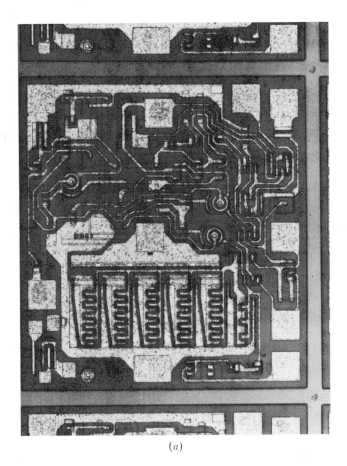

(a)

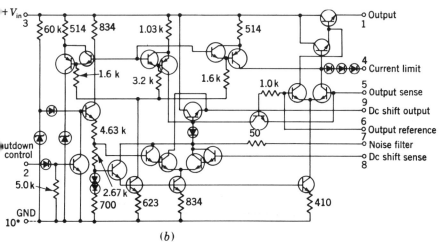

(b)

Fig. 4-14 A MC 1560 voltage regulator circuit. (*a*) Actual monolithic circuit; (*b*) circuit schematic. (*Motorola Semiconductor Products Corporation.*)

substrate. It is then etched from any point where a contact is to be made, but it remains at the crossover points. A second layer of conductors is then formed. The crossovers are thus isolated by the SiO.

Isolation should also be considered when a layout is made. At times, a circuit can be divided into groups of elements such that the isolation between the elements of any one group need not be too high. However, the isolation between elements of different groups must be high. The elements

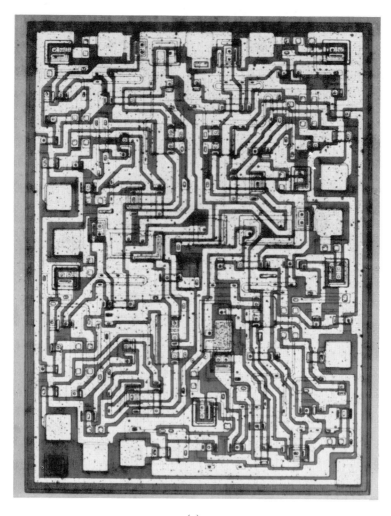

(a)

Fig. 4-15 A MC 938F decade counter. (a) Actual monolithic circuit; (b) circuit schematic. (*Motorola Semiconductor Products Corporation.*)

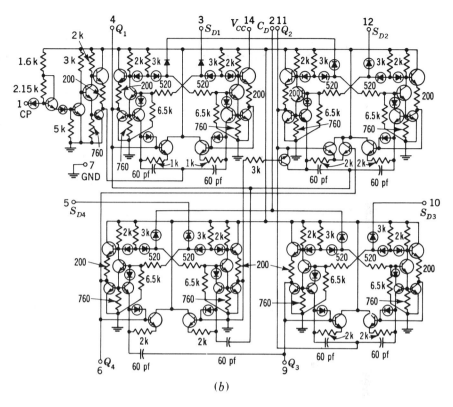

(b)

Fig. 4-15 (*Continued*)

of any one group can use *p-n*-junction isolation while the groups themselves
are isolated using EPIC or beam-lead isolation.   This should be considered
when the structure is laid out.

Let us now consider some actual monolithic circuits.   In Fig. 4-14a a
monolithic crystal is shown, and its schematic is shown in Fig. 4-14b.   This
circuit uses EPIC isolation.   It is placed in a container whose diameter is
0.375 in.   The chip itself is about 0.1 in. long.

Note that the chip of Fig. 4-14a seems to repeat itself, see the top,
bottom, and right edges.   Actually, it does.   Very often, to reduce costs, the
mask arrangement is reproduced photographically so that many identical
monolithic crystals are fabricated in a single relatively large crystal.   These
are then cut apart to form the individual devices.   Thus (see Fig. 4-14a) the
wafer would be cut along the gray lines near the top, bottom, and right side
of the photograph.

Figure 4-14 illustrates a relatively complex circuit.   However, much
more complex ones can be produced in a single monolithic structure.   One
such is shown in Fig. 4-15.

4-7 DISTRIBUTED PARAMETER DEVICES

Sometimes the resistors and capacitors in a monolithic or thin-film circuit are not fabricated as separate lumped elements, like those of Sec. 4-4, but as a single element with distributed resistance and capacitance. These distributed networks have properties which, under certain conditions, are more desirable than the ones which use lumped elements. However, under other circumstances, the lumped elements often result in circuits with more desirable characteristics.

A distributed *RC* element is shown in Fig. 4-16*a*. Note that the *n*-type region has (nonzero) resistance along its entire length. There is also capacitance between it and the metallic conductor along the entire length. A circuit representation for these elements is shown in Fig. 4-16*b*. Note that an infinite number of resistors and capacitors are required to represent the network although a finite representation often approximates it. The symbol for this circuit is shown in Fig. 4-16*c*.

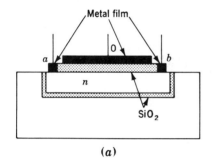

(*a*)

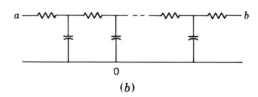

(*b*)

(*c*)

Fig. 4-16 (*a*) A distributed *RC* network; (*b*) an equivalent circuit for this network; (*c*) a symbol for this network.

4-8 THERMAL LIMITATIONS

Integrated electronic techniques can produce circuits in which many elements are incorporated in a very small volume. It may seem as though more and more elements could be put into a given volume as the size of the elements is reduced. However, there is a limit other than size which controls the *packaging density*, i.e., the number of elements per unit volume. Each element dissipates power. Thus, in general, as more and more elements are put into a volume, the power dissipated within it increases. Also, elements at the inner parts of a volume are thermally insulated by the surrounding elements. Thus, as more and more elements are incorporated in a volume, the temperature of the central parts rises. Thus, the maximum operating temperature also limits the number of elements that can be incorporated in a volume. Thus, temperature and power dissipated, as well as the size of the individual elements, limit the number of elements that can be put into a given volume.

As integrated circuits can be made smaller and as cooling techniques improve, the number of elements that can be incorporated into a fixed volume will increase. This will decrease the size and cost and improve the reliability of complex circuits.

REFERENCE

1. Levine, S. N.: "Principles of Solid State Microelectronics," pp. 136–139, Holt, Rinehart and Winston, Inc., New York, 1963.

BIBLIOGRAPHY

Chirlian, P. M.: "Integrated and Active Network Analysis and Synthesis," chap. 2, Prentice-Hall, Inc., Englewood Cliffs, N.J., 1967.
Keonjian, E.: "Microelectronics," chaps. 1, 4, and 5, McGraw-Hill Book Company, New York, 1963.
Levine, S. N.: "Principles of Solid State Microelectronics," chaps. 4 and 5, Holt, Rinehart and Winston, Inc., New York, 1963.
Meyer, C. S., D. K. Lynn, and D. J. Hamilton: "Analysis and Design of Integrated Circuits," chaps. 1 and 2, McGraw-Hill Book Company, New York, 1968.
Millman, J., and C. C. Halkias: "Electronic Devices and Circuits," chap. 15, McGraw-Hill Book Company, New York, 1967.
Schilling, D. L., and C. Belove: "Electronic Circuits: Discrete and Integrated," chap. 9, McGraw-Hill Book Company, New York, 1968.
Warner, R. M., Jr., and J. N. Fordemwalt: "Integrated Circuits," chaps. 11–15, McGraw-Hill Book Company, New York, 1965.

PROBLEMS

4-1. A bar of silicon has a single impurity whose distribution coefficient is 0.01. The silicon is 99 percent pure. A purity of 1 ppm in the first short section of the bar is desired.   How many times would the heater have to be passed over the bar in a zone-refining procedure?

4-2.   Why are several heaters used in a zone-refining procedure?   Illustrate your answer with numbers.

4-3.   Gaseous diffusion is used to dope a pure semiconductor.   Draw four curves on the same set of axes showing the impurity densities within the material.   Normalize with respect to $N(0)$, the surface concentration.   Use $Dt = 10^{-6}, 10^{-3}, 1, 10^3$.

4-4.   Explain each step in the fabrication of the transistor of Fig. 4-4.

4-5.   Repeat Prob. 4-4 for the transistor of Fig. 4-5.

4-6.   Compare the p-n-junction, EPIC, and beam-lead isolation procedures.

4-7.   If EPIC isolation is used, how can the resistance of Fig. 4-12 be simplified?

4-8.   Discuss and compare the capacitors of Fig. 4-13.

4-9.   A resistor is to be made of a rectangular slab of material whose resistance per square is 10^3 ohms.   The resistor is to be 50,000 ohms.   Compute the ratio of length to width of the resistor.

4-10.   The resistance of a material is 1000 ohm-meters.   What is the resistance per square of this resistor if its thickness is 10^{-6} meter?

4-11.   It is desired to fabricate a p-n-junction monolithic capacitance of 1000 pf.   The reverse voltage the capacitor will withstand is 5 volts.   What should the area of the p-n junction be?

4-12.   Repeat Prob. 4-11 for a 100-volt reverse voltage.

4-13.   It is desired to fabricate a MOS monolithic capacitor with a capacitance of 50,000 pf/cm².   What thickness SiO_2 layer should be used?

4-14.   What is the breakdown voltage for the capacitor of Prob. 4-13?

4-15.   Using EPIC isolation for a certain application, the capacitance across the dielectric should be no more than 10 pf/cm².   What is the minimum thickness of the dielectric layer?

4-16.   Describe how crossovers are made in monolithic circuits.

4-17.   Discuss the effects of heat on packaging density in monolithic silicon circuits.

5

Graphical Analysis of Electronic Circuits

In this chapter, we discuss basic graphical procedures for analyzing and designing electronic circuits. These procedures are used to obtain the quiescent operating point of an electronic device and to determine the response of a circuit to a signal which is so large that the *nonlinearities* of the device cannot be ignored. Graphical techniques will be considered here. In Chap. 6 linear analysis of electronic circuits will be discussed.

5-1 RULES FOR NOTATION

Before proceeding with the discussion of graphical analysis, we establish some rules for notation to be used in the remainder of the text.

1. Capital letters will be used for *time-invariant* quantities, e.g., quiescent voltages and currents, effective values of periodically varying voltage and current, and impedance. Lowercase letters will be used for *time-*

varying quantities. A voltage or current that consists of a constant plus a time-varying term will be indicated by a lowercase letter.

2. The current reference direction will be indicated by an arrow. A single subscript will be used to indicate the lead which carries the current. The voltage reference direction will be designated either by an arrow or by plus and minus signs. (Often both types of symbolism are used.) The arrow points from minus to plus; i.e., when the terminal is marked plus or, by the arrowhead, is actually positive, the value of the voltage will be positive. Double-subscript notation will also be used for voltage. The first two subscripts, for example, V_{ab}, indicate the terminals (*a* and *b*) between which the potential is measured. When the first terminal, that is, *a*, is actually positive with respect to the second, the value of the voltage is positive. If the reference node is obvious, the second subscript is often omitted.

Capital *subscripts* will be used for time-varying voltages and currents which contain direct plus alternating components; lowercase *subscripts* will be used for voltages and/or currents which contain only alternating components. For instance, if

$$v_{BE} = V_{BB} + V_1 \sin \omega t \qquad (5\text{-}1a)$$

then

$$v_{be} = V_1 \sin \omega t \qquad (5\text{-}1b)$$

An exception to this rule is the vacuum tube, where it is conventional to use the subscripts *c* and *b* for grid and plate, respectively, when total (direct plus alternating) quantities are considered and the subscripts *g* and *p* (for grid and plate, respectively) for alternating quantities alone.

3. A voltage or current with two subscripts which are the same, for example, V_{BB}, represents a power supply.

4. Additional subscripts may be added to the aforementioned ones. For instance, *Q* may be added to indicate a quiescent voltage or current, for example, V_{BEQ} or I_{BQ}.

5-2 BIASING TECHNIQUES FOR FETs

Graphical procedures are generally used to determine the quiescent operating point of electronic devices. In this chapter we shall consider biasing of FETs, bipolar junction transistors, and vacuum tubes. Since the biasing of the FET is relatively simple and its biasing procedures are similar to those of the vacuum tube, it will be considered first.

A simple FET amplifier is shown in Fig. 3-33. The gate bias is supplied by the power supply V_{GG} while the drain-bias voltage is supplied by V_{DD}. This circuit can be used for both a junction FET and a depletion

MOSFET. It has one drawback. Two power supplies are used. One establishes a positive potential for the drain, and the other establishes a negative one for the gate. To simplify the amplifier, it is usually desirable to use only one power supply.

A circuit which requires only one power supply is shown in Fig. 5-1. Let us analyze it. The drain current i_D is in R_s. Let us assume that the drain current can be written as

$$i_D = I_{DQ} + i_d \qquad (5\text{-}2)$$

where I_{DQ} is the quiescent (direct) component of drain current and i_d is the signal (alternating) component of drain current. For instance, if there is no distortion and

$$v_{gs} = V_{\max} \sin \omega t \qquad (5\text{-}3a)$$

then

$$i_d = I_{\max} \sin \omega t \qquad (5\text{-}3b)$$

The capacitance C_s is chosen such that its reactance is essentially zero at the *signal* frequency. Thus, the voltage across the parallel combination of R_s and C_s will be only the direct voltage $I_{DQ}R_s$. Then, applying Kirchhoff's voltage law around the input loop, we have

$$v_{GS} = -I_{DQ}R_s + v_{gs} \qquad (5\text{-}4)$$

The quiescent (direct) gate bias is then

$$V_{GSQ} = -I_{DQ}R_s \qquad (5\text{-}5)$$

Thus, the negative gate-bias potential has been established using only one power supply.

The capacitance C_s is placed in the circuit to cause the alternating component of voltage across R_s to be essentially zero. If C_s were not present, this alternating voltage would be in phase with the signal generator voltage. Then the alternating component of the gate-to-source voltage would equal the generator voltage *minus* the alternating component of voltage across R_s.

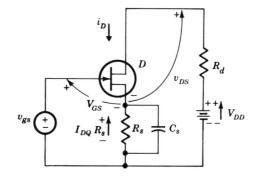

Fig. 5-1 A bias circuit for a junction FET as a depletion MOSFET that requires only one power supply.

Thus, the signal applied between gate and drain would be less than the input signal. Hence, the amplification of the circuit would be reduced. We shall discuss this effect quantitatively in Chaps. 6 and 9.

The bias circuit of Fig. 5-1 is called *self bias*, in contrast to the circuit of Fig. 3-33, which is called *battery* or *power-supply* bias.

Let us determine the operating point of the circuit of Fig. 5-1. We shall assume that the FET is characterized by the output characteristics of Fig. 5-2. In Fig. 5-1 the element values are $V_{DD} = 30$ volts, $R_D = 2000$ ohms, and $R_s = 500$ ohms. The total resistance in series with the power supply is $R_D + R_s$. Thus, the equation for the load line is

$$v_{DS} = V_{DD} - i_D(R_d + R_s) \qquad (5\text{-}6)$$

The intercepts of this load line are V_{DD} and $V_{dd}/(R_d + R_s)$, and its slope is $1/(R_d + R_s)$. The quiescent operating point must lie on this load line. The gate bias is given by Eq. (5-5). A simple procedure for obtaining the quiescent operating point is the following. The intersection of the load line with the curves of the output characteristics (or curves interpolated between

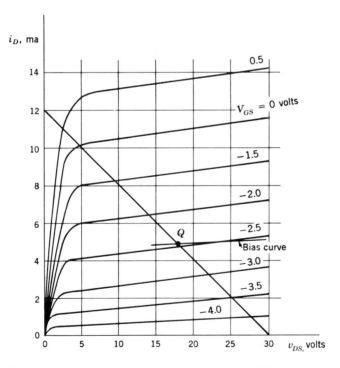

Fig. 5-2 Typical output characteristic of an FET. A bias curve and load line are drawn for the value $V_{DD} = 30$ volts, $R_d = 2000$ ohms, $R_s = 500$ ohms.

them) gives the *possible* values of quiescent operating point (I_{DQ}, V_{DSQ}, and V_{GSQ}). A value of I_{DS} is then substituted into Eq. (5-5). If the calculated value of V_{GSQ} agrees with that obtained from the load line, the correct choice has been made. If the two values of V_{GSQ} do not agree, another choice must be made.

This cut-and-try procedure can be systemized somewhat. Equation (5-5) can be plotted on Fig. 5-2, which is an unconventional plot since only one axis, that is, i_D, and the curves are used. Choose a value of i_D and compute v_{GS} using Eq. (5-5). The intersection of the chosen i_D ordinate with the v_{GS} curve in question generates a point. Repeat this procedure for different values of i_D. This results in a curve, called the *bias curve*. The intersection of the bias curve with the load line determines the quiescent operating point; i.e., the values of I_{DQ} and V_{DSQ} must lie on *both* the bias curve and the load line. This intersection is shown in Fig. 5-2 where the coordinates of the quiescent operating point are $V_{DSQ} = 18.2$ volts, $I_{DQ} = 4.9$ ma, $V_{GSQ} = -2.45$ volts. Note that the drawing of the bias curve is complicated by the fact that the slope of the static output characteristics are so small; i.e., the bias curve of Fig. 5-2 is drawn for values of i_D between 4.8 and 5.2 ma. Thus, a cut-and-try procedure should be used to determine the approximate location of the quiescent operating point. The bias curve is drawn in this region. In general, much interpolation will have to be used.

The analysis procedure just discussed can be simplified if static transfer characteristics are drawn. A typical set for an FET is shown in Fig. 5-3.

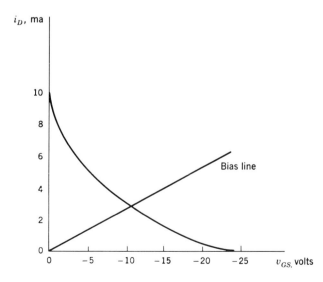

Fig. 5-3 Typical transfer characteristic for an FET. A bias line is drawn.

Note that a set of curves should be drawn for a set of values of v_{DS}. However, since the characteristics are almost independent of drain-to-source voltage, for usual operating voltages, the set of characteristics appears essentially as one characteristic (see the discussion of Fig. 3-35).

Consider Fig. 5-3. When Eq. (5-5) is plotted on the v_{GS}-versus-i_D characteristic, it is a straight line which passes through the origin. It is called the *bias line*, and its slope is $1/R_s$. The values of I_{DQ} and V_{GSQ} must lie on the bias line. In addition, they must also lie on the transfer characteristic. Thus, the intersection of the bias line and transfer characteristic gives the values of V_{GSQ} and I_{DQ}. The value of V_{DSQ} can be obtained from the output characteristic. Note that if all the transfer characteristics (for different values of v_{DS}) do not lie very close together, a cut-and-try procedure would also have to be used here. However, this is usually not the case, and the analysis proceeds without too much tedium.

The engineer is often called upon to design a circuit rather than to analyze it. In this case, the quiescent operating point is specified, usually by some other aspects of the design. The value of R_s must be determined. It can be directly found from Eq. (5-5). For instance, for the FET whose characteristics are given in Fig. 5-2, suppose that the quiescent operating point is chosen as $V_{DSQ} = 20$ volts, $I_{DQ} = 4.8$ ma, $V_{GSQ} = 2.5$ volts. Then, substitution in Eq. (5-5) yields $R_s = 521$ ohms.

In many instances, the input voltage of an amplifier consists of a large direct voltage in addition to the signal. If this direct voltage were applied to the gate, the bias would be improper. To prevent this, the circuit of Fig. 5-4 is used. The capacitor C_c, which is called the *coupling capacitor*, acts as an open circuit for direct voltage but is chosen large enough so that it acts as a short circuit for any signals. Thus, any direct voltage at the input will not affect the gate-bias voltage, but the signal voltage acts as before.

We have assumed that C_c has infinite resistance at zero frequency.

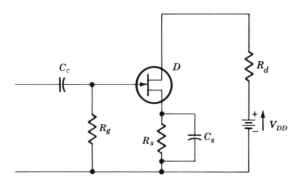

Fig. 5-4 An FET circuit illustrating a coupling capacitor.

Actually, the insulation of any capacitor will not have an infinite resistance. In a high-quality capacitor, this resistance, called the *leakage resistance*, will be of the order of 10^9 to 10^{14} ohms. The input resistance of an FET ranges between 10^8 and 10^{14} ohms. Thus, at zero frequency, a voltage divider is formed by the leakage resistance of C_c and the gate-drain impedance of the FET. If the gate-to-drain resistance of the FET is of the same order of magnitude or is greater than the leakage resistance of C_c, then much of the direct voltage will appear between the gate and drain. For example, if the leakage resistance of C_c and the gate-to-drain impedance are both 10^{10} ohms, then the direct voltage will only be halved by the inclusion of C_c. To eliminate this effect, a resistor R_g is placed in the circuit as shown. If R_g is made much less than the leakage resistance of C_c, for example, 10^6 to 10^7 ohms, then the direct voltage developed across R_g will be very much less than the input direct voltage; e.g., if the leakage resistance of C_c is 10^{10} ohms and R_g is 10^6 ohms, then the direct voltage will be reduced by a factor of 10^4.

Self bias has an advantage which we have not discussed. Such things as temperature changes can cause the characteristics of the FET to alter somewhat. The inclusion of R_s can reduce the effect of this change. Let us assume that, for some reason, the actual FET draws more current than specified (at a specific value of v_{DS} and v_{GS}). If I_{DQ} increases, then $I_{DQ}R_s$ will increase (see Fig. 5-1). This makes V_{GSQ} more negative, which tends to *reduce* I_{DQ}. Thus, I_{DQ} tends to be *stabilized* by the presence of R_s. This stabilization does not occur in the circuit of Fig. 3-33.

In general, the larger R_s, the greater will be the change in v_{GS} with changes in i_D. Thus, larger values of R_s produce more stabilization. Design requirements usually specify the quiescent operating point (I_{DQ}, V_{DSQ}, V_{GSQ}). Thus, if the circuits of Figs. 5-1 or 5-4 are used, the value of R_s is specified [see Eq. (5-5)]. If it is desired to obtain more stabilization by increasing R_s, Fig. 5-4 must be modified. This is done in Fig. 5-5, where the resistors R_{g1} and R_{g2} are added. These resistors can be very large. However (see the discussion of Fig. 5-4), the resistance of R_{g2} in parallel with R_{g1} should be much less than the leakage resistance of C_c. The direct component of voltage across R_{g2} will be

$$V = \frac{V_{DD}R_{g2}}{R_{g1} + R_{g2}} \tag{5-7}$$

This will be a positive (bias) voltage. The quiescent grid bias is then given by

$$V_{GSQ} = -I_{DQ}R_s + \frac{V_{DD}R_{g2}}{R_{g1} + R_{g2}} \tag{5-8}$$

Thus, a larger value of R_s can be used to increase $I_{DQ}R_s$. Since this offsets the positive value of V, a larger value of R_s can be used.

Note that as R_s is increased, the voltage drop across it increases. Thus,

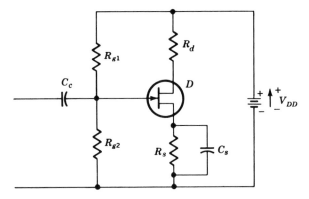

Fig. 5-5 A modification of the circuit of Fig. 5-4 which allows the use of a larger value of R_s.

if I_{DQ}, V_{DQ}, and R_D are unchanged, an increase in R_s (accompanied by an appropriate change in R_{g1} and R_{g2}) requires that the power-supply voltage V_{DD} be increased.   Limitations on V_{DD} often limit the maximum value of R_s.

It should be noted that usually FET amplifier circuits are stable enough so that the circuits of Fig. 5-1 or 5-4 can be used without the modifications of Fig. 5-5.   A quantitative discussion of bias stabilization will be given in the next section.

Biasing the enhancement MOSFET   The bias circuits we have considered are used for junction FETs and depletional MOSFETs.   The resistor R_s produces a negative gate bias.   When an enhancement MOSFET is used, a positive gate bias must be obtained.   There are several circuits which can be used to achieve this.   If the resistor R_s and capacitor C_s of Fig. 5-5 are

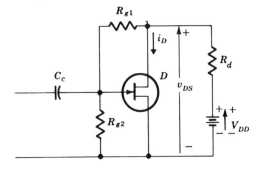

Fig. 5-6 An alternative circuit for biasing an enhancement MOS-FET.

replaced by a short circuit, the quiescent gate-to-drain voltage is given by Eq. (5-7). Thus, the required positive bias is obtained.

The complete circuit of Fig. 5-5 can be used if stabilization is desired. In this case, R_s, R_{g1}, and R_{g2} are adjusted so that the net gate-drain bias voltage is positive.

Another circuit used to bias an enhancement MOSFET is shown in Fig. 5-6. It is similar to Fig. 5-5 except that R_{g1} is connected to the drain rather than to the power supply. If i_D increases, the voltage drop across R_d will increase, reducing v_{DS}. The value of v_{GS} is

$$v_{GS} = v_{DS} \frac{R_{g2}}{R_{g1} + R_{g2}} \tag{5-9}$$

Thus, if i_D increases, then v_{GS} decreases, which tends to decrease i_D. Thus, stabilization is also introduced by the circuit. However, it has the disadvantage that its input impedance is much lower than others we have considered. This will be discussed in Sec. 6-16, where the Miller effect is presented.

Biasing the dual-gate MOSFET The second gate of the dual-gate MOSFET is usually biased with a positive potential. A circuit which accomplishes this is shown in Fig. 5-7. The resistors R_1 and R_2 form a voltage divider, which reduces the battery voltage to the desired bias voltage. The actual bias voltage is the gate 2–to–source voltage. Thus

$$V_{G2SQ} = \frac{V_{DD}R_2}{R_1 + R_2} - I_{DG}R_s$$

The capacitor C_{g2} is usually chosen large enough to act as a short circuit at all frequencies of interest.

Since there is essentially no current into either gate, the bias calculations for the dual-gate MOSFET are essentially the same as for the single-gate FET.

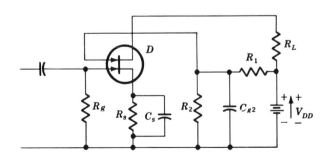

Fig. 5-7 A bias circuit for the dual-gate MOSFET.

5-3   OPERATING-POINT STABILIZATION IN THE FET

The operating point of an FET can change because the temperature of the FET varies.   That is, the current through the FET causes it to heat, which varies the characteristics and makes the operating point shift.   This shift in operating point can result in the FET's operating in an undesirable, e.g., very nonlinear, portion of the characteristic.

Two factors affect the thermal behavior of an FET.   As the temperature T is increased, the atoms of the semiconductor vibrate very rapidly, and this increases the probability of the *majority* carriers being scattered.   This is similar to the discussion of resistance in a conductor (see Sec. 1-18).   Thus, the resistance of the channel is increased, and the drain current is reduced. The second factor affecting the thermal behavior of the FET occurs only in the junction FET.   It is found that the width of the depletion layer decreases as temperature increases.   Thus, the channel becomes wider as T is increased. In the junction FET, both these effects tend to offset each other somewhat. In the MOSFET, only the first effect occurs.   In general, the thermal variation of operating point in an FET is small, and often no special means must be taken to correct it.   However, there are circumstances when temperature stabilization must be performed.

It is most convenient, when designing a stabilizing circuit, to obtain a set of transfer characteristics for the FET for the range of temperature in question.   Either these are obtained from the manufacturer's specifications,

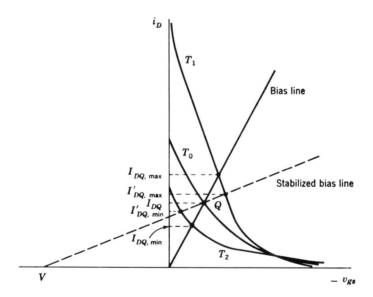

Fig. 5-8   Transfer characteristics versus temperature for an FET.   A bias line and a stabilized bias line are drawn. $T_1 < T_0 < T_2$.

or they are measured. These characteristics should be plotted on a single axis (see Fig. 5-8). Let us assume that the nominal operating temperature is T_0 and that it lies between the extreme temperatures T_1 and T_2. The curves for all the cases may intersect at a point, as shown in Fig. 5-8. *If* the FET is biased to operate at this point, there will be no thermal variation in operating point. However, this operating point may not be the desired one, in which case, the circuit of Fig. 5-5 may have to be used to obtain bias and stabilization. This circuit was discussed in Sec. 5-2. Let us now consider its design.

We shall assume that the point Q of Fig. 5-8 is the desired quiescent operating point. Let us consider at the start that an unstabilized circuit (see Fig. 5-1) is used. In this case, draw a bias line through the origin and point Q (see Fig. 5-2), as in Fig. 5-8. The intersection of the bias line with the curves for T_1 and T_2 gives the maximum and minimum values of I_{DQ} that can result as T varies from T_1 to T_2. If this variation is not excessive, the design is complete. However, if a smaller variation is desired, the circuit of Fig. 5-5 should be used. The equation for the bias line of this circuit, which we call a *stabilized bias line*, is given by Eq. (5-8). That is,

$$V_{GSQ} = -I_{DQ}R_s + V \qquad\qquad (5\text{-}10)$$

where V is given in Eq. (5-7). This is plotted as the dashed line in Fig. 5-8. Now the variation in I_{DQ} is between $I'_{DQ,max}$ and $I'_{DQ,min}$, that is, the intersection of the stabilized bias line with the curves for T_1 and T_2.

To design a stabilized circuit, draw a straight line through point Q which intersects the T_1 and T_2 curves at acceptable values of $I'_{DQ,max}$ and $I'_{DQ,min}$. The intersection with the positive v_{GS} axis yields V. The reciprocal of the slope yields R_s. In general, V_{DD} is known. R_{g2} should be chosen as large as possible (see Sec. 5-2). Then R_{g1} is determined using Eq. (5-7).

If V is larger than V_{DD}, the circuit must be modified. In this case, it may be possible either to increase V_{DD} or to use a separate power supply for the gate bias.

The addition of R_{g1} and R_{g2} will reduce the gain of the circuit somewhat. We shall discuss this in subsequent sections.

Another factor is usually considered when circuits are stabilized. Amplifiers are usually designed on the basis of average characteristics given in manuals. However, the active elements, e.g., FET, depart from these averages. The resistor R_s can be used to stabilize I_{DQ} so that it remains with specified limits, no matter which FET (of *one* given type) is placed in the circuit. Manufacturers usually specify limits on the performance of a device. For instance, the three curves in Fig. 5-8 could represent characteristics for three different devices, all operating at the same temperature. That is, the curve labeled T_0 could represent the average device, and the curves labeled T_1 and T_2 could represent the two extremes. (In such a case, the curves would not intersect but lie one below the other. However, all

other ideas would be the same.)   The design to stabilize the operating point
then proceeds exactly as it did for temperature stabilization.

5-4 BIASING TECHNIQUES FOR THE VACUUM TUBE

The details of biasing a vacuum-tube triode are essentially the same as those
for an FET, and almost all of Sec. 5-2 can be applied to biasing the vacuum-
tube triode.   Let us illustrate this using the typical bias circuit of Fig. 5-9a.
The plate current i_b is in R_k.   The capacitor C_k should be large enough to
act essentially as a short circuit for signal frequencies.   If

$$i_b = I_{bQ} + i_p \tag{5-11}$$

where i_p is the signal (alternating) component of i_b, then the quiescent grid
bias is

$$V_{CQ} = -I_{bQ}R_k \tag{5-12}$$

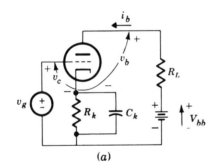

(a)

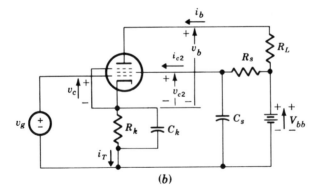

(b)

Fig. 5-9 Bias circuit for vacuum tubes using only one
power supply: (a) vacuum-tube-triode circuit and (b) vacuum-
tube-pentode circuit.

This is analogous to Eq. (5-5). Similarly, all of the discussion of Sec. 5-2 is applicable here, with one exception. When the transfer characteristics for a vacuum-tube triode are drawn, a set of curves corresponding to different values of v_b result (see Fig. 2-13). This is in contrast to the FET, where all the curves fall on the same line. Thus, it is somewhat more complicated to use the transfer characteristics to obtain the operating point for the vacuum-tube triode. Except for this one case, to apply the discussion of Sec. 5-2 to the vacuum-tube triode the drain current is replaced by plate current, the gate-source voltage is replaced by the grid voltage, and the drain-source voltage is replaced by the plate voltage. Note that, in the vacuum tube, it is conventional to refer all voltages to the cathode. Thus, the second subscript k is omitted from the voltages.

A bias circuit for the vacuum-tube pentode is shown in Fig. 5-9b. This circuit provides bias voltage for both the control and screen grids using only one power supply. The cathode current i_T consists of the sum of the plate and screen-grid currents. Thus, in this case, the quiescent control-grid bias is

$$V_{cQ} = -(I_{bQ} + I_{c2Q})R_k \tag{5-13}$$

The screen-grid bias can be found by applying Kirchhoff's voltage law to the screen-grid circuit. This yields

$$V_{c2Q} = V_{bb} - I_{c2Q}R_s - (I_{bQ} + I_{c2Q})R_K \tag{5-14a}$$

or, equivalently, substituting Eq. (5-13), we have

$$V_{c2Q} = V_{bb} + V_{cQ} - I_{c2Q}R_s \tag{5-14b}$$

The capacitor C_s performs a function similar to that of C_k. As the signal voltage v_g varies, the cathode current i_T varies with it. Thus, *both* the plate and screen-grid currents will vary with the signal. Hence the signal components of *both* the plate and screen-grid voltages will be 180° out of phase with the grid voltage (see Sec. 2-5). Since the signal components of the control-grid and screen-grid voltages will be 180° out of phase, these effects oppose each other, which tends to reduce the gain of the amplifier. To prevent this from occurring, C_s is included in the circuit. It should be chosen large enough so that it acts essentially as a short circuit at the signal frequencies. Then the alternating component of the screen-grid voltage will be zero.

The design of the bias circuit is straightforward. The operating point (V_{bQ}, I_{bQ}, V_{cQ}, V_{c2Q}, and I_{c2Q}) and the power-supply voltage V_{bb} are usually determined from some of the design specifications. We shall discuss this further in subsequent chapters. Thus, substitution in Eqs. (5-13) and (5-14) yields the values of R_k and R_s.

The analysis of the circuit of Fig. 5-9b is somewhat more complicated

than that of a vacuum-tube triode or FET.   To obtain the equation for the
load line, we apply Kirchhoff's voltage law to the plate loop.   This yields

$$v_b = V_{bb} - i_b R_L - (i_b + i_{c2})R_K \tag{5-15}$$

A typical set of static characteristics for a vacuum-tube pentode is shown in
Fig. 5-10.   In general, the load line cannot be drawn because i_{c2} is not known.
However, in almost all circumstances,

$$i_{c2}R_K \ll V_{bb} - i_b(R_L + R_K) \tag{5-16}$$

so that Eq. (5-15) can be approximated by

$$v_b = V_{bb} - i_b(R_L + R_K) \tag{5-17}$$

Thus, the load line can be drawn just as in the case of the FET (see Sec. 5-2)
or vacuum-tube triode.

The equation for the quiescent grid bias is

$$V_{cQ} = -(I_{bQ} + I_{c2Q})R_K \tag{5-18}$$

In general, I_{c2Q} *cannot* be neglected in this expression.   However, the grid-
bias curve can be drawn by making the following approximation.   In the
range of operation, i_{c2} is almost independent of v_b (see Fig. 5-10).   Thus, if
v_c is known, i_{c2} can be determined even if v_b is not known.   Note that, in

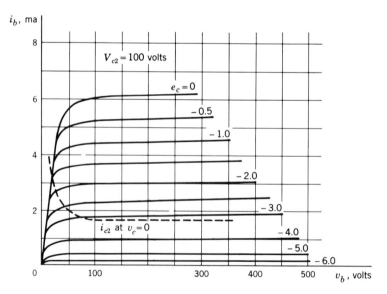

Fig. 5-10 Static output characteristics of a type 5879 vacuum-tube
pentode. (*Radio Corporation of America.*)

Fig. 5-10, only one curve of i_{c2} versus v_b is given for $v_c = 0$. However, curves for other values of v_c can be found by assuming that i_{c2} varies with v_c in the same way that i_b varies with v_c. To draw the bias curve, assume a value of V_{cQ}. A value of I_{c2Q} can then be determined. Substitution of these values into Eq. (5-18) gives the value of I_{bQ}. Then I_{bQ} and V_{cQ} can be plotted as a point on the bias curve. Repeating this procedure, the bias curve can then be constructed. This bias curve is drawn using the procedures of Sec 5-2.

If the quiescent operating point does not lie in the portion of the characteristic where i_{c2} is almost independent of v_b, a tedious cut-and-try procedure must be used [pick an operating point (I_{bQ}, V_{bQ}, I_{c2Q}, V_{cQ}) which lies on the load line and substitute the values into Eq. (5-18); if an equation is actually obtained, the quiescent operating point is correct; otherwise, choose another operating point and try again]. Fortunately, most vacuum-tube pentodes are operated in the region of the characteristic where i_{c2} is independent of v_b.

Just as for the FET, in vacuum-tube circuits the input signal sometimes contains a large direct component which must be prevented from affecting the grid bias. In such cases, the circuit of Fig. 5-11, which is analogous to Fig. 5-4, is used. The resistor R_g, called a *grid-leak resistance*, is included for a reason other than the one given in Sec. 5-2. Some of the electrons which are emitted from the cathode with sufficient energy will strike the grid. If R_g were not present, they would remain there. Thus, as time passed, the grid would acquire a larger and larger negative potential. This would eventually cause the plate current to become almost zero. However, these electrons are allowed to "leak" off the grid and return to the cathode through R_g. The size of R_g must be limited so that the magnitude of the voltage drop caused by this electron flow will be relatively small. Note that this voltage drop produces a negative grid bias.

There is another reason why the resistance of R_g is limited. Positive ions can also strike the grid. The resulting current tends to produce a positive grid bias. Also, some of the emitting material of the cathode may flake off it and adhere to the grid. This low-work-function material will allow electrons to be *emitted from the grid*. This results in an electron flow

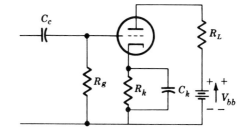

Fig. 5-11 A vacuum-tube circuit illustrating a coupling capacitor and grid-leak resistance.

in R_g, which tends to produce a positive grid bias. In this case, if the positive voltage across R_g is greater than the negative bias produced by R_k, a positive grid bias will actually result. Electrons will then be attracted from the cathode to the grid, causing the grid to be heated (see Sec. 2-12). This heating will result in further emission from the grid (see Sec. 1-20), which can cause the grid bias to become more positive. This phenomenon is cumulative, and the resulting heating can actually destroy the vacuum tube. If R_g is made small enough, the voltage drop across it will be negligible in comparison with that across R_k, so that the grid bias remains negative and this effect will not occur. Thus, the maximum value of R_g is limited. Typical maximum values lie in the range of $\frac{1}{2}$ to 2 megohms.

In general, vacuum tubes are very temperature-stable, and special temperature-stabilizing circuits do not have to be used with them.

5-5 BIASING TECHNIQUES FOR THE JUNCTION TRANSISTOR

A bias circuit for a common-emitter transistor amplifier is shown in Fig. 3-20. This circuit requires two power supplies, V_{CC} and V_{BB}. If, however, V_{BB} is set equal to V_{CC}, their negative terminals can be connected without changing the circuit conditions. Thus, only one power supply need be used. This is illustrated in Fig. 5-12. The analysis of this amplifier was discussed in Sec. 3-16 and will not be repeated here. The reader should review that section at this time. Note that in the example of Sec. 3-16 it was assumed that $V_{BB} = V_{CC} = -15$ volts. Thus, that example is directly applicable to Fig. 5-12 if $V_{CC} = -15$ volts, $R_B = 500,000$ ohms, and $R_C = 3000$ ohms.

Note that (see Sec. 3-16) if

$$|V_{CC}| \gg |V_{BEQ}| \tag{5-19}$$

the quiescent base current can be simply found from the expression

$$I_{BQ} = \frac{V_{CC}}{R_B} \tag{5-20}$$

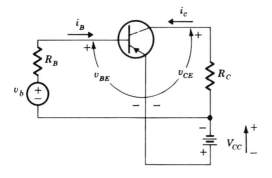

Fig. 5-12 A common-emitter transistor amplifier that requires only one power supply. Note that V_{CC} is defined as a negative number.

In almost all common-emitter transistor amplifier circuits, relation (5-19) is valid and Eq. (5-20) very accurately specifies I_{BQ}. Thus, in designing the circuit, once the quiescent operating point and V_{CC} are determined, R_B can be found using Eq. (5-20).

Usually, the somewhat more complex circuit of Fig. 5-13a is used for a common-emitter amplifier. The reasons for using this circuit will be discussed in the next section. Let us analyze it here. To make it easier we replace the portion of the circuit consisting of V_{CC}, R_{B1}, and R_{B2} by Thévenin's theorem, as shown in Fig. 5-13b, where

$$V = \frac{V_{CC}R_{B2}}{R_{B1} + R_{B2}} \tag{5-21}$$

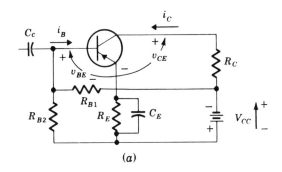

(a)

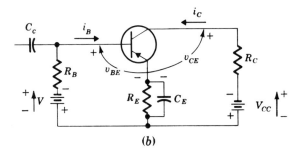

(b)

Fig. 5-13 (a) A commonly used common-emitter transistor amplifier circuit; (b) a circuit equivalent to (a), where $R_B = R_{B1}R_{B2}/(R_{B1} + R_{B2})$ and $V = V_{CC}R_{B2}/(R_{B1} + R_{B2})$. The capacitor C_c is a coupling capacitor which should act as a short circuit for signal frequencies but as an open circuit for direct current.

and

$$R_B = \frac{R_{B1} R_{B2}}{R_{B1} + R_{B2}} \tag{5-22}$$

Then, performing loop analysis, we have, for direct currents and voltages

$$V - v_{BE} = i_B(R_B + R_E) + i_C R_E \tag{5-23a}$$

$$V_{CC} - v_{CE} = i_B R_E + i_C(R_C + R_E) \tag{5-23b}$$

Solving for i_C, we have

$$i_C = \frac{(V_{CC} - v_{CE})(R_B + R_E) - (V - v_{BE})R_E}{R_B R_C + R_B R_E + R_E R_C} \tag{5-24}$$

In almost all circumstances, this equation can be simplified. Usually v_{BE} is a very small number, and we can state that

$$|(V_{CC} - v_{CE})(R_B + R_E) - VR_E| \gg |v_{BE} R_E| \tag{5-25}$$

If this is true, Eq. (5-24) can be written as

$$i_C = \frac{V_{CC}(R_B + R_E) - VR_E}{R_B R_C + R_B R_E + R_E R_C} - \frac{v_{CE}(R_B + R_E)}{R_B R_C + R_B R_E + R_C R_E} \tag{5-26a}$$

or, alternatively,

$$v_{CE} = V_{CC} - \frac{VR_E}{R_B + R_E} - \frac{R_B R_C + R_B R_E + R_C R_E}{R_B + R_E} i_C \tag{5-26b}$$

This equation is of the form

$$v_{CE} = V_1 - i_C R_1 \tag{5-27}$$

where

$$V_1 = V_{CC} - \frac{VR_E}{R_B + R_E} \tag{5-28a}$$

and

$$R_1 = \frac{R_C R_B + R_B R_E + R_C R_E}{R_B + R_E} \tag{5-28b}$$

Thus, the plot of Eqs. (5-26) or Eq. (5-27) on the static output characteristics which are given in Fig. 5-14 is a straight line, where the v_{CE} and i_C intercepts are V_1 and V_1/R_1, respectively. The slope of the straight line is $-1/R_1$.

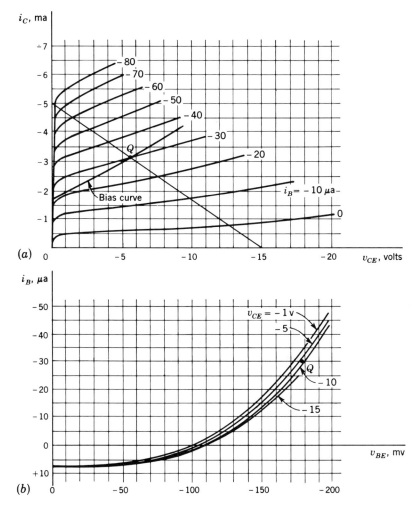

Fig. 5-14 Common-emitter characteristic of a typical *p-n-p*-junction transistor used in the analysis of Fig. 5-13. (*a*) Output characteristic; the bias curve and load line are drawn using the following element values: $V_{CC} = -15$ volts, $R_C = 2000$ ohms, $R_E = 1000$ ohms, $R_{B1} = 328{,}600$ ohms, and $R_{B2} = 511{,}100$ ohms. (*b*) Input characteristic. (*Adapted from D. DeWitt and A. L. Rossoff, "Transistor Electronics." Copyright 1957. McGraw-Hill Book Company. Used by permission.*)

Equation (5-26*b*) is a *load line*. That is, it represents the locus of all possible quiescent operating points. To determine the actual quiescent operating point, we must know i_B. Solving Eqs. (5-23) for i_B, we have

$$i_B = \frac{(V - v_{BE})(R_C + R_E) - (V_{CC} - v_{CE})R_E}{R_B R_C + R_B R_E + R_E R_C} \tag{5-29}$$

Again, for almost all transistor amplifiers, this can be simplified since v_{BE} is very small.   Usually we can write

$$|V(R_C + R_E) - (V_{CC} - v_{CE})R_E| \gg |v_{BE}(R_C + R_E)| \tag{5-30}$$

In this case we have

$$i_B = \frac{V(R_C + R_E) - (V_{CC} - v_{CE})R_E}{R_B R_C + R_B R_E + R_E R_C} \tag{5-31}$$

This can also be plotted on Fig. 5-14a.   This is a *bias curve* and is plotted using the v_{CE} axis and the i_B curves.   It is plotted in essentially the same way as the bias curve of Fig. 5-2.   The intersection of the bias curve with the load line of Eq. (5-26) yields the quiescent operating point.

In almost all cases, relations (5-25) and (5-30) will be satisfied.   If they are not, a cut-and-try procedure must be used.   The input characteristics of Fig. 5-14b are required here.   In this case, we guess at a value of v_{BE} and substitute it into Eqs. (5-26) and (5-29).   Each of these equations now has only two unknowns.   Now plot both of them on the output characteristics of Fig. 5-14a.   Their intersection yields a trial operating point.   Use this and Fig. 5-14b to obtain the value of v_{BE} at the operating point.   If this is equal to the guessed value of v_{BE}, the analysis is complete.   If the two values of v_{BE} do not agree, guess at a new v_{BE} and start again.   Repeat this procedure until the guessed and calculated values agree.   Fortunately, this tedious procedure rarely has to be used.

As an example of this procedure, let us consider that, in Fig. 5-13a, $V_{CC} = 15$ volts, $R_C = 2000$ ohms, $R_E = 1000$ ohms, $R_{B1} = 328,600$ ohms, and $R_{B2} = 511,100$ ohms.   Then $V = -9.13$ volts and $R_B = 200,000$ ohms. Substituting in Eqs. (5-26) and (5-31), we obtain

$$v_{CE} = -14.96 + 2999.5 i_C$$

and

$$v_{CE} = 602,000 i_B + 12.39$$

The resulting load line and bias curve are shown in Fig. 5-14a.   The point Q is the quiescent operating point.

Relations (5-25) and (5-30) are satisfied in this case.   For instance, from Fig. 5-14b, we have $V_{BEQ} = 0.178$ volt.   Substituting in relation (5-30) and manipulating, we have $33.4 \gg 1$.   This indicates an error of about 3 percent, which is well within the accuracy of the graph itself.

We shall discuss (Sec. 9-6) how the overall gain of the amplifier is reduced if a signal voltage appears across R_E. For this reason, C_E is included in Fig. 5-13. It should be made large enough to be essentially a short circuit at signal frequencies.

5-6 OPERATING-POINT STABILIZATION IN THE JUNCTION TRANSISTOR

Some of the parameters of a junction transistor can vary rapidly if the temperature changes. Under certain circumstances this *temperature instability* can cause the operating point to shift to a very nonlinear portion of the characteristic or even cause the transistor to destroy itself. For instance, a rise in temperature can cause the collector current i_C to increase. This can cause the power dissipated within the transistor to increase. This in turn will raise the temperature of the transistor, which further increases the current. This can further increase the power, etc. Thus, the process repeats itself and may result in temperatures high enough to destroy the transistor. This is called *thermal runaway*.

Most of the heating in the transistor occurs at the collector-base junction (see Sec. 3-27). Under quiescent conditions, this is given by $V_{CBQ}I_{CQ}$. The most important effect of the thermal instability is the change in I_C. The transistor parameter which varies very rapidly with a change in temperature is the reverse saturation current, I_{CO} [see Eqs. (3-85) and (3-33)]. It is the change in I_C with I_{CO} that leads to the thermal instability.

A measure of the effect of change of I_{CO} on I_C is the *stability factor S*, where

$$S = \frac{di_C}{di_{CO}} \qquad (5-32)$$

A small value of S implies a high degree of stability, since changes in I_{CO} will not produce a large change in S. S depends not only upon the transistor but also on its associated circuit. We shall demonstrate this with some examples. From Eqs. (3-94), (3-96), and (3-103), we have

$$I_C = -\alpha I_E + I_{CO} \qquad (5-33)$$

Let us consider that the external circuitry maintains I_E constant, independent of temperature. This often occurs in a *common-base* circuit, e.g., Fig. 3-17. In this case

$$S = 1$$

Since $|I_{CO}|$ is usually very much less than $|I_C|$, this is a stable circuit.

The common-emitter amplifier is much more important than the common-base amplifier. Equation (5-20) demonstrates that I_B is usually independent of the parameters of the transistor and hence is independent of I_{CO}. For any transistor,

$$I_E + I_B + I_C = 0 \tag{5-34}$$

Using this equation to eliminate I_E from Eq. (5-33), we obtain

$$I_C = \frac{\alpha}{1 - \alpha} I_B + \frac{1}{1 - \alpha} I_{CO} \tag{5-35}$$

Since I_B is assumed to be independent of I_{CO}, we have

$$S = \frac{1}{1 - \alpha} \tag{5-36a}$$

It is often convenient to express this relation in terms of β [see Eq. (3-123)]. Substituting this equation into Eq. (5-36a), we have

$$S = \beta + 1 \tag{5-36b}$$

This stability factor can be a large number. For instance, if $\alpha = 0.99$, then $S = 100$. Stability factors this large indicate unstable operation. There are several common-emitter amplifier circuits which reduce the stability factor. We shall consider them now.

Operating-point stabilization using an emitter resistance The circuit of Fig. 5-13a is used to reduce the stability factor of the common-emitter amplifier circuit. The effect of R_E is similar to that of R_s in the amplifier of Fig. 5-5 (see Sec. 5-2). Let us determine the stability factor of the circuit of Fig. 5-13a.

It is easier to analyze Fig. 5-13b, which is equivalent to Fig. 5-13a. As we did in Sec. 5.5, we shall assume that the voltage drop v_{BE} can be ignored. Then, writing a loop equation for the left-hand mesh of Fig. 5-13, we have

$$V = I_B R_B + (I_B + I_C) R_E \tag{5-37}$$

Solve this equation for I_B and substitute in Eq. (5-35). This yields

$$I_C = \frac{\alpha V}{(1 - \alpha) R_B + R_E} + \frac{(R_B + R_E) I_{CO}}{(1 - \alpha) R_B + R_E} \tag{5-38}$$

Substituting into Eq. (5-32) and manipulating, we obtain

$$S = \frac{1}{1 - \alpha R_B / (R_B + R_E)} = \frac{\beta + 1}{1 + \beta R_E / (R_B + R_E)} \tag{5-39}$$

The stability factor is less than $1/(1 - \alpha)$, which is S for the unstabilized amplifier. For instance, if $\alpha = 0.99$, $R_E = 1000$ ohms, and $R_B = 9000$ ohms, then $S = 9.17$. Note that S is reduced by increasing R_E and/or reducing R_B. As R_E is increased, the voltage drop across it is increased.

This must be compensated for by increasing $|V_{CC}|$. Thus, practical considerations which limit the size of the power-supply voltage also limit the maximum value of R_E. As R_B is decreased, the gain of the amplifier is decreased. Thus, the minimum size of R_B is also limited. This will be discussed in greater detail in Chap. 9.

Operating-point stabilization using a collector-to-base resistance
Another circuit which can be used to stabilize the common-emitter amplifier circuit is shown in Fig. 5-15. The stabilizing action of this circuit is similar to that of Fig. 5-6. To analyze this circuit quantitatively let us determine I_B

$$I_B = \frac{v_{CE} - v_{BE}}{R_1} \tag{5-40}$$

where

$$R_1 = R_{1a} + R_{1b} \tag{5-41}$$

In general,

$$|v_{CE}| \gg |v_{BE}| \tag{5-42}$$

Thus,

$$I_B = \frac{v_{CE}}{R_1} \tag{5-43}$$

From Fig. 5-15 we have

$$v_{CE} = V_{CC} - (I_B + I_C)R_C \tag{5-44}$$

Substituting this into Eq. (5-43), solving for I_B, substituting I_B into Eq. (5-35), and finally differentiating as in Eq. (5-32), we obtain

$$S = \frac{1}{1 - \alpha R_1/(R_1 + R_C)} = \frac{\beta + 1}{1 + \beta R_C/(R_1 + R_C)} \tag{5-45}$$

Decreasing R_1 and/or increasing R_C will reduce the stability factor.

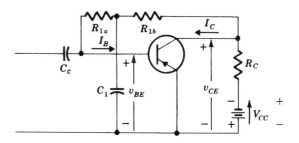

Fig. 5-15 A stabilizing circuit that uses a collector-to-base resistance. Note that V_{CC} is defined as negative.

In general, R_C is fixed by other amplifier requirements. The value of R_1 is fixed by Eq. (5-43) since I_{BQ} and V_{CEQ} are usually specified by other amplifier considerations. Thus, the circuit is somewhat limited in its utility. (It can be made more versatile by adding another resistance from base to emitter, but this reduces the gain of the amplifier.)

The resistance $R_{1a} + R_{1b}$ can feed a signal from the output circuit back to the input. At times, such feedback can be very undesirable. The capacitor C_1 is included to reduce the effect of this feedback. That is, C_1 acts as a short circuit at the signal frequencies and eliminates the feedback. (Note that C_1 does not eliminate low-frequency feedback.) However, now, at the signal frequencies, R_{1a} and R_{1b} will be effectively connected across the input and output of the amplifier, respectively. This will reduce the gain. For the aforementioned reasons, the circuit of Fig. 5-13, rather than this one, is usually used.

To determine the operating point of the circuit (again we assume that v_{BE} is sufficiently small) we modify Eq. (5-44) so that we can draw a load line on the output characteristic. Usually, $|I_C| \gg |I_B|$. Thus, Eq. (5-44) can be written as

$$v_{CE} = V_{CC} - I_C R_C \tag{5-46}$$

Note that this is the usual equation for the load line. The equation for the bias curve, to be plotted on the output characteristic, is given by Eq. (5-43). The details of the analysis will be left to the reader.

5-7 THE GENERALIZED DEVICE AND GENERALIZED CHARACTERISTICS

The graphical analyses of FETs, junction bipolar transistors, and vacuum tubes are often very similar. In fact, at times, they are almost identical. To avoid repetition, we shall now introduce a *generalized representation* that can be applied to any one of these electronic devices. This generalized representation consists of a three-terminal device which can represent an FET, a transistor, or a vacuum tube. (Note that the dual-gate FET is not a three-terminal device. However, second gate potential is often held constant, and then the analysis proceeds as if it had only three terminals.)

Figure 5-16a to c illustrates simple FET, vacuum-tube, and transistor amplifiers. Figure 5-16d is a generalized representation of any one of these circuits. The *generalized device*, i.e., the symbol shown in Fig. 5-16d, can represent any one of the actual devices (FET, transistor, or vacuum tube). The input voltage and current are labeled v_I and i_I respectively. Similarly, the output voltage and current are labeled v_O and i_O. Note that v_O corresponds to v_{DS} in the common-source FET amplifier, to v_b in the common-cathode vacuum-tube amplifier, and to v_{CE} in the common-emitter transistor amplifier.

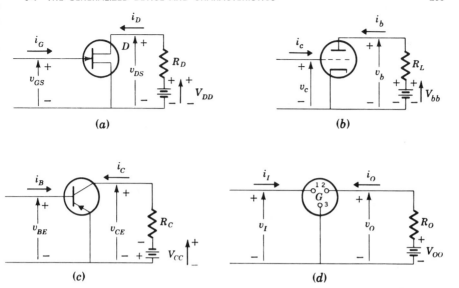

Fig. 5-16 Notation used with the generalized device: (*a*) FET circuit; (*b*) vacuum-tube circuit; (*c*) transistor circuit; (*d*) a generalized-device circuit which is equivalent to these.

Sometimes it is desirable to consider that the input generator of an amplifier circuit is a voltage generator. On the other hand, it is sometimes desirable to consider the input generator as a current generator. For instance, a FET is a voltage-operated device, and the input signal should usually be considered to be a voltage. On the other hand, the bipolar junction transistor is current-operated, and the input signal is often considered to be a current. To represent both types of inputs, the generalized generator symbol shown in Fig. 5-17 is used. The symbol x can represent either a

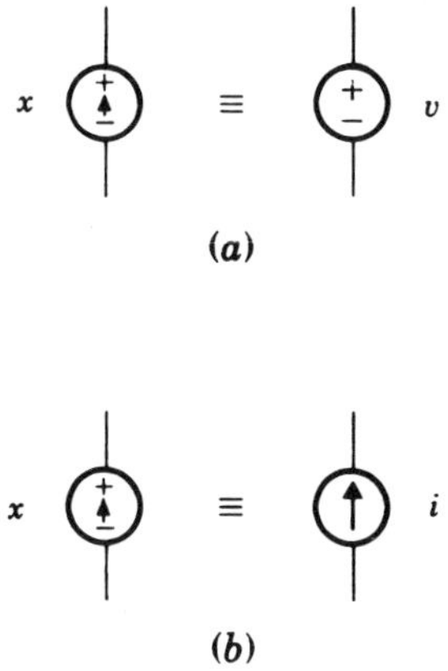

Fig. 5-17 Generalized generator symbols: generalized representation of (*a*) a voltage generator and (*b*) a current generator.

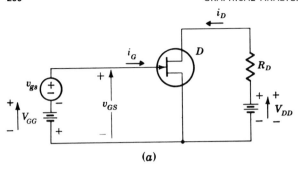

(a)

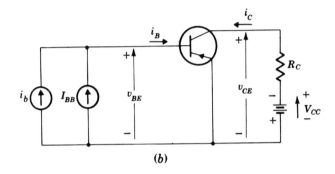

(b)

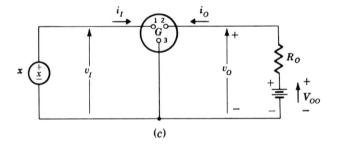

(c)

Fig. 5-18 (a) An FET circuit with voltage-generator input; (b) a transistor circuit with current input; (c) a circuit which is equivalent to (a) if x is a voltage generator, where $x = V_{GG} + v_{gs}$ or a circuit equivalent to (b) if x is a current generator, where $x = I_{BB} + i_b$. Note that I_{BB}, V_{CC}, and V_{GG} are defined as negative.

voltage or a current. When specific circuits are considered, voltage- or current-generator symbols will be used. However, when general discussions of a wide class of circuits are given, the generalized symbol can be used. For instance, Fig. 5-18c could be used to represent either Fig. 5-18a or b. If

Fig. 5-18c represents Fig. 5-18a, the generalized generator is a voltage generator with $x = V_{GG} + v_{gs}$. If Fig. 5-18c is a representation of Fig. 5-18b, the
generalized generator is a current generator with $x = I_{BB} + i_b$.

Introduction of a generalized device may appear to complicate the
situation, but in many circumstances the analysis of circuits containing FETs,
transistors, or vacuum tubes is essentially identical. In this case, the use of
the generalized device and generalized notation can be very convenient.

Usually the voltages and currents in electronic devices comprise a
direct and an alternating part. In generalized notation, the direct (time-
invariant) voltage and current will be represented by capital letters. Time-
varying terms will be represented by lowercase letters. Capital subscripts are

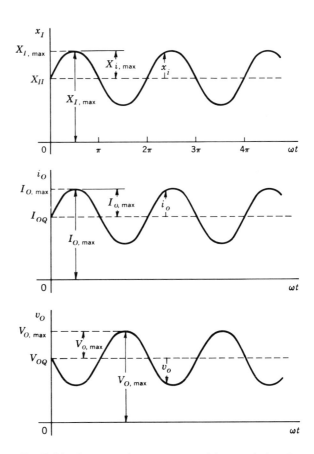

Fig. 5-19 Input and output quantities used in the
generalized device. Note the use of the upper- and
lowercase subscripts corresponding to conventional
notation for the bipolar transistor and the FET.

used for total and direct quantities and lowercase subscripts for alternating (signal) quantities only.   For instance, the output voltage v_O comprises a direct component V_{OQ} and a time-varying portion v_o.   Hence,

$$v_O = V_{OQ} + v_o \qquad (5\text{-}47)$$

The symbols for the voltages and currents of the generalized device are shown in Fig. 5-19.   As an example, let us consider the output voltage. v_O represents the total instantaneous output voltage, v_o is the instantaneous value of the signal portion of the voltage, V_{OA} is the average value of the total output voltage, V_o is the rms value of v_o, the signal component.   The maximum value of the total voltage is $V_{O,\max}$, while $V_{o,\max}$ is the maximum value of v_o, the signal component of v_O.   Remember that the capital subscripts refer to the total voltage (direct plus alternating) or direct alone, while the lowercase subscripts refer to the alternating component only.   This notation corresponds to the rules of Sec. 5-1.

Table 5-1 gives the symbols used in the generalized device and the corresponding symbols for the FET, vacuum tube, and transistor.

A very commonly used set of characteristics is the output characteristics. In Fig. 5-20 a set of generalized output characteristics is drawn, namely, a plot of the output current versus the output voltage with the input quantity as a parameter.   The input quantity x_I represents a current for the transistor and a voltage for the FET or vacuum tube.   Figure 5-20 represents output characteristics for each of the devices.   Note that the shape of the curves is similar to those of a transistor, FET, or vacuum-tube pentode.   Very often the details of the analysis of the FET and vacuum tube are the same; in such

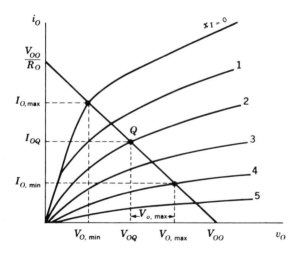

Fig. 5-20 Generalized output characteristic.   A load line is drawn for the circuit of Fig. 5-21.

Table 5-1 Definition of symbols

	Generalized device	Common-source FET amplifier	Common-cathode vacuum-tube amplifier	Common-emitter transistor amplifier
Input quantities:†				
Total instantaneous value	x_I	v_{GS}	v_c	i_B
Quiescent component	X_{IQ}	V_{GSQ}	V_{cQ}	I_{BQ}
Average value	X_{IA}	V_{GSA}	V_{cA}	I_{BA}
Direct input bias supply	X_{II}	V_{GG}	V_{CC}	I_{BB}
Instantaneous alternating component	x_i	v_{gs}	v_g	i_b
Rms value of alternating component	X_i	V_{gs}	V_g	I_b
Peak value of alternating component	$X_{i,\max}$	$V_{gs,\max}$	$V_{g,\max}$	$I_{b,\max}$
Output voltage:				
Total instantaneous voltage	v_O	v_{DS}	v_b	v_{CE}
Quiescent component	V_{OQ}	V_{DSQ}	V_{bQ}	V_{CEQ}
Average value	V_{OA}	V_{DSA}	V_{bA}	V_{CEA}
Direct bias supply	V_{OO}	V_{DD}	V_{bb}	V_{CC}
Instantaneous alternating component	v_o	v_{ds}	v_p	v_{ce}
Rms value of alternating component	V_o	V_{ds}	V_p	V_{ce}
Peak value of alternating component	$V_{o,\max}$	$V_{ds,\max}$	$V_{p,\max}$	$V_{ce,\max}$
Output current:				
Total instantaneous current	i_O	i_D	i_b	i_C
Quiescent component	I_{OQ}	I_{DQ}	I_{bQ}	I_{CQ}
Average value	I_{OA}	I_{DA}	I_{bA}	I_{CA}
Instantaneous alternating component	i_o	i_d	i_p	i_c
Rms value of alternating component	I_o	I_d	I_p	I_c
Peak value of alternating component	$I_{o,\max}$	$I_{d,\max}$	$I_{p,\max}$	$I_{c,\max}$

† In addition, the subscript s may be used in some circuits to designate an input quantity.

269

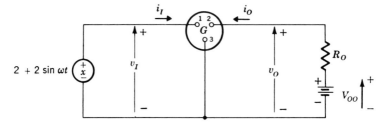

Fig. 5-21 A simple amplifier represented by generalized-device notation.

cases the discussion of the vacuum tube will be omitted. However, if the substitutions *grid* for *gate*, *plate* for *drain*, and *cathode* for *source* are made, the comments will apply to vacuum tubes.

As an example, let us consider the amplifier of Fig. 5-21, which could represent the FET amplifier of Fig. 3-33 or the transistor amplifier of Fig. 3-20 or 3-17.

The equation for the load line is

$$v_O = V_{OO} - i_O R_O \tag{5-48}$$

Thus, its v_O- and i_O-axis intercepts are V_{OO} and V_{OO}/R_O, respectively. The slope of the load line is $-1/R_O$. The quiescent operating point and the maximum and minimum values of the output voltage and current are indicated in Fig. 5-20. The analysis here is identical with that of the amplifiers of Figs. 2-10, 2-19, 3-33, 3-20, and 3-17. The details will be left to the reader.

5-8 AC LOAD LINES

In the previous graphical analyses, we assumed that the load was just a single resistance (see Fig. 5-21), but this is usually not the case. A more typical amplifier is shown in Fig. 5-22. It is called an *RC-coupled amplifier*. Let us analyze it. The coupling capacitor C_c is usually chosen large enough so that

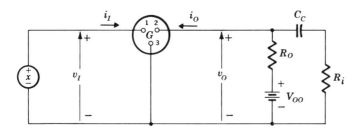

Fig. 5-22 An *RC*-coupled amplifier.

it can be considered to be a short circuit at the signal frequencies.   However, it acts as an open circuit at zero frequency.   Thus, under quiescent (direct) operating conditions, the load is just R_O; that is, the circuit acts in the same way as Fig. 5-21.   However, at signal frequencies C_c acts as a short circuit, and then the load resistance consists of R_O in parallel with R_i.   This load resistance is given by

$$R_{ac} = \frac{R_O R_i}{R_O + R_i} \tag{5-49}$$

Let us assume that the input signal is

$$x_I = X_{II} + 2\Delta x \cos \omega t \tag{5-50}$$

where Δx is a constant.   The generalized output characteristics are shown in Fig. 5-23.   (For convenience, the alternating portion of x_I is chosen to have a maximum value which is a multiple of the increment in values of x_I of Fig. 5-23.)   To determine the quiescent operating point, we consider that C_c acts as an open circuit and that $\Delta x \cos \omega t = 0$.   The load line, then, is just determined by R_O.   That is, its v_O and i_O intercepts are V_{OO} and V_{OO}/R_O, respectively, and its slope is $-1/R_O$.   This is called the *dc load line*, and is illustrated in Fig. 5-23.   The quiescent operating point Q is at the intersection of the dc load line and the characteristic curve corresponding to $x_I = x_{II}$.

Now let us consider that the signal is present.   The locus of the instantaneous value of v_O and i_O is the straight line of slope $-1/R_{ac}$ [see Eq. (5-49)].   This line is called the *ac load line*.   Let us determine its location.

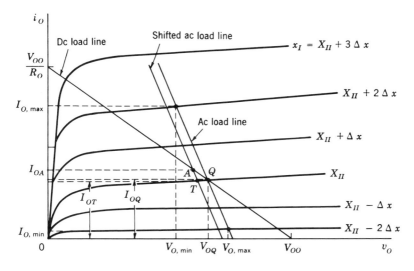

Fig. 5-23 Generalized output characteristics illustrating the graphical analysis of Fig. 5-22.

The average values of v_O and i_O are their direct components. Thus, these average values must lie on the dc load line. Since v_O and i_O are related by R_{ac}, they will have the same waveforms (with the exception of a 180° phase shift which results from the assumed direction of i_O and v_O). Then, at the instant that v_O passes through its average value V_{OA}, i_O will also pass through its average value I_{OA}. Thus, this point (V_{OA}, I_{OA}) must lie on both the ac load line and the dc load line.

For the time being, let us assume that there is no distortion. That is, the characteristics of Fig. 5-23 are straight, parallel, and equally spaced. Then, the output current and voltage will consist of their quiescent values plus sinusoids. Since the average value of a sinusoid is zero, the average value of the voltage and the current will be the quiescent values V_{OQ} and I_{OQ}, respectively. Thus, the dc load line and the ac load line intersect at the quiescent operating point, as shown in Fig. 5-23. Hence, the ac load line is obtained by drawing a line of slope $-1/R_{\mathrm{ac}}$ through the point Q.

The instantaneous operating point is the intersection of the ac load line with the characteristic corresponding to the instantaneous value of the input voltage or current. The input bias varies from $X_{II} + 2\Delta x$ to $X_{II} - 2\Delta x$ [see Eq. (5-50)]. Thus, the output currents and voltages vary from $I_{O,\max}$ to $I_{O,\min}$ and from $V_{O,\max}$ to $V_{O,\min}$ (see Fig. 5-23).

The output characteristics are actually nonlinear. Thus, the variation in v_O and i_O will not be exactly sinusoidal. The waveform is then said to be *distorted*. An example of a distorted waveform is shown in Fig. 5-24. Note that the lower loops of the sinusoid are flattened. The direct component of i_O is its average value. Thus, the average value is no longer I_{OQ} but shifts to the value I_{OA}. (Note that I_{OA} divides the upper and lower portions of the loops of i_O into equal areas.) Since the voltage and current are related by the ac load line, v_O and i_O have the same waveform (except for a 180° phase shift).

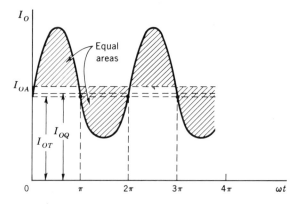

Fig. 5-24 A distorted sinusoidal waveform.

The respective average values of v_O and i_O (V_{OA} and I_{OA}) must lie on both the dc load line and the ac load line. Hence, the ac load line no longer intersects the dc load line at point Q but at point A, whose coordinates are V_{OA} and I_{OA}. Thus, the distortion causes the ac load line to *shift* parallel to itself. Note that it is not necessary for *both* V_{OA} and I_{OA} to be known to determine point A. For instance, if only I_{OA} is known, point A lies on the dc load line where the ordinate is I_{OA}. Values of the output waveform can be obtained from the shifted ac load line in the same way as before. At the instantaneous value of time when the input signal is zero, that is, $\omega t = \pi/2$, $3\pi/2$, $5\pi/2$, . . . the output current is not equal to either I_{OA} or I_{OQ} but to a different value called I_{OT}. This is (see Fig. 5-23) the value of i_O corresponding to the intersection of the shifted ac load line with the characteristic curve for $x_I = x_{II}$. This point is marked T in Fig. 5-23. If there is no distortion, points A and T fall on point Q. Methods of calculating the shift in the ac load line will be given in Sec. 5-10. This shift is often so small that it can be ignored.

For the load lines of Fig. 5-22, the resistance R_{ac} was less than the dc resistance R_O. This is not always the case if other circuits are used. If R_{ac} is greater than the resistance for direct current, then the slope of the ac load line is less negative than that of the dc load line. The procedure for drawing the ac load line and obtaining the output waveform is the same as before.

In the preceding analysis we assumed that the load was purely resistive. For instance, in Fig. 5-22 we assumed that C_c was a short circuit. However, this need not be the case; i.e., the load can have a reactive component. Let us consider this, ignoring distortion for the time being. If the load is purely resistive, the *signal components* of the voltage and current will be 180° out of phase. Thus,

$$v_o = -V_{o,\max} \cos \omega t \qquad\qquad\qquad\qquad (5\text{-}51a)$$

$$i_o = I_{o,\max} \cos \omega t \qquad\qquad\qquad\qquad (5\text{-}51b)$$

These are the parameteric equations of a straight line, which is the ac load line.

If the load is not purely resistive, then v_o and i_o will differ by a phase angle (other than 180°)

$$v_o = -V_{o,\max} \cos \omega t \qquad\qquad\qquad\qquad (5\text{-}52a)$$

$$i_o = I_{o,\max} \cos (\omega t + \theta) \qquad\qquad\qquad\qquad (5\text{-}52b)$$

These are the parametric equations of an ellipse. The load line in this case is an ellipse such as that shown in Fig. 5-25.

When the nonlinearities of the circuit are taken into account, the ellipse becomes distorted. In this case, the procedure for determining the exact location generally becomes too complicated to be useful.

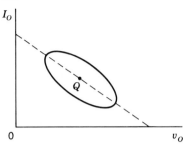

I_O

0 v_O

Fig. 5-25 An elliptical load line produced by a load containing a reactive component.

5-9 GRAPHICAL CALCULATION OF OUTPUT QUANTITIES

Let us now calculate the output voltage, current, and power of an amplifier. In addition, the power dissipated within the active device and other pertinent quantities will be determined. This analysis applies to any circuit characterized by a straight ac load line where the output current is not zero for any part of the cycle. However, to be specific, we shall discuss the circuit of Fig. 5-22. Distortion will be neglected. Assume that the generalized device has the characteristics given in Fig. 5-26 with the ac and dc load lines shown. The input voltage or current is given by

$$x_I = x_{II} + 2\Delta x \cos \omega t \tag{5-53}$$

Then, the maximum, minimum, and quiescent values of the output voltage and current are as shown in Fig. 5-26. Using standard notation for the total voltage and current,

$$v_O = V_{OQ} + v_o \tag{5-54}$$

and

$$I_O = I_{OQ} + i_o \tag{5-55}$$

The signal component of the voltage and current are

$$v_o = -\frac{V_{O,\max} - V_{O,\min}}{2} \cos \omega t = -V_{o,\max} \cos \omega t \tag{5-56}$$

$$i_o = \frac{I_{O,\max} - I_{O,\min}}{2} = I_{o,\max} \cos \omega t \tag{5-57}$$

The effective (rms) values of these quantities are

$$V_o = \frac{V_{O,\max} - V_{O,\min}}{2\sqrt{2}} \tag{5-58}$$

$$I_o = \frac{I_{O,\max} - I_{O,\min}}{2\sqrt{2}} \tag{5-59}$$

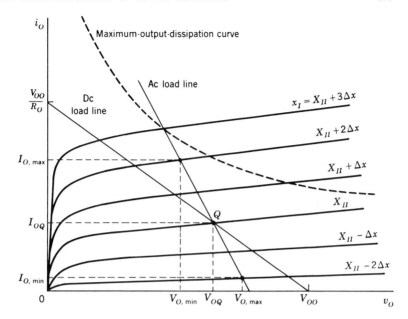

Fig. 5-26 Output characteristics of a generalized device.

Thus, the average signal (alternating) power supplied to the load (in this case R_{ac}) is

$$P_o = \frac{(V_{O,\max} - V_{O,\min})(I_{O,\max} - I_{O,\min})}{8} \tag{5-60}$$

This represents the signal power delivered to the output circuit which is connected to the active device. For example, in Fig. 5-22 it is the signal power dissipated in R_O and R_i.

Now let us determine the power supplied by the power supply V_{OO} of Fig. 5-22. The current through it consists of the entire direct component of i_o, that is, I_{OQ}, and a fraction of the alternating component of i_o, which we call $I_{ac,\max} \cos \omega t$. Thus, the instantaneous power supplied by V_{OO} is

$$p_{OO} = V_{OO}(I_{OQ} + I_{ac,\max} \cos \omega t) \tag{5-61}$$

Hence, the average power supplied by the voltage source is

$$P_{OO} = \frac{1}{2\pi} \int_0^{2\pi} V_{OO}(I_{OQ} + I_{ac,\max} \cos \omega t) \, d\omega t$$

Integrating, we obtain

$$P_{OO} = V_{OO}I_{OQ} \tag{5-62}$$

If there is distortion, I_{OQ} should be replaced by the average value I_{OA}.

The amount of power dissipated in the output portion of a device is called the *device output dissipation*. It corresponds to the power dissipated in the channel of an FET or the collector-base junction dissipation in a transistor or the plate dissipation in a vacuum tube (see Secs. 3-27 and 2-12). As discussed in these sections, the maximum device output dissipation is an important rating of active devices. Let us calculate the actual dissipation. From the law of conservation of energy, the power supplied by V_{OO} must be supplied to the load either as signal power or as direct power or it must be dissipated within the device itself. Thus, under quiescent (zero signal) conditions, the power dissipated within the device is

$$P_{OD} = P_{OO} - I_{OQ}^2 R_O \qquad (5\text{-}63a)$$

This power can also be obtained by taking the product of the quiescent output voltage and current

$$P_{OD} = V_{OQ} I_{OQ} \qquad (5\text{-}63b)$$

When an alternating signal is applied, Eq. (5-63a) must be diminished by P_o, the signal power supplied to the load. In this case

$$P_{OD} = P_{OO} - P_o - I_{OQ}^2 R_O \qquad (5\text{-}64)$$

Thus, for the type of operation considered here, the device's output dissipation decreases as the input signal is increased. In designing most amplifiers, the larger value of dissipation given by Eq. (5-63) is used. For instance, in an audio amplifier, there usually are periods when the output signal is very small (or even zero). Thus, the value of P_{OD} given by Eq. (5-63) is used so that the device's output dissipation does not exceed its rated value during the periods of no or low signal. (Other types of operation where this is not done will be considered in Chaps. 10 and 11.)

If $P_{OD,\max}$ is the maximum *rated* device output dissipation, then [see Eq. (5-63b)]

$$V_{OQ} I_{OQ} \leq P_{OD,\max} \qquad (5\text{-}65)$$

The equation $P_{OD,\max} = v_O i_O$ defines a hyperbola on the device output characteristics (see Fig. 5-26). The quiescent operating point should be chosen to lie below the hyperbola.

Another related quantity is the *output circuit efficiency*, defined as the ratio of the signal power supplied to the load to the total power supplied by the power supply. It is given by

$$\eta = \frac{(V_{O,\max} - V_{O,\min})(I_{O,\max} - I_{O,\min})}{8 P_{OO} I_{OQ}} \times 100\% \qquad (5\text{-}66)$$

This is a measure of the efficiency of the amplifier.

5-10 NONLINEAR DISTORTION

When the characteristics of the active device of an amplifier are nonlinear, the output signal waveform will not be the same shape as the input signal waveform. This is called *nonlinear distortion* or *amplitude distortion*. Another type of distortion, caused by variations of the parameters of the circuit with frequency, will be discussed in Sec. 8-7.

In analyzing the nonlinear distortion, we shall assume at the start that the input signal is of the form

$$x_i = X_{i,\max} \cos \omega t \tag{5-67}$$

We shall also assume that the load is purely resistive. The output waveform will then be periodic and symmetric about its peak value, i.e., the value that occurs when $\omega t = 0$. Such a waveform can be represented by a Fourier cosine series

$$i_o = i_{OA} + \sqrt{2}(I_{o1} \cos \omega t + I_{o2} \cos 2\omega t + I_{o3} \cos 3\omega t + \cdots) \tag{5-68}$$

where I_{OA} is the average value of i_O and I_{ok} is the effective (rms) value of the kth harmonic.

We shall perform a graphical analysis to determine the values of I_{OA} and $I_{o1}, I_{o2}, \ldots$ (note that if there is no distortion, $I_{OA} = I_{OQ}$ and all the harmonics $I_{o2}, I_{o3}, \ldots$ are zero). At first, let us assume that the location of the ac load line is known. It is shown in the output characteristics of Fig. 5-27.

In general, the Fourier series of Eq. (5-68) has an infinite number of terms. However, it often can be approximated accurately using only a finite number of them. In this case, a simple graphical procedure can be used to obtain the unknowns ($I_{OA}, I_{o1}, I_{o2}, \ldots$). To illustrate this procedure, we shall assume that i_O can be represented by a constant term, the fundamental, and the second harmonic. (Since this is usually not enough, except possibly for the vacuum-tube triode, we shall extend this analysis subsequently.) Thus,

$$i_O = I_{OA} = \sqrt{2}(I_{o1} \cos \omega t + I_{o2} \cos 2\omega t) \tag{5-69}$$

There are three unknowns. Let us obtain three simultaneous equations that can be solved for them. We assume that the input signal is of the form

$$x_I = X_{II} + 2\Delta x \cos \omega t \tag{5-70}$$

where the bias X_{II} and the peak value of the input signal $2\Delta x$ are known quantities. Now choose three values of ωt. Substitution of these values in Eq. (5-70) yields three values of x_I. Then, using Fig. 5-27, the three values of i_O corresponding to each of the values of x_I can be determined. Substitution of each pair of i_O and ωt in turn into Eq. (5-69) yields the required three

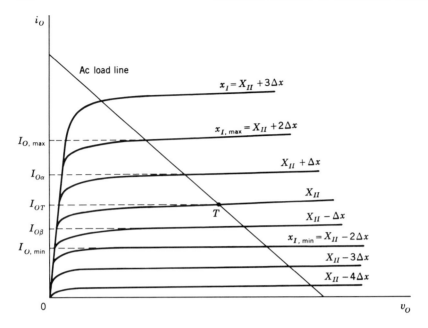

Fig. 5-27 Generalized output characteristics showing the points used in the calculation of the harmonic distortion.

simultaneous equations. Let us choose the three values of ωt to be 0, $\pi/2$, and π. Then, at $\omega t = 0$

$$x_I = X_{II} + 2\,\Delta x$$
$$i_O = I_{O,\text{max}} = I_{OA} + \sqrt{2}(I_{o1} + I_{o2}) \tag{5-71}$$

at $\omega t = \pi/2$

$$x_I = X_{II}$$
$$i_O = I_{OT} = I_{OA} + \sqrt{2}(0I_{o1} - I_{o2}) \tag{5-72}$$

and at $\omega t = \pi$

$$x_I = X_{II} - 2\,\Delta x$$
$$i_O = I_{O,\text{min}} = I_{OA} + \sqrt{2}(-I_{o1} + I_{o2}) \tag{5-73}$$

Solving Eqs. (5-71) to (5-73) for the unknowns, we obtain

$$I_{OA} = \frac{I_{O,\text{max}} + I_{O,\text{min}}}{4} + \frac{I_{OT}}{2} \tag{5-74a}$$

$$\sqrt{2}I_{o1} = \frac{I_{O,\text{max}} - I_{O,\text{min}}}{2} \tag{5-74b}$$

$$\sqrt{2}I_{o2} = \frac{I_{O,\text{max}} + I_{O,\text{min}}}{4} - \frac{I_{OT}}{2} \tag{5-74c}$$

This analysis assumed that the position of the ac load line was known. However, to draw it, I_{OA} must be known, and calculation of I_{OA} requires the use of the ac load line. To determine these quantities, a cut-and-try procedure is used. Draw the ac load line, neglecting distortion, i.e., draw it through the quiescent operating point (see Sec. 5-8). Then use Eq. (5-74a) to determine I_{OA}. If this differs substantially from I_{OQ}, draw a new ac load line using the calculated value of I_{OA} (see Sec. 5-8). Use this new load line and Eq. (5-74a) to calculate a new I_{OA} and see if it agrees with the I_{OA} used. If it does not, draw a new load line using the new I_{OA}. Repeat this procedure until the assumed and calculated value of I_{OA} agree. In most instances, the shift in the operating point is so small that we can assume that $I_{OA} = I_{OQ}$ or only one trial value of I_{OA} is needed.

If there is a resistor in series with the source of an FET or the cathode of a vacuum tube or the emitter of a transistor, then a shift in I_{OA} will change the input bias. This should be considered when the instantaneous operating points are determined.

In most cases, Eq. (5-69) is not accurate enough, and we must consider the higher-order harmonics. Let us assume that the first four terms are the important ones (usually this is sufficiently accurate). Then we write

$$i_O = I_{OA} + \sqrt{2}(I_{o1} \cos \omega t + I_{o2} \cos 2\omega t + I_{o3} \cos 3\omega t + I_{o4} \cos 4\omega t)$$

$$(5\text{-}75)$$

Five simultaneous equations are now required. We shall use the values of $\omega t = 0$, $\pi/3$, $\pi/2$, $2\pi/3$, and π. Corresponding to these we have, for x_i [see Eq. (5-70)] $X_{II} + 2 \Delta x$, $X_{II} + \Delta x$, X_{II}, $X_{II} - \Delta x$, and $X_{II} - 2 \Delta x$ and (see Fig. 5-27) for i_O: $I_{o,\max}$, $I_{o\alpha}$, I_{oT}, $I_{o\beta}$, and $I_{o,\min}$, respectively. [Note that if the magnitude of the signal is different from Eq. (5-70), then $2 \Delta x$ should be replaced by $X_{i,\max}$, the maximum value of the signal, etc.] If we substitute each pair of these values of i_O and ωt into Eq. (5-75) in turn, five simultaneous equations are obtained. Solving these, we have

$$I_{OA} = \frac{I_{o,\max} + I_{o,\min}}{6} + \frac{I_{o\alpha} + I_{o\beta}}{3} \tag{5-76a}$$

$$\sqrt{2}I_{o1} = \frac{I_{o,\max} - I_{o,\min}}{3} + \frac{I_{o\alpha} - I_{o\beta}}{3} \tag{5-76b}$$

$$\sqrt{2}I_{o2} = \frac{I_{o,\max} + I_{o,\min}}{4} - \frac{I_{oT}}{2} \tag{5-76c}$$

$$\sqrt{2}I_{o3} = \frac{I_{o,\max} - I_{o,\min}}{6} - \frac{I_{o\alpha} - I_{o\beta}}{3} \tag{5-76d}$$

$$\sqrt{2}I_{o4} = \frac{I_{o,\max} + I_{o,\min}}{12} - \frac{I_{o\alpha} + I_{o\beta}}{3} + \frac{I_{oT}}{2} \tag{5-76e}$$

Note that the expressions for I_{oA} and I_{o1} in Eqs. (5-76) and (5-74) are different because different assumptions, i.e., Eqs. (5-69) and (5-75), were used in deriving the equations. Both Eqs. (5-76) and (5-74) are approximate. Equations (5-76) are, in general, more accurate since more harmonics were assumed in deriving them.

Harmonic distortion is often used as one measure of the quality of a high-fidelity amplifier. It should be as low as possible. A good measure of the distortion is the *ratio* of the harmonics to the fundamental. The percent *harmonic distortion* for the second, third, and fourth harmonic is

$$D_2 = \left| \frac{I_{o2}}{I_{o1}} \right| \times 100\% \tag{5-77a}$$

$$D_3 = \left| \frac{I_{o3}}{I_{o1}} \right| \times 100\% \tag{5-77b}$$

$$D_4 = \left| \frac{I_{o4}}{I_{o1}} \right| \times 100\% \tag{5-77c}$$

Another measure of the distortion is the percent *total harmonic distortion*, which is the ratio of the rms value of the harmonics to the rms value of the fundamental

$$D_T = \frac{\sqrt{I_{o2}{}^2 + I_{o3}{}^2 + I_{o4}{}^2}}{I_{o1}} \times 100\% \tag{5-78}$$

Substituting Eq. (5-77), we have

$$D_T = \sqrt{D_2{}^2 + D_3{}^2 + D_4{}^2 + \cdots} \tag{5-79}$$

The total signal power output is the sum of the power contained in the fundamental and the higher harmonics. Thus,

$$P_{o,\text{tot}} = (I_{o1}{}^2 + I_{o2}{}^2 + I_{o3}{}^2 + I_{o4}{}^2 + \cdots)R_{\text{ac}} \tag{5-80}$$

The *useful signal power output* is just the power at the fundamental frequency. All the other terms are due to distortion, and we do not consider them useful

$$P_o = I_{o1}{}^2 R_{\text{ac}} \tag{5-81}$$

There is another procedure for analyzing nonlinear distortion. Let us write the output current as a Taylor's series expansion of x_i, the signal component of the input voltage or current

$$i_O = I_{OT} + a_1 x_i + a_2 x_i{}^2 + a_3 x_i{}^3 + \cdots \tag{5-82}$$

where x_i is the signal component of the input. (Note that when $x_i = 0$, $i_O = i_{OT}$, as it should.)

This power-series analysis is somewhat more general than the one previously considered since, as we shall discuss, it can be used to treat inputs other than sinusoidal ones. The $a_1, a_2, \ldots$ are unknowns. To determine them we shall again assume that the device can be accurately represented by a finite sum of terms. Equation (5-74a) or (5-76a) can be used to obtain the ac load line as before.

Now let us assume that we can accurately approximate Eq. (5-82) using only two terms (usually more terms will be required, but they can be obtained using an extension of this analysis)

$$i_O = I_{OT} + a_1 x_i + a_2 x_i{}^2 \tag{5-83}$$

Then let us choose the values of $x_i = 2\,\Delta x$ and $-2\,\Delta x$ to obtain two values of i_O which can be substituted into Eq. (5-83) to obtain two equations which can be solved for the unknowns. [These values of x_i correspond to those used in calculating Eq. (5-74).] Then, since

$$x_I = X_{II} + x_i \tag{5-84}$$

we have the two values

$$x_I = X_{II} + 2\,\Delta x$$

and

$$x_I = X_{II} - 2\,\Delta x$$

Corresponding to these values, we have $i_O = I_{O,\max}$ and $i_O = I_{O,\min}$ (see Fig. 5-27). Substituting into Eq. (5-83), we have

$$I_{O,\max} = I_{OT} + a_1(2\,\Delta x) + a_2(2\,\Delta x)^2 \tag{5-85a}$$

$$I_{O,\min} = I_{OT} - a_1(2\,\Delta x) + a_2(2\,\Delta x)^2 \tag{5-85b}$$

Solving these equations, we obtain

$$a_1 = \frac{I_{O,\max} - I_{O,\min}}{4\,\Delta x} \tag{5-86a}$$

$$a_2 = \frac{I_{O,\max} + I_{O,\min} - 2I_{OT}}{8(\Delta x)^2} \tag{5-86b}$$

Thus, the unknowns have been determined.
Let us use Eq. (5-83) to determine i_O when

$$x_I = X_{II} + X_{i,\max} \cos \omega t = X_{II} + x_i \tag{5-87}$$

Substituting x_i into Eq. (5-83) and manipulating, we obtain

$$i_O = \left(I_{OT} + \frac{a_2 X_{i,\max}^2}{2}\right) + a_1 X_{i,\max} \cos \omega t + a_2 \frac{X_{i,\max}^2}{2} \cos 2\omega t \tag{5-88}$$

The three terms of Eq. (5-88) demonstrate the shift in operating point, the presence of the fundamental, and the generation of a second-harmonic component. In the Fourier series analysis, we used the value $X_{i,\max} = 2\,\Delta x$. If this value is substituted into Eq. (5-88) and then Eqs. (5-86) are substituted for a_1 and a_2, the values of

$$I_{OA} = I_{OT} + \frac{a_2 X_{i,\max}^2}{2}$$

$$\sqrt{2}I_{o1} = a_1 X_{i,\max}$$

and

$$\sqrt{2}I_{o2} = \frac{a_2 X_{i,\max}^2}{2}$$

will be identical to those given in Eqs. (5-74). The details of this substitution will be left to the reader. If greater accuracy than that provided by Eq. (5-83) is desired, more terms of Eq. (5-82) should be used.

Now let us determine the output when the input is the sum of two sinusoidal terms of different frequencies

$$x_I = X_{II} + \sqrt{2}X_{ia} \cos \omega_a t + \sqrt{2}X_{ib} \cos \omega_b t \tag{5-89}$$

Substituting into Eq. (5-83) and manipulating and using some well-known trigonometric identities, we have

$$\begin{aligned}
i_O = {}& [I_{OT} + a_2(X_{ia}{}^2 + X_{ib}{}^2)] + a_1\sqrt{2}(X_{ia} \cos \omega_a t + X_{ib} \cos \omega_b t) \\
& + a_2(X_{ia}{}^2 \cos 2\omega_a t + X_{ib}{}^2 \cos 2\omega_b t) + 2a_2 X_{ia} X_{ib} \\
& \times [\cos (\omega_a - \omega_b)t + \cos (\omega_a + \omega_b)t] \quad (5\text{-}90)
\end{aligned}$$

These terms correspond to the shift in the average value, the original frequencies themselves, the second-harmonic terms, *and* terms whose frequencies are the sum and difference of the original frequencies, respectively. Then, in addition to harmonic distortion, a new type of distortion term appears. These sum-and-difference frequency terms are said to be produced by *intermodulation distortion*. If more terms are added to the Taylor's series, higher harmonics and *more* intermodulation or *beat* frequencies will appear.

5-11 EFFECT OF THE INPUT CIRCUIT ON NONLINEAR DISTORTION

The calculations of Sec. 5-10 were made under the assumption that the input signal x_i varied as a cosinusoid. However, the input circuit may distort the effective input waveform. This occurs in a transistor because input impedance varies with signal level. In a junction FET, this distortion can occur if the junction is not reverse-biased or if the impedance of the signal generator is extremely high. The effects of the input circuit at times must be considered when computing the distortion of the amplifier. Figure 5-28 indicates a generalized device with either a voltage source or a current source input.

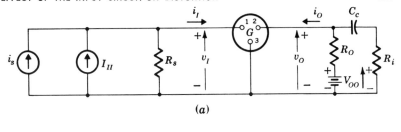

(a)

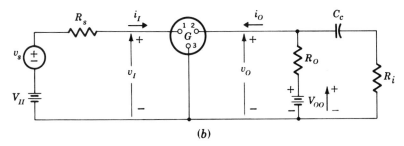

(b)

Fig. 5-28 Generalized devices: (a) with a voltage source input; (b) with a current source input.

Even though v_s and i_s are sinusoidal, the signal components of v_I and I_I may not be sinusoidal because of the nonlinearities of the input current of the active device.

The static characteristics of the generalized device are shown in Fig. 5-29. For this discussion, the output characteristics are drawn with i_I as the controlling parameter, and the input characteristic is drawn so that v_O is the controlling parameter. A trial ac load line is drawn, assuming no distortion. A curve of i_I versus v_O is found using Fig. 5-29a and the trial load line. It is then plotted as the dotted curve of Fig. 5-29b. This is called the *dynamic input characteristic*. This dynamic input characteristic is the same as the one in Sec. 3-16. The load line is then drawn on the input characteristics. Its slope is $-1/R_s$ and its ordinate intercept is $i_s + I_{II}$ if a current source is used. The abscissa intercept is $v_s + V_{II}$ for a voltage source. The instantaneous values of v_I and i_I can be obtained from the intersection of the load line and the dynamic characteristic. As i_s or v_s varies in time, the load line shifts parallel to itself. Thus, a plot of v_I and/or i_I versus time can be obtained. Once the instantaneous values of i_I are known, the instantaneous values of v_O and i_O can be obtained from Fig. 5-29a. For instance, if $R_s = 1$ ohm, $i_s = 3 \cos \omega t$, $I_{II} = 4$ and it is decided that the accuracy of Eq. (5-75) is desired, then the five-point schedule of Eq. (5-76) must be used. Five values of i_O are needed. Then the five load lines shown in Fig. 5-29b are drawn. These correspond to values of $\omega t = 0, \pi/3, \pi/2, 2\pi/3$, and π. The corresponding values of $I_{O,\max}, I_{O\alpha}, I_{OT}, I_{O\beta}$, and $I_{O,\min}$ are obtained from Fig. 5-29a.

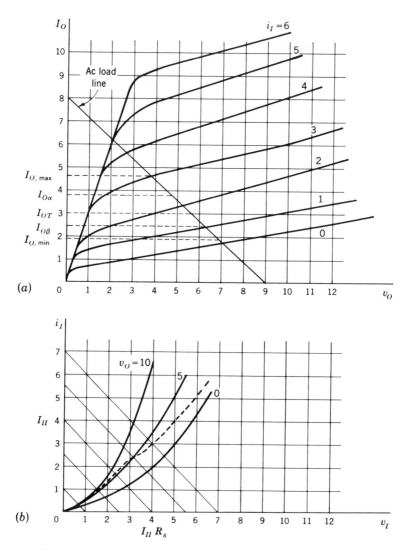

Fig. 5-29 Static characteristics of a generalized device: (*a*) output characteristic with an ac load line; (*b*) input characteristic with load line. The dynamic input characteristic is shown dotted.

If the calculated value of I_{OA} causes the output ac load line to shift appreciably, then a new one should be drawn, a new dynamic characteristic should be calculated, and the procedure should be repeated. If the dc and ac resistances of the input circuit differ, then an ac load line must be drawn on the input characteristics. The location of this load line will depend upon the instantaneous signal level and the distortion, which affects the average values V_{IA} and I_{IA}. It may be necessary to use a cut-and-try procedure similar to the one used in determining the position of the output-circuit load line.

At times, the distortion created by the input circuit is quite severe. However, there are circumstances when the distortion of the input and output circuits tend to cancel one another.

BIBLIOGRAPHY

Chirlian, P. M.: "Analysis and Design of Electronic Circuits," chap. 2, McGraw-Hill Book Company, New York, 1965.

DeWitt, D., and A. L. Rossoff: "Transistor Electronics," chap. 6, McGraw-Hill Book Company, New York, 1957.

Gibbons, J. F.: "Semiconductor Electronics," chap. 12, McGraw-Hill Book Company, New York, 1966.

Greiner, R. A.: "Semiconductor Devices and Applications," chap. 11, McGraw-Hill Book Company, New York, 1961.

Millman, J., and C. C. Halkias: "Electronic Devices and Circuits," chap. 10, pp. 405–411 and 546–549, McGraw-Hill Book Company, New York, 1967.

PROBLEMS

In the following problems it can be assumed that the reactance of any capacitors is zero at the signal frequencies.

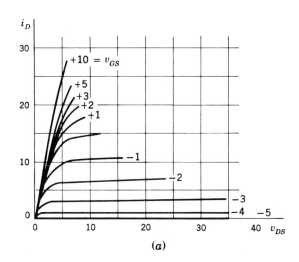

Fig. 5-30 Static characteristics of a 3N139 FET: (*a*) output characteristic; (*b*) transfer characteristic.

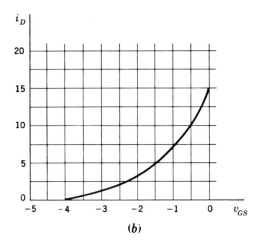

(b)

Fig. 5-30 (*Continued*)

5-1.   A 3N139 FET is to be used in the circuit of Fig. 5-1, where $V_{DD} = 30$ volts, $R_d = 2000$ ohms, $R_s = 300$ ohms.   Determine V_{DSQ}, i_{DQ}, and V_{GSQ}, that is, the coordinates of the quiescent operating point.   Use the static output characteristics given in Fig. 5-30a.

5-2.   Repeat Prob. 5-1 but now use the transfer characteristics given in Fig. 5-30b.

5-3.   The 3N139 FET is to be operated in the circuit of Fig. 5-1 such that $V_{DSQ} = 10$ volts and $V_{GSQ} = -2$ volts.   The value of R_d is 3000 ohms.   Determine V_{DD} and R_s.

5-4.   Repeat Prob. 5-3 but now assume that the coordinates of the quiescent operating point are $V_{DSQ} = 10$ volts and $I_{DSQ} = 8$ ma.

5-5.   A 3N139 is to be operated at a quiescent operating point of $V_{GSQ} = -1.45$ volts, $I_{DQ} = 5$ ma.   The average characteristics of the device are given in Fig. 5-30.   However, the transfer characteristics of individual 3N139 FETS can vary from the average.   The maximum and minimum values of I_D are 1.2 and 0.8 times that given in the curve of Fig. 5-30b.   The circuit of either Fig. 5-1 or 5-5, if it is required, should be used.   The change in I_d is to be no more than 10 percent no matter which 3N139 is used.   Design the circuit.

5-6.   Repeat Prob. 5-5 but now use a 20 percent variation.

5-7.   Repeat Prob. 5-5 but now use a 1 percent variation.

5-8.   How would the design of Prob. 5-5 differ if the shift in characteristics were due to temperature variation?

5-9.   A 3N139 FET is used in the circuit of Fig. 5-6.   The coordinates of the quiescent operating point are $V_{DSQ} = 5$ volts, $V_{GSQ} = +1$ volt. $R_d = 2000$ ohms and $R_{g2} = 10^6$ ohms.   Find V_{DD} and R_{g1}.

5-10.   A 3N139 FET is used in the circuit of Fig. 5-6.   The element values are $V_{DD} = 20$ volts, $R_d = 1000$ ohms, $R_{g1} = R_{g2} = 10^6$ ohms.   Compute the coordinates of the quiescent operating point.

5-11.   A 6C4 vacuum-tube triode is used in the circuit of Fig. 5-8.   The element values are $V_{bb} = 350$ volts, $R_L = 15,000$ ohms, and $R_k = 625$ ohms.   Determine the coordinates of the quiescent operating point.   The static output characteristics of the 6C4 vacuum-tube triode are given in Fig. 5-31.

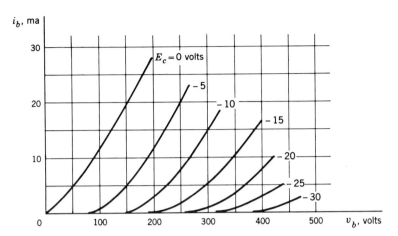

Fig. 5-31 Static output characteristics of a 6C4 vacuum-tube triode. (*Radio Corporation of America.*)

5-12. A 6C4 vacuum-tube triode is to be operated in the circuit of Fig. 5-8. The coordinates of the quiescent operating point are $V_{bQ} = 300$ volts, $I_{bQ} = 15$ ma. The value of R_L is 10,000 ohms. Find V_{bb} and R_k.

5-13. A 6C4 vacuum-tube triode is to be operated in the circuit of Fig. 5-8 such that $V_{bb} = 405$ volts, $R_L = 20,000$ ohms, and $V_{cQ} = -5$ volts. Compute the value of R_k that gives the desired operating point.

5-14. A 5879 vacuum-tube pentode is to be operated in the circuit of Fig. 5-9. The circuit values are $V_{bb} = 350$ volts, $V_{c2Q} = 100$ volts, $R_L = 50,000$ ohms and $R_k = 500$ ohms. Assume that i_{c2} is constant at 0.5 ma. Compute the coordinates of the operating point (V_{bQ}, V_{cQ}, I_{bQ}) and the value of R_s. The static output characteristics of the 5879 vacuum-tube pentode are given in Fig. 5-10.

5-15. Repeat Prob. 5-14 assuming not that i_{c2} is constant but that it varies with v_c in the same way that i_b varies with v_i.

5-16. A 5879 vacuum-tube pentode is to be operated in the circuit of Fig. 5-9. The coordinates of the quiescent operating point are $V_{bQ} = 350$ volts, $V_{cQ} = -2$ volts, $V_{c2Q} = 100$ volts. The value of R_L is 30,000 ohms. Find the values of V_{bb}, R_k, and R_s.

5-17. Discuss the operation of the circuit of Fig. 5-11 if R_g becomes open-circuited.

5-18. The transistor whose characteristics are given in Fig. 5-14 is operated in the circuit of Fig. 5-12. The element values are $V_{CC} = -20$ volts, $R_C = 4000$ ohms, $R_B = 500,000$ ohms. Determine V_{BEQ}, I_B, V_{CEQ}, and I_{CQ}, that is, the coordinates of the quiescent operating point.

5-19. The transistor whose characteristics are given in Fig. 5-14 is operated in the circuit of Fig. 5-12. Some of the circuit values are $V_{CEQ} = -10$ volts, $I_{BQ} = -20$ μa, and $R_C = 1500$ ohms. Compute the values of V_{CC} and R_B.

5-20. The transistor whose characteristics are given in Fig. 5-14 is operated in the circuit of Fig. 5-13. The elements values are $V_{CC} = -20$ volts, $R_C = 4000$ ohms, $R_E = 1000$ ohms, and $R_{B1} = R_{B2} = 10^6$ ohms. Determine the coordinates of the quiescent operating point. Make any appropriate approximations.

5-21. The transistor whose characteristics are given in Fig. 5-14 is operated in the circuit of Fig. 5-13. The coordinates of the quiescent operating point are $V_{CEQ} = -10$ volts, $I_{BQ} = -20 \ \mu a$. The value of R_C is 2000 ohms and $V_{CC} = -20$ volts. Determine the value of R_E. Determine a set of values of R_{B1} and R_{B2} which produces the required base current. Make any appropriate approximations.

5-22. Using the results of Prob. 5-21, determine the values of R_{B1} and R_{B2} such that $R_B = R_{B1}R_{B2}/(R_{B1} + R_{B2})$ is a maximum.

5-23. Repeat Prob. 5-22 but now determine the minimum value of R_B.

5-24. The transistor whose characteristics are given in Fig. 5-14 is operated in the circuit of Fig. 5-13. The coordinates of the quiescent operating point are $V_{CEQ} = -10$ volts, $I_{BQ} = -20 \ \mu a$. The element values are $R_E = 1000$ ohms, $R_C = 3000$ ohms. Determine V_{CC} and a pair of values of R_{B1} and R_{B2}.

In any of Probs. 5-25 to 5-70 which refer to transistors, assume that $v_{BE} = 0$.

5-25. The transistor of the circuit of Fig. 5-13 has an α of 0.99. The element values are $R_C = 2000$ ohms, $R_E = 2000$ ohms, $R_{B1} = R_{B2} = 10,000$ ohms. Compute the stability factor for this circuit.

5-26. Repeat Prob. 5-25 but now assume $R_E = 0$. Compare the result with Prob. 5-25.

5-27. Repeat Prob. 5-26 but now assume that $R_E = 10,000$ ohms. What practical limits are put on the value of R_E?

5-28. Repeat Prob. 5-25 but now assume that $R_{B1} = 10^6$ ohms and $R_{B2} = 2 \times 10^6$ ohms. Compare the result with Prob. 5-25.

5-29. The transistor of Fig. 5-13 is to have a quiescent operating point of $V_{CEQ} = -10$ volts, $I_{CQ} = -5$ ma, and $I_{BQ} = -100 \ \mu a$. The value of α is 0.99 and $R_C = 1000$ ohms. If the minimum value of $R_B = R_{B1}R_{B2}/(R_{B1} + R_{B2})$ is 20,000 ohms and the maximum magnitude of V_{CC} is 25 volts, what is the smallest stability factor that can be obtained with this circuit?

5-30. The transistor of Fig. 5-15 is to be operated at a quiescent operating point $V_{CEQ} = -10$ volts, $I_{CQ} = -1.0$ ma, and $I_{BQ} = -100 \ \mu a$. If $V_{CC} = -20$ volts, compute the stability factor for this circuit. Assume that $\alpha = 0.99$.

5-31. Compute the stability factor for the circuit of Fig. 5-32. Use the notation $R_1 = R_{1a} + R_{1b}$.

5-32. A 3N139 FET is connected into the circuit of Fig. 5-33. The element values are $V_{DD} = 30$ volts, $R_d = 2000$ ohms, $R_i = 2000$ ohms, $R_s = 300$ ohms. Draw the dc and

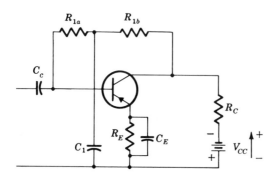

Fig. 5-32

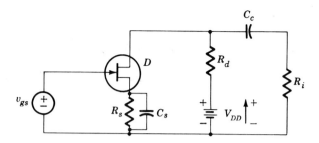

Fig. 5-33

ac load lines. Assume that v_{gs} is small enough so that distortion can be neglected. If $v_{gs} = 1 \cos \omega t$ volt, plot the waveform of v_{GS}, v_{DS}, and i_D. The characteristics of the 3N139 FET are given in Fig. 5-30.

5-33. Repeat Prob. 5-32 but now assume that distortion causes I_{DA} to be 2 ma more than I_{DQ}. Note that the gate-source direct bias will also shift.

5-34. A 6C4 vacuum-tube triode is connected into the circuit of Fig. 5-34. The element values are $V_{bb} = 400$ volts, $R_L = 20,000$ ohms, $R_k = 500$ ohms, and $R_g = 20,000$ ohms. Draw the dc and ac load lines. Assume that distortion can be neglected. Plot the waveforms of i_b, v_b, and v_c if $v_g = 5 \sin \omega t$ volts. The static characteristics of the 6C4 are given in Fig. 5-31.

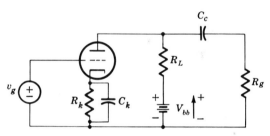

Fig. 5-34

5-35. Repeat Prob. 5-34 but now assume that distortion causes I_{bA} to be 2 ma more than I_{bQ}. Note that the grid bias will also shift.

5-36. The transistor whose characteristics are given in Fig. 5-14 is to be operated in the circuit of Fig. 5-35. The element values are $V_{CC} = -20$ volts, $R_C = 4000$ ohms,

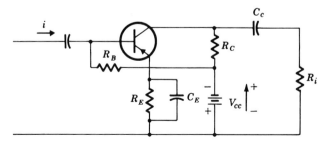

Fig. 5-35

$R_i = 3000$ ohms, $R_B = 667,000$ ohms, and $E_E = 0$. Draw the dc and ac load lines. Neglect the effect of distortion. If the signal component of the base current is 20 sin ωt μa, plot C_C, v_{CE}, and i_B.

5-37. Repeat Prob. 5-36 but now assume that distortion causes I_{CA} to be 0.5 ma greater in magnitude than I_{CQ}.

5-38. Repeat Prob. 5-36 but now assume that $R_E = 1000$ ohms and $V_{CC} = -23.3$ volts.

5-39. Repeat Prob. 5-37 but now assume that $R_E = 1000$ ohms and $V_{CC} = -23$ volts. Note that the distortion also causes the voltage across R_E to shift.

5-40. A 3N139 FET is connected into the circuit of Fig. 5-36, where $V_{DD} = 10$ volts

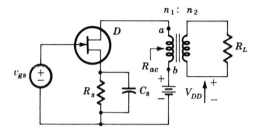

Fig. 5-36

and $V_{GSQ} = -2$ volts. The transformer has a primary resistance of 1 ohm, a secondary resistance of zero, and a turns ratio of $n_1/n_2 = 10$. The transformer operates such that at zero frequency the resistance seen between points a and b is the primary resistance R_p (1 ohm). The resistance seen between points a and b for signal frequencies is $R_{ac} = R_p + (n_1/n_2)^2 R'_L$, where R'_L is the resistance of the secondary winding plus R_L. In this case, the resistance of the secondary winding is zero. The value of R_L is 10 ohms. Thus, in this case, $R_{ac} = 1001$ ohms. Draw the ac and dc load lines and determine the value of R_s. Neglect distortion. If $v_{gs} = \cos \omega t$ volt, plot curves of v_{GS}, i_D, and v_{DS}.

5-41. Repeat Prob. 5-40 but now assume that distortion causes I_{DA} to be 2 ma less than I_{DQ}.

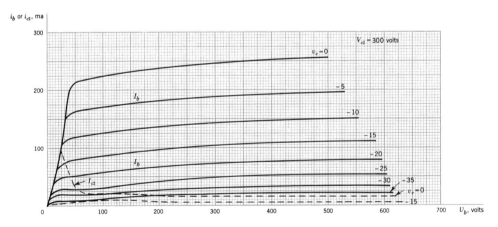

Fig. 5-37 The plate characteristic of the 7027-A beam power tube. (*Radio Corporation of America.*)

5-42. A 7027-A beam power tube is connected into the circuit of Fig. 5-38, where $V_{bb} = 315$ volts, $V_{cQ} = -15$ volts. The primary resistance of the transformer is 100 ohms, and the secondary resistance is zero. $R_1 = 4$ ohms, and $n_1/n_2 = 22.4$.

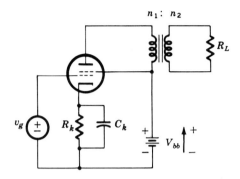

Fig. 5-38

Draw the dc and ac load lines and determine the value of R_k. Assume that the effects of distortion can be neglected. If $v_g = 5 \cos \omega t$ volts, plot curves of i_b, v_b, and v_c. The plate characteristics of the 7027 beam power tube are given in Fig. 5-37. See Prob. 5-40 for a discussion of the transformer.

5-43. Repeat Prob. 5-42 but now assume that distortion causes I_{bA} to be 10 ma more then I_{bQ}.

5-44. The transistor whose characteristics are given in Fig. 5-14 is connnected into the circuit of Fig. 5-39. The primary and secondary resistances of the transformer are

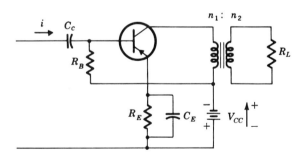

Fig. 5-39

zero, and its turns ratio is $n_1/n_2 = 26.6$. The element values are $V_{CEQ} = -8$ volts, $I_{BQ} = -20$ μa, $R_E = 1000$ ohms, $R_L = 4$ ohms. Find the value of R_B and draw the dc and ac load lines. Neglect any effect of distortion. See Prob. 5-40 for a discussion of the transformer.

5-45. Repeat Prob. 5-44 but now assume that a sinusoidal signal is present and distortion causes I_{CA} to be 0.5 ma less than I_{CQ}.

5-46. A 3N139 FET is operated as discussed in Prob. 5-40. If $v_{gs} = 1 \cos \omega t$ volt, compute the power delivered to both the transformer and R_L, the power delivered to R_L alone, the channel dissipation, the power supplied by V_{DD}, and the output circuit efficiency. Neglect any effects of distortion.

5-47. Repeat Prob. 5-46 but now assume that $v_g = 0$.

5-48. The maximum rated channel dissipation of the 3N139 FET is 0.150 watt. Draw a curve on the output characteristics of Fig. 5-30 showing an upper limit for the location of the quiescent operating point.

5-49. A 7027-A beam power tube is operated as in Prob. 5-42. If $v_g = 15 \cos \omega t$ volts, compute the power delivered to the transformer plus R_L, the power delivered to R_L alone, the plate dissipation, the screen-grid dissipation, the power supplied by V_{bb}, and the plate circuit efficiency. Neglect any effects of distortion.

5-50. Repeat Prob. 5-48 but now assume that $v_g = 0$.

5-51. The maximum rated plate dissipation of the 7027-A beam power tube is 35 watts. Draw a curve on the characteristics of Fig. 5-37 showing an upper limit for the location of the quiescent operating point.

5-52. The transistor whose characteristics are given in Fig. 5-14 is operated as discussed in Prob. 5-44. If the alternating component of base current is $20 \sin \omega t$ μa, compute the power delivered to R_L, the collector-base junction dissipation, the power supplied by V_{CC}, and the output circuit efficiency. Neglect the effects of distortion.

5-53. Repeat Prob. 5-52 but now assume that the alternating component of base current is zero.

5-54. The transistor whose characteristics are given in Fig. 5-14 has a rated collector-base junction dissipation of 0.04 watt. Draw a curve on the output characteristics of Fig. 5-14 showing an upper limit for the location of the quiescent operating point.

5-55. A 3N139 FET is operated in the circuit of Fig. 5-40. The element values are

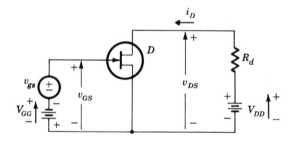

Fig. 5-40

$V_{DD} = 30$ volts, $V_{GG} = -2$ volts, $R_L = 2000$ ohms, and $v_{gs} = 2 \cos \omega t$ volts. Compute the magnitude of the second-harmonic distortion of i_D and v_{DS}.

5-56. Repeat Prob. 5-55 but now use a power-series expansion. Then, if $v_{gs} = \cos \omega_1 t + \cos \omega_2 t$ volts, use the power series to calculate the output current. Do the "constants" of the power series change if the signal level varies? Explain your answer.

5-57. Repeat Prob. 5-55 but now calculate the second, third, fourth, and total harmonic distortion.

5-58. Repeat Prob. 5-56 but now use a power series containing three terms.

5-59. A 6C4 vacuum-tube triode is connected into the circuit of Fig. 5-41, where $V_{bb} = 400$ volts, $V_{cc} = -10$ volts, $R_L = 13,333$ ohms, and $v_g = 10 \cos \omega t$ volts. Compute the magnitude of the second-harmonic distortion of i_b.

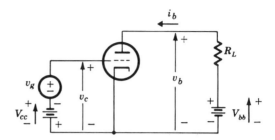

Fig. 5-41

5-60. Repeat Prob. 5-59 but now calculate the second, third, fourth, and total harmonic distortion.

5-61. The transistor whose characteristics are given in Fig. 5-14 is connected into the circuit of Fig. 5-42, where $V_{cc} = -15$ volts, $R_c = 3000$ ohms, $R_B = 500,000$ ohms, and

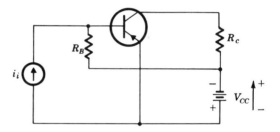

Fig. 5-42

$i_1 = 30 \cos \omega t$ μa. Calculate the magnitude of the second, third, fourth, and total harmonic distortion of i_C.

5-62. Repeat Prob. 5-61 but now use a power-series expansion. Use three terms of the power series to calculate the output current if $i_1 = 30 \cos \omega_1 t + 15 \cos \omega_2 t$ μa.

5-63. A 3N139 FET is operated in the circuit of Fig. 5-36. The primary and secondary resistances of the transformer are zero and $n_1/n_2 = 10$. The circuit elements are $V_{DD} = 10$ volts, $R_s = 308$ ohms, $R_L = 10$ ohms, and $v_g = 2 \cos \omega t$ volts. Draw the dc and ac load lines. Compute the magnitude of the second, third, fourth, and total harmonic distortion of i_D. Do not neglect the shift in the ac load line.

5-64. Repeat Prob. 5-63 using a power-series expansion.

5-65. A 7027-A beam power tube is operated in the circuit of Fig. 5-38, where $V_{bb} = 315$ volts, $R_L = 4$ ohms. Under quiescent conditions, $V_{cQ} = -15$ volts. Assume that the primary and secondary resistances of the transformer are zero and $n_1/n_2 = 26.8$. If $v_g = 15 \cos \omega t$ volts, draw the dc and ac load lines and compute the magnitude of the second, third, fourth, and total harmonic distortion of the output voltage.   Assume that the characteristics of Fig. 5-37 can be used at all times.   Do not neglect the shift in the ac load line.

5-66.   Repeat Prob. 5-65 using a power-series expansion.

5-67.   The transistor whose characteristics are given in Fig. 5-14 is operated in the circuit of Fig. 5-39.   Under quiescent conditions, $V_{CQ} = -5$ volts, $I_{BQ} = -40$ μa. The element values are $R_E = 1000$ ohms, $R_L = 4$ ohms.   The primary and secondary resistances of the transformer are zero and $n_1/n_2 = \sqrt{1000}$.   A signal is applied such that the alternating component of base current is $40 \cos \omega t$ μa.   Draw the dc and ac load lines and compute the magnitude of the second, third, fourth, and total harmonic distortion.   Do not neglect the shift in the ac load line.

5-68.   Repeat Prob. 5-67 but now use a power series.

5-69.   The generalized device whose characteristics are given in Fig. 5-29 is operated in the circuit of Fig. 5-28a such that $R_o = R_i = 2$ ohms, $VO_Q = 5$ volts, $R_s = 1.5$ ohms, $I_{I1} - 4$ amp, and $i_s - 3 \cos \omega t$ amp.   Compute the magnitude of the second, third, fourth, and total harmonic distortion.   Neglect the shift in the ac load line due to distortion.

5-70.   Repeat Prob. 5-69 but do not neglect the shift in the ac load line due to distortion.

6

Linear Models for Electronic Devices

If electronic devices are operated so that the nonlinear distortion is small, then they can often be approximated by linear equations and circuits. In such cases, all the procedures of linear-circuit analysis can be applied and complex circuits can be analyzed with a minimum of effort. In this chapter, we shall develop linear *models* or *linear equivalent* circuits that can often be used to replace electronic devices in linear-analysis procedures. It is important to realize that these models can be used to determine the effect of the electronic device on the external circuit. In general, they *do not* actually represent the internal behavior of the device. Basic amplifier circuits will also be presented and analyzed. We shall begin with a discussion of the techniques for representing *linear circuits*. These procedures will then be applied to electronic devices.

6-1 EQUIVALENT CIRCUITS FOR
THREE-TERMINAL LINEAR NETWORKS

For the time being, we shall concern ourselves with networks that have only three terminals, as shown in Fig. 6-1. Thus, there are only two independent voltages and two independent currents. Usually, a knowledge of any two of these quantities is sufficient to determine the other two.

z parameters Since we are concerned with linear circuits, we can usually write the voltages as linear functions of the currents. (Exceptions occur when open or short circuits are present.) Thus,

$$V_1 = z_{11}I_1 + z_{12}I_2 \tag{6-1}$$

$$V_2 = z_{21}I_1 + z_{22}I_2 \tag{6-2}$$

The terms z_{11}, z_{12}, z_{21}, and z_{22} have the dimensions of impedance. (Note that boldface letters are used to indicate complex quantities such as voltage or current phasors or complex impedances and admittances.) These elements are called the *z parameters* of the network and are sometimes represented by a *z-parameter matrix*.

$$\begin{bmatrix} z_{11} & z_{12} \\ z_{21} & z_{22} \end{bmatrix} \tag{6-3}$$

The *z* parameters can be obtained by a mesh analysis of the circuit within the "black box" of Fig. 6-1. An alternative procedure would be to make two sets of independent measurements of V_1, V_2, I_1, and I_2. These could be substituted into Eqs. (6-1) and (6-2) and the *z* parameters solved for. Since these parameters are constants, we can use any independent sets of voltages and currents to make the calculations. If we set I_2 and I_1 alternately equal to zero, the calculations become very simple. For instance, consider the circuit of Fig. 6-2. A current generator is applied to the input, and the output is open-circuited. Thus, $I_2 = 0$ and [see Eqs. (6-1) and (6-2)]

$$z_{11} = \frac{V_1}{I_1}\bigg|_{I_2=0} \tag{6-4}$$

$$z_{21} = \frac{V_2}{I_1}\bigg|_{I_2=0} \tag{6-5}$$

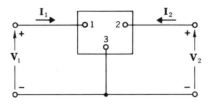

Fig. 6-1 A three-terminal network.

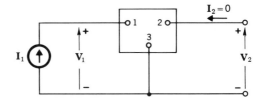

Fig. 6-2 A network used to measure z_{11} and z_{21}.

Thus, z_{11} is simply the impedance (or driving-point impedance) of the input with the output open-circuited. For this reason, z_{11} is called the *open-circuit input driving-point impedance*. Note that side 1 (terminals 1 and 3) is called the input side while side 2 (terminals 2 and 3) is called the output side. The parameter z_{21} also has the dimensions of an impedance. However, it is the ratio of the voltage at one part of a network to the current at another part. (It is assumed that the current is the driving function.) Hence, z_{21} is called a *transfer impedance*. In particular, z_{21} is the *open-circuit forward-transfer impedance*. The word "forward" is used since this is the response at the output terminals when a signal is impressed at the input terminals.

In a similar way, we can open-circuit the input terminals and apply a current generator to the output terminals. Thus,

$$z_{12} = \left.\frac{V_1}{I_2}\right|_{I_1 = 0} \tag{6-6}$$

and

$$z_{22} = \left.\frac{V_2}{I_2}\right|_{I_1 = 0} \tag{6-7}$$

where z_{12} is the *open-circuit reverse-transfer impedance*, and z_{22} is the *open-circuit output driving-point impedance*.

Equations (6-1) and (6-2) characterize the behavior of the network of Fig. 6-1. It is often convenient to represent a network by an *equivalent circuit*, that is, one whose equations are the same as Eqs. (6-1) and (6-2). Such a circuit is shown in Fig. 6-3a. It is equivalent to the black box of Fig. 6-1 as far as its external behavior is concerned. *In general, it is not representative of its internal behavior.* The voltage generators of this circuit are dependent generators. That is, their voltages depend upon currents in the network. They are treated as ordinary voltage generators. Their voltages are unknown and are grouped with the unknown terms in the mesh equations.

Another circuit that is equivalent to the one in Fig. 6-3a is shown in Fig. 6-3b. A simple mesh analysis demonstrates this equivalency. It is sometimes more convenient to use this circuit, since there is only one voltage generator. In the circuit of Fig. 6-3c the voltage generator and series

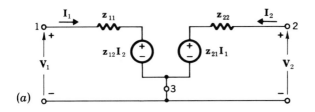

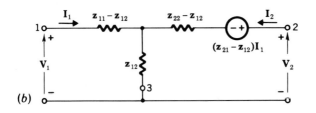

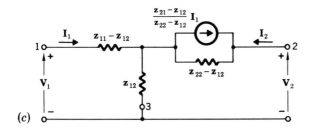

Fig. 6-3 Equivalent circuits for three-terminal networks, using the z parameters: (a) two-voltage-generator form; (b) single-voltage-generator form; (c) single-current-generator form.

impedance have been replaced by a current generator and shunt impedance. If the network is reciprocal (that is, $z_{12} = z_{21}$), then the generators are set equal to zero in Fig. 6-3b and c.

As an example, consider the network of Fig. 6-4. Its z parameters are given by $z_{11} = Z_a + Z_c$, $z_{12} = z_{21} = Z_c$, and $z_{22} = Z_b + Z_c$.

y **parameters** The currents of the network of Fig. 6-1 can usually be represented as linear functions of the voltages. Thus,

$$I_1 = y_{11}V_1 + y_{12}V_2 \tag{6-8}$$

$$I_2 = y_{21}V_1 + y_{22}V_2 \tag{6-9}$$

The parameters in these equations are called *y parameters*. They have the dimensions of admittances. It is most convenient to measure these para-

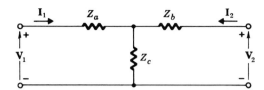

Fig. 6-4 A T section.

meters under short-circuit conditions. That is, apply a voltage generator to the input side and short-circuit the output side or vice versa. Thus,

$$y_{11} = \frac{I_1}{V_1}\bigg|_{V_2=0} \tag{6-10a}$$

$$y_{21} = \frac{I_2}{V_1}\bigg|_{V_2=0} \tag{6-10b}$$

$$y_{12} = \frac{I_1}{V_2}\bigg|_{V_1=0} \tag{6-11a}$$

$$y_{22} = \frac{I_2}{V_2}\bigg|_{V_1=0} \tag{6-11b}$$

We define these quantities as follows: y_{11} is the *short-circuit input driving-point admittance*; y_{21} is the *short-circuit forward-transfer admittance*; y_{12} is the *short-circuit reverse-transfer admittance*; and y_{22} is the *short-circuit output driving-point admittance*. Three equivalent circuits for networks characterized by Eqs. (6-8) and (6-9) are given in Fig. 6-5. Dependent generators are used in these networks, and their currents or voltages depend upon a voltage at some point in the network. If the network is reciprocal ($y_{12} = y_{21}$), the generators are set equal to zero in Fig. 6-5b and c.

h **parameters** Another convenient set of parameters is called the *hybrid parameters* or *h parameters*. These relate V_2 and I_1 to V_1 and I_2. Hence,

$$V_1 = h_{11}I_1 + h_{12}V_2 \tag{6-12}$$

$$I_2 = h_{21}I_1 + h_{22}V_2 \tag{6-13}$$

In this case, it is most convenient to determine h_{11} and h_{21} by short-circuiting the output and applying a current generator at the input. Conversely, h_{12} and h_{22} are conveniently determined by open-circuiting the input and applying a voltage generator at the output. Thus,

$$h_{11} = \frac{V_1}{I_1}\bigg|_{V_2=0} \qquad h_{21} = \frac{I_2}{I_1}\bigg|_{V_2=0} \tag{6-14}$$

$$h_{12} = \frac{V_1}{V_2}\bigg|_{I_1=0} \qquad h_{22} = \frac{I_2}{V_2}\bigg|_{I_1=0} \tag{6-15}$$

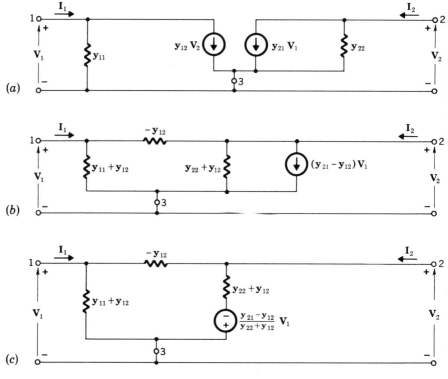

Fig. 6-5 Equivalent circuits for three-terminal networks using the y parameters: (a) two-current-generator form; (b) single-current-generator form; (c) single-voltage-generator form. The y parameters have the dimensions of admittances.

The dimensions of $\mathbf{h}_{11}$ and $\mathbf{h}_{22}$ are of an impedance and an admittance respectively, while $\mathbf{h}_{21}$ and $\mathbf{h}_{12}$ are dimensionless. They relate currents (voltages) at one part of the network to currents (voltages) at another part. Hence, they are called transfer-current (voltage) ratios. Thus: $\mathbf{h}_{11}$ is the

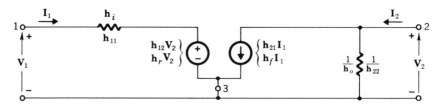

Fig. 6-6 An equivalent circuit for three-terminal networks using the h parameters. Note that both passive elements are impedances and that there is a voltage generator on the input side and a current generator on the output side.

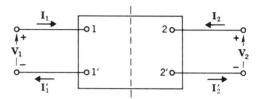

Fig. 6-7 A twoport.

short-circuit input driving-point impedance, $\mathbf{h}_{21}$ is the *short-circuit forward-transfer current ratio*, $\mathbf{h}_{12}$ is the *open-circuit reverse-transfer voltage ratio*, and $\mathbf{h}_{22}$ is the *open-circuit output driving-point admittance*. To avoid the use of double subscripts, the following notation is often used.

$$\begin{bmatrix} \mathbf{h}_{11} & \mathbf{h}_{12} \\ \mathbf{h}_{21} & \mathbf{h}_{22} \end{bmatrix} = \begin{bmatrix} \mathbf{h}_i & \mathbf{h}_r \\ \mathbf{h}_f & \mathbf{h}_o \end{bmatrix} \qquad (6\text{-}16)$$

where the subscripts i, f, r, and o stand for input, forward, reverse, and output, respectively. An equivalent circuit using h parameters is shown in Fig. 6-6.

Twoports The parameters that we have been discussing are often used to characterize a special case of networks with four terminals. Such a network is shown in Fig. 6-7. The dashed line is considered to isolate the input and output sides of the network, so that $\mathbf{I}_1 = \mathbf{I}_1'$ and $\mathbf{I}_2 = \mathbf{I}_2'$ and we cannot measure $\mathbf{V}_{12}$ or $\mathbf{V}_{1'2'}$. In this case, we can consider that $\mathbf{V}_1$, $\mathbf{V}_2$, $\mathbf{I}_1$, and $\mathbf{I}_2$ are the only independent variables and use the previously developed parameters to characterize the network. The term *twoport* is used since the four-terminal network is considered to have only two ports of entry.

In addition to the z, y, and h parameters there are other parameters which relate different combinations of $\mathbf{V}_1$, $\mathbf{V}_2$, $\mathbf{I}_1$, and $\mathbf{I}_2$. However, the ones that have been considered here are the ones commonly used for electronic devices.

6-2 RELATIONS AMONG NETWORK PARAMETERS—CHARACTERISTIC FUNCTIONS

One set of network parameters can be obtained from another by manipulating their defining equations into the same form. For instance, if Eqs. (6-1) and (6-2) are solved for $\mathbf{I}_1$ and $\mathbf{I}_2$ in terms of $\mathbf{V}_1$ and $\mathbf{V}_2$, the y parameters can be obtained as functions of the z parameters. Thus,

$$\mathbf{y}_{11} = \frac{\mathbf{z}_{22}}{\Delta_z} \qquad \mathbf{y}_{12} = -\frac{\mathbf{z}_{12}}{\Delta_z}$$

$$\mathbf{y}_{21} = -\frac{\mathbf{z}_{21}}{\Delta_z} \qquad \mathbf{y}_{22} = \frac{\mathbf{z}_{11}}{\Delta_z} \qquad (6\text{-}17)$$

where

$$\Delta_z = \mathbf{z}_{11}\mathbf{z}_{22} - \mathbf{z}_{12}\mathbf{z}_{21} \qquad (6\text{-}18)$$

Note that $\mathbf{y}_{11} \neq 1/\mathbf{z}_{11}$, since one is measured under short-circuit conditions while the other is measured under open-circuit conditions. Equations (6-12) and (6-13) can be manipulated into the form of Eqs. (6-1) and (6-2), so that

$$\mathbf{z}_{11} = \frac{\mathbf{h}_{11}\mathbf{h}_{22} - \mathbf{h}_{21}\mathbf{h}_{12}}{\mathbf{h}_{22}} \qquad \mathbf{z}_{12} = \frac{\mathbf{h}_{12}}{\mathbf{h}_{22}}$$

$$\mathbf{z}_{21} = -\frac{\mathbf{h}_{21}}{\mathbf{h}_{22}} \qquad \mathbf{z}_{22} = \frac{1}{\mathbf{h}_{22}} \qquad (6\text{-}19)$$

In a similar way, all the relationships among the parameters can be obtained.

Characteristic functions   To make the operation of converting one set of parameters to another less tedious let us consider a set of functions which can easily relate all the twoport parameters. These functions will enable us to express twoport parameters and twoport functions in a rather general way. We write each of the z parameters as the ratio of two functions,

$$\begin{bmatrix} \mathbf{z}_{11} & \mathbf{z}_{12} \\ \mathbf{z}_{21} & \mathbf{z}_{22} \end{bmatrix} = \begin{bmatrix} \dfrac{\mathbf{g}}{\mathbf{z}} & \dfrac{\mathbf{r}}{\mathbf{z}} \\ \dfrac{\mathbf{a}}{\mathbf{z}} & \dfrac{\mathbf{h}}{\mathbf{z}} \end{bmatrix} \qquad (6\text{-}20)$$

One procedure for obtaining these functions, if the z parameters are the ratio of two polynomials, is to place them all over a common denominator. $\mathbf{z}$ is the common denominator, and $\mathbf{g}$, $\mathbf{r}$, $\mathbf{a}$, and $\mathbf{h}$ are the numerators of $\mathbf{z}_{11}$, $\mathbf{z}_{12}$, $\mathbf{z}_{21}$, and $\mathbf{z}_{22}$, respectively. The functions $\mathbf{g}$, $\mathbf{r}$, $\mathbf{a}$, $\mathbf{h}$, $\mathbf{z}$, and one other function, which we shall define $\mathbf{y}$, are called the *characteristic functions* of the network. Note that if all the characteristic functions are multiplied by the *same* function then the z parameters will still be correct. Thus the characteristic functions are not unique until one of them is specified; *then* they are unique.

Now let us obtain the y parameters in terms of the characteristic functions. Substitution of the z parameters of Eq. (6-20) into Eqs. (6-17) yields

$$\begin{bmatrix} \mathbf{y}_{11} & \mathbf{y}_{12} \\ \mathbf{y}_{21} & \mathbf{y}_{22} \end{bmatrix} = \begin{bmatrix} \dfrac{\mathbf{h}}{\mathbf{y}} & \dfrac{-\mathbf{r}}{\mathbf{y}} \\ \dfrac{-\mathbf{a}}{\mathbf{y}} & \dfrac{\mathbf{g}}{\mathbf{y}} \end{bmatrix} \qquad (6\text{-}21)$$

where

$$\mathbf{y} = \frac{\mathbf{g}\mathbf{h} - \mathbf{a}\mathbf{r}}{\mathbf{z}} \qquad (6\text{-}22a)$$

or, equivalently,

$$\mathbf{zy} + \mathbf{ar} - \mathbf{gh} = 0 \tag{6-22b}$$

In general, if we solve for any of the sets of parameters in terms of the z parameters and then substitute the characteristic functions of Eq. (6-20), we obtain simple relations (the details of the substitutions are left to the reader):

$$\begin{bmatrix} z_{11} & z_{12} \\ z_{21} & z_{22} \end{bmatrix} = \begin{bmatrix} \dfrac{\mathbf{g}}{\mathbf{z}} & \dfrac{\mathbf{r}}{\mathbf{z}} \\ \dfrac{\mathbf{a}}{\mathbf{z}} & \dfrac{\mathbf{h}}{\mathbf{z}} \end{bmatrix} \tag{6-23a}$$

$$\begin{bmatrix} y_{11} & y_{12} \\ y_{21} & y_{22} \end{bmatrix} = \begin{bmatrix} \dfrac{\mathbf{h}}{\mathbf{y}} & -\dfrac{\mathbf{r}}{\mathbf{y}} \\ -\dfrac{\mathbf{a}}{\mathbf{y}} & \dfrac{\mathbf{g}}{\mathbf{y}} \end{bmatrix} \tag{6-23b}$$

$$\begin{bmatrix} h_{11} & h_{12} \\ h_{21} & h_{22} \end{bmatrix} = \begin{bmatrix} \dfrac{\mathbf{y}}{\mathbf{h}} & \dfrac{\mathbf{r}}{\mathbf{h}} \\ -\dfrac{\mathbf{a}}{\mathbf{h}} & \dfrac{\mathbf{z}}{\mathbf{h}} \end{bmatrix} \tag{6-23c}$$

6-3 LOW-FREQUENCY LINEAR-MODEL REPRESENTATIONS OF ELECTRONIC DEVICES

Electronic devices, e.g., FETs, vacuum tubes, or transistors, are not linear. However, if the signal voltages and currents are small variations about a quiescent operating point, the signal quantities can usually be obtained by a linear analysis. *The quiescent operating point cannot be obtained by these procedures.* Consider the electronic device represented by the generalized device of Fig. 6-8. For the time being, we shall both ignore reactive elements and work with instantaneous quantities. For most electronic devices, the frequency-dependent elements behave as real frequency-independent terms at sufficiently low frequencies. Thus, the linear models (equivalent circuits) that we shall develop here are *low-frequency linear models*. As in the case

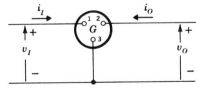

Fig. 6-8 A generalized electronic device.

of the linear network, any two variables can, in general, be expressed as functions of the other two.   For instance,

$$v_I = f_1(i_I, i_O) \qquad v_O = f_2(i_I, i_O) \tag{6-24}$$

Now, let us obtain relations for increments in v_I and v_O as functions of the increments in i_I and i_O about an operating point $i_I = I_{IQ}, i_O = I_{OQ}$.   Since f_1 and f_2 are not linear, we must use a double Taylor's series.   Hence,

$$\Delta v_I = \frac{\partial v_I}{\partial i_I} \Delta i_I + \frac{\partial v_I}{\partial i_O} \Delta i_O + \frac{\partial^2 v_I}{\partial i_I \, \partial i_O} \Delta i_I \, \Delta i_O + \frac{1}{2} \frac{\partial^2 v_I}{\partial i_I^2} \Delta i_I^2$$
$$+ \frac{1}{2} \frac{\partial^2 v_I}{\partial i_O^2} \Delta i_O^2 + \cdots \tag{6-25}$$

$$\Delta v_O = \frac{\partial v_O}{\partial i_I} \Delta i_I + \frac{\partial v_O}{\partial i_O} \Delta i_O + \frac{\partial^2 v_O}{\partial i_I \, \partial i_O} \Delta i_I \, \Delta i_O + \frac{1}{2} \frac{\partial^2 v_O}{\partial i_I^2} \Delta i_I^2$$
$$+ \frac{1}{2} \frac{\partial^2 v_O}{\partial i_O^2} \Delta i_O^2 + \cdots \tag{6-26}$$

where the derivatives are evaluated about the operating point as indicated in Eqs. (6-32).   If the deviations are small and/or the higher-order derivatives are very small, then all the terms in these equations except the first two can be ignored.   Thus, we obtain

$$\Delta v_I \approx \frac{\partial v_I}{\partial i_I} \Delta i_I + \frac{\partial v_I}{\partial i_O} \Delta i_O \tag{6-27}$$

$$\Delta v_O \approx \frac{\partial v_O}{\partial i_i} \Delta i_I + \frac{\partial v_O}{\partial i_O} \Delta i_O \tag{6-28}$$

The variation Δv_I can be considered to be the signal component of v_I.   That is, the voltages or currents have quiescent values.   The variation about these quiescent values constitutes the signal components.   For instance,

$$i_O = I_{OQ} + I_{2,\max} \cos \omega t$$

Then $I_{2,\max} \cos \omega t$ is the signal component of i_O.

We shall introduce an additional notation here which conforms with twoport notation.   The signal components of i_O and v_O will be written as i_2 and v_2, respectively.   Similarly, the signal components of i_I and v_I will be written as i_1 and v_1, respectively.   This notation is somewhat different from that used in Chap. 5, where the signal components were i_o, v_o, i_i, and v_i. Actually, either the numbers 1 and 2 or the *lowercase* subscripts i and o will be used for signal quantities.

Then, writing the variations in voltage and current as signal quantities, we have

$$\Delta v_I = v_1 \tag{6-29a}$$

$$\Delta i_I = i_1 \tag{6-29b}$$

$$\Delta v_O = v_2 \tag{6-29c}$$

$$\Delta i_O = i_2 \tag{6-29d}$$

and substitution in Eqs. (6-27) and (6-28) yields

$$v_1 = \frac{\partial v_I}{\partial i_I} i_1 + \frac{\partial v_I}{\partial i_O} i_2 \tag{6-30}$$

$$v_2 = \frac{\partial v_O}{\partial i_I} i_1 + \frac{\partial v_O}{\partial i_O} i_2 \tag{6-31}$$

If we compare these equations with Eqs. (6-1) and (6-2), we obtain

$$
\begin{aligned}
z_{11} &= \left.\frac{\partial v_I}{\partial i_I}\right|_{i_I = I_{IQ}, i_O = I_{OQ}} & z_{12} &= \left.\frac{\partial v_I}{\partial i_O}\right|_{i_I = I_{IQ}, i_O = I_{OQ}} \\
z_{21} &= \left.\frac{\partial v_O}{\partial i_I}\right|_{i_I = I_{IQ}, i_O = I_{OQ}} & z_{22} &= \left.\frac{\partial v_O}{\partial i_O}\right|_{i_I = I_{IQ}, i_O = I_{OQ}}
\end{aligned}
\tag{6-32}
$$

where the derivatives are evaluated at the operating point $i_O = I_{OQ}$, $i_I = I_{IQ}$. Thus, we can use the z-parameter equivalent circuits of Fig. 6-3 to obtain the relations for the incremental variation of voltage and current of the electronic device of Fig. 6-8. Hence these circuits are said to be linear models of the electronic device. In this case, the z parameters represent slopes of the static characteristics of the device at the operating point. We shall relate these to open-circuit measurement for the z parameters in the next section.

The other equivalent circuits can also be used to characterize the electronic devices. For instance, using the procedure of Eqs. (6-24) to (6-31), we can approximately write

$$i_1 = \frac{\partial i_I}{\partial v_I} v_1 + \frac{\partial i_I}{\partial v_O} v_2 \tag{6-33}$$

$$i_2 = \frac{\partial i_O}{\partial v_I} v_1 + \frac{\partial i_O}{\partial v_O} v_2 \tag{6-34}$$

If these equations are compared with Eqs. (6-8) and (6-9), we have

$$
\begin{aligned}
y_{11} &= \left.\frac{\partial i_I}{\partial v_I}\right|_{v_I = V_{IQ}, v_O = V_{OQ}} & y_{12} &= \left.\frac{\partial i_I}{\partial v_O}\right|_{v_I = V_{IQ}, v_O = V_{OQ}} \\
y_{21} &= \left.\frac{\partial i_O}{\partial v_I}\right|_{v_I = V_{IQ}, v_O = V_{OQ}} & y_{22} &= \left.\frac{\partial i_O}{\partial v_O}\right|_{v_I = V_{IQ}, v_O = V_{OQ}}
\end{aligned}
\tag{6-35}
$$

where the derivatives are the appropriate slopes of the static characteristics at the operating point. Thus, the y-parameter equivalent circuits of Fig. 6-5 can be used to characterize the electronic device of Fig. 6-8 for incremental changes about the operating point.

Similarly, we can relate the h parameters to the approximate slopes of the static characteristics. For instance, we can approximately write

$$v_1 = \frac{\partial v_I}{\partial i_I} i_1 + \frac{\partial v_I}{\partial v_O} v_2 \qquad (6\text{-}36a)$$

$$i_2 = \frac{\partial i_O}{\partial i_I} i_1 + \frac{\partial i_O}{\partial v_O} v_2 \qquad (6\text{-}36b)$$

Comparing these equations with Eqs. (6-12) and (6-13), we have

$$h_{11} = \frac{\partial v_I}{\partial i_I}\bigg|_{i_I = I_{IQ}, v_O = V_{OQ}} \qquad h_{12} = \frac{\partial v_I}{\partial v_O}\bigg|_{i_I = I_{IQ}, v_O = V_{OQ}} \qquad (6\text{-}37)$$

$$h_{21} = \frac{\partial i_O}{\partial i_I}\bigg|_{i_I = I_{IQ}, v_O = V_{OQ}} \qquad h_{22} = \frac{\partial i_O}{\partial v_O}\bigg|_{i_I = I_{IQ}, v_O = V_{OQ}}$$

These derivatives are evaluated at the operating point $v_O = V_{OQ}$, $i_I = I_{IQ}$. Hence the h-parameter equivalent circuit of Fig. 3-6 can be used to calculate incremental changes in voltage and current for the electronic device of Fig. 6-8.

The parameters developed in this section are real numbers. In subsequent sections, they will be extended to complex frequency-dependent terms.

6-4 GENERAL MODELS FOR ELECTRONIC DEVICES

The equations that were developed in the last section are valid only for instantaneous frequency-independent terms. However, if the instantaneous voltages and currents are replaced by phasors (which are indicated by boldface symbols) and the constant partial derivatives are replaced by frequency-dependent complex quantities, then the equivalent circuit will be valid at all frequencies. In this case, Eqs. (6-1) and (6-2), or (6-8) and (6-9), or (6-12) and (6-13) replace Eqs. (6-30) and (6-31), or (6-33) and (6-34), or (6-36a) and (6-36b), respectively. The discussion of Sec. 6-1 applies to the models of electronic devices, with one difference. When $\mathbf{I}_1 = 0$ or $\mathbf{I}_2 = 0$ for an electronic device, the signal components of the current are zero. *However, the total currents are not.* That is, if i_I and i_O are constant, so that $i_I = I_{IQ}$ and $i_O = I_{OQ}$, then $\mathbf{I}_1 = 0$ and $\mathbf{I}_2 = 0$. A similar statement can be made when $\mathbf{V}_1 = 0$ or $\mathbf{V}_2 = 0$. Thus, when the models of Sec. 6-1 are applied to electronic devices, the open-circuit and short-circuit measurements are made with respect to signal quantities but *not* with respect to quiescent voltages and currents. This is to be expected, since the equivalent circuit is used to obtain the incremental variations about the operating point. If we wish to make the open-circuit output measurement of Fig. 6-2 on an electronic device without disturbing the quiescent operating point, then the circuit of Fig. 6-9

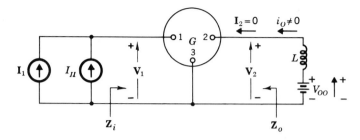

Fig. 6-9 A circuit which can be used for open-circuit measurements with electronic devices.

can be used. The generators V_{OO} and I_{II} are direct-bias generators. The inductance L should be essentially an open circuit at the frequency of I_1, but it should act as a short circuit for direct current. Thus, the direct bias of the electronic device has not been disturbed, but the output lead has been effectively open-circuited for signal quantities. Note that voltage sources could be used instead of current sources (or vice versa) in the circuit. Similarly, a capacitor can produce a short circuit for signal quantities without disturbing the quiescent operating point. The circuit of Fig. 6-10 will accomplish this. If the capacitance C acts as a short circuit at the frequency of I_1, then the desired measurements can be obtained. The output circuits of Figs. 6-9 and 6-10 can be placed on the input side of the electronic device to obtain open- or short-circuited input measurements, that is, $I_1 = 0$ or $V_1 = 0$, respectively.

Accuracy of open-circuit or short-circuit measurements If the models of electronic devices are to be valid over a wide range of frequencies, then the open-circuit and/or short-circuit measurements must be made over this frequency range. An inductance or capacitance (or any real circuit) will not be exactly an infinite impedance or a zero impedance at any frequency.

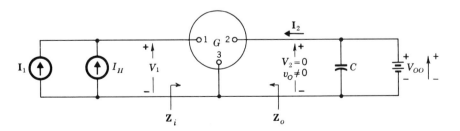

Fig. 6-10 A circuit which can be used for short-circuit measurements with electronic devices.

Thus, the measurements will be in error.   Let us see how large or how small the impedance of L or C must be if the parameter values are to be accurate. Consider the circuit of Fig. 6-10.   If the voltage $\mathbf{V}_2$ is to be essentially zero, then the magnitude of the reactance X_C of the capacitor must be very much less than the magnitude of the output impedance $\mathbf{Z}_o$ of the electronic device. Thus, for accuracy,

$$|X_C| \ll |Z_o| \tag{6-38}$$

Similarly, if X_L, the reactance of the inductor L of Fig. 6-9, is to be large enough to cause $\mathbf{I}_2$ to essentially be zero, then

$$|X_L| \gg |Z_o| \tag{6-39}$$

In general, we can state that we can obtain accurate short-circuit measurements if the impedance of the electronic device, in shunt with the short circuit, is high, while the open-circuit measurement can be accurate if the impedance of the electronic device, in series with the open circuit, is low.

Let us now consider which models are appropriate to use with FETs, vacuum tubes, and transistors.

The FET   In most FET circuits, the gate would be represented by terminal 1 of the generalized device.   The drain and source are terminals 2 and 3 of the generalized device, respectively.   Thus, the magnitude of $\mathbf{Z}_i$ of Fig. 6-9 or 6-10 will be very high.   The output impedance has the magnitude of r_d (see Secs. 3-22 and 3-25), which is also relatively high.   Thus, it is desirable to make short-circuit measurements at both the input and output sides of the network.   The y parameters should be used to characterize the FET [see Eqs. (6-10) and (6-11)].   Actually, if the gate is considered to be an open circuit, the z parameters or the h parameters cannot be used since the input impedance is infinite.

The vacuum tube   In most vacuum-tube circuits, the grid is terminal 1 of the generalized device, the plate is terminal 2, and the cathode is terminal 3. Thus, the magnitude of $\mathbf{Z}_i$ of Fig. 6-9 or 6-10 will be very high.   The output impedance $\mathbf{Z}_o$ is of the magnitude of r_p, which is very high for vacuum-tube pentodes and beam power tubes.   It is usually fairly large for triodes also. Thus, it is desirable to make short-circuit measurements at both input and output sides of the network.   The y parameters should be used to characterize the vacuum tube [see Eqs. (6-10) and (6-11)].

The transistor   In most transistor configurations, we shall see that the magnitude of the input impedance is fairly low, while the magnitude of the output impedance is high.   Thus, we desire a linear model whose parameters are obtained by open-circuit measurements at the input side and by short-circuit measurements at the output side. Thus, the *h*-parameter equivalent circuit is very often used for analysis of transistor circuits. The *z*-parameter equivalent circuit was used in the early days of the transistor. However, it is now very rarely used for actual circuit calculations.

6-5 THE LOW-FREQUENCY MODEL OF THE FET—THE COMMON-SOURCE AMPLIFIER

We shall use the methods of Sec. 6-3 to obtain the low-frequency models for the FET. In doing this, the effects of capacitance and other high-frequency effects will be neglected. They will be discussed later.

In the case of the junction FET, it will be assumed that the gate-to-source voltage v_{GS} is such that the gate-channel junction is reverse-biased. Then the gate current i_G will essentially be zero. For a MOSFET, i_G will be zero independent of the polarity of v_{GS}. The output impedance of the FET is essentially r_d (see Secs. 3-22 and 3-25). Thus, it is relatively high. Hence, we shall use the *y* parameters to obtain a linear model.

Consider the FET circuit of Fig. 6-11. The lowercase subscripts refer to signal quantities. Then, following the derivations of Eqs. (6-33) and (6-34), we obtain

$$i_G = i_g = 0 \tag{6-40a}$$

$$i_d = \frac{\partial i_D}{\partial v_{GS}} v_{gs} + \frac{\partial i_D}{\partial v_{DS}} v_{ds} \tag{6-40b}$$

Comparing Eqs. (6-40a) and (6-33), we have

$$\frac{\partial i_G}{\partial v_{GS}} = \frac{\partial i_G}{\partial v_{DS}} = 0 \tag{6-41}$$

Note that the derivatives are evaluated at the operating point $v_{GS} = V_{GSQ}$, $v_{DS} = V_{DSQ}$.

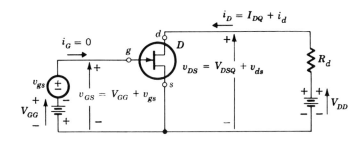

Fig. 6-11 An elementary FET amplifier.

Using the FET dynamic parameters [see Eqs. (3-166) to (3-168)], Eq. (6-40b) becomes

$$i_d = g_m v_{gs} + \frac{1}{r_d} v_{ds} \tag{6-42}$$

Then, comparing Eqs. (6-40a) to (6-42) with Eqs. (6-33) to (6-35) and Fig. 6-5a, we obtain the low-frequency model for the FET shown in Fig. 6-12a.

At times it is desirable to work with voltage generators rather than with current generators. In this case, the circuit of Fig. 6-12b can be used. (It is obtained from Fig. 6-12a using Thévenin's theorem.)

To use these models the FET is "removed" from the circuit and the model is redrawn in its place. In addition, all direct bias supplies are replaced by their internal impedances. Ideally, no signal voltage should appear across a bias voltage source and no signal current should be in a bias current source. Thus, ideally, voltage source power supplies are replaced by short circuits while current source power supplies are replaced by open circuits Phasor notation, as well as instantaneous notation, can be used in the analysis. In this way the effect of reactive elements can be studied. As an example the model for Fig. 6-11 is drawn in Fig. 6-13b using phasor notation.

Now let us consider a linear model which can be used for the dual-gate FET. A simple dual-gate MOSFET amplifier is shown in Fig. 6-13a. If the capacitor C_{g2} is a short circuit at the signal frequency, then the gate 2–to–source potential will be independent of the signal voltage. Since the gate

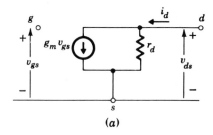

(a)

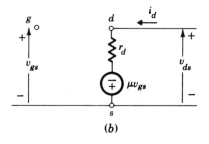

(b)

Fig. 6-12 (a) A current-generator model for the FET and (b) a voltage-generator model for the FET. $\mu = g_m r_p$.

currents are zero, the dual-gate MOSFET is characterized by Eqs. (6-40). Thus, it can be represented by the linear models of Fig. 6-12. The generalized linear model for the dual-gate MOSFET where the potential of the second gate is allowed to vary will be discussed in Sec. 6-22.

Let us calculate the *voltage amplification*, or *voltage gain*, $\mathbf{A}_v$ of the amplifier of Fig. 6-13b. This is the ratio of the output-voltage phasor to the input-voltage phasor when the input actually is a sinusoid. Thus, $\mathbf{A}_v$ is a complex quantity which has a magnitude and a phase angle. Boldface letters are used for phasors throughout this book. The magnitude of a voltage or current phasor will usually be its rms value unless the subscript max is added. In addition, the notation of Table 5-1 will be used. Then, for the circuit of Fig. 6-13, the input voltage is $\mathbf{V}_{gs}$ and the output voltage is $\mathbf{V}_{ds}$. Hence,

$$\mathbf{A}_v = \frac{\mathbf{V}_{ds}}{\mathbf{V}_{gs}} = -\frac{g_m R_d}{1 + R_d/r_p} \tag{6-43}$$

Using the relation $\mu = g_m r_d$, we obtain the equivalent expression

$$\mathbf{A}_v = -\frac{\mu}{1 + r_d/R_d} \tag{6-44}$$

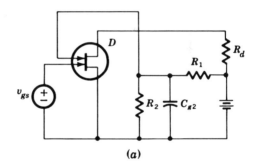

(a)

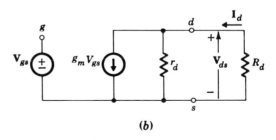

(b)

Fig. 6-13 (a) Elementary dual-gate MOSFET amplifier; (b) linear model of the amplifiers of Figs. 6-11 and 6-13a. Phasor notation is used.

The minus signs in Eqs. (6-43) and (6-44) indicate the 180° phase shift between the input and output voltages. The maximum magnitude of A_v occurs when $R_d \gg r_d$, and then $A_{v,\max}$ is equal to μ. Thus, the amplification factor is the maximum voltage gain that this circuit can have.

The value of r_d is often very large. If $r_d \gg R_d$, Eq. (6-43) becomes

$$A_v \approx -g_m R_d \tag{6-45}$$

The source lead is common to both the input and output circuits in the amplifier of Fig. 6-11. For this reason, it is called a *common-source amplifier*.

Let us now consider the circuit of Fig. 6-14a, which includes a self-bias circuit. The linear model is shown in Fig. 6-14b. Writing mesh equations, we obtain

$$\mu V_{gs} = I_d(r_d + R_d + Z_s) \tag{6-46}$$

The quantity V_{gs} is unknown. It should be substituted for before Eq. (6-46) is solved. *If this is not done, the "solution" will contain an unknown.* Then summing the voltage drops from gate to source, we obtain

$$V_{gs} = V_1 - I_d Z_s$$

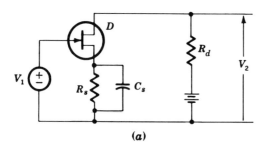

(a)

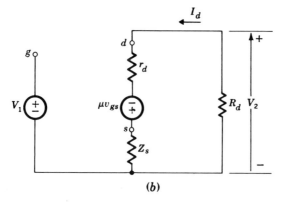

(b)

Fig. 6-14 (a) Common-source FET amplifier with a source bias impedance and (b) its linear model, where $Z_s = R_s/(1 + j\omega R_s C_s)$.

The output voltage is

$$\mathbf{V}_2 = -\mathbf{I}_d R_d$$

Thus, substituting for $\mathbf{V}_{gs}$ in Eq. (6-45) and solving for $\mathbf{V}_2/\mathbf{V}_1$, we have

$$\mathbf{A}_v = \frac{\mathbf{V}_2}{\mathbf{V}_1} = \frac{-\mu R_d}{r_d + (1 + \mu)\mathbf{Z}_s + R_d} \tag{6-47}$$

Since $\mathbf{Z}_s$ represents a complex number, the phase angle of $\mathbf{A}_v$ will not be 180°. Thus, there will no longer be an exact phase reversal between the input and output voltages.

The impedance $\mathbf{Z}_s$ acts as a much larger impedance $\mathbf{Z}_s(1 + \mu)$ because its presence affects the gate circuit as well as the drain circuit. This phenomenon will be discussed in great detail in Chap. 13. The term $(1 + \mu)\mathbf{Z}_s$ in the denominator of Eq. (6-47) tends to reduce the voltage gain. The value of R_s is fixed by bias requirements. However, the value of C_s is usually made large enough so that $(1 + \mu)\mathbf{Z}_s$ is small at all frequencies of interest.

6-6 THE LOW-FREQUENCY MODEL OF THE VACUUM TUBE—THE COMMON-CATHODE AMPLIFIER

The discussion of the last section can be directly applied to the vacuum-tube triode if we substitute *grid* for *gate*, *plate* for *drain*, and *cathode* for *source* where they occur. For instance, the drain current i_D becomes the plate current i_b. As an example consider the simple common-cathode vacuum-tube-triode amplifier of Fig. 6-15. Proceeding as in Sec. 6-5, we have

$$i_c = 0 \tag{6-48a}$$

$$i_b = \frac{\partial i_b}{\partial v_c} v_g + \frac{\partial i_b}{\partial v_c} v_p \tag{6-48b}$$

Then, using the dynamic parameters of Eqs. (2-24) to (2-26) we can rewrite Eq. (6-48b) as

$$i_b = g_m v_g + \frac{1}{r_p} v_p \tag{6-49}$$

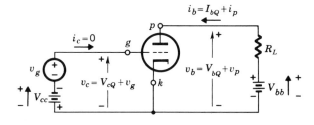

Fig. 6-15 An elementary vacuum-tube-triode amplifier.

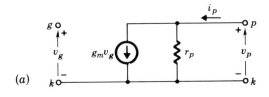

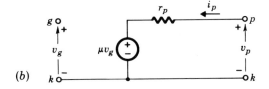

Fig. 6-16 (a) Current-generator model for the vacuum tube and (b) voltage-generator model for the vacuum tube.

Thus (see Sec. 6-5) two forms of the linear model for a vacuum-tube triode are shown in Fig. 6-16.

Now let us consider a linear model which can often be used for the vacuum-tube pentode. A simple vacuum-tube-pentode circuit is shown in Fig. 6-17a. If the capacitor C_s is a short circuit at the signal frequency, then the screen-grid potential will be independent of the signal voltage. In addition, the suppressor grid is often connected to the cathode so that its potential does not vary. Then if the control-grid current is zero, the pentode

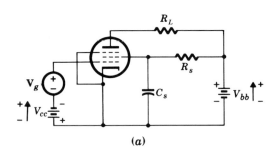

(a)

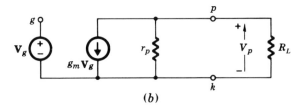

(b)

Fig. 6-17 (a) Elementary vacuum-tube-pentode voltage amplifier and (b) model for the amplifiers of Figs. 6-17a and 6-15.

is characterized by Eqs. (6-48) and (6-49). Thus, it can be represented by the models of Fig. 6-16. The generalized linear models for the vacuum-tube pentode where the potential of all the grids is allowed to vary will be discussed in Sec. 6-22. The linear model of Fig. 6-16 can be used for a vacuum-tube tetrode or a beam power tube if the screen-grid potential does not vary.

The analysis of common-cathode amplifiers directly parallels the analysis of common-source FET amplifiers. For instance, the model of the amplifier of Fig. 6-15 or 6-17a is shown in Fig. 6-17b. Then the voltage amplification of this circuit is

$$\mathbf{A}_v = \frac{\mathbf{V}_p}{\mathbf{V}_g} = -\frac{g_m R_L}{1 + R_L/r_p} \tag{6-50a}$$

Using the relation $\mu = g_m r_p$, we have

$$\mathbf{A}_v = -\frac{\mu}{1 + r_p/R_L} \tag{6-50b}$$

A common-cathode amplifier with a cathode-bias impedance is shown in Fig. 6-18a. Its linear model is given in Fig. 6-18b. Proceeding as in Sec. 6-5, we obtain

$$\mathbf{A}_v = \frac{\mathbf{V}_2}{\mathbf{V}_1} = -\frac{\mu R_L}{r_p + (1 + \mu)\mathbf{Z}_k + R_L} \tag{6-51}$$

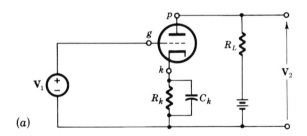

(a)

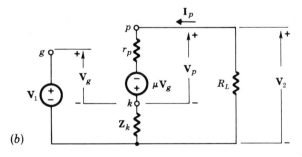

(b)

Fig. 6-18 (a) Common-cathode vacuum-tube amplifier with a cathode-bias impedance and (b) its linear model, where $\mathbf{Z}_k = R_k/(1 + j\omega C_k R_k)$.

A comparison of this section and the last one indicates that the analysis of FET amplifiers and that of vacuum-tube amplifiers are often essentially the same. To avoid duplication, only the FET amplifier will be discussed. The details for the vacuum-tube amplifier can be obtained by substituting *grid* for *gate*, *plate* for *drain*, *cathode* for *source*, r_p for r_d, V_g for V_{gs}, etc. When such substitutions cannot be made, it will be noted in the text.

6-7 THE COMMON-DRAIN FET AMPLIFIER—THE SOURCE FOLLOWER

We shall consider another amplifier configuration in this section. Consider the amplifier of Fig. 6-19a. Its linear model is shown in Fig. 6-19b. The drain lead is common to both the input and output circuits; thus this amplifier is called a *common-drain amplifier*. The circuit of Fig. 6-19b yields the equations

$$\mu V_{gs} = I_d(r_d + R_L) \tag{6-52}$$

$$V_{gs} = V_1 - I_d R_L \tag{6-53}$$

Then, solving for I_d and using the relation $V_2 = I_d R_L$, we obtain

$$A_v = \frac{\mu}{1 + \mu} \frac{1}{1 + r_d/[(1 + \mu)R_L]} \tag{6-54}$$

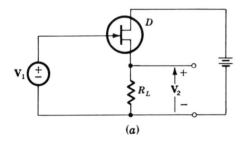

(a)

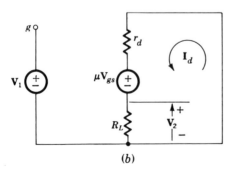

(b)

Fig. 6-19 (a) Source-follower amplifier and (b) linear model.

This is a real positive number, so there is no phase reversal between the input and output voltages. The voltage gain of this circuit approaches its maximum value when R_L becomes so large that $r_d/[(1 + \mu)R_L] \ll 1$. Thus,

$$|A_v| \leq A_{v,\max} = \frac{\mu}{1 + \mu} \qquad (6\text{-}55)$$

This is a number that is less than unity. In many instances $\mu \gg 1$, and the gain is essentially 1. For this reason, the common-drain amplifier is called a *source follower*, since the source voltage "follows" the input voltage. (The corresponding vacuum-tube circuit is called a *cathode follower*.)

Even though there is no actual voltage gain, the source follower has many applications. We shall see in a subsequent section that when interelectrode capacitances are considered, the input impedance of the source follower is usually very much greater than that of other amplifiers. In addition, the output impedance of the source follower is usually much lower than that of other amplifiers. Common-drain amplifiers are often used as the input stages of high-frequency voltage-measuring devices such as vacuumtube voltmeters and oscilloscopes where their high input impedance does not "load down" the circuit to be measured. These circuits are also frequently used as the output stages of audio preamplifiers. These preamplifiers require low output impedances so that they can be connected to lowimpedance loads without appreciable loss of signal level. Low-impedance circuits also are used where it is necessary to minimize interference.

When the impedance viewed into a pair of terminals is to be calculated, all independent generators should be replaced by their internal impedances. However, the dependent generators represent the effect of the electronic device on the circuit. Thus, they are not replaced. The impedance can then be obtained by placing a voltage generator across the pair of terminals in question and then determining the current through it. Impedance is the ratio of the voltage to the current. (Current generators can also be used in these calculations.) Thus, the circuit of Fig. 6-20 can be used to obtain the output

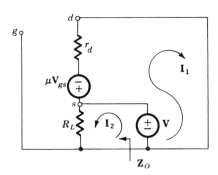

Fig. 6-20 Linear model used to calculate the output impedance of the source follower.

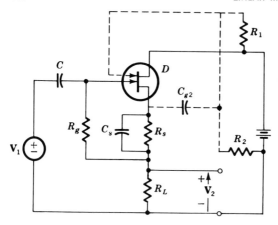

Fig. 6-21 Source follower with a practical bias circuit; connections for a dual-gate MOSFET are shown dashed.

impedance of the source (cathode) follower. The output impedance is $\mathbf{Z}_o = \mathbf{V}/(\mathbf{I}_1 + \mathbf{I}_2)$. Hence,

$$\mathbf{Z}_o = \frac{1}{1/r_d + \mu/r_d + 1/R_L} \tag{6-56}$$

This is a pure resistance which represents the parallel combination of r_d, $1/g_m$, and R_L. Usually, this is very much less than the parallel combination of r_d and R_L.

If the gain of the source follower is to approach unity, then $R_L \gg r_d/(1 + \mu) \approx 1/g_m$. Often, this requires relatively large values of R_L. This resistance not only serves as an output load resistance but also produces the direct-gate bias. If large values of R_L are used, the gate bias often becomes excessive. To prevent this, the circuit of Fig. 6-21, which also illustrates a dual-gate MOSFET source follower, is often used. The direct current through R_g is zero. Thus, the direct-voltage drop across it is zero. Hence, the direct-gate bias is equal to $-I_{DQ}R_s$. The value of R_s is chosen to provide the correct grid bias. If the capacitors are chosen large enough so that they can be considered short circuits at the signal frequency, and if R_g is chosen large enough so that there is negligible signal current through it, then the model of Fig. 6-19b is valid for these circuits also.

6-8 THE COMMON-GATE FET AMPLIFIER

Another FET amplifier configuration is shown in Fig. 6-22a. Its linear model is shown in Fig. 6-22b. Since the gate lead is common to both the

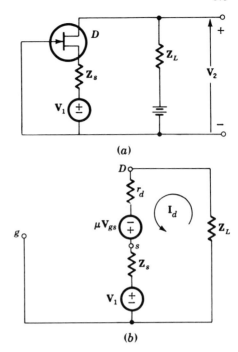

Fig. 6-22 (*a*) Common-gate amplifier and (*b*) its linear model.

input and output circuit, this is called a *common-gate amplifier*. The voltage gain is

$$A_v = \frac{(1 + \mu)Z_L}{r_d + (1 + \mu)Z_s + Z_L} \tag{6-57}$$

Note that if Z_s and Z_L are purely resistive, then the voltage amplification is a real positive number. That is, there is no $180°$ phase shift between the input and output waveforms. The maximum value of A_v is equal to $1 + \mu$ and is obtained when $|Z_L| \gg |r_d + (1 + \mu)Z_s|$. Thus, the maximum voltage gain of the common-gate amplifier is potentially greater than that of the common-source amplifier. However, the common-source amplifier finds far more use than the common-gate amplifier. In the common-gate amplifier, the input generator is in series with the source lead. This eliminates one of the primary advantages of the FET amplifier: its infinite, or extremely high, input impedance. In addition the gain of the common-gate amplifier is usually much less than the maximum value because of the factor $(1 + \mu)Z_s$. If Z_s represents the internal impedance of the signal generator, then it cannot be bypassed with a capacitor. Thus, the common-source amplifier often provides much more gain than the common-gate amplifier.

In a common-grid amplifier, the grid tends to isolate the input (cathode) circuit from the output (plate) circuit, providing the input-output isolation of the vacuum-tube pentode with a vacuum-tube triode. At times, this is useful and in such circumstances common-grid circuits are used.

6-9 PHYSICAL DISCUSSION OF LOW-FREQUENCY JUNCTION TRANSISTOR MODELS

Before considering the circuit aspects of transistor models we shall develop a model using physical arguments. The common-base circuit will be used. In the model of Fig. 6-23a, r_c' represents the dynamic resistance of the reverse-biased collector-base junction with the emitter lead open-circuited. Similarly, r_e' represents the dynamic resistance of the forward-biased emitter-base junction with $v_c = 0$. For incremental changes in i_e, the change in collector current is α times the emitter current. Thus, the generator αi_e is included. As v_c varies, the collector-base junction depletion-layer width varies. This, in turn, changes the width of the base. This is called the *Early effect* (see Sec. 3-12). As the base width changes, the rate of change of minority-carrier density with distance also varies. This changes i_e. Thus, i_e is not independent of v_c. The μv_c generator takes this dependence into account. The linear model of Fig. 6-23a has the same form as that of the h-parameter equivalent circuit of Fig. 6-6. If Fig. 6-23a were the linear model of the transistor, then the h parameters would correspond to r_e', $1/r_c'$, α, and μ. However, we have ignored the ohmic resistance of the semiconductor

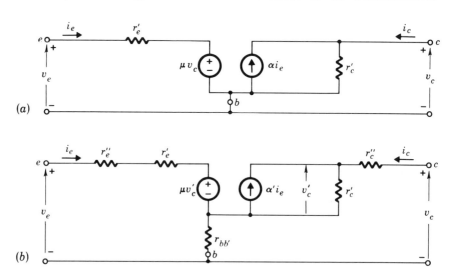

Fig. 6-23 Low-frequency models for the junction transistor developed from physical arguments: (*a*) an ideal model that does not include the ohmic resistances and (*b*) a model with the ohmic resistances, including the base spreading resistance $r_{bb'}$.

material in the regions removed from the junctions. The largest resistance is in the base region, since the base current is transverse to the narrow base region and, thus, the cross-sectional area presented to the current is small. This resistance, called the *base-spreading resistance*, must be added to the equivalent circuit of Fig. 6-23*a*. It is shown in Fig. 6-23*b* as $r_{bb'}$. Resistances also occur in the bulk of the emitter and collector materials. These are shown as r_e'' and r_c'' in Fig. 6-23*b*. However, the cross-sectional areas presented to the currents are much larger here and these lower resistances are often neglected. The value of α has been replaced by α', since by definition $i_c = \alpha i_e$ if $v_c = 0$. In general, $r_c' \gg r_{bb'} + r_c''$, hence $\alpha' \approx \alpha$. The common-base *h*-parameter linear model for the transistor will be of the form of Fig. 6-6. However, there will not be a simple relationship between the *h* parameters and the elements of Fig. 6-23*b*.

The direct-bias current through the base produces an alternating voltage drop, since the base-spreading resistance varies with base width. An additional voltage can be included in the base lead to take this alternating voltage into account. However, it is small and can often be ignored.

6-10 LOW-FREQUENCY *h*-PARAMETER MODELS FOR COMMON-BASE, COMMON-EMITTER, AND COMMON-COLLECTOR TRANSISTORS

We shall now obtain *h*-parameter low-frequency models for the bipolar junction transistor. When the *h* parameters are used, it is conventional to use the same *form* of the equivalent circuit for the common-base, common-emitter, and common-collector amplifier configurations, but different *numerical* values of the *h* parameters are used in each of the three equivalent circuits. The general form of these three models is shown in Fig. 6-6. It should be stressed that all these models are general and can be used to represent the transistor, no matter which lead is taken as common, just as the circuits of Fig. 6-12 can always represent the FET. However, it is often more convenient or more accurate to use one model rather than another. This is why so many forms of transistor models are used. For instance, the generator $\mathbf{h}_f\mathbf{I}_1$ of Fig. 6-6 is of prime importance. Its presence causes the circuit to have a gain. Usually, more insight can be gained if $\mathbf{I}_1$ represents the input current. It is often more accurate to do this, since the generator current can be expressed in terms of the input directly rather than in terms of the difference among variables.

We shall now define the *h*-parameter linear models for the common-base, common-emitter, and common-collector transistor amplifiers and relate them to each other. The circuit of Fig. 6-6 can be used as the linear model for any three-terminal device. Thus, the linear model for the common-base transistor amplifier of Fig. 6-24*a* is shown in Fig. 6-24*b*. The subscript *b* is

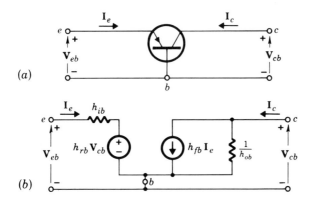

Fig. 6-24 (*a*) Common-base transistor and (*b*) its *h*-parameter model.

added to the *h* parameters to avoid confusion, since we shall consider all three configurations in this section.   To avoid an excessive number of subscripts, the notation of Eq. (6-16) will be employed.   That is, $h_{11} = h_i$, $h_{12} = h_r$, $h_{21} = h_f$, and $h_{22} = h_o$.   The equations that characterize Fig. 6-24 are

$$\mathbf{V}_{eb} = h_{ib}\mathbf{I}_e + h_{rb}\mathbf{V}_{cb} \qquad\qquad (6\text{-}58a)$$

$$\mathbf{I}_c = h_{fb}\mathbf{I}_e + h_{ob}\mathbf{V}_{cb} \qquad\qquad (6\text{-}58b)$$

Similarly, Fig. 6-25 illustrates the common-emitter transistor and its linear model.   The equations that characterize it are

$$\mathbf{V}_{be} = h_{ie}\mathbf{I}_b + h_{re}\mathbf{V}_{ce} \qquad\qquad (6\text{-}59a)$$

$$\mathbf{I}_c = h_{fe}\mathbf{I}_b + h_{oe}\mathbf{V}_{ce} \qquad\qquad (6\text{-}59b)$$

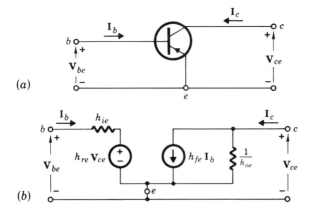

Fig. 6-25 (*a*) Common-emitter transistor and (*b*) its *h*-parameter model.

Finally, Fig. 6-26 shows the common-collector transistor and its linear model.   The equations that characterize it are

$$\mathbf{V}_{bc} = h_{ic}\mathbf{I}_b + h_{rc}\mathbf{V}_{ec} \tag{6-60a}$$

$$\mathbf{I}_e = h_{fc}\mathbf{I}_b + h_{oc}\mathbf{V}_{ec} \tag{6-60b}$$

The h parameters for one configuration can be related to those for another configuration simply by making some elementary substitutions and rearranging the equations.   For instance, to relate the common-emitter h parameters to the common-base h parameters, use the following substitutions:

$$\begin{aligned} \mathbf{V}_{eb} &= -\mathbf{V}_{be} \\ \mathbf{V}_{cb} &= \mathbf{V}_{ce} - \mathbf{V}_{be} \\ \mathbf{I}_e &= -(\mathbf{I}_c + \mathbf{I}_b) \end{aligned} \tag{6-61}$$

Substitute Eqs. (6-61) into Eqs. (6-58) and rearrange them into the form of Eqs. (6-59).   We then obtain

$$\mathbf{V}_{be} = \frac{h_{ib}}{(1 + h_{fb})(1 - h_{rb}) + h_{ob}h_{ib}}\,\mathbf{I}_b + \frac{h_{ib}h_{ob} - h_{rb}(h_{fb} + 1)}{(1 + h_{fb})(1 - h_{rb}) + h_{ob}h_{ib}}\,\mathbf{V}_{ce} \tag{6-62a}$$

$$\mathbf{I}_c = \frac{-h_{ob}h_{ib} - h_{fb}(1 - h_{rb})}{(1 + h_{fb})(1 - h_{rb}) + h_{ob}h_{ib}}\,\mathbf{I}_b + \frac{h_{ob}}{(1 + h_{fb})(1 - h_{rb}) + h_{ob}h_{ib}}\,\mathbf{V}_{ce} \tag{6-62b}$$

Comparing these with Eqs. (6-59), we have

$$h_{ie} = \frac{h_{ib}}{(1 + h_{fb})(1 - h_{rb}) + h_{ob}h_{ib}} \tag{6-63a}$$

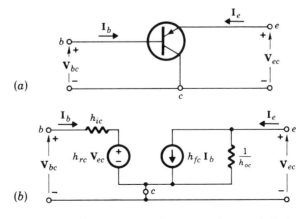

(a)

(b)

Fig. 6-26 (a) Common-collector transistor and (b) its h-parameter model.

$$h_{re} = \frac{h_{ib}h_{ob} - h_{rb}(h_{fb} + 1)}{(1 + h_{fb})(1 - h_{rb}) + h_{ob}h_{ib}} \tag{6-63b}$$

$$h_{fe} = \frac{-h_{ib}h_{ob} - h_{fb}(1 - h_{rb})}{(1 + h_{if})(1 - h_{rb}) + h_{ob}h_{ib}} \tag{6-63c}$$

$$h_{oe} = \frac{h_{ob}}{(1 + h_{fb})(1 - h_{rb}) + h_{ob}h_{ib}} \tag{6-63d}$$

If we proceed in a similar fashion, we can relate any two sets of h parameters. These relationships are given below.[1]

$$h_{ib} = \frac{h_{ie}}{(1 + h_{fe})(1 - h_{re}) + h_{ie}h_{oe}} = \frac{h_{ic}}{h_{ic}h_{oc} - h_{fc}h_{rc}} \tag{6-64a}$$

$$h_{rb} = \frac{h_{ie}h_{oe} - h_{re}(1 + h_{fe})}{(1 + h_{fe})(1 - h_{re}) + h_{ie}h_{oe}} = \frac{h_{fc}(1 - h_{rc}) + h_{ic}h_{oc}}{h_{ic}h_{oc} - h_{fc}h_{rc}} \tag{6-64b}$$

$$h_{fb} = \frac{-h_{fe}(1 - h_{re}) - h_{ie}h_{oe}}{(1 + h_{fe})(1 - h_{re}) + h_{ie}h_{oe}} = \frac{h_{rc}(1 + h_{fc}) - h_{ic}h_{oc}}{h_{ic}h_{oc} - h_{fc}h_{rc}} \tag{6-64c}$$

$$h_{ob} = \frac{h_{oe}}{(1 + h_{fe})(1 - h_{re}) + h_{ie}h_{oe}} = \frac{h_{oc}}{h_{ic}h_{oc} - h_{fc}h_{rc}} \tag{6-64d}$$

and

$$h_{ie} = \frac{h_{ib}}{(1 + h_{fb})(1 - h_{rb}) + h_{ob}h_{ib}} = h_{ic} \tag{6-65a}$$

$$h_{re} = \frac{h_{ib}h_{ob} - h_{rb}(1 + h_{fb})}{(1 + h_{fb})(1 - h_{rb}) + h_{ob}h_{ib}} = 1 - h_{rc} \tag{6-65b}$$

$$h_{fe} = \frac{-h_{fb}(1 - h_{rb}) - h_{ob}h_{ib}}{(1 + h_{fb})(1 - h_{rb}) + h_{ob}h_{ib}} = -(1 + h_{fc}) \tag{6-65c}$$

$$h_{oe} = \frac{h_{ob}}{(1 + h_{fb})(1 - h_{rb}) + h_{ob}h_{ib}} = h_{oc} \tag{6-65d}$$

and

$$h_{ic} = \frac{h_{ib}}{(1 + h_{fb})(1 - h_{rb}) + h_{ob}h_{ib}} = h_{ie} \tag{6-66a}$$

$$h_{rc} = \frac{1 + h_{fb}}{(1 + h_{fb})(1 - h_{rb}) + h_{ob}h_{ib}} = 1 - h_{re} \tag{6-66b}$$

$$h_{fc} = \frac{h_{rb} - 1}{(1 + h_{fb})(1 - h_{rb}) + h_{ob}h_{ib}} = -(1 + h_{fe}) \tag{6-66c}$$

$$h_{oc} = \frac{h_{ob}}{(1 + h_{fb})(1 - h_{rb}) + h_{ob}h_{ib}} = h_{oe} \tag{6-66d}$$

With the exception of the relationships between the common-emitter and common-collector h parameters, these equations are very cumbersome. The h parameters of actual transistors are such that approximations can often be made which simplify these equations greatly. Let us consider some typical values (see Table 6-1) in order to see what approximations can be made. The following approximations are valid for almost all bipolar junction transistors.

$$h_{re} \ll 1 \tag{6-67a}$$

$$h_{ie}h_{oe} \ll 1 \tag{6-67b}$$

$$h_{rb} \ll 1 \tag{6-67c}$$

$$h_{ib}h_{ob} \ll 1 \tag{6-67d}$$

$$h_{rc} \approx 1 \tag{6-67e}$$

$$h_{ic}h_{oc} \ll 1 \tag{6-67f}$$

Thus, we can use the following approximate relationships

$$h_{ib} \approx \frac{h_{ie}}{1 + h_{fe}} \approx -\frac{h_{ic}}{h_{fc}} \tag{6-68a}$$

$$h_{rb} \approx \frac{h_{ie}h_{oe}}{1 + h_{fe}} - h_{re} \approx h_{rc} - 1 - \frac{h_{ic}h_{oc}}{h_{fc}} \tag{6-68b}$$

$$h_{fb} \approx \frac{-h_{fe}}{1 + h_{fe}} \approx -\frac{1 + h_{fc}}{h_{fc}} \tag{6-68c}$$

$$h_{ob} \approx \frac{h_{oe}}{1 + h_{fe}} \approx -\frac{h_{oc}}{h_{fc}} \tag{6-68d}$$

and

$$h_{ie} \approx \frac{h_{ib}}{1 + h_{fb}} \tag{6-69a}$$

$$h_{re} \approx \frac{h_{ib}h_{ob}}{1 + h_{fb}} - h_{rb} \tag{6-69b}$$

Table 6-1   Values of the h parameters for a typical transistor

Parameter	Common base	Common emitter	Common collector
h_i, ohms	39	2000	2000
h_r	3.8×10^{-4}	6×10^{-4}	1
h_f	-0.9804	50	-51
h_o, mhos	0.49×10^{-6}	25×10^{-6}	25×10^{-6}

$$h_{fe} \approx \frac{-h_{fb}}{1 + h_{fb}} \qquad (6\text{-}69c)$$

$$h_{oe} \approx \frac{h_{ob}}{1 + h_{fb}} \qquad (6\text{-}69d)$$

and

$$h_{ic} \approx \frac{h_{ib}}{1 + h_{fb}} \qquad (6\text{-}70a)$$

$$h_{rc} \approx 1 \qquad (6\text{-}70b)$$

$$h_{fc} \approx \frac{-1}{1 + h_{fb}} \qquad (6\text{-}70c)$$

$$h_{oc} \approx \frac{h_{ob}}{1 + h_{fb}} \qquad (6\text{-}70d)$$

Although the h-parameter models are now most commonly used, at one time the r-parameter models were used. The z-parameter models were actually used here. Since at low frequencies all the elements were real the notation r parameter was adopted.

6-11 COMPARISON OF THE h PARAMETERS OF A BIPOLAR JUNCTION TRANSISTOR

Let us now compare the h parameters for the various configurations and relate them to other parameters of the transistor. The current-amplifying ability of the transistor, in any configuration, depends directly upon h_f, since it relates the output circuit current to the input current. From Fig. 6-24, we have

$$h_{fb} = \frac{\mathbf{I}_c}{\mathbf{I}_e}\bigg|_{\mathbf{v}_{cb} = 0} \qquad (6\text{-}71)$$

The currents and voltages represent incremental changes. Then, if this is compared with Eq. (3-71), we have

$$h_{fb} = -\alpha \qquad (6\text{-}72)$$

Thus, the significance of α is again illustrated. Then, using Eqs. (6-69) and (6-70), we have

$$h_{fe} = \frac{\alpha}{1 - \alpha} \qquad (6\text{-}73)$$

$$h_{fc} = -\frac{1}{1 - \alpha} \qquad (6\text{-}74)$$

The value of h_{fe} is the *common-emitter short-circuit forward-current amplification factor*, and is denoted by the symbol β (see Sec. 3-16). This is to the common-emitter circuit what α is to the common-base circuit. Thus [see also Eq. (3-123)]

$$\beta = \frac{\alpha}{1 - \alpha} \tag{6-75}$$

In the usual transistor, α is a positive number that is slightly less than unity. Thus, h_{fe} and h_{fc} are usually very much greater than 1. We shall see that the common-emitter and common-collector amplifier configurations are capable of much greater current gains than the common-base configuration. In the transistor, the current gain is usually of prime importance. We are usually concerned with the gain of cascaded amplifiers (where the output of one amplifier is connected to the input of the next). The output generator of the transistor is controlled by the input current (not by the input voltage). Thus, knowledge of current gains can be used *directly* to obtain the gain of a cascaded amplifier. The input current can be obtained from the input voltage, but this involves tedious calculations involving the input admittance.

Now let us consider the admittance h_o that shunts the output current generator. In general,

$$h_{oe} \approx h_{oc} \approx \frac{h_{ob}}{1 - \alpha} \tag{6-76}$$

Thus, the shunting effect of h_{oe} and h_{oc} are considerably greater than that of h_{ob}. This shunting admittance tends to reduce the current gain of the amplifier. It is desirable for the admittance to be small.

The resistance that is in series with the input generator is h_{ie}. Here we have

$$h_{ie} \approx h_{ic} \approx \frac{h_{ib}}{1 - \alpha} \tag{6-77}$$

Here h_{ie} and h_{ic} are considerably greater than h_{ib}. This series resistance tends to reduce the gain of the amplifier. It is desirable for it to be small. At first glance, Eqs. (6-76) and (6-77) seem quite similar. However, it should be remembered that h_o represents an admittance whereas h_i represents an impedance.

6-12 VARIATION IN THE HYBRID PARAMETERS WITH OPERATING POINT AND TEMPERATURE

When a transistor is operated linearly, much of the pertinent low-frequency information about it can be obtained from the hybrid parameters. If these change, then such characteristics as amplification, input impedance, and output impedance will vary. Thus, it is desirable to know how the h parameters change with the operating point of the transistor. This knowledge enables the circuit designer to vary the operating point to obtain the most desirable characteristics. If the h parameters of the transistor vary very rapidly with a change in operating point, the operating point should be well stabilized so that the characteristics of the amplifier do not change too much.

The parameters of the transistor also vary with temperature. This change should be known since it indicates to the designer how much temperature variation can be tolerated.

The change of a transistor's parameters with operating point and/or temperature can be found, in an ideal case, from the theoretical equations for a transistor (see Secs. 3-13 and 3-14). However, the actual variations are

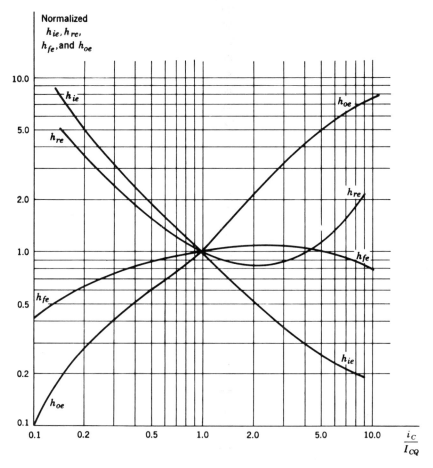

Fig. 6-27 Typical variation of h_{ie}, h_{re}, h_{fe}, and h_{oe} with i_C. The h parameters are normalized to their values where $i_C = I_{CQ}$. It is assumed that v_{CE} and the temperature are constant.

often somewhat different than those predicted by the ideal equations. For these reasons, manufacturers often supply experimentally measured graphical information which indicates the variation of the important parameters with operating point and/or temperature. Let us consider some typical diagrams. We shall consider the common-emitter parameters here since they are most often used.

In Fig. 6-27, the variation of the h parameters with collector current is presented. A typical operating point is chosen, that is, $i_c = I_{CQ}$, $v_{CE} = V_{CEQ}$, and the parameters are normalized with respect to their values at that operating point. In Fig. 6-27, v_{CE} and the temperature T are assumed to be constant. Let us consider the variation of h_{fe}. In the next section we shall demonstrate that the amplification varies directly with it. Note that it has a maximum for some values of i_C. Thus, it may be desirable to operate the transistor such that h_{fe} is maximized. However, there are factors other than h_{fe} which enter into the choice of an operating point. The collector-base junction dissipation and the nonlinearities of the transistor must also be considered when the location of the operating point is chosen.

The variation of the h parameters with temperature is also often presented graphically, a typical plot being shown in Fig. 6-28. The operating

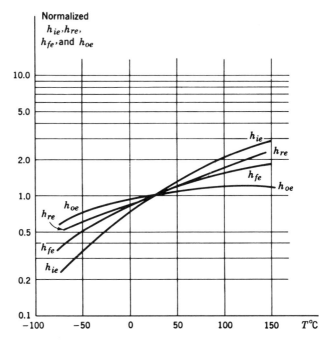

Fig. 6-28 Typical variation of h_{ie}, h_{re}, h_{fe}, and h_{oe} with temperature. The h parameters are normalized to their values when $T = 25°C$.

point of the transistor is assumed to be constant. The h parameters are normalized to their respective values at $T = 25°C$. This is often the nominal operating temperature of electronic devices. Note that all the parameters fall off as temperature decreases. Usually, a falloff in h_{fe} means that the behavior of the transistor has deteriorated. Thus, it may seem desirable to operate the transistor at high temperatures. However, this could require the use of cumbersome heaters or damage the transistor or result in reduced power-dissipation ratings.

At times, manufacturers supply additional characteristics which give the variation of the h parameters with other terms such as i_B or v_{CE}.

6-13 AN ANALYSIS OF ELEMENTARY COMMON-BASE, COMMON-EMITTER, AND COMMON-COLLECTOR TRANSISTOR AMPLIFIERS

Since the form of the h-parameter equivalent circuits of the common-base, common-emitter, and common-collector transistor configurations are the same, a single linear model will suffice for the three elementary amplifiers. That is, the amplifier circuits of Fig. 6-29 can be represented by the linear model of Fig. 6-30a, provided that the substitutions of Table 6-2 are used.

Writing a mesh equation for the input side and a nodal equation for the output side of Fig. 6-30a or its equivalent Fig. 6-30b, we obtain

$$\mathbf{I}_s R_s = (R_s + h_i)\mathbf{I}_1 + h_r\mathbf{V}_2 \tag{6-78a}$$

$$0 = h_f\mathbf{I}_1 + \left(h_o + \frac{1}{R_L}\right)\mathbf{V}_2 \tag{6-78b}$$

As we discussed in Sec. 6-11, the current gains are of prime importance. There are two different ones that can be considered. The first is the *current amplification (or gain)* $\mathbf{A}_i$, which is defined as

$$\mathbf{A}_i = \frac{\mathbf{I}_2}{\mathbf{I}_1} \tag{6-79}$$

Table 6–2   Substitutions to be used with the h-parameter equivalent circuits of Fig. 6-30

Quantity	Common base	Common emitter	Common collector
h_i	h_{ib}	h_{ie}	h_{ic}
h_r	h_{rb}	h_{re}	h_{rc}
h_f	h_{fb}	h_{fe}	h_{fc}
h_o	h_{ob}	h_{oe}	h_{oc}
$\mathbf{V}_1$	$\mathbf{V}_{eb}$	$\mathbf{V}_{be}$	$\mathbf{V}_{bc}$
$\mathbf{V}_2$	$\mathbf{V}_{cb}$	$\mathbf{V}_{ce}$	$\mathbf{V}_{ec}$
$\mathbf{I}_1$	$\mathbf{I}_e$	$\mathbf{I}_b$	$\mathbf{I}_b$
$\mathbf{I}_2$	$\mathbf{I}_c$	$\mathbf{I}_c$	$\mathbf{I}_e$

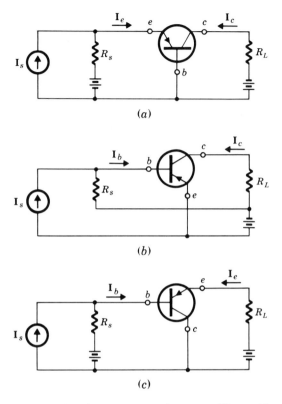

Fig. 6-29 Elementary transistor amplifiers: (*a*) common-base; (*b*) common-emitter; (*c*) common-collector.

This is the ratio of the transistor output current to its input current and is quite useful in calculating the current gain of cascaded amplifier stages. The other current gain is $\mathbf{K}_i$, the *composite-current amplification (or gain)*, which is defined as

$$\mathbf{K}_i = \frac{\mathbf{I}_2}{\mathbf{I}_s} \tag{6-80}$$

This is the ratio of the circuit's output current to its input current. Thus, $\mathbf{K}_i$ is the current gain for the complete circuit. Then, solving Eqs. (6-78) for $\mathbf{V}_2$, and dividing by $-\mathbf{I}_s R_L$, we obtain

$$\mathbf{K}_i = \frac{h_f R_s}{(h_i + R_s)(1 + h_o R_L) - h_f h_r R_L} \tag{6-81}$$

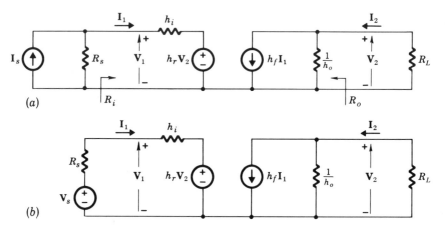

Fig. 6-30 (a) An h-parameter model which can be used to represent the elementary common-base, common-emitter, and common-collector transistor amplifiers of Fig. 6-29; (b) the same circuit with a voltage-generator input.

The current gain $\mathbf{A}_i$ is different from $\mathbf{K}_i$ because of the current through R_s. $\mathbf{A}_i$ can be obtained from $\mathbf{K}_i$ by letting $R_s \to \infty$. Thus,

$$\mathbf{A}_i = \frac{h_f}{1 + h_o R_L} \tag{6-82}$$

The maximum value of $\mathbf{K}_i$ occurs when R_s is infinite and R_L is zero. Letting $R_s \to \infty$ maximizes $\mathbf{I}_1$ independently of R_L, and setting $R_L = 0$ maximizes $\mathbf{I}_2$ independently of R_s. Similarly, the maximum value of $\mathbf{A}_i$ occurs when $R_L = 0$. Thus,

$$K_{i,\max} = A_{i,\max} = h_f \tag{6-83}$$

These equations again illustrate the significance of the function h_f.

Now let us consider the voltage amplifications of the circuit. Note that, in a transistor amplifier, the current gains are far more significant than the voltage gains. We shall use the circuit of Fig. 6-30b, where the current-generator input has been replaced by a voltage-generator input to permit us to define a composite voltage gain. The *composite voltage amplification (or gain)* $\mathbf{K}_v$ is

$$\mathbf{K}_v = \frac{\mathbf{V}_2}{\mathbf{V}_s} \tag{6-84}$$

The *voltage amplification (or gain)* $\mathbf{A}_v$ is defined by

$$\mathbf{A}_v = \frac{\mathbf{V}_2}{\mathbf{V}_1} \tag{6-85}$$

The significance of $\mathbf{K}_v$ and $\mathbf{A}_v$ is analogous to that of $\mathbf{K}_i$ and $\mathbf{A}_i$. Note that the value of $\mathbf{A}_v$ does not depend on whether Fig. (6-30) *a* or *b* is used since they are equivalent. Then, replacing $\mathbf{I}_s R_s$ by $\mathbf{V}_s$ in Eq. (6-78a) and solving Eqs. (6-78), we obtain

$$\mathbf{K}_v = \frac{-h_f R_L}{(h_i + R_s)(1 + h_o R_L) - h_f h_r R_L} \tag{6-86}$$

The voltage gain $\mathbf{A}_v$ can be obtained from $\mathbf{K}_v$ by setting $R_s = 0$. Thus,

$$\mathbf{A}_v = \frac{-h_f R_L}{h_i(1 + h_o R_L) - h_f h_r R_L} \tag{6-87}$$

The maximum value of $\mathbf{K}_v$ occurs when $R_s = 0$ and $R_L \rightarrow \infty$. Similarly, the maximum value of $\mathbf{A}_v$ occurs when $R_L \rightarrow \infty$. Thus,

$$K_{v,\max} = A_{v,\max} = \frac{-h_f}{h_i h_o - h_f h_r} \tag{6-88}$$

The input and output resistances of transistor circuits can be used to calculate the effect of the external circuit on the amplifier and vice versa (see Sec. 8-2). Solving for these, we obtain

$$R_i = \frac{\mathbf{V}_1}{\mathbf{I}_1}\bigg|_{\mathbf{I}_2 = -\mathbf{V}_2/R_L} = h_i - \frac{h_f h_r R_L}{1 + h_o R_L} \tag{6-89}$$

and

$$R_o = \frac{\mathbf{V}_2}{\mathbf{I}_2}\bigg|_{\mathbf{I}_1 = -\mathbf{V}_1/R_S} = \frac{R_s + h_i}{h_o(h_i + R_s) - h_f h_r} \tag{6-90}$$

where R_o is measured with the input generator replaced by its internal impedance.

Since the input resistance of a transistor circuit is not infinite, power will be taken from the input generator. We can define two operating power gains: K_p, the *composite power gain*, and A_p, the *power gain*. Using Fig. 6-30a, we have

$$K_p = \frac{|\mathbf{V}_2|\,|I_2|}{|\mathbf{V}_1|\,|I_s|} = |A_v|\,|K_i| \tag{6-91}$$

and

$$A_p = \frac{|\mathbf{V}_2|\,|I_2|}{|\mathbf{V}_1|\,|I_1|} = |A_v|\,|A_i| \tag{6-92}$$

where K_p is the ratio of the power dissipated in R_L to the power supplied by I_s, and A_p is the ratio of the power dissipated in R_L to the power entering the transistor.   These are called *operating* gains since they represent the ratios of actual powers.   Then, substituting in Eqs. (6-91) and (6-92) we obtain

$$K_p = \frac{h_f^2 R_s R_L}{[(h_i + R_s)(1 + h_o R_L) - h_f h_r R_L][h_i(1 + h_o R_L) - h_f h_r R_L]} \quad (6\text{-}93)$$

The value of A_p can be found from K_p by letting $R_s \to \infty$, since this will cause the power dissipated in R_s to become zero.   Hence,

$$A_p = \frac{h_f^2 R_L}{h_i(1 + h_o R_L)^2 - h_f h_r R_L(1 + h_o R_L)} \quad (6\text{-}94)$$

To maximize K_p with respect to R_s, let $R_s \to \infty$, since this will simultaneously maximize the output power and eliminate the power dissipated in R_s, independent of R_L.   Thus, the maximum value of A_p will also be the maximum value of K_p (with respect to R_s).   To maximize A_p with respect to R_L, differentiate and set the derivative equal to zero.   This yields

$$R_{L,\text{opt}} = \sqrt{\frac{h_i}{h_o(h_i h_o - h_r h_f)}} \quad (6\text{-}95)$$

Note that this is not equal to R_o given by Eq. (6-90).   If $R_L = R_o$, the output power will be maximized.   However, the power gain is a ratio of output to input power.   Hence, maximizing the output power does not necessarily maximize the ratio.   Substituting Eq. (6-95) into Eq. (6-94), we obtain

$$K_{p,\text{max}} = A_{p,\text{max}} = \frac{h_f^2}{(\sqrt{h_i h_o - h_f h_r} + \sqrt{h_i h_o})^2} \quad (6\text{-}96)$$

Another type of power gain, called the *transducer gain* K_T, is defined as the ratio of the output power delivered to R_L to the power that the input generator could supply to a matched load.   This is *not* an operating power gain, since a matched load is not usually presented.   The transducer gain is a measure of the advantage gained by using a transistor, since it is the ratio of the output power to the power that *could* be supplied to a matched load without a transistor.   Then

$$K_T = \frac{|I_2|^2 R_L}{|I_s|^2 R_s/4} = \frac{4K_i^2 R_L}{R_s} \quad (6\text{-}97a)$$

Hence

$$K_T = \frac{4R_s R_L h_f^2}{[(h_i + R_s)(1 + h_o R_L) - h_f h_r R_L]^2} \quad (6\text{-}97b)$$

Since the denominator of Eq. (6-97a) is independent of the actual circuit conditions, K_T will be maximized with respect to R_L when the output power is maximized, i.e., when $R_L = R_o$. This maximized value of K_T is called the *available power gain* K_{AP}. Substituting Eq. (6-90) into Eq. (6-97b), we obtain

$$K_{AP} = \frac{h_f{}^2 R_s}{(h_i + R_s)[h_o(h_i + R_s) - h_f h_r]} \tag{6-98}$$

Maximizing this expression with respect to R_s, we have

$$R_{s,\text{opt}} = \sqrt{\frac{h_i(h_i h_o - h_f h_r)}{h_o}} \tag{6-99}$$

Substituting Eq. (6-99) into Eq. (6-98), we obtain

$$K_{AP,\text{max}} = \frac{h_f{}^2}{(\sqrt{h_i h_o - h_f h_r} + \sqrt{h_i h_o})^2} \tag{6-100}$$

This is the same as Eq. (6-96). Thus, $K_{P,\text{max}}$, $A_{p,\text{max}}$, and $K_{AP,\text{max}}$ are all equal. This quantity is sometimes used as a figure of merit for the transistor.

Let us now consider the relative merits of the common-base, common-emitter, and the common-collector amplifiers. The current gain is usually of prime importance. Its maximum value is given by h_f. Thus,

$$K_{ib,\text{max}} = \alpha \tag{6-101a}$$

$$K_{ie,\text{max}} = \frac{\alpha}{1 - \alpha} = \beta \tag{6-101b}$$

$$K_{ic,\text{max}} = \frac{1}{1 - \alpha} \tag{6-101c}$$

The subscripts b, e, and c stand for common base, common emitter, and common collector, respectively. Since α is a number that is, in general, less than, but almost equal to, unity, we can write

$$K_{ib,\text{max}} \approx 1 \tag{6-102a}$$

$$K_{ie,\text{max}} \approx K_{ic,\text{max}} \gg K_{ib,\text{max}} \tag{6-102b}$$

The maximum current gain available from the common-base amplifier is less than unity, while it is considerably greater than unity for the common-emitter and common-collector amplifiers. The largest value is that for the common-collector amplifier. Before drawing any conclusions about the desirability of one configuration over another, we must consider the actual current gain $\mathbf{K}_i$, rather than the theoretical maximum values of Eqs. (6-101). Equation (6-81) can be written as

$$K_i = \frac{h_f R_s}{(1 + h_o R_L)[R_s + h_i - h_f h_r R_L/(1 + h_o R_L)]} \tag{6-103}$$

Substituting Eq. (6-89), we obtain

$$\mathbf{K}_i = h_f \left[\frac{R_s}{(R_s + R_i)} \right] \left[\frac{1}{(1 + h_o R_L)} \right] \tag{6-104}$$

Let us interpret the various factors of this equation. h_f represents the value of I_2/I_1 when R_L is set equal to zero and R_s approaches infinity. That is, it is the short-circuit current gain of the transistor. It is also the maximum value of $\mathbf{K}_i$. The other two factors reduce the actual current gain below the maximum value. All the current that is supplied by the input current generator $\mathbf{I}_s$ does not enter the transistor as $\mathbf{I}_1$. Some of it is shunted by R_s (see Fig. 6-30a). Thus, the gain is reduced by the fraction

$$\frac{\mathbf{I}_1}{\mathbf{I}_s} = \frac{R_s}{R_s + R_i} \tag{6-105}$$

In the same way, a fraction of the current of the output current generator $h_f \mathbf{I}_1$ is shunted by the resistance $1/h_o$. Thus, the gain is also reduced by

$$\frac{\mathbf{I}_2}{h_f \mathbf{I}_1} = \frac{1/h_o}{1/h_o + R_L} = \frac{1}{1 + h_o R_L} \tag{6-106}$$

In general, $R_{ib} < R_{ie} < R_{ic}$. Some typical values are $R_{ib} = 60$ ohms, $R_{ie} = 1000$ ohms, and $R_{ic} = 30,000$ ohms. Thus, the value of $R_s/(R_s + R_i)$ will be smallest for the common-collector circuit and largest for the common-base circuit. Of course, if R_s is made large enough, the fraction will be close to unity for all three circuits. In practice, when cascaded amplifiers are considered, $R_s/(R_s + R_i)$ is almost unity for the common-base circuit, somewhat less than unity for the common-emitter circuit, and very much less than unity for the common-collector circuit. Finally, $h_{ob} < h_{oe} \approx h_{oc}$. Some average values are $h_{ob} = 0.49 \times 10^{-6}$ mho and $h_{oc} = h_{oc} = 25 \times 10^{-6}$ mho. Then $1/(1 + h_o R_L)$ will be largest for the common-base circuit. Often R_L is such that this ratio is fairly close to unity for all three circuits. When transistor circuits are cascaded, the common-emitter amplifier is almost always used. The common-base circuit cannot provide an actual current gain since h_{ib} is less than unity. The factor $R_s/(R_s + R_i)$ is usually very much smaller for the common-collector circuit than it is for the common-emitter circuit. Hence, the current gain of the common-emitter circuit will be considerably larger than the current gain of the common-collector circuit. Thus, in cascaded circuits, the common-emitter circuit is usually employed.

Although most transistor amplifiers have the common-emitter configuration, it is by no means the only one that is used. Current gain is not the only factor that is considered when a circuit is chosen. For instance, if a device is to be used to measure voltage, it is desirable that its input impedance be high so that it does not load down the circuit to be measured. In such cases, the input stage of the device would be a common-collector amplifier. Conversely, if the device were to measure current, a low-impedance input would be desirable and the common-base circuit would be used as the input stage. The output impedance of the common-collector circuit is usually low; hence, it is often used as an impedance match between a high-impedance input and a low-impedance output. The converse is true for the common-base circuit. The voltage gain of the common-base circuit is usually high.

The voltage gain of the common-collector amplifier is often slightly less than, but very close to, unity. Hence, the emitter voltage "follows" the input voltage. For this reason, the common-collector amplifier is called an *emitter follower*. This terminology is somewhat undesirable since it focuses attention on the voltage gain of the transistor amplifier. Actually, the current gain is of prime importance.

6-14   THE HIGH-FREQUENCY LINEAR MODEL OF THE FET

The linear model of the FET discussed in Sec. 6-5 is very accurate at low frequencies. However, as the frequency of the signal is increased, this model is no longer adequate. A linear model of the FET which is accurate at high frequencies can be obtained by modifying Fig. 6-12. In Fig. 3-37, we represented three stray capacitances of the FET. These are between the gate and drain, gate and source, and source and drain. In most instances, inclusion of these capacitances in the linear model will accurately account for the high-frequency effects.

However, at the start, we shall consider a more accurate model, shown in Fig. 6-31. In addition, we have included a substrate lead (see Figs. 3-38, 3-40, and 3-42). Often, the substrate lead is connected to the source, in which case, the lead is omitted. The stray capacitances of Fig. 3-37, C_{gs}, C_{gd}, and C_{ds}, have been included. In addition, we have included the resistances r_{gs} and r_{gd} in parallel with them. These resistances (see Sec. 3-25) are usually very large (of the order of 10^8 ohms in a junction FET and 10^{14} ohms in a MOSFET). In many instances they can be ignored, i.e., considered to be open circuits.

Note that the current generator's current is not proportional to the input voltage but to the voltage across C_a. That is,

$$\mathbf{V}_a = \frac{\mathbf{V}_{gs}}{1 + j\omega r_a C_a} \tag{6-107}$$

Note that the current of the current generator, and hence the amplification, falls off as ω is increased. This is caused by two effects. One is that the reactances of the capacitances C_{gd}, C_{gs}, and C_{ds} become smaller as the frequency is increased. If these reactances become small enough, they tend to "short-circuit" the signal. Thus, the input voltage will become smaller.

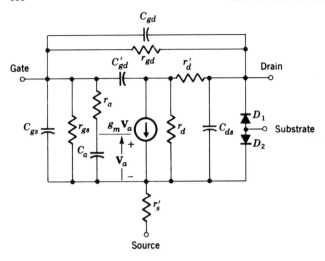

Fig. 6-31 High-frequency model of an FET.

In addition the actual amplifying ability of the FET falls off as frequency is increased. This occurs for several reasons. As an example, consider the following. As the signal varies, the width of the channel is varied (see Sec. 3-20). This varying channel width accounts for the varying resistance and varying output current of the FET. It takes a finite time for a single charge carrier to traverse the channel. This time is called the *transit time*, T_T. At low frequencies, T_T is very much shorter than the period of the signal. Thus, during the time that any one charge carrier is in the channel, the gate-source potential is essentially constant. On the other hand, if T_T is not very much less than the period of the signal, then each individual charge carrier will "see" a varying gate potential. It will act in accordance with the "average" of the gate potential. This will reduce the gain. It also can be shown that the motion of the charge carriers, when T_T becomes of the same order of magnitude as the period of the signal, also causes a component of gate current to be in phase with the gate-source voltage. This acts as though there were a resistance connected between the gate and source. These effects are accounted for by the inclusion of r_a and C_a. However, it is often found that at those frequencies where the effects of r_a and C_a *just* become noticeable, the gain has been reduced *very substantially* by the stray capacitance and the amplifier is no longer usable. In this case, the effect of r_a and C_a can be ignored. That is, they can be considered open circuits, and $g_m V_a$ can be replaced by $g_m V_{gs}$ in Fig. 6-31.

The elements r'_s, r'_d, and C'_{gd} are included to make the performance of the model closely approach measured values; for example, r'_s accounts for some resistance in series with the source. However, their effect is often small

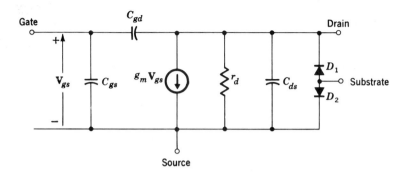

Fig. 6-32   Simplified high-frequency model of an FET.

in the useful range of frequency, and they are often omitted from the linear model.

In general, to be completely accurate, any linear model would have to have an infinite number of elements, but then it would be impractical to use it. Thus, approximations are made to obtain useful circuits. Often, linear models which contain only a few terms are very accurate. In general, as we have discussed, many of the elements of Fig. 6-31 can often be omitted. The resultant linear model is shown in Fig. 6-32.

The diodes D_1 and D_2 of Fig. 6-31 or 6-32 represent the isolation be-

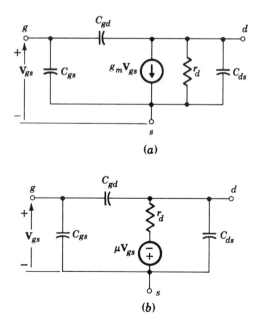

Fig. 6-33   Commonly used high-frequency models of the FET: (*a*) current-generator form and (*b*) voltage-generator form.

tween the FET and the substrate. These diodes are usually reverse-biased and often are omitted or replaced by capacitors in the model. In many instances where individual FETs are used the substrate is connected to the source. In this case, D_2 is short-circuited. The capacitance across the reverse-biased D_1 can then be considered to be part of C_{ds}. Thus, a very commonly used form of FET linear model is shown in Fig. 6-33a. Another form of this model is given in Fig. 6-33b. Here the current generator in shunt with r_d is replaced by a voltage generator in series with r_d.

When a dual-gate MOSFET is operated so that the gate 2–to–source potential does not vary, the models of Fig. 6-33 can be used to represent it. In this case, C_{gs} is replaced by C_{in} and C_{ds} replaced by C_{out}, where

$$C_{\text{in}} = C_{gs} + C_{gg2} \qquad C_{\text{out}} = C_{ds} + C_{dg2}$$

This is discussed in detail in Sec. 3-28.

6-15 THE HIGH-FREQUENCY LINEAR MODEL OF THE VACUUM TUBE

The linear model of the vacuum tube discussed in Sec. 6-6 must be modified if it is to be useful at high frequencies. Up to relatively high frequencies, the

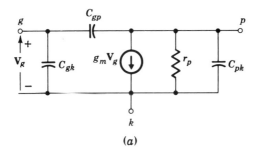

(a)

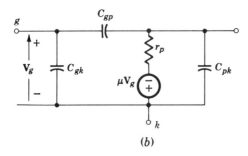

(b)

Fig. 6-34 High-frequency linear models for the vacuum tube: (a) current-generator form and (b) voltage-generator form.

only modification that must be made is the inclusion of the stray capacitances discussed in Secs. 2-7 and 2-10.   Then for the vacuum-tube triode the high-frequency linear model will be as shown in Fig. 6-34a.   This is obtained from the low-frequency model of Fig. 6-16a by adding the capacitances C_{gk}, C_{gp}, and C_{pk}.   This can be modified as shown in Fig. 6-34b by replacing the voltage generator by a current generator.

When a vacuum-tube pentode is operated such that its screen- and suppressor-grid potentials do not vary, the low-frequency model of Fig. 6-16 can be used to represent it (see Sec. 6-6).   At high frequencies, the bypass capacitor C_s (see Fig. 6-17a) can almost always be considered to be a short circuit.   Hence, the model of Fig. 6-16 can be used to represent the vacuum-tube pentode provided that the appropriate stray capacitances are added. This is done in Fig. 6-35a where it is assumed that the screen- and suppressor-

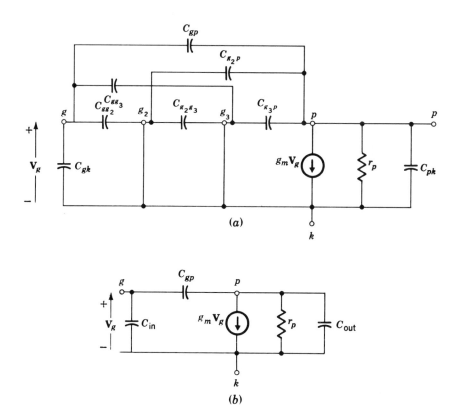

(a)

(b)

Fig. 6-35   (a) High-frequency linear model for the vacuum-tube pentode.   It is assumed that the screen and suppressor grids are effectively short-circuited to the cathode at all signal frequencies.   (b) The model redrawn with all parallel capacitors combined. $C_{in} = C_{gk} + C_{gg2} + C_{gg3}$; $C_{out} = C_{pk} + C_{g2p} + C_{g3p}$.

grid potentials are not allowed to vary; i.e., they are effectively short-circuited to the cathode at signal frequencies.

Many of the capacitances of Fig. 6-35a are connected in parallel. Thus, the circuit can be simplified by combining them. This is done in Fig. 6-35b, where

$$C_{\text{in}} = C_{gk} + C_{gg2} + C_{gg3} \tag{6-108a}$$

and

$$C_{\text{out}} = C_{pk} + C_{g2p} + C_{g3p} \tag{6-108b}$$

The performance of vacuum tubes also deteriorates because of transit-time effects (see Sec. 6-14). The primary effect is the apparent introduction of a resistance between the grid and cathode. At extremely high frequencies, transit-time effects limit the use of ordinary vacuum tubes. However, special vacuum tubes such as *klystrons*, *magnetrons*, and *traveling-wave tubes*, actually utilize transit-time effects in their operation.

The high-frequency model for the vacuum tube is essentially the same as the high-frequency model for the FET. (Compare Figs. 6-33 to 6-35.) Thus, as we have stated (see Sec. 6-6), to avoid duplication, only the FET circuit will be considered. The discussion can be applied to vacuum tubes by substituting *grid* for *gate*, *plate* for *drain*, *cathode* for *source*, $\mathbf{V}_g$ for $\mathbf{V}_{gs}$, r_p for r_d, C_{gp} for C_{gd}, etc. Unless otherwise noted, these substitutions can be made.

6-16 HIGH-FREQUENCY INPUT ADMITTANCE OF THE COMMON-SOURCE FET AMPLIFIER—MILLER EFFECT

Let us compute the input admittance of the common-source amplifier shown in Fig. 6-36b. Using Fig. 6-36b, we obtain

$$\mathbf{Y}_i = \frac{\mathbf{I}_1}{\mathbf{V}_{GS}} \tag{6-109}$$

where

$$\mathbf{I}_1 = \mathbf{I}_{gs} + \mathbf{I}_{gd} \tag{6-110}$$

From Fig. 6-36b we have

$$\mathbf{I}_{gs} = \mathbf{V}_1 j\omega C_{gs} \tag{6-111a}$$

and

$$\mathbf{I}_{gd} = (\mathbf{V}_1 - \mathbf{V}_2)j\omega C_{gd} \tag{6-111b}$$

The voltage $\mathbf{V}_2$ is not known. However, we can express it in terms of $\mathbf{V}_{gs}$ and the voltage amplification $\mathbf{A}_v$

$$\mathbf{A}_v = \frac{\mathbf{V}_2}{\mathbf{V}_{gs}} \tag{6-112}$$

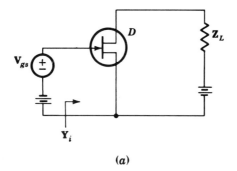

(a)

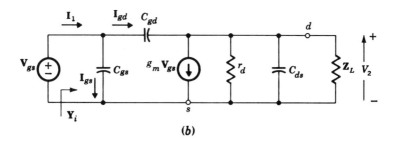

(b)

Fig. 6-36 (a) Elementary common-source FET amplifier and (b) its high-frequency linear model.

Thus,

$$\mathbf{I}_{gd} = \mathbf{V}_1(1 - \mathbf{A}_v)j\omega C_{gd} \tag{6-113}$$

Substituting Eqs. (6-111a) and (6-113) into Eq. (6-110) and then into Eq. (6-109), we obtain

$$\mathbf{Y}_i = j\omega[C_{gs} + (1 - \mathbf{A}_v)C_{gd}] \tag{6-114}$$

The voltage gain is a complex number. Let us write it as the sum of its real and imaginary components

$$\mathbf{A}_v = A_R + jA_X \tag{6-115}$$

Substituting this into Eq. (6-114) and separating it into its real and imaginary components, we have

$$G_i = \text{Re } (\mathbf{Y}_i) = \omega A_X C_{gd} \tag{6-116a}$$

$$B_i = \text{Im } (\mathbf{Y}_i) = \omega[C_{gs} + (1 - A_R)C_{gd}] \tag{6-116b}$$

Equations (6-116) represent a conductance G_i in *parallel* with a susceptance jB_i. This susceptance represents a capacitance. It is the input capacitance C_i of the amplifier, where

$$C_i = C_{gs} + (1 - A_R)C_{gd} \tag{6-117}$$

Often, A_v has a real negative component whose magnitude is much greater than 1.　In this case, A_R is a large negative number, and C_i is very much greater than can be expected from the magnitude of the capacitances C_{gs} and C_{gd}.　This increase in capacitance is called the *Miller effect*.　Since a *small* input capacitance is desirable, both C_{gs} and C_{gd} should be small.　It is especially important that C_{gd} be small since it is multiplied by $1 - A_R$.　In an FET, C_{gs} will be of the order of several picofarads, for example, 5 pf.　In those FETs which are to be used at high frequencies, C_{gd} must be kept very small.　A typical value is 0.1 pf.　(If a dual-gate FET is used, this figure can be reduced by an order of magnitude or more.)　Note that, for the figures given, if $-A_R$ is larger than 50, the predominant effect of C_i will be due to C_{gd}.

The *conductance in shunt* with C_i is G_i [see Eq. (6-116a)].　It is also desirable for this conductance to be small, i.e., be a large shunting resistance. This again demonstrates the necessity of having a small C_{gd}.　In general, A_X can be either positive or negative.　If it is negative, a negative input conductance results.　This can, at times, result in improper operation, as will be discussed in Secs. 9-26 and 11-7.　For the above reasons it is desirable for C_{gd} to be small.　The value of C_{gd} in a dual-gate MOSFET can be an order of magnitude, or more, less than that of the single-gate FET.　This is one of the great advantages of the dual-gate FET.

In the vacuum tube, Eq. (6-117) will be

$$C_i = C_{gk} + (1 - A_R)C_{gp} \tag{6-118}$$

Thus, it is important to keep C_{gp} small.　In the vacuum-tube triode C_{gp} will be on the order of several picofarads.　However, in the vacuum-tube pentode, with the shielding action of the screen grid, C_{gp} can be on the order of 0.001 pf.　Thus, one of the advantages of the vacuum-tube pentode over the vacuum-tube triode at high frequencies is demonstrated.　For the vacuum-tube pentode, C_{gk} is replaced by C_{in} (see Sec. 6-15).

In order to use Eqs. (6-116), $\mathbf{A}_v$ must be known.　An analysis of Fig. 6-36b yields

$$\mathbf{A}_v = \frac{\mathbf{V}_2}{\mathbf{V}_{gs}} = \frac{-g_m + j\omega C_{gd}}{j\omega(C_{gd} + C_{ds}) + r_d^{-1} + \mathbf{Z}_L^{-1}} \tag{6-119}$$

6-17 HIGH-FREQUENCY INPUT ADMITTANCE OF THE COMMON-DRAIN FET AMPLIFIER

One of the most important advantages of the common-drain amplifier is that its input admittance is very much lower than that of the other commonly used amplifier configurations, especially when the stray capacitances are con-

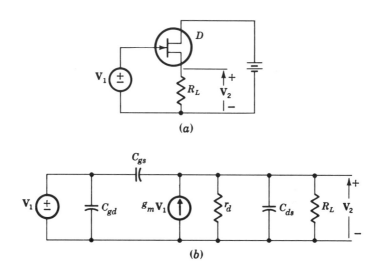

Fig. 6-37 (*a*) An FET source follower and (*b*) its high-frequency linear model.

sidered. We shall demonstrate this with the source-follower amplifier and linear model of Fig. 6-37. The input admittance is found by using the procedure of Sec. 6-16. Thus,

$$\mathbf{Y}_i = j\omega[C_{gd} + (1 - \mathbf{A}_v)C_{gs}] \tag{6-120}$$

where $\mathbf{A}_v = \mathbf{V}_2/\mathbf{V}_1$. Equation (6-120) has the same form as Eq. (6-114) except that the roles of C_{gd} and C_{gs} have been interchanged. However, in the source follower, $\mathbf{A}_v$ can often be considered to be approximately unity. Hence, the factor $1 - \mathbf{A}_v$ will be extremely small instead of large. Thus, the input admittance of Eq. (6-120) can often be approximated by

$$\mathbf{Y}_i \approx j\omega C_{gd} \tag{6-121}$$

In general, $\mathbf{A}_v$ will be a complex number that varies with frequency, so that this approximation is valid only for those frequencies where $\mathbf{A}_v \approx 1$. However, this approximation usually is very good over most of the frequencies of interest. Equations (6-120) and (6-121) can be used with vacuum tubes by replacing C_{gd} by C_{gp} and C_{gs} by C_{gk} for the vacuum-tube triode and C_{in} for the vacuum-tube pentode.

The use of dual-gate MOSFETs in common-drain circuits usually results in a large reduction in the input admittance because of the very low value of C_{gd}.

6-18 SOURCE- (OR CATHODE-) LEAD INDUCTANCE

All circuits possess some inductance. The inductance of all the leads which are connected to an FET will, in general, tend to reduce the high-frequency gain of the amplifier. The inductance in series with the source (or cathode) is particularly troublesome since the voltage produced across it will affect the input circuit. In this section, we shall discuss FETs or vacuum-tube pentodes. In general, the Miller effect causes the gain of vacuum-tube triodes to become very small before cathode-lead-inductance effects become important. Consider the linear model of an FET amplifier (see Fig. 6-38) where we have considered an inductance in series with the source. We shall make several approximations here which may be valid in wide-band amplifiers. If they are not, the complete circuit of Fig. 6-38 should be analyzed. This will be left to the reader. We shall assume that

$$r_d \gg |Z_L + j\omega L| \tag{6-122}$$

If this is true, we can neglect the current in r_d. We shall also assume that, at frequencies of interest,

$$|Z_L| \ll 1/j\omega C_{gd} \tag{6-123}$$

If Eqs. (6-122) and (6-123) are valid, the generator current $g_m V_{gs}$ will all be in the inductor L. Then, applying Kirchhoff's law to Fig. 6-38, we have

$$\mathbf{I}_a = \mathbf{V}_{gs} j\omega C_{gs} \tag{6-124a}$$

and

$$\mathbf{V}_1 = \mathbf{V}_{gs} + j\omega L g_m \mathbf{V}_{gs} \tag{6-124b}$$

Also

$$\mathbf{I}_b = \mathbf{V}_1(1 - \mathbf{A}_v)j\omega C_{gd} \tag{6-124c}$$

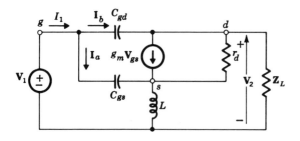

Fig. 6-38 Circuit illustrating a source-lead inductance.

where

$$\mathbf{A}_v = \frac{\mathbf{V}_2}{\mathbf{V}_1} \qquad (6\text{-}124d)$$

The input admittance is given by

$$\mathbf{Y}_i = \frac{\mathbf{I}_1}{\mathbf{V}_1} = \frac{\mathbf{I}_a + \mathbf{I}_b}{\mathbf{V}_1} \qquad (6\text{-}125)$$

Substituting Eqs. (6-124) into Eq. (6-125) and manipulating, we obtain

$$\mathbf{Y}_i = \frac{\omega^2 g_m C_{gs} L}{1 + \omega^2 g_m{}^2 L^2} + j\omega \left[\frac{C_{gs}}{1 + \omega^2 g_m{}^2 L^2} + (1 - A_v)C_{gd} \right] \qquad (6\text{-}126)$$

The last term is essentially the Miller effect capacitance (see Sec. 6-16); usually, $1 + \omega^2 g_m{}^2 L^2 \approx 1$ for frequencies of interest. In addition, because of the source-lead inductance, a conductance $\omega^2 g_m C_{gs} L/(1 + \omega^2 g_m{}^2 L^2)$ is added. It increases the input conductance of the amplifier and generally reduces the gain.

The use of integrated circuits can lessen this effect since the lead length, and hence this inductance, can be made very small. This reduces the shunt conductance [see Eq. (6-126)].

Often, the effects of stray capacitance reduce the gain far more than the effect of source-lead inductance does. In this case, it can be ignored. This is especially true in integrated circuits.

6-19 HIGH-FREQUENCY LINEAR MODELS FOR THE JUNCTION TRANSISTOR

High-frequency linear models for a bipolar junction transistor can be obtained by modifying the low-frequency model of Fig. 6-23b. We shall make use of the results of Sec. 3-18 here. There we discussed [see Eq. (3-132)] how α varies with frequency as

$$\alpha = \frac{\alpha_0}{1 + j\omega/\omega_\alpha} \qquad (6\text{-}127)$$

The capacitance across the emitter-base and collector-base junctions were also considered there. The high-frequency behavior of a transistor is very complex, and any linear model which uses a finite number of terms is a compromise between accuracy and simplicity. However, we shall consider models that are sufficiently accurate to analyze and design transistor circuits. At the start, let us consider the model of Fig. 6-23b, which was obtained on a physical basis, and modify it. Such a modification is shown in Fig. 6-39. In general, the quantity α' of Fig. 6-23b is such that $\alpha' \approx \alpha$. Thus, the current generator has been replaced by the value $\alpha_0 \mathbf{I}_e/(1 + j\omega/\omega_\alpha)$ which was

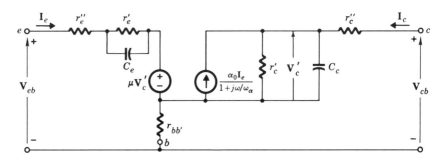

Fig. 6-39 A modification of the circuit of Fig. 6-23b which is valid at high frequencies.

derived in Sec. 3-18. In addition, the capacitances that exist across the transistor junctions must also be included. This is done by adding the capacitors C_e and C_c across the appropriate junction resistances. The capacitor C_e is usually larger than C_c. However, r_c' is usually very much greater than r_e'. The value of r_e' is small, since the emitter-base junction is forward-biased. For this reason, C_e often is neglected in high-frequency calculations.

Let us obtain the high-frequency common-base h-parameter linear model from the model of Fig. 6-39. To obtain $\mathbf{h}_{ie}$ and $\mathbf{h}_{fe}$, the output is short-circuited (see Sec. 6-1). Thus, in Fig. 6-39, $V_c = 0$. (Note that $V_c' \neq 0$.) We shall also make the following approximations which are usually very accurate. The impedances r_e'' and r_c'' of Fig. 6-39 are usually so small that they can be neglected. In addition, usually, the impedance of r_c' in parallel with C_c is much greater than $r_{bb'}$ at all frequencies of interest. Hence,

$$\left| \frac{r_c'}{1 + j\omega r_c' C_c} \right| \gg r_{bb'} \tag{6-128}$$

Thus, all the current from the current generator will be in r_{bb} and the output short circuit. Assume that an input generator I_c is applied. Then,

$$\mathbf{h}_{fb} = \frac{\mathbf{I}_c}{\mathbf{I}_e}$$

$$\mathbf{h}_{fb} = \frac{\alpha_0}{1 + j\omega/\omega_\alpha} \tag{6-129}$$

Similarly,

$$\mathbf{h}_{ib} = \frac{\mathbf{V}_{eb}}{\mathbf{I}_e}$$

$$\mathbf{h}_{ib} = \frac{r_e'}{1 + j\omega r_e' C_e} + r_{bb'}\left(1 - \frac{\alpha_0}{1 + j\omega/\omega_\alpha}\right)(1 - \mu) \tag{6-130a}$$

In general, $\mu \ll 1$, for example, $\mu = 10^{-4}$. Thus, $1 - \mu \approx 1$. Substituting this and manipulating, we obtain

$$\mathbf{h}_{ib} = \frac{r'_e}{1 + j\omega r'_e C_e} + (1 - \alpha_0)r_{bb'} + \frac{1}{\frac{1}{\alpha_0 r_{bb'}} + \frac{1}{j\alpha_0 r_{bb'}\omega/\omega_\alpha}} \qquad (6\text{-}130b)$$

This can be represented by the input circuit shown in Fig. 6-40. To determine $\mathbf{h}_{rb}$ and $\mathbf{h}_{ob}$, the input is open-circuited in Fig. 6-39. A voltage $\mathbf{V}_{cb}$ is then applied at the output

$$\mathbf{h}_{rb} = \frac{\mathbf{V}_{eb}}{\mathbf{V}_{cb}}$$

In general, at most frequencies of interest

$$\left| \frac{r'_c}{1 + j\omega r'_c C_c} \right| \gg r_{bb'} \qquad (6\text{-}131)$$

Thus,

$$\mathbf{V}'_c \approx \mathbf{V}_{cb} \qquad (6\text{-}132)$$

Then,

$$\mathbf{h}_{rb} = \mu + \frac{r_{bb'}}{r'_c}(1 + j\omega r'_c C_c) \qquad (6\text{-}133)$$

Similarly, using relation (6-131), we have

$$\mathbf{h}_{ob} = \frac{r'_c}{1 + j\omega r'_c C_c} \qquad (6\text{-}134)$$

Thus, the common-base h-parameter model has the form shown in Fig. 6-40.

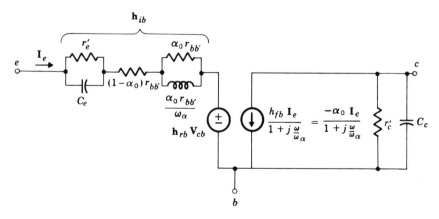

Fig. 6-40 An h-parameter representation of Fig. 6-39.

Note that the reactance of the inductor in parallel with $r_{bb'}$ becomes equal to it at $\omega = \omega_\alpha$. At frequencies far below ω_α this inductance can be considered to be essentially a short circuit. In addition, since $\alpha_0 \approx 1$, $(1 - \alpha_0)r_{bb'}$ will, in general, be very much less than the impedance of r_e in parallel with C_e. Thus, it can be omitted from the linear model. An approximate common-base h-parameter model based on these assumptions is shown in Fig. 6-41. At zero frequency this model should reduce to that of Fig. 6-24. Thus, r'_e is equal to h_{ib} and r'_c to $1/h_{ob}$. Note that the boldface h parameter represents the total expression, while the lightface expression represents the low-frequency terms. For instance,

$$\mathbf{h}_{fb} = \frac{h_{fb}}{1 + j\omega/\omega_\beta} \tag{6-135}$$

It is often just as easy to use the linear model of Fig. 6-39 as that of Fig. 6-40. However, if h parameters are used for the low-frequency calculations, it is sometimes desirable to use them for high-frequency calculations as well. This permits the high-frequency and low-frequency response to be related.

The most important transistor configuration is the common-emitter configuration. The common-emitter high-frequency model can be derived from Fig. 6-39 by using the emitter lead as the common one. However, another model that is more often used gives very good experimental results. Called the *hybrid-pi model* or *Giacoletto model*, it is shown in Fig. 6-42. The dependent current generator does not depend upon a terminal voltage or current. Instead, it is a function of the voltage $\mathbf{V}_{b'e}$ which appears between the *internal* terminal b' and the emitter lead. The difference between the input voltage $\mathbf{V}_{be}$ and $\mathbf{V}_{b'e}$ is the voltage drop across $r_{bb'}$. This represents the base spreading resistance. The voltage $\mathbf{V}_{b'e}$ falls off as frequency is increased because of the capacitance $C_{b'e}$ (and $C_{b'c}$). If $r_{bb'}$ were zero, this would not occur. This demonstrates the importance of the base spreading resistance.

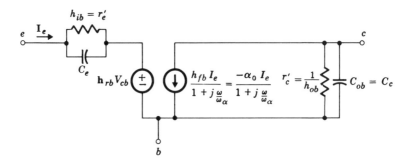

Fig. 6-41   An approximate common-base h-parameter model of a transistor.

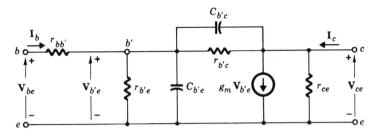

Fig. 6-42 A high-frequency common-emitter hybrid-pi linear model for the transistor.

Note, however, that any internal resistance of the input voltage, or current, generator (applied to terminals be) is added in series with $r_{bb'}$. It is this series combination that plays an important role in determining the frequency response.

The capacitance $C_{b'c}$ and the resistance $r_{b'c}$ represent the impedance across the reverse-biased collector-base junction. Often, $r_{b'c}$ is so large that it can be omitted, i.e., open-circuited. Let us consider some typical values of the parameters of the hybrid-pi equivalent circuit. These are $g_m = 50,000$ μmhos, $r_{bb'} = 80$ ohms, $r_{b'e} = 800$ ohms, $C_{b'e} = 100$ pf, $r_{b'c} = 5 \times 10^6$ ohms, $C_{b'c} = 3$ pf, $r_{ce} = 100,000$ ohms.

The hybrid-pi model is often used to analyze transistor circuits. However, there are times when h-parameter models have been used for low-frequency analysis. It is then desirable to relate the hybrid-pi model to the h parameters. Let us do this by obtaining the common-emitter h-parameter model from the hybrid-pi model of Fig. 6-42. To obtain $\mathbf{h}_{ie}$ and $\mathbf{h}_{fe}$, a short circuit is placed across the output. Thus, $\mathbf{h}_{ie}$ represents the impedance of $r_{bb'}$ in series with the parallel combination of $r_{b'e}$, $C_{b'e}$, $C_{b'c}$, and $r_{b'c}$. $r_{b'e}$ and $C_{b'e}$ represent the resistance and diffusion capacitance of the forward-biased emitter-base junction while $r_{b'c}$ and $C_{b'c}$ represent the resistance and transition capacitance of the reverse-biased collector-base junction. Thus,

$$r_{b'c} \gg r_{b'e} \tag{6-136a}$$

$$C_{b'c} \ll C_{b'e} \tag{6-136b}$$

In this case, we can write

$$\mathbf{h}_{ie} = r_{bb'} + \frac{r_{b'e}}{1 + j\omega r_{b'e} C_{b'e}} \tag{6-137}$$

which can be represented by the impedance shown in Fig. 6-43. Again making use of relation (6-136), we have (remember that the output is short-circuited)

$$\mathbf{V}_{b'e} = \frac{\mathbf{I}_b r_{b'e}}{1 + j\omega r_{b'e} C_{b'e}} \tag{6-138}$$

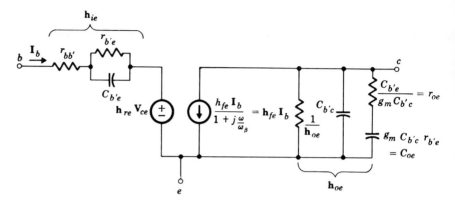

Fig. 6-43 A high-frequency common-emitter h-parameter model of the transistor. All resistance values are in ohms and capacitor values are in farads.

Then,

$$\mathbf{h}_{fe} = \frac{h_{fe}}{1 + j\omega/\omega_\beta} \tag{6-139}$$

where

$$h_{fe} = g_m r_{b'e} \tag{6-140a}$$

and

$$\omega_\beta = \frac{1}{r_{b'e} C_{b'e}} \tag{6-140b}$$

Note that at $\omega = 0$, $\mathbf{h}_{fe}$ becomes h_{fe}. If relations (6-136) are not valid, then replace $r_{b'e}$ by the parallel combination of $r_{b'e}$ and $r_{b'c}$ and replace $C_{b'e}$ by $C_{b'e} + C_{b'c}$ in Eqs. (6-139) to Eq. (6-140) and in Fig. 6-43.

To obtain $\mathbf{h}_{re}$ and $\mathbf{h}_{oe}$, we open-circuit the input and apply a voltage generator across the output. When a voltage generator is placed in parallel with a current generator, the current generator does not affect the rest of the network, except for the current in the voltage generator. Thus,

$$\mathbf{h}_{re} = \frac{r_{b'e}/(1 + j\omega r_{b'e} C_{b'e})}{r_{b'e}/(1 + j\omega r_{b'e} C_{b'e}) + r_{b'c}/(1 + j\omega r_{b'c} C_{b'c})} \tag{6-141}$$

Making use of Eqs. (6-136), we obtain

$$\mathbf{h}_{re} = h_{re} \frac{1 + j\omega r_{b'c} C_{b'c}}{1 + j\omega r_{b'e} C_{b'e}} \tag{6-142a}$$

where

$$h_{re} = \frac{r_{b'e}}{r_{b'c}} \tag{6-142b}$$

Thus, at $\omega = 0$, $\mathbf{h}_{re}$ becomes h_{re}.   Finally,

$$\mathbf{h}_{oe} = \frac{1}{r_{ce}} + \cfrac{1}{\cfrac{r_{b'c}}{1 + j\omega r_{b'c}C_{b'c}} + \cfrac{r_{b'e}}{1 + j\omega r_{b'e}C_{b'e}}} + g_m \frac{r_{b'e}}{r_{b'c}} \frac{1 + j\omega r_{b'c}C_{b'c}}{1 + j\omega r_{b'e}C_{b'e}}$$

(6-143a)

where we have used relation (6-142) to obtain the last term.   Applying relation (6-136) to the second term and manipulating the last one, we have

$$\mathbf{h}_{oe} = \frac{1}{r_{ce}} + \frac{1 + j\omega r_{b'c}C_{b'c}}{r_{b'c}} + \frac{g_m C_{b'c}}{C_{b'e}} \cfrac{\cfrac{1}{r_{b'c}C_{b'c}} + j\omega}{\cfrac{1}{r_{b'e}C_{b'e}} + j\omega}$$

(6-143b)

In general, for almost all transistors

$$r_{b'c}C_{b'c} \gg r_{b'e}C_{b'e}$$

(6-144)

Then, we can write

$$\mathbf{h}_{oe} = \frac{1}{r_{ce}} + \frac{r_{b'e}g_m}{r_{b'c}} + \frac{1}{r_{b'c}} + j\omega C_{b'c} + \frac{(g_m C_{b'c}/C_{b'e})j\omega}{j\omega + 1/r_{b'e}C_{b'e}}$$

(6-145a)

If relations (6-144) are not valid, the last term of Eq. (6-145a) should be multiplied by $1 - r_{b'e}C_{b'e}/r_{b'c}C_{b'c}$.   At zero frequency Eq. (6-145a) should reduce to h_{oe}.   Then,

$$\mathbf{h}_{oe} = h_{oe} + j\omega C_{b'c} + \frac{(g_m C_{b'c}/C_{b'e})j\omega}{j\omega + 1/r_{b'e}C_{b'e}}$$

(6-145b)

where

$$h_{oe} = \frac{1}{r_{ce}} + \frac{r_{b'e}g_m}{r_{b'c}} + \frac{1}{r_{b'c}}$$

(6-146)

The complete representation of this model is shown in Fig. 6-43.   Note that, at zero frequency, $\mathbf{h}_{ie}$ should reduce to h_{ie}.   Thus,

$$h_{ie} = r_{bb'} + r_{b'e}$$

(6-147)

If relations (6-136) are not valid, use Eq. (6-141) for $\mathbf{h}_{re}$ and Eq. (6-143a) with the last term obtained using Eq. (6-141) and not Eq. (6-142).

The capacitance $C_{b'c}$ is relatively small.   Usually, at those frequencies where the effect of the single shunting $C_{b'c}$ just becomes noticeable, the gain of the transistor amplifier has fallen off to unusable values.   Thus, $C_{b'c}$ often is omitted from the h-parameter model.   This is shown in Fig. 6-44.   Note that the effect of $C_{b'c}$ appears at several other parts of that model.

The reactance of the capacitance C_{oe} is equal to the resistance of r_{oe} (see Fig. 6-44) at the frequency $\omega = 1/C_{b'e}r_{b'e}$.   This is equal to ω_β [see Eq.

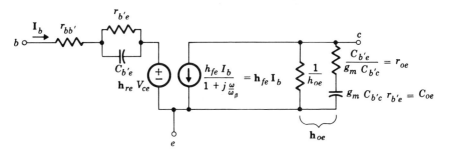

Fig. 6-44 A high-frequency common-emitter h-parameter model of the transistor which is valid at all except the highest frequencies. All resistances and capacitance values are in ohms or farads.

(6-140b)]. At frequencies far below ω_β, the resistance r_{oe} often can be considered to be a short circuit.

At times, the capacitance $C_{b'e}$ is omitted (open-circuited) in calculations.

The value of h_{re} is given by Eq. (6-142b). This is a very small number. If the voltage gain of the amplifier is not too large, so that $h_{re}V_{ce}$ is small in comparison with V_{eb} (see Fig. 6-44), then h_{re} is often neglected, i.e., considered zero. At high frequencies, this approximation may no longer be valid. That is, at very high frequencies [see Eq. (6-142b)]

$$\mathbf{h}_{re} = \frac{C_{b'c}}{C_{b'e}} \tag{6-148}$$

This is still a small number, but it is not as small as h_{re}. However, in many cases, Eq. (6-142a) does not become large enough to be considered over most of the frequencies of interest.

An important effect of $\mathbf{h}_{re}$ is on the input impedance of the amplifier. If $|\mathbf{h}_{re}V_{ce}|$ is small in comparison with $|V_{be}|$, then $\mathbf{h}_{re}$ can be neglected in computing the input impedance. This approximation will be valid if the voltage amplification is not too large.

Alternately, we can demonstrate this by using the hybrid-pi model (see Fig. 6-45a). The input admittance $\mathbf{Y}_i$ consists of $\mathbf{Y}'_i$ in series with $r_{bb'}$. $\mathbf{Y}'_i$ is given by

$$\mathbf{Y}'_i = \frac{\mathbf{I}_b}{\mathbf{V}_{b'e}}$$

Then, from Fig. 6-45a,

$$\mathbf{I}_b = \frac{\mathbf{V}_{b'e}(1 + j\omega r_{b'e}C_{b'e})}{r_{b'e}} + \frac{(\mathbf{V}_{b'e} - \mathbf{V}_{b'c})(1 + j\omega r_{b'c}C_{b'c})}{r_{b'c}} \tag{6-149}$$

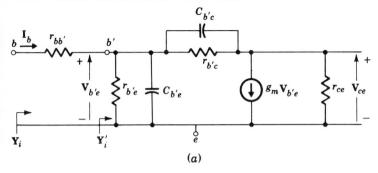

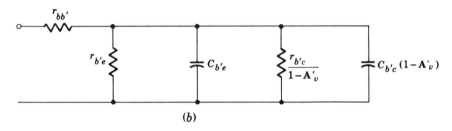

Fig. 6-45 (a) A hybrid-pi model of a transistor; (b) a representation of the input admittance of this device showing the Miller effect.

Let us define a voltage gain from point b' to e

$$A'_v = \frac{\mathbf{V}_{b'c}}{\mathbf{V}_{b'e}} \tag{6-150}$$

Then, substituting in Eq. (6-148), we have

$$\mathbf{Y}'_i = \frac{1 + j\omega r_{b'e}C_{b'e}}{r_{b'e}} + \frac{(1 - \mathbf{A}'_v)(1 + j\omega r_{b'c}C_{b'c})}{r_{b'c}} \tag{6-151}$$

The total $\mathbf{Y}_i$ is shown in Fig. 6-45b, where it is assumed that $\mathbf{A}'_v$ is real (and negative). Note that the actual admittance of the parallel combination of $r_{b'c}$ and $C_{b'c}$ has been multiplied by $1 - \mathbf{A}'_v$. This is the *Miller effect* in the transistor. Since the impedance of $r_{b'c}$ in parallel with $C_{b'c}$ is much greater than the impedance of $r_{b'e}$ in parallel with $C_{b'e}$, the $r_{b'c}$ and $C_{b'c}$ can at times be omitted from Fig. 6-45b unless $|\mathbf{A}'_v|$ is a large number. This substantiates the previous discussion.

6-20 A LINEAR MODEL FOR THE TUNNEL DIODE

When the tunnel diode is used as a linear device, it is operated in the negative-resistance portion of its characteristics (see Sec. 3-10). At low frequencies, the tunnel-diode model is just a negative resistance equal to the reciprocal of the slope of its output characteristics (see Fig. 3-13) at the operating point.

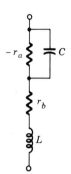

Fig. 6-46 A linear model for the tunnel diode. Note that $-r_a$ is negative.

This resistance is called the *dynamic resistance* of the tunnel diode. It can be considered to be the sum of two terms, $-r_a$ and r_b. The negative term $-r_a$ represents the net effect of the tunneling current and the ordinary diode currents while r_b accounts for ohmic resistance at the contacts and in the bulk of the semiconductor.

At high frequencies, the effect of the junction capacitor must be considered. This capacitor should be placed across $-r_a$ since this represents the effect of the junction, as shown in Fig. 6-46.

The leads of the tunnel diode possess an inductance accounted for by the inductor L in Fig. 6-46.

When tunnel diodes are used as linear amplifiers, the negative resistance in conjunction with the lead inductance L, the capacitor C, and the other circuit elements can cause the circuit to oscillate and not function properly. Care should be taken to see that this oscillation does not occur.

6-21 SOME EXAMPLES OF THE USE OF LINEAR MODELS

As an example of the use of linear models, we shall compute the voltage amplification of the FET amplifier of Fig. 6-47a. This type of amplifier is called a *feedback amplifier* since a fraction of the output voltage is returned to the input circuit. Usually, such a feedback amplifier would have an odd number of stages. However, we shall use only two stages in the example to simplify and better illustrate the analysis. Feedback amplifiers will be discussed in detail in Chap. 13. To further simplify the analysis, we shall assume that the frequency of operation is such that high-frequency models do not have to be used. In addition, we shall assume that C_1 and C_2 are chosen large enough so that they can be considered to be short circuits at the signal frequency. The model for Fig. 6-47a is shown in Fig. 6-47b.

We shall perform a loop analysis on this circuit. Choosing loop currents as shown, we can write

$$\mathbf{V}_1 + \mu_2\mathbf{V}_{g2} = (R_1 + R_2 + r_{d2} + \mathbf{Z}_6)\mathbf{I}_1 + (r_{d2} + \mathbf{Z}_6)\mathbf{I}_2 \qquad (6\text{-}152a)$$

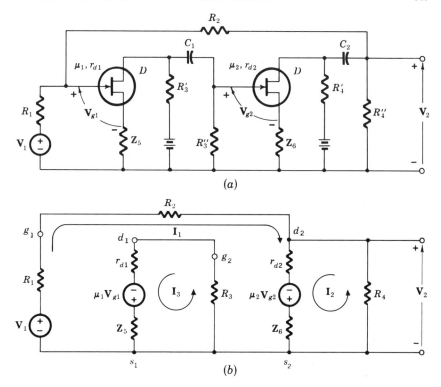

Fig. 6-47 (a) A two-stage FET amplifier and (b) its linear model, where $R_3 = R_3'$ $R_3''/(R_3' + R_3'')$ and $R_4 = R_4' R_4''/(R_3' + R_3'')$. It is assumed that C_1 and C_2 are short circuits at the signal frequency.

$$\mu_2 V_{g2} = (r_{d2} + Z_6)I_1 + (r_{d2} + Z_6 + R_4)I_2 \qquad (6\text{-}152b)$$

$$\mu_1 V_{g1} = (r_{d1} + Z_5 + R_3)I_3 \qquad (6\text{-}152c)$$

The gate-source voltages are given by

$$V_{g1} = V_1 - R_1 I_1 - Z_5 I_3 \qquad (6\text{-}153a)$$

$$V_{g2} = -R_3 I_3 - Z_6(I_1 + I_2) \qquad (6\text{-}153b)$$

We can eliminate two of the five unknown quantities by substituting Eqs. (6-153) into (6-152). *It should be emphasized that these substitutions should be made at this point, since this will considerably reduce the labor required to solve the equations.* The resulting equations are

$$V_1 = [R_1 + R_2 + r_{d2} + (1 + \mu_2)Z_6]I_1$$
$$+ [r_{d2} + (1 + \mu_2)Z_6]I_2 + \mu_2 R_3 I_3 \qquad (6\text{-}154a)$$

$$0 = [r_{d2} + (1 + \mu_2)Z_6]I_1 + [r_{d2} + (1 + \mu_2)Z_6 + R_4]I_2 + \mu_2 R_3 I_3$$
$$(6\text{-}154b)$$

$$\mu_1 \mathbf{V}_1 = \mu_1 R_1 \mathbf{I}_1 + 0\mathbf{I}_2 + [r_{d1} + (1 + \mu_1)\mathbf{Z}_5 + R_3]\mathbf{I}_3 \qquad (6\text{-}154c)$$

Using standard determinant techniques to solve these equations for $\mathbf{I}_2$ and then multiplying by $-R_4$ and dividing by $\mathbf{V}_1$, we obtain the following expression for the voltage gain:

$$A_v = \frac{\mathbf{V}_2}{\mathbf{V}_1}$$

$$= -R_4 \frac{\begin{vmatrix} R_1 + R_2 + r_{d2} + (1 + \mu_2)\mathbf{Z}_6 & 1 & \mu_2 R_3 \\ r_{d2} + (1 + \mu_2)\mathbf{Z}_6 & 0 & \mu_2 R_3 \\ \mu_1 R_1 & \mu_1 & r_{d1} + (1 + \mu_1)\mathbf{Z}_6 + R_3 \end{vmatrix}}{\begin{vmatrix} R_1 + R_2 + r_{d2} + (1 + \mu_2)\mathbf{Z}_6 & r_{d2} + (1 + \mu_2)\mathbf{Z}_6 & \mu_2 R_3 \\ r_{d2} + (1 + \mu_2)\mathbf{Z}_6 & r_{d2} + (1 + \mu_2)\mathbf{Z}_6 + R_4 & \mu_2 R_3 \\ \mu_1 R_1 & 0 & r_{d1} + (1 + \mu_1)\mathbf{Z}_5 + R_3 \end{vmatrix}}$$

$$(6\text{-}155)$$

The answer will be left in determinant form.

As a further example, let us compute the current gain of the transistor amplifier shown in Fig. 6-48a. Its linear model is shown in Fig. 6-48b. We have used the hybrid-pi model for the transistor here. The notation $G = 1/R$, $g = 1/r$, and $\mathbf{Y} = 1/\mathbf{Z}$ will be used. The appropriate subscripts will be added to these terms. Then, applying nodal analysis, we have

$$\mathbf{I}_1 = (G_1 + g_{bb'1})\mathbf{V}_1 - g_{bb'1}\mathbf{V}_2 - 0\mathbf{V}_3 - 0\mathbf{V}_4 - 0\mathbf{V}_5 - 0\mathbf{V}_6 - 0\mathbf{V}_7$$
$$(6\text{-}156a)$$

$$0 = -g_{b'b}\mathbf{V}_1 + [g_{bb'1} + g_{b'e1} + g_{b'c1} + j\omega(C_{b'e1} + C_{b'c1})]\mathbf{V}_2$$
$$-(g_{b'e1} + j\omega C_{b'e1})\mathbf{V}_3 - (g_{b'c1} + j\omega C_{b'c1})\mathbf{V}_4 - 0\mathbf{V}_5 - 0\mathbf{V}_6 - 0\mathbf{V}_7$$
$$(6\text{-}156b)$$

$$g_{m1}(\mathbf{V}_2 - \mathbf{V}_3) = 0\mathbf{V}_1 - (g_{b'e1} + j\omega C_{b'e1})\mathbf{V}_2 + (g_{b'e1} + g_{ce1}$$
$$+ j\omega C_{b'e1} + \mathbf{Y}_5)\mathbf{V}_3 - g_{ce1}\mathbf{V}_4 - 0\mathbf{V}_5 - 0\mathbf{V}_6 - 0\mathbf{V}_7 \quad (6\text{-}156c)$$

$$-g_{m1}(\mathbf{V}_2 - \mathbf{V}_3) = 0\mathbf{V}_1 - (g_{b'c1} + j\omega C_{b'c1})\mathbf{V}_2 - g_{ce}\mathbf{V}_3$$
$$+ (g_{ce1} + G_3 + g_{bb'2} + g_{b'c1} + j\omega C_{b'c1})\mathbf{V}_4$$
$$- g_{bb'2}\mathbf{V}_5 - 0\mathbf{V}_6 - 0\mathbf{V}_7 \quad (6\text{-}156d)$$

$$0 = 0\mathbf{V}_1 - 0\mathbf{V}_2 - 0\mathbf{V}_3 - g_{bb'2}\mathbf{V}_4 + [g_{bb'2} + g_{b'e2} + g_{b'c2}$$
$$+ j\omega(C_{b'e2} + C_{b'c2})]\mathbf{V}_5 - (g_{b'e2} + j\omega C_{b'e2})\mathbf{V}_6 - (g_{b'c2} + j\omega C_{b'c2})\mathbf{V}_7$$
$$(6\text{-}156e)$$

$$g_{m2}(\mathbf{V}_5 - \mathbf{V}_6) = 0\mathbf{V}_1 - 0\mathbf{V}_2 - 0\mathbf{V}_3 - 0\mathbf{V}_4 - (g_{b'e2} + j\omega C_{b'e2})\mathbf{V}_5$$
$$+ (g_{b'e2} + g_{ce2} + j\omega C_{b'e2} + \mathbf{Z}_6)\mathbf{V}_6 - g_{ce2}\mathbf{V}_7 \quad (6\text{-}156f)$$

$$-g_{m2}(\mathbf{V}_5 - \mathbf{V}_6) = 0\mathbf{V}_1 - 0\mathbf{V}_2 - 0\mathbf{V}_3 - 0\mathbf{V}_4 - (g_{b'c2} + j\omega C_{b'c2})\mathbf{V}_5$$
$$- g_{ce2}\mathbf{V}_6 + (g_{b'c2} + g_{ce2} + G_4 + j\omega C_{b'c2})\mathbf{V}_7$$
$$(6\text{-}156g)$$

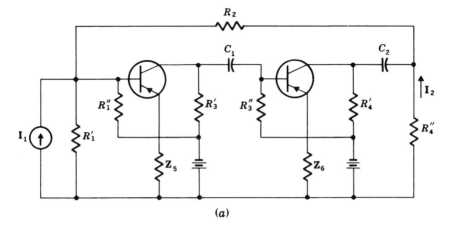

(a)

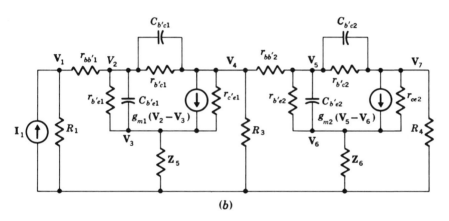

(b)

Fig. 6-48 (a) A two-stage transistor amplifier and (b) its hybrid-pi linear model, where $R_3 = R_3' R_3''/(R_3' + R_3'')$, $R_4 = R_4' R_4''/(R_4' + R_4'')$. It is assumed that C_1 and C_2 are short circuits at the signal frequency.

The dependent generator voltages are in terms of the unknown nodal voltages. Then, Eq. (6-156) should be manipulated into a form suitable for solution. Doing this, we obtain

$$I_1 = (G_1 + g_{bb'1})V_1 - g_{bb'1}V_2 - 0V_3 - 0V_4 - 0V_5 - 0V_6 - 0V_7$$

$$(6\text{-}157a)$$

$$0 = -g_{b'b1}V_1 + [g_{bb'1} + g_{b'e1} + g_{b'c1} + j\omega(C_{b'e1} + C_{b'c1})]V_2$$

$$- (g_{b'e1} + j\omega C_{b'e1})V_3 - (g_{b'c1} + j\omega C_{b'c1})V_4 - 0V_5 - 0V_6 - 0V_7$$

$$(6\text{-}157b)$$

$$0 = 0\mathbf{V}_1 - (g_{m1} + g_{b'e1} + j\omega C_{b'e1})\mathbf{V}_2$$
$$+ (g_{m1} + g_{b'e1} + g_{ce1} + j\omega C_{b'e1} + \mathbf{Y}_5)\mathbf{V}_3 - g_{ce1}\mathbf{V}_4$$
$$- 0\mathbf{V}_5 - 0\mathbf{V}_6 - 0\mathbf{V}_7 \quad (6\text{-}157c)$$

$$0 = 0\mathbf{V}_1 - (-g_{m1} + g_{b'c1} + j\omega C_{b'c1})\mathbf{V}_2 - (g_{m1} + g_{ce})\mathbf{V}_3$$
$$+ (g_{ce1} + G_3 + g_{bb'2} + g_{b'c1} + j\omega C_{b'c1})\mathbf{V}_4 - g_{bb'2}\mathbf{V}_5 - 0\mathbf{V}_6 - 0\mathbf{V}_7$$
$$\quad (6\text{-}157d)$$

$$0 = 0\mathbf{V}_1 - 0\mathbf{V}_2 - 0\mathbf{V}_3 - g_{bb'2}\mathbf{V}_4$$
$$+ [g_{bb'2} + g_{b'e2} + g_{b'c2} + j\omega(C_{b'e2} + C_{b'c2})]\mathbf{V}_5$$
$$- (g_{b'e2} + j\omega C_{b'e2})\mathbf{V}_6 - (g_{b'c2} + j\omega C_{b'c2})\mathbf{V}_7 \quad (6\text{-}157e)$$

$$0 = 0\mathbf{V}_1 - 0\mathbf{V}_2 - 0\mathbf{V}_3 - 0\mathbf{V}_4 - (g_{m2} + g_{b'e2} + j\omega C_{b'e2})\mathbf{V}_5$$
$$+ (g_{m2} + g_{b'e2} + g_{ce2} + j\omega C_{b'e2} + \mathbf{Z}_6)\mathbf{V}_6 - g_{ce2}\mathbf{V}_7 \quad (6\text{-}157f)$$

$$0 = 0\mathbf{V}_1 - 0\mathbf{V}_2 - 0\mathbf{V}_3 - 0\mathbf{V}_4 - (-g_{m2} + g_{b'c2} + j\omega C_{b'c2})\mathbf{V}_5$$
$$- (g_{m2} + g_{ce2})\mathbf{V}_6 + (g_{b'c2} + g_{ce2} + G_4 + j\omega C_{b'c2})\mathbf{V}_7 \quad (6\text{-}157g)$$

To obtain the current amplification of the device, we require $\mathbf{I}_2$ (see Fig. 6-48a)

$$\mathbf{I}_2 = \frac{\mathbf{V}_7}{R_4''} \quad (6\text{-}158)$$

Then solve Eqs. (6-157) for $\mathbf{V}_7$ and substitute in Eq. (6-158). Then the current amplification is

$$\mathbf{A}_i = \frac{\mathbf{I}_2}{\mathbf{I}_1} \quad (6\text{-}159)$$

The details of the solution of the simultaneous equations will not be presented here.

6-22 LINEAR MODELS FOR MULTITERMINAL DEVICES

The procedures of Secs. 6-3 and 6-4 can be extended to obtain low-frequency models for devices with more than three terminals. For instance, consider the $(n + 1)$-terminal device of Fig. 6-49. The reference terminal is numbered zero, and all other terminal voltages are measured with respect to it. Thus, there are n independent terminal voltages, $v_1, v_2, \ldots, v_n$. There are also n independent terminal currents since the reference current is the negative of the sum of all the other terminal currents. These currents are $i_1, i_2, \ldots, i_n$.

Let us first consider the case where the device is voltage-controlled, e.g., an FET. In this case, the voltages are the independent variables. In

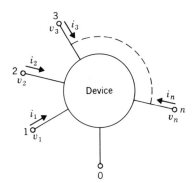

Fig. 6-49 The $(n + 1)$-terminal device. All voltages are measured with respect to the reference terminal 0.

obtaining linear models, we are interested in changes in the instantaneous operating point about a quiescent operating point. These changes can be obtained by means of a Taylor's series [see Eq. (6-26)]. In this case, the series will be a function of all the terminal voltages. We shall neglect the higher-order terms in the Taylor's series (see Sec. 6-3). Then, for each terminal in turn, we have

$$\Delta i_k = \frac{\partial i_k}{\partial v_1} \Delta v_1 + \frac{\partial i_k}{\partial v_2} \Delta v_2 + \cdots + \frac{\partial i_k}{\partial v_n} \Delta v_n \qquad k = 1, 2, \ldots, n$$

$$(6\text{-}160)$$

The changes in the voltages and currents are the signal components. Thus, we replace them by signal voltages and currents. We shall use phasors for these. Hence, Eq. (6-160) becomes

$$\mathbf{I}_k = \frac{\partial i_k}{\partial v_1} \mathbf{V}_1 + \frac{\partial i_k}{\partial v_2} \mathbf{V}_2 + \cdots + \frac{\partial i_k}{\partial v_n} \mathbf{V}_n \qquad k = 1, 2, \ldots, n \quad (6\text{-}161)$$

We shall use the following notation

$$g_{kj} = \frac{\partial i_k}{\partial v_j} \tag{6-162}$$

When $k = j$, g_{kk} represents a *dynamic conductance*. When $k \neq j$, g_{kj} represents a *transconductance*, i.e., the change in i_k produced by a change in v_j when all other terminal voltages are constant. Then, Eq. (6-161) can be written

$$\mathbf{I}_k = \mathbf{g}_{k1}\mathbf{V}_1 + \mathbf{g}_{k2}\mathbf{V}_2 + \cdots + \mathbf{g}_{kn}\mathbf{V}_n \qquad k = 1, 2, \ldots, n \quad (6\text{-}163)$$

For any particular k, this equation can be represented by the linear model of Fig. 6-50a. Note that there is no $g_{kk}\mathbf{V}_k$ generator. The conductance g_{kk} represents this term in Eq. (6-163).

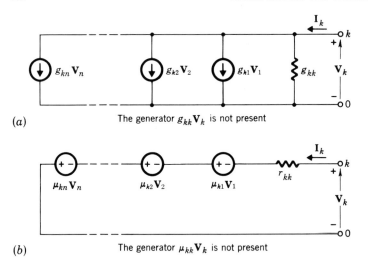

(a)   The generator $g_{kk}\mathbf{V}_k$ is not present

(b)   The generator $\mu_{kk}\mathbf{V}_k$ is not present

Fig. 6-50 Linear models between the k and reference terminals for the multiterminal device of Fig. 6-49, where the terminal voltages are the independent variables: (a) using current generators and (b) using voltage generators.

Figure 6-50a represents a model between the k and reference terminals. There are n such models, one for each terminal. The complete model for the device of Fig. 6-49 consists of the n models (of the form of Fig. 6-50a) *all* of which are connected at their (individual) reference terminals. This model replaces the device in an analysis just as the three-terminal model does.

At times, it is convenient to use voltage generators rather than current generators. The circuit of Fig. 6-50b can be obtained by applying Thévenin's theorem to Fig. 6-50a. In this circuit

$$r_{kk} = 1/g_{kk} \tag{6-164}$$

and

$$\mu_{kj} = \frac{g_{kj}}{g_{kk}} \qquad j = 1, 2, \ldots, n \qquad j \neq k \tag{6-165}$$

The μ_{kj} are *voltage amplification factors*. They represent the open-circuit voltage between terminal k and reference in response to a voltage applied between terminal j and reference when all other terminal voltages are held constant; i.e., these signal voltages are zero.

Let us now consider a device, e.g., a transistor, which is current-controlled; i.e., the terminal currents are the independent variables. Proceeding in a fashion which is dual to the derivation of Eq. (6-163), we obtain

$$\mathbf{V}_k = r_{k1}\mathbf{I}_1 + r_{k2}\mathbf{I}_2 + \cdots + r_{kn}\mathbf{I}_n \qquad k = 1, 2, \ldots, n \tag{6-166}$$

where

$$r_{kj} = \frac{\partial v_k}{\partial i_j} \qquad (6\text{-}167)$$

r_{kk} is a *dynamic resistance*, and r_{kj}, $j \neq k$, is a *transresistance*; that is, r_{kj} is the change in v_k in response to a change in i_k when all other terminal currents are constant. The linear model for one of these equations is shown in Fig. 6-51a. The complete model consists of n such circuits all connected together at their reference terminals.

At times it is desirable to use models containing current generators rather than voltage generators. The circuit of Fig. 6-51b can be obtained by applying Norton's theorem to the circuit of Fig. 6-51a. In this case

$$g_{kk} = \frac{1}{r_{kk}} \qquad (6\text{-}168)$$

and

$$\alpha_{kj} = \frac{r_{kj}}{r_{kk}} \qquad j = 1, 2, \ldots, n \qquad j \neq k \qquad (6\text{-}169)$$

g_{kk} represents a *dynamic conductance* while α_{kj} is a *current amplification factor*, i.e., the ratio of the short-circuit current between terminal k and reference in response to the current into terminal j when the signal components of all other terminal currents are zero.

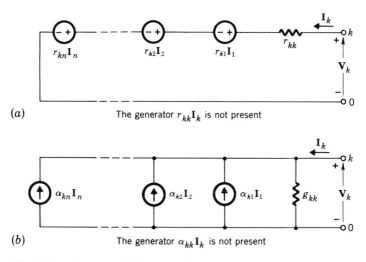

(a)   The generator $r_{kk}I_k$ is not present

(b)   The generator $\alpha_{kk}I_k$ is not present

Fig. 6-51 Linear models between the k and reference terminals for the multiterminal device of Fig. 6-49, where the terminal currents are the independent variables: (a) using voltage generators and (b) using current generators.

As an example of the use of these linear models, we shall consider the vacuum-tube-pentode amplifier of Fig. 6-52a. It will not be assumed that C_s and C_k are short circuits at the signal frequency. In this case, the screen-grid potential can vary with the signal. Hence, the models of Fig. 6-16 are not adequate. We shall assume, as is usually the case in linear amplifiers, that the control grid is always at a negative potential with respect to the cathode. Thus, the control-grid current will be zero, and it will not be necessary to draw a model for the control grid, although the control-grid voltage will affect the other models. The suppressor grid is directly connected to the cathode. Thus, its signal voltage is zero, and suppressor-grid generators are *not* present in the model. Since the suppressor-grid current is usually not of interest and it does not pass through any of the elements, the suppressor-grid model is omitted. The total linear model for the complete circuit is shown in Fig. 6-52b.

The model for the dual-gate MOSFET is much simpler than that for the vacuum-tube pentode. The second gate does not have current through it. Thus, at low frequencies, the gate 2–to–source potential will not vary. The only mechanisms that can vary the gate 2–to–drain potential are stray-capacitance coupling, i.e., the capacitance C_{g2d} and C_{gg2}, and also some coupling from the channel. These stray capacitances are of the order of 1 pf.

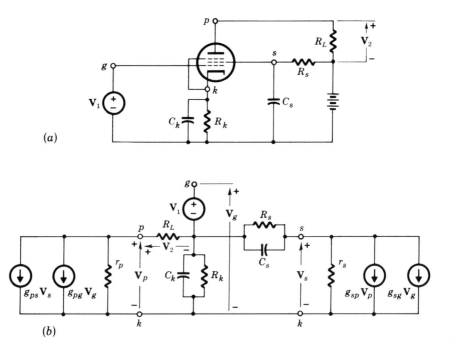

Fig. 6-52 (*a*) Simple vacuum-tube-pentode amplifier and (*b*) its complete linear model.

The external bypass capacitor C_{g2} (see Fig. 6-13a) acts as the shunt arm in a voltage divider.   The series arm is the stray capacitance.   Thus, if C_{g2} is very much larger than the stray capacitance, very little voltage will be "coupled" to the second gate.   Usually, C_{g2} can be 10^6 or more times larger than the stray capacitances.   Thus, in almost all circumstances, the linear model for the single-gate FET can be used for the dual-gate MOSFET.

The models we have derived in this section are low-frequency models. High-frequency modifications can be obtained by using the procedures discussed in this chapter.

REFERENCES

1. Texas Instruments, Inc.: "Transistor Circuit Design," pp. 96–97, McGraw-Hill Book Company, New York, 1963.
2. Hunter, L. P.: "Handbook of Semiconductor Electronics," 2d ed., sec. 11-1, McGraw-Hill Book Company, New York, 1962.

BIBLIOGRAPHY

Chirlian, P. M., and A. H. Zemanian: "Electronics," chap. 11, McGraw-Hill Book Company, New York, 1961.
Gibbons, J. F.: "Semiconductor Electronics," chap. 11, McGraw-Hill Book Company, New York, 1966.
Greiner, R. A.: "Semiconductor Devices and Applications," chap. 12, McGraw-Hill Book Company, New York, 1961.
Hunter, L. P.: "Handbook of Semiconductor Electronics," 2d ed., pp. 11-5 to 11-35, 12-2 to 12-23, McGraw-Hill Book Company, New York, 1962.
Linvill, J. G.: "Models of Transistors and Diodes," chap. 5, McGraw-Hill Book Company, New York, 1963.
Millman, J., and C. C. Halkais: "Electronic Devices and Circuits," pp. 369–378, McGraw-Hill Book Company, New York, 1967.
Pritchard, R. L.: Electric-network Representation of Transistors: A Survey, *IRE Trans. Circuit Theory*, vol. CT-3, pp. 5–21, March, 1956.
Wallmark, J. T., and H. Johnson: "Field-effect Transistors," chap. 11, Prentice-Hall, Inc., Englewood Cliffs, N.J., 1966.

PROBLEMS

6-1. Obtain the open-circuit impedance parameters of the networks shown in Fig. 6-53.

6-2. Obtain the short-circuit admittance parameters of the networks of Fig. 6-53. Work with the networks directly.

6-3. Obtain the hybrid parameters for the networks of Fig. 6-53.   Work with the networks directly.

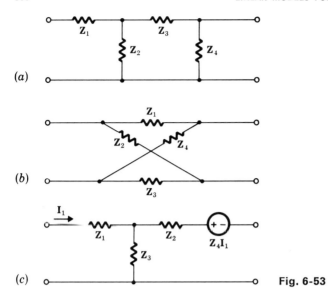

(a)

(b)

(c)   **Fig. 6-53**

6-4. A network is characterized by the following open-circuit impedance-parameter matrix:

$$\begin{bmatrix} 10 & 5 \\ 5 & 15 \end{bmatrix}$$

Determine three equivalent circuits which have these z parameters. Is it necessary that the equivalent circuit of this network have a voltage or a current generator?

6-5. Repeat Prob. 6-4 using an open-circuit impedance-parameter matrix which is

$$\begin{bmatrix} 10 & 5 \\ 4 & 15 \end{bmatrix}$$

6-6. A network is characterized by the following short-circuit admittance-parameter matrix:

$$\begin{bmatrix} 10 & -5 \\ -5 & 15 \end{bmatrix}$$

Determine three equivalent circuits which have these y parameters. Is it necessary that the equivalent circuit of this network possess a voltage or a current generator?

6-7. Repeat Prob. 6-6, using the following short-circuit admittance-parameter matrix:

$$\begin{bmatrix} 10 & -5 \\ -4 & 15 \end{bmatrix}$$

6-8. Obtain an equivalent circuit whose hybrid matrix is given by

$$\begin{bmatrix} 10 & -5 \\ -4 & 15 \end{bmatrix}$$

6-9. Derive a set of equations which expresses the open-circuit impedance parameters in terms of the short-circuit admittance parameters.

6-10. Derive a set of equations which expresses the short-circuit admittance parameters in terms of the hybrid parameters.

6-11. Derive a set of equations which expresses the hybrid parameters in terms of the open-circuit impedance parameters.

6-12. Obtain the characteristic functions for the network of Fig. 6-53.

6-13. Derive Eqs. (6-23).

In the following problems where a plot of gain versus frequency is called for, semilog paper should be used, and the frequency should be plotted against the log scale.

6-14. Plot the voltage gain of the amplifier shown in Fig. 6-54 for frequencies from 10 to 10^6 Hz. Assume that C_c is a short circuit at the signal frequencies.

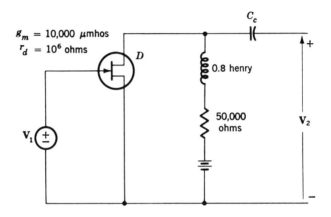

Fig. 6-54

6-15. Plot the voltage gain of the amplifier shown in Fig. 6-55 for frequencies from 1 to 100,000 Hz. Assume that C_c has zero reactance in this frequency range.

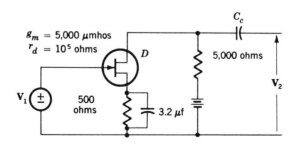

Fig. 6-55

6-16. Compute the voltage gain of the amplifier of Fig. 6-56. Assume that g_m and

r_d are known and that the reactance of C_c is zero at the signal frequency. Let $1/R_3 = 1/R_3' + 1/R_3'' + 1/r_d$.

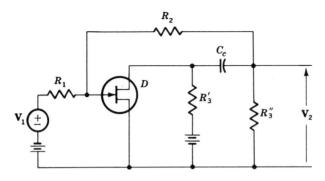

Fig. 6-56

6-17. Repeat Prob. 6-16 for the amplifier of Fig. 6-57.

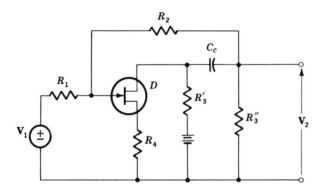

Fig. 6-57

6-18. Plot the voltage gain of the amplifier shown in Fig. 6-58 for frequencies from 10 to 100,000 Hz. Assume that the capacitor C_c is a short circuit at all signal frequencies.

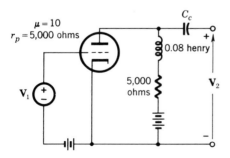

Fig. 6-58

6-19. Plot the voltage gain of the amplifier shown in Fig. 6-59 for frequencies from 1 to 10,000 Hz. Assume that the reactance of the capacitor C_c is zero in this frequency range.

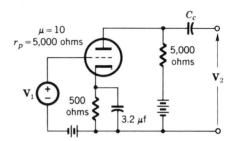

Fig. 6-59

6-20. Plot the voltage gain of the amplifier shown in Fig. 6-60 for frequencies from 1 to 10,000 Hz. Assume that the reactance of the capacitor C_s is zero in this frequency range.

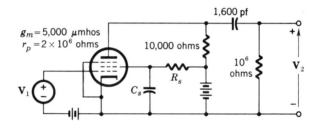

Fig. 6-60

6-21. Compute the voltage gain of the amplifier shown in Fig. 6-61. Assume that the reactances of C_1, C_c, and C_s are zero at the signal frequency and that the value of g_m is known and $r_p \gg R_3$.

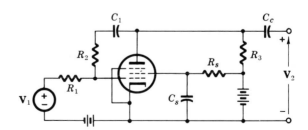

Fig. 6-61

6-22. Compute the voltage gain of the amplifier shown in Fig. 6-62. Assume that the reactances of C_1 and C_c are zero at the signal frequency.

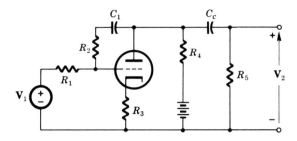

Fig. 6-62

6-23. Compute the voltage gain of the FET amplifier shown in Fig. 6-63. If R_1 and R are varied, what is the maximum value that the voltage gain can attain?

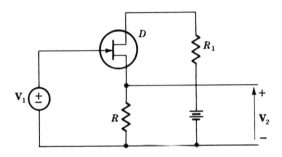

Fig. 6-63

6-24. Repeat Prob. 6-23 for the amplifier of Fig. 6-64.

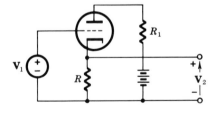

Fig. 6-64

6-25. Calculate the input impedance Z_i and the output impedance Z_o for the amplifier of Fig. 6-65. Assume that the reactance of C_c is zero at all frequencies of interest.

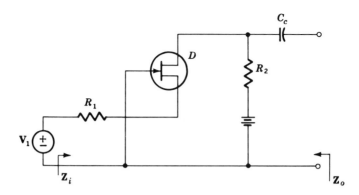

Fig. 6-65

6-26. A transistor whose model is illustrated in Fig. 6-23a, is found to have the following parameter values: $r'_e = 30$ ohms, $r'_c = 1.2 \times 10^6$ ohms, $\mu = 4 \times 10^{-5}$ and $\alpha = 0.98$. Compute the value of α in the linear model of Fig. 6-23b, if $r''_b = 100$ ohms. Comment on the accuracy of the approximation $\alpha \approx \alpha'$ in this case. Assume that r''_e and r''_c are zero.

6-27. Compute the h parameters for the transistor of Prob. 6-26.

6-28. A transistor has the following common-base h parameters: $h_{ib} = 40$ ohms, $h_{rb} = 4 \times 10^{-4}$ ohm, $h_{fb} = -0.98$, and $h_{ob} = 0.50 \times 10^{-6}$ mho. Compute the common-emitter and common-collector h parameters. Use exact expressions.

6-29. For the transistor of Prob. 6-28, comment on the accuracy of the approximate expressions of Eqs. (6-69) and (6-70).

6-30. The transistor whose h parameters are given in Prob. 6-28 is connected into the elementary common-base amplifier circuit of Fig. 6-29a, where $R_s = 1000$ ohms and $R_L = 1000$ ohms. Compute the following quantities: $\mathbf{K}_i$, $\mathbf{A}_i$, $\mathbf{A}_v$, R_i, R_o, K_p, A_p, K_T, K_{AP}, $K_{AP,\max}$. Also consider that the input current source is replaced by a voltage source. Then compute $\mathbf{K}_v$ and $\mathbf{A}_v$.

6-31. Repeat Prob. 6-30, but now assume that the transistor is connected into the elementary common-emitter amplifier circuit of Fig. 6-29b.

6-32. Repeat Prob. 6-30, but now assume that the transistor is connected into the elementary common-collector amplifier circuit of Fig. 6-29c, where $R_s = 20,000$ ohms and $R_L = 500$ ohms.

6-33. Compute the current gain $\mathbf{K}_i$ for the amplifier of Prob. 6-32, but now assume that $R_s = 1000$ ohms and $R_L = 1000$ ohms. Compare this result with those of the last three problems.

6-34. Discuss the relative merits of the elementary common-base, common-emitter, and common-collector transistor amplifiers.

6-35. Compute the current gain I_2/I_1 and the voltage gain V_2/V_1 for the transistor amplifier shown in Fig. 6-66, where $h_{ie} = 2000$ ohms, $h_{re} = 6 \times 10^{-4}$, $h_{fe} = 50$, and $h_{oe} = 25 \times 10^{-6}$ mho.

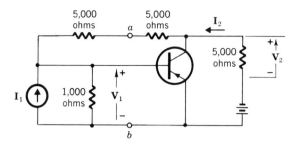

Fig. 6-66

6-36. Repeat Prob. 6-35, but consider Fig. 6-66 to be modified by placing a capacitor which acts as a short circuit at the signal frequencies between points *a* and *b*.

6-37. Plot the current gain I_2/I_1 for the transistor amplifier shown in Fig. 6-67 for frequencies from 1 to 10,000 Hz. Assume that C_1 acts as a short circuit at the signal frequencies. The *h* parameters for the transistor are: $h_{ie} = 2000$ ohms, $h_{re} = 6 \times 10^{-4}$, $h_{fe} = 50$, and $h_{oe} = 25 \times 10^{-6}$ mho.

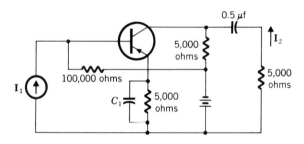

Fig. 6-67

6-38. Repeat Prob. 6-37, but now assume that $C_1 = 2$ μf.

6-39. Repeat Prob. 6-38 but now double the sizes of all capacitors.

6-40. Compute the current gain I_2/I_1 for the transistor amplifier shown in Fig. 6-68.

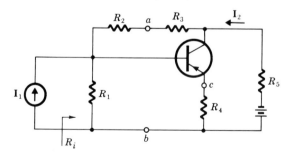

Fig. 6-68

6-41. Repeat Prob. 6-40, but now assume that capacitors whose reactances are zero at the signal frequency have been connected between points ab and bc. Compare the relations obtained in this problem with those calculated in Prob. 6-40.

6-42. Compute the input resistance R_i of the circuit shown in Fig. 6-68.

6-43. For the FET amplifier shown in Fig. 6-36, $C_{gs} = 2$ pf, $C_{ds} = 2$ pf, and $C_{gd} = 0.1$ pf. Assume that Z_L is such that the voltage gain of this circuit is -100. Compute the effective input capacitance of the amplifier.

6-44. Plot a curve of $|A_v|$ and the phase angle of A_v versus frequency for the amplifier shown in Fig. 6-36. Use frequencies from 1 to 10^6 Hz. The parameters of the FET are $g_m = 10,000$ μmhos, $r_d = 10^6$ ohms, $C_{gd} = 1.0$ pf, $C_{ds} = 5$ pf, $C_{gs} = 5$ pf. Z_L is a 10,000-ohm resistance.

6-45. Repeat Prob. 6-44 but now assume that all the capacitances are halved.

6-46. Repeat Prob. 6-44 but now assume that all the capacitances are doubled.

6-47. Repeat Prob. 6-44 but now assume that the voltage generator has an internal series resistance of 100,000 ohms.

6-48. Derive an expression that is valid at all frequencies for the input impedance of the amplifier of Fig. 6-69. Use the parameters for the FET given in Prob. 6-44. Consider that C_s and C_c are short-circuited at all signal frequencies.

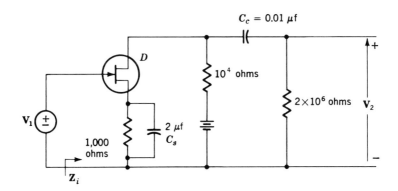

Fig. 6-69

6-49. Repeat Prob. 6-48 but do not assume that the reactances of C_s and C_c are zero at the signal frequencies.

6-50. For the source follower of Fig. 6-37a, $C_{gd} = 0.1$ pf, $C_{ds} = 5$ pf, $C_{gs} = 5$ pf. Assume that R_L is such that $A_v = 0.99$. Determine the input admittance of the amplifier.

6-51. Derive an expression for the input admittance of the source follower of Fig. 6-21 that is valid at all frequencies. Do not neglect the stray capacitances but assume that C and C_s act as short circuits at all frequencies of interest.

6-52. For the vacuum-tube-triode amplifier shown in Fig. 6-70, $C_{gk} = 2$ pf, $C_{gp} = 2$ pf, and $C_{pk} = 2$ pf. Assume that Z_L is such that the voltage gain of this circuit is -50. Compute the effective input capacitance of this amplifier.

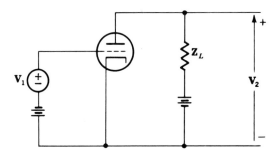

Fig. 6-70

6-53. For the vacuum-tube-pentode amplifier of Fig. 6-71a, $C_{gk} = 2$ pf, $C_{gg2} = 2$ pf, $C_{gp} = 0.002$ pf, $C_{g2p} = 2$ pf, and $C_{pk} = 2$ pf. Assume that $\mathbf{Z}_L$ is such that the voltage gain of the circuit is -50 and that the reactances of C_k and C_s are zero at the signal frequency. Compute the effective input capacitance of this amplifier. Compare this answer with the result of Prob. 6-52. The capacitances between the cathode and any electrode include the capacitance between electrode and the suppressor grid.

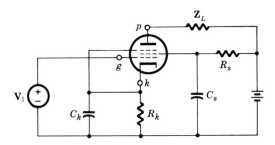

Fig. 6-71

6-54. Plot a curve of voltage gain versus frequency for the amplifier shown in Fig. 6-72.

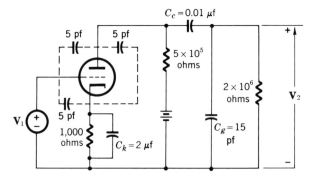

Fig. 6-72

Use frequencies from 1 to 100,000 Hz. Assume that the reactances of C_k and C_c are zero at all signal frequencies. The parameters of the vacuum tube are $\mu = 100$ and $r_p = 200,000$ ohms.

6-55. Repeat Prob. 6-54, assuming that all capacitances are halved.

6-56. Repeat Prob. 6-54, but now assume that the voltage generator V_1 has an internal resistance of 100,000 ohms.

6-57. Derive an expression for the input admittance and voltage gain of the vacuum-tube amplifier shown in Fig. 6-72 that is valid for all frequencies. Assume that $\mu = 100$ and $r_p = 200,000$ ohms.

6-58. Repeat Prob. 6-57 but neglect the grid-to-plate capacitance. This would usually be the case when a vacuum-tube pentode is used.

6-59. For a vacuum-tube-triode cathode-follower amplifier which is analogous to Fig. 6-37a, $C_{gk} = 2$ pf, $C_{gp} = 2$ pf, and $C_{pk} = 2$ pf. Assume that R_L is such that the voltage gain of this circuit is 0.90. Compute an expression for the input admittance of this amplifier. Find a parallel-RC network that has the same input admittance.

6-60. Repeat Prob. 6-59 for a pentode cathode-follower circuit which is analogous to Fig. 6-21 where $C_{gk} = 2$ pf, $C_{gg2} = 2$ pf, $C_{pk} = 2$ pf, $C_{pg2} = 2$ pf, and $C_{gp} = 0.02$ pf. Assume that the voltage gain is 0.99, $R_g = 10^6$ ohms, and that the bypass and coupling capacitances are short circuits at the signal frequency. The capacitance between any electrode and the suppressor grid is included in the capacitance between that electrode and the cathode.

6-61. Derive expressions for the voltage gain and input admittance of a vacuum-tube pentode cathode-follower circuit which is analogous to Fig. 6-21 that is valid at all frequencies. Do not neglect the interelectrode capacitances but consider that the bypass and coupling capacitances are short circuits.

6-62. The FET whose model is shown in Fig. 6-38 has a $g_m = 10,000$ μmhos, $C_{gd} = 0.1$ pf, $C_{ds} = 5$ pf, and $C_{gs} = 5$ pf. The inductor $L = 0.01$ μh. Compute the input admittance at 100×10^6 Hz. Assume that the voltage gain of the amplifier is -20.

6-63. The parameters of the transistor of Fig. 6-73 are $r_{e'} = 40$ ohms, $C_e = 100$ pf, $r_{bb'} = 80$ ohms, $r_{c'} = 10^6$ ohms, $\alpha = 0.98$, $\omega_a = 10 \times 10^6$ Hz, $\mu = 0$, and $C_c = 10$ pf. Plot curves of current gain I_2/I_1 and voltage gain V_2/V_1 for frequencies from 10^4 to 10^8 Hz.

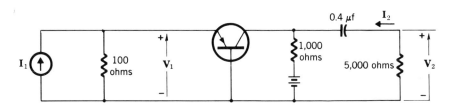

Fig. 6-73

6-64. Compute the common-base h parameters for the transistor of Prob. 6-63.

6-65. The transistor of Prob. 6-63 is connected into the circuit of Fig. 6-74. Plot curves of current gain I_2/I_1 for frequencies from 10,000 to 10^8 Hz.   Assume that C_1 is a short circuit at all frequencies of interest.

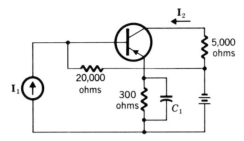

Fig. 6-74

6-66.   The transistor of Prob. 6-63 is connected into the circuit of Fig. 6-29c, where $R_s = 10,000$ ohms and $R_L = 500$ ohms.   Plot curves of current gain I_2/I_1 for frequencies from 10,000 to 10^7 Hz.

6-67.   Compute the current gain I_2/I_1, the voltage gain V_2/V_1, the input impedance, and the output impedance of the circuit of Fig. 6-75.   Use the model of Fig. 6-39.   Assume that $r_{e''}$ and $r_{c''}$ are zero.

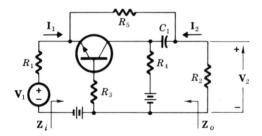

Fig. 6-75

6-68.   A p-n-p-junction transistor is connected into the circuit of Fig. 6-74.   The parameters of the transistor are given by $r_{bb'} = 100$ ohms, $r_{b'e} = 900$ ohms, $r_{b'c} = 3.3 \times 10^6$ ohms, $r_{ce} = 100,000$ ohms, $C_{b'e} = 90$ pf, $C_{b'c} = 3$ pf, and $g_m = 20,000$ μmhos. Plot a curve of current gain I_2/I_1 for frequencies from 10,000 to 10^8 Hz.   Assume that C_1 acts as a short circuit at all signal frequencies.   Use the model of Fig. 6-42.

6-69.   Obtain the exact common-emitter h-parameter model for the transistor of Prob. 6-68.

6-70.   Repeat Prob. 6-68 but now use the model of Fig. 6-43.   Compare the h parameters with those obtained in Prob. 6-69.   Do they differ significantly for most frequencies?

6-71.   Repeat Prob. 6-70 but now use the model of Fig. 6-44.

6-72.   Determine the voltage gain V_2/V_1 for the tunnel-diode amplifier of Fig. 6-76. Take the reactance of C_1 and L_1 into account.

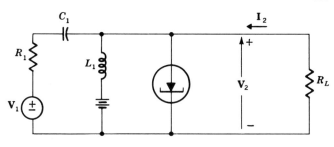

Fig. 6-76

6-73. Compute the voltage gain, input resistance, and output resistance for the circuit of Fig. 6-77. Assume that C_1 and C_2 act as short circuits at the signal frequencies and that any stray capacitances can be neglected.

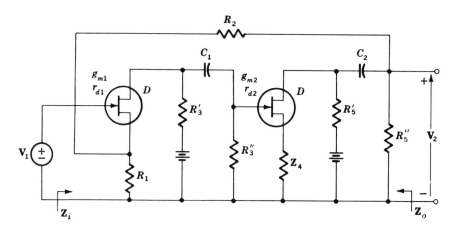

Fig. 6-77

6-74. Repeat Prob. 6-73 but now take the stray capacitances into account. Note that A_v becomes complex and the input and output impedances (rather than resistances) must be found.

6-75. Compute the voltage gain, the input resistance, and the output resistance for the circuit of Fig. 6-78. Assume that C_1, C_2, C_3, and C_4 act as short circuits at the signal frequencies and that any stray capacitances can be neglected.

6-76. Repeat Prob. 6-75, but now take the stray capacitances into account. Note that in this case, the amplification becomes complex and the input and output impedances (rather than resistances) must be found.

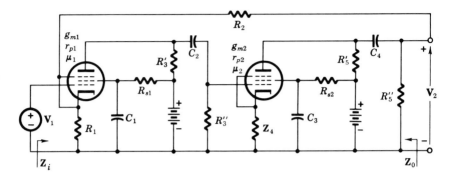

Fig. 6-78

6-77. Compute the current gain I_2/I_1, the input impedance Z_i, and the output impedance Z_o for the transistor circuit of Fig. 6-79. Assume that the reactances C_1, C_2, and C_3 are zero at the signal frequencies. Use low-frequency h-parameter models for the transistors.

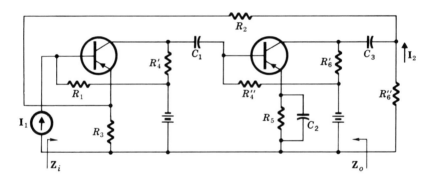

Fig. 6-79

6-78. Repeat Prob. 6-77 but now use the high-frequency hybrid-pi linear model.

6-79. Repeat Prob. 6-77 but now use the h-parameter model of Fig. 6-43.

6-80. Repeat Prob. 6-77 but now use the h-parameter model of Fig. 6-44.

6-81. For the vacuum-tube-pentode amplifier shown in Fig. 6-52a, $R_k = 50$ ohms, $R_s = 100,000$ ohms, $R_L = 10,000$ ohms, $g_{pg} = 9000$ μmhos, $g_{ps} = 100$ μmhos, $r_p = 2 \times 10^6$ ohms, $g_{sp} = 500$ μmhos, $g_{sg} = 9000$ μmhos, and $r_s = 10,000$ ohms. Compute the voltage gain V_2/V_1 of this amplifier under each of the following conditions:

    (a) C_k acts as a short circuit; C_s acts as a short circuit.

    (b) C_k acts as a short circuit; C_s acts as an open circuit.

    (c) C_k acts as an open circuit; C_s acts as a short circuit.

    (d) C_k acts as an open circuit; C_s acts as an open circuit.

7

Piecewise-linear Models for Electronic Devices

The linear models developed in Chap. 6 can be used to calculate the response of electronic devices to small signals. For instance, at low frequencies, the models represented only small regions of the static characteristics. These models are accurate when small signals are encountered and *should* be used to analyze such circuits. However, there are times when a model is needed which can be used when the changes in the voltage and currents are large. In this case, one procedure is to use the piecewise-linear model we shall discuss here. Such models represent large regions of the static characteristics. Some applications for piecewise-linear models are in pulse circuits and waveshaping circuits. The piecewise-linear models do not replace the linear ones but augment them.

When piecewise-linear models are used, nonlinear characteristics are approximated by a set of confluent straight-line segments. Such a *piecewise-linear approximation* is shown in Fig. 7-1.

We shall consider low-frequency models in this chapter. High-frequency piecewise-linear models will be developed in Secs. 15-1 and 15-2.

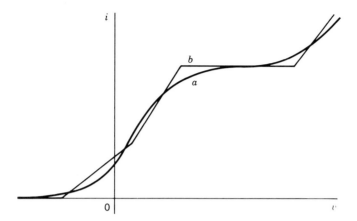

Fig. 7-1 A piecewise-linear approximation. Curve *a* is the non-linear characteristic, and curve *b* is the approximation.

7-1 BASIC BUILDING BLOCKS FOR PIECEWISE-LINEAR MODELS

The nonlinear voltage-current characteristics of electronic devices will be represented by models which are made up of basic elements, or *building blocks*. In this section we discuss these building blocks and in the next we demonstrate how they are interconnected to produce the desired nonlinear characteristics.

The building blocks consist of voltage generators, current generators, resistors, and *ideal diodes* or *ideal rectifiers*. Since the other elements are familiar, let us start by discussing the ideal diode. Its symbol and voltage-current characteristic are given in Fig. 7-2. The ideal diode acts as a short circuit when a forward voltage is applied and as an open circuit when a reverse voltage is applied. The arrowhead in the symbol points in the forward-current direction. Note that the ideal diode consumes no power since, at any instant, *either* the voltage across it or the current through it is zero. The voltage-current characteristic consists of two semifinite lines of zero and

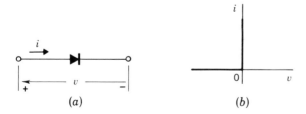

Fig. 7-2 The ideal diode: (*a*) symbol and (*b*) voltage-current characteristic.

infinite slope which intersect at the origin. The point of intersection is called the *breakpoint*.

To obtain a slope which is not infinite, the building block of Fig. 7-3a can be used. Here a resistance is placed in series with the ideal diode. The resulting characteristic is also shown in Fig. 7-3a. When a forward bias is applied, the diode conducts and the circuit acts just like the resistance R.

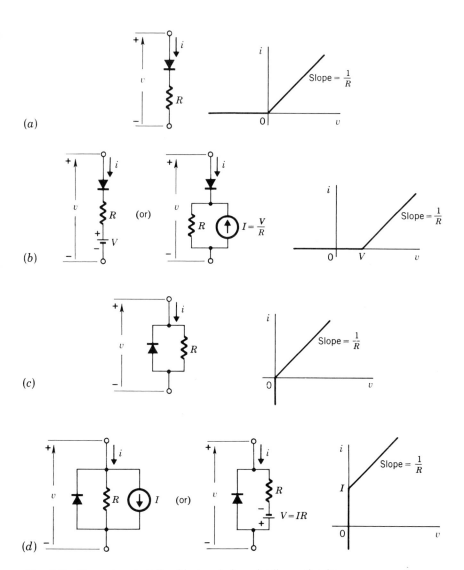

Fig. 7-3 Elementary building blocks of piecewise-linear circuits.

Then, the slope of the characteristic (where $v > 0$) is just $1/R$. When a reverse bias is applied, the circuit acts as an open circuit.

Let us now shift the breakpoint from the origin. Consider the first circuit of Fig. 7-3b. The ideal diode will not conduct until it is forward-biased. That is, the ideal diode of Fig. 7-3b will not conduct until $v > V$.

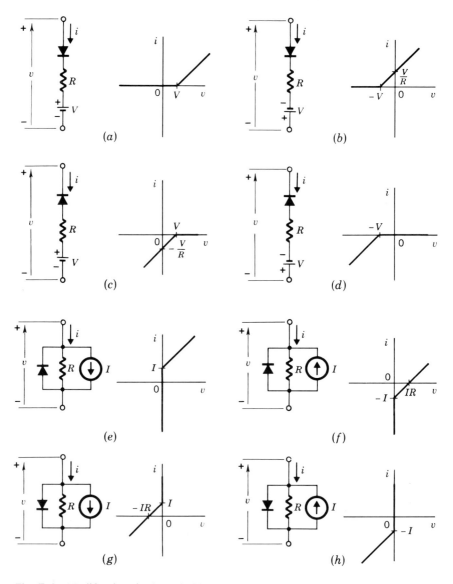

Fig. 7-4 Modifications in the polarities of the elementary building blocks.

When the ideal diode conducts, it acts as a short circuit. The circuit then acts as a resistor R in series with the voltage V. Thus, the voltage-current characteristic has the form shown in Fig. 7-3b. The second diagram of Fig. 7-3b is obtained from the first one by replacing the voltage generator in series with R by a current generator in shunt with R.

The building blocks of Fig. 7-3a and b act either as open circuits or as finite resistors. Now let us consider some circuits that act as short circuits or finite resistors. Consider Fig. 7-3c. If v is positive, the ideal diode will be an open circuit and the entire circuit acts as a resistor R. On the other hand, if v tends to be negative, the diode will be a short circuit. This will cause the voltage of any practical generator to be zero. The characteristic curve is shown in Fig. 7-3c. Note that the breakpoint is at the origin.

Let us now shift the breakpoint by using the circuit of Fig. 7-3d. Consider the first circuit. There a current generator I is placed in shunt with the circuit. If $i < I$, then, using Kirchhoff's current law, there must be a current $I - i$ upward through either the ideal diode or R. If it is in R, the polarity of the voltage drop across it will be such that the diode is a short circuit. Hence, $v = 0$. In this case, the current in R is $v/R = 0$. Thus, all the (upward) current $I - i$ will be in the ideal diode, and $v = 0$. If $i > I$, then the current $i - I$ must be in either R or the ideal diode and in the downward direction. The ideal diode cannot carry current in this direction. Thus, the current must be in R and produce the voltage drop $v = (i - I)R$. This reverse-biases the diode. Thus, the circuit of Fig. 7-3d has the voltage-current characteristic given there. Note that if R approaches an open circuit, the portion of the characteristic to the right of the breakpoint becomes horizontal.

The second network of Fig. 7-3d is obtained from the first one by replacing the current generator in shunt with a resistor by a voltage generator in series with the same resistor.

The characteristics of the building blocks can be modified by reversing the polarity of the ideal diode and/or the generator. These provide additional characteristics. Such modifications are shown in Fig. 7-4. The basic ideas involved here are the same as for the building blocks of Fig. 7-3.

7-2 SYNTHESIS OF PIECEWISE-LINEAR VOLTAGE-CURRENT CHARACTERISTICS

We shall now discuss the synthesis of piecewise-linear characteristics. We start by considering a nonlinear resistance, and the synthesis is then extended to more complex devices. In general, there are several procedures which can be used to synthesize a desired characteristic. They yield different networks. We shall demonstrate one procedure here.

The nonlinear characteristic is approximated by confluent straight-line

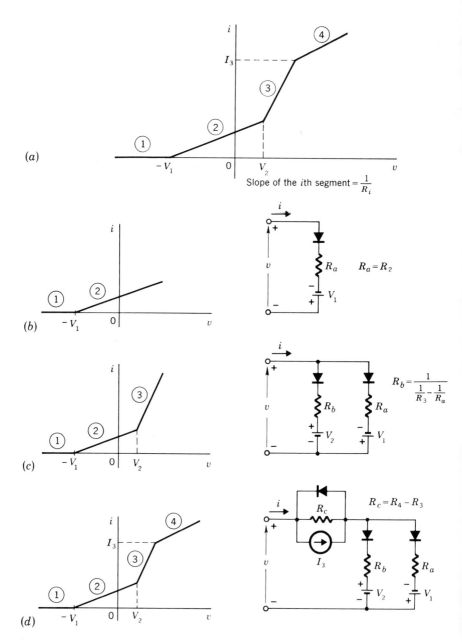

Slope of the ith segment $= \dfrac{1}{R_i}$

$R_a = R_2$

$R_b = \dfrac{1}{\dfrac{1}{R_3} - \dfrac{1}{R_a}}$

$R_c = R_4 - R_3$

Fig. 7-5 The synthesis of a piecewise-linear resistance: (*a*) piecewise-linear resistance; (*b*) realization of the first segment; (*c*) realization of the second segment; (*d*) total resistance.

segments (see Fig. 7-1). Then, each segment of the characteristic is realized proceeding from *left to right*. A building block is added for each segment. Let us illustrate this by realizing the piecewise-linear characteristic of Fig. 7-5a. The first two segments are realized by the building block shown in Fig. 7-5b (see Fig. 7-4b). $R_a = R_2$, the reciprocal of the slope of segment 2.

The slope of segment 3 is greater than that of segment 2. Thus, when $v > V_2$, the input resistance must decrease. This is accomplished by placing a building block, which acts as an open circuit for $v < V_2$ and as a resistance for $v > V_2$, in *parallel* with the first building block. The resultant network is shown in Fig. 7-5b. R_b must be such that the parallel combination of R_c and R_b is equal to the resistance R_3, that is, the reciprocal of the slope of segment 3 (see Fig. 7-5a).

The slope of segment 4 is less than that of segment 3. Thus, when $i > I_3$, resistance must be added in series with the circuit. This can be accomplished using a building block of the type of Fig. 7-3d. Thus, the final network has the form shown in Fig. 7-5d. The value of the resistance R_c

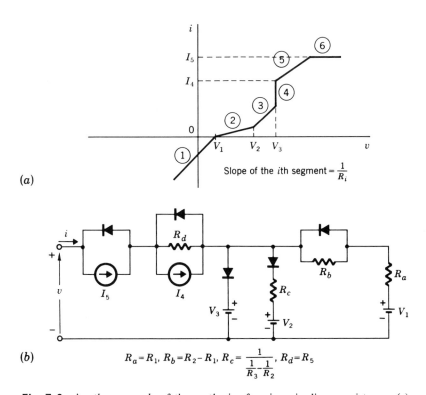

(a)

(b)

$$R_a = R_1, \ R_b = R_2 - R_1, \ R_c = \frac{1}{\frac{1}{R_3} - \frac{1}{R_2}}, \ R_d = R_5$$

Fig. 7-6 Another example of the synthesis of a piecewise-linear resistance: (a) piecewise-linear resistance and (b) its realization.

should be such that R_c plus the reciprocal of the slope of segment 3 is equal to the reciprocal of the slope of segment 4.

At times in this example we concerned ourselves with the value of the voltage at the breakpoint while at other times we were concerned with the value of the current.   In general, it is usually easier to work with the voltage across a shunt branch and the current in a series branch.   This assumes that

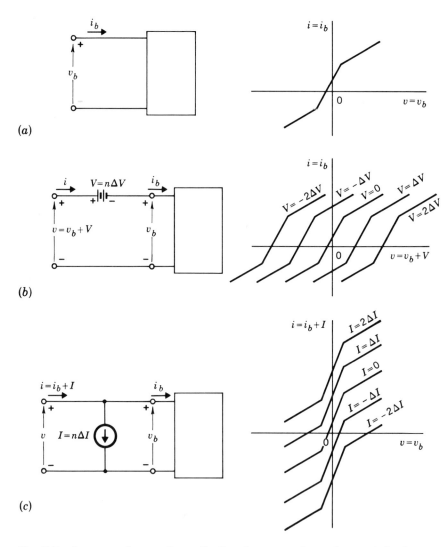

Fig. 7-7 A means of generating a family of current-voltage characteristics from a single characteristic: (a) the characteristic; (b) the family generated by shifting in voltage; (c) the family generated by shifting in current.

the characteristic is realized from left to right and does not have a negative slope.

Another example, presented in Fig. 7-6, uses essentially the same procedure as the preceding one. Note that the first segment *does not* require an ideal diode.

If positive resistances are used in the synthesis, a voltage-current characteristic with a negative slope cannot result. In order to obtain a negative slope negative resistances must be used. This will be illustrated in Sec. 7-8.

When piecewise-linear characteristics for FETs, vacuum tubes, or transistors are synthesized, families of curves are required. Let us discuss a procedure whereby a family of characteristics can be generated from a single one. Two techniques for doing this are indicated in Fig. 7-7. The device of Fig. 7-7a is assumed to have the piecewise-linear characteristics shown. (Actually, the characteristics need not be piecewise-linear.) If a voltage $V = n \Delta V$, $n = \pm 1$, ± 2, . . ., is added in series with the device (see Fig. 7-7b), the characteristic will be shifted horizontally as shown in Fig. 7-7b. This is because, at any given $i = i_b$, the terminal voltage of the complete network is equal to the terminal voltage of the device plus V. In a similar fashion, vertical shifting of the characteristic can be obtained by adding a current generator in shunt with the device, as shown in Fig. 7-7c. By combining both these procedures, the characteristic can be shifted in any direction desired.

The basic building blocks of Sec. 7-1 all have their breakpoints on at least one of the axes. The shifting procedure of Fig. 7-7 can be used to shift the breakpoint to any position desired.

7-3   PIECEWISE-LINEAR CIRCUIT ANALYSIS

In Sec. 7-2, we synthesized a circuit composed of basic building blocks from a given piecewise-linear characteristic. Now let us do the converse. That is, given a network composed of basic building blocks, let us determine its voltage-current characteristic. Such devices have linear characteristics between any two breakpoints. On any straight-line segment, no ideal diode changes its *state*, i.e., whether it is an open or short circuit. If the *states* of the ideal diodes are known (for a given value of terminal voltage or current), then the current (or voltage) can be found using linear analysis since the diodes can all be replaced by open or short circuits. The analysis actually consists of determining the state of the ideal diodes and the locations of the breakpoints.

The value of voltage and current where an ideal diode changes its state is called the *critical point* of the diode. Since it is passing from its conductive state to its nonconductive state, or vice versa, the voltage across it and the current through it are *both* zero. This fact is used to simplify the circuit and obtain the location of the breakpoint. Once the breakpoints are known, the voltage and current characteristic is obtained by connecting them with straight line segments whose slopes are never negative (if all the resistances of the circuit are positive). The two end segments of the characteristic are determined by calculating their slopes.

Let us illustrate the procedure by finding the voltage-current characteristic of Fig. 7-8a. First, let us determine the breakpoint which corresponds to the critical point of ideal diode D_1. At its critical point, the voltage across it and the current through it are both zero. Thus, an ideal diode, at its critical point, can be replaced by a short circuit with no current in it or, alternatively, an open circuit with no voltage across it. The former is done in Fig. 7-8b, which is called a *degenerate circuit*. Since the current through the 1-ohm resistor is zero, the voltage drop across it is also zero. Thus, it too is replaced by a short circuit in Fig. 7-8b. This circuit must be analyzed to determine the terminal voltage and current. These are the location of the breakpoint of D_1. To do this, the state of ideal diode D_2 must be known. One procedure is to guess at the state of D_2. If the guess is wrong, an inconsistency will occur. If there is only one ideal diode, then the result is simple, because then the other choice of the state of D_2 must be picked. If there are many diodes, the state of all of them must be guessed. (Note that the guess might be that some were conducting and others were not conducting.) If the guess is proved wrong, another guess must be made. The number of possible choices is equal to 2^n, where n is the number of ideal diodes. Thus, this can be a tedious calculation.

In the case of Fig. 7-8b, the correct guess can actually be obtained by inspection since $v = 10$ (see Fig. 7-8b). Thus, D_2 is open-circuited because of the 20-volt battery. Hence, $i = 0$. Thus, the coordinates of the breakpoint are $v = 10$ volts, $i = 0$ amp.

To obtain the breakpoint corresponding to the critical point of D_2, we use the network of Fig. 7-8c. Note that the 3-ohm resistor is replaced by a short circuit here since the voltage across it is zero. Thus, $v = 20$ volts. Again, the circuit is simple enough so that we do not have to guess at the state of D_1 since $20 > 10$. Hence, D_1 is conducting. The 2-ohm resistor is short-circuited by it. There are $20 - 10$ volts across the 1-ohm resistor; thus the current through it and the terminal current are equal to 10 amp. The breakpoint is at $v = 20$ volts, $i = 10$ amp.

The two breakpoints are shown in Fig. 7-8d. Since there are only two rectifiers, there are at most two breakpoints. They are connected by a straight-line segment.

Let us now obtain the slope of the end segment. If $v > 20$, both D_1 and D_2 will conduct. The input resistance of the circuit, with all generators replaced by their internal impedances, is a 3-ohm resistor in parallel with a

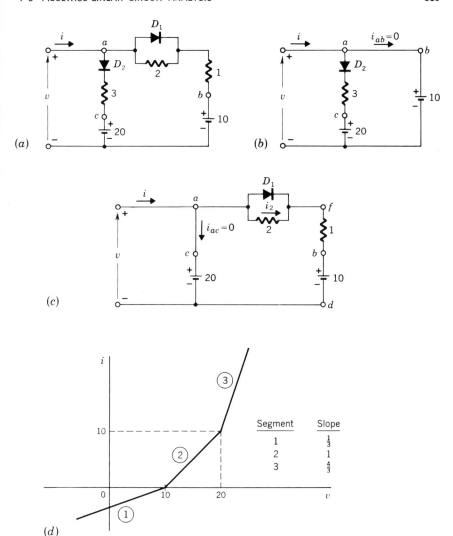

Fig. 7-8 Analysis of a piecewise-linear circuit: (*a*) the circuit; (*b*) the degenerate circuit when D_1 is at its critical point; (*c*) the degenerate circuit when D_2 is at its critical point; (*d*) the piecewise-linear characteristic. All element values are in volts, amperes, or ohms.

1-ohm resistor or $\frac{3}{4}$ ohm. Thus, the slope of the characteristic for $v > 20$ is $\frac{4}{3}$. If $v < 10$, both diodes are open-circuited and the input resistance is 3 ohms. Thus, the slope of the characteristic for $v < 10$ is $\frac{1}{3}$. The complete characteristic is shown in Fig. 7-8*d*. Note that the states of the ideal diodes for the end segment will usually be known since their states at the breakpoints have been determined.

When the circuits containing many ideal diodes are analyzed, the guessing procedure discussed can result in an analysis which is so tedious that it often becomes impractical. In this case, computer analysis can be used to reduce the tedium. Fortunately, many practical circuits have relatively simple piecewise-linear models.

7-4 PIECEWISE-LINEAR MODELS FOR VARIOUS DIODES

In this and subsequent sections we shall discuss the piecewise-linear models of various electric devices. Here, we shall consider diodes. In Fig. 7-9a, the voltage-current characteristic of a vacuum-tube diode is shown and approximated by two straight-line segments. The slope in the first quadrant is picked to approximate the characteristic over the region of operation. The model is also shown in Fig. 7-9a and is the one generally used. However, if more accuracy is desired, the approximations and model of Fig. 7-9b can be used.

Piecewise-linear models for the semiconductor diode are shown in Fig. 7-10. Figure 7-10a is the same as Fig. 7-9a. It neglects the reverse resistance; i.e., it is considered infinite. Figure 7-10b takes the reverse resistance into account. The model of Fig. 7-10c is very accurate, and, in addition, it

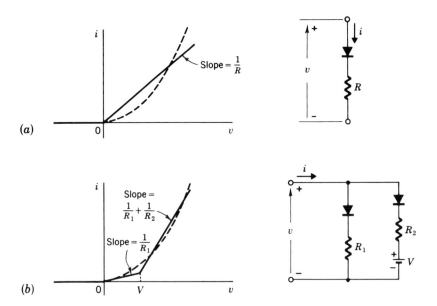

Fig. 7-9 Piecewise-linear models for the vacuum-tube diode. The actual characteristic is shown by the dashed curve. (a) The usual two-segment approximation and (b) a three-segment approximation.

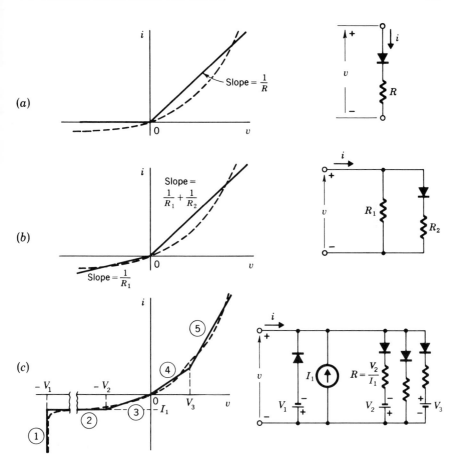

Fig. 7-10 Piecewise-linear models for the semiconductor diode.   The scales of the negative axes are different from those of the positive axes to show the reverse characteristic. (a) A two-segment approximation; (b) a two-segment approximation which takes the reverse characteristic into account; (c) a multisegment approximation that takes both the reverse characteristic and the reverse breakdown. into account.

takes the reverse breakdown into account.   Models this accurate are not often used.

   At times, all diodes are approximated by a simple ideal rectifier.   Often, this results in a small error.

7-5   PIECEWISE-LINEAR MODEL FOR THE FET

Typical static output characteristics for the FET are shown in Fig. 7-11a. Some of the distortion of these characteristics has been neglected.   It has been assumed that the almost horizontal portion of the characteristic can be

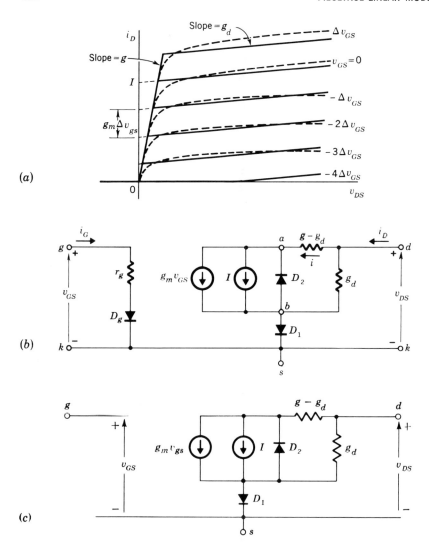

Fig. 7-11   (a) A piecewise-linear approximation for the FET or vacuum-tube pentode output characteristics; (b) a piecewise-linear model for the junction FET or the vacuum-tube pentode; (c) the piecewise-linear model for a MOSFET.

approximated by parallel straight-line segments which are equally spaced for equal increments in v_{GS}.   (This discussion can also be applied to the vacuum-tube pentode if we assume that the potentials of the screen and suppressor grids do not vary with respect to the cathode.)

A piecewise-linear model for the junction FET is shown in Fig. 7-11b.

At the start, consider that D_1 is replaced by a short circuit and that $v_{GS} = 0$. Then if v_{DS} is positive but small enough so that the current i (in the conductance $g - g_d$) is less than I, then D_2 will act as a short circuit (see Fig. 7-3d). The circuit then consists of the conductances $g - g_d$ and g_d in parallel. This yields a net conductance of g. The value of g is chosen to be relatively large. This leads to the segment of slope g in Fig. 7-11a. Thus, for the value of v_{GS} which results in a value of $i < I$, the slope of the characteristic will be g, that is, a line whose equation is $i_D = gv_{DS}$. Now suppose that v_{DS} is increased. This will result in an increase in i. When it becomes equal to I, it cannot increase any further. Then, any additional increase in the current i_D must be through g_d. This results in a characteristic of slope g_d.

The breakpoint occurs at a value of $i = I$. The drain current corresponding to this value is

$$i_D = I + \frac{Ig_d}{g - g_d} = \frac{I_g}{g - g_d} \tag{7-1}$$

Note that the intersection of the extension of the line of slope g_s with the i_D axis is I. The value of v_{DS} at the breakpoint is obtained from the equation

$$v_{DS} = \frac{i_{DBP}}{g} \tag{7-2}$$

where i_{DBP} is the value of i_D at the breakpoint.

If $v_{GS} \neq 0$, the current generator of Fig. 7-11b no longer is I but becomes $I + g_m v_{GS}$. Then this value is substituted in all the previous discussion. Thus, the characteristics of Fig. 7-11a are obtained.

Now let us consider the reason for the inclusion of D_1. If it were not present, i_D would become negative if v_{GS} became negative enough, even though v_{DS} were positive. For instance, consider the actual characteristics for $v_{GS} = -4 \, \Delta v_{GS}$. This has a breakpoint where it intersects the v_{DS} axis and, hence, does not go negative. If D_1 were not present, this breakpoint would not be there and i_D would become negative. Neither the FET nor the vacuum-tube pentode acts this way. Thus, D_1 is added. As long as i_D is positive, D_1 will conduct and not change with the operation, as discussed in the previous paragraph. However, D_1 acts as an open circuit if i_D tends to become negative.

The current in an FET will not reverse if v_{GS} becomes sufficiently negative. However, it will reverse if v_{DS} is reversed. The diode D_1 acts to prevent this from occurring in the model. Then, if it is desired to operate the FET with both positive and negative values of v_{DS}, a more extensive model should be used. Usually, this type of operation is not used, and the model of Fig. 7-11b is adequate.

The input circuit of Fig. 7-11b represents the gate-channel diode of a junction FET. As long as the gate is at a negative potential with respect to the source this diode acts as an open circuit. D_g represents the diode. The resistor r_g represents the resistance of the gate-channel diode when it is forward-biased.

In the MOSFET, there is no diode but an actual layer of insulator material. Thus, the gate is actually insulated from the channel. At low frequencies, the gate terminal acts essentially as an open circuit, e.g., there is a resistance between the gate and source of about 10^{14} ohms. Thus, in the piecewise-linear model, the input circuit is represented by an open circuit. This is shown in Fig. 7-11c. This figure can also be used as a piecewise-linear model for the dual-gate MOSFET if the gate 2–source potential does not vary.

7-6 PIECEWISE-LINEAR MODEL FOR THE VACUUM-TUBE TRIODE

Piecewise-linear approximations to the vacuum-tube-triode plate characteristics are given in Fig. 7-12a. We have assumed that the curves are

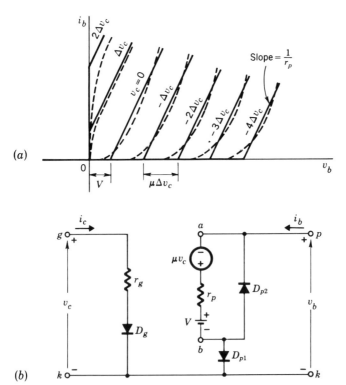

Fig. 7-12 (a) Piecewise-linear approximation for the vacuum-tube-triode plate characteristics and (b) a piecewise-linear model for the vacuum-tube triode.

straight, parallel, and equally spaced for equal increments in v_c. The piecewise-linear model is given in Fig. 7-12b. To simplify the explanation of this circuit assume, for the time being, that D_{p2} is open-circuited. Then, the model is of the form of Fig. 7-3b. (The voltage generator is $V - \mu v_c$.) Thus, the form curves of Fig. 7-12a result.

If D_{p2} were not present, the curves for $v_c = +\Delta v_c$ and $v_c = +2\,\Delta v_c$ would have their breakpoints on the negative v_b axis instead of on the i_b axis. That is, if v_c were positive and large enough, these plate currents would result even if v_b were negative. Vacuum-tube triodes do not operate this way. The inclusion of D_{p2} causes the characteristics of the model to be of the form shown. It prevents v_{ab} from ever being negative. If v_b is positive (and larger than $V + \mu v_c$), then D_{p1} will conduct and D_{p2} will act as an open circuit. Thus, all the characteristics in the first quadrant will be as discussed.

Now consider that v_b is negative. If v_c is positive and large enough so that $|\mu v_c| > v$, then i_b would not be zero if D_{p2} were absent. Note that, in this case, v_{ab} would be negative. Now consider that D_{p2} is present. It will conduct and cause v_{ab} to be zero. Then D_{p1} will be reverse-biased by v_b, and i_b will be zero. Thus, the operation of the model will be as shown in Fig. 7-12a.

The input circuit consisting of r_g and D_g acts in the same way as it does for the vacuum-tube pentode (see Sec. 7-5).

7-7 PIECEWISE-LINEAR MODELS FOR THE TRANSISTOR

A typical set of transistor characteristics has been drawn in Fig. 7-13b and c. To simplify the explanation of the piecewise-linear model, we have drawn these characteristics so that the first quadrant represents positive values of voltage and current. Note that this is not the conventional way of drawing p-n-p transistor characteristics. The piecewise-linear characteristics that we shall use are drawn dashed on these characteristics. The actual output characteristics of Fig. 7-13b are essentially linear and equally spaced for $i_E \geq 0$ and $v_{CB} \leq 0$. Thus, the piecewise-linear approximation lies on the curves in the quadrant. We shall approximate the curves for $v_{CB} \geq 0$ by the i_C axis. The variation of the input characteristics with v_{CB} will also be ignored as is shown by the dashed curve of Fig. 7-13c. Thus, the piecewise-linear equivalent circuit has the form shown in Fig. 7-14. The parameter h_{fb} is negative. A very simple model results if it is assumed that h_{ib}, h_{ob}, and V are zero. Some accuracy is lost in this case. However, the results of an analysis using such a circuit are often satisfactory.

If greater accuracy than that provided by the model of Fig. 7-14 is desired, then the model of Fig. 7-15 can be used. The addition of the conductance $g - h_{ob}$ plays essentially the same role here as does the conductance $g - g_d$ of Fig. 7-11. The curves to the right of the breakpoint will no longer

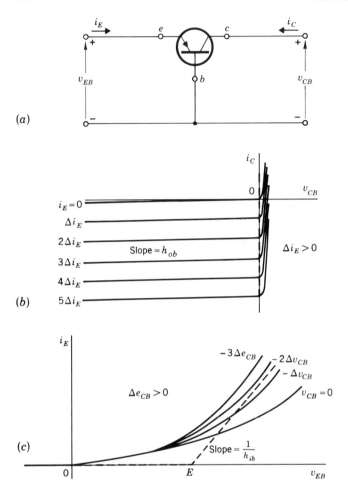

Fig. 7-13 (a) A p-n-p common-base transistor; (b) the common-base output characteristics, with the piecewise-linear approximation shown dashed; (c) the common-base input characteristics with the piecewise-linear approximation shown dashed.

be vertical, but will have a slope of g. The breakpoints will occur at (see Sec. 7-5)

$$i_{CBP} = \frac{g h_{fb} i_E}{g - h_{ob}} \tag{7-3a}$$

$$v_{CB} = g i_{CBP} \tag{7-3b}$$

The generator $h_{rb} v_{CB}$ has been included in the input side to account for the variation of the input characteristic with V_{CB}. The breakpoint now lies

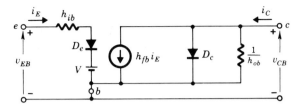

Fig. 7-14 A common-base piecewise-linear model for the *p-n-p* transistor. Note that h_{fb} is negative.

at $V + h_{rb}v_{CB}$. (For normal operation, v_{CB} is negative.) Since the emitter-base junction has a finite back resistance, the resistance r_{bb} has been placed in shunt with the diode.

Typical common-emitter characteristics for the *p-n-p* transistor are given in Fig. 7-16. A piecewise-linear approximation has been shown dashed. A typical circuit that produces the piecewise-linear characteristics is given in Fig. 7-17. Note that if i_B is made somewhat positive (for normal operation, it is negative), the transistor will *essentially* be cut off for much of the region of operation. The diode D_{c2} is shunted by the resistance r_{bc} since a small collector current can exist even if the transistor is "cut off." This small current is not shown in Fig. 7-16.

The input circuit is essentially that of Fig. 7-15 with the polarities reversed. If the collector-base junction becomes forward-biased, a very large collector current will exist. This circuit makes no provision for this. However, it can be accounted for by the diode D_{cb} (shown dashed). It is not necessary to include this diode if the collector-base voltage is maintained at a negative potential.

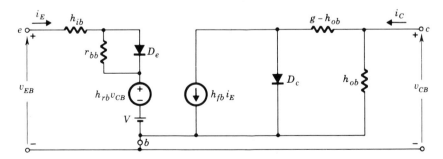

Fig. 7-15 A more complex form of the common-base piecewise-linear model for the *p-n-p* transistor. Note that h_{ob} and g are conductances and that h_{fb} is negative.

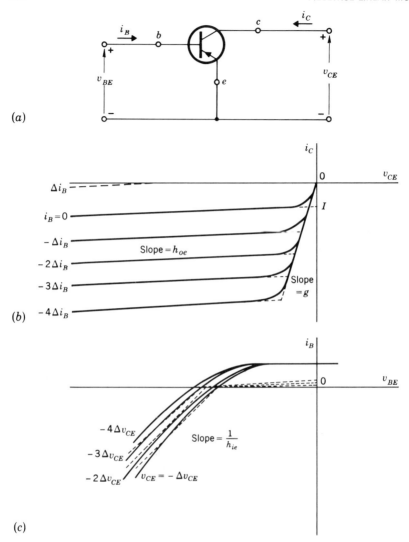

Fig. 7-16 (*a*) A *p-n-p* common-emitter transistor; (*b*) the common-emitter output characteristics with the piecewise-linear approximation shown dashed; (*c*) the common-emitter input characteristic with the piecewise-linear approximation shown dashed.

This piecewise-linear model can be often simplified by omitting r_{be}, r_{bc}, and D_{cb}. At times, the $h_{re}v_{CE}$ generator can be replaced by a short circuit.

If *n-p-n* transistors are used instead of *p-n-p* transistors, the piecewise-linear equivalent circuits are the same except for a modification of the polarities of the voltages and the currents and the orientations of the diodes.

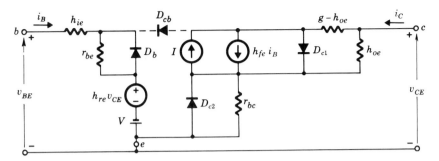

Fig. 7-17 A common-emitter piecewise-linear model for the transistor. Note that h_{ie}, r_{be}, and r_{bc} are resistances while h_{oe} and g are conductances.

7-8 PIECEWISE-LINEAR MODEL FOR THE TUNNEL DIODE

A current-voltage characteristic for a tunnel diode and its piecewise-linear approximation are shown in Fig. 7-18a and b, respectively. The corresponding piecewise-linear model is shown in Fig. 7-18c. This characteristic has a negative slope. Thus, a negative resistance must be used to represent it. When the circuit is analyzed, $-R_2$ is treated using the same procedures that would be applied to a positive resistance.

If a current source whose value lies between I_1 and I_2 is applied to the tunnel diode, the resulting voltage v_b can take on one of three possible values. This implies instability, which is inherent in any negative-resistance device. This instability is one of the reasons tunnel diodes are used in pulse circuits. If a voltage generator is used as the power supply, this instability does not result. Actually, the occurrence of the instability depends upon the magnitude of the power-supply voltage or current source and its internal resistance.

7-9 COMPARISON OF THE PARAMETERS OF PIECEWISE-LINEAR MODELS WITH THOSE OF LINEAR MODELS

In some of the piecewise-linear models that have been developed, the symbolism is the same as that used in the linear models for the same device. In general, the parameters of the linear models represent different quantities than the corresponding parameters used in the piecewise-linear models. The parameters of the linear models are the slopes of characteristic curves at the operating *point*. The parameters of the piecewise-linear models represent an average of a slope over a very wide operating *range*. Of course if the device is essentially linear in this range, then the parameters will be the same. Thus, these parameters cannot be interchanged without a loss of accuracy.

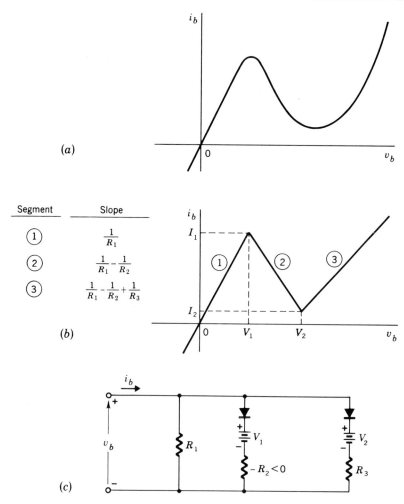

Fig. 7-18 (*a*) The current-voltage characteristic of the tunnel diode; (*b*) a three-segment piecewise-linear approximation to these characteristics; (*c*) a piecewise-linear model whose characteristics are given in (*b*).

Also, note that the form of the piecewise-linear model is often different from that of the linear model.   This is done to allow the model to be accurate over a wide range.

BIBLIOGRAPHY

Chirlian, P. M., and A. H. Zemanian: "Electronics," chap. 12, McGraw-Hill Book Company, New York, 1961.

Zimmermann, H. J., and S. J. Mason: "Electronic Circuit Theory," pp. 56–78, 171–174, 225–228, 304, John Wiley & Sons, Inc., New York, 1960.

PROBLEMS

7-1. Sketch the characteristic curves for the circuits of Fig. 7-4a to d when all the resistances are replaced by short circuits.

7-2. Sketch the characteristic curves for the circuits of Fig. 7-4e to h when all the resistances are replaced by open circuits.

7-3. Obtain a network that realizes the piecewise-linear characteristic shown in Fig. 7-19.

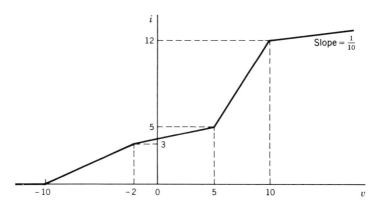

Fig. 7-19

7-4. Obtain a network that realizes the piecewise-linear characteristic shown in Fig. 7-20.

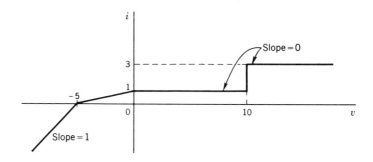

Fig. 7-20

7-5. Obtain a network that realizes the piecewise-linear characteristic shown in Fig. 7-21.

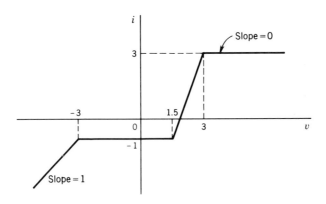

Fig. 7-21

7-6. Approximate the curve of Fig. 7-22 in a piecewise-linear fashion and derive a network that realizes this approximation.

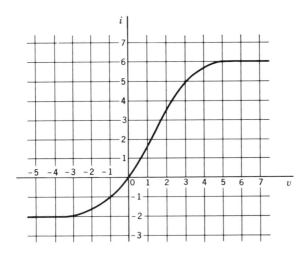

Fig. 7-22

7-7. Synthesize a network that produces the family of piecewise-linear characteristics shown in Fig. 7-23. Each curve is composed of four segments, one of which is horizontal and another vertical.

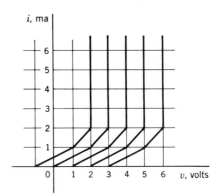

Fig. 7-23

7-8. Synthesize a network that produces the family of piecewise-linear curves shown in Fig. 7-24. Each curve is composed of three segments, one of which is vertical and another horizontal.

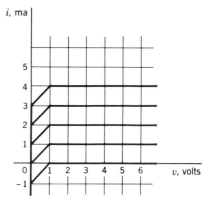

Fig. 7-24

7-9. Obtain a plot of i versus v for the piecewise-linear circuit of Fig. 7-25.

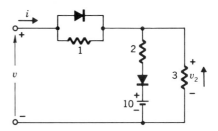

Fig. 7-25

7-10. Obtain a plot of i versus v for the piecewise-linear circuit of Fig. 7-26.

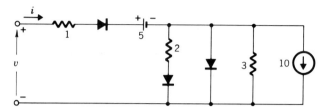

Fig. 7-26

7-11. Obtain a plot of v_2 versus v for the piecewise-linear circuit of Fig. 7-25.

7-12. Obtain a piecewise-linear model for the diode characteristic shown in Fig. 7-27,

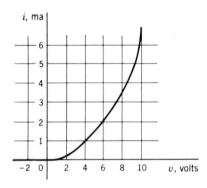

Fig. 7-27

using only one ideal diode. Then, using this model, calculate the operating point of this diode when it is connected into the circuit of Fig. 7-28 when $V = 10$ volts. Repeat this calculation for $V = 4$ volts. Then find the operating points by drawing load lines on the characteristic curve. Compare these results.

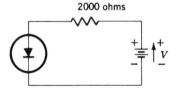

2000 ohms

Fig. 7-28

7-13. Repeat Prob. 7-12, but now use a piecewise-linear circuit containing two ideal diodes. Compare these results with those of Prob. 7-12.

7-14. Sketch the piecewise-linear characteristic of the FET piecewise-linear model of Fig. 7-11b if D_1 is replaced by a short circuit. Why is D_1 included in Fig. 7-11b?

7-15. Determine the parameter values for the piecewise-linear model of Fig. 7-11c for the 3N139 FET. The state characteristics of this FET are given in Fig. 5-30. Use this model to determine the operating point when the FET is connected into the circuit of Fig. 7-29. Compare this result with that obtained by graphical analysis.

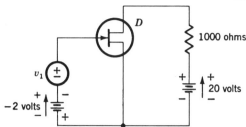

Fig. 7-29

7-16. Obtain a linear model for the 3N139 FET which is valid for small incremental changes about the operating point determined in Prob. 7-15. Compare this model with the piecewise-linear one determined in Prob. 7-15.

7-17. Discuss how the linear model for the FET can be determined from the piecewise-linear model of Fig. 7-11. Will the parameter values always be the same?

7-18. Sketch the i_b-versus-v_b characteristics of the piecewise-linear model for the vacuum-tube triode of Fig. 7-12b if D_{p2} is replaced by an open circuit.

7-19. Obtain a piecewise-linear model for the vacuum-tube triode which approximates each characteristic curve with three straight-line segments, rather than the two shown in Fig. 7-12a.

7-20. Determine the parameter values for the piecewise-linear model of Fig. 7-12b for the 6C4 vacuum-tube triode. Use this model to determine the quiescent operating point when this tube is connected into the circuit of Fig. 7-30. The plate characteristics

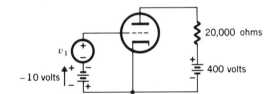

Fig. 7-30

of the 6C4 are given in Fig. 5-31. Compare this result with the value of the quiescent operating point obtained by a graphical analysis that uses a load line.

7-21. Obtain the linear model for the 6C4 vacuum-tube triode which is valid for incremental changes about the graphically determined operating point obtained in Prob. 7-20 Compare this circuit with the piecewise-linear model determined in Prob. 7-20.

7-22. Determine the parameter values of the piecewise-linear model shown in Fig. 7-11b for the 5879 vacuum-tube pentode. Use this model to obtain the operating point of the circuit shown in Fig. 7-31 and compare it to the value obtained graphically.

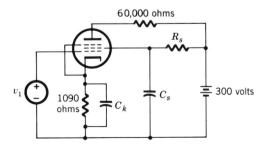

Fig. 7-31

Assume that the screen grid–to–cathode voltage is 100 volts.   The plate characteristics of the 5879 vacuum-tube pentode are given in Fig. 5-10.

7-23.   Obtain piecewise-linear models for the *p-n-p* transistor whose characteristics are shown in Fig. 7-32, using first the circuit of Fig. 7-14 and then that of Fig. 7-15.

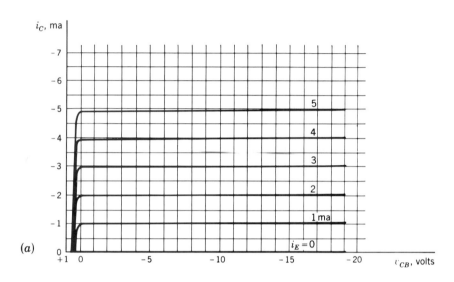

(a)

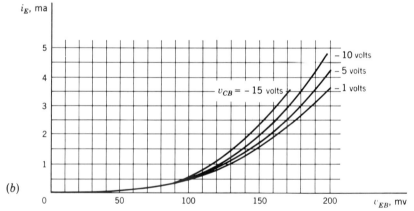

(b)

Fig. 7-32

7-24.   Draw the input and output characteristics, that is, i_B versus v_{BE} with v_{CE} as a parameter, and i_C versus v_{CE} with i_B as a parameter, for the piecewise-linear model of Fig. 7-17.

7-25.   Use the piecewise-linear model of Fig. 7-14 to obtain expressions for all four coordinates of the quiescent operating point of the *p-n-p* transistor shown in Fig. 7-33. Note that V_{CC} is defined as negative.

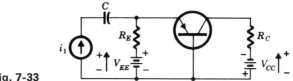

Fig. 7-33

7-26. Repeat Prob. 7-25, but now use the piecewise-linear model of Fig. 7-15.

7-27. Use the piecewise-linear model of Fig. 7-17 to obtain expressions for all four coordinates of the quiescent operating point of the *p-n-p* transistor of Fig. 7-34. Assume

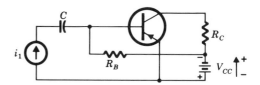

Fig. 7-34

that $g - h_{oe}$ is a short circuit and r_{bc} and r_{be} are open circuits. Note that V_{CC} is defined as negative.

7-28. Repeat Prob. 7-27 but do not neglect any elements.

7-29. Use the piecewise-linear model of Fig. 7-17 to obtain expressions for all four coordinates of the quiescent operating point of the *p-n-p* transistor shown in Fig. 7-35.

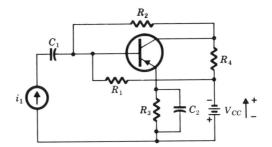

Fig. 7-35

Note that V_{CC} is defined as negative. Assume that $g - h_{oe}$ is a short circuit and that r_{be} and r_{bc} are open circuits.

7-30. Make a five-segment piecewise-linear approximation of the tunnel diode characteristic of Fig. 7-18*a*, and synthesize the corresponding piecewise-linear model, specifying all resistors in terms of the slopes of the segments.

8
Amplifier Fundamentals

One of the most important functions that FETs, transistors, and vacuum tubes perform is amplification. That is, a small controlling signal is used to produce a larger signal of the same waveshape. For instance, in a high-fidelity phonograph system, the extremely small signal from the phonograph pickup is amplified to a large signal which can drive the loudspeaker. In this chapter, we shall discuss amplifiers qualitatively and defer a discussion of their analysis and design to subsequent chapters.

8-1 CASCADING OF AMPLIFIERS

FET, vacuum-tube, and transistor circuits can produce voltage, current, and power gains. Note that the words amplification and gain are used interchangeably. In many instances, the gain of a single amplifier circuit is not sufficient, so amplifiers are cascaded. That is, the output of one amplifier is

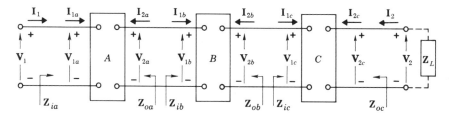

Fig. 8-1 A representation of a cascade of amplifier stages.

used to drive a succeeding one (see Fig. 8-1). The overall voltage and current gains of this device are given by

$$A_v = \frac{V_2}{V_1} \tag{8-1}$$

$$A_i = \frac{I_2}{I_1} \tag{8-2}$$

The overall power gain is given by

$$A_p = \frac{|V_2|\,|I_2|\cos\theta_2}{|V_1|\,|I_1|\cos\theta_1} \tag{8-3}$$

where θ_1 and θ_2 are the phase angles between V_1 and I_1 and between V_2 and I_2, respectively. The voltage and current amplifications for the individual stages are given by

$$\begin{aligned}
A_{av} &= \frac{V_{2a}}{V_{1a}} & A_{ai} &= \frac{I_{2a}}{I_{1a}} \\
A_{bv} &= \frac{V_{2b}}{V_{1b}} & A_{bi} &= \frac{I_{2b}}{I_{1b}} \\
A_{cv} &= \frac{V_{2c}}{V_{1c}} & A_{ci} &= \frac{I_{2c}}{I_{1c}}
\end{aligned} \tag{8-4}$$

Making use of the relations

$$V_1 = V_{1a} \qquad V_{2a} = V_{1b} \qquad V_{2b} = V_{1c} \qquad V_{2c} = V_2$$

and

$$\tag{8-5}$$

$$I_1 = I_{1a} \qquad I_{2a} = -I_{1b} \qquad I_{2b} = -I_{1c} \qquad I_{2c} = I_2$$

we obtain

$$A_v = \frac{V_2}{V_1} = A_{av}A_{bv}A_{cv} \tag{8-6}$$

and

$$A_i = \frac{I_2}{I_1} = A_{ai}A_{bi}A_{ci} \tag{8-7}$$

In general, if we cascade n stages, we obtain

$$\mathbf{A}_v = \mathbf{A}_{1v}\mathbf{A}_{2v} \cdot \cdot \cdot \mathbf{A}_{nv} \tag{8-8}$$

$$\mathbf{A}_i = (-1)^{n+1}\mathbf{A}_{1i}\mathbf{A}_{2i} \cdot \cdot \cdot \mathbf{A}_{ni} \tag{8-9}$$

The factor $(-1)^{n+1}$ occurs in Eq. (8-9) because of the convention used in assigning the directions of the currents.

The overall power gain is given by

$$\mathbf{A}_p = |A_v| \, |A_i| \frac{\cos \theta_2}{\cos \theta_1} \tag{8-10}$$

If we define the power gain of an individual stage as the ratio of the power delivered to the next stage (or to the load) to its input power, then we have

$$\mathbf{A}_p = A_{1p}A_{2p} \cdot \cdot \cdot A_{np} \tag{8-11}$$

Thus the overall voltage, current, and power gains are the products of the voltage gains, the current gains, and the power gains of the individual stages, respectively. Hence, extremely large gains can be obtained from amplifier stages that have only moderate gains.

8-2 EFFECT OF INPUT AND OUTPUT IMPEDANCES ON THE GAINS OF CASCADED AMPLIFIER STAGES

In the discussion of the preceding section, we assumed that the gains of the amplifier stages were the actual operating gains. For instance, in Fig. 8-1, $\mathbf{A}_{av} = \mathbf{V}_{1a}/\mathbf{V}_{2a}$ represents the voltage gain of stage A *when it is terminated in the cascade of stages B and C and the load* $\mathbf{Z}_L$. In general, if the terminating impedance of stage A were changed, then the voltage gain would change. This also applies to current and power gains. Thus, when devices are cascaded, a knowledge of their input impedance is necessary if their operation is to be predicted. It is often tedious to determine the input impedance. For example, to determine $\mathbf{Z}_{ib}$, the input impedance of stage B, the terminating impedance of stage B must be known. This is given by $\mathbf{Z}_{ic}$, the input impedance of stage C. Thus, $\mathbf{Z}_{ic}$ must be calculated before $\mathbf{Z}_{ib}$ can be, and so forth. At times, there is isolation between the stages, so that the input impedance of one stage does not depend upon the succeeding stages. This greatly simplifies the calculations.

The output impedance of each amplifier stage is also important. Any amplifier can be characterized by Thévenin's theorem as a voltage generator in series with the output impedance. If the voltage source is replaced by a current source, then the amplifier can alternately be represented by a current generator in shunt with the output impedance (Norton's theorem). A convenient way of representing amplifiers is shown in Fig. 8-2. The voltage of

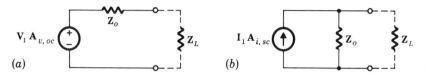

Fig. 8-2 (*a*) Thévenin's model of an amplifier; $A_{v,oc}$ = voltage gain of the amplifier when the load impedance is an open circuit and V_1 = input voltage of the amplifier; (*b*) Norton's equivalent circuit of an amplifier; $A_{i,sc}$ = current gain of the amplifier when the load impedance is a short circuit and I_1 = input current of the amplifier. Note that (*a*) and (*b*) are not equivalent.

Thévenin's generator is equal to the open-circuit voltage gain or the amplifier times the input voltage. Such a representation is shown in Fig. 8-2*a*. Similarly, the amplifier can be represented by Norton's equivalent circuit of Fig. 8-2*b*. Note that Fig. 8-2*a* and *b* are *not* equivalent, since the amplifier inputs are different in each case. If the open-circuit voltage gain $A_{v,oc}$ and the output impedance are known, then the voltage gain for any termination can be found. Similarly, the current gain, for any value of load impedance can be found from the short-circuit current gain $A_{i,sc}$ and Z_o. From Fig. 8-2*a* we have that if $|Z_o| \ll |Z_L|$, the voltage gain will be approximately equal to $A_{v,oc}$. Similarly, using Fig. 8-2*b*, if $|Z_o| \gg |Z_L|$, the current gain is essentially given by $A_{i,sc}$. Hence, if the impedance conditions are correct, the calculation of either the voltage gain or the current gain of an individual stage will depend only upon the parameters of that stage.

8-3 COUPLING NETWORKS

Amplifier stages are not cascaded by just connecting the output of one stage to the input of the next. This would be done if only signal considerations were involved. However, the output bias voltage of an amplifier stage is usually very different from the input bias voltage of the next amplifier stage, so more complex coupling techniques must be used. For instance, in a vacuum-tube amplifier, the plate voltage may be several hundred volts positive, while the grid voltage is several volts negative. We shall present the important amplifier coupling techniques in this section. Quantitative discussions of the properties of these amplifiers will be given in Chap. 9.

Resistance-capacitance-coupled amplifiers The direct bias voltage at the output of one stage can be isolated from the input to the next stage by placing a capacitor in series with the output, as shown in Fig. 8-3. The coupling capacitors C_c act as open circuits for the direct bias voltages and prevent interaction of the output bias voltage of one stage with the input bias voltage of the next stage. The value of C_c should be chosen so that it acts

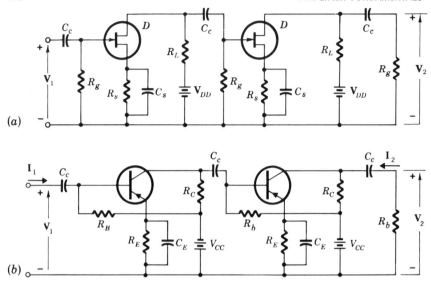

Fig. 8-3 *RC*-coupled amplifiers: (*a*) common-source FET amplifier and (*b*) common-emitter transistor amplifier.

essentially as a short circuit at the signal frequencies.   Actually we have over-simplified the problem somewhat.   When very low frequencies are used, C_c can no longer be considered to be a short circuit.   It acts as the series arm in a voltage divider and causes the amplification to decrease.   Although we have illustrated only the common-source FET amplifier and the common-emitter transistor amplifier, the same coupling procedure can be used with other amplifier configurations.   The elements of this coupling are resistances and capacitances, hence, the name *resistance-capacitance coupling*, often abbreviated as *RC* coupling.

Transformer-coupled amplifiers   A transformer performs the functions of a coupling network.   That is, it transmits the alternating signal while "blocking" the direct bias voltage or current.   Typical transformer-coupled amplifiers are shown in Fig. 8-4.   Transformers can be used as impedance-matching circuits.   In addition, the direct current through their windings does not dissipate any power as it does in a load resistance.   The ability of a transformer to step up the voltage or the current enables it to increase the voltage gain or the current gain of an amplifier.   However, transformer coupling usually results in amplifiers that have poorer frequency responses and that are larger, heavier, and more expensive than *RC*-coupled amplifiers.

Direct-coupled amplifiers   An ideal coupling circuit is often considered to be one that blocks the passage of direct voltages and currents but permits

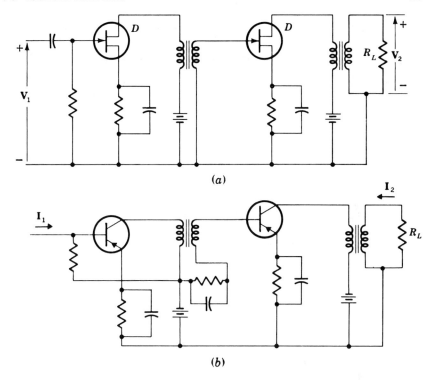

Fig. 8-4 Transformer-coupled amplifiers: using (*a*) FETs and (*b*) transistors.

the passage of signal components. Direct voltage is zero-frequency voltage and therefore these coupling circuits will not transmit zero-frequency *signals*. The previously discussed coupling networks greatly attenuate signals that have extremely low frequency components. Thus those circuits are not suitable for use in amplifiers which amplify very low frequencies. One procedure that is used to amplify low-frequency signals is to connect the output of one stage directly to the input of the next one. Additional power supplies are then used to eliminate the effect of the unwanted bias voltages. Such direct-coupled circuits will amplify all frequencies down to zero frequency. However, there are problems associated with direct-coupled amplifiers; hence they are only used where necessary. These amplifiers are discussed in Sec. 9-27.

Tuned amplifiers The amplifier interstages that have been discussed amplify a broad range of frequencies. It is often desirable to amplify only a range of frequencies and to reject all others. Resonant circuits are usually used in such applications. Figure 8-5*a* is a simple tuned amplifier. C_c is a blocking capacitor that functions as it does in the *RC*-coupled amplifier of

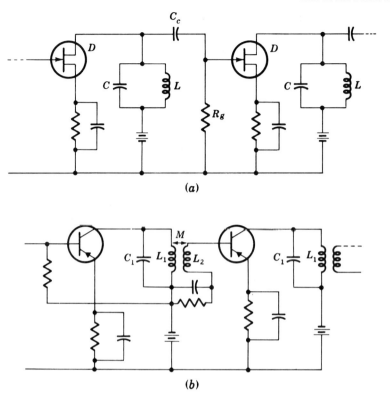

Fig. 8-5 Tuned amplifiers: (*a*) capacitor coupled; (*b*) mutual inductance coupled.

Fig. 8-3.   The resonant circuit consisting of the inductor L and the capacitor C produces the frequency discrimination.   It presents a high impedance at the resonant frequency $1/(2\pi\sqrt{LC})$ and a low impedance at frequencies far removed from resonance.   The circuit of Fig. 8-5*b* also utilizes resonance. The two coils are coupled by mutual inductance, and, hence, no blocking capacitor is required.

8-4   DECIBEL NOTATION

Often it is desirable to express the power gain of a device in logarithmic form. This is true in audio devices, since the human ear functions logarithmically. If P_2 is the output power supplied to a load and P_1 is the input power, then the number of bels of power gain is given by

$$\text{No. of bels} = \log\frac{P_2}{P_1} \tag{8-12}$$

The bel is usually too large a unit. For this reason, the decibel, which is one-tenth of a bel, is usually used. The number of decibels is given by

$$\text{No. of db} = 10 \log \frac{P_2}{P_1} \qquad (8\text{-}13)$$

If the input impedance of the device is purely resistive and equal to R_1, and if the load impedance is purely resistive and equal to R_2, we have

$$\text{No. of db} = 10 \log \frac{|\mathbf{V}_2|^2/R_2}{|\mathbf{V}_1|^2/R_1} = 10 \log \frac{|I_2|^2 R_2}{|I_1|^2 R_1}$$

If $R_1 = R_2$, we have

$$\text{No. of db} = 20 \log \left|\frac{\mathbf{V}_2}{\mathbf{V}_1}\right| = 20 \log \left|\frac{I_2}{I_1}\right| \qquad (8\text{-}14)$$

Strictly speaking, the only time that Eq. (8-14) can be used is when the input and load resistances are equal. However, this relation is widely misused in that voltage ratios and current ratios are expressed in decibels even though $R_1 \ne R_2$. In such cases, the decibel voltage and decibel current ratios are not equal. *It is permissible to use decibels in this way as long as it is understood that only a voltage ratio or a current ratio is expressed.* The voltage, current, and power ratios will no longer be equal. If an amplifier has a voltage gain whose magnitude is A_v and a current gain whose magnitude is A_i, these can be expressed in decibels as

$$A_{v,\text{db}} = 20 \log A_v \qquad (8\text{-}15)$$

$$A_{i,\text{db}} = 20 \log A_i \qquad (8\text{-}16)$$

Note that $A_v \ne A_i$ and $A_{v,\text{db}} \ne A_{i,\text{db}}$. When amplifiers are cascaded, the overall gain is found by multiplying the gains of the individual stages. If the amplification of each stage is expressed in decibels, the overall gain in decibels is found by adding the individual gains in decibels.

Although the decibel notation is a power ratio, at times it is modified to indicate an absolute level of power. In such cases, a standard reference level is chosen. For instance, the dbm is the number of decibels above 1 mw and is given by

$$\text{No. of dbm} = 10 \log \frac{P}{10^{-3}} = 10 \log 10^3 P \qquad (8\text{-}17)$$

where P is the power level in watts.

8-5 CLASSIFICATION OF AMPLIFIERS

Many adjectives are used to describe amplifiers. For instance, the active device is usually specified, e.g., transistor FET, or vacuum-tube amplifier. There are many other descriptive terms, and we shall discuss them here.

Voltage, current, and power amplifiers   Usually an amplifier is designed to amplify either voltage, current, or power. For instance, if FET or vacuum-tube amplifiers are cascaded, the function of each of the stages, except the last, is to provide a voltage that drives the next stage. Thus, these stages are called *voltage amplifiers* even though their current and power gains are large (and might be even larger than their voltage gain). Similarly, when transistor amplifiers are cascaded, all the stages but the last could be called *current amplifiers*. When the function of the amplifier is to supply signal power to a load, such as a loudspeaker or antenna, then it is classified as a *power amplifier*.

Small-signal and large-signal amplifiers   If an amplifier is operated such that linear analysis can be used, it is called a *small-signal amplifier*. If the operation is over such a large region of the static characteristics that graphical or piecewise-linear analysis techniques are required, then it is called a *large-signal amplifier*. Note that this classification depends upon the linearity of operation, not on any arbitrary signal level.

Classification according to operating frequency   Amplifiers are designed to amplify specific ranges of frequency. For instance, an amplifier used in a sound system amplifies frequencies in the audible range, that is, 20 to 20,000 Hz. Such an amplifier is called an *audio amplifier*.

The information in a standard television picture contains frequencies up to 4.5×10^6 Hz. An amplifier designed to amplify such signals is called a *video amplifier*. Actually, the term video amplifier is applied to any *broadband amplifier* whose frequency response is considerably greater than that of an audio amplifier.

Certain amplifiers are designed to pass a certain range of frequencies and to reject others. Two such amplifiers are shown in Fig. 8-5. These amplifiers utilize tuned circuits and are called *tuned amplifiers*. These can be contrasted with audio and video amplifiers, which do not use tuned circuits and are therefore called *untuned amplifiers*.

Class A, B, and C amplifiers   When an alternating signal is applied to an electronic device, e.g., FET, vacuum tube, or transistor, the instantaneous operating point will vary. If the biasing voltage or current and the amplitude of the signal are such that the output current is never zero, then this is said to be *class A operation*. (In the examples in Chap. 5, the operation was class A.) If we consider the generalized circuit of Fig. 8-6, where the input bias is $X_{II} = -4\,\Delta x$ and the signal is $x_1 = 2\,\Delta x \sin \omega t$, the operation will be class A. If the input signal increases to $x_1 = 4\,\Delta x \sin \omega t$, then i_O will be

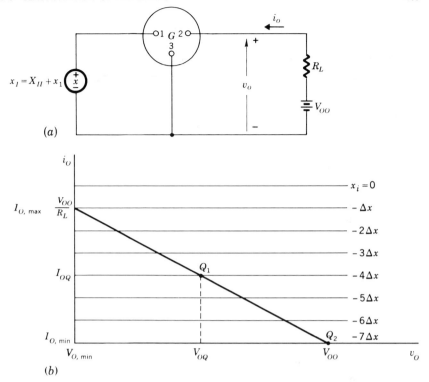

Fig. 8-6 (a) A simple amplifier circuit using a generalized device; (b) idealized characteristics for the generalized device and the load line for the amplifier. $V_{o,min}$ and $I_{o,min}$ correspond to $x_1 = 4\Delta x \sin \omega t$.

zero for those times when $x_1 < -3\,\Delta x$. This will then not be class A operation.

If we change the quiescent input bias to $-7\,\Delta x$, the quiescent operating point will shift from point Q_1 to point Q_2. The current i_o will be nonzero only when x_1 is positive, which is for one-half the cycle. This is called *class B operation*. If current is nonzero for more than one-half cycle but less than a full cycle, then the operation is called *class AB*. For instance, if we return the quiescent operating point to Q_1 and apply a signal $x_1 = 4\,\Delta x \sin \omega t$, the operation will be class AB.

When output current is nonzero for substantially less than one half-cycle, we have *class C* operation. If the quiescent input bias is $X_{II} = -10\,\Delta x$ and $x_1 = 6\,\Delta x \sin \omega t$, then i_o will be nonzero only when $x_1 > 3\,\Delta x$. This will be class C operation. Note that when $x_I < -7\,\Delta x$, $i_o = 0$. Hence the curve labeled $-7\,\Delta x$ in Fig. 8-6b actually represents all the curves for values of input bias equal to or less than $-7\,\Delta x$.

8-6 EFFICIENCY OF IDEAL AMPLIFIERS

In Sec. 5-9 we discussed the output-circuit efficiency of generalized amplifiers. Let us now compute the maximum efficiency that an amplifier can have. It should be emphasized here that these calculations involve idealized characteristics and, thus, the efficiencies are larger than in actual practice. The output-circuit efficiency is given by

$$\eta_2 = \frac{\text{ac output power}}{\text{power supplied by power supply}} \times 100 = \frac{P_2}{P_{OO}} \times 100$$

where P_2 is the signal power delivered to the load impedance and P_{OO} is the power supplied by the battery V_{OO}.

Let us now consider the amplifier of Fig. 8-6, restricting the operation to class A. There is no distortion, so $P_{OO} = E_{OO}I_{OQ}$. The power P_{OO} is independent of the signal level. Hence, to obtain maximum efficiency, we use the largest signal which does not cause distortion. For the operating point shown, we have [see Eq. (5-66)]

$$\eta_{2,\max} = \frac{(V_{OO} - 0)(I_{O,\max} - 0)}{8E_{OO}I_{OQ}} \times 100$$

But $I_{O,\max} = 2I_{OQ}$; therefore

$$\eta_{2,\max} = 25\% \tag{8-18}$$

This efficiency is very low. One reason is that the direct current I_{OQ} is through R_L and dissipates power in it. The use of the transformer-coupled circuit of Fig. 8-7a eliminates this problem. The load line in Fig. 8-7b is drawn with the assumption that the transformer is ideal; e.g., the primary winding resistance is zero. In order to obtain the largest possible output the operating point and R_L are adjusted so that $V_{O,\max} = 2V_{OO}$. Note that the ideal transformer operates such that the impedance, at signal frequencies, into the primary, is $R_{ac} = (n_1/n_2)^2 R_L$ (see Sec. 9-17). Then the efficiency is given by

$$\eta_{2,\max} = \frac{(I_{O,\max} - 0)(2V_{OO} - 0)}{8V_{OO}I_{OQ}}$$

Therefore

$$\eta_{2,\max} = 50\% \tag{8-19}$$

This is a considerable improvement, but the efficiency is still low. So far we have only permitted class A operation. If this restriction is removed, the efficiency can be greatly increased.

Let us now assume that the operation is class B. That is, for the circuit of Fig. 8-7, the quiescent input bias is shifted from $-4\,\Delta x$ to $-7\,\Delta x$.

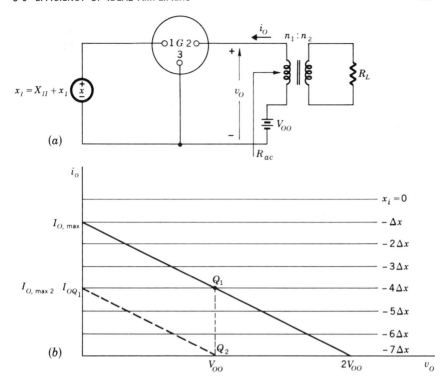

Fig. 8-7 (a) A simple transformer-coupled amplifier; (b) idealized characteristics for the generalized device and the load line for the amplifier. The slope of the load line is $-(n_1/n_2)^2 R_L$. The dashed load line is for class B operation.

Note that if no signal is present, then $i_O = 0$ and $P_{OO} = 0$. We shall again assume maximum signal swing without distortion so that $x_1 = 3\,\Delta x \sin \omega t$. In this case

$$i_O = \begin{cases} I_{O;\text{max},2} \sin \omega t & \text{for } 0 \le \omega t \le \pi \\ 0 & \text{for } \pi \le \omega t \le 2\pi \end{cases}$$

Then $P_{OO} = E_{OO} I_{OA}$ where

$$I_{OA} = \frac{1}{2\pi} \int_0^{2\pi} i_O \, d\omega t$$

$$I_{OA} = \frac{I_{O;\text{max},2}}{\pi}$$

The instantaneous sinusoidal current is nonzero for only one half-cycle. Thus,

$$\eta_2 = \frac{(E_{OO} - 0)(I_{O,\text{max},2} - 0)(\tfrac{1}{4})}{E_{OO} I_{O,\text{max},2}/\pi} \times 100$$

$$\eta_{2,\text{max}} = \frac{\pi}{4} \times 100 = 78.5\% \tag{8-20}$$

If we use class C operation, the maximum efficiency will be increased still further. In fact, it is theoretically possible to approach 100 percent efficiency. If class A operation is not used, then the signal will be distorted, since the output current will be zero for a portion of the cycle. This does not mean that we are always restricted to class A operation. In Chap. 10 we shall demonstrate that this distortion can be eliminated for class AB and for class B operation. In Chap. 11 we shall show how class C amplifiers can be utilized.

The calculations made in this section involved idealized characteristics. If characteristics of actual devices are used, the swing in output voltage and current has to be limited to prevent excessive distortion. Thus, the maximum efficiencies given here are higher than those actually obtained. For instance, in actual practice with vacuum tubes, the actual efficiencies may only be one-half of the predicted values. Larger swings are usually possible with transistors, and the efficiencies are closer to the maximum values. For class B and C operation, the reduction in efficiency is not as great. Class B efficiencies of 50 percent or more can be obtained readily. For class C operation, it is possible to obtain efficiencies of 85 to 90 percent or more. These calculations are based on sinusoidal signals. If other waveforms are used, the efficiencies can be higher. For instance, with class A operation, the circuit of Fig. 8-7a can have efficiencies that approach 100 percent if the input signal is a square wave. However, in most linear applications, the results obtained with sinusoids are typical.

8-7 DISTORTION

The output waveform of an ideal amplifier should be an exact reproduction of the input waveform multiplied by a constant. In an actual amplifier the output waveform will differ to some extent from that of the input. Such a difference in waveforms is termed *distortion*. There are two basic causes of distortion. One is the nonlinearity of the active element and is termed *nonlinear distortion*. This was discussed in Secs. 5-10 and 5-11. The other is the variation of the parameters of the amplifier with frequency and is called *frequency distortion*. To illustrate this latter case, let us assume that a square wave, such as that shown in Fig. 8-8a, is applied to an amplifier. A Fourier analysis of this waveform yields

$$v_1(t) = \frac{4}{\pi}(\cos t - \tfrac{1}{3}\cos 3t + \tfrac{1}{5}\cos 5t - \tfrac{1}{7}\cos 7t + \cdot\cdot\cdot) \qquad (8\text{-}21)$$

If this signal were amplified by an ideal amplifier of voltage gain A, the output signal would be

$$v_2(t) = \frac{4A}{\pi}(\cos t - \tfrac{1}{3}\cos 3t + \tfrac{1}{5}\cos 5t - \tfrac{1}{7}\cos 7t + \cdot\cdot\cdot) \qquad (8\text{-}22)$$

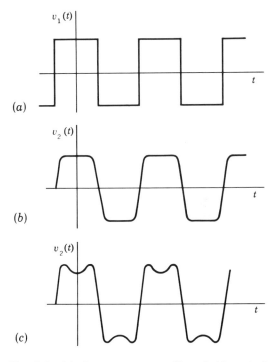

Fig. 8-8 (*a*) A square wave; (*b*) and (*c*) typical effects of frequency distortion.

If the amplification of all the frequencies is not the same, then the output and input waveforms will differ. The amplification is a complex number. Its magnitude is the magnitude, or amplitude, of the amplification; its phase angle is the phase shift of the amplifier. If there is to be no frequency distortion, then:

1. The magnitude of the amplification must not vary over the range of the input frequencies.
2. The phase shift over the range of input frequencies must be 0 or $\pm n\pi$, where n is an integer; or it must vary linearly with frequency such that the phase shift is given by $-k\omega$, where k is a positive constant.

Conditions 1 and 2 must be met if there is to be no frequency distortion. Distortion due to 1 is called *amplitude distortion*; that due to 2 is termed *phase distortion*. Typical effects of these distortions are shown in Fig. 8-8*b* and *c*.

If the magnitude of the amplification varies with frequency, then the relative magnitudes of the harmonics will vary with respect to each other. This will change the shape of the output waveform.

If the phase shift is $0°$, then the phases of the various harmonics are undisturbed. Shifting the phase by an integral multiple of π rad is equivalent to multiplying the output by ± 1; this may produce a phase reversal but not distortion. The only other kind of phase characteristic that does not lead to distortion is one that just delays the signal in time. For instance, if $v_2(t) = v_1(t - \tau)$, that is, if the output waveform is the same as the input delayed by τ sec, then

$$v_2(t) = \frac{4}{\pi} \left[\cos (t - \tau) - \tfrac{1}{3} \cos 3(t - \tau) + \tfrac{1}{5} \cos 5 (t - \tau) - \cdots\right]$$

or

$$v_2(t) = \frac{4}{\pi} \left[\cos (t - \tau) - \tfrac{1}{3} \cos (3t - 3\tau) + \tfrac{1}{5} \cos (5t - 5\tau) - \cdots\right]$$

$$(8\text{-}23)$$

In this case the phase shift $-k\omega = -\tau\omega$. Any other phase shift changes the phase angles among the various harmonics and leads to distortion.

Although we have discussed amplitude and phase distortion separately,

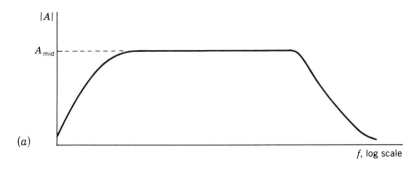

(a)

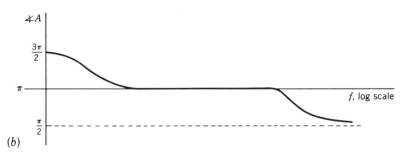

(b)

Fig. 8-9 A typical plot of (a) the magnitude of amplification versus frequency and (b) the phase shift of an amplifier versus frequency. The frequency is plotted on a log scale so that the high- and low-frequency regions can be adequately displayed.

they are related.   In fact, very often, it is possible to calculate one from the knowledge of the other.

One means of rating the frequency distortion of an amplifier is to compare an input square wave (or other standard waveform) with the output waveform.   This is called the *transient response* of the amplifier and will be discussed further in Chap. 9.   Another means of rating the amplifier is to plot the magnitude and phase of the amplifier versus frequency.   Such plots are given in Fig. 8-9a and b.   Since the frequency content of the input signal is usually known, these curves provide a means of determining the frequency distortion.

Very often there is a region where the magnitude of amplification remains essentially constant.   Such a region is shown in Fig. 8-9a.   The value of this amplification is designated A_{mid}.   It is often convenient to normalize the curve by plotting $|A/A_{\text{mid}}|$ versus frequency.   Such a graph is shown in Fig. 8-10a.   This can be done since the amplitude distortion depends only upon the difference among the amplifications at the frequencies of interest and not upon the absolute values of the amplification at any one frequency.   Thus, if the ordinate of Fig. 8-9 is divided by a constant, no information

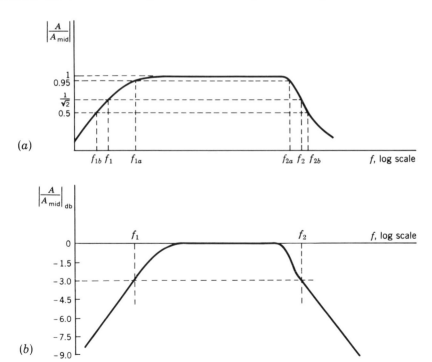

Fig. 8-10 (a) The normalized frequency response of an amplifier and (b) the normalized response plotted on a decibel basis.

concerning frequency distortion is lost. A_{mid} is a convenient constant to divide by, since the response in the flat midband region becomes unity, and the relative response at other frequencies can be read off the graph. The *bandwidth* is defined as the useful range of frequencies of the amplifier. For instance, if the amplifier is to be used to amplify signals for an accurate voltmeter, the bandwidth might contain those frequencies where $0.95 \leq |A/A_{\mathrm{mid}}| \leq 1$. Such a bandwidth lies between f_{1a} and f_{2a} of Fig. 8-10a. On the other hand, for a less precise application, the bandwidth might lie between f_{1b} and f_{2b} where $0.5 \leq |A/A_{\mathrm{mid}}| \leq 1$. *Thus, for any specific device, the bandwidth depends upon the application for which it is to be used.* If such specific information is not present then the bandwidth is usually considered to be those frequencies between f_1 and f_2 where $0.707 = 1/\sqrt{2} \leq |A/A_{\mathrm{mid}}| \leq 1$. This is called *half-power bandwidth* and the frequencies f_1 and f_2 are called the *lower half-power frequency* and the *upper half-power frequency*, respectively. Note that if the output voltage falls off by $1/\sqrt{2}$, then the power delivered to a fixed resistance is halved.

Since the ear is a logarithmic device, the relative response of audio amplifiers is often plotted on a decibel basis. That is, we plot

$$\left|\frac{A}{A_{\mathrm{mid}}}\right|_{\mathrm{db}} = 20 \log_{10}\left|\frac{A}{A_{\mathrm{mid}}}\right| \tag{8-24}$$

Such a plot is shown in Fig. 8-10b. On a decibel basis, $1/\sqrt{2}$ corresponds to -3.0103 db ≈ -3 db. For this reason, the half-power frequencies are often called the *3-db frequencies*. In many applications, plots of frequency response in decibels versus frequency on a log scale approach a straight line. The logarithmic nature of the decibel allows both large and small amplitude variations to be displayed on the same set of axes. For these reasons, plots of response in decibels are often used in applications other than audio amplifiers.

8-8 A COMPARISON OF THE FET, VACUUM TUBE, AND TRANSISTOR

There are many circuits in which the same functions can be performed by FETs, vacuum tubes, and (bipolar junction) transistors. Let us consider some of the relative merits of each of these devices. The solid-state devices, FETs, and transistors are, in general, much smaller, more efficient, more rugged, and much more reliable than the vacuum tube. The vacuum tube requires a heater. This eventually ceases to function, and the vacuum tube fails. In addition, the heater must be supplied with power and causes the circuit to dissipate more heat. Solid-state devices do not have these problems.

Vacuum tubes are subject to microphonic noise, i.e., noise that comes about from motion of the elements of the tube caused by mechanical shock. Solid-state devices are not subject to this noise.

Solid-state devices are smaller and lighter than the vacuum-tube ones. When integrated circuits are used, this advantage is increased by an extreme amount. In addition, the use of integrated circuits makes for far more reliable operation (after an initial test period) since wiring errors or badly soldered joints are eliminated. The circuit characteristics of the transistor make it more suitable for use in pulse or digital circuits than the vacuum tube. The use of both *p-n-p* or *n-p-n* transistors in certain circuits provides a (see Sec. 10-10) simplification that cannot be obtained with vacuum tubes. The input impedance of the transistor is much lower than that of the FET. In certain circuits such as tuned amplifiers, this is a great disadvantage. The FET can perform better in such circuits. In general, the transistor can operate at higher frequencies and higher power levels than the FET.

For all these reasons solid-state devices have replaced or are replacing vacuum tubes in many applications. However, there are still occasions when vacuum tubes are superior. Vacuum tubes, at present, are capable of supplying much more power than semiconductor devices, for example, 500,000 watts for vacuum tubes and 500 watts for transistors and much smaller amounts for FETs. Semiconductor devices can be damaged by very short power overloads while vacuum tubes, in general, are not. Higher output voltages can be obtained from vacuum tubes. The vacuum tube is far less temperature-sensitive than the transistor. However, the FET is not as temperature-sensitive as the transistor. The transistor is very sensitive to ionizing radiation, while the vacuum tube is not. Special-purpose vacuum tubes can operate at much higher frequencies than semiconductor devices. Thus, the semiconductor devices have replaced vacuum tubes in most applications, but there still are occasions when the vacuum tube is superior.

BIBLIOGRAPHY

Seely, S.: "Electron-tube Circuits," 2d ed., chap. 3, McGraw-Hill Book Company, New York, 1958.

PROBLEMS

8-1. Three identical amplifiers are cascaded as shown in Fig. 8-1. The voltage gains of stages *A* and *B* are each -10, and the voltage gain of stage *C* is -5. The current gains of stages *A* and *B* are each $+5$, while the current gain of stage *C* is $+15$. Compute the voltage and current gains of the overall amplifier.

8-2. If the input impedance and the load impedance of the amplifier of Prob. 8-1 are purely resistive, what is the overall power gain?

8-3. Each one of the amplifiers of Fig. 8-1 has the following characteristics: open-circuit voltage gain -20; input impedance 1000 ohms, independent of load impedance;

output impedance 500 ohms, independent of input impedance. If $Z_L = 700$ ohms, compute the voltage, current, and power gains of the overall amplifier. Repeat this problem, but now assume that the open-circuit voltage gain is unknown and that the short-circuit current gain is 40.

8-4. Repeat Prob. 8-3, but now assume that the load impedance is $100 + j1000$ ohms.

8-5. An amplifier is to be made up of a cascade of amplifiers of the first type specified in Prob. 8-3. The overall voltage gain is to have a magnitude of at least 10,000, and the load impedance is to be 100 ohms. What is the minimum number of stages in cascade that can produce the required amplification?

8-6. The input impedance of a certain amplifier is 1000 ohms. Its load impedance is also 1000 ohms. The voltage gain of the amplifier is 20. Express the voltage gain, the current gain, and the power gain in decibels.

8-7. Repeat Prob. 8-6, but now assume that the load impedance is 2000 ohms. Assume that the input impedance and the voltage amplification do not change. Explain why the gains in decibels do not equal each other.

8-8. The voltage gain of each amplifier in a cascade is 30 db. There are five amplifiers in the cascade. What is the voltage gain of the overall amplifier in decibels? What is the numerical voltage gain of the amplifier?

8-9. The amplifier of Fig. 8-6a is operated such that $X_{11} = -5\Delta x$. If the operation is to be class A, what is the maximum signal that can be applied? Repeat this problem for the amplifier of Fig. 8-7a.

8-10. A generalized device has the characteristics shown in Fig. 8-11. The device is to

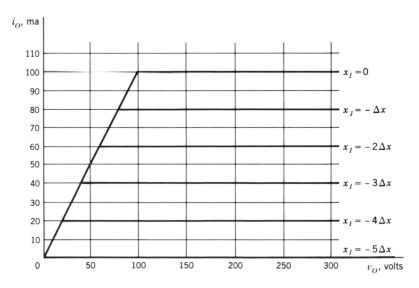

Fig. 8-11

be operated class A in the circuit of Fig. 8-7a. What is the maximum output power that can be obtained if there is to be no distortion? Use a power-supply voltage $V_{OO} = 250$ volts. Also determine the value of ac load resistance, the output-circuit efficiency, the coordinates of the quiescent operating point, and the alternating input signal for operation at maximum efficiency. Assume that the characteristics extend linearly above $v_O = 300$ volts.

8-11. Plot one period of the voltage of Eq. (8-21) using the first three terms in the Fourier series. Now assume that this waveform is applied to an amplifier with the amplification

$$A = \frac{10}{1 + j\omega}$$

Plot the output waveform.

8-12. An amplifier has a response such that

$$\frac{A}{A_{\text{mid}}} = \frac{1}{1 + j\omega/10,000} = \frac{1}{\sqrt{1 + (\omega/10,000)^2}} \quad \underline{/-\tan^{-1} \omega/10,000}$$

Plot the amplitude and phase response of this amplifier on semilog paper for frequencies from 100 to 100,000 Hz. Find the upper half-power frequency. Find the frequency where the phase shift is $-45°$. Find the frequency where $|A/A_{\text{mid}}| = 0.9$.

8-13. An amplifier has a response such that

$$\frac{A}{A_{\text{mid}}} = \frac{1}{1 - j10/\omega} \frac{1}{1 + j\omega/10,000}$$

Plot the amplitude and phase response of this amplifier on semilog paper for frequencies from 1 to 100,000 Hz. Find the upper and lower half-power frequencies. What approximations can be made in this problem?

8-14. Repeat Prob. 8-13, but now plot the amplitude response of the amplifier in decibels.

9
Small-signal Linear Amplifiers

Ideally the interstage networks that couple amplifier stages would pass the signal frequencies without attenuation and prevent the interaction of the bias voltages. Actually these networks do attenuate the signals, and this attenuation varies with frequency. The electronic devices themselves function differently at different frequencies. Thus, amplifiers will have responses that are functions of frequency.

In this chapter we shall determine the frequency response of commonly used amplifiers, and also consider amplifiers whose response is deliberately made to vary with frequency. We shall assume that the operation is class A and that the signal levels are small enough so that the operation is linear.

In many applications involving FETs or vacuum tubes, the equations and discussion for the vacuum tube will exactly follow that for the FET if we substitute *grid* for *gate*, *plate* for *drain*, and *cathode* for *source* (see Sec. 6-15). It will be assumed that the reader will make these substitutions unless indicated otherwise.

9-1 FREQUENCY RESPONSE OF THE *RC*-COUPLED COMMON-SOURCE FET AMPLIFIER

Resistance-capacitance coupling is a simple, inexpensive technique for cascading amplifier stages. It is used extensively for moderately broadband amplifiers. In Fig. 9-1, *RC*-coupled amplifiers are shown. When the frequency response of these amplifiers is to be determined, the stray capacitances must be considered as well as the elements of the coupling network. For the time being we shall assume that the bypass capacitors C_s and C_{g2} are short circuits at the signal frequencies. The elements that will be considered in a single-stage FET amplifier are shown in Fig. 9-2. The capacitor C_o represents the drain-to-source capacitance C_{ds} plus any wiring capacitance between the leads to the drain and to the source. The stray capacitance between C_c and the lead connected to the source is included here also. The capacitor C_i represents the input capacitance of the next stage plus any stray wiring capacitance beyond C_c. In an FET, C_i may be very much greater than the gate-to-source capacitance C_{gs}, because of the Miller effect (see Sec. 6-16). Usually for the dual-gate MOSFET the Miller effect can be ignored. Actually, the input impedance of the FET is not purely capacitive. This is shown by Eqs. (6-116). In most cases, however, accurate results are obtained if we consider that the input impedance is capacitive. C_c is the *coupling capacitor*. This is somewhat different from the others in that it is placed there deliberately. It is usually very much larger than C_o or C_i.

An exact analysis of this amplifier would show that the output voltage would not be zero even if the μ and g_m of the FET were reduced to zero, because of the direct transmission of the signal through C_{gd}. This direct-transmission voltage can be neglected in most cases, since it is usually 1000 or more times smaller than the voltage due to the amplification of the FET. We can then often neglect the presence of C_{gd} *provided that we compensate for it* in the following ways: (1) the capacitance C_{gd} cannot be ignored when C_i

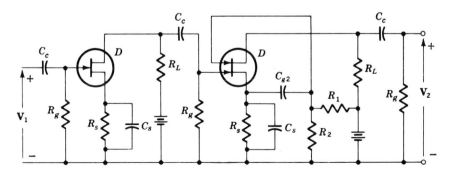

Fig. 9-1 *RC*-coupled common-source FET. For purposes of illustration a single-gate FET stage is cascaded with a dual-gate FET stage.

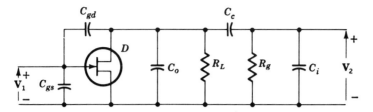

Fig. 9-2 A representation of an *RC*-coupled amplifier showing only those elements which will be used in the calculation of frequency response.

is computed, (2) the capacitance C_o tends to load down the output at high frequencies and, thus, reduce the gain. The component of the drain current through C_o is given by $j\omega C_o V_{ds}$. Similarly, the component of the drain current through C_{gd} is

$$j\omega C_{gd}(V_{ds} - V_1) = j\omega C_{gp} V_{ds}\left(1 - \frac{V_1}{V_{ds}}\right)$$

Because of the amplification $|V_{ds}| \gg |V_1|$. Hence, the component of the plate current through C_{gd} is approximately $j\omega C_{gd} V_{ds}$. We can increase C_o by C_{gd} to account for this effect of C_{gd}. Thus, if we use C_{gd} in the computation of C_i, and if we increase C_o by C_{gd}, we can, to a high degree of accuracy, neglect C_{gd} otherwise. The symbol C_o will be considered to include C_{gd} henceforth.

If, in the dual-gate FET of Fig. 9-1, we assume that the bypass capacitors C_s and C_{g2} are short circuits, the representation of Fig. 9-2 becomes a valid one. Note that gate 2 is effectively connected to the source. The capacitance C_o now represents the output capacitance of the dual-gate FET plus the wiring capacitance up to C_c. This capacitance should be increased by C_{gd} as it should be the case of the single-gate FET. However, in dual-gate FETs, C_{gd} is usually so small that it can be neglected. The output capacitance of a dual-gate MOSFET is given by the sum of the capacitances between the drain and the source and second gate (see Sec. 3-28):

$$C_{\text{out}} = C_{ds} + C_{dg2} \tag{9-1}$$

Similarly, the input capacitance of a dual-gate MOSFET is the capacitance between the gate and the source and second gate:

$$C_{\text{in}} = C_{gs} + C_{gg2} \tag{9-2}$$

Similarly Eqs. (6-108) can be used to obtain C_{out} and C_{in} for the vacuum-tube pentode. Actually, the Miller effect should be considered in computing C_i, but C_{gd} is so small for dual-gate MOSFETs or for pentodes that it can usually be neglected.

The linear model for the amplifier of Fig. 9-2, subject to the modifications that we have discussed, is given in Fig. 9-3. Note that the capacitance C_{gs} has been neglected. This will affect the gain of a preceding stage but not that of this one. Noting that $V_{gs} = V_1$, we can write the following nodal equations:

$$-g_m V_1 = \left[\frac{1}{r_d} + \frac{1}{R_L} + j\omega(C_o + C_c)\right]V_d - j\omega C_c V_2 \qquad (9\text{-}3a)$$

$$0 = -j\omega C_c V_d + \left[\frac{1}{R_g} + j\omega(C_i + C_c)\right]V_2 \qquad (9\text{-}3b)$$

Solving for the voltage gain $A_v = V_2/V_1$, we obtain

$$A_v = \frac{-j\omega C_c g_m}{[1/r_d + 1/R_L + j\omega(C_o + C_c)][1/R_g + j\omega(C_i + C_c)] + \omega^2 C_c^2} \qquad (9\text{-}4)$$

This expression can be simplified. However, we shall not do so, since we shall obtain much simpler expressions subsequently. The voltage gain A_v is a complex number that varies with frequency. A typical plot of the magnitude and phase of A_v versus frequency is shown in Fig. 9-4. The magnitude of the response is zero at zero frequency. It then rises to the value of $A_{v,\text{mid}}$ as the frequency increases. It remains *essentially constant* at this value as the frequency further increases and then finally begins to decrease. It falls off to zero as the frequency approaches infinity. In a similar way, the phase shift is 270° at zero frequency, decreases to 180°, remains *essentially constant* over a wide range of frequencies, and finally approaches 90°. Let us consider the reasons for this response. In the midband region, where $|A_v| \approx A_{v,\text{mid}}$ and $\angle A_v \approx 180°$, the reactance of the coupling capacitor is very much smaller than the resistance of R_g; the reactances of the shunt capacitors C_o and C_i are very much greater than the resistance of the parallel combination of R_L, r_d, and R_g. Here, C_c can be approximated by a short circuit, and C_i and C_o can be approximated by open circuits. Thus, there is no variation of A_v with frequency. As the frequency is increased, the reactance of C_c decreases so that it still can be considered to be a short circuit.

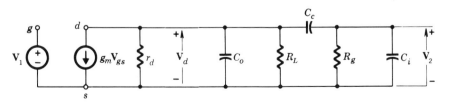

Fig. 9-3 A linear model for the amplifier of Fig. 9-2. The modifications discussed in the text have been incorporated.

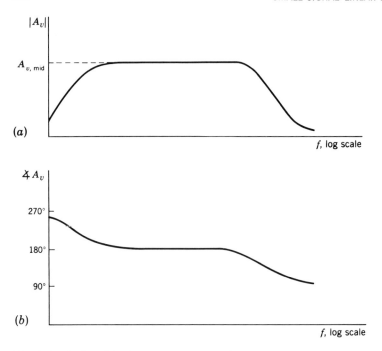

Fig. 9-4 A plot of the frequency response of an *RC*-coupled amplifier: (*a*) the amplitude response; (*b*) the phase response.

The reactances of C_o and C_i also decrease and can no longer be neglected. They now reduce the load impedance of the amplifier. As the load impedance decreases, the output voltage falls off and the phase shift departs from 180°. At frequencies below the midband range, the capacitors C_o and C_i can again be neglected, but now C_c can no longer be considered to be a short circuit. It acts as the series arm in a voltage divider and causes the gain to fall off. In the preceding discussion, we have assumed that there are three well-defined regions. Actually, this need not be true. We can make C_c very small or add shunt capacitance to make C_o or C_i very large. Then there will be no range of frequencies where the capacitors can be ignored. There would then be no region of constant amplification. This would not be a practical amplifier. Actually, C_o and C_i represent stray capacitances and lie in the range 5 to 30 pf. C_c is a coupling capacitor which is deliberately placed in the circuit; its range is usually between 0.01 and 0.5 μf. Thus, C_c may be 100,000 times as large as C_o or C_i. It is relatively easy to obtain a region of flat response. If we have an amplifier with a well-defined midband region, then it is valid to neglect C_o and C_i at low and mid-frequencies and to consider C_c to be a short circuit at mid- and high frequencies. We shall now analyze the amplifier by dividing it into three frequency regions. This will make the expression of the voltage gain much more understandable. The accuracy of this procedure will be discussed subsequently.

Mid-frequency region The modified form of Fig. 9-3 that is valid in the mid-frequency range is given in Fig. 9-5a. Let R_{sh} be the total resistance shunting the current generator. That is, R_{sh} is the parallel combination of r_d, R_L, and R_g.

$$\frac{1}{R_{sh}} = \frac{1}{r_d} + \frac{1}{R_L} + \frac{1}{R_g} = \frac{r_d R_L + r_d R_g + R_L R_g}{r_d R_L R_g} \tag{9-5}$$

Then

$$\mathbf{A}_{v,\text{mid}} = -g_m R_{sh} = g_m R_{sh} \quad \underline{/180°} \tag{9-6}$$

High-frequency region The model that is valid at high frequencies is given in Fig. 9-5b. Let C_{sh} be the total shunting capacitance

$$C_{sh} = C_o + C_i \tag{9-7}$$

Then

$$\mathbf{A}_{v,\text{high}} = \frac{-g_m R_{sh}}{1 + j\omega R_{sh} C_{sh}} \tag{9-8}$$

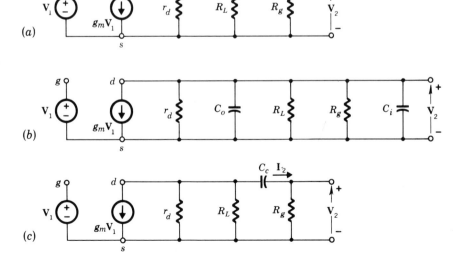

Fig. 9-5 (a) The mid-frequency model of an *RC*-coupled amplifier; (b) the high-frequency model; and (c) the low-frequency model.

We are often interested in the relative response of the amplifier (see Sec. 8-7).

$$\frac{A_{v,\text{high}}}{A_{v,\text{mid}}} = \frac{1}{1 + j\omega R_{\text{sh}} C_{\text{sh}}} \tag{9-9}$$

It is often convenient to express this relationship in terms of a constant that is more general than a specific R_{sh} and C_{sh}. To do this we let

$$\omega_2 = \frac{1}{R_{\text{sh}} C_{\text{sh}}} \qquad \text{or} \qquad f_2 = \frac{1}{2\pi R_{\text{sh}} C_{\text{sh}}} \tag{9-10}$$

Then

$$\frac{A_{v,\text{high}}}{A_{v,\text{mid}}} = \frac{1}{1 + jf/f_2} = \frac{1}{\sqrt{1 + (f/f_2)^2}} \quad \underline{/-\tan^{-1}(f/f_2)} \tag{9-11}$$

The significance of this equation will be discussed after we consider the low-frequency response.

Low-frequency region   The model for the low-frequency region is shown in Fig. 9-5c.   The current I_2 is

$$I_2 = \frac{-g_m V_1 r_d R_L / (r_d + R_L)}{[r_d R_L / (r_d + R_L)] + R_g - j/\omega C_c}$$

Let

$$R_{\text{low}} = R_g + \frac{r_d R_L}{r_d + R_L} \tag{9-12}$$

Note that R_{low} represents R_g in series with the parallel combination of r_d and R_L.   Then, since $A_{v,\text{low}} = I_2 R_g / V_1$ and $R_{\text{sh}} = r_d R_L R_g / R_{\text{low}} (r_d + R_L)$, we have

$$A_{v,\text{low}} = \frac{-g_m R_{\text{sh}}}{1 - j(1/\omega C_c R_{\text{low}})} \tag{9-13}$$

If we let

$$\omega_1 = \frac{1}{C_c R_{\text{low}}} \qquad \text{or} \qquad f_1 = \frac{1}{2\pi C_c R_{\text{low}}} \tag{9-14}$$

Then

$$\frac{A_{v,\text{low}}}{A_{v,\text{mid}}} = \frac{1}{1 - jf_1/f} = \frac{1}{\sqrt{1 + (f_1/f)^2}} \quad \underline{/\tan^{-1}(f_1/f)} \tag{9-15}$$

Figure 9-6 is a plot of amplitude and the phase of $A_{v,\text{low}}/A_{v,\text{mid}}$ and $A_{v,\text{high}}/A_{v,\text{mid}}$.   The values of f_1 and f_2 correspond to the lower and upper half-power frequencies, respectively (see Sec. 8-7).   The phase angles at f_1 and f_2 are $+45°$ and $-45°$, respectively.   Note that these phase angles represent departures from the midband phase angle of $180°$.

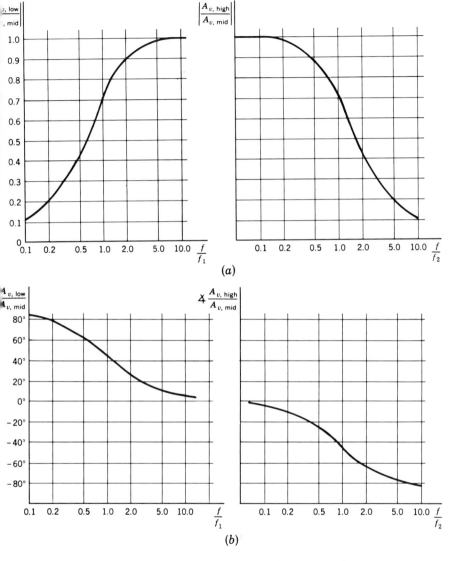

Fig. 9-6 (*a*) The normalized amplitude response of an *RC*-coupled common-source FET amplifier and (*b*) the normalized phase response.

In the midband region and at higher frequencies $A_{low}/A_{mid} \approx 1$, while in the midband region and at lower frequencies $A_{high}/A_{mid} \approx 1$. Thus, an approximate expression for the normalized gain that is valid at all frequencies is

$$\frac{A}{A_{mid}} = \frac{1}{(1 - jf_1/f)(1 + jf/f_2)} \qquad (9\text{-}16)$$

If the upper and lower half-power frequencies are known, then the frequency response of any RC-coupled FET or vacuum-tube amplifier is determined. That is, insofar as the frequency response is concerned, only f_1 and f_2 need be known but not any of the circuit elements. The approximations made here depend upon having a well-defined mid-frequency region. This will occur if $f_2 \gg f_1$. If the approximate response given by Eqs. (9-11) and (9-15) or by Eq. (9-16) is compared with the actual response given by Eq. (9-4), it is found [1] that the error in the amplitude will be less than 0.5 percent if $f_2 \geq 100f_1$. If $f_2 \geq 25f_1$, then the error in the amplitude will be less than 2 percent. If f_2 is not at least $10f_1$ the approximations should not be used. Actually, these requirements are not very stringent. Even poor audio amplifiers (for example, $f_1 = 50$ Hz and $f_2 = 5000$ Hz) are such that $f_2 = 100f_1$. Actually, in most practical cases, $f_2 \gg 100f_1$ and the approximate expressions are very accurate.

Logarithmic plots of $|A_v/A_{\text{mid}}|$ are quite useful (see Sec. 8-7).

$$\left|\frac{A_{v,\text{high}}}{A_{v,\text{mid}}}\right|_{\text{db}} = 20 \log \frac{1}{\sqrt{1 + (f/f_2)^2}}$$

Thus,

$$\left|\frac{A_{v,\text{high}}}{A_{v,\text{mid}}}\right|_{\text{db}} = -10 \log \left[1 + \left(\frac{f}{f_2}\right)^2\right] \tag{9-17}$$

Let us consider the asymptotes of this response. If $f/f_2 \ll 1$,

$$\left|\frac{A_{v,\text{low}}}{A_{v,\text{mid}}}\right|_{\text{db}} = 0 \tag{9-18}$$

and if $f/f_2 \gg 1$,

$$\left|\frac{A_{v,\text{high}}}{A_{v,\text{mid}}}\right|_{\text{db}} = -20 \log \frac{f}{f_2} \tag{9-19}$$

If Eqs. (9-18) and (9-19) are plotted to a log (f/f_2) frequency scale, they will be straight lines. These asymptotes, as well as the actual curve, are shown in Fig. 9-7. Let us determine the slope of the asymptotic response. A band of frequencies from f_a to f_b is called an *octave* if $f_b = 2f_a$. If $f_b = 10f_a$ then the frequency band is called a *decade*. Log $2 \approx 0.3$ and log $10 = 1$. Thus, the asymptotic slope of Eq. (9-19) when plotted to a log frequency scale is -6 db/octave or, equivalently, -20 db/decade. We can make an equivalent set of statements for the low-frequency response.

$$\left|\frac{A_{v,\text{low}}}{A_{v,\text{mid}}}\right|_{\text{db}} = -10 \log \left[1 + \left(\frac{f_1}{f}\right)^2\right] \tag{9-20}$$

If $f_1/f \ll 1$,

$$\left|\frac{A_{v,\text{low}}}{A_{v,\text{mid}}}\right|_{\text{db}} = 0 \tag{9-21}$$

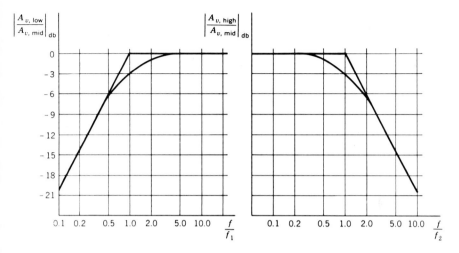

Fig. 9-7 The normalized amplitude response of an RC-coupled common-source FET amplifier plotted on a decibel basis.   The asymptotes are also shown.

If $f_1/f \gg 1$,

$$\left|\frac{A_{v,\text{low}}}{A_{v,\text{mid}}}\right|_{\text{db}} = -20 \log \left(\frac{f_1}{f}\right) \tag{9-22}$$

A plot of this is also given in Fig. 9-7.   The fact that the asymptotes can be drawn very easily and that the curve is fairly well approximated by them makes the decibel plot convenient to use.

9-2   FACTORS AFFECTING THE FREQUENCY RESPONSE OF RC-COUPLED FET AMPLIFIERS

The amplification of an RC-coupled FET amplifier is completely specified if we know $A_{v,\text{mid}} = -g_m R_{\text{sh}}$, $f_1 = 1/2\pi R_{\text{low}} C_c$, and $f_2 = 1/2\pi R_{\text{sh}} C_{\text{sh}}$.   The overall bandwidth of the amplifier is increased by increasing f_2 and by decreasing f_1.   Let us consider what is involved in doing this.   In order to decrease f_1, we must increase R_{low} or C_c.   The resistance R_{low} consists of R_g in series with the parallel combination of R_L and r_d.   The size of R_L is limited by high-frequency considerations, as we shall discuss, and by the fact that it is in series with the power supply. R_L is usually very much less than R_g. Thus

$$R_{\text{low}} \approx R_g \tag{9-23}$$

To obtain as low a value of f_1 as possible, R_g or C_c should be made large. For the FET, the size of R_g is limited by the leakage resistance of C_c.   This is discussed in Sec. 5-2. In the vacuum tube, R_g is limited by grid leak considerations (see Sec. 5-4). If we wish to reduce f_1 any further, then C_c must be increased. In theory, C_c can be made as large as desired. In practice, the size of C_c is limited. If C_c is larger than 0.5 to 1.0 μf, it becomes large and expensive. The increased physical size not only increases the dimensions of the amplifier, but also increases C_{sh}. This is because C_c possesses stray capacitance to the substrate or chassis, which is usually at the same potential as the source of the FET at high frequencies. Thus, if the physical size of C_c is too great, the high-frequency response will suffer. (Note that the value of C_c itself does not affect the high-frequency response; rather it is the stray capacitance between it and the substrate or chassis.) *Electrolytic capacitors* combine large capacitance with small size. Unfortunately, they are not suitable for use as coupling capacitors in FET circuits, since their leakage resistance is too low in comparison with R_g. Their leakage resistance also tends to fluctuate. The lowest value of f_1 that is obtained with an *RC*-coupled amplifier is usually in the vicinity of 0.1 to 1 Hz. If lower values of f_1 are required, then other coupling techniques should be used.

To increase the high-frequency bandwidth, the value of f_2 should be increased. This can be done by decreasing R_{sh} or C_{sh}. The shunt capacitance can be minimized by choosing FETs with small stray capacitances. (If values of f_2 greater than 50 kHz are desired, vacuum-tube pentodes rather than vacuum-tube triodes should be used because of the Miller effect.) The Miller effect also limits the high-frequency response of the FET. However, it is possible to obtain FETs with relatively small C_{gd}, for example, 0.1 pf, so that the Miller effect is not too troublesome if the gain per stage is small. Dual-gate MOSFETs can be used to further reduce C_{gd}.

Let us consider that identical stages are cascaded. C_{sh} consists of the sum of the input and output capacitances of the FET plus any stray wiring capacitance C_w. Careful wiring can reduce the value of C_w. In integrated circuits, the lead length can be kept very short, thus reducing C_w. However, the isolation problem (see Sec. 4-3) can increase C_w. The proper isolation procedures can reduce C_w; for example, EPIC isolation leads to relatively low stray capacitance.

There is a certain minimum value below which C_{sh} cannot be reduced. To increase f_2, we must reduce R_{sh}. This can make the value of f_2 as large as desired. However, reducing R_{sh} also reduces the magnitude of the midband gain, $|A_{mid}| = g_m R_{sh}$. The product of *the midband gain and high-frequency bandwidth* or, more simply, the *gain-bandwidth product* can be obtained from Eqs. (9-6) and (9-10). Their product yields

$$|A_{v,\text{mid}}|f_2 = \frac{g_m}{2\pi C_{sh}} \tag{9-24}$$

Thus, the product of midband gain and f_2 is a constant. For a single stage, as R_{sh} is reduced, $A_{v,\text{mid}}$ will decrease and f_2 will increase in accordance with Eq. (9-24). However, if the Miller effect capacitance is important, then the Miller effect capacitance will be reduced when $|A_{v,\text{mid}}|$ is reduced. Thus, the f_2 of the *preceding* stage will also be increased by reducing R_{sh}.

In general, it is desirable to make $|A_{v,\text{mid}}|f_2$ as large as possible. A figure of merit for it is the ratio $g_m/2\pi C_{\text{sh}}$. If the Miller effect is substantial, then the result is complicated (see above). However, for the dual-gate FET and for the FET with low C_{gd} and relatively low $|A_{v,\text{mid}}|$, the Miller effect will not be important. Then, a figure of merit for an FET is the ratio of g_m to the sum of the input and the output capacitance of the device.

We can adjust the midband gain and f_2 by varying R_{sh}, which consists of r_d, R_L, and R_g in parallel. Usually R_g is made as large as possible because of low-frequency considerations. The drain resistance r_d is usually quite large and cannot be easily changed in any event. Usually in FET or pentode amplifiers, $r_d \gg R_L$, so that

$$R_{\text{sh}} \approx R_L \qquad\qquad\qquad (9\text{-}25)$$

Thus variations in R_{sh} are obtained by varying R_L.

9-3 FREQUENCY RESPONSE OF THE *RC*-COUPLED COMMON-EMITTER TRANSISTOR AMPLIFIER

We shall now obtain expressions for the gain of *RC*-coupled common-emitter transistor amplifiers. A typical cascade of such stages is shown in Fig. 9.8. In general, as in the case of the FET or vacuum-tube *RC*-coupled amplifier, this amplifier will have a midband region where the gain is essentially constant. The gain will fall off at frequencies above and below the midband region. We shall analyze each of these regions separately. The low-frequency common-emitter *h*-parameter model (see Sec. 6-10) will be used to represent the transistor in the low- and mid-frequency regions. The

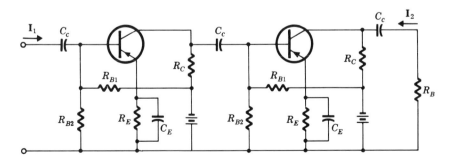

Fig. 9-8 A cascade of *RC*-coupled common-emitter transistor amplifier stages.

hybrid-pi model, or the high-frequency h-parameter model derived from the hybrid-pi model (see Sec. 6-19) will be used in the high-frequency region. We shall use the h parameters since the response in the high-frequency region can then be easily related to the response in the mid-frequency region. The reader should note that the high-frequency h-parameter model is derived from the hybrid-pi model and has the same accuracy.

We shall consider that C_E acts as a short circuit at all signal frequencies. Its effect will be considered in Sec. 9-6. Then, using the h-parameter model of Fig. 6-43, we obtain the h-parameter model of a single stage shown in Fig. 9-9. To simplify the notation, we have made the substitutions indicated in the caption. The impedance $\mathbf{Z}_i$ represents a load impedance or the input impedance of the next amplifier stage in the cascade. At low frequencies or mid-frequencies, this usually is a pure resistance, which we shall call R_i. Let us now consider the mid-, low-, and high-frequency regions of operation.

Mid-frequency region   In the mid-frequency region, the frequencies are low enough so that the capacitors C_{oe} and $C_{b'c}$ can be considered to be open circuits and $1 + j\omega/\omega_\beta \approx 1$. However, the frequencies are high enough so that C_C can be considered to be a short circuit. Remember that the value of C_C can be 10,000 times or more greater than the values of the shunting capacitors. Then, making these approximations, we obtain the mid-frequency model of Fig. 9-10. Note that, in the mid- and low-frequency regions

$$h_{ie} = r_{bb'} + r_{b'e} \tag{9-26}$$

The current gain $\mathbf{A}_{i,\mathrm{mid}} = \mathbf{I}_2/\mathbf{I}_1$ can be obtained from Fig. 9-10 by noting that $\mathbf{I}_2 = \mathbf{V}_{ce}/R_i$. Then, if we let

$$\frac{1}{R_{\mathrm{sh}}} = h_{oe} + \frac{1}{R_c} + \frac{1}{R_B} + \frac{1}{R_i} \tag{9-27}$$

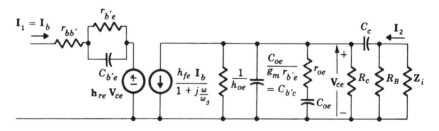

Fig. 9-9   A linear model of one stage of the RC-coupled common-emitter amplifier. $C_{oe} = g_m r_{b'e} C_{b'c}$, $r_{oe} = 1/\omega_\beta C_{oe}$, and $\omega_\beta = 1/r_{b'e} C_{b'e}$. The resistor R_B is the parallel combination of R_{B1} and R_{B2}, $1/R_B = 1/R_{B1} + 1/R_{B2}$. $\mathbf{Z}_i$ is the load impedance or the input impedance of the next amplifier stage.

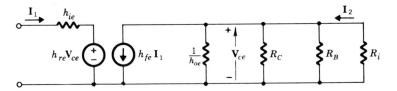

Fig. 9-10 The mid-frequency linear model of the circuit of Fig. 9-9.

we obtain

$$A_{i,\text{mld}} = \frac{h_{fe}R_{\text{sh}}}{R_i} \tag{9-28}$$

Note that R_{sh} is the parallel combination of the resistors $1/h_{oe}$, R_c, R_B, and R_i. If $R_i \to 0$, then $R_{\text{sh}} \to R_i \to 0$ and $A_{i,\text{mld}} = h_{fe}$. Note that h_{ie} and h_{re} do not enter into the expression for current gain. This is because the input current $\mathbf{I}_1$ is the current into the base lead. The primary effect of h_{ie} and h_{re} is on the input impedance of the amplifier. Thus, they may affect the establishment of $\mathbf{I}_1$. However, in computing the gain of this stage, the $\mathbf{I}_1$ is the assumed input current. Thus, h_{ie} and h_{re} do not affect it. If $\mathbf{Z}_i$ represents the input impedance of the next transistor in the cascade, then $\mathbf{Z}_i$ in Fig. 9-9 or R_i in Fig. 9-10 is a function of h_{ie} and h_{re} of the following amplifier stage. Thus, these terms do actually affect the gain. The gain is measured from the input (base) lead of one stage to the input lead of the next stage. Thus, the gain of a cascade of stages is equal to the product of the individual gains.

Low-frequency region In the low-frequency region, we can ignore the effect of the shunting capacitances and still consider that $1 + j\omega/\omega_\beta \approx 1$. However, C_c can no longer be considered to be a short circuit. Then, the linear model that is valid in the low-frequency region is given in Fig. 9-11. We can write

$$A_{i,\text{low}} = \frac{\mathbf{I}_2}{\mathbf{I}_1} = \frac{\mathbf{I}_2'}{\mathbf{I}_1}\frac{\mathbf{I}_2}{\mathbf{I}_2'}$$

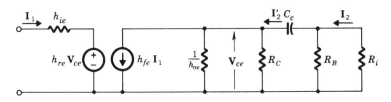

Fig. 9-11 The low-frequency linear model of the circuit of Fig. 9-9.

Hence

$$\mathbf{A}_{i,\text{low}} = h_{fe} \frac{R_C/(1 + h_{oe}R_C)}{R_C/(1 + h_{oe}R_C) + R_B R_i/(R_B + R_i) + 1/j\omega C_c} \frac{R_B}{R_B + R_i}$$

Let

$$R_{\text{low}} = \frac{R_C}{1 + h_{oe}R_C} + \frac{R_B R_i}{R_B + R_i} \tag{9-29}$$

Thus

$$\mathbf{A}_{i,\text{low}} = \frac{h_{fe}R_B R_C}{R_C(R_B + R_i) + R_B R_i(1 + h_{oe}R_C)} \frac{1}{1 - j/\omega C_c R_{\text{low}}} \tag{9-30}$$

Then, rearranging and substituting Eq. (9-28), we obtain

$$\frac{\mathbf{A}_{i,\text{low}}}{\mathbf{A}_{i,\text{mid}}} = \frac{1}{1 - j/\omega C_c R_{\text{low}}} \tag{9-31}$$

Let

$$\omega_1 = \frac{1}{C_c R_{\text{low}}} \tag{9-32a}$$

or

$$f_1 = \frac{1}{2\pi C_c R_{\text{low}}} \tag{9-32b}$$

Therefore

$$\frac{\mathbf{A}_{i,\text{low}}}{\mathbf{A}_{i,\text{mid}}} = \frac{1}{1 - j f_1/f} = \frac{1}{\sqrt{1 + (f_1/f)^2}} \quad \underline{/\tan^{-1} f_1/f} \tag{9-33}$$

Equation (9-33) has the same form as Eq. (9-15), which gives the low-frequency response of the common-source FET amplifier. Thus, the low-frequency plots of Fig. 9-6a and b apply here also. Again f_1 is the lower half-power frequency and the phase angle of Eq. (9-33) at this frequency is 45°.

High-frequency region In the high-frequency region, all the elements of the model of Fig. 9-9 must be considered except C_c, which acts as a short circuit. Before proceeding with the analysis let us consider an approximation which is almost always accurate. Consider two of the shunt branches of Fig. 9-9. One consists of r_{oe} in series with C_{oe} and the other is $C_{b'c}$. These two branches are in parallel. However, in general

$$g_m r_{b'e} \gg 1 \tag{9-34a}$$

Thus (see the caption of Fig. 9-9)

$$C_{oe} \gg C_{b'c} = C_{oe}/g_m r_{b'e} \tag{9-34b}$$

A typical value of $g_m r_{b'e}$ is 50. The reactance of C_{oe} is equal to the resistance of r_{oe} when $\omega = \omega_\beta$. Thus, at frequencies far below ω_β, the branch consisting of r_{oe} and C_{oe} in series can be approximated by C_{oe} alone. However, C_{oe} in parallel with $C_{b'c}$ can also be approximated by C_{oe} alone [see Eq. (9-34b)]. At $\omega = \omega_\beta$, the impedance of the branch containing r_{oe} and C_{oe} has a magnitude $\sqrt{2}/\omega C_{oe}$. Thus, it is still much less than $1/\omega C_{b'c}$. Hence, $C_{b'c}$ can still be neglected. At frequencies much above ω_β, the r_{oe}, C_{oe} branch will have an impedance which is essentially equal to $r_{oe} = 1/\omega_\beta C_{oe}$. Thus, at a frequency of $5\omega_\beta$, its impedance will still be very small in comparison with the impedance of $C_{b'c}$. For example, $g_m r_{b'e} = 50$, then at $\omega = 5\omega_\beta$, $1/\omega C_{b'c}$ is 10 times as large as $r_{b'e}$. Thus, it is still valid to neglect $C_{b'c}$ at frequencies as high as $5\omega_\beta$. Now consider the following. At $\omega = 5\omega_\beta$, $|h_{fe}/(1 + j\omega/\omega_\beta)| = h_{fe}/\sqrt{26}$. Thus, at $\omega = 5\omega_\beta$, the current gain will be less than 20 percent of its midband value. (Note that this only consists of the falloff due to $\mathbf{h}_{fe}$. There will be additional falloff due to C_{oe}. Thus, the current gain will be smaller than 20 percent of its midband value.) As the frequency increases, the current gain decreases still further.

The capacitor $C_{b'c}$ need be considered only at those frequencies where $1/\omega C_{b'c}$ is not very much greater than r_{oe}. However, when ω becomes large enough for this to occur, the current gain is usually so small that it is no longer of any interest. Thus, $C_{b'c}$ can be omitted from the high-frequency model of the *RC*-coupled amplifier, since its effect becomes important only at those frequencies where the gain is very small.

At high frequencies, the input impedance of a transistor amplifier often is not a pure resistance. Thus (see Fig. 9-9) if $\mathbf{Z}_i$ represents the input impedance of the next transistor stage, it is not resistive. However, there are times when the input impedance of a transistor is *essentially* resistive over all frequencies of interest. In addition, the load may not be a transistor but an actual resistor. In this case, $\mathbf{Z}_i$ will be R_i, a resistance. In addition, if we assume that the input impedance of the transistor is a resistance, valid design equations are often obtained. At the start, let us assume that $\mathbf{Z}_i$ is purely resistive.

The high-frequency model of Fig. 9-9 is modified according to the discussion of the last three paragraphs, as shown in Fig. 9-12. Analyzing this circuit, we obtain

$$\mathbf{I}_2 = \frac{h_{fe}\mathbf{I}_1}{1 + j\dfrac{\omega}{\omega_\beta}} \cdot \frac{1}{\dfrac{1}{R_{\rm sh}} + \dfrac{1}{r_{oe} + 1/j\omega C_{oe}}} \cdot \frac{1}{R_i}$$

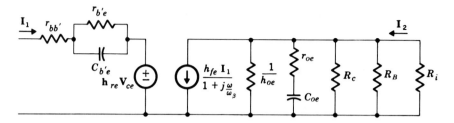

Fig. 9-12 The high-frequency linear model of the circuit of Fig. 9-9 with a resistive load. The modifications discussed in the text have been incorporated.

where R_{sh} is defined in Eq. (9-27).   Then, $\mathbf{A}_{i,\text{high}} = \mathbf{I}_2/\mathbf{I}_1$.   Dividing by $\mathbf{A}_{i,\text{mid}}$ [see Eq. (9-28)], we obtain

$$\frac{\mathbf{A}_{i,\text{high}}}{\mathbf{A}_{i,\text{mid}}} = \frac{1}{1 + j\omega/\omega_\beta} \frac{1 + j\omega r_{oe}C_{oe}}{1 + j\omega(r_{oe} + R_{\text{sh}})C_{oe}} \tag{9-35}$$

However,

$$\omega_\beta = \frac{1}{r_{oe}C_{oe}}$$

This is discussed in the second paragraph following Eq. (6-147).   Thus, Eq. (9-35) becomes

$$\frac{\mathbf{A}_{i,\text{high}}}{\mathbf{A}_{i,\text{mid}}} = \frac{1}{1 + j\omega(r_{oe} + R_{\text{sh}})C_{oe}} \tag{9-36}$$

Let

$$\omega_2 = \frac{1}{(r_{oe} + R_{\text{sh}})C_{oe}} \tag{9-37a}$$

and

$$f_2 = \frac{1}{2\pi(r_{oe} + R_{\text{sh}})C_{oe}} \tag{9-37b}$$

Then

$$\frac{\mathbf{A}_{i,\text{high}}}{\mathbf{A}_{i,\text{mid}}} = \frac{1}{1 + jf/f_2} \tag{9-38}$$

Equation (9-38) has the same form as Eq. (9-11), which gives the high-frequency response of the common-source FET amplifier.   Thus, the high-frequency plot of Fig. 9-6a and b applies here also.   Thus, f_2 is the upper half-power frequency, and the phase angle of Eq. (9-38) at this frequency is 45°.   The decibel plots of Fig. 9-7 are valid here also.

When transistor amplifiers are cascaded, the input impedance of one stage acts as the load impedance of the preceding one. As we have discussed, the impedance $\mathbf{Z}_i$ of Fig. 9-9 often cannot be considered to be a simple resistance. The input impedance of a common-emitter transistor amplifier, including Miller effect, was discussed in Sec. 6-19. The form of the input impedance is given in Fig. 6-45b. Thus, in Fig. 9-12, if the complex form of the input impedance of the transistor is to be considered, R_i should be replaced by Fig. 6-45b. This is done in Fig. 9-13. The capacitor C_e is given by (see Fig 6-45).

$$C_e = C_{b'e} + C_{b'c}(1 - A'_{v,\text{mid}})$$ (9-39)

where $A'_{v,\text{mid}}$ is defined in Eq. (6-150). Actually, we have simplified this by using $A'_{v,\text{mid}}$ rather than the actual voltage gain $\mathbf{A}'_v$. ($A'_{v,\text{mid}}$ can be obtained from an analysis of Fig. 9-10.) However, this approximation will have little effect on the current gain for almost all frequencies of interest. Actually, $r_{b'e}$ should be replaced by the parallel combination of $r_{b'e}$ and $r_{b'c}/(1 - A'_{v,\text{mid}})$. However, $r_{b'c}$ is usually so large that $r_{b'c}/(1 - A'_{v,\text{mid}})$ can be neglected here. At low frequencies, this should reduce to the midband model. Then,

$$R_i = r_{bb'} + r_{b'e}$$ (9-40)

Thus, the model of Fig. 9-13 represents a modification of Fig. 9-12, where C_e is added. Actually, this tends to improve the high-frequency current gain somewhat. As the frequency is increased, the value of $\mathbf{Z}_i$ decreases. This causes a greater proportion of the current from the current generator $\mathbf{h}_{fe}\mathbf{I}_1$ to appear as $\mathbf{I}_2$. This effect can be minor if the input impedance of the transistor is small in comparison with the other elements at all frequencies. However, it does offset the effect of r_{oe} and C_{oe} somewhat. If we analyze Fig. 9-13, we have

$$\mathbf{A}_{i,\text{high}} = \frac{h_{fe}}{1 + j\dfrac{\omega}{\omega_\beta}} \cdot \frac{1}{h_{oe} + \dfrac{1}{r_{oe} + \dfrac{1}{j\omega C_{oe}}} + \dfrac{1}{R_C} + \dfrac{1}{R_B} + \dfrac{1}{r_{bb'} + \dfrac{r_{b'e}}{1 + j\omega r_{b'e} C_e}}}$$

$$\times \frac{1}{r_{bb'} + \dfrac{r_{b'e}}{1 + j\omega r_{b'e} C_e}}$$

Manipulating and substituting Eqs. (9-40), (9-37), (9-28), and (9-27), we obtain

$$\frac{\mathbf{A}_{i,\text{high}}}{\mathbf{A}_{i,\text{mid}}} = \frac{1}{1 + j\dfrac{\omega}{\omega_2} + \dfrac{R_{\text{sh}}}{R_i} j \dfrac{\omega (1 + j\omega/\omega_\beta)}{\omega_a (1 + j\omega/\omega_b)}} \cdot \frac{1 + j\omega/\omega_c}{1 + j\omega/\omega_b}$$ (9-41)

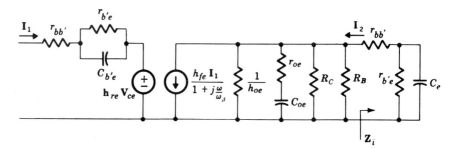

Fig. 9-13 A modification of Fig. 9-12 where a more-complex load impedance is considered.

where

$$\omega_a = \frac{r_{b'e} + r_{bb'}}{r_{b'e}^2 C_e} \tag{9-42a}$$

$$\omega_b = \frac{r_{b'e} + r_{bb'}}{r_{b'e} r_{bb'} C_e} \tag{9-42b}$$

$$\omega_c = \frac{1}{r_{b'e} C_e} \tag{9-42c}$$

Equation (9-41) is relatively complex. Plots can be made to ascertain the actual frequency response. Often, when designs are made, the load is assumed to be resistive. This is a safe approximation since the inclusion of the capacitor Z_i improves the frequency response. Thus, the design which ignores C_e is on the safe side. After a trial design is made, the element values can be substituted in the exact expression to see if the amplifier has been overdesigned.

Decibel plots can simplify the plotting of amplifier expressions. For instance, Eq. (9-41), after manipulation, can be written as

$$\frac{A_{i,\text{high}}}{A_{i,\text{mid}}} = \frac{1 + j\omega/\omega_c}{(1 + j\omega/\omega_{d1})(1 + j\omega/\omega_{d2})} \tag{9-43}$$

where ω_{d1} and ω_{d2} are obtained by multiplying the denominator of Eq. (9-41) by $1 + j\omega/\omega_b$ as indicated in the equation and then factoring the denominator. On a logarithmic basis, the magnitude is

$$\left| \frac{A_{i,\text{high}}}{A_{i,\text{mid}}} \right|_{\text{db}} = 20 \log \sqrt{1 + (\omega/\omega_c)^2}$$

$$- [20 \log \sqrt{1 + (\omega/\omega_{d1})^2} + 20 \log \sqrt{1 + (\omega/\omega_{d2})^2}] \tag{9-44}$$

Each of these terms is of the form of Eq. (9-17). Thus, each term has two asymptotes, one of zero slope and the other having a slope of 6 db/octave. Their breakpoints are at ω_c, ω_{d1}, and ω_{d2}. The numerator term has a posi-

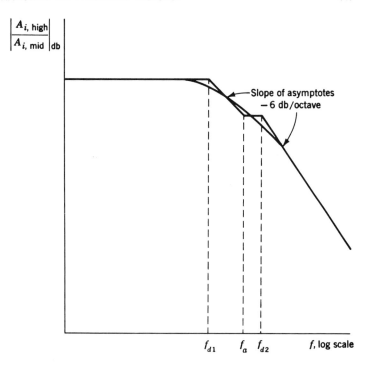

Fig. 9-14 A typical plot of Eq. (9-44) for the high-frequency current gain of an *RC*-coupled transistor amplifier.

tive slope, while the denominator terms have negative slopes. The overall asymptotes are obtained by taking the sum of the asymptotes for the individual terms. A typical plot of Eq. (9-44) is shown with its asymptotes in Fig. 9-14.

9-4 FACTORS AFFECTING THE FREQUENCY RESPONSE OF *RC*-COUPLED COMMON-EMITTER TRANSISTOR AMPLIFIERS

The amplification of the *RC*-coupled common-emitter transistor amplifier with a resistive load is completely specified if $A_{i,\text{mid}} = h_{fe}R_{\text{sh}}/R_i$, $f_1 = 1/2\pi R_{\text{low}}C_c$, and $f_2 = 1/2\pi(r_{oe} + R_{\text{sh}})C_{oe}$ are known. The overall bandwidth will increase if we decrease the lower half-power frequency f_1 and we increase the upper half-power frequency f_2. Let us consider what is involved in obtaining a required midband gain and high-frequency bandwidth.

The value of $h_{fe} = \beta_0$ depends upon the transistor itself. The larger β_0 is, the larger will be the midband gain. The term R_{sh}/R_i is the ratio of the parallel combination of $1/h_{oe}$, R_c, R_B, and R_i to R_i. If R_i is reduced, then R_{sh}/R_i increases and approaches unity as $R_i \to 0$. This increases $A_{i,\text{mid}}$.

However, R_i often depends almost entirely upon the parameters of the transistor in the next stage and cannot be varied at will. If R_{sh} is varied without changing R_i, then $A_{i,mid}$ will vary directly with R_{sh}.

In order to decrease f_1 we must increase the size of R_{low} or C_c. The resistance R_{low} is made up of the parallel combination of $1/h_{oe}$ and R_C in series with the parallel combination of R_B and R_i. It is usually desirable to have $1/h_{oe}$, R_C, and R_B as large as possible. However, the size of R_C is limited, since the direct-bias current must pass through it. The value of R_B is determined from bias and stability considerations. Thus, R_{low} cannot be varied too readily. The principal way to lower f_1 is to increase C_c. In general, R_{low} for a common-emitter transistor is considerably less than it is for an FET or a vacuum tube. Thus, comparatively large values of C_c are required. The resistance levels in transistor circuits are relatively low. Hence, electrolytic capacitors can be used as the coupling capacitors, since their leakage resistance will be thousands of times greater than the bias impedances. This, and the fact that low voltages are encountered in transistor circuits, results in large capacitances with relatively small physical size. Note that the physical size of a capacitor varies directly with its rated working voltage.

High-frequency response depends upon f_2. The frequency f_2 is given by $1/2\pi(r_{oe} + R_{sh})C_{oe}$. The value of f_2 can be increased by decreasing R_{sh}. It is presumed that C_{oe} is kept small by the proper choice of a transistor. Then any increase in f_2 must be accomplished by decreasing R_{sh}. If this is done by decreasing R_i, then the midband gain and f_2 will both increase. However, as we have seen, R_i cannot easily be varied. If R_{sh} is reduced without varying R_i (probably by reducing R_C), then $A_{i,mid}$ will decrease. From Eqs. (9-28) and (9-37), we have

$$A_{i,mid}f_2 = \frac{h_{fe}}{2\pi R_i(1 + r_{oe}/R_{sh})C_{oe}} \tag{9-45}$$

Note that this product depends not only on the transistor parameters but also upon R_{sh} and R_i. We can now trade midband gain for f_2. However, note that as f_2 is increased by decreasing R_{sh}, the gain-bandwidth product also decreases. This indicates that the maximum bandwidth is limited and that gain cannot be traded for bandwidth (by varying R_{sh}) as freely as in the FET. However, the bandwidths of transistor circuits are often far greater than those of FET circuits. A figure of merit for transistors is $g_m/r_{oe}C_{oe}$.

9-5 EFFECT OF IMPEDANCE IN SOURCE, SECOND GATE, CATHODE, AND SCREEN-GRID CIRCUITS

In the analysis of Sec. 9-1, we assumed that the source, cathode, and screen-grid bypass capacitors had zero impedance at any signal frequencies. At low frequencies, the reactance of these capacitors increases and this assumption is not valid. The low-frequency response must therefore be modified. The cases of the FET and vacuum-tube triode will be considered first. A low-frequency linear model for an FET circuit with a source impedance is given in Fig. 9-15. In general, $R_L \ll R_g$. Thus, $\mathbf{Z} \approx R_L$. The voltage gain $\mathbf{A}'_{v,\text{low}} = \mathbf{V}'_2/\mathbf{V}'_1$ is then given by Eq. (6-47)

$$\mathbf{A}'_{v,\text{low}} = \frac{-\mu R_L}{r_d + R_L + \mathbf{Z}_s(1 + \mu)} \tag{9-46}$$

where

$$\mathbf{Z}_s = \frac{R_s}{1 + j\omega C_s R_s} \tag{9-47}$$

Then, substituting and rearranging, we obtain

$$\mathbf{A}'_{v,\text{low}} = \frac{-g_m r_d R_L}{r_d + R_L} \frac{1}{1 + \dfrac{R_s(1 + \mu)}{r_d + R_L}} \frac{1 + j\omega C_s R_s}{1 + \dfrac{j\omega C_s R_s}{1 + R_s(1 + \mu)/(r_d + R_L)}}$$

Since $R_g \gg R_L$, we can write

$$\frac{r_d R_L}{r_d + R_L} \approx R_{\text{sh}}$$

Therefore [see Eq. (9-6)]

$$\frac{\mathbf{A}'_{v,\text{low}}}{\mathbf{A}_{v,\text{mid}}} = \frac{1}{1 + \dfrac{R_s(1 + \mu)}{r_d + R_L}} \frac{1 + j\omega C_s R_s}{1 + \dfrac{j\omega C_s R_s}{1 + R_s(1 + \mu)/(r_d + R_L)}} \tag{9-48}$$

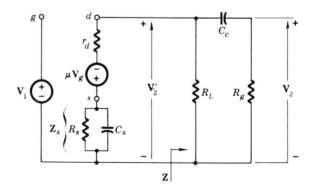

Fig. 9-15 A low-frequency linear model for an FET amplifier stage with a source-bias impedance.

At sufficiently high frequencies $A'_{v,\text{low}}/A_{v,\text{mid}}$ approaches unity as it should, because C_s then acts as a short circuit. As the frequency decreases, $A'_{v,\text{low}}/A_{v,\text{mid}}$ decreases. Its minimum value is given by

$$\left.\frac{\mathbf{A}'_{v,\text{low}}}{\mathbf{A}_{v,\text{mid}}}\right|_{\min} = \frac{r_d + R_L}{r_d + R_L + R_s(1 + \mu)} \tag{9-49}$$

Notice that the unbypassed source impedance does not cause the gain to become zero. Let

$$f_{s1} = \frac{1}{2\pi C_s R_s} \tag{9-50}$$

and

$$f_{s2} = \frac{1 + R_s(1 + \mu)/(r_d + R_L)}{2\pi C_s R_s} \tag{9-51}$$

Note

$$f_{s2} > f_{s1}$$

Then

$$\frac{\mathbf{A}'_{v,\text{low}}}{\mathbf{A}_{v,\text{max}}} = \frac{f_{s1}}{f_{s2}}\frac{1 + jf/f_{s1}}{1 + jf/f_{s2}} = \frac{f_{s1}}{f_{s2}}\sqrt{\frac{1 + (f/f_{s1})^2}{1 + (f/f_{s2})^2}} \left/ \tan^{-1}\frac{f}{f_{s1}} - \tan^{-1}\frac{f}{f_{s2}}\right. \tag{9-52}$$

Plots of the magnitude and phase of this expression are given in Fig. 9-16a and b. Note that there is a positive phase angle which approaches zero at sufficiently low or high frequencies. On a decibel basis

$$\left|\frac{\mathbf{A}'_{v,\text{low}}}{\mathbf{A}_{v,\text{mid}}}\right|_{\text{db}} = -20\log\frac{f_{s2}}{f_{s1}} + 10\log\left[1 + \left(\frac{f}{f_{s1}}\right)^2\right] - 10\log\left[1 + \left(\frac{f}{f_{s2}}\right)^2\right] \tag{9-53}$$

A plot of this expression, with its asymptotes, is shown in Fig. 9-16c. Again note that we can draw the asymptotes between the breakpoints very simply.

To obtain the frequency response of the entire stage, we must include the effect of the coupling network. If $R_g \gg R_L$, we can assume that R_g and C_c have no effect of $\mathbf{V}'_2$ and that $\mathbf{V}_2/\mathbf{V}'_2$ is given by Eq. (9-15). The overall gain of the amplifier can be found by taking the product of Eqs. (9-15) and (9-52). Hence,

$$\frac{\mathbf{A}_{v,\text{low}}}{\mathbf{A}_{v,\text{mid}}} = \frac{f_{s1}}{f_{s2}}\frac{1 + jf/f_{s1}}{1 + jf/f_{s2}}\frac{1}{1 - jf_1/f} \tag{9-54}$$

A plot of $|A_{v,\text{low}}/A_{v,\text{mid}}|$ on a decibel basis is shown in Fig. 9-17.

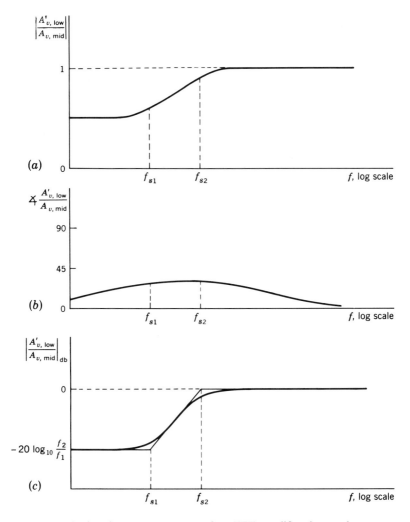

Fig. 9-16 The low-frequency response of an FET amplifier due to the source-bias circuit: (*a*) the amplitude response; (*b*) the phase response; (*c*) the amplitude response plotted on a decibel basis.

The source-bias circuit causes the gain to fall off for frequencies near and between f_{s1} and f_{s2}. To improve the low-frequency response, f_{s1} and f_{s2} should be made small. Since the value of R_s is fixed by gate-bias considerations, C_s is used to adjust the frequency response. Values of C_s between 20 and 1000 μf are usually required, and electrolytic capacitors are used. Because of the small direct-bias voltages, these capacitors occupy relatively small spaces. If C_s is reduced to zero, then f_{s1} and f_{s2} both approach

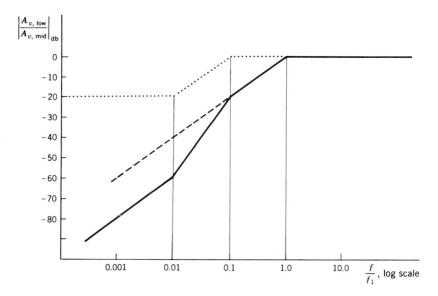

Fig. 9-17 Typical low-frequency response of an *RC*-coupled amplifier. The dashed curve is the response due to the coupling network alone, and the dotted one is the response due to the source, cathode (or emitter), impedance alone. Only the asymptotes have been drawn.

infinity. There is no longer any variation of gain with frequency. However, the gain at all frequencies will be reduced by the factor given in Eq. (9-49). Sometimes this loss in gain is tolerated, because the frequency response is improved. Actually, C_s cannot be reduced to zero, because of stray capacitance across R_s. If C_s is to be ignored, then f_{s1}, which is calculated on the basis of the stray capacitance, must be somewhat higher than the highest input frequency.

When vacuum-tube pentodes are used, we must consider the effect not only of the cathode-bias impedance but also of the impedance in the screen-grid circuit. The screen potential cannot be considered constant, and the more general form of the equivalent circuit of Sec. 6-22 must be used. The pentode circuit of Fig. 6-52 is the one that we shall analyze here. It is cumbersome, and we shall make some approximations[2,3] that simplify our results without creating a large error. These are:

1. The plate resistance r_p is very much larger than any resistance shunting it, so that we can consider r_p to be an open circuit.
2. The plate voltage is sufficiently high so that both the plate and screen

currents are independent of the plate voltage.   We can then write the approximate relation

$$\mathbf{I}_s = \delta \mathbf{I}_p \tag{9-55}$$

where δ is a constant.

3. $R_g \gg R_L$, so that the effective load resistance is R_L.

Using these assumptions, the equivalent circuit of Fig. 6-52 becomes that of Fig. 9-18.   The notation $g_m = g_{pg}$ has been used here.   The voltage across R_L is given by

$$\mathbf{V}_2' = -\mathbf{I}_p R_L$$

and

$$\mathbf{I}_p = g_{ps}\mathbf{V}_s + g_m\mathbf{V}_g \tag{9-56}$$

Let

$$\mathbf{Z}_k = \frac{R_k}{1 + j\omega C_k R_k} \tag{9-57}$$

and

$$\mathbf{Z}_s = \frac{R_s}{1 + j\omega C_s R_s} \tag{9-58}$$

Then

$$\mathbf{V}_g = \mathbf{V}_1 - \mathbf{I}_p(1 + \delta)\mathbf{Z}_k \tag{9-59a}$$

$$\mathbf{V}_s = -\mathbf{I}_p[\delta\mathbf{Z}_s + (1 + \delta)\mathbf{Z}_k] \tag{9-59b}$$

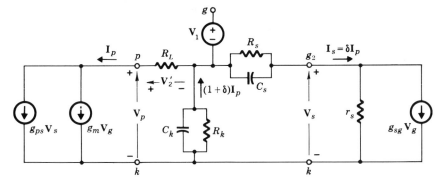

Fig. 9-18 A linear model for the vacuum-tube pentode which can be used to account for the effects of the cathode and screen-grid bias circuits.

Substituting in Eq. (9-56) and rearranging, we obtain

$$\mathbf{A}'_{v,\text{low}} = \frac{\mathbf{V}'_2}{\mathbf{V}_1} = \frac{-g_m R_L}{1 + (1 + \delta)(g_m + g_{ps})\mathbf{Z}_k + \delta g_{ps}\mathbf{Z}_s} \tag{9-60}$$

Since $R_L \gg R_g$ and r_p approaches ∞, we can write

$$R_L \approx R_{sh} \tag{9-61}$$

Let

$$f_{k1} = \frac{1}{2\pi R_k C_k} \tag{9-62}$$

$$f_{s1} = \frac{1}{2\pi R_s C_s} \tag{9-63}$$

Then

$$\frac{\mathbf{A}'_{v,\text{low}}}{\mathbf{A}_{v,\text{mid}}} = \frac{1}{1 + \dfrac{R_k(1 + \delta)(g_m + g_{ps})}{1 + jf/f_{k1}} + \dfrac{R_s\,\delta g_{ps}}{1 + jf/f_{s1}}} \tag{9-64}$$

At sufficiently high frequencies, $\mathbf{A}'_{v,\text{low}}/\mathbf{A}_{v,\text{mid}}$ becomes unity.   Its minimum value is

$$\left|\frac{\mathbf{A}'_{v,\text{low}}}{\mathbf{A}_{v,\text{mid}}}\right|_{\min} = \frac{1}{1 + R_k(1 + \delta)(g_m + g_{ps}) + R_s\,\delta g_{ps}} \tag{9-65}$$

To simplify this expression, let

$$\gamma_k = R_k(1 + \delta)(g_m + g_{ps}) \tag{9-66}$$

$$\gamma_s = R_s\,\delta g_{ps} \tag{9-67}$$

Then

$$\frac{\mathbf{A}'_{v,\text{low}}}{\mathbf{A}_{v,\text{mid}}} = \frac{(1 + jf/f_{k1})(1 + jf/f_{s1})}{(1 + \gamma_k + \gamma_s)\left[1 + \dfrac{jf}{1 + \gamma_k + \gamma_s}\left(\dfrac{1 + \gamma_s}{f_{k1}} + \dfrac{1 + \gamma_k}{f_{s1}}\right) + \dfrac{(jf)^2}{(1 + \gamma_k + \gamma_s)f_{k1}f_{s1}}\right]} \tag{9-68}$$

The term in the bracket is a quadratic in the variable jf.   It can always be factored into the form $(1 + jf/f_{k2})(1 + jf/f_{s2})$.   Hence

$$\frac{\mathbf{A}'_{v,\text{low}}}{\mathbf{A}_{v,\text{mid}}} = \frac{1}{1 + \gamma_k + \gamma_s}\frac{(1 + jf/f_{k1})(1 + jf/f_{s1})}{(1 + jf/f_{k2})(1 + jf/f_{s2})} \tag{9-69}$$

Since $\mathbf{A}'_{v,\text{low}}/\mathbf{A}_{v,\text{mid}} \to 1$ as $f \to \infty$, we have

$$\frac{f_{k2}f_{s2}}{f_{k1}f_{s1}} = 1 + \gamma_k + \gamma_s \tag{9-70}$$

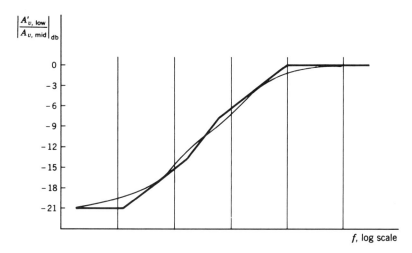

Fig. 9-19 A typical low-frequency amplitude response of a vacuum-tube-pentode amplifier due to the cathode and screen-bias circuits. Each division on the frequency scale corresponds to an octave. The asymptotes as well as the curve have been drawn.

The frequencies f_{k2} and f_{s2} cannot be associated with the screen or cathode impedances in any simple fashion. A typical plot in decibels of $|A'_{v,\text{low}}/A_{v,\text{mid}}|$ is given in Fig. 9-19. As in the case of the vacuum-tube triode, the overall low-frequency gain can be found by multiplying Eq. (9-69) by Eq. (9-15), thus

$$\frac{\mathbf{A}_{v,\text{low}}}{\mathbf{A}_{v,\text{mid}}} = \frac{1}{1 + \gamma_k + \gamma_s} \frac{(1 + jf/f_{k1})(1 + jf/f_{s1})}{(1 + jf/f_{k2})(1 + jf/f_{s2})} \frac{1}{1 - jf_1/f}. \tag{9-71}$$

The second gate bypass impedance has much less effect on the low-frequency response of the dual-gate FET than the screen bypass impedance has on the low-frequency response of the vacuum-tube pentode. In general (see the next to last paragraph of Sec. 6-22) if C_{g2} is much larger than the stray capacitances, the second gate-to-source voltage can be considered constant for all frequencies. Thus, the second gate will not affect the frequency response to any great extent.

9-6 EFFECT OF IMPEDANCE IN THE EMITTER CIRCUIT

In the analysis of Sec. 9-3, we assumed that the stabilizing impedance, consisting of C_E in parallel with R_E, had zero impedance at all frequencies of interest. Its effect will now be taken into account. The linear model that will be used is shown in Fig. 9-20. The conventional h-parameter model has

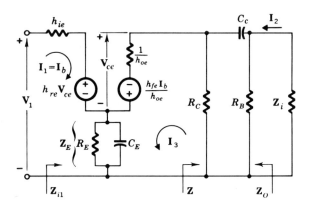

Fig. 9-20 A low-frequency linear model for the *RC*-coupled transistor amplifier.

been modified slightly by replacing the current generator with a voltage generator. Then, writing mesh equations, and making use of the relation $\mathbf{V}_{ce} = -(h_{fe}/h_{oe})\mathbf{I}_b + (1/h_{oe})\mathbf{I}_3$, we have

$$\mathbf{V}_1 = \left(h_{ie} + \mathbf{Z}_E - \frac{h_{re}h_{fe}}{h_{oe}}\right)\mathbf{I}_1 + \left(\mathbf{Z}_E + \frac{h_{re}}{h_{oe}}\right)\mathbf{I}_3 \qquad (9\text{-}72a)$$

$$0 = \left(\mathbf{Z}_E - \frac{h_{fe}}{h_{oe}}\right)\mathbf{I}_1 + \left(\mathbf{Z}_E + \frac{1}{h_{oe}} + \mathbf{Z}\right)\mathbf{I}_3 \qquad (9\text{-}72b)$$

where

$$\mathbf{Z}_E = \frac{R_E}{1 + j\omega R_E C_E} \qquad (9\text{-}73)$$

The effect that $\mathbf{Z}_E$ has on the current gain can be determined by considering the ratio $\mathbf{I}_3/\mathbf{I}_1$ [see Eq. (9-72b)].

$$\frac{\mathbf{I}_3}{\mathbf{I}_1} = \frac{h_{fe} - h_{oe}\mathbf{Z}_E}{1 + h_{oe}\mathbf{Z} + h_{oe}\mathbf{Z}_E} \qquad (9\text{-}74)$$

Since R_E is usually no larger than several thousand ohms, $|h_{oe}\mathbf{Z}_E| \ll 1$. Equation (9-74) then becomes

$$\frac{\mathbf{I}_3}{\mathbf{I}_1} = \frac{h_{fe}}{1 + h_{oe}\mathbf{Z}}$$

This is independent of $\mathbf{Z}_E$. This seems to indicate that the emitter stabilizing impedance will not affect the gain of a cascade of amplifiers. However, it does, since the *input impedance* of the amplifier varies greatly with $\mathbf{Z}_E$. Thus, a change in $\mathbf{Z}_E$ in the next stage will vary $\mathbf{I}_2/\mathbf{I}_3$ and, consequently, the current gain.   It will be assumed that the input impedance $\mathbf{Z}_i$ of each stage in the cascade is identical and that the impedance $\mathbf{Z}$ is purely resistive and equal to the parallel combination of R_C, R_B, and R_i.   (Note that R_i is the midband value of $\mathbf{Z}_i$.)   The magnitude of $\mathbf{Z}$ can never be greater than R_c; thus, it will not increase greatly at low frequencies even though the impedance of C_c and $\mathbf{Z}_i$ will.   Then, replacing $\mathbf{Z}$ by R, where

$$\frac{1}{R} = \frac{1}{R_C} + \frac{1}{R_B} + \frac{1}{R_i} \tag{9-75}$$

and solving Eqs. (9-72a) and (9-72b), we obtain

$$\mathbf{Z}_i = \frac{h_{ie}(1 + h_{oe}R) - h_{re}h_{fe}R + \mathbf{Z}_E(1 + h_{oe}R + h_{ie}h_{oe} - h_{re}h_{fe} - h_{re} + h_{fe})}{1 + h_{oe}R + h_{oe}\mathbf{Z}_E} \tag{9-76}$$

Making use of the relation $1 + h_{oe}\mathbf{Z}_E \approx 1$, and Eq. (6-89), we have

$$\mathbf{Z}_i = R_i + \frac{\mathbf{Z}_E(1 + h_{oe}R + h_{ie}h_{oe} - h_{re}h_{fe} - h_{re} + h_{fe})}{1 + h_{oe}R} \tag{9-77}$$

Using the inequalities of relation (6-67) and noting that $h_{fe} \gg 1 + h_{oe}R$, results in

$$\mathbf{Z}_i \approx R_i + \frac{\mathbf{Z}_E h_{fe}}{1 + h_{oe}R} \tag{9-78}$$

In order to determine the effect of $\mathbf{Z}_i$ on the current gain, we replace all the elements to the left of $\mathbf{Z}_i$ by their Norton's equivalent circuit.   This impedance $\mathbf{Z}_o$ is shown in Fig. 9-20.   To simplify the results, we shall use the midband value of $\mathbf{Z}_o$.   (This is accurate as long as the gain does not fall off by a large amount in the frequencies of interest.)   Then, we approximately have $\mathbf{Z}_o = R_o$ where, in Fig. 9-20,

$$\frac{1}{R_o} = \frac{1}{R_B} + \frac{1}{R_C} + h_{oe} \tag{9-79}$$

Then the frequency response of the ratio $\mathbf{I}_2'/\mathbf{I}_2$ (see Fig. 9-21) yields the effect of $\mathbf{Z}_E$ on the frequency response of the amplifier.   The ratio $\mathbf{I}_2'/\mathbf{I}_2$ is

$$\frac{\mathbf{I}_2}{\mathbf{I}_2'} = \frac{R_o}{R_o + \mathbf{Z}_i}$$

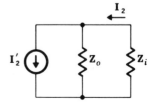

Fig. 9-21 A Norton's equivalent circuit for the linear model of Fig. 9-20.

Then

$$\frac{\mathbf{I}_2}{\mathbf{I}_2'} = \frac{R_o}{R_o + R_i} \frac{1}{1 + \gamma_E} \frac{1 + jf/f_{e1}}{1 + jf/f_{e2}} \tag{9-80}$$

where

$$\gamma_E = \frac{R_E h_{fe}}{(1 + h_{oe}R)(R_o + R_i)} \tag{9-81a}$$

$$f_{e1} = \frac{1}{2\pi R_E C_E} \tag{9-81b}$$

$$f_{e2} = (1 + \gamma_E)f_{e1} \tag{9-81c}$$

The magnitude of $\mathbf{I}_2'/\mathbf{I}_2$ varies between $R_o/(R_o + R_i)$, the midband value, and $R_o/[(R_o + R_i)(1 + \gamma_E)]$, the value at zero frequency. Plots of the magnitude and phase of $\mathbf{I}_2'/\mathbf{I}_2$ versus frequency will have the same shape as the curve of Fig. 9-16. To obtain the expression for the overall current gain, multiply Eq. (9-33) by

$$\frac{\mathbf{I}_2}{\mathbf{I}_2'} \frac{R_o + R_i}{R_o} \tag{9-82}$$

[Note that the factor $(R_o + R_i)/R_o$ has already been taken into account in Eq. (9-33).] Then

$$\frac{\mathbf{A}_{i,\text{low}}}{\mathbf{A}_{i,\text{mid}}} = \frac{1}{1 + \gamma_E} \frac{1 + jf/f_{e1}}{1 + jf/f_{e2}} \frac{1}{1 - jf_1/f} \tag{9-83}$$

This curve has the same shape as the low-frequency response of the FET RC-coupled amplifier, with source bias. Thus, Fig. 9-16 applies here if the ordinate axis is labeled $|A_{i,\text{low}}/A_{i,\text{mid}}|_{\text{db}}$.

The capacitor C_E has the same effect on the response of the transistor amplifier as C_s does on the response of the FET amplifier. The discussion of C_s in Sec. 9-5 also applies to C_E.

9-7 INPUT AND OUTPUT STAGES IN A CASCADE OF AMPLIFIERS

We have thus far considered the internal stages in a cascade of amplifiers. Let us now consider the input and output circuits. The output impedance of many amplifiers can often be considered to be a resistor. In all the amplifiers that have been considered, we have made provision for such a load. Thus, we can directly apply the results of the previous sections to most output stages.

Insofar as the input stage is concerned, we need only find the voltage across it in the case of the FET, or the current into it in the case of the transistor. Once these quantities are known, the output of the first stage,

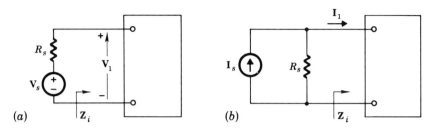

Fig. 9-22 Representations of the input to (*a*) a voltage amplifier and (*b*) a current amplifier.

which is the input to the next stage, can be found by multiplying by the amplification. To illustrate the calculation of the input quantities, consider Fig. 9-22*a*. The input voltage of the amplifier is given by

$$\mathbf{V}_1 = \frac{\mathbf{V}_s \mathbf{Z}_i}{R_s + \mathbf{Z}_i} \tag{9-84}$$

Similarly, from Fig. 9-22*b*, the amplifier input current is given by

$$\mathbf{I}_1 = \frac{\mathbf{I}_s R_s}{R_s + \mathbf{Z}_i} \tag{9-85}$$

A simple input circuit for an amplifier is shown in Fig. 9-23. Note that the input current is only considered to be the current in R_i. This is often the case in an actual amplifier. Then,

$$\frac{\mathbf{V}_1}{\mathbf{V}_s} = \frac{R_i}{R_s + R_i} \frac{1}{1 + jf/f_2} \tag{9-86}$$

$$\frac{\mathbf{I}_1}{\mathbf{I}_s} = \frac{R_s}{R_s + R_i} \frac{1}{1 + jf/f_2} \tag{9-87}$$

where

$$f_2 = \frac{R_s + R_i}{2\pi C_i R_s R_i} \tag{9-88}$$

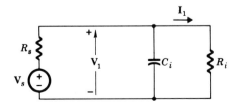

Fig. 9-23 A simple amplifier input.

and

$$\mathbf{I}_s = \frac{\mathbf{V}_s}{R_s} \tag{9-89}$$

Note that Eqs. (9-86) and (9-87) indicate a high-frequency-response falloff.

9-8 BANDWIDTH OF CASCADED AMPLIFIER STAGES

The gain of an amplifier is the product of the gains of its individual stages.   If RC-coupled amplifiers are cascaded, the bandwidth of the overall amplifier will be less than that of any one stage.   For instance, let us consider an amplifier whose high-frequency response is given by

$$\frac{A_{\text{high}}}{A_{\text{mid}}} = \frac{1}{1 + jf/f_2} = \frac{1}{\sqrt{1 + (f/f_2)^2}} \quad \underline{\big/{-\tan^{-1} f/f_2}} \tag{9-90}$$

If n of these are cascaded, then for the entire amplifier

$$\frac{A_{T,\text{high}}}{A_{T,\text{mid}}} = \frac{1}{(1 + jf/f_2)^n} = \frac{1}{[1 + (f/f_2)^2]^{n/2}} \quad \underline{\big/{-n \tan^{-1} f/f_2}} \tag{9-91}$$

On a decibel basis

$$\left|\frac{A_{T,\text{high}}}{A_{T,\text{mid}}}\right|_{\text{db}} = -10n \log\left[1 + \left(\frac{f}{f_2}\right)^2\right] \tag{9-92}$$

Comparing this with Eqs. (9-17) to (9-19), we see that the breakpoint of the asymptotes is f_2 and the asymptotic slope is $-6n$ db/octave or $-20n$ db/decade.   The phase shift of the overall amplifier is just n times the phase shift of an individual stage.   A plot of $|A_{T,\text{high}}/A_{T,\text{mid}}|_{\text{db}}$ is given in Fig. 9-24.

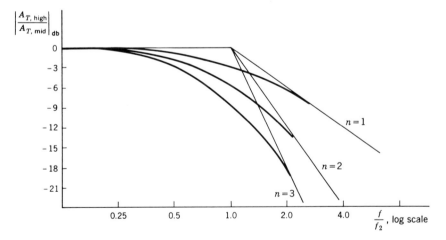

Fig. 9-24 Plots of the amplitude response of one-stage, two-stage, and three-stage amplifiers whose amplifications are given in Eq. (9-91).

The half-power bandwidth of the amplifier f_{2T} decreases with the number of stages and is found by solving the following equation

$$[1 + (f_{2T}/f_2)^2]^{n/2} = \sqrt{2}$$

Thus

$$f_{2T} = f_2\sqrt{2^{1/n} - 1} \qquad (9\text{-}93)$$

Values of f_{2T}/f_2 are given in Table 9-1.

Although high-frequency-response curves have been drawn, these results are directly applicable to the low-frequency response of cascaded amplifiers.

These results can be applied to the high-frequency response of FETs and transistors with resistive loads and to the low-frequency response of FETs and transistors.

When identical amplifier stages are cascaded, the overall bandwidth is reduced. On the other hand, if the gain-bandwidth product of each stage is constant and the midband gain of the overall amplifier is kept constant (independent of the number of stages), then an increase in the number of stages may actually increase the bandwidth. For instance, let us assume for an amplifier characterized by Eq. (9-90) that $|A_{\text{mid}}|f_2 = 100 \times 10^6$ Hz. A single-stage amplifier with a midband gain of 100 will have an upper half-power frequency of 1 MHz. If we desire the same midband gain, we can cascade two stages, each with a midband gain of 10. The half-power frequency of each stage will then be 10 MHz, and the half-power frequency of the cascade will be 6.4 MHz (see Table 9-1). Thus, the overall bandwidth has been increased. As the number of stages is increased (with constant total midband gain), f_{2T} will increase and then start to decrease. There is an

Table 9-1†

n	f_{2T}/f_2
1	1.00
2	0.64
3	0.51
4	0.44
5	0.39
6	0.35
7	0.32
8	0.30
9	0.28

† From G. E. Valley, Jr., and H. Wallman, "Vacuum Tube Amplifiers." Copyright 1948. McGraw-Hill Book Company. Used by permission.

optimum number of stages to use for maximum bandwidth.   It can be shown that the maximum bandwidth occurs when the gain per stage is approximately equal to

$$\sqrt{\epsilon} = \sqrt{2.7183} = 1.649 \qquad \text{or} \qquad 4.34 \text{ db}$$

The previous discussion assumed that the gain-bandwidth product is a constant.   This is essentially true (except for Miller effect) for the FET.   In the transistor, the gain-bandwidth product is not a constant.   However, the previous discussion does apply in part.   These ideas will be illustrated in the next section, where the design of an RC-coupled amplifier is discussed.

9-9   DESIGN OF RC-COUPLED AMPLIFIERS

To illustrate the ideas of the previous sections of this chapter, we shall design FET and transistor RC-coupled amplifiers.

The FET amplifier   The amplifier is to have the following specifications. There is to be a well-defined midband region with $|A_{v,\text{mid}}| = 400$, $|A_{v,\text{high}}/A_{v\text{mid}}| \geq 0.95$ at 10^5 Hz, $|A_{v,\text{low}}/A_{v,\text{mid}}| \geq 1/\sqrt{2} = 0.707$ at 20 Hz. The amplifier is to have the minimum number of stages.   The load resistance is 10^6 ohms shunt by 5 pf.   For any stage, $R_{g,\text{max}} = 10^6$ ohms.   An FET with the following characteristics will be used: $g_m = 5000$ μmhos, $r_d = 100,000$ ohms, $C_{gs} = 5$ pf, $C_{ds} = 5$ pf, $C_{gd} = 0.2$ pf.   The coordinates of the quiescent operating point are $V_{DSQ} = 15$ volts, $I_{DQ} = 10$ ma, $V_{GSQ} = -1$ volt. Assume that there is $C_w = 4.8$ pf of stray wiring capacitance per stage.

A cut-and-try procedure will be used to determine the number of stages. The midband and high-frequency gains are considered first since these determine the number of stages that must be used or whether the design can be achieved.   Let us try one stage.   In this case, the Miller effect does not enter the problem.   The total shunt capacitance $C_{\text{sh}} = C_{ds} + C_{gd} + C_w + 5 = 15$ pf.   The 5 represents the capacitance across the load. $|A_{v,\text{mid}}| = 400$.   Substituting in Eq. (9-24), we have

$$f_2 = \frac{g_m}{2\pi C_{\text{sh}} |A_{v,\text{mid}}|} = 1.326 \times 10^5 \text{ Hz}$$

Thus, at $f = 100,000$ Hz,

$$\frac{A_{v,\text{high}}}{A_{v,\text{mid}}} = \frac{1}{\sqrt{1 + [10^5/(1.326 \times 10^5)]^2}} = 0.8 < 0.95$$

Thus, one stage does not achieve the design.   Now try two stages.   In this case

$$|A_{v,\text{mid}}| = \sqrt{400} = 20$$

Now, for the second stage, f_2 will be 20 times the previous value

$$f_{22} = 2.652 \times 10^6 \text{ Hz}$$

The shunt capacitance is larger for the first stage because of the Miller effect. The Miller effect capacitance is $C_{ds}|A_{v,\text{mid}}| = 4$ pf. Thus, $C_{\text{sh}} = C_{ds} + C_{gs} + C_{gd} + C_w + C_{\text{Miller}} = 19$ pf. Then, for the second stage,

$$f_{21} = \tfrac{15}{19} f_{22} = 2.092 \times 10^6 \text{ Hz}$$

Then, the response of the amplifier at 100,000 Hz is given by

$$\left|\frac{A_{v,\text{high}}}{A_{v,\text{mid}}}\right| = \frac{1}{\sqrt{1 + [10^5/(2.652 \times 10^6)]^2}} \frac{1}{\sqrt{1 + [10^5/(2.092 \times 10^6)]^2}}$$

$$= 0.998 > 0.95$$

Thus, two stages can be used. A complete amplifier is shown in Fig. 9-25. The load resistance is labeled R_g. The stray capacitances are not shown.

Now we are in a position to determine the values of all the resistances and the power-supply voltage. The value of R_{sh} is [see Eq. (9-6)]

$$R_{\text{sh}} = \frac{|A_{v,\text{mid}}|}{g_m} = \frac{20}{5000 \times 10^{-6}} = 4000 \text{ ohms}$$

R_{sh} consists of the parallel combination of r_d, R_c, and R_g. We shall use $R_g = 10^6$ ohms. (The maximum value of R_g is used to keep C_c small.) In addition, $r_d = 100,000$ ohms. Thus,

$$\frac{1}{R_L} = \frac{1}{R_{\text{sh}}} - \frac{1}{R_g} - \frac{1}{r_d}$$

$$R_L = 4184 \text{ ohms}$$

Then

$$R_s = -\frac{V_{GSQ}}{I_D} = \frac{1}{10 \times 10^{-3}} = 100 \text{ ohms}$$

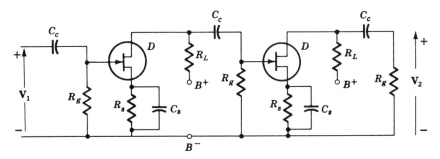

Fig. 9-25 The two-stage *RC*-coupled FET amplifier.

The required power-supply voltage is

$$V_{DD} = I_{DQ}R_L + V_{DSQ} - V_{GSQ} = 41.8 + 15 + 1 = 57.8 \text{ volts}$$

Now to complete the design we must find the values of C_c and C_s. There are two amplifier stages; in addition, a coupling network consisting of a C_c and R_s is placed in the input circuit. This protects the input FET from any direct voltage that might be present in V_1. This input circuit acts as a third RC-coupled stage at low frequencies.

To simplify the analysis, at the start, we shall assume that the source bypass capacitors act as short circuits. Their effect will be considered subsequently. The resistance R_{low} consists of R_g in series with r_d and R_L in parallel. Thus, $R_{low} \approx R_g = 10^6$ ohms. Then, if the three coupling capacitors are equal,

$$\left|\frac{A_{vT,low}}{A_{vT,mid}}\right| = \left[\frac{1}{\sqrt{1 + (f_1/f)^2}}\right]^3$$

where the subscript T indicates the total amplifier and not just a single stage. Then, at 20 Hz,

$$\frac{1}{[1 + (f_1/20)^2]^{\frac{3}{2}}} = \frac{1}{\sqrt{2}}$$

Solving, we obtain $f_1 = 10.2$ Hz. Substituting in Eq. (9-14), we have

$$C_c = \frac{1}{2\pi R_{low} f_1} = \frac{1}{2\pi \times 10^6 \times 10.2} = 0.0156 \ \mu\text{f}$$

This value of C_c does not allow for any loss in gain due to the source impedance. Let us increase C_c so that some loss due to the source impedance can be tolerated. Let us try a value of $C_c = 0.03 \ \mu\text{f}$. Then, substituting in Eq. (9-14) yields $f_1 = 5.31$ Hz. Then, at 20 Hz,

$$\left|\frac{A_{vT,low}}{A_{vT,mid}}\right| = \frac{1}{[1 + (5.31/20)^2]^{3/2}} = 0.903$$

At 20 Hz, the gain can be 0.707 of the midband value. Thus, the allowable loss due to the source impedances is

$$\left|\frac{A_{vT',low}}{A_{vT,mid}}\right| = \frac{0.707}{0.903} = 0.783$$

Since there are two stages, the allowable loss per stage is $\sqrt{0.783} = 0.885$. Then, using Eqs. (9-50) to (9-52), we have

$$\frac{f_{s1}}{f_{s2}} \sqrt{\frac{1 + (20/f_{s1})^2}{1 + (20/f_{s2})^2}} = 0.885$$

where

$$f_{s2} = 1 + \frac{R_s(1 + \mu)}{r_d + R_L} f_{s1} = 1 + \frac{100(501)}{104,000} f_{s1} = 1.482 f_{s1}$$

Substituting and solving, we have $f_{s1} = 10.99$ Hz. Then, using Eq. (9-50),

$$C_s = \frac{1}{2\pi R_s f_{s1}} = \frac{1}{2\pi (100)(10.99)} = 145 \ \mu\text{f}$$

This value may seem large. However it is very acceptable since electrolytic capacitors can be used. Actually, much larger values of C_s could be obtained in practice using electrolytic capacitors. The value of C_s can be decreased somewhat if C_c is increased. However, eventually, large increases in C_c will result in essentially no decrease in C_s. Possibly several values of C_c should be tried to establish an optimum design.

The design of the FET amplifier is now complete. In summary, $V_{DD} = 57.8$ volts, $R_c = 4184$ ohms, $R_g = 10^6$ ohms, $R_s = 100$ ohms, $C_c = 0.03 \ \mu\text{f}$, and $C_s = 145 \ \mu\text{f}$.

The values of the resistors and capacitors that are calculated may not be the same as those which are commonly manufactured. In the case of the capacitors, the next larger size can be chosen. The standard resistor values that are closest to the calculated ones should be selected. These values should be checked to verify that the operating point, gain, and frequency response are not varied beyond allowable limits.

If dual-gate MOSFETs are used, the Miller effect need not be considered. Otherwise, the design is essentially the same as for the single-gate FET. A bias circuit and bypass capacitor must be added for the second gate. A typical amplifier is shown in Fig. 9-26.

The vacuum-tube amplifier The design of a vacuum-tube amplifier closely follows that of the FET amplifier. Vacuum-tube pentodes should be used so that the Miller effect does not become important. The high-

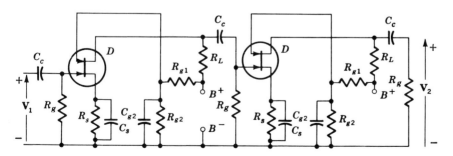

Fig. 9-26 A two-stage *RC*-coupled dual-gate FET amplifier.

frequency design essentially parallels the preceding one. The low-frequency design must consider both cathode- and screen-bias impedances (see Sec. 9-5).

Transistor amplifier   The amplifier is to have the following specifications. There is to be a well-defined midband region; the magnitude of the current gain in the midband region is to be equal to or greater than 42, $|A_{i,\text{high}}/A_{i,\text{low}}|$ ≥ 0.96 at 10^5 Hz, $|A_{i,\text{low}}/A_{i,\text{mid}}| \geq 1/\sqrt{2} = 0.707$ at 20 Hz; the minimum number of amplifier stages is to be used; and the stability factor of any stage is to be equal to or less than 5. The load impedance is 1500 ohms, and the internal impedance of the input current generator is 10,000 ohms.

The transistor to be used has the following (hybrid-pi) parameter values: $r_{bb'} = 100$ ohms, $r_{b'e} = 1400$ ohms, $C_{b'e} = 56.8$ pf, $r_{b'c} = 4.67 \times 10^6$ ohms, $C_{b'c} = 5$ pf, $g_m = 71,400$ μmhos, $r_{ce} = 34,500$ ohms. The quiescent operating point is $I_{CQ} = -6$ ma, $V_{CEQ} = -5$ volts, $I_{BQ} - -100$ μamp, and $V_{BEQ} \approx 0$ volts.

Before proceeding, let us determine the pertinent h parameters to be used in the linear model of Fig. 9-12. Substituting in Eqs. (6-137) to (6-147) and Fig. 6-43, we have $h_{ie} = 1500$ ohms, $h_{re} = 300 \times 10^{-6}$, $h_{fe} = 100$, $h_{oe} = 50 \times 10^{-6}$, $f_\beta = 2 \times 10^6$ Hz, $C_{oe} = 500$ pf, and $r_{oe} = 159.1$ ohms.

A typical amplifier is shown in Fig. 9-27. Two stages have been drawn, although at the present time we do not know the number of stages that are needed. It will be more convenient to work with the ratio I_2/I_1 rather than with I_2/I_s in the mid- and high-frequency regions. To do this, we must know the ratio I_1/I_s. At mid- and high frequencies, this is

$$\frac{I_1}{I_s} = \frac{R_s'}{R_s' + R_i}$$

where $R_s' = R_s R_B/(R_s + R_B)$, $R_B = R_{B1}R_{B2}/(R_{B1} + R_{B2})$, and R_i is the input resistance between the base and the common terminal. At low frequencies this ratio falls off, because of the presence of C_{ci}, R_E, and C_E. We can

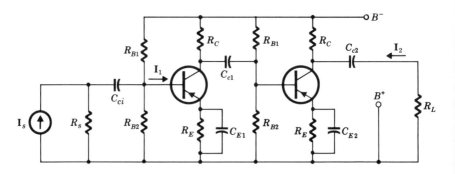

Fig. 9-27   The two-stage RC-coupled transistor amplifier.

obtain a trial value for R_B by considering the stability factor $S = dI_C/dI_{CO}$. From Eq. (5-39), we have

$$S = \frac{1}{1 - \alpha R_B/(R_B + R_E)} = \frac{1}{1 - [\beta/(\beta + 1)][R_B/(R_B + R_E)]}$$

Let us try $R_E = 1000$ ohms. Too large a value of R_E will result in too large a power-supply voltage. If R_E is too small, then R_B will be small and will shunt the input signal and reduce the current gain.

$$S = \frac{1}{1 - \frac{100}{101}[R_B/(R_B + 1000)]} = 5$$

Solving for R_B, we obtain

$$R_B = 4208 \text{ ohms}$$

If more than one stage is necessary, then we shall use this value for R_B also (if it proves to be suitable). Since R_B consists of R_{B1} in parallel with R_{B2}, it corresponds to the R_B that was discussed in Sec. 9-3. We do not know the input impedance of the amplifier, since the value of R_C is not known. However, R_i can be approximated. From Eq. (6-89) we have in the mid-frequency region

$$R_i = h_{ie} - \frac{h_{re}h_{fe}R_{sh}}{1 + h_{oe}R_{sh}}$$

Substituting, we have

$$R_i = 1500 - \frac{3 \times 10^{-2}R_{sh}}{1 + 50 \times 10^{-6}R_{sh}}$$

The second term will, in general, be very small, so that we can approximate R_i by 1500 ohms. We shall verify this approximation subsequently. Then, substituting, we obtain $I_1/I_s = 0.664$. Thus

$$|A_{iT,\text{mid}}| = \frac{|I_2|}{|I_1|} = \frac{42}{0.664} = 63.3$$

We shall use the value $A_{iT,\text{mid}} = 64$. Note that the subscript T will be added to indicate a quantity for both stages, differentiating the symbol from one which applies to a single stage.

The midband gain and the high-frequency response will determine the number of stages to be used or whether the design will succeed. Let us try one stage. From Eq. (9-28) we have

$$R_{sh} = \frac{A_{i,\text{mid}}R_i}{h_{fe}}$$

R_i is the load impedance if there is only one stage. Then

$$R_{sh} = \frac{64 \times 1500}{100} = 960 \text{ ohms}$$

Then [see Eq. (9-37b)]

$$f_2 = \frac{1}{2\pi(r_{oe} + R_{sh})C_{oe}} = \frac{1}{2\pi(159.1 + 960)500 \times 10^{-12}} = 2.845 \times 10^5$$

Then, at 100,000 Hz

$$\left|\frac{A_{i,\text{high}}}{A_{i,\text{mid}}}\right| = \frac{1}{\sqrt{1 + [10^5/(2.845 \times 10^5)]^2}} = 0.943 < 0.96$$

Thus, we must try two stages. In this case, $A_{i,\text{mid}} = \sqrt{64} = 8$. Hence,

$$R_{sh} = 120 \text{ ohms}$$

Then,

$$f_2 = \frac{1}{2\pi(159.1 + 120)500 \times 10^{-12}} = 1.14 \times 10^6 \text{ Hz}$$

Then,

$$\left|\frac{A_{iT,\text{high}}}{A_{iT,\text{mid}}}\right| = \frac{1}{1 + [10^5/(1.14 \times 10^6)]^2} = 0.992 > 0.96$$

Actually, if the design just failed with two stages, the more accurate expression of Eq. (9-41) should be used to compute the gain of the first stage, since this takes the capacitive component of the input circuit into account. Note that if the value $R_{sh} = 120$ is substituted into the relation for R_i, we have $R_i = 1496.4$ ohms. Thus, the assumption that $R_i = 1500$ ohms is justified.

The design can be met with two stages. We can now determine the unknown resistances in the circuit. For the first stage,

$$\frac{1}{R_{sh}} = h_{oe} + \frac{1}{R_C} + \frac{1}{R_B} + \frac{1}{R_i}$$

Substituting, and solving for R_C, we obtain

$$R_C = 135 \text{ ohms}$$

For the second stage, R_B is missing. The value of R_C is then given by $1/R_C = 1/R_{sh} - h_{oe} - 1/R_i$; hence, $R_C = 131$ ohms. If we use $R_C = 135$ ohms, the change in frequency response will be negligible. Hence, for simplicity, we shall do so. Since R_C is 135 ohms, the shunting effect of R_B is very small. Therefore, we need not use a value of R_E greater than 1000 ohms. *Actually, R_C is much smaller than is typical.* However, the numbers were deliberately chosen in this way to demonstrate how gain and bandwidth can be manipulated in a transistor. The power-supply voltage V_{CC} is connected between the points B^- and B^+, where

$$V_{CC} = I_{CQ}R_C + V_{CQ} + (I_{BQ} + I_{CQ})R_E = -11.91 \text{ volts}$$

The minus sign indicates that the terminal marked B^- is negative.   Since the base-to-emitter quiescent voltage can be neglected, we can combine Eqs. (5-21) to (5-23) and obtain

$$V_{CC} = I_{BQ}R_{B1} + \frac{(I_{BQ} + I_{CQ})R_E R_{B1}}{R_B}$$

Substituting and solving for R_{B1}, we have

$$R_{B1} = 7684 \text{ ohms}$$

Then

$$R_{B2} = 9305 \text{ ohms}$$

The low-frequency design will now be obtained.   We shall, for the time being, neglect the effect of the emitter stabilizing impedance.   There are three coupling capacitors; thus, there are effectively three stages.   The subscripts *i*, 1, and 2 will be used to differentiate among these three stages. Then, proceeding as in Sec. 9-3, we have

$$R_{\text{low},1} = \frac{R_C}{1 + h_{oe}R_C} + \frac{R_B R_i}{R_B + R_i}$$

$$R_{\text{low},2} = \frac{R_C}{1 + h_{oe}R_C} + 1500$$

$$R_{\text{low},i} = R_s + \frac{R_B R_i}{R_B + R_i}$$

Substituting, we obtain

$$R_{\text{low},1} = 1240 \text{ ohms} \qquad R_{\text{low},2} = 1634 \text{ ohms} \qquad R_{\text{low},i} = 11{,}100 \text{ ohms}$$

The low-frequency response is then given by

$$\left| \frac{A_{iT,\text{low}}}{A_{iT,\text{mid}}} \right| = \frac{1}{\sqrt{1 + (f_{11}/f)^2}} \frac{1}{\sqrt{1 + (f_{12}/f)^2}} \frac{1}{\sqrt{1 + (f_{1i}/f)^2}}$$

where

$$f_{11} = \frac{1}{2\pi R_{\text{low},1}C_{c1}} \qquad f_{12} = \frac{1}{2\pi R_{\text{low},2}C_{c2}} \qquad f_{1i} = \frac{1}{2\pi R_{\text{low},i}C_{ci}}$$

We shall adjust C_{c2} and C_{ci} so that $f_{11} = f_{12} = f_{1i} = f_1$.

There are instances when it is not desirable to make the three breakpoints equal.   However, we shall do so here to simplify the problem.   [Since $R_{\text{low},i}$ is considerably greater than $R_{\text{low},1}$ and $R_{\text{low},2}$, an alternative procedure would be to make f_{1i} very much less than f_{11} and f_{12}.   In this case, over much of the low-frequency range, the low-frequency behavior would be of the form

$1/[\sqrt{1 + (f_{11}/f)^2}\sqrt{1 + (f_{12}/f)^2}].]$ In the case of equal breakpoints, $C_{c2} = (R_{\text{low},1}/R_{\text{low},2})C_{c1} = 0.759C_{c1}$, $C_{ci} = (R_{\text{low},1}/R_{\text{low},i})C_{c1} = 0.112C_{c1}$. Then

$$\left|\frac{A_{iT,\text{low}}}{A_{iT,\text{mid}}}\right| = \frac{1}{[1 + (f_1/f)^2]^{\frac{3}{2}}}$$

and, at 20 Hz, $[1 + (f_1/20)^2]^{\frac{3}{2}} = \sqrt{2}$. Solving for f_1, we obtain $f_1 = 10.2$ Hz. Then, $C_{c1} = 1/2\pi R_{\text{low},1}f_1 = 12.6$ μf. In computing this value, the emitter stabilizing impedance is ignored. A larger value of C_{c1} should be used to account for the loss due to C_E and R_E. Let us use $C_{c1} = 20$ μf as a trial. Then $f_1 = 6.42$ Hz and at 20 Hz the response due to the coupling capacitors is given by

$$\frac{1}{[1 + (6.42/20)^2]^{3/2}} = 0.863$$

The allowable loss due to the two emitter lead impedances at 20 Hz is then

$$\left|\frac{A'_{T,\text{low}}}{A_{iT,\text{mid}}}\right| = \frac{0.707}{0.863} = 0.819$$

The allowable loss per stage is $|A'_{i,\text{low}}/A_{i,\text{mid}}| = \sqrt{0.819} = 0.905$. Then, using Eqs. (9-81) to (9-83), we obtain

$$\gamma_E = \frac{R_E h_{fe}}{(1 + h_{oe}R)(R_o + R_i)}$$

where

$$\frac{1}{R} = \frac{1}{R_C} + \frac{1}{R_B} + \frac{1}{R_i}$$

For the second stage, R_B is omitted from the relation for R. For the first stage, R_o consists of R_B and R_s in parallel, while for the second stage, R_o consists of R_B, R_C, and h_{oe} in parallel. Thus, for the second stage, $R_o = 130$ ohms, $R = 124$ ohms, $\gamma_E = 61.0$. Then, at 20 Hz,

$$\sqrt{0.819} = \frac{1}{62.0}\sqrt{\frac{1 + (20/f_{e1})^2}{1 + (1/62.0)^2(20/f_{e1})^2}}$$

Solving, we obtain $f_{e1} = 0.152$. Then,

$$C_{E2} = \frac{1}{2\pi R_E f_{e1}} = 1047 \ \mu\text{f}$$

where the subscript 2 is used since this is in the second stage. This is a large value. However, it is not unacceptable since an electrolytic capacitor can be used. For the first stage, $R_o = 2962$ ohms, $R = 120$ ohms, $\gamma_E = 22.3$. Then, substituting as before, we have

$$\sqrt{0.819} = \frac{1}{23.3} \sqrt{\frac{1 + (20/f_{e1})^2}{1 + (1/23.3)^2(20/f_{e1})^2}}$$

Solving, we obtain $f_{e1} = 0.403$. Thus, $C_{E1} = 395 \ \mu f$.

If the sizes of the coupling capacitors are increased, then the emitter bypass capacitors can be reduced somewhat. However, it is probably not advisable to do so, since the leakage resistance of a capacitor usually decreases as the capacitance increases. The emitter bypass capacitors are shunted by small resistances and their leakage resistance can be ignored. However, the coupling capacitors must have a relatively high leakage resistance. Thus, it is desirable to keep their capacitance relatively small. Hence, the trial value of 20 μf for C_{c1} will be used. Therefore

$$C_{c2} = 15.2 \ \mu f \qquad \text{and} \qquad C_{ci} = 2.24 \ \mu f$$

The design is now complete. To summarize: $V_{CC} = -11.91$ volts, $R_C = 135$ ohms, $R_{B1} = 7684$ ohms, $R_{B2} = 9305$ ohms, $R_E = 1000$ ohms, $C_{c1} = 20 \ \mu f$, $C_{c2} = 15.2 \ \mu f$, $C_{ci} = 2.24 \ \mu f$, $C_{E1} = 1047 \ \mu f$, and $C_{E2} = 395 \ \mu f$. As in the case of the FET amplifier, these values are usually adjusted to ones that are commercially available. We have at times specified element values to four significant figures. Usual components have tolerances of 5 to 10 percent. Thus such accuracy is usually neither necessary nor practical when components are specified. However, it is often desirable to use high accuracy for all computations to prevent large round off errors. The final results are then rounded off.

In the FET amplifier and the transistor amplifier, the high-frequency response was better (broader) than the specifications, while the midband gain just met specifications. In such cases, the shunting resistors can be increased somewhat so that both the midband gain and the high-frequency response exceed specifications.

9-10 LOW- AND HIGH-FREQUENCY COMPENSATION WITH *RC* NETWORKS

The frequency response of an *RC*-coupled amplifier can be improved if a *compensating network* is added to the coupling network. In general, compensating networks are *RC* networks, or utilize resonance phenomena and contain inductance, in addition to resistance and capacitance. We shall consider the *RC* compensating networks in this section and the others in the next two.

Low-frequency compensation Low-frequency-compensated RC-coupled FET and transistor amplifiers are shown in Fig. 9-28a and b, respectively. A linear model that is valid for both these amplifiers is shown in Fig. 9-28c. The bypass capacitors C_s and C_E are assumed to be short circuits at the signal frequencies. Their effect can be accounted for by using the procedures of Secs. 9-5 and 9-6. We can treat FET and transistor amplifiers simultaneously throughout much of this analysis. *However, because of differences in the impedance levels of these circuits, there will be some differences in the approximations that can be made.* The parameters of the equivalent circuit are related to the parameters of the amplifiers by the substitutions of Table 9-2.

The following assumptions will be made at the start: The impedance $\mathbf{Z}$ is such that $r \gg |Z|$, so r can be considered to be an open circuit; and that $R_d \gg 1/\omega C_d$ at all frequencies of interest, so R_d can be neglected. An analysis of this amplifier then yields

$$\frac{\mathbf{V}_2}{\mathbf{I}} = -\frac{(R_1 + 1/j\omega C_d)R_2}{R_1 + 1/j\omega C_d + R_2 + 1/j\omega C_c} \tag{9-94}$$

The input voltage and current of the FET and the transistor circuits both equal $\mathbf{I}$ multiplied by a constant that is independent of frequency. The output voltage is $\mathbf{V}_2$, and the output current, for the transistor circuit, is $-\mathbf{V}_2/R_i$. Thus, the frequency response of both the voltage gain and the current gain is given by Eq. (9-94). Manipulating this equation, we obtain

$$\frac{\mathbf{V}_2}{\mathbf{I}} = \frac{R_2}{1 + [(1 + j\omega R_2 C_c)/(1 + j\omega R_1 C_d)]C_d/C_c} \tag{9-95}$$

If

$$R_2 C_c = R_1 C_d \tag{9-96}$$

$$\frac{\mathbf{V}_2}{\mathbf{I}} = \frac{R_2}{1 + C_d/C_c} = \frac{R_1 R_2}{R_1 + R_2} \tag{9-97}$$

Equation (9-97) indicates that the frequency response is a constant, independent of frequency. However, C_c becomes an open circuit at zero fre-

Table 9-2

Equivalent circuit	FET amplifier	Transistor amplifier
r	r_d	$1/h_{oe}$
R_1	R_L	R_C
R_2	R_g	$R_B R_i/(R_B + R_i)$
$\mathbf{I}$	$g_m \mathbf{V}_1$	$h_{fe} \mathbf{I}_1$

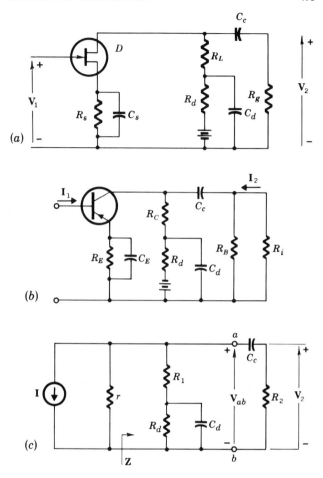

Fig. 9-28 Low-frequency-compensated *RC*-coupled amplifiers: (a) common-source FET amplifier; (b) common-emitter transistor amplifier; (c) a linear model that is valid for both. The bypass capacitors C_s and C_E are assumed to be short circuits.

quency; hence the gain should fall off. This discrepancy results because the approximations that were made are not valid at extremely low frequencies. For instance, at sufficiently low frequencies, $1/\omega C_d > R_d$, not $R_d \gg 1/\omega C_d$.

The preceding analysis provides some insight into the operation of compensated amplifiers. However, the approximations are not very valid. We shall now make some approximations that are very accurate for junction FET and vacuum-tube-pentode amplifiers. They may not be very accurate for the transistor.

Let us assume that

$$R_2 + \frac{1}{j\omega C_c} \gg R_1 + \frac{R_d}{1 + j\omega C_d R_d} \tag{9-98}$$

and

$$r \gg |Z| \tag{9-99}$$

Note that both these approximations can be valid down to zero frequency. The second of these relations allows us to ignore the effect of r, while the first indicates that the voltage $\mathbf{V}_{ab}$ is given approximately by

$$\mathbf{V}_{ab} \approx \mathbf{I}\left(R_1 + \frac{R_d}{1 + j\omega R_d C_d}\right) \tag{9-100}$$

Then, solving for $\mathbf{V}_2$, we obtain

$$\frac{\mathbf{V}_2}{\mathbf{I}} = \frac{R_1[1 + (R_1 + R_d)/j\omega C_d R_1 R_d]}{(1 + 1/j\omega C_d R_d)(1 + 1/j\omega C_c R_2)} \tag{9-101}$$

If $R_2 \gg R_1$, then $R_2 = R_{\text{low}}$ [see Eqs. (9-12) and (9-29)], so that $f_1 = 1/2\pi C_c R_2$ is the lower half-power frequency of the amplifier without compensation. In addition, let

$$f_3 = \frac{1}{2\pi C_d R_d} \tag{9-102}$$

and

$$f_4 = \frac{R_1 + R_d}{2\pi C_d R_1 R_d} \tag{9-103}$$

Making use of the fact that $\mathbf{V}_2/\mathbf{I} \approx R_1$ in the midband region, we can write

$$\frac{\mathbf{A}_{\text{low}}}{\mathbf{A}_{\text{mid}}} = \frac{1 - jf_4/f}{(1 - jf_3/f)(1 - jf_1/f)} \tag{9-104}$$

Let

$$R_1' = \frac{R_1 R_d}{R_1 + R_d} \tag{9-105}$$

If $R_1' C_d = R_2 C_c$, then $f_1 = f_4$ and

$$\frac{\mathbf{A}_{\text{low}}}{\mathbf{A}_{\text{mid}}} = \frac{1}{1 - jf_3/f} \tag{9-106}$$

This has the same form as that of the low-frequency response of the uncompensated amplifier, except that f_1 has been replaced by f_3. If we are to achieve any improvement through compensation, $f_3 < f_1$. Since $R_d > R_1'$ and $f_1 = f_4$, then $f_1 > f_3$ and some improvement will always be obtained.

If $r \gg R_1$ and $R_1 \ll R_2$, there will usually be values of R_d for which R_d is greater than R_1' and for which the relations (9-98) and (9-99) will be met. Then there can be substantial improvement in the low-frequency response.

At the start of this section we mentioned that the differences in impedance levels in the FET and transistor circuits produced differences in the operation of these circuits. We shall consider these now. In the junction FET amplifier, in general, $r_d \gg R_L$ and $R_g \gg R_L$. Thus, relations (9-98) and (9-99) can be easily satisfied. In the MOSFET, r_d is not as large as in the junction FET. Thus, the approximations may not be valid. (However, there are circumstances when they are.) In the transistor amplifier, we cannot, in general, state that $R_i \gg R_C$, so the approximate solution of Eq. (9-104) may be of limited use in transistor amplifiers. However, the compensation procedure itself may be useful.

If $R_1'C_d = R_2 C_c$ and $R_1' \ll R_2$, then $C_d \gg C_c$. The size of C_c is usually limited by its leakage resistance and by its stray capacitance to the common lead. The capacitor C_d is not limited in these ways; hence it can usually be made very much larger than C_c.

We have assumed that $f_4 = f_1$. If the value of f_4 is adjusted so that $f_4 > f_1$, then the frequency response will actually rise before it starts to fall off. This is sometimes done to partially account for the effects of source-bias impedance, or emitter compensating impedance. This procedure also will partially compensate for a coupling network in another amplifier stage.

In a multistage amplifier, all the stages usually use the same power supply. Since the impedance of the power supply cannot be zero, some components of the signal will appear across the power-supply terminals. This can result in undesirable signal feedback. The circuit consisting of R_d and C_d will attenuate any alternating voltage across the power-supply terminals and thus tend to prevent the output of one amplifier stage from being coupled back into another one. For this reason, the network consisting of R_d and C_d is called a *decoupling filter*. The decoupling filter also will tend to reduce the effect of any power-line frequency components that may be present in the output of the power supply.

High-frequency compensation   Consider the circuit of Fig. 9-29, which could represent the linear model of an amplifier, whose shunt capacitances can be neglected. Solving for $\mathbf{I}_2/\mathbf{I}$, we obtain

$$\frac{\mathbf{I}_2}{\mathbf{I}} = \frac{r(1 + j\omega C_1 R_1)}{(r + R_1 + R_2)[1 + j\omega C_1 R_1(r + R_2)/(r + R_1 + R_2)]} \qquad (9\text{-}107)$$

In the low- and mid-frequency regions, the capacitor C_1 can be considered to be an open circuit. Thus, for both the voltage gain and the current gain

$$\frac{\mathbf{A}_{\text{high}}}{\mathbf{A}_{\text{mid}}} = \frac{1 + jf/f_5}{1 + jf/f_6} \qquad (9\text{-}108)$$

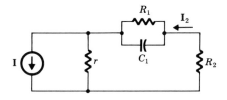

Fig. 9-29   A model of a high-frequency
RC-compensating network.

where

$$f_5 = \frac{1}{2\pi C_1 R_1} \tag{9-109}$$

and

$$f_6 = \frac{r + R_1 + R_2}{2\pi C_1 R_1 (r + R_2)} \tag{9-110}$$

A typical plot of $|A_{\text{high}}/A_{\text{mid}}|_{\text{db}}$ is shown in Fig. 9-30.   The asymptotic slope between f_5 and f_6 is 6 db/octave or 20 db/decade.   The response in the high-frequency region is greater than the response in the mid-frequency region. Actually, when the compensating network consisting of the parallel combination of R_1 and C_1 is placed into the circuit, the midband gain is reduced while the high-frequency gain is unaffected.

Suppose that the current generator I is frequency-dependent, as it would be if the high-frequency response of some stages preceding this one fell off; then Eq. (9-108) could become

$$\frac{A_{\text{high}}}{A_{\text{mid}}} = \frac{1}{1 + jf/f_a} \frac{1 + jf/f_5}{1 + jf/f_6} \tag{9-111}$$

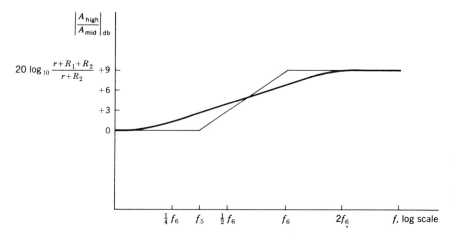

Fig. 9-30   The amplitude response of the RC-compensating network of Fig. 9-29.

Then, if the circuit parameters are adjusted so that $f_5 = f_a$, we have

$$\frac{A_{\text{high}}}{A_{\text{mid}}} = \frac{1}{1 + jf/f_6} \qquad (9\text{-}112)$$

The upper half-power frequency has been increased from f_a to f_6, and the midband gain has been reduced by the factor $f_5/f_6 = f_a/f_6$. Thus, the gain-bandwidth product remains constant. [Note that if there were no compensation, R_1 would be replaced by a short circuit. Then the midband gain would be $r/(R_2 + r)$. Thus the loss in midband gain due to compensation is f_5/f_6.]

This compensating network could partially offset the effect of the shunting capacitance in a FET or vacuum-tube amplifier. However, these results can be more easily obtained by reducing R_{sh}. In addition, we shall see in the next sections that the addition of inductance will permit us to compensate for C_{sh} somewhat without sacrificing midband gain. If shunt capacitances are present, then the results of the previous analysis are only approximate.

9-11 HIGH-FREQUENCY COMPENSATION USING SHUNT-PEAKED NETWORKS

In this section we shall discuss a procedure whereby the high-frequency response can be improved without reducing the midband gain. The analysis and approximations will apply to FET amplifiers but usually will not be valid for transistor amplifiers. In the next section we shall discuss shunt-peaked transistor amplifiers.

The circuit we shall use, see Fig. 9-31, is called a *shunt-peaked* network since the combination of R_L in series with the inductance L forms a very low Q coil that is in parallel with C_{sh}. Compensation of this type is usually needed only for relatively broadband amplifiers. Consequently, these amplifiers are also called *shunt-peaked video amplifiers*. At low and mid-frequencies, $R_L \gg \omega L$ for the usual values of inductance, and the response of the amplifier is independent of L. A model that is valid in the high-frequency region is given in Fig. 9-31b. The capacitor C_{sh} represents the total shunting capacitance and is defined by Eq. (9-7). In analyzing this circuit, we shall assume that

$$r_d \gg R_L + j\omega L \qquad (9\text{-}113)$$

and

$$R_g \gg R_L + j\omega L \qquad (9\text{-}114)$$

for frequencies from zero to several times the upper half-power frequency of

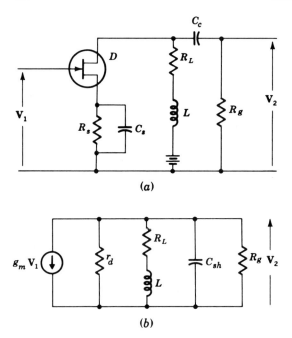

Fig. 9-31 Shunt-peaked amplifiers: (*a*) common-source FET amplifier and (*b*) its linear model.

the uncompensated amplifier. These assumptions are usually very good. If the inequalities of relations (9-113) and (9-114) hold, we can write

$$\frac{V_2}{V_1} = \frac{-g_m(R_L + j\omega L)/j\omega C_{\text{sh}}}{R_L + j(\omega L - 1/\omega C_{\text{sh}})} = \frac{-g_m R_L(1 + j\omega L/R_L)}{1 - \omega^2 L C_{\text{sh}} + j\omega R_L C_{\text{sh}}} \tag{9-115}$$

For small values of ω, which would be encountered in the mid- and low-frequency regions, $V_2/V_1 = -g_m R_L$. Thus, we have

$$\frac{A_{v,\text{high}}}{A_{v,\text{mid}}} = \frac{1 + j\omega L/R_L}{1 - \omega^2 L C_{\text{sh}} + j\omega R_L C_{\text{sh}}} \tag{9-116}$$

The easiest way to obtain useful information from Eq. (9-116) is to plot its amplitude and phase angle versus frequency. Before doing this, we shall make some substitutions that present the results in a more general fashion. Let

$$f_2 = \frac{1}{2\pi R_L C_{\text{sh}}} \tag{9-117}$$

Since $R_L \ll R_g$ and $R_L \ll r$, then $R_L \approx R_{\text{sh}}$ [see Eqs. (9-5) and (9-10)], and f_2 is the upper half-power frequency of the uncompensated amplifier. The only other parameter that we need to know is the Q of the RL circuit at the frequency f_2. That is,

$$Q_2 = \frac{2\pi f_2 L}{R_L} = \frac{\omega_2 L}{R_L} \tag{9-118}$$

Then, after substituting and manipulating, we obtain

$$\frac{\mathbf{A}_{v,\text{high}}}{\mathbf{A}_{v,\text{mid}}} = \frac{1 + jQ_2(f/f_2)}{1 - Q_2(f/f_2)^2 + j(f/f_2)} \tag{9-119}$$

or, equivalently,

$$\left|\frac{\mathbf{A}_{v,\text{high}}}{\mathbf{A}_{v,\text{mid}}}\right| = \sqrt{\frac{1 + Q_2{}^2(f/f_2)^2}{[1 - Q_2(f/f_2)^2]^2 + j(f/f_2)^2}} \tag{9-120}$$

and

$$\measuredangle \frac{A_{v,\text{high}}}{A_{v,\text{mid}}} = -\tan^{-1}\left\{\frac{f}{f_2}\left[1 - Q_2 + Q_2{}^2\left(\frac{f}{f_2}\right)^2\right]\right\} \tag{9-121}$$

A plot of $|A_{v,\text{high}}/A_{v,\text{mid}}|$ versus frequency, with Q_2 as a parameter, is given in Fig. 9-32.[5] When $Q_2 = 0$, the response is that of the uncompensated amplifier. As Q_2 increases, the bandwidth increases. $|A_{v,\text{high}}/A_{v,\text{mid}}|$ falls off monotonically with frequency for values of Q_2 between 0 and 0.414. The

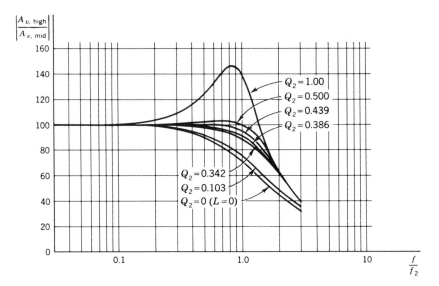

Fig. 9-32 Curves of the amplitude response of the shunt-peaked amplifiers of Fig. 9-31. (*Adapted with permission from A. V. Bedford and G. L. Fredendall, Transient Response of Multistage Video-frequency Amplifiers, Proc. IRE, vol. 27, pp. 277–284, 1939.*)

curve for $Q_2 = 0.439$ has an extremely small rise. If absolutely no rise can be tolerated, $Q_2 = 0.414$ should be used. For values of $Q_2 > 0.414$, the amplitude response rises and then falls. The upper half-power frequency tends to increase as Q_2 increases. However, if Q_2 is made too large, then the rise in the frequency response usually introduces a frequency distortion that is more severe than the one it corrects. If a maximally flat frequency response is desired, then $Q_2 = 0.414$ is chosen. The value of $Q_2 = 0.5$ is used at times, since this increases the upper half-power frequency without causing the gain to rise too much above the midband value.

The discussion of the previous paragraph pertains only to the amplitude response. If phase distortion is considered, then other restrictions are placed on the value of Q_2. In general, phase distortion occurs when the phase shift of the amplifier does not vary linearly with frequency (see Sec. 8-7). Thus, $\angle(A_{v,\text{high}}/A_{v,\text{mid}})/f$ should be constant. If there is no frequency distortion, then the time delay τ_d is given by [see Eq. (8-23)]

$$\tau_d = \frac{-\angle(A_{v,\text{high}}/A_{v,\text{mid}})}{\omega} \tag{9-122}$$

If τ_d is plotted, then departure from a constant is an indication of the amount of phase distortion. Since we usually plot normalized frequency f/f_2, the expression for τ_d will be normalized in the following way

$$\tau_{dn} = -\frac{\omega_2}{\omega} \angle \frac{A_{v,\text{high}}}{A_{v,\text{mid}}} = -\frac{\angle(A_{v,\text{high}}/A_{v,\text{mid}})}{f/f_2} \tag{9-123}$$

We shall call τ_{dn} the *normalized relative time delay*; it is plotted versus frequency, with Q_2 as a parameter, in Fig. 9-33.[5] As Q_2 is increased from 0 to 0.342, the phase distortion, or the *delay distortion*, is reduced. The value of τ_{dn} decreases monotonically with frequency for these values of Q_2. As Q_2 is increased above 0.342, the delay distortion increases.

The optimum value of Q_2 depends upon the criterion used in choosing it. If amplitude distortion is the primary consideration, then a value of 0.414 to 0.5 might be used. If delay distortion is of utmost importance, then a value of 0.342 would be used. If both amplitude and delay distortion are weighted equally, then a value of Q_2 between 0.342 and 0.414 is usually used. We shall see that if transient response is considered, other criteria are used in choosing Q_2.

When amplifiers are cascaded, their amplitude responses are multiplied and their phase shifts are added. Thus, the relative response of a cascade of amplifiers can be obtained from Figs. 9-32 and 9-33. If a value of Q_2 is chosen such that the amplitude response is not monotonic and if identical stages are cascaded, then the nonmonotonicity will be exaggerated. Hence, if many stages are used, it is desirable to keep Q_2 equal to or less than 0.414.

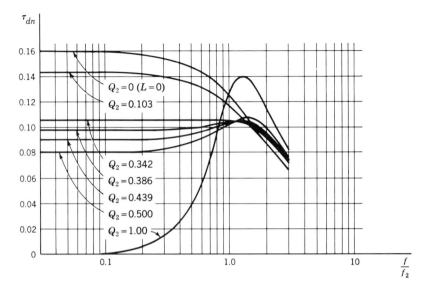

Fig. 9-33 Curves of the normalized relative time delay of the amplifiers of Fig. 9-31. The units of τ_{dn} are ω_2 sec. (*Adapted with permission from A. V. Bedford and G. L. Fredendall, Transient Response of Multistage Video-frequency Amplifiers, Proc. IRE, vol. 27, pp. 277–284, 1939.*)

9-12 A PROCEDURE FOR HIGH-FREQUENCY COMPENSATION OF THE COMMON-EMITTER TRANSISTOR AMPLIFIER

The equations of the last section often are of limited use in analyzing the high-frequency response of cascaded common-emitter transistor amplifiers since the approximations made there are usually not valid. A more accurate and general compensating procedure, due to Gärtner,[6] will be presented here. We shall consider a cascade of identical amplifiers such as that shown in Fig. 9-34, where $\mathbf{Z}$ and $\mathbf{Y}$ are the compensating networks. Their forms will be considered subsequently. Note that $\mathbf{Y}$ must be such that the bias voltage can be applied to the transistor. In addition, $\mathbf{Z}$ and $\mathbf{Y}$ should be such that the low- and mid-frequency performance of the amplifier is unaffected by the compensation. For increased accuracy, at high frequencies, we shall use the hybrid-pi linear model of Fig. 6-42. A linear model for one stage of the amplifier is as shown in Fig. 9-35. Since this is a high-frequency analysis, C_c and C_s are assumed to be short circuits at all frequencies of interest. In addition, the impedance of $R_B = R_{B1}R_{B2}/(R_{B1} + R_{B2})$ will usually be much greater than the elements shunting it. Thus, it can be ignored. The input impedance of the next transistor stage is designated $\mathbf{Y}_i$. The input impedance given in Fig. 9-13 is used here. That is, $C_e = C_{b'e} + C_{b'c}(1 - A'_{v,\text{mid}})$ [see Eq. (9-39)]. Actually, this is an approximation since $A'_v = \mathbf{V}_2/\mathbf{V}_1$ should be

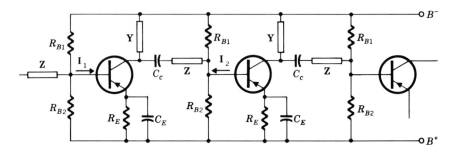

Fig. 9-34 A cascade of compensated common-emitter transistor amplifiers.

used rather than its midband value, but the use of $A'_{v,\text{mid}}$ simplifies the design equations. However, after a trial design is obtained, the result should be checked by analyzing the *total* amplifier using the hybrid-pi model of Fig. 6-42 for *each* transistor.

For the last amplifier in the stage, $\mathbf{Z}_i = R_i$, the load resistance. In addition, even for the input impedance of a transistor, R_i represents the midband value of $\mathbf{Z}_i$.

Now let us apply nodal analysis to Fig. 9-35. This yields

$$\mathbf{I}_1 = [g_{b'e} + g_{b'c} + j\omega(C_{b'e} + C_{b'c})]\mathbf{V}_1 - (g_{b'c} + j\omega C_{b'c})\mathbf{V}_2 \qquad (9\text{-}124a)$$

$$0 = (g_m - g_{b'c} - j\omega C_{b'c})\mathbf{V}_1 + (g_{ce} + g_{b'c} + j\omega C_{b'c} + \mathbf{Y} + \mathbf{Y}_1)\mathbf{V}_2 \qquad (9\text{-}124b)$$

where $g = 1/r$ and

$$\mathbf{Y}_1 = \frac{1}{\mathbf{Z} + \mathbf{Z}_i} \qquad (9\text{-}125)$$

Then,

$$\mathbf{I}_2 = -\mathbf{V}_2\mathbf{Y}_1 \qquad (9\text{-}126)$$

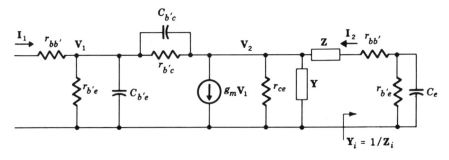

Fig. 9-35 A linear model of one stage of the cascade of Fig. 9-34. The bypass and coupling capacitors are considered to be short circuits at all frequencies of interest.

Then, solving Eqs. (9-124), we obtain

$$\mathbf{A}_{i,high} = \frac{(g_m - g_{b'c} - j\omega C_{b'c})\mathbf{Y}_1}{[g_{b'e} + g_{b'c} + j\omega(C_{b'e} + C_{b'c})](g_{ce} + g_{b'c} + j\omega C_{b'c} + \mathbf{Y} + \mathbf{Y}_1)}$$
$$+ (g_{b'c} + j\omega C_{b'c})(g_m - g_{b'c} - j\omega C_{b'c}) \quad (9\text{-}127)$$

If $\mathbf{Y}$ and $\mathbf{Z}$ are left as general terms, it becomes extremely difficult to optimize this expression. To simplify the procedure, we shall assume a specific value for both $\mathbf{Y}$ and $\mathbf{Z}$. Consider that $\mathbf{Y}$ has the same form that it does in the shunt-peaked amplifier, a resistance in series with an inductance

$$\mathbf{Y} = \frac{1}{R_1 + j\omega L_1} \quad (9\text{-}128)$$

We choose $\mathbf{Z}$ to be just an inductance

$$\mathbf{Z} = j\omega L_2 \quad (9\text{-}129)$$

The value of $A_{i,mid}$ can be obtained from Eq. (9-127) by substituting Eqs. (9-128) and (9-129) and then letting ω approach zero. Thus,

$$A_{i,mid} = \frac{(g_m - g_{b'c})G_i}{g_{b'e}(g_{ce} + g_{b'c} + G_1 + G_i) + g_{b'c}(g_{ce} + G_1 + g_m + G_i)}$$
$$(9\text{-}130)$$

where $G_i = 1/R_i$ and $G_1 = 1/R_1$. Then,

$$\frac{\mathbf{A}_{i,high}}{A_{i,mid}} =$$

$$\frac{\mathbf{Y}_i(g_m - g_{b'c} - j\omega C_{b'c})\dfrac{(g_{ce} + g_{b'c} + G_1 + G_i)g_{b'e} + g_{b'c}(g_{ce} + G_1 + g_m + G_i)}{(g_m - g_{b'c})G_i}}{(g_{b'e} + j\omega C_{b'e})\left[(1 + j\omega L_2 \mathbf{Y}_i)\dfrac{g_{ce} + g_{b'c} + j\omega C_{b'c} + G_1}{1 + j\omega L_1 G_1} + \mathbf{Y}_i\right]}$$
$$+ (g_{b'c} + j\omega C_{b'c})\left[(1 + j\omega L_2 \mathbf{Y}_i)\frac{g_m + g_{ce} + G_1}{1 + j\omega L_1 G_1} + \mathbf{Y}_i\right]$$
$$(9\text{-}131)$$

where

$$\mathbf{Y}_i = \frac{1}{r_{bb'} + r_{b'e}/(1 + j\omega r_{b'e}C_e)} \quad (9\text{-}132)$$

Often, these equations can be simplified since $g_{b'c}$ and g_{ce} can be considered to be zero. In any event, Eq. (9-131) is too complex to obtain any useful design relations, and there are too many variables to permit plotting a set of universal curves as was done for the shunt-peaked amplifier. Instead, the following procedure can be used.

Choose a particular transistor; its parameters are known constants. Substitute them in Eqs. (9-130) and (9-131). The only unknowns are

$G_1 = 1/R_1$, L_1, and L_2. Now choose the highest frequency of interest, f_0. At this frequency, the design requirements should specify $|A_{i,high}/A_{i,mid}|$ to be some fraction of unity. Call this fraction δ. Thus, manipulate Eq. (9-131) to be of the form

$$\delta = \left| \frac{A_{i,high}}{A_{i,mid}} \right|_{f=f_0} \tag{9-133}$$

Thus, we obtain an equation which contains (and relates) the unknowns R_1, L_1, and L_2. The value of R_1 can be obtained from Eq. (9-130). Manipulation of this equation yields

$$G_1 = \frac{1}{R_1}$$

$$= \frac{G_i(g_m - g_{b'c}) - A_{i,mid}[g_{b'e}(g_{ce} + g_{b'c} + G_i) + g_{b'c}(g_{ce} + g_m + G_i)]}{(g_{b'e} + g_{b'c})A_{i,mid}} \tag{9-134}$$

Equation (9-134) does not uniquely determine R_1, since $A_{i,mid}$ is the midband current gain per stage and depends upon the number of stages. Start by trying one stage. Substitute the value of R_1 obtained from Eq. (9-134) into Eq. (9-133). That is, in Eq. (9-133), $|A_{i,high}/A_{i,mid}|_{f=f_0}$ represents the magnitude of the right-hand side of Eq. (9-131) where the known $\omega_0 = 2\pi f_0$ has been substituted for ω. This then yields an equation that relates L_1 to L_2. Curves of $|A_{i,high}/A_{i,mid}|$ should be plotted using values of L_1 and L_2 which satisfy this equation. This is done to determine the optimum values of L_1 and L_2. The shape of the resulting frequency response must be suitable; e.g., there should not be large peaks, and the magnitude of the normalized response should not be less than δ in the frequency range for any frequencies less than f_0. If this can be done, then the design is complete. It is assumed that R_1, L_1, and L_2 are real positive constants. If R_1 is negative, the required gain per stage is too large. This can be corrected by using more stages or by obtaining a transistor with a larger value of g_m. Note that even if R_1 is positive, the value of L_1 or L_2 obtained may be imaginary or negative. Even if they are real and positive, the shape of the response may be unacceptable. In such cases more stages should be tried, since this reduces the value of R_1 and may reduce the effect of the shunting capacitors. As the number of stages increases, the requirements on the frequency response of any one stage also increase. If Eq. (9-133) is valid for any one stage, and if n stages are used, we have

$$\delta_n = \delta^{1/n} \tag{9-135}$$

Now, δ_n replaces δ in Eq. (9-133). This compensation procedure may not always work; if it does not, a new transistor with a higher g_m and/or lower shunting capacitances should be used.

This procedure did not consider the phase shift at all.   Once the final form of the response is attained, the phase distortion should be checked to see if it is excessive.   An alternative procedure would be to replace Eq. (9-133) with an equation for the phase shift.

Procedures of this type can be extended to more complex coupling networks.   The algebraic manipulations become more difficult as the complexity of the network is increased.   Such complex coupling networks are used in both FET and transistor circuits, where they provide some improvement over the simple shunt-peaked circuits.

The network considered here used both series and shunt peaking.   If only a shunt-peaked amplifier is desired, then $L_2 = 0$ should be substituted into all the relations of the section.

9-13   POLES AND ZEROS

We have thus far characterized frequency response by the behavior of the amplitude response and the phase shift as a function of ω.   In this section we shall consider a different approach.   For the circuits that we have considered, the only frequency-dependent parameters encountered are inductance, capacitance, and the variation of α with frequency.   In all these cases, the term ω never appears by itself but is always multiplied by $j = \sqrt{-1}$.   For instance, in the case of an inductance,

$$\mathbf{Z}_L = j\omega L \quad \text{and} \quad \mathbf{Y}_L = \frac{1}{j\omega L}$$

for a capacitance

$$\mathbf{Z}_C = \frac{1}{j\omega C} \quad \text{and} \quad \mathbf{Y}_C = j\omega C$$

and for a transistor

$$\alpha = \frac{\alpha_0}{1 + j\omega/\omega_\alpha} \qquad \beta = \frac{\beta_0}{1 + j\omega/\omega_\beta} \qquad \mathbf{h}_{fe} = \frac{h_{fe}}{1 + j\omega/\omega_\beta} \qquad \text{etc.}$$

The response of networks containing these elements will be made up of the algebraic combinations of terms of this type.   Thus whenever ω appears in such networks, it will be multiplied by j.   Hence, we can always make the substitution

$$s = j\omega \tag{9-136}$$

and replace all the $j\omega$ terms.   Then, for an inductance

$$\mathbf{Z}_L = sL \qquad \mathbf{Y}_L = \frac{1}{sL} \tag{9-137a}$$

for a capacitance

$$\mathbf{Z}_C = \frac{1}{sC} \qquad \mathbf{Y}_C = sC \tag{9-137b}$$

and, for the transistor

$$\alpha = \frac{\alpha_0}{1 + s/\omega_\alpha} \qquad \beta = \frac{\beta_0}{1 + s/\omega_\beta} \qquad \mathbf{h}_{fe} = \frac{h_{fe}}{1 + s/\omega_\beta} \qquad \text{etc.} \tag{9-138}$$

The solution of the mesh or nodal equations of a network can always be expressed as the ratio of two determinants. After they are expanded and any fractions are cleared, the solution will be in the form of the ratio of two polynomials in the variable s. For instance, Eq. (9-11) can be written as

$$\frac{\mathbf{A}_{v,\text{high}}}{\mathbf{A}_{v,\text{mid}}} = \frac{1}{1 + s/\omega_2} \tag{9-139}$$

and Eq. (9-119) becomes

$$\frac{\mathbf{A}_{\text{high}}}{\mathbf{A}_{\text{mid}}} = \frac{1 + (Q_2/\omega_2)s}{1 + (1/\omega_2)s + (Q_2/\omega_2{}^2)s^2} \tag{9-140}$$

The general form of the response of a network can be written as

$$\mathbf{A}(s) = \frac{a_n s^n + a_{n-1} s^{n-1} + \cdots + a_1 s + a_0}{b_m s^m + b_{m-1} s^{m-1} + \cdots + b_1 s + b_0} \tag{9-141}$$

The s in the parentheses indicates that $\mathbf{A}$ *is a function of the variable* s. In addition, the a_i, $i = 1, 2, \ldots, n$, and the b_k, $k = 1, 2, \ldots, m$, are real numbers that are independent of frequency and that depend only upon the parameters of the network, i.e., the resistance, inductance, capacitance, transconductance, low-frequency short-circuit current gain, etc. We can always express a polynomial in terms of its roots and a constant multiplier. Thus,

$$\mathbf{A}(s) = K \frac{(s - s_1)(s - s_3) \cdots (s - s_{2n-1})}{(s - s_2)(s - s_4) \cdots (s - s_{2m})} \tag{9-142}$$

Note that the roots of the numerator are given odd-numbered subscripts, while the roots of the denominator have even-numbered subscripts. The roots are constants which depend only upon the parameters of the network. They need not necessarily be real numbers; they can be imaginary or complex. Since the coefficients of Eq. (9-141) are real, then if the roots of the numerator or the denominator are complex or imaginary numbers, they must occur in conjugate pairs.

The frequency response of Eq. (9-142) does not depend upon the value of the constant multiplier and is completely specified if we know the location of the roots of the numerator and the denominator. The location of these roots can be marked on a two-dimensional plot. The axis of real numbers is labeled σ and is called the σ *axis*. The axis of imaginary numbers is labeled $j\omega$ and is called the $j\omega$ axis. Note that if s is replaced by $j\omega$, the expression for the frequency response results. Usually, the roots of the numerator are marked with circles, while the roots of the denominator are marked with $\times$'s. Such a plot is shown in Fig. 9-36. A polynomial is zero when it is evaluated at one of its roots. Thus, at a root of the numerator $|A|$ is zero. Therefore, the roots of the numerator are called *zeros*. At a root of the denominator $|A|$ will be infinite. These roots are called *poles*. A diagram such as that of Fig. 9-36 is called a *pole-zero diagram* or a *pole-zero plot*. The entire plane of the plot is called the *s plane*. The $j\omega$ axis divides it into a *left half-plane* and a *right half-plane*. We shall discuss the significance of these half-planes subsequently.

In order to obtain the frequency response we replace s by $j\omega$, so that for Eq. (9-142)

$$\mathbf{A}(j\omega) = K\frac{(j\omega - s_1)(j\omega - s_3) \cdots (j\omega - s_{2n-1})}{(j\omega - s_2)(j\omega - s_4) \cdots (j\omega - s_m)} \tag{9-143}$$

Thus

$$|A(j\omega)| = K\frac{|j\omega - s_1|\,|j\omega - s_3| \cdots |j\omega - s_{2n-1}|}{|j\omega - s_2|\,|j\omega - s_4| \cdots |j\omega - s_{2m}|} \tag{9-144}$$

and

$$\angle A(j\omega) = \angle(j\omega - s_1) + \angle(j\omega - s_3) + \cdots + \angle(j\omega - s_{2n-1})$$
$$- [\angle(j\omega - s_2) + \angle(j\omega - s_4) + \cdots$$
$$+ \angle(j\omega - s_{2m})] \tag{9-145}$$

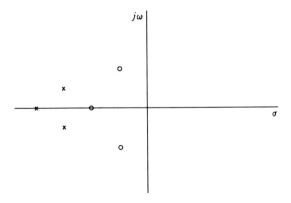

Fig. 9-36 A typical pole-zero diagram.

If the pole-zero plot is available, these magnitudes and angles can be calculated by means of the very simple graphical construction of Fig. 9-37. The frequency ω_0 represents any one frequency, and s_v represents either a pole or a zero. The length of the vector drawn from s_v to $j\omega_0$ is equal to $|j\omega_0 - s_v|$ and its angle is $\angle(j\omega_0 - s_v)$. To obtain the frequency response at any frequency ω_0, draw vectors from all the poles and zeros to the point $j\omega_0$. The lengths of the vectors and their phase angles are then measured. The amplitude response is obtained by multiplying the lengths of all the vectors from the zeros and then dividing this product by the product of the lengths of all the vectors from the poles. The phase shift is equal to the sum of the angles of all the vectors drawn from the zeros minus the sum of the angles of all the vectors drawn from the poles.

If a pole or a zero is very close to the $j\omega$ axis, then as ω_0 passes along the axis near the pole the length of the vector $j\omega_0 - s_v$ and its angle will change very rapidly. If s_v is very far from $j\omega_0$, then the magnitude and angle of the vector will vary only slightly as ω_0 varies. Thus, the response at any frequency ω_0 is determined primarily by the poles and zeros near $j\omega_0$. At times the variations due to poles and zeros that are the furthest from $j\omega_0$ can be neglected.

Note that there may be multiple poles and zeros. That is, some of the roots of the numerator and/or the denominator may be multiple. These can be indicated by multiple circles or ×'s on the pole-zero plot. The above discussion holds for multiple poles and zeros. Each pole or zero is counted in accordance with its multiplicity. For example, if there is a second-order pole at $s = s_a$, then Eqs. (9-144) and (9-145) would contain a term $|j\omega - s_a|^2$ and $2\angle(j\omega - s_a)$, respectively.

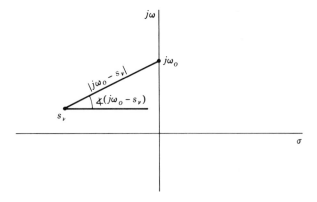

Fig. 9-37 A graphical construction useful in determining the frequency response.

Let us now consider the pole-zero diagram of some of the amplifiers we have considered. A typical low-frequency response is of the form

$$\frac{A_{\text{low}}}{A_{\text{mid}}} = \frac{1}{1 + \omega_1/s} = \frac{s}{s + \omega_1} \tag{9-146}$$

Its pole-zero pattern is given in Fig. 9-38a. The zero at the origin causes the gain to be zero at zero frequency. As ω_0 increases, the lengths of the vectors drawn from the pole and from the zero increase and approach each other so that at mid- and high frequencies the gain approaches unity.

The high-frequency response of the RC-coupled amplifier stages is

$$\frac{A_{i,\text{high}}}{A_{i,\text{low}}} = \frac{1}{1 + s/\omega_a} \frac{1}{1 + s/\omega_b} = \frac{\omega_a \omega_b}{(s + \omega_a)(s + \omega_b)} \tag{9-147}$$

The pole-zero plot is shown in Fig. 9-38b. The response in the low- and mid-frequency regions is essentially constant, and the phase angle is zero, because at these frequencies the lengths of the vectors drawn from the poles at $-\omega_a$ and $-\omega_b$ to the $j\omega$ axis remain almost constant at the lengths ω_a and ω_b, respectively, and their phase angles are almost zero. In the high-frequency region, the lengths of the vectors and their phase angles increase as ω increases. Figure 9-38a and b are not drawn to the same scale. In general, ω_a or ω_b is usually 100 or more times ω_1.

An unbypassed bias impedance will produce a response of the form

$$\frac{A}{A_{\text{mid}}} = \frac{s + \omega_3}{s + \omega_4} \tag{9-148}$$

Its pole-zero plot is shown in Fig. 9-38c. At low frequencies, such as ω_{01}, the vector drawn from the pole is much longer than the vector drawn from the zero. This results in diminished response. At higher frequencies, such as ω_{02}, the length and angle of both vectors approach each other, and the response approaches unity.

Figure 9-38d shows the pole-zero diagrams for a low-frequency-compensated amplifier. From Eq. (9-104) we have

$$\frac{A_{\text{low}}}{A_{\text{mid}}} = \frac{s(s + \omega_4)}{(s + \omega_3)(s + \omega_4)} \tag{9-149}$$

When the network is adjusted so that the $f_4 = f_1$, a zero cancels a pole, so that the pole-zero diagram then has the same form as that of Fig. 9-38a. Since $\omega_3 < \omega_1$, the frequency response will be improved.

Let us now obtain the pole-zero diagram of the shunt-peaked amplifier. From Eq. (9-119) we have

$$\frac{A_{\text{high}}}{A_{\text{mid}}} = \frac{\omega_2(s + \omega_2/Q_2)}{s^2 + (\omega_2/Q_2)s + \omega_2{}^2/Q_2} \tag{9-150}$$

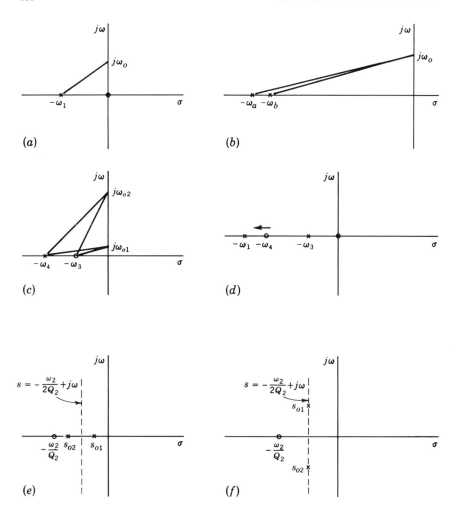

Fig. 9-38 Pole-zero diagrams for typical amplifiers: (*a*) low frequency; (*b*) two-stage amplifier high-frequency response; (*c*) unbypassed bias lead; (*d*) low-frequency compensation; (*e*) shunt peaking with $Q < 0.25$; and (*f*) shunt peaking with $Q > 0.25$.

The roots of the denominator are given by

$$s_2, s_4 = -\frac{\omega_2}{2Q_2} \pm \sqrt{\frac{\omega_2{}^2}{4Q_2}\left(\frac{1}{Q_2} - 4\right)} \qquad (9\text{-}151)$$

If $Q_2 < \frac{1}{4}$, then the poles will be real and lie on the negative σ axis on either side of the point $-\omega_2/2Q_2$, as shown in Fig. 9-38*e*. As Q_2 increases the poles move along the σ axis toward the point $-\omega_2/2Q_2$. When $Q_2 = \frac{1}{4}$, there is a double pole at $-\omega_2/2Q_2$. As Q_2 increases further, the poles become complex and move along the vertical line whose equation is

$$s = \frac{-\omega_2}{2Q_2} + j\omega \qquad (9\text{-}152)$$

(see Fig. 9-38f). At first glance, it may appear that the nonmonotonicity in the amplitude or the phase response could be related to the fact that the poles do not lie on the negative σ axis. However, this is not a *simple* function of the location of the poles and zeros.

9-14 TRANSIENT RESPONSE

The ultimate reason for considering the frequency response of an amplifier is to determine the amount of distortion of the output signal (see Sec. 8-7) which is a function of time. That is, the frequency response can be utilized to determine the output as a function of time in response to an arbitrary input. The two signals can then be compared. The response of an amplifier as a function of time is called the *transient response*. In this section we shall consider distortion on a transient basis and relate it to the frequency distortion.

An irregular input signal applied to a network will produce an irregular output signal. It is then difficult, unless tedious measurements are made, to estimate the distortion. On the other hand, if a regular input signal is applied, any distortion in the output waveform will be readily discernible. An input signal that is commonly used for such testing is the *unit step*. This is symbolically represented by $u(t)$ and is given by

$$u(t) = \begin{cases} 1 & t > 0 \\ 0 & t < 0 \end{cases} \qquad (9\text{-}153)$$

Figure 9-39 illustrates such a function. The response of a network to a voltage or current whose input waveform is $u(t)$ is called the *unit-step response*. We shall illustrate this with the circuit of Fig. 9-40a, which is a simple form

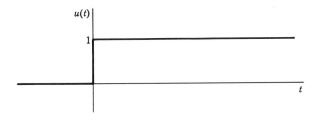

Fig. 9-39 The unit-step function.

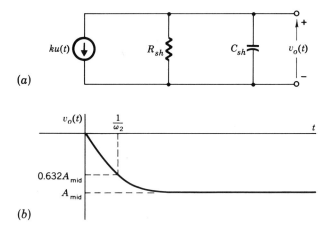

(a)

(b)

Fig. 9-40 (a) A simple high-frequency linear model with a
unit-step input and (b) its unit-step response.

of the high-frequency model of Sec. 9-1.   The differential equation for this
circuit is

$$-k = \frac{1}{R_{\text{sh}}} v_o + C_{\text{sh}} \frac{dv_o}{dt} \tag{9-154}$$

Solving, and assuming that there is no initial stored charge, we obtain

$$v_o(t) = -kR_{\text{sh}}(1 - e^{-t/R_{\text{sh}}C_{\text{sh}}}) \tag{9-155}$$

but $-kR_{\text{sh}} = A_{\text{mid}}$ and $\omega_2 = 1/R_{\text{sh}}C_{\text{sh}}$.   Thus,

$$v_o(t) = A_{\text{mid}}(1 - e^{-t\omega_2}) \tag{9-156}$$

This voltage is illustrated in Fig. 9-40b.   The t in the parentheses indicates

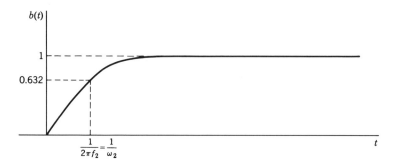

Fig. 9-41 The normalized unit-step response of the amplifier of Fig.
9-40a.

that v_o is a function of time. The waveform approaches a steady magnitude of $|A_{\text{mid}}|$, and the time constant is $1/\omega_2$, the reciprocal of the upper half-power angular frequency. To normalize, we often plot the output divided by A_{mid}. This will be denoted by the symbol $b(t)$. Hence,

$$b(t) = 1 - e^{-t\omega_2} \qquad (9\text{-}157)$$

This waveform is shown in Fig. 9-41. Its departure from the unit step can be seen immediately. As f_2 increases, $b(t)$ rises more rapidly and better approximates the unit step.

Let us now investigate the effects of a coupling capacitor upon the unit-step response. Consider the circuit of Fig. 9-42a. The differential equation of this circuit is

$$kR_1 = (R_1 + R_2)i + \frac{1}{C_c} \int i \, dt \qquad (9\text{-}158)$$

and

$$v_o = -iR_2 \qquad (9\text{-}159)$$

Thus

$$v_o(t) = -kR_{\text{sh}}e^{-t/R_{\text{low}}C_c} \qquad (9\text{-}160)$$

where, using the notation of Secs. 9-1 and 9-3,

$$R_{\text{sh}} = \frac{R_1 R_2}{R_1 + R_2} \qquad \text{and} \qquad R_{\text{low}} = R_1 + R_2$$

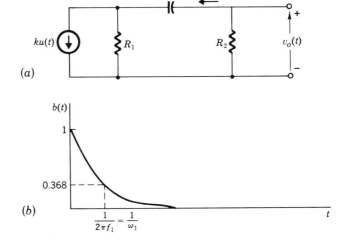

(a)

(b)

Fig. 9-42 (a) A simple low-frequency linear model and (b) its normalized unit-step response.

Thus, in normalized form

$$b(t) = e^{-t\omega_1} \qquad\qquad (9\text{-}161)$$

This is illustrated in Fig. 9-42. The response does not appear to be very much like a unit step. However, as f_1 decreases to zero, the 0.368 point moves out toward infinite time and $b(t)$ does approach $u(t)$. The lower half-power frequency f_1 should be small enough so that $b(t)$ is close to unity for all times of interest. This will be discussed subsequently in terms of sag.

We shall consider the complete time response by combining the circuits of Figs. 9-40a and 9-42a. This is shown in Fig. 9-43a. Let

$$\frac{1}{R_{sh}} = \frac{1}{R_1} + \frac{1}{R_2} \qquad \text{and} \qquad C_{sh} = C_1 + C_2$$

If $f_2 = 1/2\pi R_{sh}C_{sh} \gg f_1 = 1/2\pi R_{low}C_c$, then an approximate analysis yields the waveform shown in Fig. 9-43b. If there is a well-defined midband region, then the response will essentially rise to unity, remain there for a time, and then fall off. Note that there is a break in the time axis. Even with this break, Fig. 9-43b is not too representative, because the time constant of the exponential decay actually is very much greater than that of the exponential rise. Figure 9-43b is actually a combination of Figs. 9-41 and 9-42b. The response of Fig. 9-41 usually takes place in the first hundredth of an inch or so of the time axis of Fig. 9-42b. If there is not a well-defined midband region, then there will not be a flat region of the unit-step-response curve.

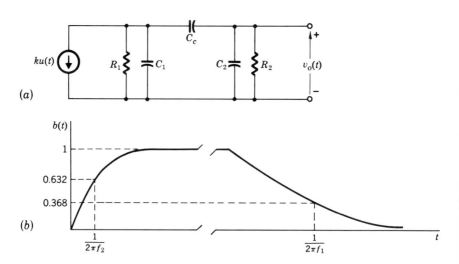

Fig. 9-43 (a) A simple linear model with both low- and high-frequency response and (b) its unit-step response.

In most practical amplifiers, the midband region is well defined, and the buildup and the decay of the unit-step response can be considered separately. Often, in such cases, it is possible to obtain some simple numbers, or figures of merit, that can be used to rate the transient response. These will now be discussed.

Rise of the unit-step response   Consider the unit-step response of Fig. 9-41.   One criterion of the distortion is the length of time it takes for the response to rise to unity.   Often, as in Fig. 9-41, this time is infinite.   Thus, the time it takes for the response to reach a value somewhat less than 1 is more representative.   Nine-tenths is the value that is usually chosen.   There is one other factor that must be considered.   A network may introduce a time delay without producing distortion.   For instance, if $A/A_{\text{mid}} = 1\underline{/-k\omega}$, then the output will be a faithful reproduction of the input, but it will be delayed by k sec.   This time should not be "charged" against the response time of the network.   Often it is considered that the response has not started until it has reached 10 percent of its final value.   Hence, a criterion for the speed of the response is defined as

$$\tau_r = \text{time for } b(t) \text{ to reach } 0.9 - \text{time for } b(t) \text{ to reach } 0.1 \qquad (9\text{-}162)$$

This is called the 10 to 90 *percent rise time* or simply the *rise time*.   It is indicated on the unit-step response of Fig. 9-44.   This unit-step response is typical of many networks.   Notice that the response does not asymptotically approach unity, but actually overshoots and then approaches unity in a damped oscillatory fashion.   The ratio of the maximum value of $b(t)$ to unity (the final value) is called the *overshoot*.   We shall indicate it by δ_o.   The 10 to 90 percent rise time and the overshoot are two important figures of merit

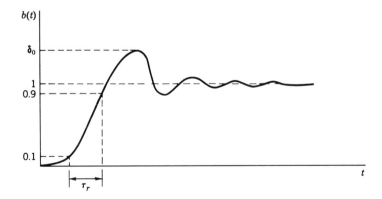

Fig. 9-44   A typical unit-step response illustrating the 10 to 90 percent rise time and the overshoot.

for the rising portion of the unit-step response. Of course, they do not convey all of the information about $b(t)$, since two numbers cannot completely characterize a general curve.

In certain computer applications the total speed of response is important. In such cases any delay time should be charged against the rise time of the amplifier. The 0 to 90 percent rise time could be considered in such cases.

The response of an amplifier to a train of pulses is an important criterion of its transient response. For instance, in a television amplifier, this indicates the amount of resolution in the picture, since it indicates how rapidly the image can be switched from black to white. It is also of importance in a radar amplifier, since the location of a pulse in time is an indication of the distance of the object sighted upon. A pulse train and some typical responses are shown in Fig. 8-8. In terms of the examples, if the rise time is too long, (1) the television picture cannot go rapidly from black to white and will have a blurred gray area between; (2) a radar pulse that does not have a well-defined leading edge cannot be fixed accurately in time, and, thus, the radar will not give accurate information about range. In general, τ_r should be considerably less than the width of the pulse. The overshoot is somewhat more important in the television image since severe overshoot will distort the signal. It can be tolerated in the radar pulse if it is not so severe that it prevents successive pulses from being identified.

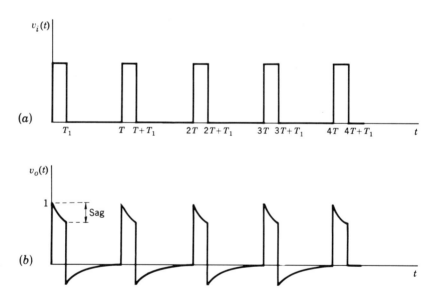

Fig. 9-45 (*a*) A train of pulses and (*b*) the effect of the low-frequency response on the pulse train.

Decay of the unit-step response Consider the curve of Fig. 9-42*b*. One way of rating it would be to determine the time it takes for the response to fall to 90 percent of its initial value. The longer this *fall time*, the better the response. However, the pulse response is usually used to obtain a figure of merit for the decay. For instance, if the input to the network of Fig. 9-42*a* is a train of pulses such as that shown in Fig. 9-45*a*, the response will be that given in Fig. 9-45*b*. For convenience, we have assumed that the period *T* is long enough so that the response becomes almost zero between pulses. We would ideally have the top of each pulse horizontal. Thus, the amount that it falls off is a criterion of the distortion. If the pulses are normalized so that the maximum height is unity, then the *sag* is equal to 1 minus the magnitude of $v_o(t)$ at the end of the pulse. In general, as the pulse duration T_1 becomes longer, the sag increases. Conversely, if there is a maximum sag that will be tolerated, the lower half-power frequency must decrease as the pulse length increases [see Eq. (9-161)]. The top of the pulse need not be just a simple exponential decay. For instance, in certain cases of low-frequency compensation, the response may actually rise before it falls off. In such cases, an overshoot can be spoken of in the decay.

9-15 RELATION OF THE POLE-ZERO DIAGRAMS TO TRANSIENT RESPONSE

Readers who are familiar with the Laplace transform will find this section to be a review. The response of a network to an applied signal is characterized by a differential equation. There are operational methods for solving such equations. These relate the pole-zero diagram to the response of the network. This process is too lengthy to be considered at this time, but some results of such an analysis will be given in this section. Networks of the type that we are considering are characterized by *linear integrodifferential equations with constant coefficients*. When an operational method called the *Laplace transform* is used to solve these equations, the operations of differentiation and integration with respect to time become multiplication and division by a new variable. We shall denote this variable by the letter *s*. The integrodifferential equation then becomes algebraic, and its solution is called the *response of the network in transformed form*. A function of time can be *transformed* into a function of *s*. Conversely, a function of *s* can be *inverse-transformed* into a function of time. In transformed form, the output of an amplifier in response to an arbitrary input is equal to the transformed form of the amplification times the transform of the input. For a great many networks, the transformed form of the amplification can be obtained from the frequency response if *jω* is replaced by *s*. We shall present, without proof, some functions of time and their Laplace transforms in Table 9-3. It is assumed that these functions of time are zero for $t < 0$.

Table 9-3 The Laplace transform of some simple functions

$f(t)$	$F(s)$
$u(t)$	$\dfrac{1}{s}$
$\sin \omega_o t$	$\dfrac{\omega_o}{s^2 + \omega_o{}^2} = \dfrac{\omega_o}{(s + j\omega_o)(s - j\omega_o)}$
$\cos \omega_o t$	$\dfrac{s}{s^2 + \omega_o{}^2} = \dfrac{s}{(s + j\omega_o)(s - j\omega_o)}$
$e^{-at} \sin \omega_o t$	$\dfrac{\omega_o}{(s + a)^2 + \omega_o{}^2} = \dfrac{\omega_o}{(s + a + j\omega_o)(s + a - j\omega_o)}$
$e^{-at} \cos \omega_o t$	$\dfrac{s + a}{(s + a)^2 + \omega_o{}^2} = \dfrac{s + a}{(s + a + j\omega_o)(s + a - j\omega_o)}$
e^{-at}	$\dfrac{1}{s + a}$
e^{+at}	$\dfrac{1}{s - a}$

We shall state some general facts about the Laplace transform. The transient response is characterized by the location of the poles. For instance, a pair of simple poles on the $j\omega$ axis at $s = \pm j\omega_o$ gives rise to sines and/or cosines of frequency ω_o. A simple pole at the origin transforms into the unit step. Any pole in the left half-plane will transform into a function of time multiplied by a decaying exponential. A damped exponential falls off very rapidly with time, so that any response whose transform is a pole, or a pair of poles in the left half-plane, will approach zero as t approaches infinity. Similarly, poles in the right half-plane will have a transform that is multiplied by an increasing exponential, so that the poles in the right half-plane lead to unstable circuits wherein the response builds up with time. A simple pole on the σ axis produces an exponential rise or decay. A pair of simple poles not on the σ axis will lead to a sinusoid multiplied by the factor e^{-at} if the poles are in the left half-plane and to a sinusoid multiplied by e^{+at} if the poles are in the right half-plane. It is assumed that a is a real positive constant.

The ratio of two polynomials can be expanded in a series so that each term in the series contains only one pole. For instance

$$\frac{s}{(s + 1)(s + 2)} = \frac{-1}{s + 1} + \frac{2}{s + 2} \tag{9-163}$$

The functions of time whose transform is given by Eq. (9-163) is obtained by taking the inverse transform of each term

$$f(t) = -e^{-t} + 2e^{-2t}$$

Thus, we can determine the type of time functions that are present in the output signal simply by inspecting the pole-zero plot of the amplifier.

In all of this discussion nothing was mentioned about the zeros. The location of the zeros determines the relative magnitudes of the various time functions and the phase angle of any sinusoids. The zeros do not determine what components are present. (If a zero and a pole occur at the same point, the zero will cancel the pole and its transform will not appear in the output.)

Now let us use the Laplace transform to obtain the transient response of an amplifier to an arbitrary input waveform. The Laplace transform of the output waveform is obtained by multiplying the transformed form of the gain by the transform of the input waveform. It is often desirable to normalize the response by dividing it by the constant value A_{mid}. For instance, let us calculate $b(t)$, the normalized unit-step response. Its Laplace transform $B(s)$ is given by

$$\mathbf{B}(s) = \frac{1}{s} \frac{\mathbf{A}(s)}{\mathbf{A}_{mid}} \tag{9-164}$$

As an example, let us obtain the unit-step response of the amplifier of Fig. 9-42a. From Eq. (9-146), we have

$$\frac{\mathbf{A}(s)}{\mathbf{A}_{mid}} = \frac{s}{s + \omega_1}$$

Then, using Eq. (9-164) we obtain

$$\mathbf{B}(s) = \frac{1}{s} \cdot \frac{s}{s + \omega_1} = \frac{1}{s + \omega_1}$$

and $b(t) = e^{-\omega_1 t}$ for $t > 0$. This is verified by Eq. (9-161). The output does not have a unit step as one of its components, since the pole at $s = 0$ is canceled by the zero there.

Let us now consider the unit-step response of the shunt-peaked amplifier of Sec. 9-11. The normalized gain in transformed form is given by Eq. (9-150). The transform of the unit-step response is then

$$\mathbf{B}(s) = \frac{\omega_2(s + \omega_2/Q_2)}{s[s^2 + (\omega_2/Q_2)s + \omega_2^2/Q_2]} \tag{9-165}$$

The form of $b(t)$ is relatively complicated and can be discussed most easily if the values are plotted. This is done in Fig. 9-46. The rise time of the unit-step response decreases as Q_2 is increased. However, if $Q_2 > 0.25$, an overshoot develops. This can be explained in terms of the pole-zero diagram which is given in Fig. 9-38e and f, except that a pole must be added at the origin. If $Q_2 < 0.25$, the response will consist of the sum of decaying exponentials, since the poles all lie on the σ axis. If $Q_2 > 0.25$, the poles

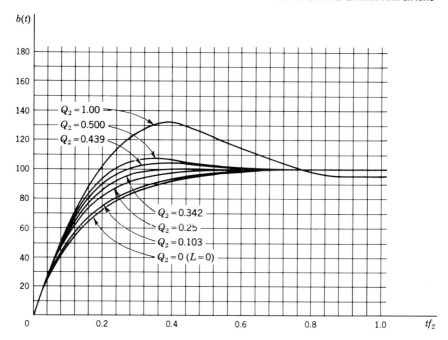

Fig. 9-46 Curves of the normalized unit-step response of the amplifiers of Fig. 9-31. (*Adapted with permission from A. V. Bedford and G. L. Fredendall, Transient Response of Multistage Video-frequency Amplifiers, Proc. IRE, vol. 27, pp. 277–284, 1939.*)

become complex and consequently the output will contain damped sinusoids. This is the reason for the change in the character of the response when Q_2 exceeds 0.25. The rise time decreases as the overshoot increases. This happens in a great many networks. A compromise must usually be made between rise time and overshoot. If no overshoot is allowed, then, for the shunt-peaked amplifier, the critically damped case of $Q_2 = 0.25$ is used. This value is less than those discussed in Sec. 9-11, where the amplitude distortion or the phase distortion was considered. Thus, we can see that there is no *simple* interrelation among the three types of response. If a value of $Q_2 = 0.342$ is used, the rise time will be decreased and the overshoot will still be small; the frequency and phase distortion will also be reduced.

The rise time and overshoot of a single stage are not of prime importance, but the rise time and overshoot of the overall amplifier are. Unfortunately, the rise time and overshoot of the cascade cannot be determined from a knowledge of just the rise time and overshoot of the individual stages. However, there are some *approximate* rules that work quite well in most cases when the transform of the amplification does not have zeros in the right half-plane.[7] These rules are:

1. If there are n stages, with rise times $\tau_{r1}, \tau_{r2}, \ldots, \tau_{rn}$, and all the stages are free of overshoot, then the overall rise time is

$$\tau_{rT} \approx \sqrt{\tau_{r1}^2 + \tau_{r2}^2 + \cdots + \tau_{rn}^2} \qquad (9\text{-}166)$$

If n identical stages are used,

$$\tau_{rT} \approx \tau_{r1}\sqrt{n} \qquad (9\text{-}167)$$

If the overshoot per stage is very small (less than 1 or 2 percent), then Eqs. (9-166) and (9-167) are still valid. The overshoot of the overall amplifier will not increase as the number of stages is increased.

2. If the overshoot is about 5 to 10 percent per stage and there are n identical stages, the overshoot of the cascade will be

$$\delta_{oT} = \sqrt{n}\, \delta_o \qquad (9\text{-}168)$$

where δ_o is the overshoot of one stage. In such cases, the rise time increases at a slower rate than is indicated by Eqs. (9-166) and (9-167).

The transform of the unit-step response of the low-frequency-compensated amplifier whose response is given by Eq. (9-104) is

$$\mathbf{B}(s) = \frac{s + \omega_4}{(s + \omega_3)(s + \omega_1)} = \frac{\omega_4 - \omega_3}{\omega_1 - \omega_3}\frac{1}{s + \omega_3} + \frac{\omega_4 - \omega_1}{\omega_3 - \omega_1}\frac{1}{s + \omega_1}$$

$$(9\text{-}169)$$

From Eqs. (9-102) and (9-103) we have $\omega_4 > \omega_3$. The unit-step response is given by

$$b(t) = \frac{1}{\omega_1 - \omega_3}[(\omega_4 - \omega_3)e^{-\omega_3 t} - (\omega_4 - \omega_1)e^{-\omega_1 t}] \qquad (9\text{-}170)$$

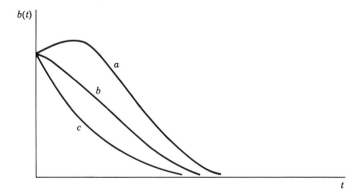

Fig. 9-47 The unit-step response of the low-frequency-compensated amplifier: (a) $\omega_4 > \omega_1$; (b) $\omega_4 = \omega_1$; and (c) $\omega_4 < \omega_1$. It is assumed that $\omega_3 < \omega_1$.

There are three general forms that the unit-step response will take. (We shall assume that $\omega_3 < \omega_1$.) These are illustrated in Fig. 9-47. If $\omega_1 < \omega_4$, the response actually overshoots before it falls off. If $\omega_1 > \omega_4$, the rate of falloff increases. By varying the value of ω_4 we can trade overshoot for sag.

9-16 FREQUENCY RESPONSE OF SOME COMMONLY USED AMPLIFIERS

With some modifications the analysis of the previous sections can be applied to the other amplifier configurations. We shall discuss some of them here.

The common-drain amplifier An RC-coupled source-follower amplifier is shown in Fig. 9-48a. Its linear model is given in Fig. 9-48b, where we have assumed that the capacitor C_s is a short circuit at all frequencies of interest. Since the gain of the source follower is usually close to unity, the effect of R_{g1}

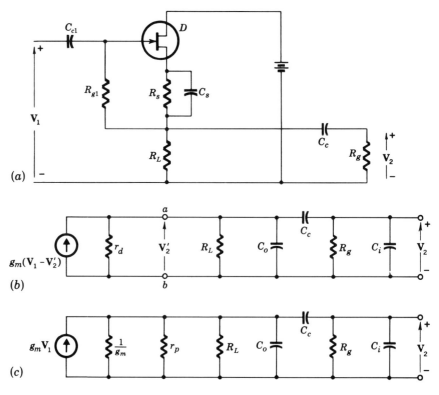

Fig. 9-48 (a) A source-follower amplifier; (b) its linear model; (c) a modification of the linear model.

can, in general, be neglected (see Sec. 6-17).   The effect of the first coupling capacitor C_{c1} is not included in the gain of this stage.   We shall consider it subsequently.   The capacitance C_o is given by

$$C_o = C_{ds} + C_w \tag{9-171a}$$

For the vacuum-tube pentode, it is

$$C_o = C_{\text{out}} + C_w + C_{hk} \tag{9-171b}$$

where C_{out} is defined by Eq. (9-1), C_w represents half of the stray wiring capacitance, and C_{hk} is the capacitance between the cathode and the heater of the vacuum tube.

The resistor R_g is the gate resistance of the next stage, and C_i is the sum of the remainder of the wiring capacitance plus the input capacitance of the next stage.   Let us replace the circuit to the left of terminals ab by its Norton's equivalent circuit.   Since $V_2' = 0$ under short-circuit conditions, we have

$$\mathbf{I}_{sc} = g_m \mathbf{V}_1$$

The open-circuit voltage is

$$\mathbf{V}_{oc} = \frac{g_m \mathbf{V}_1}{g_m + 1/r_d}$$

Thus, the model can be redrawn as in Fig. 9-48c.   This is essentially the same as Fig. 9-3, which is the model for the common-source RC-coupled amplifier. The only differences are that the resistance $1/g_m$ is placed in parallel with r_d and the polarity of the current generator has been reversed.   We can thus use all the results of Sec. 9-1 if we use new values for R_{sh} and R_{low}.   These are given by

$$\frac{1}{R_{\text{sh}}'} = g_m + \frac{1}{r_d} + \frac{1}{R_L} + \frac{1}{R_g} \tag{9-172a}$$

and

$$R_{\text{low}}' = \frac{1}{g_m + 1/r_d + 1/R_L} + R_g \tag{9-172b}$$

The midband gain will not have a phase reversal, so that

$$A_{v,\text{mid}} = g_m R_{\text{sh}}' \tag{9-173}$$

The value of R_{sh}' is always less than $1/g_m$.   Hence, the midband gain is less than unity, and the upper half-power frequency f_2 is quite high.   The gain-bandwidth product for a source-follower amplifier is still $g_m/2\pi C_{\text{sh}}$, however.

The input resistance of the source follower is usually many times the value of R_{g1}.   If the ratio of V_2'/V_1 is equal to d, then the input resistance is $R_{g1}/(1 - d)$ (see Sec. 6-17).   Usually d is very close to unity.   Thus, the lower half-power frequency of the input circuit, consisting of C_{c1} and the input resistance, is given by $(1 - d)/2\pi R_{g1}C_{c1}$. This half-power frequency may be many times less than that of the other amplifier stages. Source followers are not cascaded, since their voltage gains are less than unity.

The common-base transistor amplifier A common-base transistor amplifier and its linear model are given in Fig. 9-49a. The linear model is obtained from the h-parameter model of Fig. 6-41. If more accuracy is desired, the model of Fig. 6-39 can be used. In the low- and mid-frequency region, Fig. 9-47b is the same as the model for the common-emitter amplifier of Fig. 9-9 except that the subscript e has been replaced by the subscript b. Thus, in the low- and mid-frequency regions, the results of the analysis of the common-emitter amplifier can be applied to the common-base amplifier by appropriately modifying the subscripts. Note that $h_{fB} = -\alpha_0$. Hence, for the common-base amplifier using junction transistors, the maximum current gain is less than unity. In the high-frequency region, an analysis yields

$$\frac{A_{i,\text{high}}}{A_{i,\text{mid}}} = \frac{1}{1 + j\omega/\omega_\alpha} \frac{1}{1 + j\omega/\omega_2} \qquad (9\text{-}174a)$$

where

$$\omega_2 = \frac{1}{2\pi R_{\text{sh}}C_{ob}} \qquad (9\text{-}174b)$$

In general, the high-frequency bandwidth of the common-base circuit will be considerably greater than that of the common-emitter amplifier. As in the

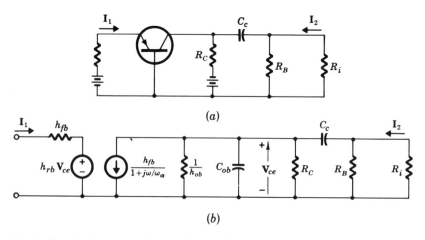

(a)

(b)

Fig. 9-49 (a) A common-base RC-coupled transistor amplifier and (b) its linear model based on the approximate model of Fig. 6-41.

case of the source follower, common-base amplifiers are usually not cascaded but are used for special-purpose input or output stages.

The common-collector amplifier can be analyzed using the linear model of Fig. 6-42 connected appropriately. The details will be left to the reader.

9-17 THE IDEAL TRANSFORMER

In Sec. 8-3 we mentioned the advantages and disadvantages of the transformer as a coupling network. Now, we shall develop the fundamental relations of the *ideal transformer*. In the next section practical transformers will be considered. A representation of an ideal transformer is shown in Fig. 9-50a. Two coils of wire are wound on a core that is assumed to be lossless and of zero reluctance. Thus, all of the flux set up by any turn of one coil links all the turns of both coils. It is also assumed that the wire possesses zero resistance. Since the same flux ϕ links both coils, we can write

$$v_1 = n_1 \frac{d\phi}{dt} \quad \text{and} \quad v_2 = n_2 \frac{d\phi}{dt}$$

Thus

$$\frac{v_1}{v_2} = \frac{n_1}{n_2} \tag{9-175}$$

The net magnetomotive force (mmf) around any closed loop is zero. Since the core is ideal, we have

$$n_1 i_1 + n_2 i_2 = 0 \tag{9-176}$$

so that

$$\frac{v_1}{v_2} = -\frac{i_2}{i_1} = \frac{n_1}{n_2} \tag{9-177}$$

A schematic representation for the ideal transformer is shown in Fig. 9-50b. The dots are used to indicate the polarity of the windings. If the current

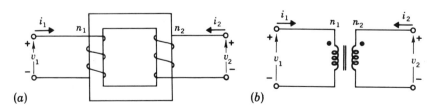

(a) (b)

Fig. 9-50 (a) An ideal transformer and (b) its schematic representation.

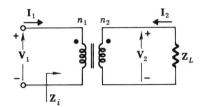

Fig. 9-51 A circuit illustrating the impedance-transforming properties of the ideal transformer.

into one dotted terminal increases constantly, the other dotted terminal is the "positive end" of its coil.

Transformers can be used to transform impedance levels as well as voltage and current levels. In fact, this is one of their most important applications in amplifier work. Consider the circuit of Fig. 9-51. The input impedance is given by

$$\mathbf{Z}_i = \frac{\mathbf{V}_1}{\mathbf{I}_1} = \frac{(n_1/n_2)\mathbf{V}_2}{-(n_2/n_1)\mathbf{I}_2}$$

Thus

$$\mathbf{Z}_i = \left(\frac{n_1}{n_2}\right)^2 \mathbf{Z}_L \tag{9-178}$$

Hence, the impedance transformation ratio is the square of the turns ratio.

9-18 LINEAR MODELS FOR ACTUAL TRANSFORMERS

The ideal transformer introduces no frequency distortion. However, the frequency response of an actual transformer is far from perfect. In order to obtain the frequency characteristics of a practical transformer, we must obtain its linear model. This circuit is only approximate, as are all models. It represents a compromise between accuracy and a reasonable number of elements. The linear model that we shall use here is shown in Fig. 9-52a. It contains an ideal transformer whose turns ratio is the same as that of the actual transformer, plus other elements which cause the circuit to perform in essentially the same way as the actual transformer does. Equation (9-176) indicates that $\mathbf{I}_1 = 0$ if $\mathbf{I}_2 = 0$. A transformer with an open-circuited secondary is just an inductance. Hence, if $\mathbf{I}_1 = 0$, then this inductance must be infinite. The shunt *magnetizing inductance* L_m is added to account for the fact that the primary inductance is finite. The power dissipated by R_c is approximately equal to the eddy-current and hysteresis losses in the core. The less the core loss, the greater is the value of R_c. Both the primary and secondary coils set up flux that link their own turns but not those of each other. Such flux does not produce transformer action, but it does produce a voltage drop in each winding which is the same as the one that would be

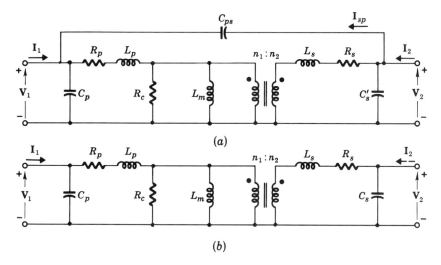

Fig. 9-52 (*a*) A linear model for an actual transformer and (*b*) a modification that does not have the capacitive coupling between the primary and the secondary.

produced by an inductance in series with the transformer windings. The *leakage inductances* L_p and L_s account for this voltage drop. The resistances R_p and R_s are equal to the resistance of the primary and secondary windings. As L_p, L_s, R_p, and R_s are decreased, the quality of the transformer is increased. Any coil will possess capacitance between successive turns. The capacitors C_p and C'_s take this into account. For usual operation, one end of the primary and one end of the secondary windings are connected together as shown. C_{ps} represents the capacitive coupling *between* the windings. It is desirable to have all the capacitances as small as possible. A question can be raised whether these elements have been placed in the right position. For instance, why are L_p and L_s, but not C_p and C'_s, placed adjacent to the transformer? Actually, neither would be totally correct. An exact equivalent circuit for the transformer would use distributed parameters, i.e., an infinite number of infinitesimal elements. This circuit is just a useful approximation.

The capacitor C_{ps}, coupling the primary to the secondary, complicates the calculations. It can be accounted for approximately by the following procedure. The current through C_{ps} is given by

$$\mathbf{I}_{sp} = (\mathbf{V}_2 - \mathbf{V}_1)j\omega C_{ps}$$

If the drops in R_p, L_p, R_s, and L_s are neglected, we have

$$\mathbf{I}_{sp} = \mathbf{V}_2\left(1 \mp \frac{n_1}{n_2}\right)j\omega C_{ps} \tag{9-179}$$

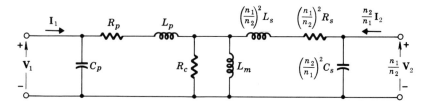

Fig. 9-53 The linear model of Fig. 9-52b referred to the primary side. Note that C_s is multiplied by $(n_2/n_1)^2$ since the impedance is inversely proportional to the capacitance.

where the upper sign is used if the dots are as shown. We then partially account for C_{ps} by placing a capacitor $(1 \mp n_1/n_2)C_{ps}$ in shunt with C'_s so that it draws the same current $\mathbf{I}_{sp}$. Such a circuit is shown in Fig. 9-52b, where

$$ C_s = C'_s + \left(1 \mp \frac{n_1}{n_2}\right)C_{ps} \tag{9-180} $$

If $1 \mp n_1/n_2$ is negative, then to avoid confusion the procedure should be modified so that a positive capacitance is added to C_p, that is, to the primary side. It should be stressed that either of these procedures only approximately accounts for C_{ps}.

If there is no coupling capacitance between the primary and secondary of the transformer, the circuit can be reduced still further. We can eliminate the ideal transformer from the circuit of Fig. 9-52b by raising the impedance level of the secondary circuit by the amount $(n_1/n_2)^2$ as indicated in Eq. (9-178). The voltage and current levels are then transformed in accordance with Eq. (9-177). Such a circuit, called a *linear model referred to the primary side*, is shown in Fig. 9-53. Similarly, we can also obtain a linear model referred to the secondary side.

9-19   THE TRANSFORMER-COUPLED AMPLIFIER

The primary purpose for using transformer coupling is to impedance-match a fixed load to an FET or to a transistor. Three typical circuits are shown in Fig. 9-54a to c. Transformers can be used to produce a voltage or a current gain in circuits that normally do not provide it, e.g., current gain in the common-base transistor amplifier. In most cases, transformer-coupled amplifiers have a poorer frequency response, are more costly, and are larger than RC-coupled amplifiers. Thus, transformers are usually not used as interstage elements. An exception to this is when good low-frequency response is not important, e.g., when short pulses are to be amplified. Then small and inexpensive transformers can be built and are used. Figure 9-54c shows such a circuit.

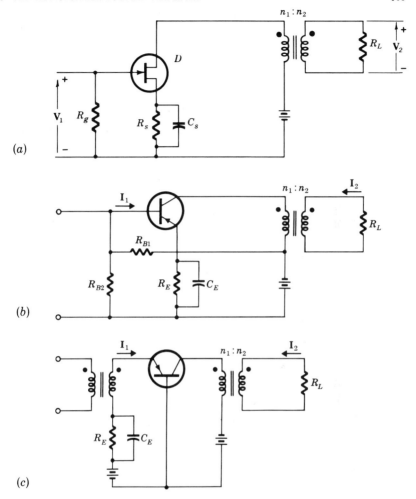

Fig. 9-54 Transformer-coupled amplifiers: (*a*) FET; (*b*) common-emitter transistor; and (*c*) common-base transistor.

Figure 9-55 shows a linear model that is valid if the active element is a common-source FET, common-cathode vacuum tube, or any of the three transistor-amplifier configurations and if the substitutions of Table 9-4 are made. It is assumed that the high-frequency response of the transformer reduces the gain to insignificant values well below those frequencies where the stray capacitances of the transistor (see Fig. 6-42) have any effect. This assumption is usually valid. We have used the transformer equivalent circuit of Fig. 9-53 here.

Capacitor C_o represents the output capacitance of the active element

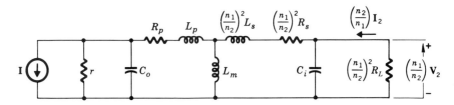

Fig. 9-55 A linear model for the transformer-coupled amplifier.

plus the capacitance C_p of the transformer. Similarly, the capacitor C_i
represents the input capacitance of the load (transformed to the primary side)
plus the capacitor $(n_2/n_1)^2 C_s$ of the transformer. At all frequencies of
interest, the core-loss resistance R_c is usually very much larger than the
impedance in shunt with it, and it has been omitted from the equivalent
circuit. It has also been assumed that the impedance of any bypass capacitors is zero. Their effect can be taken into account by means of the procedure of Secs. 9-5 and 9-6.

A useful wideband transformer-coupled amplifier will have a well-
defined midband region, where the response is almost independent of
frequency. The gain will fall off at low and high frequencies. At low
frequencies the impedance of L_m becomes small, which causes the gain to fall
off. The series inductances L_p and $(n_1/n_2)^2 L_s$ are small, and their impedance
can be considered to be a short circuit at low and mid-frequencies. The
capacitors C_i and C_o can be considered to be open circuits at these frequencies. At high frequencies, the effect of L_m can be ignored, since its impedance
becomes very large. However, we can no longer ignore L_p, $(n_1/n_2)^2 L_s$, C_i,
and C_o. The three ranges will be considered separately.

The mid-frequency region The mid-frequency equivalent circuit is shown
in Fig. 9-56, where the current generator has been replaced by a voltage
generator. For convenience, we shall write the gain $\mathbf{A}_{\mathrm{mid}} = \mathbf{I}_2/\mathbf{I}$. To obtain
the current gain of a transistor amplifier, this quantity must be multiplied by
h_f. The voltage gain of a common-source FET amplifier is obtained by
multiplying $\mathbf{A}$ by $-g_m R_L$. Thus,

$$\mathbf{A}_{\mathrm{mid}} = \frac{n_1}{n_2} \frac{r}{r + R_p + (n_1/n_2)^2 (R_s + R_L)} \tag{9-181}$$

Table 9-4

Model	FET	Transistor
r	r_d	$1/h_o$
$\mathbf{I}$	$g_m \mathbf{V}_1$	$h_f \mathbf{I}_1$

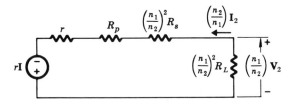

Fig. 9-56 A modification of Fig. 9-55 valid in the mid-frequency range.

If the dots on the transformer winding are reversed, this amplification should be multiplied by -1.

The low-frequency region   A linear model that is valid in the low-frequency region is shown in Fig. 9-57.   The mesh equations are

$$-r\mathbf{I} = (r + R_p + j\omega L_m)\mathbf{I}_a + j\omega L_m \frac{n_2}{n_1}\mathbf{I}_2$$

$$0 = j\omega L_m \mathbf{I}_a + \left[\left(\frac{n_1}{n_2}\right)^2 (R_s + R_L) + j\omega L_m\right] \frac{n_2}{n_1}\mathbf{I}_2$$

Solving and dividing by $\mathbf{A}_{\text{mid}}$, we obtain

$$\frac{\mathbf{A}_{\text{low}}}{\mathbf{A}_{\text{mid}}} = \frac{1}{1 + R_{\text{low}T}/j\omega L_m} \tag{9-182}$$

where

$$R_{\text{low}T} = \frac{(r + R_p)[(n_1/n_2)^2(R_s + R_L)]}{r + R_p + (n_1/n_2)^2(R_s + R_L)} \tag{9-183}$$

Let

$$\omega_1 = \frac{R_{\text{low}T}}{L_m} \quad \text{and} \quad f_1 = \frac{R_{\text{low}T}}{2\pi L_m} \tag{9-184}$$

Then

$$\frac{\mathbf{A}_{\text{low}}}{\mathbf{A}_{\text{mid}}} = \frac{1}{1 - jf_1/f} \tag{9-185}$$

Fig. 9-57 A modification of Fig. 9-55 valid in the low-frequency region.

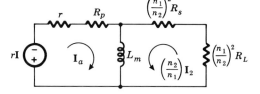

This is exactly the same as the expression for the low-frequency response of the RC-coupled amplifier [see Eqs. (9-15) and (9-33)]. Hence, a plot of the low-frequency response of the transformer-coupled amplifier is given by the low-frequency portion of the curves of Figs. 9-6 and 9-7.

Let us see what is involved in obtaining a low value of f_1. As $R_{\text{low}T}$ is reduced, f_1 decreases. The resistance $R_{\text{low}T}$ is the parallel combination of $r + R_p$ and $(n_1/n_2)^2(R_s + R_L)$. In a good transformer, $R_p \ll r$ and $R_s \ll R_L$. Thus, $R_{\text{low}T}$ is essentially $(n_1/n_2)^2 R_L$ in parallel with r. The value of $(n_1/n_2)^2 R_L$ can be reduced somewhat, but the design requirements often fix its value. The magnitude of r cannot be varied at will, since it represents r_d or $1/h_{oe}$. However, a resistance can be placed in shunt with the FET, or the transistor to reduce the value of r. If it is decreased too much, A_{mid} will fall off. Thus, if we are to have a good low-frequency response without reducing the value of A_{mid}, the value of L_m must be high. The cores of transformers are made of ferromagnetic material. This causes both the coupling between the coils and the value of L_m to be high. However, such cores can become saturated and lose their effectiveness. The direct flux, which is set up by the direct-bias current through the primary winding, can cause such saturation. To prevent this, the core must contain a relatively large amount of iron, which makes the transformer large, heavy, and expensive. There are some circuits where the saturation due to the direct current is not present. In such cases, the transformer can be smaller. These circuits will be discussed in the next chapter. In order to obtain good low-frequency response with FETs, they are chosen so that their plate resistance is not too high or their outputs are shunted by resistors.

The high-frequency region The high-frequency model for the transformer-coupled amplifier is shown in Fig. 9-58. The complete solution of this circuit is very complicated. We shall eventually obtain it; however, let us start by making some approximations that are often valid. Usually, low-frequency considerations keep r small, so that we often have

$$r \ll \frac{1}{\omega C_o} \tag{9-186}$$

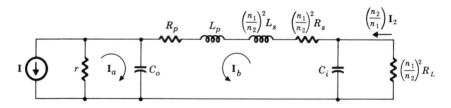

Fig. 9-58 The high-frequency linear model for the amplifier of Fig. 9-55.

over all frequencies of interest. The effect of C_o can then be ignored. Writing two current-divider ratios and clearing fractions, we obtain

$$\mathbf{A}_{\text{high}} = \frac{(n_1/n_2)r}{(n_1/n_2)^2 R_L + [1 + j\omega C_i(n_1/n_2)^2 R_L]} \tag{9-187}$$
$$\times \{r + R_p + (n_1/n_2)^2 R_s + j\omega[L_p + (n_1/n_2)^2 L_s]\}$$

Then

$$\frac{\mathbf{A}_{\text{high}}}{\mathbf{A}_{\text{mid}}} = \frac{1}{\dfrac{1 - \omega^2 C_i L_T (n_1/n_2)^2 R_L}{R_T} + j\omega \dfrac{L_T + C_i R_{Ta}(n_1/n_2)^2 R_L}{R_T}} \tag{9-188}$$

where

$$R_T = r + R_p + \left(\frac{n_1}{n_2}\right)^2 (R_s + R_L) \tag{9-189}$$

$$R_{Ta} = r + R_p + \left(\frac{n_1}{n_1}\right)^2 R_s \tag{9-190}$$

and

$$L_T = L_p + \left(\frac{n_1}{n_2}\right)^2 L_s \tag{9-191}$$

There are many circumstances when the value of $(n_1/n_2)^2 R_L$ is very small; at other times it is extremely large. For instance, for an output circuit $(n_1/n_2)^2 R_L$ may be only several thousand ohms. Let us assume that, at all frequencies of interest,

$$\left(\frac{n_1}{n_2}\right)^2 R_L \ll \frac{1}{\omega C_i} \tag{9-192}$$

We can then neglect C_i so that Eq. (9-188) becomes

$$\frac{\mathbf{A}_{\text{high}}}{\mathbf{A}_{\text{mid}}} = \frac{1}{1 + j\omega L_T/R_T} \tag{9-193}$$

Let

$$f_2 = R_T/2\pi L_T \tag{9-194}$$

then

$$\frac{\mathbf{A}_{\text{high}}}{\mathbf{A}_{\text{mid}}} = \frac{1}{1 + jf/f_2} \tag{9-195}$$

The response has the same form as the RC-coupled amplifier, and the high-frequency portion of Figs. 9-6 and 9-7 can represent it. The upper half-power frequency is increased by increasing R_T or by reducing L_T. Usually, $R_T \approx r + (n_1/n_2)^2 R_L$. The value of R_L is usually fixed. A change in n_1/n_2

will also change L_T and thus may not achieve any significant improvement. The value of r cannot be made too large, because of low-frequency considerations. If good high-frequency response is desired, the *equivalent leakage inductance* L_T must be kept small. This is done by careful winding on high-quality cores. In general, it is more difficult to achieve broadband response with a transformer-coupled amplifier than it is with an RC-coupled amplifier.

Now let us consider an additional approximation which can be used when $(n_1/n_2)^2 R_L$ is very large. We shall assume that

$$\left(\frac{n_1}{n_2}\right)^2 R_L \gg R_{Ta} \tag{9-196}$$

so that

$$R_T \approx \left(\frac{n_1}{n_2}\right)^2 R_L$$

In addition, we shall assume that

$$\left(\frac{n_1}{n_2}\right)^2 R_L R_{Ta} C_i \gg L_T \tag{9-197}$$

Thus, Eq. (9-188) becomes

$$\frac{\mathbf{A}_{\text{high}}}{\mathbf{A}_{\text{mid}}} = \frac{1}{1 - \omega^2 C_i L_T + j\omega C_i R_{Ta}}$$

In order to obtain a set of general curves, we shall introduce the following terminology:

$$\omega_0 = \frac{1}{\sqrt{C_i L_T}} \qquad f_0 = \frac{1}{2\pi\sqrt{C_i L_T}} \tag{9-198}$$

$$Q_0 = \frac{\omega_0 L_T}{R_{Ta}} = \frac{1}{R_{Ta}\omega_0 C_i} \tag{9-199}$$

Then, substituting, we obtain

$$\frac{\mathbf{A}_{\text{high}}}{\mathbf{A}_{\text{mid}}} = \frac{1}{1 - (f/f_0)^2 + j(f/f_0)(1/Q_0)} \tag{9-200}$$

Curves of $|A_{\text{high}}/A_{\text{mid}}|$ and $\angle(A_{\text{high}}/A_{\text{mid}})$ are given in Fig. 9-59.[8] Note that these curves are not normalized with respect to f_2 but with respect to f_0, which is the resonant frequency of L_T and C_i. Thus, the high-frequency bandwidth is increased if the leakage inductance and the stray capacitance are reduced. In transformed form Eq. (9-200) is

$$\frac{\mathbf{A}_{\text{high}}}{\mathbf{A}_{\text{low}}} = \frac{\omega_0^2}{s^2 + (\omega_0/Q_0)s + \omega_0^2} \tag{9-201}$$

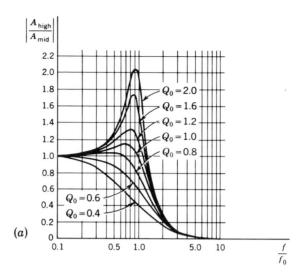

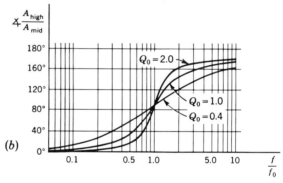

Fig. 9-59 Frequency response of the transformer-coupled amplifier assuming that $r << 1/\omega c_0$, $R_T \approx (n_1/n_2)^2 R_L$, and $(n_1/n_2)^2 R_L R_{Ta} C_i >> L_T$: (a) amplitude response and (b) phase response. (*From F. E. Terman, " Radio Engineers' Handbook." Copyright 1943. McGraw-Hill Book Company. Used by permission.*)

The poles of this network occur at

$$s = -\frac{\omega_0}{2Q_0} \pm \frac{\omega_0}{2Q_0} \sqrt{1 - 4Q_0{}^2} \qquad (9\text{-}202)$$

As Q_0 is increased, the rise time decreases. However, if $Q_0 > \frac{1}{2}$, the unit-step response will overshoot.

If the inequality of relation (9-197) does not hold but all the other assumptions are valid, we can still use all the above results if we redefine Q_0 as

$$Q_0 = \frac{R_T}{\omega_0[L_T + C_i R_{Ta}(n_1/n_2)^2 R_L]}$$

We have thus far obtained the high-frequency response subject to the assumption, among others, that $r \ll 1/\omega C_0$. This assumption is often valid for common-source FET amplifiers and common-cathode vacuum-tube amplifiers. However, it is not always valid when transistors are used. If the current generator of Fig. 9-58 is replaced by a voltage generator, a mesh analysis yields

$$-\mathbf{I}r = \left(r + \frac{1}{j\omega C_0}\right)\mathbf{I}_a + \frac{1}{j\omega C_0}\mathbf{I}_b \qquad (9\text{-}203a)$$

$$0 = \frac{1}{j\omega C_0}\mathbf{I}_a + \left(R_a + j\omega L_T + \frac{1}{j\omega C_0} + \frac{R_L'}{1 + j\omega R_L' C_i}\right)\mathbf{I}_b \qquad (9\text{-}203b)$$

where

$$R_a = R_p + \left(\frac{n_1}{n_2}\right)^2 R_s \qquad (9\text{-}204)$$

and

$$R_L' = \left(\frac{n_1}{n_2}\right)^2 R_L \qquad (9\text{-}205)$$

Then

$$\frac{n_2}{n_1}\mathbf{I}_2 = \frac{\mathbf{I}_b}{1 + j\omega R_L' C_i}$$

Solving and manipulating, we obtain

$$\frac{\mathbf{A}_{\text{high}}}{\mathbf{A}_{\text{mid}}} =$$

$$\frac{1}{1 + \dfrac{j\omega}{R_T}\{(R_a + j\omega L_T)[rC_0(1 + j\omega R_L' C_i) + R_L' C_i] + R_L' r(C_i + C_0) + L_T\}}$$

$$(9\text{-}206)$$

This is fairly complex, and there are too many variables to conveniently plot a set of curves. In general, a frequency response that has a form somewhat similar to that of Fig. 9-59 will be obtained. The denominator of Eq. (9-206) is a cubic equation in the variable $s = j\omega$. General solutions to cubic equations do exist. However, the form is so involved that numerical procedures are usually used to solve them. One pole of Eq. (9-206) will always lie on the negative σ axis.   The other two may lie on the negative σ axis or in the left half-plane.   If these roots are off the σ axis, then the unit-step response will overshoot.   Again, to increase the bandwidth, the leakage inductance and the stray capacitance should be reduced.

9-20 TUNED AMPLIFIERS—THE PARALLEL-RESONANT CIRCUIT

Thus far we have concerned ourselves with obtaining amplifiers with as broad a bandwidth as possible.   We shall now consider amplifiers that would, ideally, amplify a certain range of frequencies and reject all others.   One application of such a circuit would be in radio receivers, which amplify the signals received from one station but reject the signals from all other stations. These amplifiers are called *tuned amplifiers* or *bandpass amplifiers*.   They use tuned circuits of varying complexity.   Two typical ones are shown in Fig. 9-60.   Before considering them, we shall analyze the simple parallel-resonant circuit shown in Fig. 9-61.   Circuits of this type are useful in a frequency range of from tens of kilohertz to several hundred megahertz, and, for these

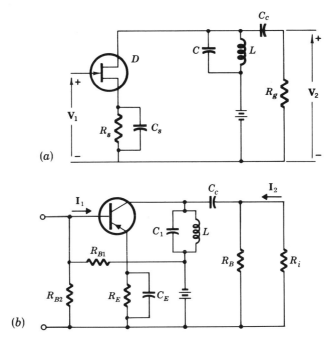

Fig. 9-60 *RC*-coupled single-tuned amplifiers: (*a*) common-source FET amplifier and (*b*) common-emitter transistor amplifier.

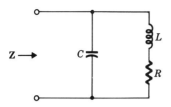

Fig. 9-61 A simple parallel-resonant circuit.

frequencies, the losses in the capacitor can often be neglected. The impedance is given by

$$\mathbf{Z} = \frac{(1/j\omega C)(R + j\omega L)}{R + j(\omega L - 1/\omega C)}$$

Manipulating, we have

$$\mathbf{Z} = \frac{(L/C)(1 - jR/\omega L)}{R[1 + j(\omega L/R)(1 - 1/\omega^2 LC)]} \tag{9-207}$$

To generalize, let

$$\omega_0 = \frac{1}{\sqrt{LC}} \qquad f_0 = \frac{1}{2\pi\sqrt{LC}} \tag{9-208}$$

and

$$Q_0 = \frac{\omega_0 L}{R} = \frac{1}{\omega_0 RC} = \frac{1}{R}\sqrt{\frac{L}{C}} \tag{9-209}$$

Substituting, we obtain

$$\mathbf{Z} = \frac{Q_0^2 R[1 - j(f_0/f)(1/Q_0)]}{1 + jQ_0[(f/f_0) - (f_0/f)]} = \frac{Q_0^2 R(f/f_0 - j1/Q_0)}{(f/f_0) + jQ_0(f^2/f_0^2 - 1)} \tag{9-210}$$

For most tuned amplifiers, $Q_0 > 10$. In fact, very often, $Q_0 > 100$, so that the second term in the denominator is very important. Even though Eq. (9-210) is exact, erroneous results may be obtained when values of f are substituted, unless many significant figures are used. *In general, large errors can be obtained when two nearly equal numbers are subtracted.* To eliminate the need for extreme accuracy, we shall introduce a new normalized frequency variable δ. Let

$$\delta = \frac{f - f_0}{f_0} \tag{9-211}$$

Substituting, we obtain

$$\mathbf{Z} = \frac{Q_0^2 R[1 + \delta - j(1/Q_0)]}{1 + \delta + jQ_0\,\delta(\delta + 2)} \tag{9-212}$$

Note that the difference between two nearly equal numbers no longer appears. If $Q \gg 1$, we can approximate Eq. (9-212) by

$$\mathbf{Z} = \frac{Q_0{}^2 R}{1 + jQ_0 \; \delta(\delta + 2)/(\delta + 1)} \tag{9-213}$$

Under these conditions, the maximum magnitude of the impedance occurs when $f = f_0$ or $\delta = 0$.

$$Z_{max} = Q_0{}^2 R = (\omega_0 L)Q_0 = R_0 \tag{9-214}$$

In normalized form

$$\frac{\mathbf{Z}}{R_0} = \frac{1}{1 + jQ_0 \; \delta(\delta + 2)/(\delta + 1)} \tag{9-215}$$

A plot of the magnitude of this expression for various values of Q_0 is given in Fig. 9-62. Such a plot is called a *resonance curve*. Notice that it becomes sharper as Q_0 is increased. The circuit is said to become more *selective* as the width of the resonance curve decreases. We shall develop tuned amplifiers whose amplification varies with frequency in the same way that Fig. 9-62 does. Let us define the half-power bandwidth B of a parallel-resonant circuit, such that

$$B = f_2 - f_1 \tag{9-216}$$

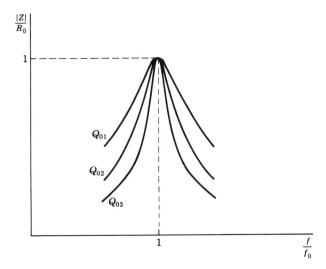

Fig. 9-62 Typical curves of the normalized impedance of a parallel-resonant circuit $Q_{03} > Q_{02} > Q_{01}$.

where

$$f_2 = \text{upper frequency where} \left| \frac{Z}{Q_0{}^2 R} \right| = \frac{1}{\sqrt{2}} \tag{9-217}$$

$$f_1 = \text{lower frequency where} \left| \frac{Z}{Q_0{}^2 R} \right| = \frac{1}{\sqrt{2}} \tag{9-218}$$

The bandwidth of a resonant circuit does not have to be the half-power bandwidth; e.g., for a precise application, the bandwidth could be defined as those frequencies where $|Z/Q_0{}^2 R|$ lies between 1.0 and 0.9. If $Q_0 \gg 1$, the magnitude of Eq. (9-210) becomes

$$\left| \frac{Z}{R_0} \right| = \frac{1}{|1 + jQ_0(f/f_0 - f_0/f)|} = \frac{1}{\sqrt{1 + Q_0{}^2(f/f_0 - f_0/f)^2}} \tag{9-219}$$

The magnitude of the impedance function is an even function of frequency. That is, the response for negative f is the same as that for positive f. (The phase angle is an odd function of frequency.) In obtaining the values of f_1 and f_2, we must be careful to obtain the positive frequency values. Thus

$$Q_0 \left(\frac{f_2}{f_0} - \frac{f_0}{f_2} \right) = 1 \tag{9-220}$$

and

$$Q_0 \left(\frac{f_0}{f_1} - \frac{f_1}{f_0} \right) = 1 \tag{9-221}$$

Equating, and solving, we obtain

$$f_1 f_2 = f_0{}^2 \tag{9-222}$$

Substituting in Eq. (9-220), we have

$$B = f_2 - f_1 = \frac{f_0}{Q_0} \tag{9-223}$$

Thus, the frequencies f_1 and f_2 are spaced with *geometric symmetry* about f_0. In fact, the entire curve of Eq. (9-219) has geometric symmetry about f_0. In addition, the bandwidth $f_2 - f_1$ varies directly with f_0 and inversely with Q_0.

Let us now obtain expressions for f_1 and f_2. From Eqs. (9-222) and (9-223), we obtain

$$f_2{}^2 - f_2 \frac{f_0}{Q_0} - f_0{}^2 = 0$$

Solving for f_2, and using the positive value, we have

$$f_2 = \frac{f_0}{2Q_0} + \sqrt{f_0{}^2 \left(1 + \frac{1}{4Q_0{}^2} \right)} \tag{9-224a}$$

Similarly

$$f_1 = -\frac{f_0}{2Q_0} + \sqrt{f_0^2\left(1 + \frac{1}{4Q_0^2}\right)} \tag{9-224b}$$

If $Q_0 \gg 1$, we can make some approximations that simplify these expressions. Expanding the square root of Eq. (9-224) in a power series, we obtain

$$f_2 = \frac{f_0}{2Q_0} + f_0\left(1 + \frac{1}{8Q_0^2} + \cdots\right)$$

If $Q_0 \gg 1$, we can neglect those terms containing all powers of Q_0 except the first. Hence,

$$f_2 \approx f_0\left(1 + \frac{1}{2Q_0}\right)$$

In a similar way, Eq. (9-225) can be manipulated to obtain

$$f_1 \approx f_0\left(1 - \frac{1}{2Q_0}\right)$$

For the high-Q case, f_0 and f_1 exhibit approximate *arithmetic symmetry* about f_0. In fact, if $Q_0 \gg 1$, then for frequencies that are not far from f_0, we can assume that the resonance curve has arithmetic symmetry about f_0. This often proves convenient.

9-21 SINGLE-TUNED *RC*-COUPLED AMPLIFIERS AND SOME MODELS OF ACTIVE DEVICES

Before we analyze the amplifiers of Fig. 9-60, let us consider the models of the active devices that will be used. When vacuum tubes are used, they are usually vacuum-tube pentodes rather than vacuum-tube triodes. The linear model of Fig. 6-35 can then be used. C_{gp} is usually so small that the Miller effect can be neglected. In this case, C_{gp} can be omitted from the model of the vacuum-tube pentode. The input admittance of the vacuum-tube pentode can then be represented by the capacitor C_{in}. The output admittance can be represented by the capacitor C_{out} in parallel with the resistor r_p.

The linear model of Fig. 6-33 can be used for the FET. Often C_{gd} is not small enough so that it can be ignored. In this case, the input admittance of the FET must include the Miller effect. It can then be represented by a resistance in parallel with a capacitance [see Eq. (6-116)]. The output admittance of the FET consists of $C_{ds} + C_{gd}$ in parallel with r_d (see Sec. 9-1). If a dual-gate MOSFET is used, the Miller effect can be neglected. The input admittance is represented by C_{in} while the output admittance is represented by C_{out} in parallel with r_d.

The hybrid-pi linear model of Fig. 6-42 or its equivalent h-parameter model of Fig. 6-43 will be used to represent the common-emitter transistor. The input impedance is given by Fig. 6-45b.   We shall approximate this by assuming that A_v' is not measured at the frequency in question but at the resonant frequency.   It will then be designated A_{v_0}'.   A more exact representation of this will be considered in Sec. 9-26.   Here we approximate the input impedance as shown in Fig. 9-63a.   The input impedance is given by

$$\mathbf{Z}_i = r_{bb'} + \frac{r_{b'e}}{1 + j\omega r_{b'e}C_e}$$

This can be manipulated into the form

$$\mathbf{Z}_i = r_{bb'} + \frac{r_{b'e}(1 - j\omega r_{b'e}C_e)}{1 + \omega^2 r_{b'e}^2 C_e^2}$$

Very often the transistor is operated *well* below its ω_β frequency so that

$$\frac{1}{\omega C_e} \gg r_{b'e} \tag{9-225}$$

Then the expression for the impedance can be approximated by

$$\mathbf{Z}_i = r_{bb'} + r_{b'e} + j\omega r_{b'e}^2 C_e$$

Note that we have only approximated the denominator of $\mathbf{Z}_i$.   This is done for two reasons: (1) the approximation is much more accurate there because

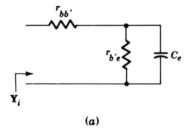

(a)

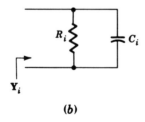

(b)

Fig. 9-63 (*a*) A representation of the input admittance of a common-emitter transistor amplifier and (*b*) a modification of the representation which is valid if $r_{b'e} \ll 1/\omega C_e$, $R_i = r_{bb'} + r_{b'e}$, and $C_i = r_{b'e}C_e/R_i$.

of the squared terms, and (2) the reactive component is important in resonance phenomena and should not be ignored.   Solving for the admittance, we have

$$Y_i = \frac{1}{Z_i} = \frac{r_{bb'} + r_{b'e} - j\omega r_{b'e}C_e}{(r_{bb'} + r_{b'e})^2 + (\omega r_{b'e}^2 C_e)^2}$$

Again, making use of relation (9-225), we obtain

$$Y_i = \frac{1}{r_{bb'} + r_{b'e}} + \frac{j\omega r_{b'e}C_e}{r_{bb'} + r_{b'e}}$$

Now let $r_{bb'} + r_{b'e} = R_i$.   The equation for Y_i represents the input admittance of Fig. 9-63b.   Thus, this figure can be used to represent the input admittance of the transistor if relation (9-225) is valid.

Let us now consider the output admittance of the transistor.   If $|\mathbf{h}_{re}|$ is small, which is true at frequencies far below ω_β, then the output impedance is given by $\mathbf{h}_{oe}$ (see Fig. 6-43).   This impedance is shown in Fig. 9-64.   The input admittance of the branch consisting of r_{oe} and C_{oe} in series is

$$Y = \frac{1}{r_{oe} + 1/j\omega C_{oe}} = \frac{r_{oe} + j(1/\omega C_{oe})}{r_{oe}^2 + (1/\omega C_{oe})^2}$$

At frequencies far below ω_β,

$$\frac{1}{\omega C_{oe}} \gg r_{oe} \tag{9-226}$$

Then, approximating as before,

$$Y = r_{oe}(\omega C_{oe})^2 + j\omega C_{oe}$$

The conductive portion of Y is $r_{oe}(\omega C_{oe})$.   This varies with frequency.   In general, we shall be working in a range of frequencies that is very close to ω_0,

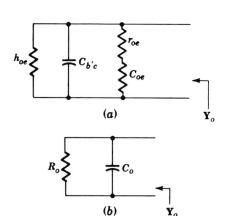

(a)

Y_o

Fig. 9-64 (a) A representation of the output admittance of a common-emitter transistor amplifier and (b) a modification of (a) which is valid if $r_{oe} << 1/\omega C_{oe}$. $1/R_o = h_{oe} + r_{oe}(\omega_0 C_{oe})^2$ and $C_o = C_{b'c} + C_{oe}$.

(b)

Y_o

the resonant frequency. Thus, $\omega \approx \omega_0$. Hence, we can approximate the conductance by the constant $r_{oe}(\omega_0 C_{oe})^2$. The admittance of the shunt branch then is

$$\mathbf{Y} = r_{oe}(\omega_0 C_{oe})^2 + j\omega C_{oe}$$

The susceptive portion of the admittance is *not* approximated by a constant. It is more convenient not to do so. In addition, in resonant circuits, *reactances* often enter relations as the difference between two nearly equal numbers. Thus, great care should be taken if they are approximated. The admittance $\mathbf{Y}$ represents a resistance $1/r_{oe}(\omega_0 C_{oe})^2$ in parallel with a capacitance C_{oe}. When this is combined in parallel with the resistance $1/h_{oe}$ and the capacitance $C_{b'c}$ (see Fig. 9-64a), the circuit of Fig. 9-64b results.

Now let us analyze the amplifiers of Fig. 9-60. Each has only one tuned circuit and uses a coupling capacitor to prevent the bias voltages of adjacent stages from interacting. Thus, they are called *single-tuned RC-coupled amplifiers*. At the frequencies where such amplifiers are used, we can always assume that C_s and C_E are short circuits. The frequencies are usually well below ω_β for the transistor. A linear model that is valid for the common-source FET amplifier and the common-emitter transistor amplifier is shown in Fig. 9-65. Then the capacitor C represents the total shunt capacitance; i.e., it is the sum of the capacitances due to the output admittance of the active device and the input admittance of the next active device in the cascade and also the sum of the capacitance C_1 that is actually placed in the circuit. The resistor r represents the output shunt resistance of the active device (see the discussion at the beginning of this section). In addition, R_T is equivalent to R_g in parallel with any input resistance for the FET. For the transistor $R_T = R_B R_i/(R_B + R_i)$. Then

$$\mathbf{V}_2 = \frac{-\mathbf{I}}{1/r + 1/\mathbf{Z} + 1/R_T}$$

where $\mathbf{Z}$ is given by Eq. (9-215). Substituting and manipulating, we have

$$\mathbf{V}_2 = \frac{-\mathbf{I}R_{sh}}{1 + jQ_0(R_{sh}/R_0)[\delta(\delta + 2)/(\delta + 1)]} \tag{9-227}$$

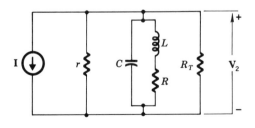

Fig. 9-65 A linear model for the single-tuned amplifier.

where

$$\frac{1}{R_{\text{sh}}} = \frac{1}{r} + \frac{1}{R_T} + \frac{1}{R_0} \tag{9-228}$$

Let us define an effective Q for this circuit

$$Q_{\text{eff}} = \frac{Q_0 R_{\text{sh}}}{R_0} \tag{9-229}$$

Since R_{sh} is the parallel combination of r, R_T, and R_0,

$$Q_{\text{eff}} < Q_0 \tag{9-230}$$

Then, for an FET or a vacuum tube

$$\mathbf{A}_v = \frac{-g_m R_{\text{sh}}}{1 + jQ_{\text{eff}}\,\delta(\delta + 2)/(\delta + 1)} \tag{9-231}$$

At $f = f_0$, the gain is maximum and is

$$\mathbf{A}_{v0} = -g_m R_{\text{sh}} \tag{9-232}$$

The normalized response is given by

$$\frac{\mathbf{A}_v}{\mathbf{A}_{v0}} = \frac{1}{1 + jQ_{\text{eff}}\,\delta(\delta + 2)/(\delta + 1)} \tag{9-233}$$

This has exactly the same form as Eq. (9-215), except that Q_0 has been replaced by Q_{eff}, and thus Fig. 9-62 is a plot of the normalized amplitude response of this amplifier. Hence, the half-power bandwidth is given by

$$B = \frac{f_0}{Q_{\text{eff}}} \tag{9-234}$$

At the half-power frequencies, the phase shift is $\pm 45°$. The gain-bandwidth product is

$$|A_{v0}|B = \frac{g_m R_{\text{sh}} f_0}{Q_{\text{eff}}} = \frac{g_m}{2\pi C} \tag{9-235}$$

This result is the same as that given by Eq. (9-24) for the simple *RC*-coupled amplifier.

For a transistor amplifier $\mathbf{I}_2 = -\mathbf{V}_2/R_i$. Thus,

$$\mathbf{A}_i = \frac{h_f R_{\text{sh}}/R_i}{1 + jQ_{\text{eff}}\,\delta(\delta + 2)/(\delta + 1)} \tag{9-236a}$$

At $f = f_0$

$$A_{i0} = \frac{h_f R_{\text{sh}}}{R_i} \tag{9-236b}$$

The normalized form of this expression is the same as Eq. (9-233). If R_i could be reduced to zero, then R_{sh} also approaches zero such that $R_{\text{sh}}/R_i = 1$.

The current gain is then a maximum. However, Q_{eff} will also be zero, and the circuit will not provide any selectivity. It is sometimes difficult to obtain the desired selectivity with transistor amplifiers because the value of R_i is too low. If Q_0 is increased, then Q_{eff} will also increase [see Eq. (9-229)], and the bandwidth will be reduced. To increase Q_0, the ratio of L to R must be increased. We can very roughly say that the inductance of an inductor increases with the square of the number of turns while its resistance increases linearly with the number of turns. Thus, Q_0 will increase if L is increased. However, the parasitic capacitance limits the minimum value of C and, hence, the maximum value of L is fixed by the relation $f_0 = 1/2\pi\sqrt{LC}$. Thus, we cannot always obtain the desired selectivity by increasing L. In the next section, we shall see that a low value of R_i need not prevent us from obtaining the desired selectivity.

We shall now demonstrate that, in general, it is desirable to use as large a value of L as possible. The gain-bandwidth product for the transistor amplifier is given by

$$A_{i0}B = \frac{h_f/R_i}{2\pi C} \tag{9-237}$$

This is somewhat different from the case of the RC-coupled transistor amplifier since we have assumed that the operating frequency is far below ω_β and that capacitor C_1 is added to the circuit. From Eqs. (9-235) and (9-237) we can conclude that, for both the vacuum-tube and the transistor amplifiers, it is desirable to make C as small as possible. Thus, L should be made as large as possible. It is often desirable to vary $f_0 = 1/2\pi\sqrt{LC}$. This is done so that the amplifier can be tuned to different signals. Even if the amplifier is only to be used at one frequency, there is always provision made to vary f_0 slightly, for purposes of adjustment. If L is made adjustable, often by moving a low-loss ferromagnetic core into or out of it, then the capacitor C need only be the parasitic capacitance of the circuit. Hence the minimum value of C will always be used. If a variable capacitor is used to tune the circuit, then values of C that are larger than the parasitic capacitance will be required and the gain-bandwidth product will be reduced. In some frequency ranges, the losses due to the ferromagnetic core become very large. It is somewhat easier to construct a variable capacitor than a variable inductor. For these reasons, both variable-inductance and variable-capacitance tuned circuits are used.

When tuned amplifiers are cascaded, the overall amplification is the product of the responses of the individual stages. Thus, the midband gain increases and the bandwidth decreases. It can be shown that the decrease in half-power bandwidth as the number of stages increases is given by Eq. (9-93). Again, we see that the bandwidth of the simple RC-coupled amplifier and that of the single-tuned amplifier are related. In the case of the tuned amplifier, the decrease in bandwidth may actually be desirable since it increases the selectivity of the circuit.

9-22 IMPEDANCE-LEVEL CONTROL IN TUNED AMPLIFIERS—TAPPED INDUCTANCES

The input resistance of a transistor amplifier is often such that Q_{eff} is too small and the amplifier does not possess the required selectivity. In such cases, the effective input resistance of the transistor must be made to appear larger. An impedance-matching transformer placed between the output of the tuned circuit and the input to the transistor will accomplish this. In Fig. 9-66 we have so modified the model of Fig. 9-65. The input bias is supplied through the secondary of the transformer and the resistor R_B can be omitted. Thus, the resistor R_T has been replaced by R_i. Any input capacitance should be referred to the primary side of the transformer (see Sec. 9-18). Let us assume that the transformer is ideal. Then $R_i' = (n_1/n_2)^2 R_i$ can be adjusted to be any value that is desired.

There is an optimum turns ratio that will provide maximum current gain. If the load resistance is fixed, then the maximum power dissipation in the load and maximum load current occur simultaneously. (If the load resistance is varied, then maximum load current will occur when the load resistance is zero, but maximum power dissipation occurs when the load is matched to the generator resistance.) If R_0 represents the impedance of the tuned circuit at resonance, then maximum current gain occurs when

$$\left(\frac{n_1}{n_2}\right)^2 R_i = \frac{R_0 r}{R_0 + r}$$

$$\left.\frac{n_1}{n_2}\right|_{\text{opt}} = \sqrt{\frac{R_0 r}{R_i(R_0 + r)}} \tag{9-238}$$

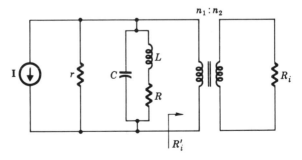

Fig. 9-66 A single-tuned circuit that uses a transformer as an impedance-matching device.

This equation is not as important as it may seem, since selectivity requirements often govern the choice of the impedance level rather than the current
gain.   In addition, we shall see in Sec. 9-26 that mismatch is at times
deliberately introduced to prevent the circuit from oscillating.

   The circuit of Fig. 9-66 is rarely used, because essentially the same effect
can be achieved by using the circuit of Fig. 9-65 and tapping the coil.   Such
a circuit is shown in Fig. 9-67a.   The input impedance of the coil will be
obtained from the circuit of Fig. 9-67b.   We have assumed that all the
resistance of the coil is in series with L_1.   Since L_2 is usually considerably
less than L_1, the assumption is very good.   Then, from Fig. 9-67b, we have

$$\mathbf{V} = j\omega(L_1 + L_2 + 2M)\mathbf{I}_a + j\omega(M + L_2)\mathbf{I}_b$$
$$0 = j\omega(M + L_2)\mathbf{I}_a + (j\omega L_2 + R_T)\mathbf{I}_b$$

Solving for the impedance $\mathbf{Z}_1 = \mathbf{V}/\mathbf{I}_a$ and noting that $L = L_1 + L_2 + 2M$,
we obtain

$$\mathbf{Z}_i = j\omega L + \frac{\omega^2(L_2 + M)^2}{R_T + j\omega L_2} \tag{9-239}$$

For most applications the impedance of $\omega L_2 \ll R_T$, so that

$$\mathbf{Z}_i = j\omega L + \frac{\omega^2(L_2 + M)^2}{R_T} \tag{9-240}$$

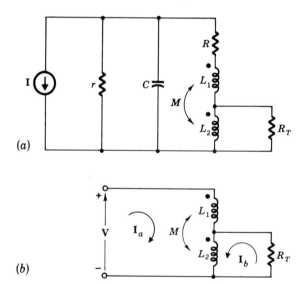

(a)

(b)

Fig. 9-67   (a) A single-tuned circuit that uses a tapped
coil as an impedance-matching device and (b) a circuit used
to calculate the input impedance of the coil.

This can be represented as an inductance L in series with a resistance $\omega^2(L_2 + M)^2/R_T$. The resistance varies with frequency. In general, the frequencies of interest are very close to ω_0, so that we can assume that the resistance does not change with frequency. Hence,

$$\mathbf{Z}_i = j\omega L + \frac{\omega_0{}^2(L_2 + M)^2}{R_T} \tag{9-241}$$

The reactive portion of the impedance must be left as a function of frequency, since it results in the difference of two nearly equal terms [see Eq. (9-207)]. The term $L_2 + M$ depends upon the position of the tap. Its minimum value is zero, so that the component of series resistance due to R_T can be made as small as desired. It is assumed that the resistance R of the coil is small enough and r is large enough so that the desired selectivity can then be obtained.

A tapped inductance is used in this example. Instead of this, we could use a tapped capacitor. That is, C could be replaced by two capacitors in series, with R_T connected between their junction and the common terminal. The results for this circuit are similar to those for the tapped inductance.

9-23 MUTUAL-INDUCTANCE-COUPLED SINGLE-TUNED CIRCUITS

Coupled coils are often used to produce an impedance transformation. Two such circuits are shown in Fig. 9-68. When mutual-inductance coupling is used, no coupling capacitor, R_g, grid-leak resistance, or shunting base-bias resistance is needed. Thus, these circuits are very commonly used. The untuned winding is placed in the circuit of lowest impedance. Hence, Fig. 9-68a is typical of the equivalent circuits of common-emitter transistor amplifiers, while 9-68b is typical of common-source FET amplifiers. Such circuits are also used to couple an antenna, which has a low impedance, to an amplifier. We shall analyze each of these circuits separately.

Tuned primary, untuned secondary Proceeding as we did to obtain Eq. (9-239), the impedance $\mathbf{Z}_1$ is given by

$$\mathbf{Z}_1 = R_1 + j\omega L_1 + \frac{\omega^2 M^2}{R_2 + R_i + j\omega L_2}$$

For most practical circuits, $R_2 + R_i \gg \omega L_2$ at all frequencies of interest. Also, as in the case of Eq. (9-241), we can consider the term $\omega^2 M^2$ to be a constant equal to $\omega_0{}^2 M^2$. Thus, we have

$$\mathbf{Z}_1 = R_1 + \frac{\omega_0{}^2 M^2}{R_2 + R_i} + j\omega L_1$$

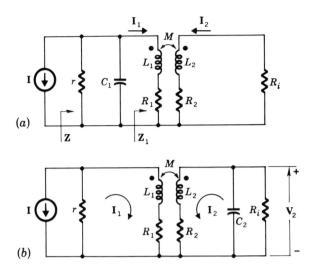

Fig. 9-68 Two single-tuned mutually inductive coupled circuits. (*a*) Tuned primary, untuned secondary and (*b*) untuned primary, tuned secondary.

where

$$\omega_0 = \frac{1}{\sqrt{L_1 C_1}} \tag{9-242}$$

Hence, $\mathbf{Z}_1$ appears as a constant resistance in series with an inductance. At ω_0 the Q of this circuit is given by

$$Q_1 = \frac{\omega_0 L_1}{R_1 + \omega_0{}^2 M^2/(R_2 + R_i)} \tag{9-243}$$

Then, using the results of Secs. 9-20 and 9-21

$$\mathbf{Z} = \frac{R_{\mathrm{sh}}}{1 + jQ_{\mathrm{eff},1}\,\delta(\delta + 2)/(\delta + 1)}$$

where

$$Q_{\mathrm{eff},1} = \frac{Q_1 r}{r + Q_1 \omega_0 L_1} \tag{9-244}$$

and

$$R_{\mathrm{sh}} = \frac{Q_1 \omega_0 L_1 r}{r + Q_1 \omega_0 L_1} \tag{9-245}$$

Then

$$I_2 = \frac{j\omega M I_1}{R_i + R_2 + j\omega L_2}$$

and

$$I_1 = I\frac{Z}{Z_1}$$

Thus, the current gain I_2/I is given by

$$A_i = \frac{j\omega M Z}{(R_i + R_2 + j\omega L_2)[R_1 + \omega_0^2 M^2/(R_2 + R_i) + j\omega L_1]}$$

In general, the effective Q of the primary inductance will be large, so that $\omega L_1 \gg R_1 + \omega_0^2 M^2/(R_2 + R_i)$. In addition, $R_i + R_2 \gg \omega L_2$. Therefore,

$$A_i \approx \frac{M R_{\text{sh}}/(R_i + R_2) L_1}{1 + j Q_{\text{eff},1}\, \delta(\delta + 2)/(\delta + 1)} \tag{9-246}$$

If Eq. (9-246) represents the gain of a transistor amplifier, then it should be multiplied by h_f. It is assumed that $\omega_0 \ll \omega_\beta$. The gain at resonance is

$$A_{i0} = \frac{M R_{\text{sh}}}{L_1(R_i + R_2)} = \frac{M \omega_0^2 L_1 r}{(R_i + R_2)[\omega_0^2 L_1^2 + R_1 r + \omega_0^2 M^2 r/(R_2 + R_i)]} \tag{9-247}$$

To obtain the value of M that gives the largest current gain, differentiate this with respect to M and set the derivative equal to zero.

$$M_{\text{opt}} = \frac{1}{\omega_0} \sqrt{\frac{(\omega_0^2 L_1^2 + R_1 r)(R_2 + R_i)}{r}} \tag{9-248}$$

Selectivity considerations often cause smaller values of M to be used. The normalized gain is

$$\frac{A_i}{A_{i0}} = \frac{1}{1 + j Q_{\text{eff},1}\, \delta(\delta + 2)/(\delta + 1)} \tag{9-249}$$

This has exactly the same form as Eq. (9-215) and, hence, the half-power bandwidth is

$$B = \frac{f_0}{Q_{\text{eff},1}} \tag{9-250}$$

If r is not large enough, $Q_{\text{eff},1}$ will be too small. In addition, the output capacitance of the active element (transistor) may be quite large, which results in too small a value of L_1. Both of these effects can be reduced by connecting the output of the transistor to a tap on L_1.

Untuned primary, tuned secondary   The circuit of Fig. 9-68b is usually used with FETs or vacuum tubes, and often we can consider R_i to be an open circuit.   Alternatively, the shunt resistance can be computed as a resistance effectively in series with C_2 (see Sec. 9-21).   In this case, the value of R_2 is increased by this amount.   In the case of the FET we assume that C_{gd} is small enough so that the shunting conductance due to the Miller effect is negligible. Replacing the current generator by a voltage generator and writing mesh equations, we have

$$-r\mathbf{I} = (r_1 + j\omega L_1)\mathbf{I}_1 + j\omega M \mathbf{I}_2 \tag{9-251a}$$

$$0 = j\omega M \mathbf{I}_1 + \left[R_2 + j\left(\omega L_2 - \frac{1}{\omega C_2}\right)\right]\mathbf{I}_2 \tag{9-251b}$$

where $r_1 = r + R_1$.   Then

$$\mathbf{I}_2 = \frac{r\mathbf{I}j\omega M}{(r_1 + j\omega L_1)[R_2 + j(\omega L_2 - 1/\omega C_2)] + \omega^2 M^2}$$

For FETs or vacuum-tube pentodes, which are usually used in such circuits, $r_1 \gg \omega L_1$ for frequencies of interest.   We can then write $r_1 + j\omega L_1 \approx r_1$. Special care should be taken when such approximations are made in resonant circuits to ensure that highly critical terms do not become inaccurate.   The approximation is usually valid in this case.

Since $\mathbf{V}_2 = -\mathbf{I}_2/j\omega C_2$, we have

$$\frac{\mathbf{V}_2}{\mathbf{I}} = \frac{-Mr/C_2 r_1 R_2}{1 + \dfrac{\omega^2 M^2}{r_1 R_2} + \dfrac{j\omega L_2}{R_2}(1 - 1/\omega^2 L_2 C_2)} \tag{9-252}$$

As in the case of Eq. (9-241), we can approximate $1 + \omega^2 M^2/r_1 R_2$ by $1 + \omega_0^2 M^2/r_1 R_2$.   In addition, we shall use the substitutions

$$\omega_0 = \frac{1}{\sqrt{L_2 C_2}} \qquad f_0 = \frac{1}{2\pi\sqrt{L_2 C_2}} \tag{9-253}$$

$$Q_2 = \frac{\omega_0 L_2}{R_2} \tag{9-254}$$

and

$$\delta = \frac{f - f_0}{f_0}$$

Then, proceeding as in Sec. 9-20, we obtain

$$\frac{\mathbf{V}_2}{\mathbf{I}} = \frac{-(Mr/C_2 r_1 R_2)/(1 + \omega_0^2 M^2/r_1 R_2)}{1 + j\dfrac{Q_2}{1 + \omega_0^2 M^2/r_1 R_2}\delta\dfrac{2 + \delta}{1 + \delta}}$$

If Fig. 9-68b is the linear model of an FET amplifier, then $\mathbf{I} = g_m\mathbf{V}_1$ and $r = r_d$. Then, at ω_0, we have

$$\mathbf{A}_{v0} = \frac{-g_m M r_d / C_2 r_1 R_2}{1 + \omega_0{}^2 M^2 / r_1 R_2} = \frac{-g_m \omega_0 M Q_2 r_d / r_1}{1 + \omega_0{}^2 M^2 / r_1 R_2} \tag{9-255}$$

and

$$\frac{\mathbf{A}_v}{\mathbf{A}_{v0}} = \frac{1}{1 + jQ_{\text{eff},2} \, \delta(\delta + 2)/(\delta + 1)} \tag{9-256}$$

where

$$Q_{\text{eff},2} = \frac{Q_2}{1 + \omega_0{}^2 M^2 / r_1 R_2} \tag{9-257}$$

and the bandwidth is given by

$$B = \frac{f_0}{Q_{\text{eff},2}} \tag{9-258}$$

If we maximize A_{v0} with respect to M, we obtain

$$M = \frac{1}{\omega_0} \sqrt{r_1 R_2} \tag{9-259}$$

Often, $r_d \gg R_1$ so that $r_1 \approx r_d$. Thus

$$A_{v0} = -g_m \omega_0 M Q_{\text{eff},2} \tag{9-260}$$

9-24 DOUBLE-TUNED AMPLIFIERS

Amplifiers that use more than one tuned circuit have frequency-response characteristics that are more versatile than those we have considered. A linear model for such an amplifier is shown in Fig. 9-69a. The analysis of this circuit is very tedious. To obtain the results that can be easily used, we shall make some simplifying approximations. If a resistor R is in parallel with an inductance L, the impedance of the combination is given by

$$\mathbf{Z} = \frac{j\omega L R}{R + j\omega L} = \frac{\omega^2 L^2 R + j\omega L R^2}{R^2 + \omega^2 L^2}$$

If $R \gg \omega L$ and if we work in a narrow range of frequencies, so that the frequency dependence of the effective series resistance can be neglected, we can write

$$\mathbf{Z} \approx \frac{\omega_0{}^2 L^2}{R} + j\omega L \tag{9-261}$$

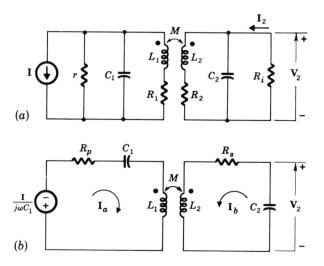

Fig. 9-69 (*a*) A double-tuned amplifier circuit and (*b*) an approximation of this circuit that will be used for analysis.

We shall assume that when the resistance of the coil itself is added to $\omega_0{}^2L^2/R$, the total effective series resistance is obtained.

$$R_p = \frac{\omega_0{}^2L_1{}^2}{r} + R_1 \tag{9-262}$$

and

$$R_s = \frac{\omega_0{}^2L_2{}^2}{R_i} + R_2 \tag{9-263}$$

If these modifications are made and the current generator shunted by C_1 is replaced by a voltage generator in series with C_1, the circuit of Fig. 9-69*b* results. Writing mesh equations, we obtain

$$\frac{-\mathbf{I}}{j\omega C_1} = \mathbf{Z}_p\mathbf{I}_a + j\omega M\mathbf{I}_b \tag{9-264a}$$

$$0 = j\omega M\mathbf{I}_a + \mathbf{Z}_s\mathbf{I}_b \tag{9-264b}$$

where

$$\mathbf{Z}_p = R_p\left[1 + j\frac{\omega L_1}{R_p}\left(1 - \frac{1}{\omega^2L_1C_1}\right)\right] \tag{9-265}$$

and

$$\mathbf{Z}_s = R_s\left[1 + j\frac{\omega L_2}{R_s}\left(1 - \frac{1}{\omega^2L_2C_2}\right)\right] \tag{9-266}$$

Let us assume that the primary and secondary circuits are adjusted so that

$$f_0 = \frac{1}{2\pi\sqrt{L_1 C_1}} = \frac{1}{2\pi\sqrt{L_2 C_2}} \tag{9-267}$$

Then let

$$Q_1 = \frac{\omega_0 L_1}{R_p} \tag{9-268}$$

and

$$Q_2 = \frac{\omega_0 L_2}{R_s} \tag{9-269}$$

Proceeding as in Sec. 9-20, we have

$$\mathbf{Z}_p = R_p\left[1 + jQ_1 \frac{\delta(\delta + 2)}{\delta + 1}\right] \tag{9-270a}$$

$$\mathbf{Z}_s = R_s\left[1 + jQ_2 \frac{\delta(\delta + 2)}{\delta + 1}\right] \tag{9-270b}$$

Usually $\delta = (f - f_0)/f_0 \ll 1$, so that $(\delta + 2)/(\delta + 1) \approx 2$. This approximation could have been made in the preceding sections. However, there was no need. It is done here to simplify the relatively complex results. Thus,

$$\mathbf{Z}_p = R_p(1 + j2Q_1 \delta) \tag{9-271}$$

$$\mathbf{Z}_s = R_s(1 + j2Q_2 \delta) \tag{9-272}$$

Substitute these expressions into Eqs. (9-264) and solve for $\mathbf{V}_2/\mathbf{I}$.

$$\frac{\mathbf{V}_2}{\mathbf{I}} = \frac{-M/j\omega_0 C_1 C_2 R_p R_s}{1 - 4\delta^2 Q_1 Q_2 + j2\delta(Q_1 + Q_2) + \omega_0^2 M^2/R_p R_s}$$

where we have again assumed that $\omega M \approx \omega_0 M$ and $\omega C_2 \approx \omega_0 C_2$ over all frequencies of interest [see Eq. (9-241)]. Let

$$b = \frac{\omega_0 M}{\sqrt{R_p R_s}} \tag{9-273}$$

Then

$$\frac{\mathbf{V}_2}{\mathbf{I}} = \frac{-(1/j\omega_0^2 C_1 C_2 \sqrt{R_p R_s})[b/(1 + b^2)]}{1 - 4\delta^2 Q_1 Q_2/(1 + b^2) + j2\delta(Q_1 + Q_2)/(1 + b^2)} \tag{9-274}$$

If Fig. 9-69 represents the model of an FET, then Eq. (9-274) must be multiplied by g_m to obtain the voltage gain. Similarly, for a transistor, the current gain is obtained by multiplying by $-h_f/R_i$. Then, when $f = f_0$ for the FET amplifier

$$\mathbf{A}_{v0} = \frac{-g_m}{j\omega_0{}^2 C_1 C_2 \sqrt{R_p R_s}} \frac{b}{b^2 + 1} \qquad (9\text{-}275)$$

and for the transistor amplifier

$$\mathbf{A}_{i0} = \frac{h_{fe}}{j\omega_0{}^2 C_1 C_2 R_i \sqrt{R_p R_s}} \frac{b}{b^2 + 1} \qquad (9\text{-}276)$$

where we have assumed that the input impedance of the transistor is essentially resistive.   If either of these expressions is maximized with respect to b, we obtain

$$b_{\mathrm{opt}} = \pm 1 \qquad (9\text{-}277)$$

$$M_{\mathrm{opt}} = \frac{\pm \sqrt{R_p R_s}}{\omega_0} \qquad (9\text{-}278)$$

For convenience, we shall normalize with respect to the maximum gain at resonance $\mathbf{A}_{0,\max}$.

$$\frac{\mathbf{A}}{\mathbf{A}_{0,\max}} = \frac{2b/(b^2 + 1)}{1 - 4\,\delta^2 Q_1 Q_2/(1 + b^2) + j2\,\delta(Q_1 + Q_2)/(1 + b^2)} \qquad (9\text{-}279)$$

A plot of $|A/A_{0,\max}|$ versus frequency for various values of b is shown in Fig. 9-70.   The case $Q_1 = Q_2$ has been plotted here.   For values of $b \le 1$,

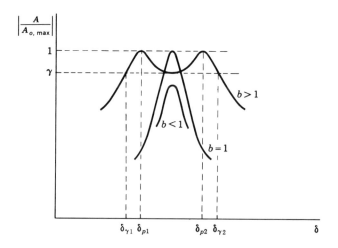

Fig. 9-70 Resonance curves for the double-tuned amplifier. These curves are drawn for $Q_1 = Q_2$.

the response resembles the usual resonance curve.   However, for $b > 1$, the shape changes considerably.   The maximum of the response no longer occurs at $f = f_0$, and the curve has two peaks.   We shall discuss the utility of this type of response subsequently.   To determine the frequencies where the peaks occur, set $(d/d\delta)|A/A_{0,\max}| = 0$.   Solving for δ, we obtain

$$\delta = 0$$

$$\delta_{p1,p2} = \pm\frac{1 + b^2}{2Q_1Q_2}\sqrt{\frac{Q_1Q_2}{1 + b^2} - \frac{(Q_1 + Q_2)^2}{2(1 + b^2)^2}} \tag{9-280}$$

If $Q_1Q_2/(1 + b^2) \le (Q_1 + Q_2)^2/2(1 + b^2)^2$, the value of δ_{p1} and δ_{p2} are imaginary, there is only one peak in the response curve, and $\delta = 0$ is a maximum.   However, if the inequality is reversed, then there will be a double hump and $\delta = 0$ will be a minimum.   The critical value of b is given by

$$b_{\text{crit}} = \frac{1}{\sqrt{2}}\sqrt{\frac{Q_1}{Q_2} + \frac{Q_2}{Q_1}} \tag{9-281}$$

When $b > b_{\text{crit}}$, the double-humped response results.
     Let us now consider that $Q_1 = Q_2 = Q_0$.   Actually, we shall see that we can achieve this in most practical cases.   Then

$$\delta_{p1,p2} = \frac{\pm 1}{2Q_0}\sqrt{b^2 - 1} \tag{9-282}$$

and $b_{\text{crit}} = 1$.   The frequencies where the peaks occur can be found from the relation $f/f_0 = 1 + \delta$.
     In Secs. 9-20 to 9-23 we determined the half-power bandwidth.   In practice, the bandwidth is set by the design requirements.   For instance, we could consider the bandwidth to be those frequencies where

$$\gamma \le \left|\frac{A}{A_{0,\max}}\right| \le 1 \tag{9-283}$$

γ is an arbitrary positive number less than 1.   In order to obtain the broadest bandwidth, for the double-humped curve, the minimum at $\delta = 0$ should be adjusted to be equal to γ.   The bandwidth B_γ then lies between $\delta_{\gamma 1}$ and $\delta_{\gamma 2}$, as shown in Fig. 9-70.   From Eq. (9-279) we have

$$\gamma = \frac{2b}{b^2 + 1} \tag{9-284}$$

Solve for b and choose the value greater than $b_{\text{crit}} = 1$.

$$= \frac{1}{\gamma} + \sqrt{\frac{1}{\gamma^2} - 1} \tag{9-285}$$

Note that $\gamma < 1$, so that b_γ is real. Then, setting the magnitude of Eq. (9-279) equal to $2b/(b^2 + 1)$ and solving for $\delta_{\gamma1,\gamma2}$, we obtain

$$\delta_{\gamma1,\gamma2} = \pm \frac{1}{\sqrt{2}Q_0} \sqrt{b^2 - 1} \qquad (9\text{-}286)$$

If we compare this with Eq. (9-282), we see that

$$\delta_{\gamma1} = \sqrt{2}\delta_{p1} \qquad (9\text{-}287a)$$

$$\delta_{\gamma2} = \sqrt{2}\delta_{p2} \qquad (9\text{-}287b)$$

Then, using the relation $\delta = f/f_0 - 1$, we have

$$B_\gamma = \frac{\sqrt{2}}{Q_0} f_0 \sqrt{b^2 - 1} \qquad (9\text{-}288)$$

The value of b can be related to the *coefficient of coupling* of the coils. This is defined by

$$k = \frac{M}{\sqrt{L_1 L_2}} \qquad (9\text{-}289)$$

Manipulating Eq. (9-273), we obtain

$$b = k\sqrt{Q_1 Q_2} \qquad (9\text{-}290)$$

The maximum value that the coefficient of coupling can have is unity. Thus,

$$b_{\max} = \sqrt{Q_1 Q_2} \qquad (9\text{-}291)$$

A procedure especially useful in transistor circuits, and which can be used to raise Q_1 and Q_2, is to tap the coils L_1 and L_2 and connect the load and the transistor to these taps. By properly adjusting the taps, the values

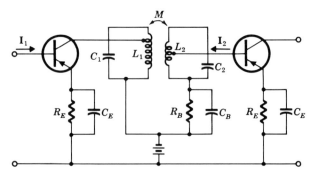

Fig. 9-71 A double-tuned transistor amplifier circuit using tapped coils.

of Q_1 and Q_2 can be made equal.   A typical circuit utilizing these connections is shown in Fig. 9-71.   The procedure of Sec. 9-22 can be used to calculate the impedances of this circuit.

9-25 MORE-COMPLEX TUNED CIRCUITS—
THE DESIGN OF BANDPASS AMPLIFIERS

An ideal bandpass amplifier would have a frequency characteristic like that shown in Fig. 9-72a.   That is, the response should be constant for a specified range of frequencies and zero elsewhere.   However, this characteristic cannot be realized in practice.   Practical design specifications require that the response lie within the crosshatched area of Fig. 9-72b.   The region between $f_{\rho 1}$ and $f_{\rho 2}$ is called the *passband*.   Here the normalized response is held close to unity. $\gamma \leq |A/A_0| \leq 1$.   The frequencies from zero to f_{r1} and from f_{r2} to ∞ constitute the *stop band*, where the normalized response must be less than a specified value r.   The remaining frequencies, those between f_{r1} and $f_{\rho 1}$, and $f_{\rho 2}$ and f_{r2}, make up the *transition band*.   No specific requirements are placed in this interval.   However, it is assumed that $|A/A_0|$ falls from the

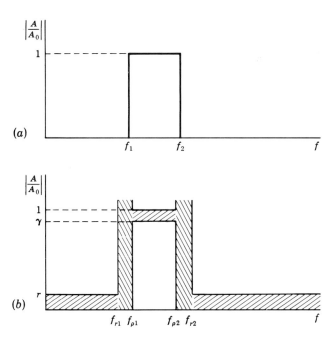

Fig. 9-72 (*a*) The frequency response of an ideal bandpass amplifier and (*b*) design requirements for a practical bandpass amplifier.   The response must lie within the crosshatched area.

passband value to the stop-band value in this region. In addition to the frequency requirements, the magnitude of A_0 will also be specified.

Let us consider how a simple single-tuned RC-coupled amplifier would be designed in view of these requirements. (Much of the discussion of Sec. 9-8 applies here.) Choose f_0 such that

$$f_0 = \sqrt{f_{\rho 1} f_{\rho 2}} \tag{9-292}$$

The minimum value of capacitance should be used to maximize the gain-bandwidth product. Equation (9-208) then determines L. The maximum Q that can be conveniently obtained should be used for Q_0. Try one stage. The required value of R_{sh} is found from A_0 using Eq. (9-232) or (9-236b). If the actual value of R_{sh} calculated by Eq. (9-228) is greater than this value, shunt resistance should be placed across R_T. If the value calculated from Eq. (9-228) is too small, an impedance-matching technique must be used and/or Q_0 must be increased. We shall assume that the actual R_{sh} of Eq. (9-228) is equal to or greater than the required one. The value of Q_{eff} is obtained from Eq. (9-229) and the frequency response if then given by Eq. (9-233). The passband requirements are then checked at $f_{\rho 1}$ or $f_{\rho 2}$, and if they are met, we proceed to the stop-band requirements. If they are not met, try additional stages and repeat the procedure until a broad enough passband is obtained. It may not be possible to do this. In that case, an FET with a higher $g_m/2\pi C$ or a transistor with a higher g_m or lower capacitance should be chosen. If the gain-bandwidth product is larger than required, then the gain of each amplifier stage should be increased, if possible, until the passband requirements are exactly obtained. This will improve the selectivity in the stop band. When the passband design is completed, the stop-band response should be checked. If $f_{r1} f_{r2} = f_0{}^2$, then, because of the geometric symmetry, the stop-band response need be verified only at either f_{r1} or f_{r2}. If $f_{r1} f_{r2} > f_0{}^2$, then check the response at f_{r1}, and if $f_{r1} f_{r2} < f_0{}^2$, check the response at f_{r2}. If the stop-band requirements are not met, increase the number of stages while adjusting their Q's so that the passband specifications are exactly realized. If too many stages are needed, it is possible that the passband specifications cannot be achieved. In such a case, a more complex coupling network or an active element that provides a higher gain-bandwidth product is needed.

If r or R_T is too low to obtain the desired Q_{eff}, then an impedance-matching circuit, using either tapped coils or mutual inductance, should be used. There are additional degrees of freedom in this case, but the basic procedure is the same.

In general, double-tuned circuits are used when the design specifications are somewhat more severe. We shall assume that coils with equal Q's are used, to determine b_y from γ [see Eq. (9-285)]. Then, establish the value of Q_0 from Eq. (9-288). Use the smallest values of capacitors that are feasible.

These will determine the inductances. Then we can calculate the effective resistance and the actual Q of the coils. Assume that the calculated Q_0 is less than the actual Q_0 given by Eq. (9-268) or (9-269). If this is so, then shunt resistance can be added to reduce the Q to the desired value. We assume here that the Q's of the primary and secondary can be made equal and that $b > 1$. In this case, the gain at the peaks of the response curve can be obtained from Eq. (9-275) or (9-276) with $b = 1$. Thus,

$$A_{v,\max} = \frac{g_m Q_0^2 \sqrt{R_p R_s}}{2} \quad \text{or} \quad A_{i,\max} = \frac{h_{fe} Q_0^2 \sqrt{R_p R_s}}{2R_i}$$

If these gains are not sufficiently large, try two stages. In this case use a new value of γ which is the square root of the original γ. Continue to increase the number of stages until the passband requirements are met. This may not always be possible. In that case g_m or h_{fe}/R_i must be raised and/or the shunting capacitors reduced. The stop-band design then proceeds in essentially the same way that it does for the single-tuned amplifier. The use of tapped inductances can prove helpful here also, especially for transistor circuits.

The networks that we have considered are called *synchronously tuned.* That is, all the circuits are tuned to the same resonant frequency. If stringent design requirements are imposed, that is, γ very close to unity, r very small, and the width of the transition bands quite narrow, it is possible that these procedures will not produce an acceptable circuit. In such cases, a more general procedure called *filter synthesis* is used to design the network. The resonant frequencies of the various tuned circuits may not all be the same when this general procedure is used. Such networks are called *stagger tuned.*

9-26 NEUTRALIZATION

Thus far in our discussion of tuned amplifiers, we have neglected the fact that any coupling that allows an output signal to be fed back to the input circuit may cause the amplifier to oscillate. The phenomenon of oscillation is very complex. We shall discuss it briefly here and defer a detailed discussion of it until Chap. 13. The oscillation can be analyzed by considering the input admittance of the active element. In Sec. 6-16 we demonstrated that the input admittance of a common-source FET amplifier whose voltage gain was A_v is given by

$$\mathbf{Y}_i = j\omega[C_{gs} + (1 - \mathbf{A}_v)C_{gd}] \tag{9-293}$$

For a dual-gate FET, C_{gs} is replaced by C_{in}. Let us assume that the voltage gain $\mathbf{A}_v$ is a complex number such that

$$\mathbf{A}_v = A_R + jA_x \tag{9-294}$$

Then

$$\mathbf{Y}_i = \omega A_x C_{gd} + j\omega[C_{gs} + (1 - A_R)C_{gd}] \qquad (9\text{-}295)$$

The first term is a shunt conductance, which can be positive or *negative*, depending upon the phase angle of the load impedance.

The input admittance of a common-emitter transistor is found in Sec. 6-19 [see Eq. (6-151) and Fig. 6-45]. From this figure we have

$$\frac{1}{\mathbf{Y}_i} = r_{bb'} + \frac{1}{\mathbf{Y}_i'} \qquad (9\text{-}296)$$

where

$$\mathbf{Y}_i' = \frac{1}{r_{b'e}} + j\omega C_{b'e} + \left(\frac{1}{r_{b'c}} + j\omega C_{b'c}\right)(1 - \mathbf{A}_v') \qquad (9\text{-}297)$$

In general, A_v' is a complex number, so that we can write

$$\mathbf{A}_v' = A_R + jA_x \qquad (9\text{-}298)$$

Then, substituting in Eq. (9-297), we obtain

$$\mathbf{Y}_i' = \frac{1}{r_{b'e}} + \frac{1 - A_R}{r_{b'c}} + \omega C_{b'c} A_x + j\left[\omega C_{b'e} + \omega C_{b'c}(1 - A_R) - \frac{A_x}{r_{b'c}}\right] \qquad (9\text{-}299)$$

The conductive portion of this admittance is

$$G_i' = \frac{1}{r_{b'e}} + \frac{1 - A_R}{r_{b'c}} + \omega C_{b'c} A_x \qquad (9\text{-}300)$$

If A_x is negative, this can be a negative conductance. The input conductance is found by substituting Eq. (9-299) into Eq. (9-296). Substitution yields

$$\frac{1}{\mathbf{Y}_i} = r_{bb'} + \frac{1/r_{b'e} + (1 - A_R)/r_{b'c} + \omega C_{b'c} A_x}{\left\{\left(\dfrac{1}{r_{b'e}} + \dfrac{1 - A_R}{r_{b'c}} + \omega C_{b'c} A_x\right)^2\right.}$$

$$\left. + \left[\omega C_{b'e} + \omega C_{b'c}(1 - A_R) - \dfrac{A_x}{r_{b'c}}\right]^2\right\}$$

$$- \frac{j[\omega C_{b'e} + \omega C_{b'c}(1 - A_R) - A_x/r_{b'c}]}{\left\{\left(\dfrac{1}{r_{b'e}} + \dfrac{1 - A_R}{r_{b'c}} + \omega C_{b'c} A_x\right)^2\right.}$$

$$\left. + \left[\omega C_{b'e} + \omega C_{b'c}(1 - A_R) - \dfrac{A_x}{r_{b'c}}\right]^2\right\} \qquad (9\text{-}301)$$

If A_x is negative and $|\omega C_{b'c} A_x|$ is large enough, then the real part of $1/\mathbf{Y}_i$ will be negative. In this case, Re (Y_i) will also be negative.

Thus, it is possible that the input conductance of the FET, vacuum-tube, or transistor amplifier can be negative. Note that in all three cases, the negative input conductance is due to the capacitor (or parallel RC network) connected from the output to the input, for example, C_{gd} for the FET and $C_{b'c}$ in parallel with $r_{b'c}$ for the transistor. These are called *feedback elements* since they feed an output signal back to the input.

Now let us consider the effect a negative conductance can have when it is placed in shunt with a parallel-resonant circuit.

If we have a high-Q parallel-resonant circuit whose impedance is given by

$$\mathbf{Z}_1 = \frac{R_0}{1 + jQ_0(f/f_0 - f_0/f)}$$

and we shunt it by a negative resistance $-R$, the resulting impedance is

$$\mathbf{Z} = \frac{R_0 R/(R - R_0)}{1 + jQ_{\text{eff}}(f/f_0 - f_0/f)} \tag{9-302}$$

where

$$Q_{\text{eff}} = \frac{Q_0 R}{R - R_0} \tag{9-303}$$

In transformed form, this becomes

$$\mathbf{Z} = \frac{s\omega_0 R_0 R/(R - R_0)Q_{\text{eff}}}{s^2 + (\omega_0/Q_{\text{eff}})s + \omega_0{}^2} \tag{9-304}$$

The poles of this expression occur at

$$s_{1,2} = \frac{-\omega_0}{2Q_{\text{eff}}} \pm j\frac{\omega_0}{2Q_{\text{eff}}}\sqrt{4Q_{\text{eff}} - 1} \tag{9-305}$$

If $R < R_0$, then $Q_{\text{eff}} < 0$, the poles lie in the right half-plane, and the response of the amplifier will contain an exponentially increasing sinusoid. This is oscillation. (Any active element will saturate, and thus the signal level will eventually stabilize.) To prevent oscillation, we must either make C_{gd} or $C_{b'c}$ in parallel with $r_{b'c}$ very small admittances or eliminate their effect. In the dual-gate FET this is accomplished by actually reducing C_{gd} to extremely small values.

To eliminate the effects of the feedback elements in FET or transistor amplifiers, another current which is equal to, but 180° out of phase with, the current through them is introduced at the input terminal. Circuits which accomplish this are called *neutralizing circuits*. Several of them are illustrated in Fig. 9-73. In each case, the coil is center-tapped so that $\mathbf{V}_1 = -\mathbf{V}_2$. In the case of the FET, $C_N = C_{gd}$, and the net current fed back to the gate node is zero. In a transistor, the feedback impedance is somewhat more

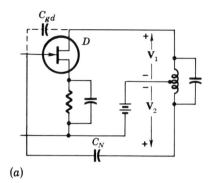

(a)

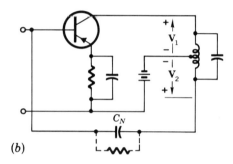

(b)

Fig. 9-73 (a) A neutralized common-source FET amplifier and (b) a neutralized common-emitter transistor amplifier.

complex. At times, $C_N \approx C_{b'c}$ provides neutralization. However, there are times when this value must be adjusted and a shunt resistor included. The circuits of Fig. 9-73 can be modified by using a tapped tuning capacitor, consisting of two capacitors in series, instead of the tapped inductance.

Neutralization often proves quite troublesome. An additional capacitor must be added to the circuit, and its adjustment is critical. Also, C_N must be adjusted if f_0 is changed, because V_2 is not exactly equal to $-V_1$ in an actual circuit and the feedback impedance is complex in the case of a transistor.

In the case of the FET, we can almost always avoid the need for neutralization by using dual-gate MOSFETs or by choosing an FET with a very small C_{gd}, if possible. Otherwise, the proper choice of circuitry can eliminate the need for neutralization. This circuitry can also be used in the case of the transistor. If $R > R_0$ [see Eq. (9-305)], the circuit will not oscillate. Consider Fig. 9-67a with R_T a negative resistance. The magnitude of the apparent shunting negative resistance $-R$ can be made as large as desired by making L_2 small enough [see Eq. (9-241)]. Thus, transistor circuits which do not oscillate and which do not require a neutralizing circuit can be built using tapped coils. When the circuit is adjusted so that it is stable, i.e., does not oscillate, the gain will be reduced somewhat. This is usually a small price to pay for the advantage of not needing a neutralizing capacitor.

A common-grid vacuum-tube amplifier (see Fig. 6-22b) usually does not require neutralization. The common grid shields the plate from the cathode and reduces the feedback effect greatly. Because of their low input impedance, common-grid circuits are not used too often. They are used, at times, as low-noise input stages of radio and television receivers.

9-27 DIRECT-COUPLED AMPLIFIERS

In Secs. 9-1 to 9-6 and 9-10 we discussed the low-frequency response of amplifiers and the means for extending this response. However, there are applications where signals of extremely low frequencies (on the order of fractions of a hertz or less) must be amplified. In such cases, RC-coupled amplifiers are not suitable. If the amplifier is not required to amplify very high frequencies, so that the effects of stray capacitance can be neglected, then the source or emitter-bypass capacitance can be omitted. This will eliminate the dependence of the frequency response on these elements and also reduce the gain. However, a principal cause of the loss in gain at low frequencies is the coupling capacitor C_c. If it is short-circuited, then the low-frequency response can become perfect. The bias voltages of the various circuits will then interact. For instance, if the gate of an FET is connected directly to the drain of one preceding it, a large positive direct voltage will be applied between the gate and the source. In the common-emitter transistor amplifier, if a base of one stage is connected directly to the collector of the preceding one, then too large a negative voltage will be applied between the base and the emitter. In both cases, improper operation will result. The use of two power supplies can correct this situation. Consider the FET circuit of Fig. 9-74. If R_1, R_2, and the negative power supply $-V_{GG}$ are adjusted properly, the proper negative grid bias will result. Thus, this circuit eliminates the problem of bias interaction. The voltage divider, consisting of R_1 and R_2, will reduce the signal by the ratio $R_2/(R_1 + R_2)$. At times R_1 is replaced by a zener diode. Since the voltage drop across it is constant, this circuit does *not* act as a voltage divider for signal quantities. There are circuits which do not require the voltage divider. However, they are cumbersome in that they require many power supplies or power supplies with very high voltages. For this reason, they are seldom used. Figure 9-74b illustrates a direct-coupled transistor amplifier that operates on the same principles.

The first FET uses a source-bias resistance. The successive stages do not require it because the power supply V_{GG} can be used to obtain the required negative bias. The emitter resistors are included in each transistor stage for stabilizing purposes. If the output resistances R_1' and R_2' are properly

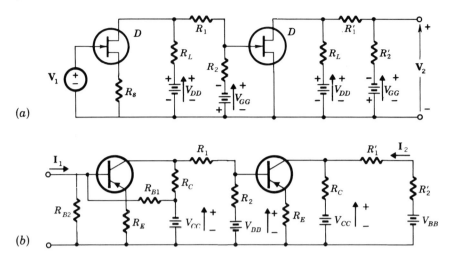

(a)

(b)

Fig. 9-74   Direct-coupled amplifier: (a) common-source FET amplifier and (b) common-emitter transistor amplifier.

chosen, the output can be made to be zero if the input signal is zero.   The various voltages and currents can be found by an application of Kirchhoff's laws.

Although obtaining the correct bias voltages is a problem in direct-coupled amplifiers, it is a very minor one in comparison with the problem of *operating-point stability*.   To illustrate this, let us consider a cascade of *RC*-coupled amplifiers, each with a voltage gain of 10.   Because of temperature fluctuations and power-supply changes, the operating point of each stage will fluctuate very slowly.   For instance, assume that the input bias voltage of the first stage fluctuates ± 0.1 volt over a period of several minutes.   This would appear as a very low-frequency signal.   However, the *RC*-coupled network would almost completely reject signals of such low frequency. Hence, there would be no harmful results.   On the other hand, if the amplifier were direct-coupled, it could not distinguish between these bias-voltage shifts and low-frequency signals.   Thus, the voltage of the second stage would shift by ∓ 1 volt, and that of the third stage by ± 10 volts, etc.   Thus, minute variations in bias potentials can cause serious effects in direct-coupled amplifiers.   The drift acts as a spurious input signal.   Often, there is no convenient way of distinguishing between drift in bias voltages and a very low frequency signal.   The smallest signal to be amplified should be much greater than the effective "drift signal" at the input.   In severe cases of drift, operating-point shifts in the latter stages of the amplifier may result in very nonlinear operation or excessive dissipation.   For these reasons the power-supply voltage should be well regulated.   However, minute changes in power-supply voltage cannot be eliminated. In addition, much of the drift is caused by changes in the circuit elements themselves. These changes are due primarily to thermal effects and are especially troublesome in transistor circuits. One means of reducing these thermal effects is to include additional temperature-sensitive elements which compensate for changes in other circuit elements. For instance, consider the circuit of Fig. 9-75. The semiconductor diode and the transistor are mounted close together, so that each operates at essentially the same temperature. An increase in the temperature tends to increase the collector current of the transistor. However, the increase in temperature also decreases the resistance of the reverse-biased diode. This, in turn, will reduce the base current, which will reduce the collector current. Thus, the inclusion of the diode tends to reduce the thermal sensitivity of the circuit. The diode must be properly matched to the transistor. If its resistance does not change enough, then the collector current will rise with increasing temperature. If it changes too much, then the collector current can actually decrease with increasing temperature. It may prove difficult to match the diode and the transistor.

If we use two active elements in each stage instead of one, many of the effects of drift can actually be canceled. Consider the circuit of Fig. 9-76. This is called a *balanced amplifier*. Assume that the two FETs or the two transistors are identical. If the power-supply voltage shifts, then the drain or collector voltage of each active element will change equally. Thus, the output voltage V_2 will be unaffected. Similarly, there will be no output voltage resulting from thermal drifts or any other changes *provided that the changes in both halves of the circuit are equal*. To accomplish this, the active elements should be picked so that they are as nearly identical as possible. In addition, they should be mounted very close together so that their temperatures will be equal. Succeeding stages of the amplifier are also balanced. In these stages instead of connecting one gate or one base to the common lead, one is connected to point *a* while the other is connected to point *b*. An arrangement similar to that of Fig. 9-74 must be used to prevent bias interaction. The use of balanced amplifiers allows direct-coupled amplifiers to amplify much smaller signals. (The tendency for the operating points to

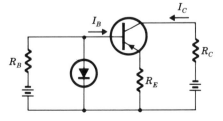

Fig. 9-75 Use of a semiconductor diode as a thermal-compensating element. Actually only one power supply is needed.

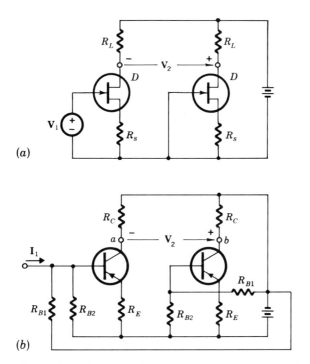

Fig. 9-76 Balanced amplifiers: (*a*) common-source FET amplifier and (*b*) common-emitter transistor amplifier.

drift is still present. However, this drift no longer appears as an output signal.)

One means of eliminating the problem of the drift of direct-coupled amplifiers is to avoid using them. This can be accomplished if we can obtain a high-frequency voltage or current whose amplitude varies in accordance with the low-frequency signal. This high-frequency signal can then be amplified by an ordinary *RC*-coupled amplifier. Its amplitude will be an amplified replica of the low-frequency signal, and an amplified signal can be recovered from it. Such processes, called *modulation and demodulation*, will be considered in detail in Chap. 16. We shall consider a very simple circuit for accomplishing it here (see Fig. 9-77). The switch sw_1 is a mechanically driven switch. A typical rate for driving this switch is 60 Hz. If an input voltage v_1, which is shown by the solid curve of Fig. 9-78, is applied to the system, then the voltage v_1' will be of the form shown in the dotted curve (this assumes that $R_1 \ll R_i$). One-half of the input signal is removed. For this reason, this is called a *chopper amplifier*. If information regarding the input waveform is not to be lost, then the frequency ω_a at which the switches are driven must be much greater than the highest frequency of v_1, ω_b. We have

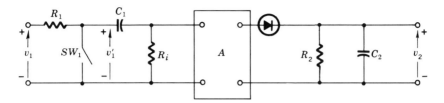

Fig. 9-77 A chopper amplifier.

obtained a higher frequency signal whose amplitude varies in accordance with the input signal. If ω_a is the frequency at which the switches are driven and if $1/\omega_a C_1 \ll R_i$, then input voltages or currents of the amplifier will have the same waveform as the dashed curve of Fig. 9-78, but the direct component will be removed from them. This alternating signal then can be amplified by the RC-coupled amplifier.

The output circuit removes the alternations from the output signal, so that v_2 has the same form as v_1. The diode allows current to be in only one direction. As a consequence, the alternations are removed from the circuit and the input waveform is realized. (At times, more-complex circuits are used. However, the general ideas of operation are the same.) The operation of this circuit, which is called a *linear detector*, is discussed in great detail in Chap. 16 and will not be repeated here. However (see Sec. 16-4), if it is to function properly, $1/R_2 C_2$ must be much smaller than ω_a and, in addition, $1/R_2 C_2$ must be much larger than ω_b. Thus, as discussed previously, if the circuit is to operate properly, ω_a must be much larger than ω_b. In practice, ω_a must be at least 10 times ω_b if this amplifier is to function properly. Thus, if $f_a = 60$ Hz, which is a fairly rapid rate at which to drive a switch, then the usable upper frequency limit of the amplifier is 6 Hz. This is adequate for a great many instrumentation problems. However, the very limited high-frequency response does restrict the usefulness of mechanical

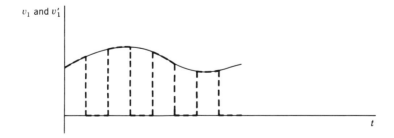

Fig. 9-78 Waveforms of a chopper amplifier.

chopper amplifiers. There are chopper circuits that use FETs as electronic switches. These can be driven at higher frequencies. These circuits have a better high-frequency response.

9-28 NOISE-AMPLIFIER SENSITIVITY

The function of an amplifier is to increase the amplitude of a signal to a usable value. For instance, the input signal of a radio receiver is often on the order of microvolts. It may appear as though any signal, no matter how small, can be amplified to any desired value by using an amplifier with enough gain. However, this is not the case. All electronic devices produce unwanted signals called *noise*. The most important noise can often be considered to be produced in the first stage of the amplifier. Then, as the amplification is increased, the noise output will also be increased. If the level of the input signal is not larger than the noise, the output signal will be obscured by the noise. For instance, in a radio receiver, noise often manifests itself as a hissing sound. In television receivers, noise appears as "snow." If these noise signals are large enough, the signal will be masked. The *sensitivity* of a receiver is defined as the minimum signal that can be detected by it. As the gain of the amplifiers of the receiver is increased, the sensitivity increases. However, eventually, the noise becomes so large that it obscures the signal. Any further increase in gain *will not* increase the sensitivity, since a very weak signal would be so masked by noise that it would not be recognizable. Let us now consider the origin of noise in electronic devices.

Resistor noise—Johnson noise The electrons in any conductor are always thermally agitated. These randomly moving electrons cause a voltage to appear across the conductor called *thermal noise* or *Johnson noise*. The waveform of the voltage is random and cannot be predicted at any instant. However, some facts about it can be ascertained. The energy contained in a frequency range $\Delta f = f_2 - f_1$ is dependent only upon the difference between f_2 and f_1 but not upon their absolute values. The energy in any Δf is proportional to the temperature of the resistance. The effective (rms) value of the noise voltage is proportional to the square root of the energy. It is found that

$$V_n = 2\sqrt{keTR\,\Delta f} \tag{9-306}$$

where Δf = bandwidth, Hz

R = resistance, ohms

T = temperature, °K

e = charge of electron, coul

k = Boltzmann's constant, eV/°K

The noise power is independent of the center frequency of the bandwidth. This is called *white noise*.

Random noise will also be produced by an antenna. Every antenna has an effective radiation resistance which is indicative of the energy it can radiate. It is a physical fact that the noise voltage produced is a function of the radiation resistance and average temperature of the antenna. (This temperature may be difficult to calculate. It depends upon the temperature of all parts within the radiation pattern of the antenna and the shape of the radiation pattern.) Then, since all radio receivers use an antenna, their sensitivity is limited by the noise produced in the antenna resistance.

Noise figure If amplifiers were ideal, in that they produced no noise, the sensitivity of a radio receiver or amplifier would depend upon the noise produced in the signal source, e.g., antenna. However, amplifiers are far from ideal. Often, they produce much more noise than the source. If the output noise voltage, which can be due to noise produced in several parts of the amplifier, is measured and then it is divided by the magnitude of the gain of the amplifier, an effective input noise voltage is determined. That is, this is an input voltage which, if it were applied at the input of an ideal amplifier, would produce the same noise output as the actual amplifier. Often the amplifier noise input voltage is much greater than that produced by the input source.

To rate an amplifier in terms of the noise it produces, a quantity called the *noise figure* is used. This is defined as

$$\text{NF} = 10 \log \frac{P_{No}}{A_P P_{Ni}} \tag{9-307}$$

where P_{No} = the total noise power output

P_{Ni} = noise produced by the input generator

A_P = power gain of amplifier

Thus, NF is the ratio in decibels of the total noise output power to the noise output power that would be produced if the amplifier were ideal. A noise figure of 0 db is the best that can be obtained. Another definition of noise figure, which is equivalent if the input and output impedances of the amplifier are resistive and equal, is

$$\text{NF} = 20 \log \frac{V_{No}}{A_v V_{Ni}} \tag{9-308}$$

where V_{No} = rms noise output voltage (produced by all noise sources)

V_{Ni} = rms noise voltage produced by input generator

A_v = voltage gain of amplifier

To obtain the lowest noise figure, the bandwidth of the amplifier should be no larger than required by the signals.

The noise voltage or power is not significant by itself.   The ratio of the signal to the noise is important.   Thus, we can define a *voltage signal-to-noise ratio* and a *power signal-to-noise ratio*.   These are

$$S_v = \frac{V_S}{V_N} \tag{9-309a}$$

$$S_p = \frac{P_S}{P_N} \tag{9-309b}$$

where V_S and V_N are the rms values of the signal and noise voltages and P_S and P_N are the signal and noise average powers.   We can express the noise figure in terms of the signal-to-noise ratio.   For instance, for an amplifier,

$$A_v = \frac{V_{So}}{V_{Si}} \tag{9-310}$$

where the subscripts i and o refer to input and output values.   Thus,

$$\text{NF} = 20 \log \frac{V_{Si}}{V_{Ni}} - 20 \log \frac{V_{So}}{V_{No}} \tag{9-311a}$$

or

$$\text{NF} = 20 \log S_{Vi} - 20 \log S_{Vo} \tag{9-311b}$$

Thus, the noise figure is the difference between the input signal-to-noise ratio in decibels and the output signal-to-noise ratio in decibels.   Now let us consider the mechanisms whereby amplifiers generate noise.

Vacuum-tube noise   One of the primary causes of noise in a vacuum tube is the random emission of electrons from the cathode.   This random emission causes a random variation in the plate current.   This noise is called *shot noise*.   If the tube is *temperature-limited*, the random component of plate current is found to have an rms value of

$$I_n = \sqrt{2eI_b \, \Delta f} \tag{9-312}$$

where e = charge of electron, coul

$\quad I_b$ = plate current, amp

$\quad \Delta f$ = bandwidth, Hz

Usually, vacuum tubes are not operated temperature-limited but space-charge-limited.   This reduces the dependence of the plate current on the emission from the cathode.   In such cases, the noise current will be substantially less than that predicted by Eq. (9-312).

In vacuum-tube pentodes or tetrodes the noise is increased, above the shot noise, by the fact that the current divides between the screen grid and the plate.   This division will vary randomly and lead to noise which is called *partition noise*.   It may increase the noise by a factor of 10 or more above the shot noise.   For these reasons, vacuum-tube triodes, rather than pentodes are often used as the input stages of low-noise vacuum-tube devices.

The noise produced in the first stages of the amplifier is of prime importance.   Consider that each stage produces the same noise.   The noise of the input stage will be amplified most and will contribute most to the noise output.   At times the input stage is a source (or cathode) follower, e.g., in some oscilloscopes.   This stage actually produces a loss.   In this case the noise produced in the second stage is as important as, or more important than, the noise produced in the first stage.

Both partition and shot noise are white noise; i.e., their energies do not vary with frequency.

There are other sources of noise in vacuum tubes.   In addition to the random emission from a cathode, the emission level varies randomly.   This is called *flicker effect*.   The noise produced by this effect is not white noise but varies as $1/f$.   It falls off at high frequencies and is thus important only for low-frequency devices, such as audio amplifiers.

Noise is also caused in a vacuum tube by random collision of electrons with gas molecules and random secondary-emission effects.

Transistor noise   Noise in transistors is caused by several effects.   Besides the Johnson noise produced in the ohmic portion of the transistor, the charge carriers diffuse across the base.   Since this is a random motion, it results in a random noise component.   The charge carriers which diffuse to a forward-biased junction, e.g., the emitter-base junction, and diffuse across it also move randomly.   Thus, the motion across this junction is also random and contributes to noise.   Note that the average value of the current is constant. The noise causes the current to fluctuate slightly about the average value.

There is also a *partition effect* in transistors.   Some charge carriers recombine in the base and contribute to base current.   Most of the charge carriers diffuse to the collector-base junction, where they contribute to the collector current.   This division is on a random basis and contributes to the noise.   All the noise mechanisms discussed above lead to white noise.

There is noise that varies as $1/f$ in the transistor.   This is analogous to the flicker effect in vacuum tubes.   The noise is thought to be due to effects which occur on the surface of the transistor.

The noise produced by the transistor varies with frequency.   At low frequencies, it is high because of the flicker effect.   The noise then falls off and levels off over a range of frequencies.   The noise figure falls off at high frequencies where the gain, and hence the output signal, falls off.   Much of the noise current in any one transistor is not affected by this falloff in gain.

The noise figure of a transistor is also found to be a function of the collector current and the impedance of the input generator.   Manufacturers often supply curves which specify the noise figure of a transistor over a wide range of operation.

FET noise   The noise in an FET is produced from several sources.   Johnson noise occurs in the ohmic resistance of the channel.   There is an extremely small component of current from the gate to the channel.   This introduces a small noise current.   Finally, the surface effects lead to a $1/f$ flicker-effect noise (see the discussion of noise in the transistor).   In general, the noise figure of FETs is very low.   Often they are superior to vacuum tubes or transistors as low-noise devices.

Hum   In addition to random noise, there is another noise source.   Most amplifiers operate in the vicinity of 60-Hz fields produced by the power lines or power transformers.   Stray pickup of the fields can introduce a 60-Hz (and its harmonics) signal.   This noise can be reduced by shielding the amplifier and, in the case of vacuum tubes, by operating the heaters with direct current.

REFERENCES

1. Gray, T. S.: "Applied Electronics," 2d ed., pp. 520–521, John Wiley & Sons, Inc., New York, 1954.
2. Terman, F. E.: "Electronic and Radio Engineering," 4th ed., pp. 265–266, McGraw-Hill Book Company, New York, 1955.
3. Angelo, E. J., Jr.: "Electronic Circuits," pp. 310–313, McGraw-Hill Book Company, New York, 1958.
4. Valley, G. E., Jr., and H. Wallman: "Vacuum Tube Amplifiers," McGraw-Hill Book Company, pp. 172–173, New York, 1948.
5. Bedford, A. V., and G. L. Fredendall: Transient Response of Multistage Video-frequency Amplifiers, *Proc. IRE*, vol. 27, pp. 277–284, 1939.
6. Gärtner, W. W.: "Transistors: Principles, Design, and Applications," chap. 15, D. Van Nostrand Company, Inc., Princeton, N.J., 1960.
7. Valley, G. E., Jr., and H. Wallman: "Vacuum Tube Amplifiers," McGraw-Hill Book Company, pp. 77–78, New York, 1948.
8. Terman, F. E.: "Radio Engineers' Handbook," p. 372, McGraw-Hill Book Company, New York, 1943.

BIBLIOGRAPHY

Gärtner, W. W.: "Transistors: Principles, Design, and Applications," chaps. 12, 14, and 15, D. Van Nostrand Company, Inc., Princeton, N.J., 1960.
Gibbons, J. F.: "Semiconductor Electronics," chap. 13, McGraw-Hill Book Company, New York, 1966.
Pettit, J. M., and M. M. McWhorter: "Electronic Amplifier Circuits: Theory and Design," chaps. 3–5, 7, 9–11, McGraw-Hill Book Company, New York, 1961.
Valley, G. E., Jr., and H. Wallman: "Vacuum Tube Amplifiers," chaps. 2, 4, and 5, McGraw-Hill Book Company, New York, 1948.

PROBLEMS

9-1. Determine the voltage gain of the amplifier of Fig. 9-1. Make no approximations except that all bypass capacitors are short circuits at the signal frequencies. Do not neglect the stray capacitances.

9-2. Compute the magnitude of the mid-frequency voltage gain, the upper and lower half-power frequencies, and plot the normalized frequency response (amplitude and phase) of the amplifier of Fig. 9-2. The FET has the following parameter values: $g_m = 5000$ μmhos, $r_d = 10{,}000$ ohms, $C_{gd} = 1.0$ pf, $C_{gs} = 3.0$ pf, $C_{ds} = 3.0$ pf. The circuit constants are $R_L = 10{,}000$ ohms, $C_c = 0.1$ μf, $R_g = 10^6$ ohms. Assume that the wiring capacitance is 5 pf and that C_i is 15 pf. Plot the low-frequency response and the high-frequency response separately. Use semilog paper.

9-3. Repeat Prob. 9-2 but now assume that C_i represents the input capacitance of an identical amplifier stage. For convenience, assume that the voltage gain of the second stage remains constant at the midband value. How would the results change if this assumption were not made?

9-4. An RC-coupled FET amplifier has the linear model shown in Fig. 9-3. The parameters of the FET are $g_m = 10{,}000$ μmhos, $r_d = 2 \times 10^6$ ohms. $C_{gs} = 3$ pf, $C_{ds} = 3$ pf, $C_{gd} = 0.1$ pf. The circuit constants are $R_L = 5000$ ohms, $R_g = 10^6$ ohms, $C_i = 3$ pf, and $C_c = 0.1$ μf. Assume that the wiring capacitance is 2 pf and that $C_i = 18.9$ pf. Find the magnitude of the midband voltage gain and the upper and lower half-power frequencies and plot the normalized frequency response (amplitude and phase) of this amplifier.

9-5. Repeat Prob. 9-4 but now assume that C_i represents the input capacitance of an identical amplifier stage. For convenience, assume that the voltage gain of the second stage remains constant at the midband value. Compare this answer with that of Prob. 9-4.

9-6. Plot the normalized amplitude response of the amplifier of Prob. 9-4 in decibels.

9-7. The FET of Prob. 9-4 is to be used in an amplifier. What is the maximum magnitude that $A_{v,\text{mid}}$ can have? What upper half-power frequency corresponds to this $A_{v,\text{mid}}$? What is the gain-bandwidth product of the amplifier?

9-8. An RC-coupled vacuum-tube-pentode amplifier has the model shown in Fig. 9-3. The parameters of the pentode are $g_m = 5000$ μmhos, $r_p \geq 2 \times 10^6$ ohms, $C_{in} = 10$ pf, $C_{out} = 10$ pf, $C_{gp} = 0.001$ pf. The circuit constants are $R_L = 5000$ ohms, $R_g = 10^6$ ohms, and $C_c = 0.1$ μf. Assume that the wiring capacitance is 5 pf, and that C_i is 10 pf. Find the magnitude of the midband voltage gain and the upper and lower half-power frequencies and plot the normalized frequency response (amplitude and phase) of the amplifier.

9-9. Repeat Prob. 9-8, but now assume that C_i represents the input capacitance of an identical amplifier stage. For convenience, assume that the voltage gain of the second stage remains constant at the midband value. Compare and discuss the answers of Probs. 9-5 and 9-8. Plot the low-frequency response and the high-frequency response separately. Use semilog paper.

9-10. Plot the normalized amplitude response of the amplifier of Prob. 9-4 in decibels.

9-11. If the plate resistance of the vacuum-tube pentode of Prob. 9-8 is exactly 2×10^6 ohms, what is the maximum magnitude that $A_{v,\text{mid}}$ can have? What is the upper half-power frequency that corresponds to this value of midband gain? What is the gain-bandwidth product of the amplifier?

9-12. Three identical amplifier stages, of the type given in Prob. 9-4, are cascaded.

Determine the midband voltage gain of the overall amplifier and plot the normalized frequency response (amplitude, amplitude in decibels, and phase) of the amplifier.

9-13. Repeat Prob. 9-12, but now assume that the coupling capacitance and the parasitic capacitance of the last stage are halved.

9-14. Compute an exact expression for the current gain of the two-stage transistor amplifier of Fig. 9-8. Use the hybrid-pi model. Assume that the capacitor C_E is a short circuit at the signal frequency.

9-15. A transistor has the following parameter values: $h_{ie} = 5000$ ohms, $h_{re} = 2 \times 10^{-4}$, $h_{fe} = 100$, $h_{oe} = 60 \times 10^{-6}$ mho, $C_{oe} = 300$ pf, and $f_{\beta} = 20 \times 10^4$ Hz. It is used as the active element in an RC-coupled amplifier whose linear model is given in Fig. 9-9. The parameters of the circuit are $R_C = 10,000$ ohms, $R_B = 50,000$ ohms, $R_i = 5000$ ohms, and $C_c = 5$ μf. Determine the midband current gain and plot the normalized frequency response (amplitude and phase) of the amplifier.

9-16. Repeat Prob. 9-15 but now assume that the parameters of the transistor are $r_{bb'} = 100$ ohms, $r_{b'e} = 1500$ ohms, $C_{b'e} = 60$ pf, $r_{b'c} = 5 \times 10^6$ ohms, $C_{b'c} = 6$ pf, $g_m = 75,000$ μmhos, and $r_{ce} = 50,000$ ohms.

9-17. Repeat Prob. 9-16 but halve the values of all the capacitances.

9-18. Plot the asymptotes of the normalized amplitude response in decibels for the amplifiers of Probs. 9-16 and 9-17.

9-19. Discuss the concept of a gain-bandwidth product in a transistor amplifier. Compare it with the gain-bandwidth product in an FET amplifier.

9-20. An RC-coupled transistor amplifier is made up of three identical stages. The parameters of the transistor are $r_{bb'} = 100$ ohms, $r_{b'e} = 1500$ ohms, $C_{b'e} = 60$ pf, $r_{b'c} = 10^{12}$ ohms, $C_{b'c} = 6$ pf, $g_m = 75,000$ μmhos, and $r_{ce} = 50,000$ ohms. The values of the circuit elements are (see Fig. 9-9) $R_B = 50,000$ ohms, $R_i = 1600$ ohms, and $C_i = 10$ μf. Determine the midband current gain of the amplifier. Plot the normalized frequency response (amplitude, amplitude in decibels, and phase) of the amplifier.

9-21. Repeat Prob. 9-20 but now assume that $r_{b'c} = 10^3$ ohms. The load resistor for the last stage is 1500 ohms. Do not assume that the input impedance of each stage is 1500 ohms.

9-22. An FET whose linear model is given in Fig. 9-15 requires a quiescent gate bias of -5 volts and a quiescent plate current of 25 ma. The FET has the parameters $r_d = 10,000$ ohms and $g_m = 10,000$ μmhos. The element values are $R_L = 10,000$ ohms and $R_g = 10^6$ ohms. Assume that C_c acts as a short circuit at signal frequencies. Find a C_s such that $|A_v/A_{v,\text{mid}}| \geq 0.9$, at 20 Hz. After C_s is found, plot the normalized frequency response (amplitude and phase) of this circuit.

9-23. A vacuum-tube triode, whose model is given in Fig. 9-15, requires a quiescent grid bias of -5 volts and a quiescent plate current of 25 ma. The vacuum tube is operated such that $r_p = 10,000$ ohms and $\mu = 100$. The element values are $R_L = 10,000$ ohms and $R_g = 10^6$ ohms. Find a value for C_k such that $|A_v/A_{v,\text{mid}}| \geq 0.9$ at 20 Hz. Consider only the effect of the cathode-bias impedance in this example. After the value of C_k is determined, plot the normalized frequency response (amplitude and phase) of the circuit.

9-24. A vacuum-tube pentode has the following parameter values: $g_m = 600$ μmhos, $g_{ps} = 1500$ μmhos, $r_p \geq 2 \times 10^6$ ohms, and $I_s = 0.1I_p$. It is operated in an amplifier whose model is given in Fig. 9-18, where $R_s = 100,000$ ohms, $R_k = 1000$ ohms, $R_L = 10,000$ ohms, $C_k = 100$ μf, and $C_s = 2.0$ μf. Determine the low-frequency response of this amplifier due to the cathode- and screen-grid bias impedances. Plot the normalized frequency response (amplitude and phase) for this circuit.

9-25. A vacuum-tube pentode which is used in the amplifier of Fig. 9-18 is operated at the following operating point: $V_{bQ} = 300$ volts, $I_{bQ} = 10$ ma, $V_{cQ} = -9$ volts, $V_{c2Q} = 250$ volts, $I_{c2Q} = 1.5$ ma. At this operating point, the parameters of the vacuum tube are $g_m = 6000$ μmhos, $g_{ps} = 1500$ μmhos, $r_p \geq 2 \times 10^6$ ohm. The load resistance in the circuit is $R_L = 9100$ ohms. Determine values for C_k and C_s such that $|A_v/A_{v,\text{mid}}| \geq 0.8$ at 50 Hz. Consider only the effects of the cathode-bias impedance and the screen-grid bias impedance in this problem.

9-26. A transistor has these low-frequency parameters: $h_{ie} = 1500$ ohms, $h_{re} = 300 \times 10^{-6}$, $h_{fe} = 100$, $h_{oe} = 50 \times 10^{-6}$ mho. It is operated in the circuit of Fig. 9-20 where $R_C = 2000$ ohms, $R_B = 20,000$ ohms, the input impedance of the next stage $Z_i = 2000$ ohms, $R_E = 1000$ ohms, and $C_E = 300$ μf. The reactance of C_c is assumed to be zero. Will the emitter stabilizing impedance affect the gain I_2/I_i to any great extent? Now, assume that the impedance Z_i is equal to Z_{i1} (where Z_{i1} is calculated when $Z_i = 2000$ ohms) and compute the current gain of the amplifier as a function of frequency. Plot the amplitude and phase response of this amplifier. What is the mid-band gain?

9-27. The element values of Fig. 9-23 are $R_s = 10,000$ ohms, $R_i = 20,000$ ohms, and $C_i = 200$ pf. Determine the upper half-power frequency of the ratio $|V_1/V_s|$. Repeat this for the ratio $|I_1/V_s|$.

9-28. Three identical RC-coupled FET amplifier stages are cascaded. The upper and lower half-power frequencies of the amplifier are 2 and 100,000 Hz, respectively. What are the upper and lower half-power frequencies of the individual stages?

9-29. Prove this statement: If an amplifier is composed of n identical stages whose gain-bandwidth product is constant, then the maximum gain-bandwidth product of the overall amplifier occurs when the gain of each individual stage is approximately equal to 4.34 decibels. Hint: Use the approximation $2^{1/n} - 1 \approx (\ln 2)/n$.

9-30. Design an RC-coupled voltage amplifier, using the minimum number of stages, that meets the following specifications: $|A_{v,\text{mid}}| \geq 64$. At a frequency of 2×10^6 Hz, $|A_v/A_{v,\text{mid}}| \geq 0.9$, and at a frequency of 50 Hz, $|A_v/A_{v,\text{mid}}| \geq 0.8$. The amplifier is to have a dc blocking capacitor in its input stage. The load is a 10^6-ohm resistor shunted by 4 pf. (See Fig. 9-25 for the form of the amplifier.) Use FETs with the following characteristics: $g_m = 8000$ μmhos, $r_d = 10^6$ ohms, $R_{g,\text{max}} = 10^6$ ohms, $C_{gd} = 1$ pf, $C_{gs} = 4$ pf, $C_{ds} = 4$ pf. The coordinates of the quiescent operating point are $V_{DSQ} = 10$ volts, $I_{DQ} = 1$ ma, $V_{GSQ} = -1$ volt. Assume that the stray wiring capacitance is 2 pf for any stage.

9-31. Consider the design of Prob. 9-30 but now assume that a new FET is available with a g_m that is sufficiently high so that only one stage is needed. All other parameters are the same as in Prob. 9-30. Determine the value of g_m needed.

9-32. Design an RC-coupled voltage amplifier, using the minimum number of stages, that meets the following specifications: $|A_{\text{mid}}| \geq 64$; at a frequency of 10^6 Hz, $|A/A_{\text{mid}}| \geq 0.9$; and at a frequency of 50 Hz, $|A/A_{\text{mid}}| \geq 0.8$. The amplifier is to have a dc blocking capacitor in its input stage. The load is a 10^6-ohm resistance shunted by 12 pf. Use vacuum-tube pentodes with the following characteristics: $g_m = 8000$ μmhos, $g_{ps} = 1500$ μmhos, $r_p \geq 3 \times 10^6$ ohms, $R_{g,\text{max}} = 10^6$ ohms, $C_{\text{in}} = 12$ pf, and $C_{\text{out}} = 8$ pf. The coordinates of the operating point are $V_{bQ} = 350$ volts, $I_{bQ} = 30$ ma, $V_{c2Q} = 250$ volts, $I_{c2Q} = 2$ ma, and $V_{cQ} = -5$ volts. The wiring capacity is 5 pf for any stage.

9-33. Consider the design of Prob. 9-32, but now assume that a new pentode is available with a g_m that is sufficiently high so that only one stage is needed. Determine this value of g_m.

9-34. Using the minimum number of stages, design an RC-coupled vacuum-tube amplifier that meets the following specifications: $|A_{\text{mid}}| \geq 20$, the lower and upper half-power frequencies are to be 20 Hz and 20,000 Hz, respectively. Cathode bias is to be used, and the maximum power-supply voltage is to be 405 volts. A dc blocking capacitor should be included in the input circuit. Use vacuum-tube triodes with the following specifications: $\mu = 20$, $r_p = 20,000$, $C_{gp} = 2$ pf, $C_{gk} = 2$ pf, and $C_{pk} = 1.5$ pf. The coordinates of the operating point are $V_{bQ} = 300$ volts, $I_{bQ} = 10$ ma, and $V_{cQ} = -5$ volts. The maximum value at R_g is 10^6 ohms. The stray wiring capacitance is 5 pf. The output load resistance is 10^6 ohms.

9-35. Design an RC-coupled transistor amplifier of the type shown in Fig. 9-27, using the following specifications: $|A_{i,\text{mid}}| = |I_s/I_2| \geq 49$; at a frequency of 0.4×10^6 Hz, $|A_i/A_{i,\text{mid}}| \geq 0.8$; and at a frequency of 50 Hz, $|A_i/A_{i,\text{mid}}| \geq 0.8$. The minimum number of amplifier stages are to be used and the stability factor of any stage is to be equal to or less than 7. The load impedance and the internal impedance of the input current generator are each 2000 ohms. Use p-n-p transistors with the following characteristics: $h_{ie} = 2000$ ohms, $h_{re} = 30 \times 10^{-6}$, $h_{fe} = 50$, $h_{oe} = 40 \times 10^{-6}$ mho, $C_{oe} = 200$ pf, and $f_\beta = 2 \times 10^6$ Hz. The coordinates of the operating point are given by $I_{CQ} = -5$ ma, $I_{BQ} = -100$ μamp, $V_{CQ} = -6$ volts, and $V_{BQ} \approx 0$ volts. Assume that the stray wiring capacitance can be neglected.

9-36. If the transistor of Prob. 9-35 were replaced by an n-p-n transistor, how would the design change?

9-37. Repeat Prob. 9-35 but now use a transistor with the following specifications: $r_{bb'} = 100$ ohms, $r_{b'e} = 1900$ ohms, $g_m = 26,300$ μmhos, $C_{b'e} = 4.2$ pf, $r_{b'c} = 63.3 \times 10^6$ ohms, $C_{b'c} = 4$ pf, and $r_{ce} = 25,500$ ohms.

9-38. The amplifier of Fig. 9-28a has the following element values: $R_L = 10,000$ ohms, $R_d = 10,000$ ohms, $R_g = 10^6$ ohms, $C_c = 0.005$ μf, and $C_d = 1.0$ μf. The FET has the following parameter values: $g_m = 5000$ μmhos, $r_p = 2 \times 10^6$ ohms. Assume that C_k and C_s are short circuits at the signal frequencies. Determine $A_{v,\text{mid}}$ and plot $|A_{v,\text{low}}/A_{v,\text{mid}}|$ for this amplifier. First use the approximate expression of Eq. (9-104) and then use exact calculations. Comment on the accuracy of the approximate relation in this case. If R_d is replaced by a short circuit, how do these results change?

9-39. Repeat Prob. 9-38, but now use a value of $C_d = 2.0$ μf and then use a value of $C_d = 0.5$ μf.

9-40. An RC-coupled vacuum-tube-pentode amplifier is to have a lower half-power frequency of 20 Hz. The form of the circuit is to be equivalent to that of Fig. 9-28a, where $R_L = 10,000$ ohms, $R_g = 10^6$ ohms, $g_m = 5000$ μmhos, and $r_p \geq 2 \times 10^6$ ohms. The coordinates of the operating point are $V_{bQ} = 250$ volts, $I_{bQ} = 10$ ma, $V_{CQ} = -5$ volts, $V_{C2Q} = 250$ volts, and $I_{C2Q} = 1$ ma. If $R_d = 0$, what value of C_i is required to obtain the desired low-frequency response? Now use a coupling capacitor that is one-half of this value and find the value of R_d and C_d such that the low-frequency response remains unchanged. Compute the value of V_{bb}, R_s, and R_k for both cases. Assume that C_k and C_s are short circuits at all frequencies of interest.

9-41. The transistor of Fig. 9-28c has the following parameter values: $h_{ie} = 2000$ ohms, $h_{re} = 300 \times 10^{-6}$, $h_{fe} = 50$, $h_{oe} = 10 \times 10^{-6}$ mho. The coordinates of the operating point are $V_{CQ} = -5$ volts, $I_{CQ} = -1$ ma, and $I_{BQ} = -100$ μa. The circuit elements are $R_E = 1000$ ohms, $R_C = 1000$ ohms, $R_d = 10,000$ ohms, $R_B = 10,000$ ohms, $R_i = 2500$ ohms, $C_c = 1$ μf, and $C_d = 2$ μf. Plot the low-frequency current gain (magnitude and phase) using the approximate expression of Eq. (9-104) and then using an exact expression. Calculate the value of V_{CC}.

9-42. Repeat Prob. 9-40, but now use a value of $R_d = 100,000$ ohms.

9-43. Repeat Probs. 9-40 and 9-41, but change the value of C_d to 4 μf and then repeat the calculations using a value of $C_d = 1$ μf.

9-44. For the amplifier of Prob. 9-41, consider that R_d and C_d are variable. The low-frequency response is to be constant, within approximately 10 percent, down to 10 Hz. Determine the values of R_d, C_d, C_c, and V_{CC} if this design is to be realized. If $R_d = 0$, what value of C_c is required to make $|A_{t,\text{low}}/A_{t,\text{mid}}| = 0.9$ at 10 Hz?

9-45. A single-stage RC-coupled amplifier has the following element values: $R_c = 10,000$ ohms, $R_g = 10^6$ ohms and $C_c = 0.01$ μf. The parameters of the FET are $g_m = 10,000$ μmhos, $r_d = 500,000$ ohms, $C_{gs} = 2$ pf, $C_{ds} = 2$ pf, and $C_{gd} = 0.1$ pf. Assume that this is cascaded with an identical amplifier and the wiring capacitance is 2 pf. Find the upper and lower half-power frequencies of the one-stage amplifier if no shunt peaking is used. Then find a value of L which maximizes the upper half-power frequency and also keeps the amplitude response monotonic.

9-46. Repeat Prob. 9-45 but now assume that the amplitude response is allowed to rise 2 or 3 percent above the midband value.

9-47. Repeat Prob. 9-45 but now adjust the value of L for minimum delay distortion.

9-48. A single-stage RC-coupled amplifier equivalent to the type shown in Fig. 9-31a has the following element values: $R_L = 10,000$ ohms, $R_g = 10^6$ ohms, and $C_c = 0.01$ μf. The parameters of the vacuum-tube pentode are $g_m = 5000$ μmhos, $r_p \geq 2 \times 10^6$ ohms, $C_{\text{out}} = 8$ pf, $C_{\text{in}} = 10$ pf. Assume that this is cascaded with an identical amplifier and that the wiring capacitance is 5 pf. Find the upper half-power frequency of the one-stage amplifier if no shunt peaking is used. Then find a value of L which maximizes the upper half-power frequency and also keeps the amplitude response monotonic.

9-49. Repeat Prob. 9-48 but now assume that the amplitude response is allowed to rise 2 or 3 percent above the midband value.

9-50. Repeat Prob. 9-48 but now adjust the value of L for the minimum delay distortion.

9-51. Discuss how the equations of Sec. 9-12 would be modified if the common-emitter h-parameter model of Fig. 6-43 were used.

9-52. Use the constructions of Fig. 9-37 to plot the amplitude and phase response of the shunt-peaked amplifier of Fig. 9-31a for values of $Q_2 = 1.00$, 0.439, 0.342, and 0.200. (The notation is that of Sec. 9-11.)

9-53. Determine the 10 to 90 percent rise time for the amplifier of Prob. 9-45 when no shunt peaking is used. Find a value of L that minimizes the 10 to 90 percent rise time without producing any overshoot. What is the 10 to 90 percent rise time in this case? Now repeat this calculation assuming that above 5 percent overshoot is allowed.

9-54. Compare and discuss the amplifiers of Probs. 9-45 to 9-47, and 9-53.

9-55. Plot the unit-step response of the amplifier of Probs. 9-38 and 9-39, when $C_d = 2.0$ μf. (Assume that the approximate relations for low-frequency compensation can be used.)

9-56. The amplifiers of Probs. 9-38 and 9-39 are to amplify a rectangular pulse whose width is $\frac{1}{10}$ sec. Compute the sag. Assume that the pulse-repetition rate is very long.

9-57. Repeat Prob. 9-56 but now assume that the pulse width is $\frac{1}{1000}$ sec.

9-58. An amplifier has a normalized gain in transformed form given by

$$A(s) = 1 + \frac{0.1s(s + a)}{(s + a)^2 + \omega_0^2}$$

What is the unit-step response of this amplifier?

9-59. An amplifier has a normalized unit-step response that is given by

$$f(t) = 1 + 0.1e^{-0.2t} + 0.1e^{-0.3t} \cos 4t$$

Find the normalized amplification as a function of $j\omega$.

9-60. Determine the midband amplification and the lower and upper half-power frequencies and plot the normalized frequency response (amplitude and phase) of the source-follower amplifier of Fig. 9-48a. The circuit elements have the following values: $R_L = 10,000$ ohms, $R_g = 10^6$ ohms, $R_{g1} = 10^6$ ohms, $R_s = 200$ ohms, $C_{c1} = 0.01$ μf, $C_c = 0.1$ μf. The parameters of the FET are $g_m = 10,000$ μmhos, $r_d = 10^6$ ohms, $C_{gs} = 2$ pf, $C_{ds} = 2$ pf, $C_{gd} = 0.1$ pf. In the low-frequency region neglect the effect of C_s. The stray wiring capacitance is 2 pf, and the input capacitance of the next amplifier stage is 3 pf.

9-61. Determine the midband amplification and the lower and upper half-power frequencies and plot the normalized frequency response (amplitude and phase) of the cathode-follower amplifier which is equivalent to Fig. 9-48a. The circuit elements have the following values: $R_L = 10,000$ ohms, $R_g = 10^6$ ohms, $R_{g1} = 10^6$ ohms, $R_k = 200$ ohms, $C_{c1} = 0.01$ μf, and $C_c = 0.1$ μf. The parameters of the vacuum tube are $g_m = 5000$ μmhos, $r_p \geq 2 \times 10^6$ ohms, $C_{out} = 8$ pf, $C_{in} = 12$ pf, $C_{gp} = 0.001$ pf, and $C_{hk} = 10$ pf. Assume that C_k and C_s are short circuits at all frequencies of interest. In the low-frequency region, consider the effects of both coupling capacitors. The wiring capacity is 5 pf and the input capacitance of the next amplifier stage is 12 pf.

9-62. Determine the midband amplification and plot the normalized frequency response (amplitude and phase) of the common-base transistor amplifier of Fig. 9-49a. The circuit elements have the following values: $R_C = 10,000$ ohms, $R_B = 1500$ ohms, $R_i = 40$ ohms, and $C_c = 5$ μf. The parameters of the transistor are $h_{ib} = 40$ ohms, $h_{rb} = 4 \times 10^{-6}$, $h_{fb} = -0.99$, $h_{ob} = 10^{-6}$ mho, $f_\alpha = 200 \times 10^6$ Hz, and $C_{ob} = 5$ pf. Assume that the stray wiring capacitance plus the input capacitance of the next stage is 3 pf.

9-63. Compute the input resistance of the ideal transformer shown in Fig. 9-79. The turns ratios are $n_1/n_2 = 10$, $n_1/n_3 = 5$.

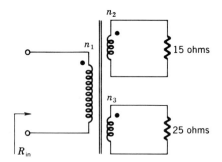

Fig. 9-79

9-64. The transformer-coupled amplifier whose linear model is shown in Fig. 9-55 has the following parameter values: $R_p = 500$ ohms, $R_s = 0.5$ ohm, $L_p = 0.025$ henry, $L_s = 15 \times 10^{-6}$ henry, $L_m = 30$ henrys, $n_1/n_2 = 40$, $r = 400$ ohms, and $R_L = 2$ ohms. The active element is an FET with $g_m = 5000$ μmhos, and $r_d = 5000$ ohms. Compute the mid-frequency voltage gain and the upper and lower half-power frequencies for the amplifier. Assume that $1/\omega C_0 \gg r$ and $1/\omega C_i \gg (n_1/n_2)^2 R_L$ for all frequencies of interest.

9-65. Repeat Prob. 9-64 but now assume that R_L is an open circuit and $C_i = 200$ pf. Plot the high-frequency response of this amplifier.

9-66. The transformer-coupled amplifier whose linear model is shown in Fig. 9-55 has the following parameter values: $R_p = 500$ ohms, $R_s = 1$ ohm, $L_p = 0.025$ henry, $L_s = 300 \times 10^{-6}$ henry, $C_o = 400$ pf, $C_i = 200$ pf, $L_m = 30$ henrys, $n_1/n_2 = 9$, $R_L = 40$ ohms, and $r = 100,000$ ohms. If the active element is a common-base transistor where h_{fb} is -0.99 and where $h_{ob}{}^{-1} = r = 100,000$ ohms, compute the mid-frequency current gain and plot the frequency response of the amplifier.

9-67. For the parallel-resonant circuit of Fig. 9-61, plot a curve of $|Z|/R_0$ versus δ and f/f_0 for values of $Q_0 = 10, 100, 1000$. What are the half-power bandwidths in each of these cases? The notation of Sec. 9-20 is used in this problem.

9-68. The voltage gain of the single-tuned RC-coupled amplifier of Fig. 9-60a is to have a half-power bandwidth of exactly 10,000 Hz, a center frequency $f_0 = 500,000$ Hz, and as large a midband voltage gain as possible. The parameters of the FET are $g_m = 10,000$ ohms, $r_d = 500,000$ ohms, $C_{gs} = 2$ pf, $C_{ds} = 2$ pf, $C_{gd} = 0.1$ pf. The stray wiring capacitance is 5 pf. The input capacitance of the next stage is 3 pf. Find the value of the inductance L. If L has a $Q_0 = 200$, what size resistor must be placed in parallel with R_g to obtain the desired bandwidth? $R_g = 2 \times 10^6$ ohms. What is the voltage gain at f_0? Assume that all bypass capacitances are short circuits at the signal frequencies.

9-69. The voltage gain of the single-tuned RC-coupled amplifier equivalent to Fig. 9-60a is to have a half-power bandwidth of exactly 10,000 Hz, a center frequency of $f_0 = 500,000$ Hz, and as large a midband voltage gain as possible. The output capacitance of the pentode is 20 pf. Assume that the input capacitance of the next stage is 20 pf and the stray wiring capacitance is 10 pf. For the pentode $g_m = 5000$ μmhos and $r_p = 2 \times 10^6$ ohms. The value of R_g is 2×10^6 ohms. Find the value of the inductance L. If L has a $Q_0 = 100$, what size resistance must be placed in parallel with R_g to obtain the desired bandwidth? What is the midband voltage gain? Assume that all bypass capacitors are short circuits at the signal frequencies.

9-70. The current gain of the single-tuned RC-coupled transistor amplifier of Fig. 9-60c is to have a half-power bandwidth of exactly 10,000 Hz, a center frequency of $f_0 = 500,000$ Hz, and as large a midband current gain as possible. Assume that the transistor has the following parameter values: $r_{bb'} = 200$ ohms, $r_{b'e} = 4800$ ohms, $r_{b'c} = 10^{10}$ ohms, $C_{b'c} = 0.1$ pf, $C_{b'e} = 10$ pf, $C_{oe} = 30$ pf, $h_{oe} = 0.5 \times 10^{-6}$ mho, $r_{oe} = 56$ ohms, and $g_m = 20,800$ μmhos. The next stage in the cascade uses a similar transistor. To prevent the size of L from becoming more than a desired value add capacitance, if necessary, so that the total shunt capacitance across it is not less than 50 pf. The value of R_B is 50,000 ohms. The wiring capacitance is 3 pf. Neglect the input capacitance of the next stage. Find the value of the inductance L. If L has a $Q_0 = 100$, can the design be achieved with this circuit? Now add the ideal transformer as shown in Fig. 9-66. Determine the turns ratio necessary to obtain the required bandwidth. What is the current gain at $f = f_0$ in this case? Assume that all bypass capacitors are short circuits at the signal frequencies. Does the resistor R_B have to be used when the impedance-matching transformer is added to the circuit?

9-71. Repeat Prob. 9-70, but instead of the ideal transformer, use the tapped coil of Fig. 9-67. Find the values of $L = L_1 + L_2 + 2M$ and $L_2 + M$ and the current gain at $f = f_0$.

9-72. Repeat Prob. 9-70, but now assume that $h_{oe} = 5 \times 10^{-6}$ mho, $r_{oe} = 506$ ohms, and $C_{oe} = 300$ pf. In this case, two impedance-matching transformers can be used. Place one between the transistor and the tuned circuit so that the transistor's output impedance appears to be the same as it was in Prob. 9-70. The second transformer is used as it was in Prob. 9-70. Determine the turns ratio of both transformers. What is the current gain at $f = f_0$?

9-73. Repeat Prob. 9-71, but now use the circuit of Fig. 9-80 with two capacitors, instead of the tapped inductor. Assume that $C_{oe} = 20$ pf. What effect does this reduction in C_{oe} produce?

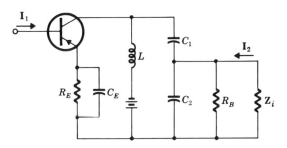

Fig. 9-80

9-74. Repeat Prob. 9-70, but now use the mutual-inductance-coupled circuit of Fig. 9-68a. Assume that the Q of the primary coil alone is 100, that $R_2 = 0$, and that R_B is not present in this circuit.

9-75. The double-tuned amplifier of Fig. 9-69a has the following parameter values: $C_1 = C_2 = 50$ pf, the Q of the primary and secondary coils alone are each 100, $r = R_i = 10^6$ ohms. The resonant frequency is to be 500,000 Hz and the bandwidth where $|A/A_0| \geq 0.8$ is to be 25,000 Hz. Find the values of M, L_1, L_2 and any resistances that are to be placed across r and R_i to obtain the desired bandwidth. If the active element is an FET with $g_m = 5000$ μmhos, what is the maximum voltage gain of the circuit? At what frequencies does this maximum voltage gain occur?

9-76. Repeat Prob. 9-75, but now assume that r and R_i are each 10,000 ohms. Use the circuit of Fig. 9-71 to bring the primary and secondary Q's up to the required value. In this case, if the active element is a transistor, with an $h_{fe} = 100$, what will be the magnitude of the maximum current gain? Assume that C_1 and C_2 are each 50 pf.

9-77. For the amplifier of Prob. 9-69, compute the normalized voltage gain at a bandwidth of 20,000 Hz. The bandwidth is defined by $f_b - f_a = 20,000$ where $f_b f_a = f_0^2$. Then redesign the amplifier of Prob. 9-69 so that two stages are used. What is the normalized voltage gain at f_a and f_b in this case?

9-78. A direct-coupled amplifier has a voltage gain of 10^4. The power-supply voltage changes slightly, which causes the effective input voltage to increase by 0.001 volt. What will be the change in the direct-output voltage? If an RC-coupled amplifier were used, what would this change become?

9-79. Obtain the noise figure of a device in terms of its power signal-to-noise ratios.

10

Untuned Large-signal Amplifiers

When the signal levels present in an amplifier become so large that the non-linearity of the active elements can no longer be ignored, they are spoken of as *large signals*. Large-signal amplifiers are usually, but not always, power amplifiers (see Sec. 8-5). We shall consider the analysis and design of these amplifiers here. Much of the preliminary material necessary for this discussion has been presented in Chap. 5 and in Sec. 8-6. In this chapter, we shall consider untuned amplifiers that amplify a relatively broad range of frequencies. The generalized-device notation of Sec. 5-7 will be used wherever possible.

10-1 CLASS A SINGLE-ENDED AMPLIFIERS

A typical *single-ended amplifier* is shown in Fig. 10-1. Transformer coupling has been illustrated, but this need not be the case. The term single-ended is used to differentiate this type from the push-pull amplifiers that will be

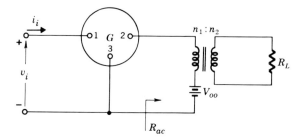

Fig. 10-1 A generalized-device representation of a single-ended amplifier.

discussed in Sec. 10-4. To avoid excessive distortion, single-ended amplifiers are operated class A. A typical set of output characteristics is shown in Fig. 10-2. The quantity x_I is used to represent either the input voltage or the input current (but not both). The labeling of the x_I parameter is typical of a transistor. However, there is no loss of generality, and all the results can be applied equally well to FETs or vacuum tubes.

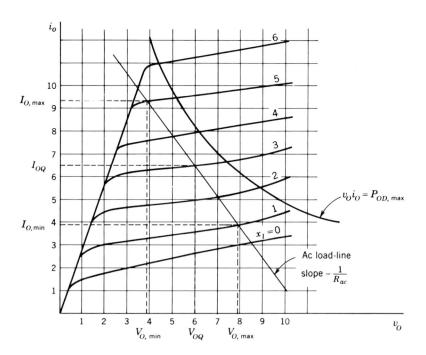

Fig. 10-2 The output characteristics of a generalized device. Relative scales have been used. The quantity x_i represents either v_i or i_i. The value of P_{OD} is chosen to be 49.

If we assume that the distortion is very small, then the procedures of Secs. 5-2 to 5-6 and 5-8 can be used to determine the operating point and the ac load line. If the distortion is appreciable, the procedures of Secs. 5-10 and 5-11 should be used. The quantities that are of interest are P_2, the signal power delivered to the load; the power P_{OO} supplied by the battery; the efficiency of the output circuit η_2; the power dissipated within the output of the device P_{OD}; the rms signal output voltage and current V_2 and I_2, respectively; the rms signal input voltage and/or current V_1 and I_1, respectively; and the distortion. The procedure for calculating all these quantities when distortion is negligible was given in Sec. 5-9. We shall summarize these procedures here using the quantities defined in Fig. 10-2, where it is assumed that coordinates of the quiescent operating point are $V_{OQ} = 6$, $I_{OQ} = 6.5$, and $X_{IQ} = 3$. (Relative values are used here.) The input signal is given by $x_1 = 2 \cos \omega t$. If the transformer is ideal,

$$P_2 = \frac{(V_{O,\max} - V_{O,\min})(I_{O,\max} - I_{O,\min})}{8} \tag{10-1}$$

$$V_2 = \frac{V_{O,\max} - V_{O,\min}}{2\sqrt{2}} \tag{10-2}$$

$$I_2 = \frac{I_{O,\max} - I_{O,\min}}{2\sqrt{2}} \tag{10-3}$$

$$P_{OO} = V_{OO}I_{OQ} \tag{10-4}$$

$$\eta_2 = \frac{P_2}{P_{OO}} \tag{10-5}$$

$$P_{OD} = P_{OO} - P_2 \tag{10-6}$$

If there is a resistance in series with the power supply, the power dissipated in it should be subtracted from P_{OD} in Eq. (10-6). A distortion analysis using the procedures of Secs. 5-10 and 5-11 should also be performed to determine the distortion and to see whether Eqs. (10-1) to (10-6) are valid. When the distortion is large, Eqs. (10-1) to (10-6) should be modified. If the output current is of the form

$$i_2 = I_{OA} + \sqrt{2}(I_{o1} \cos \omega t + I_{o2} \cos 2\omega t + I_{o3} \cos 3\omega t + \cdots) \tag{10-7}$$

we can write

$$P_2 = I_{o1}{}^2 R_{ac} \tag{10-8}$$

$$V_2 = I_{o1} R_{ac} \tag{10-9}$$

$$I_2 = I_{o1} \tag{10-10}$$

$$P_{OO} = V_{OO} \frac{1}{2\pi} \int_0^{2\pi} i_2 \, d\omega t \tag{10-11}$$

$$P_{OO} = V_{OO} I_{oA} \tag{10-12}$$

$$\eta_2 = \frac{P_2}{P_{OO}} \tag{10-13}$$

$$P_{OD} = P_{OO} - (I_{o1}^2 + I_{o2}^2 + \cdots)R_{ac} = P_{OO} - P_{2T} \tag{10-14}$$

If there is resistance in series with the power supply, the power dissipated in it should also be subtracted from P_{OO} to obtain P_{OD}. Thus, a complete analysis of this amplifier can be performed. We must now consider how these results can be used in the design of an amplifier.

10-2 DESIGN OF CLASS A SINGLE-ENDED AMPLIFIERS

The design of a power amplifier consists of choosing a device and determining the coordinates of the operating point, the value of R_{ac}, and the required input signal so that the desired output power is delivered to R_L, the distortion is equal to or less than a specified amount, and the device output dissipation is equal to or less than the rated value. The procedures for determining some of these quantities differ greatly for the vacuum-tube triode, for the vacuum-tube pentode or beam power tube or FET, and for the transistor. In such cases, we shall have to consider their individual characteristics and not use the generalized device.

The maximum allowable device output dissipation $P_{OD,\max}$, that is, the plate dissipation in the vacuum tube, the channel dissipation in an FET, and the collector-junction dissipation in a transistor, is specified by the manufacturer. It represents the maximum *average* power that can be dissipated in the output circuit of the device. The actual value of P_{OD} is given by Eq. (10-6) or (10-14) and depends upon the signal level. It decreases if the signal increases. There are usually times when signals are absent, so that the plate dissipation should be designated for quiescent conditions. That is,

$$V_{OQ}I_{OQ} \leq P_{OD,\max} \tag{10-15}$$

The equation

$$v_O i_O = P_{OD,\max} \tag{10-16}$$

is a hyperbola. Such a curve is shown in Fig. 10-2. The quiescent operating point should not be located above this curve if the device output dissipation is not to exceed the rated value.

At low power levels, up to 500 watts output, the transistor has almost completely replaced the vacuum tube as a power amplifier. However, the vacuum tube is still used extensively when many kilowatts of output signal are required, e.g., in modulation circuits (see Chap. 16). Thus, we shall discuss vacuum-tube design in some detail. At the present time, the FET is limited to output power in the order of 1 watt or less. Now let us consider specific devices and see how the amplifier design proceeds.

The vacuum-tube triode In order to determine a starting point in the choice of R_{ac}, we shall idealize the vacuum-tube-triode characteristics by assuming that they are linear as long as the plate current is not less than a specified value I_a. In Fig. 10-3 vacuum-tube-triode characteristics that are equally spaced and linear for $i_b > I_a$ have been drawn. When the grid is positively biased, grid current results, which often produces excessive distortion. For instance, consider the circuit of Fig. 10-4. If $v_s < |V_{cQ}|$, the net grid bias is negative and the full signal voltage appears between the grid and the cathode. (The capacitor C_k is assumed to be a short circuit at signal frequencies.) If $v_s > |V_{cQ}|$, grid current will result and there will be a voltage drop in R_s. Thus, the positive peak of the sine wave will be flattened. We shall restrict our operation such that

$$v_c \leq 0 \qquad\qquad (10\text{-}17a)$$

$$i_b \geq I_a \qquad\qquad (10\text{-}17b)$$

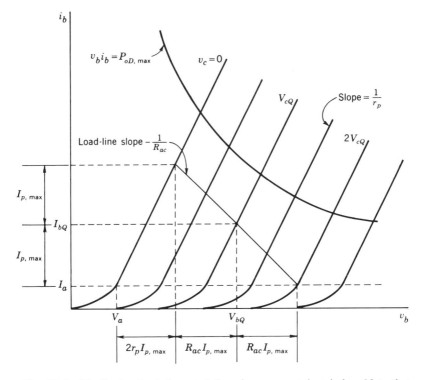

Fig. 10-3 Idealized output characteristics of a vacuum-tube triode. Note that V_{cQ} is negative.

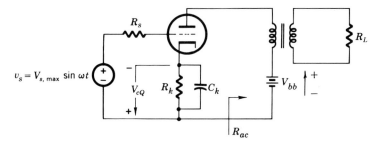

Fig. 10-4 A vacuum-tube-triode power amplifier.

A load line has been drawn on the output characteristics of Fig. 10-3. To maximize the power delivered to R_{ac}, the signal level and grid bias are adjusted so that relations (10-17) are satisfied with the equal signs. The quiescent plate voltage is specified at times because of power-supply considerations. The output power will be maximized with respect to R_{ac}, subject to the above restrictions. The various lengths that have been marked off in Fig. 10-3 are obtained by multiplying the peak signal current $I_{p,max}$ by the appropriate slopes. Then

$$V_{bQ} - V_a = I_{p,max}(2r_p + R_{ac}) \tag{10-18}$$

$$P_2 = \frac{I_{p,max}^2}{2} R_{ac} \tag{10-19}$$

Thus

$$P_2 = \frac{(V_{bQ} - V_a)^2}{2(2r_p + R_{ac})^2} R_{ac} \tag{10-20}$$

Setting dP_2/dR_{ac} equal to zero and solving for R_{ac}, we obtain

$$R_{ac} = 2r_p \tag{10-21}$$

If we had chosen other constraints, a different relationship might have been obtained, since V_{bQ} might not be independent of R_{ac}.

If a triode amplifier is operated at very low fixed signal levels, so that the operation is linear, and if R_{ac} is varied, then the maximum power output occurs when $R_{ac} = r_p$. It is only when the nonlinearities of the device are considered and additional constraints are imposed that other results are obtained.

Actual triode characteristics are nonlinear over their entire operating range with the nonlinearities increasing as i_b decreases. If the input signal and the operating point are held constant while R_{ac} is varied, then the curve of P_2 versus R_{ac} will peak when $R_{ac} \approx r_p$ (if the distortion is not too large). However, if R_{ac} is increased further, then the distortion decreases. Typical curves of power output and percent harmonic distortion versus load resistance are shown in Fig. 10-5. Note that the distortion falls off very rapidly with increasing R_{ac}, but the curve of P_2 versus R_{ac} has a broad peak. If the value of $R_{ac} = 2r_p$ is chosen, P_2 is approximately 89 percent of the maximum value while the distortion decreases considerably. If we set $R_{ac} = 2r_p$ and then increase the input signal level, the output power can be increased to more than the value obtained when $R_{ac} = r_p$ but the distortion will be less.

Let us consider the design of a vacuum-tube-triode power amplifier. It is assumed that the following quantities are specified: the required output power P_2, the maximum allowable distortion, the quiescent plate voltage (if the transformer is good, this is approximately equal to $V_{bb} + V_{cQ}$), and the maximum plate dissipation.

1. For various triodes, determine I_a, V_a, and the average value of r_p. Then use Eq. (10-20), with $R_{ac} = 2r_p$, to determine the triode to be used. Remember that this is very approximate, since I_a and r_p really cannot be accurately specified and Eq. (10-20) is an approximation.
2. Determine $I_{p,\text{max}}$ from the equation

$$I_{p,\text{max}} = \sqrt{\frac{2P_2}{R_{ac}}}$$

Use a value of P_2 that is slightly greater than the required value.

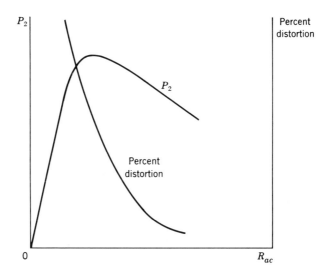

Fig. 10-5 Typical curves of power output and percent distortion versus load resistance for a vacuum-tube-triode amplifier.

3. Then,

$$I_{bQ} = I_a + I_{p,\max}$$

Since V_{bQ} is specified, the coordinates of the operating point are now determined. Verify that they lie below the grid-bias hyperbola.
4. Compute the actual power output and the distortion. If P_2 is large enough and the distortion and the plate dissipation are small enough, the design is complete and the required input signal can be determined. It must be emphasized that this procedure is very approximate and yields only a first trial for the design. It may be necessary to vary R_{ac}. Increasing R_{ac} will reduce the distortion; reducing R_{ac} will increase P_2. The operating point can also be shifted to vary P_2, the distortion, or the plate dissipation. If the design cannot be achieved, then try a larger tube, i.e., one with greater i_b for the same v_b and v_c; it will also have a greater allowable plate dissipation.

Equations (10-18) to (10-21) were derived on the basis of a constant value of r_p in a linear region. In the actual triode, no such region exists. In addition, the design is based on an assumed value of I_a, but until the design is complete, the relationship between I_a and the distortion is unknown. Thus, it again must be stressed that this procedure is very approximate.

FET, vacuum-tube pentode, and beam power tube The output characteristics of the FET and the vacuum-tube pentode or beam power tube are very similar. Thus, essentially the same design procedures can be used for each of these devices. Note that the power output for vacuum-tube pentodes can be much greater than that for FETs, i.e., up to kilowatts for vacuum-tube pentodes but up to the order of 1 watt for an FET. Note that for the MOSFET, operation is *not* restricted to negative values of the gate-source voltage.

Typical characteristics for an FET are shown in Fig. 10-6. There are severe nonlinearities in the region of the knees of the curves, and the curves become crowded together for large negative grid voltages. Load lines have been drawn for several values of R_{ac}. The operation will be restricted to negative grid voltages for the pentode. Thus, the input signal is assumed to be $v_{gs} = -V_{GSQ} \cos \omega t$. Typical curves of power output and distortion versus R_{ac} are shown in Fig. 10-7. The distortion for the negative half of the current cycle is almost independent of R_{ac}. However, the clipping of the positive half-cycle varies directly with R_{ac}. The second-harmonic distortion becomes zero when the flattening of the positive and negative peaks is equal [see Eq. (5-76c)]. Thus, the distortion is minimum for an optimum value of R_{ac}. If the load resistance is increased further, the distortion increases rapidly because of the increased clipping of the positive peak. If the operation were

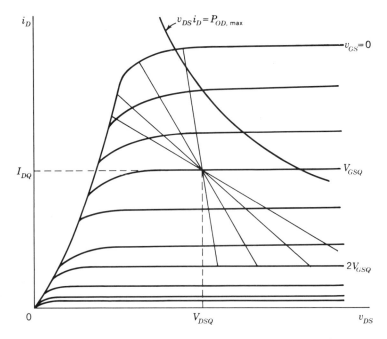

Fig. 10-6 Typical output characteristics for an FET. Note that V_{GSQ} is negative.

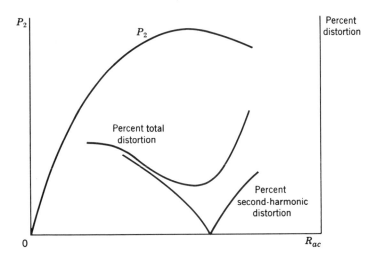

Fig. 10-7 Typical curves of power output and percent distortion for a vacuum-tube pentode, a beam power tube, or an FET.

linear, the maximum output power would occur when $R_{ac} = r_d$ (which is larger than the value that produces minimum distortion). However, for large signal levels, the clipping of the signal that occurs at small values of R_{ac} limits the output power. The maximum power output usually occurs at a value of R_{ac} that is very close to the one that produces minimum distortion.

If the required power output, the maximum allowable distortion, the quiescent plate voltage, and the maximum plate dissipation are specified, then an optimum value of R_{ac} can be found for any given operating point. Try various operating points, subject to the requirements on the channel dissipation and the drain-source voltage, until the output requirements are met. If the design cannot be achieved, then the requirements on V_{DSQ} may have to be relaxed or a larger device used.

If the signal is reduced from its maximum value, there will no longer be cancellation of the second harmonic. Thus, the distortion should also be checked at smaller values of input signal.

The class A amplifier has a maximum theoretical efficiency of 50 percent. In practice, it may only be half of this value. Thus, the plate dissipation has a minimum value which is equal to P_2. Its probable value is closer to $3P_2$. This should be considered when the vacuum tube or FET is chosen.

The transistor   A typical set of characteristics for the common-emitter transistor is shown in Fig. 10-8. There are several differences in the allowed operation of the vacuum tube and the transistor. The vacuum tube is often restricted to operation below the zero-grid-voltage curve. However, operation at large magnitudes of base current is permissible with the transistor. There is a maximum allowable base current, but the collector-junction dissipation often limits the operation before it is reached. In a vacuum tube, the efficiency is usually much less than the theoretical maximum. However, the knees of the transistor output characteristics are very close to the axis of ordinates. Thus, large signal swings can be attained, and the efficiency of operation can be very close to the theoretical maximum value of 50 percent. Hence, the allowable collector-junction dissipation need be only slightly greater than the required power output.

Even if the actual collector-junction dissipation is less than that specified by the manufacturer, the transistor may still be overheated. This is because its temperature depends not only upon the power dissipated in it but also upon the means provided for removing the resultant heat. (Procedures for cooling transistors are discussed in detail in Sec. 10-8.) The rated power dissipation assumes that certain cooling procedures are used and that the ambient temperature is below a specified value. If these assumptions are not valid, the transistor may be damaged by overheating even though the power dissipation is less than the rated value. The results of Sec. 10-8 can be used to determine the maximum allowable power dissipation in such cases.

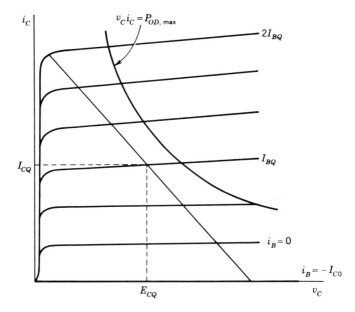

Fig. 10-8 Typical output characteristics for a common-emitter transistor.

Since the input circuit of the transistor also introduces distortion, the analysis of Sec. 5-11 should be used. The distortion is a function of the impedance of the preceding stage. At times, if this impedance is the proper value, the total distortion is minimized, since the distortion due to the input characteristics can tend to cancel the distortion due to the output characteristics. Resistance is sometimes placed in series or shunt with the input to achieve this optimum condition.

If the required power output, the maximum allowable distortion, and the quiescent collector voltage are specified, then the following design procedure can be used to obtain the required circuit. Choose a transistor with a collector dissipation somewhat greater than the required power output. Pick an operating point, using the required V_{CEQ}, close to (but below) the allowable dissipation hyperbola, choose a load line, and check the output quantities. The signal component of the base current should be chosen to cause i_B to vary between $i_B \approx 0$ and $i_B \approx 2I_{BQ}$. If high efficiency is desired, the load line should be drawn into the knees of the curves as shown. The distortion can be reduced somewhat at the expense of efficiency and output by reducing R_{ac}. Again, a cut-and-try procedure should be used once the first operating point is located. If the design cannot be achieved, a transistor with a larger rated output dissipation should be chosen.

For the vacuum tube, FET, and transistor, we have shown the operating point below the device output dissipation curve (see Figs. 10-3, 10-6, and 10-8). It may not be necessary to leave a safety factor here. Manufacturers sometimes specify maximum ratings as the maximum permissible value, in which case some safety factor should be allowed for. On the other hand, if a maximum design value is specified, no additional safety factor is needed in most cases. The device output dissipation should not be made any larger than is necessary so that the efficiency will be as large as possible. The device should be chosen so that the output dissipation is close to the maximum rated value. This can eliminate the need for a larger and more expensive device.

In addition to the device output dissipation, a maximum output voltage rating is usually specified. In the transistor or FET, it is limited by junction breakdown. In a vacuum tube or FET it may be limited by arc over between electrodes. At maximum signal levels the maximum output voltage is somewhat less than twice the power-supply voltage. In the transistor, the collector voltage can swing almost down to zero, because of the location and shape of the knees of the static output characteristic. Hence, the maximum collector voltage will be approximately $2V_{CC}$. It should be verified that these voltages do not exceed rated values. Maximum current ratings may also be specified. The amplifier should be designed so that these ratings are not exceeded.

10-3 PARALLEL OPERATION

If two identical generalized devices are connected in parallel, i.e., terminals 1 connected to each other, terminals 2 connected to each other, and terminals 3 connected to each other, the characteristics of the resultant device can be obtained from those of the original by doubling all current scales, including those of the input parameter, while holding all voltage scales constant.

If, for instance, two devices whose output characteristics are given in Fig. 10-2 are paralleled, if the new device is operated so that the value of R_{ac} is one-half of the value used for one device, and if the quiescent input current is doubled, then the locus of operation will be that shown in Fig. 10-2 (with the current scales doubled). Thus, the output power will be doubled while the distortion remains constant. The allowable device output dissipation will also be doubled. Parallel operation can be used to increase power output without increasing distortion. However, there are two reasons why this is not often done. First, if the two devices are not exactly the same, the power dissipated within them will not be equal. Hence, even if the two parallel devices are nominally the same, one may actually have a considerably greater power dissipation than the other. Thus, if the devices are to be used at, or near, their rated dissipation, they must be carefully matched. This often proves inconvenient. Second, another circuit which also uses two devices offers greater advantages. We shall discuss it next.

10-4 PUSH-PULL AMPLIFIERS

A commonly used power-amplifier configuration is shown in Fig. 10-9. This circuit provides all the advantages of parallel operation and more. It is assumed that both generalized devices are identical and that their input signals differ by 180°. Thus, when the output current of one device increases, the other decreases. This is called a *push-pull* amplifier. It has several advantages which we shall illustrate with the following discussion.

If the input signal to device 1 is $x_{11} = X_{1,\max} \cos \omega t$, then the output current i_{o1} will be of the form

$$i_{o1} = i_{o1}(\omega t) = I_{OA} + \sqrt{2}(I_{o1} \cos \omega t + I_{o2} \cos 2\omega t + I_{o3} \cos 3\omega t$$
$$+ I_{o4} \cos 4\omega t + \cdots) \quad (10\text{-}22)$$

Since the input signals are 180° out of phase, $x_{12} = X_{1,\max} \cos(\omega t + \pi)$ and we have

$$i_{o2} = i_{o1}(\omega t + \pi) = I_{OA} + \sqrt{2}[I_{o1} \cos(\omega t + \pi) + I_{o2} \cos 2(\omega t + \pi)$$
$$+ I_{o3} \cos 3(\omega t + \pi) + I_{o4} \cos 4(\omega t + \pi) + \cdots] \quad (10\text{-}23)$$

The load current i_L and the flux in the core of the transformer are proportional to

$$i_{OT} = i_{o1} - i_{o2} \quad (10\text{-}24)$$

Substituting, and using the relation $\cos(x + n\pi) = (-1)^n \cos x$, we obtain

$$i_{OT} = 2\sqrt{2}(I_{o1} \cos \omega t + I_{o3} \cos 3\omega t + I_{o5} \cos 5\omega t + \cdots) \quad (10\text{-}25)$$

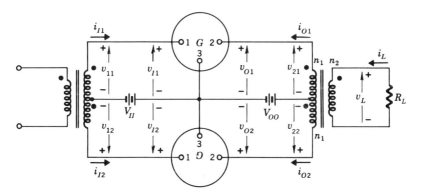

Fig. 10-9 A push-pull amplifier.

All the even harmonics have been canceled. This is an important advantage of the push-pull circuit. A second advantage is that there is no direct current that tends to saturate the core of the transformer (see Sec. 9-19). It can then contain much less ferromagnetic material. Output transformers for push-pull circuits are lighter, smaller, and less expensive than transformers of comparable quality used in single-ended circuits.

The turns ratio of the transformer is $2n_1/n_2$. The effective resistance R_{dd}, viewed across the primary winding, is

$$R_{dd} = 4\left(\frac{n_1}{n_2}\right)^2 R_L \tag{10-26}$$

Therefore, each device seems to have an ac load resistance of

$$\frac{R_{dd}}{2} = 2\left(\frac{n_1}{n_2}\right)^2 R_L \tag{10-27}$$

Actually the situation is not this simple. Note that if one device were made inoperative by opening the lead to its terminal 2, the remaining device would effectively be connected to a transformer whose turns ratio is n_1/n_2, and its ac load resistance would be $(n_1/n_2)^2 R_L$. The reason for the apparent discrepancy is that when both devices operate, they interact with each other through the transformer. For this reason, the load may not be the resistance given in Eq. (10-27). For instance, i_{o1} sets up a flux that affects v_{22}. An important fact is that the flux linking each half of the secondary is ideally the same. Thus

$$v_{21} = -v_{22} \tag{10-28}$$

Since the devices are not necessarily linear, this would not be the case if the transformer were replaced by two resistors. Equation (10-28) is said to come about because of *transformer action*. Since this occurs in a common winding it is also called *autotransformer action*. In Sec. 10-10 we shall discuss procedures whereby the transformer can be eliminated from the push-pull circuit.

A single source resistance will provide gate bias for both FETs of a push-pull amplifier as shown in Fig. 10-10a. The current through the resistor R_s is

$$i_{o1} + i_{o2} = 2I_{OA} + 2\sqrt{2}(I_{o2}\cos 2\omega t + I_{o4}\cos 4\omega t + \cdots) \tag{10-29}$$

No (fundamental) component of current of frequency ω is through R_s. Thus, in theory, there is no reason to bypass it. However, in practice, a bypass capacitor is usually used, because two identical FETs can never be found. Thus, $i_{o2}(\omega t)$ is not exactly equal to $i_{o1}(\omega t + \pi)$ and there will not be exact cancellation of the fundamental.

An emitter resistance is not used to obtain bias but to stabilize the collector current (see Sec. 5-6). The voltage across it should depend only upon the collector current of one transistor, since it cannot be assumed that the

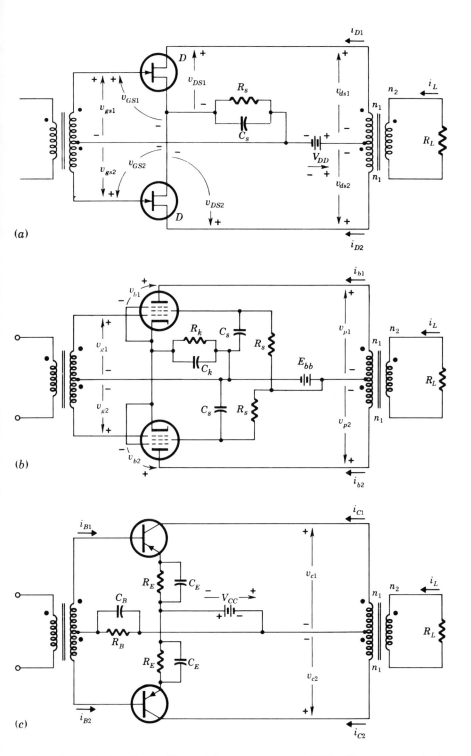

Fig. 10-10 Push-pull amplifiers: (*a*) common-source FET; (*b*) common-cathode vacuum-tube pentode; (*c*) common-emitter transistor.

same instabilities will develop in each transistor. Thus, separate emitter resistors, as shown in Fig. 10-10c, are used, and they are bypassed. The resistor R_B limits the direct base current. It is bypassed so that it does not affect the signal current.

A source or cathode-bias resistance tends to stabilize FET or vacuum-tube operation (see Sec. 5-3). Since balance is very important in push-pull circuits, this extra stability is desirable. Thus, FET or vacuum-tube circuits, at times, use two separate source or cathode-bias impedances.

10-5 THE COMPOSITE DEVICE

To completely determine the output of a push-pull amplifier, a graphical analysis should be performed. We shall do this by replacing the two active elements by a single *composite device* which produces the same load current i_L as the push-pull circuit. From Fig. 10-9 and Eq. (10-24) we have

$$i_L = \frac{n_1}{n_2}(i_{o1} - i_{o2}) = \frac{n_1}{n_2}i_{OT} \tag{10-30}$$

Thus, the composite device shown in Fig. 10-11 works into a transformer of turns ratio n_1/n_2 and has an output current equal to i_{OT}. The quantity x_I will be used to represent either v_i or i_i. We shall neglect the distortion due to the input circuit. Its effect will be considered subsequently. The output current of a device is a function of its output voltage and its input current or voltage. Thus (see Fig. 10-9)

$$\begin{aligned} i_{o1} &= f(x_{I1}, v_{o1}) \\ i_{o2} &= f(x_{I2}, v_{o2}) \end{aligned} \tag{10-31}$$

The two functions are the same, since the two devices are identical. Neglecting any direct-voltage drop in the transformer, we have

$$v_{o1} = V_{OO} + v_{21} \tag{10-32}$$

$$v_{o2} = V_{OO} + v_{22} \tag{10-33}$$

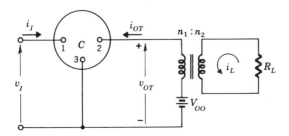

Fig. 10-11   The composite device.

Then, using Eq. (10-28) and substituting, we obtain

$$v_{O2} = 2V_{OO} - v_{O1} \tag{10-34}$$

Note that this equation is a result of the autotransformer action. If there are bypassed cathode-bias resistances or emitter-stabilizing resistances, the value of V_{OO} should be reduced by an amount equal to the voltage drop across them. (This voltage drop is a function of I_{OA} and can vary with signal level.) The input quantity x_I is the sum of the signal and the direct bias.

$$x_{I1} = X_{II} + x_{11} \tag{10-35}$$

$$x_{I2} = X_{II} + x_{12} \tag{10-36}$$

We assume that the input signals x_{11} and x_{12} are 180° out of phase. Then

$$x_{I2} = X_{II} - x_{11} \tag{10-37}$$

Substituting Eqs. (10-31) to (10-37) and (10-28) into Eq. (10-24), we obtain

$$i_{OT} = f(X_{II} + x_{11}, V_{OO} + v_{21}) - f(X_{II} - x_{11}, V_{OO} - v_{21}) \tag{10-38}$$

$$i_{OT} = f(X_{II} + x_{11}, v_{01}) - f(X_{II} - x_{11}, 2V_{OO} - v_{01}) \tag{10-39}$$

Equation (10-38) or (10-39) is an expression for the static characteristic output curves of the composite device. To construct them, we require the static output characteristics of an individual device and the location of two of the coordinates of the operating point. The *composite output characteristic* is a plot of i_{OT} versus $v_{OT} = v_{O1}$, with the input *signal* x_{11} as a parameter. Figure 10-12 illustrates the construction of two such curves for $x_{11} = 0$ and $+1$. The procedure used is to specify values for X_{II} and V_{OO} and then subtract the individual curves for $X_{II} + x_{11}$ and $X_{II} - x_{11}$ from each other as indicated in Eq. (10-39). To do this conveniently, line up the abscissas of two characteristics so that zero of one corresponds to $2V_{OO}$ of the other, as shown in Fig. 10-12. The V_{OO} points are then adjacent to each other. The two curves can be directly subtracted on a point-by-point basis. If this is repeated for other values of x_{11}, the entire composite characteristic can be obtained. Figure 10-13 illustrates such a set of composite characteristics.

Since $i_L = (n_1/n_2)i_{OT}$, the effective load resistance for the composite device is

$$R_{ac} = \left(\frac{n_1}{n_2}\right)^2 R_L \tag{10-40}$$

so that the slope of the load line is $-1/(n_1/n_2)^2 R_L$. If no signal is present, $i_{OT} = 0$ and $v_{O1} = v_{OT} = V_{OO}$. Thus, the abscissa intercept of the load line is V_{OO}. The intersection of the load line with the appropriate composite characteristic curve yields the instantaneous value of i_{OT}, just as it would on a set of ordinary output characteristics. Thus, the usual distortion and power-

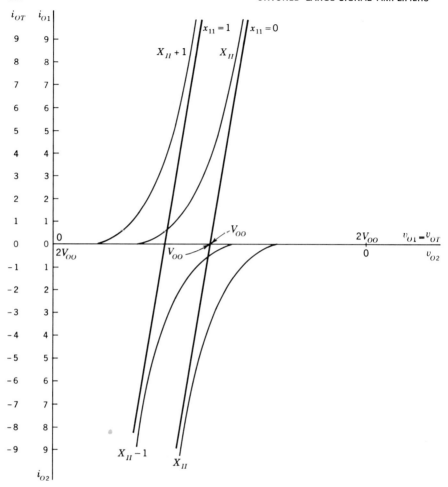

Fig. 10-12 Construction of the composite-device output characteristics.

output calculations can be made. The locus of the output of the composite device lies along the ac load line.

The locus of operation of the individual devices is found by reversing the construction procedure. That is, at a point where R_{ac} intersects a composite curve, project straight up and down until the device characteristics that were used to construct the composite curve are intersected. These points are the instantaneous operating points of devices 1 and 2. The locus of operation of both devices is shown in Fig. 10-13. It is *not* a straight line, since the load that each individual device sees is not a simple resistance, due to the interaction of the two devices.

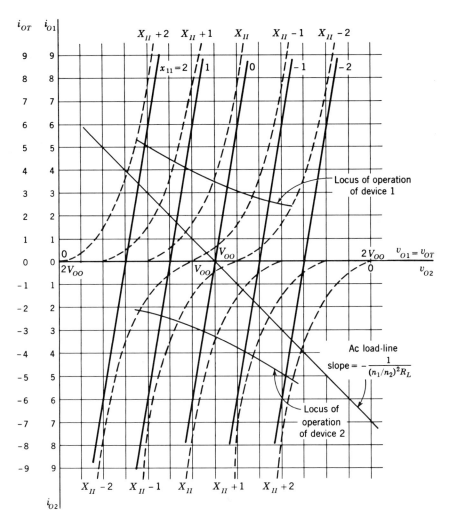

Fig. 10-13 Composite output characteristics of two devices operating at a specific operating point, in push-pull.

Thus far, the distortion due to the input characteristics has been neglected. It is very important to consider it for transistors and also for vacuum tubes if there is grid current. Once the locus of operation of the individual device is known, we can obtain a plot of x_I versus v_O. The procedure of Sec. 5-11 can then be applied directly to the individual devices to determine their input voltage and current. If the advantages of push-pull operation are to be obtained, x_{11} must equal $-x_{12}$. If this is not the case

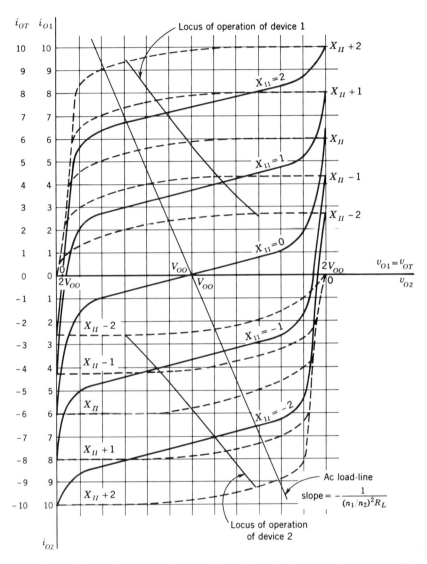

Fig. 10-14 Composite output characteristics of two devices operating at a specific operating point, in push-pull.

(because of distortion), then the input circuit should be adjusted to make it essentially true. We shall consider this in Sec. 10-9.

We have thus far used generalized-device characteristics that resemble those of the vacuum-tube triode. Since even harmonics predominate here, the composite-device characteristics are very linear. If the device characteristics resembled those of a pentode, FET, or transistor, a set of curves similar to those of Fig. 10-14 would result. Note that there is more non-linearity of the composite characteristics, since the devices themselves produce a substantial amount of odd-harmonic distortion.

The upper and lower portions of these curves are symmetric, so that only the upper half of the composite characteristics need be constructed and the information can be obtained from one set of output characteristics.

10-6 CLASS AB AND CLASS B PUSH-PULL OPERATION

In Sec. 8-6, we demonstrated that the output-circuit efficiency would be increased if the operation were shifted from class A to class AB or B. Single-ended amplifiers are restricted to class A operation because of the excessive distortion that results in any other mode of operation. This is not the case when push-pull amplifiers are used. In class B operation, each device will conduct for an alternate half-cycle and the output waveform need not be distorted. Such operation is represented in Fig. 10-15. In actual circuits,

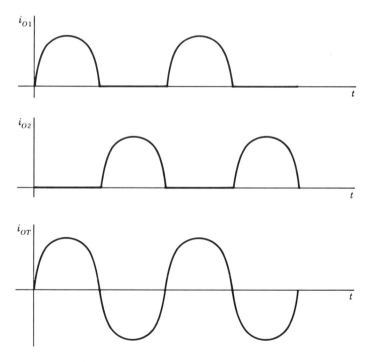

Fig. 10-15 Curves of individual-device output currents i_{O1} and i_{O2} and composite-device output current i_{OT} in an ideal class B push-pull amplifier.

true class B operation, where there is output current for exactly one-half of the cycle, is not used, because excessive distortion can result. In class B operation, at any time, one device always has zero output current, so that the composite characteristic is composed of the individual device characteristics with no subtraction performed. The vacuum tube, FET, and the transistor have characteristics that are quite nonlinear near cutoff. If a small

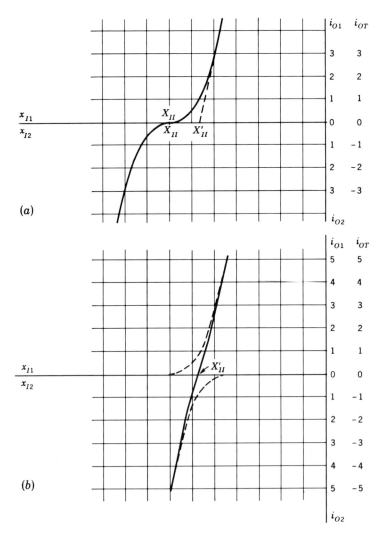

Fig. 10-16 Composite transfer characteristics: (a) biased at exact cutoff and (b) biased at projected cutoff.

signal is applied, the operation will be entirely in this region and the distortion will be very high. [For class A operation, the subtractive process linearizes this highly curved region near cutoff (see Fig. 10-13).] This effect can best be seen by considering the *transfer characteristics* of the composite device. This is a plot of output current versus x_I with e_{OT} as a parameter. The same variables are plotted here as in the output characteristics, and the construction

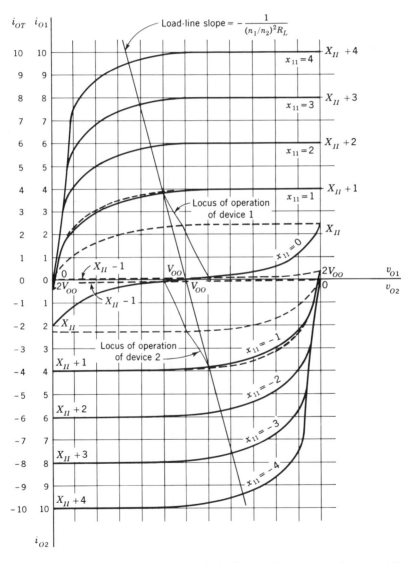

Fig. 10-17 Composite output characteristics for two devices operating class AB.

is similar. Figure 10-16a shows one composite transfer characteristic curve for $v_{O1} = v_{O2} = v_{OT} = V_{OO}$ and $x_{11} = 0$. The input bias X_{II} is adjusted for exact class B operation. The composite characteristic is very nonlinear. A procedure for avoiding much of the distortion is to operate so that the currents i_{O1} and i_{O2} are not zero for somewhat more than one half-cycle. One means of obtaining X_{II} is to pick a point where the transfer characteristics have become fairly linear. Then draw a tangent to the curve at this point. Assume that the transfer characteristic follows this straight line. The value of input bias is found from the intersection of the straight line with the x_I axis. Call this value X'_{II}. The straight line is called the *projected curve* and the bias X'_{II} is called the *projected cutoff bias*. Figure 10-16b shows a composite transfer characteristic drawn using the projected cutoff bias X'_{II}. When composite transfer curves are constructed, the abscissa axes are lined up so that the direct-bias points coincide.) Note that almost all the non-linearity is gone. To avoid the distortion of Fig. 10-16a, which is called *crossover distortion*, class B amplifiers are usually operated at projected cutoff bias. This is not true class B operation; it is actually class AB operation. It is sometimes called class B, but class ABB might be a better name. A typical set of class AB output characteristics is shown in Fig. 10-17. Notice that over most of the region of operation, the characteristics are those of the individual devices themselves, as it would be in class B operation. The composite-device characteristics are so similar to those of the individual devices that it is often unnecessary to draw the composite-device characteristics. If the input bias is shifted so that the operation proceeds from class A to class ABB, the distortion and efficiency will, in general, increase.

10-7 DESIGN OF PUSH-PULL AMPLIFIERS

The design of a push-pull amplifier is considerably different from that of a single-ended amplifier. For instance, a class A vacuum-tube-triode push-pull amplifier is usually so linear that the maximum-power-transfer theorem can be used in determining the effective load resistance and Eq. (10-21) is not used. The internal resistance r_{pd} of the composite device is given by the reciprocal of the slope of the composite output characteristic. Thus, for maximum output power

$$\frac{n_1}{n_2} = \sqrt{\frac{r_{pd}}{R_L}} \tag{10-41}$$

For vacuum-tube pentodes or FETs operating class A, at maximum signal level, the curve of power output versus load resistance peaks at a value of a load resistance considerably less than that predicted by the maximum-power-transfer theorem. This is similar to the clipping that occurs in a single-ended vacuum-tube pentode or FET stage. If the load resistance is increased further, severe clipping of the signal results and the power output is limited. The distortion curve does not exhibit a minimum, such as that shown in Fig. 10-7, since the even harmonics are canceled by the push-pull circuit.

If vacuum-tube pentodes or FETs are operated class B or class ABB, a minimum in the distortion curve does result at an optimum value of load resistance, $R_{ac,opt}$. This is because the third harmonic can be canceled. For values of load resistance that are less than the optimum value

$$\tfrac{1}{6}(I_{O,\max} - I_{O,\min}) > \tfrac{1}{3}(I_{O\alpha} - I_{O\beta})$$

[see Eq. (5-76d)]. This is due to the crowding of the class ABB composite characteristics at low signal levels. As the load resistance is increased, the locus of operation crosses the knees of the characteristic curves (see Figs 10-14 and 10-17), which reduces $I_{O,\max} - I_{O,\min}$ in relation to $I_{O\alpha} - I_{O\beta}$. A minimum in the third-harmonic distortion results at some optimum value of load resistance $R_{ac,opt}$. There is no exact cancellation of the harmonic since Eq. (5-76d) is only approximate. The higher harmonics, such as the fifth and seventh, cannot be neglected in this case. However, the total harmonic distortion will have a minimum value when $R_{ac,opt}$ is used. When the signal level decreases from the maximum value, the third harmonic will no longer be canceled. Thus, the distortion should be checked not only at the maximum signal level but also at smaller ones. The power output tends to peak at a value of load resistance near $R_{ac,opt}$ for the same reason that it does in class A operation. Class AB operation lies between class A and class B operation. Thus, the distortion curve may or may not have a minimum. However, if the load resistance is increased above the value that yields maximum power output, the distortion increases greatly.

The statements concerning power output can also be applied to transistors. However, the shape of their static characteristics is such that the minimum in the distortion does not result.

The design of push-pull amplifiers is complicated by the fact that the composite characteristics cannot be drawn until the operating point is fixed and vice versa. If V_{OQ} is specified, then an input bias value can be picked and a first trial design obtained. Experience will aid in choosing the operating point. The fact that the distortion, available power output, and efficiency increase as the operation moves closer to class B can be used here. This assumes that the input signal is increased as the operation shifts toward class B.

There may be distortion due to nonlinearities in the input circuit. These occur in the transistor, and in the vacuum tube if there is grid current. The driver stage (see Sec. 10-9) should be designed to minimize this distortion.

The individual device output dissipation P_{OD} is just half of the output dissipation of the composite device P_{OCD}. Thus,

$$P_{OD} = \tfrac{1}{2}P_{OCD}$$

where

$$P_{OCD} = P_{OO} - P_2 \tag{10-42}$$

The power dissipated in any resistance in series with the power supply should be subtracted from P_{OCD}. The dissipation, for class A operation, is usually determined for quiescent operation. However, the devices themselves may operate very nonlinearly. In this case, P_{OO} may increase with signal level, and graphical means should be used to determine P_{OCD} at the maximum signal level. Hence, the greater of

$$P_{OCD} = 2V_{OQ}I_{OQ} \tag{10-43}$$

and

$$P_{OCD} = 2V_{OO}I_{OA} - P_{2T} \tag{10-44}$$

should be used [see Eqs. (10-12) and (10-14)]. Note that I_{OQ} and I_{OA} are the quiescent and average output currents of the individual devices and P_{2T} is the total output power of the fundamental and all the harmonics.

If a vacuum tube or FET is operated class B or class ABB, there is very little plate or drain current during quiescent operation. If a cathode or source resistance were used to obtain bias, its value would be excessive, and so fixed bias is usually used instead.

For class ABB operation, the specified quiescent output voltage and projected cutoff bias determine the operating point. The characteristics can then be drawn. For vacuum-tube pentodes, FETs, or transistors, they will resemble Fig. 10-17. The knees of the curves limit the value of $(n_1/n_2)^2 R_L$. In this type of operation, V_{OO} supplies very little power until a signal is applied. (For this reason, this circuit is often used in battery-operated transistor amplifiers.) Equation (10-44) is used to calculate the device output dissipation. If the currents are sinusoidal, then I_{OA} can be obtained by the analysis of Sec. 8-6. If the peak signal current in each device is $I_{O,\max}$,

$$I_{OA} = \frac{2I_{O,\max}}{\pi}$$

$$P_2 = \tfrac{1}{2}I_{0,\max}^2 \left(\frac{n_1}{n_2}\right)^2 R_L$$

and

$$P_{OCD} = \frac{2I_{O,\max}V_{OO}}{\pi} - \tfrac{1}{2}I_{0,\max}^2 \left(\frac{n_1}{n_2}\right)^2 R_L \tag{10-45}$$

If there is no distortion, or if the input signal is not a sine wave, then Eq. (10-45) is no longer valid. However, it is often sufficiently accurate for design purposes since the device output dissipation is usually less for non-sinusoidal signals. If there is a great deal of distortion, I_{OA} can be found by using Eq. (5-76a). The power supplied by the power supply is then $2V_{OO}I_{OA}$ and $P_{OCD} = 2V_{OO}I_{OA} - P_{2T}$.

10-8 THERMAL EFFECTS

The maximum device output dissipation is specified to limit the operating temperature of the device. The device can be cooled by the surrounding atmosphere, with forced air or, at very high power levels, with water. Transistors are not usually operated at power levels that warrant water cooling. Thermal conduction and radiation are usually used to cool them. At high power levels, the transistor is placed in contact with a large piece of metal called a *heatsink* to increase the heat flow to the surrounding area. The temperature problem is more critical in transistors than in vacuum tubes, because transistors are damaged at lower temperatures and because the characteristics of transistor currents can vary greatly with temperature. In addition, most power transistors are designed to be attached to an external heatsink. We shall consider the thermal aspects of a transistor connected to a heatsink.

In order to make temperature calculations, we shall introduce the concept of a *thermal resistance* θ. If a power of P_J watts is dissipated in a junction, and if the ambient temperature, i.e., the temperature of the surroundings, is T_A, then the temperature of the junction is

$$T_J = T_A + P_J\theta_T \tag{10-46}$$

where θ_T is defined as the thermal resistance (in degrees centigrade per watt) between the region and the ambient surroundings. Thermal resistance is analogous to electrical resistance. In a transistor, there are several thermal resistances that must be considered. These are diagrammatically illustrated in Fig. 10-18. There is resistance θ_J between the junction itself and the case of the transistor. The resistance θ_I occurs between the case and the heatsink. The heatsink itself possesses some thermal resistance θ_H. Finally, heat leaves the heatsink through the parallel resistances θ_R and θ_C, which are due to radiation and conduction, respectively. The function of the heatsink is to reduce the values of θ_R and θ_C. Figure 10-18 is actually oversimplified. Conduction and radiation take place from all parts of the system and the temperature varies over the surface of the elements. Thus, an exact thermal network would require an infinite number of elements. However, the results obtained with Fig. 10-18 are usually accurate enough to be used in design calculations. The value of θ_J depends upon the construction of the transistor. Typical values for power transistors range from 0.2 to 2.0°C/watt.

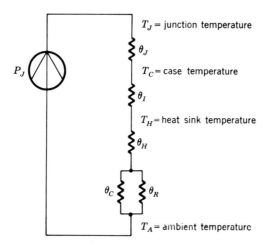

T_J = junction temperature

T_C = case temperature

T_H = heat sink temperature

T_A = ambient temperature

Fig. 10-18 A simplified thermal circuit for a transistor.

A thin mica spacer is often used to electrically insulate the transistor from the heatsink. The spacer introduces a resistance of approximately[1] 25.4°C (cm²)/(watt) for each millimeter of thickness. Silicone compounds (greases) are often placed between the spacer and the heatsink to reduce the thermal resistance. The thermal resistance of the heatsink θ_H depends upon the thermal resistivity of the material. Typical values[1] are $\rho = 0.26$°C(cm)/ (watt) for copper, $\rho = 0.443$°C (cm)/(watt) for pure aluminium, and $\rho = 0.66$°C (cm)/(watt) for commercial aluminium. Thermal resistance is calculated from resistivity in the same way that electrical resistance is. For instance, the thermal resistance between the inner and outer edges of an annular circle of inner radius r_1, outer radius r_2, and thickness d, is[1]

$$\theta_H = \frac{2.3\rho}{2\pi d} \log \frac{r_2}{r_1} \tag{10-47}$$

If the ring is a heatsink, the actual value of θ_H is quite difficult to obtain, since heat flows from it at all points. Equation (10-47) gives a value that is high.

The largest resistances in the system are often those between the heatsink and the ambient temperature. They vary with the cross-sectional area of the heatsink and its position. An empirical formula[1] for the conduction resistance θ_C is

$$\theta_C = \frac{2900}{A} \left(\frac{L}{T_H - T_A} \right)^{0.25} \qquad °\text{C/watt} \tag{10-48}$$

where A is the total surface area of the plate in square centimeters and T is the temperature in degrees Kelvin. Usually A includes the area of both sides. The dimension L is the length in the vertical direction. The resistance θ_C increases with L, since the cooling air rises along the heatsink. For horizontal plates, use L = area of one surface/(length + width). Note that L can be fairly large for horizontal plates, this accounts for the fact that the convection from the lower surface is very small. If forced-air cooling is used, this resistance can be reduced by a factor of $\frac{1}{4}$ or more.

The radiation resistance can be expressed by the relation[1]

$$\theta_R = \frac{1.78 \times 10^{11}}{\epsilon A} \frac{T_H - T_A}{T_H{}^4 - T_A{}^4} \qquad °\text{C/watt} \tag{10-49}$$

where ϵ = emissivity

A = area, cm^2

T = temperature, °K

Some typical values of ϵ are: ideal black body, 1; dull black paint or lacquer, 0.96; polished copper, 0.03; polished aluminium, 0.09. Thus, the importance of using dull black radiators can be seen. It should be emphasized that the formulas given here are empirical and are not exact.

Equations (10-48) and (10-49) are functions of the surface temperature of the heatsink. If that temperature varies from point to point, then these equations cannot be used. If the thermal conductivity of the heatsink is large enough, then this temperature variation can be neglected. If the maximum dimension from the transistor to the edge of the heatsink is less than 5 cm and the heatsink is made of copper that is thicker than 0.2 cm, or aluminium that is thicker than 0.32 cm, the heatsink temperature can be assumed to be constant.

In order to design a heatsink, the values of θ_J and θ_I should be determined. The temperature T_H can then be calculated using the relation

$$T_H = T_J - P_J(\theta_J + \theta_I) \tag{10-50}$$

The total heatsink resistance $\theta_H + \theta_C\theta_R/(\theta_C + \theta_R)$ can then be found from Eq. (10-46) and the heatsink designed. If P_J is too large, then the resistance of $\theta_J + \theta_I$ may cause T_J to become excessive even if the heatsink resistance is zero. However, if rated dissipation values are not exceeded, this usually will not occur.

The value of thermal resistance calculated from Eq. (10-46) may not be satisfactory because of thermal runaway (see Sec. 5-6). That is, we have assumed that P_J is constant, whereas it is actually a function of T_J. If P_J is independent of T_J, then, from Eq. (10-46), the derivative's reciprocal is

$$\frac{dP_J}{dT_J} = \frac{1}{\theta_T} \tag{10-51}$$

On the other hand, if at the operating temperature

$$\frac{dP_J}{dT_J} > \frac{1}{\theta_T} \tag{10-52}$$

then the power increases with T_J and instability *may* occur. In any event, the power and the temperature will tend to increase above the design value. Let us consider the significance of relation (10-52) for class A amplifiers. The power P_J is the product $V_{CQ}I_{CQ}$. If the quiescent collector voltage is constant, then P_J varies directly with the collector current I_C. On the other hand, if I_C is constant, P_J will actually decrease as T_J increases, since the collector voltage will decrease. Thus, thermal runaway is usually no problem in RC-coupled amplifiers where the large series resistance tends to keep the value of I_{CQ} constant. Let us assume the worst possible case, where the collector voltage is constant at V_{CQ}. Then, for stability [see Eq. (10-52)]

$$V_{CQ} \frac{dI_{CQ}}{dT_J} \leq \frac{1}{\theta_T} \tag{10-53}$$

Let us write

$$\frac{dI_{CQ}}{dT_J} = \frac{dI_{CQ}}{dI_{C0}} \frac{dI_{C0}}{dT_J} \tag{10-54}$$

where I_{C0} is the reverse collector saturation current. But the stability factor (see Sec. 5-6) is $S = dI_C/dI_{C0}$. Substituting and manipulating in Eq. (10-53), we obtain

$$S\theta_T V_{CQ} \frac{dI_{C0}}{dT_J} \leq 1 \tag{10-55}$$

The quantity dI_{C0}/dT_J is temperature-dependent and should be determined at the operating temperature of the transistor. Typical variations of I_{C0} with temperature are given by Eqs. (3-33). It is often experimentally found that the saturation current increases 7 percent for a 1°C increase in temperature. Then, $dI_{C0}/dT = 0.07I_{C0}$. This value can be substituted in Eq. (10-55). In addition the manufacturer often supplies experimental data which can be used in Eq. (10-55). Relation (10-55) thus imposes an upper limit of S, θ_T, and E_{CQ}, which ensures stability.

Each of the thermal resistances of Fig. 10-18 is actually shunted by thermal capacitance. They take into account the fact that if P_J is changed, the various temperatures in the circuit do not change instantaneously, but take a finite time to reach equilibrium. This often proves useful, since it allows the instantaneous power (but not the average power) to be greater than the maximum rated power. The duty cycle in such cases must be much shorter than the thermal time constants so that excessive temperature rise does not occur during a portion of the cycle.

10-9   PHASE-INVERTER CIRCUITS

The push-pull amplifier requires two input signals 180° out of phase with each other.   These are called *balanced* signals, whereas the usual single-ended systems are *unbalanced*.   We have made the transition from an unbalanced system to a balanced one by means of an input transformer (see Figs. 10-9

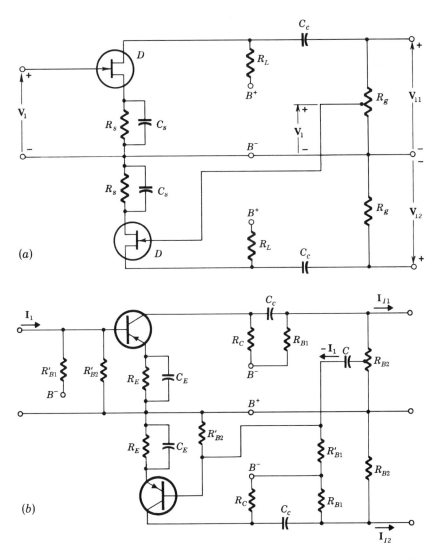

Fig. 10-19 Basic phase-inverter circuits using (*a*) common-source FET amplifier and (*b*) common-emitter transistor amplifier.

and 10-10).   Circuits called *phase inverters* can be used to replace the input transformer.   There are other procedures for obtaining input signals for push-pull amplifiers.   These will be discussed in the next section.   Phase-inverter circuits are shown in Fig. 10-19*a* and *b*.   Their operation is similar and we shall discuss them simultaneously.   The upper *RC*-coupled amplifier is conventional and it produces a 180° phase shift in voltage.   A portion of the signal across R_g or R_{B2} is tapped off and used to drive the lower *RC*-coupled amplifier.   Thus, the driving signals for the upper and lower amplifiers are 180° out of phase.   If the position of the tap is adjusted so that the magnitudes of these driving signals are equal, then the desired balanced output signal will be obtained (if loading of the output circuits is neglected). The transistor phase inverter is more complex because it must supply a direct-bias current as well as a signal to the push-pull amplifier.   This accounts for the two resistances R_{B1} and R_{B2}.   The capacitor C is a dc

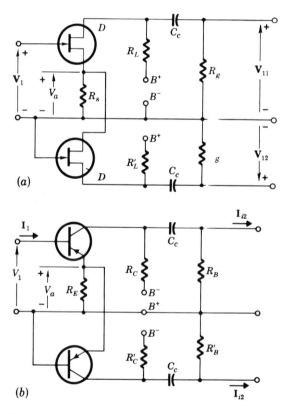

(a)

(b)

Fig. 10-20 (*a*) Source-coupled FET phase inverter and (*b*) emitter-coupled transistor phase inverter. For simplicity, the biasing circuits have been omitted.

blocking capacitor and should be large enough to be ignored at signal frequencies.

If the parameters of the devices change (possibly due to aging), the output signals may no longer be equal in magnitude. The location of the tap should be adjusted periodically in critical applications. Two circuits that tend to compensate for changes in the device parameters are shown in Fig. 10-20. The voltage drop across R_s or R_E is in phase with the input voltage. Thus, the input of the lower amplifier will be 180° out of phase with the input of the upper amplifier. If the two output signals are to be equal in magnitude, then

$$V_a = \tfrac{1}{2}V_1 \tag{10-56}$$

This is a condition that never can be exactly achieved, so that the gain of the lower amplifier may have to be somewhat larger than that of the upper one. This circuit tends to be self-balancing. If the gain of the upper stage

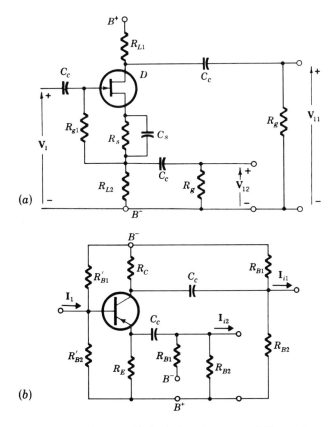

Fig. 10-21 (a) FET split-load phase inverter and (b) transistor split-load phase inverter.

decreases (increases), then so will the signal applied to the lower circuit, which will tend to decrease (increase) its output. If the gain of the lower stage decreases (increases), the voltage V_a will increase (decrease) and tend to offset this effect. The phase inverters of Fig. 10-19 compensate for changes in the gain of the upper stages but not the lower ones.

Two very simple phase-inverter circuits, called *split-load* phase inverters, each of which uses only one device, are shown in Fig. 10-21. One circuit is essentially a common-source or common-emitter amplifier, while the other is a common-drain or a common-collector amplifier. In the FET circuit, the current through R_{g1} usually can be ignored, so the output voltages will be equal in magnitude and 180° out of phase if $R_{L1} = R_{L2}$. Since the maximum voltage gain of a source follower is unity, the voltages V_{11} and V_{12} cannot be greater than V_1. Thus, this phase inverter provides no gain, which is one of its disadvantages. Since the emitter current of a transistor is somewhat greater than the collector current, R_E must be less than R_C. The current gain of this circuit can be substantially in excess of unity. The primary disadvantage of both these circuits is that the output impedances of the upper and lower circuits are not equal, so that an unbalance can result when the load is connected. This is especially true when nonlinearities in the push-pull input circuit are taken into account.

One fact that we have ignored is the frequency response of these amplifiers. The methods of Chap. 9 can be used to perform any necessary analyses. If the amplifiers of the phase inverters introduce phase shift, then the two output signals will no longer be 180° out of phase. Thus, they should always be operated well within the midband region.

In addition to causing distortion, the nonlinearity of the input circuit of a push-pull amplifier may cause the input signals to be no longer equal in magnitude and 180° out of phase.

There is base current in a transistor at all times and the input characteristics are nonlinear. (A representative input circuit is shown in Fig.

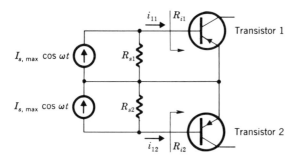

Fig. 10-22 Representation of the input of a push-pull transistor amplifier.

10-22.) These nonlinearities will cause the input signals to be distorted and to be unequal in magnitude and 180° out of phase. The input characteristic can be linearized by placing a resistance in series with the base. This series resistance will tend to limit the base current and thus reduce the gain. If the values of R_s can be increased, the base currents will exhibit less distortion. If $R_s \gg R_i$, the distortion can be neglected since i_{11} and i_{12} become equal to their respective generator currents in this case.

10-10 USE OF TRANSISTORS WITH COMPLEMENTARY SYMMETRY AND QUASI-COMPLEMENTARY SYMMETRY IN PUSH-PULL CIRCUITS

The output transformer in a push-pull circuit is often a heavy, large, and expensive component. In addition, it usually introduces frequency distortion. Thus, it would be an advantage not to have to use it. The transformer performs two functions: (1) it impedance-matches the load to the active device, and (2) it causes $v_{21} = -v_{22}$ [see Fig. 10-9 and Eq. (10-28)].

The output impedance of many transistor circuits is often low enough so that the impedance-matching properties of the transformer are not required. The second function of the transformer can be obtained in a transistorless circuit if we make use of both p-n-p and n-p-n transistors. That is, the active devices of the push-pull stage consist of two transistors which are identical *except* that one is p-n-p and the other is n-p-n. Thus, the characteristics of both transistors are the same except for *polarity* differences. Two transistors of this type are said to exhibit *complementary symmetry*.

A typical complementary-symmetry push-pull transistor amplifier is shown in Fig. 10-23. The resistors R_{B1} and R_{B2} supply the base bias current. The capacitors C_1 and C_2 prevent the output signal from being fed back to the input.

Let us now consider the output circuit. The voltages are

$$v_{CE1} = V_{CC1} + v_2 \qquad (10\text{-}57a)$$

$$v_{CE2} = V_{CC2} + v_2 \qquad (10\text{-}57b)$$

but $V_{CC2} = -V_{CC1}$. Thus, manipulating, we obtain

$$v_{CE1} = V_{CC1} + v_2 \qquad (10\text{-}58a)$$

$$-v_{CE2} = V_{CC1} - v_2 \qquad (10\text{-}58b)$$

Note that we have written the voltage for the lower transistor as $-v_{CE}$. In the p-n-p transistor, the collector-to-emitter voltage is negative. Then v_{CE1} and $-v_{CE2}$ should be compared. This is done in Eqs. (10-58). The signal voltages are equal in magnitude and opposite in polarity, as they should be. (Note that when the collector-emitter voltage of one transistor increases in magnitude, the collector-emitter voltage of the other transistor decreases in magnitude.) Thus, transformer action has been achieved in a circuit which does not have a transformer.

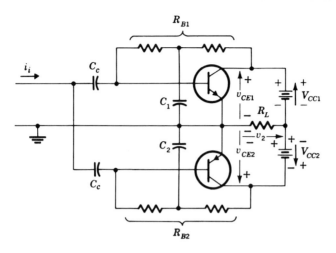

Fig. 10-23 A push-pull common-emitter complementary-symmetry amplifier. $V_{CC2} = -V_{CC1}$.

Another advantage of the complementary-symmetry circuit is that a phase inverter is not required. When i_i is of such polarity that it increases the collector current of the upper transistor, then it decreases the current of the lower one and vice versa. Thus the transistors are effectively driven by signals 180° out of phase even though there is no input transformer or phase inverter.

The circuit of Fig. 10-23 has several disadvantages. It is almost always necessary to have one side of the load resistance-grounded, i.e., connected to the common lead. Thus, in Fig. 10-23, one side of the power supplies cannot be grounded. This often requires that a separate power supply for the push-pull stage be constructed. In addition, the output impedance of a common-emitter stage is often higher than desired. A common-collector complementary-symmetry circuit which does not have these disadvantages is shown in Fig. 10-24. Note that, as far as the signals are concerned, both collectors are grounded. Thus, this is a common-collector amplifier. An analysis of the output voltage yields

$$v_{EC1} = V_{EE1} + v_2 \tag{10-59a}$$

$$-v_{EC2} = V_{EE1} - v_2 \tag{10-59b}$$

Thus, the desired relations for the output voltage are obtained.

Note that one side of each power supply and the load resistance are grounded. Thus, this circuit does not have the previously discussed difficulties.

The input circuit of Fig. 10-24 does not require a phase inverter. The discussion of the input of Fig. 10-23 applies here also.

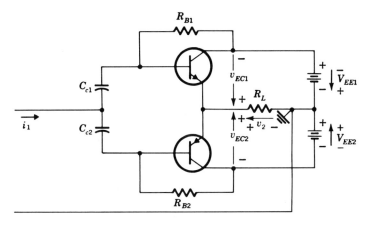

Fig. 10-24 A push-pull common-collector complementary-symmetry amplifier.

At times, it is desirable to have a direct coupled input to a push-pull amplifier. This can be done simply by replacing the coupling capacitors by resistors (see Fig. 10-25). The resistors R_{B1} and R_{B2} are chosen to be large enough so that the biases of the two transistors and the driving stage do not interact with each other to any great extent. These resistors must be small enough so that the input currents are not reduced too much.

All push-pull amplifiers require that the two active devices be matched, i.e., that they have essentially the same characteristics (except for a difference in polarity in the case of complementary symmetry). The use of

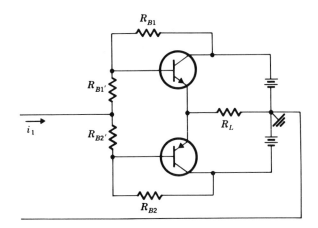

Fig. 10-25 A modification of Fig. 10-24 that is direct-coupled.

complementary symmetry greatly complicates the problem of matching the devices, since *n-p-n* and *p-n-p* transistors have somewhat different characteristics and transistors cannot be picked from the same production run. There are circuits which use the same type of transistors, i.e., two *p-n-p* transistors or two *n-p-n* transistors, which act properly as a push-pull amplifier and do not require an output transformer. These circuits are called *quasi-complementary-symmetry amplifiers*. One such circuit is shown in Fig. 10-26. It uses an input transformer. Note that the current in the input circuit is very much less than the current in the output circuit. Thus, there is less tendency for the core to saturate and the input transformer can be much smaller, lighter, and less expensive than an output transformer of corresponding quality.

Two input signals 180° out of phase are applied between the base and the collector of each transistor. Thus, both circuits function as common-collector devices. R_{B1} and R_{B2} provide bias. The capacitors C should be short circuits at the signal frequencies. The output voltages are (note that $V_{EE1} = V_{EE2}$)

$$v_{EC1} = V_{EE1} - v_2 \tag{10-60a}$$

$$v_{EC2} = V_{EE1} + v_2 \tag{10-60b}$$

Thus, the proper voltages are obtained.

The circuit of Fig. 10-26 can be made a common-emitter circuit by connecting one lead of each secondary winding to the emitter rather than to the collector. (The bias circuits must be modified somewhat.) This circuit has a higher output impedance.

The transformer of the quasi-complementary-symmetry amplifier can be replaced by a pair of transistors. This is shown in Fig. 10-27, for the

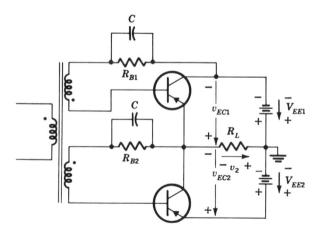

Fig. 10-26 A quasi-complementary-symmetry amplifier.

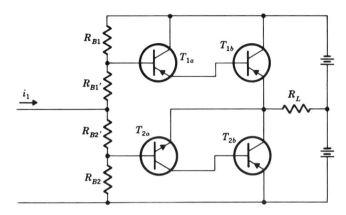

Fig. 10-27 A quasi-complementary-symmetry push-pull amplifier which does not require an input transformer.

common-collector output configuration.   Transistors T_{1a} and T_{2a} supply the signals for transistors T_{2a} and T_{2b}, respectively.   Note that their outputs replace the transformer secondaries of Fig. 10-26.   In order to obtain the desired 180° phase difference in the driving signals, T_{1a} and T_{1b} must have complementary symmetry.   However, it is easier to obtain a reasonably good match in the low-power driving transistors than in the power transistors. Note that Fig. 10-27 does have complementary-symmetry matching problems, which Fig. 10-26 does not, but Fig. 10-26 requires a transformer.

When amplifiers are direct-coupled, diodes are often added to stabilize the operating point (see Sec. 9-27).

REFERENCES

1. "Thermal Resistance as Applied to Transistors," Tung-Sol Electric, Inc., Application Note 2-62, July 5, 1962.

BIBLIOGRAPHY

Alley, C. L., and K. W. Atwood: "Electronic Engineering," 2d ed., chap. 10, John Wiley & Sons, Inc., New York, 1962.
Gärtner, W. W.: "Transistors: Principles, Design, and Applications," chap. 13, D. Van Nostrand Company, Inc., Princeton, N.J., 1960.
Gibbons, J. F.: "Semiconductor Electronics," pp. 528–546, McGraw-Hill Book Company, New York, 1966.
Gray, T. S.: "Applied Electronics," 2d ed., pp. 460–476, 530–533, 609–619, John Wiley & Sons, Inc., New York, 1954.
Greiner, R. A.: "Semiconductor Devices and Applications," chap. 14, McGraw-Hill Book Company, New York, 1961.
Millman, J., and C. C. Halkias: "Electronic Devices and Circuits," chap. 18, McGraw-Hill Book Company, New York, 1967.

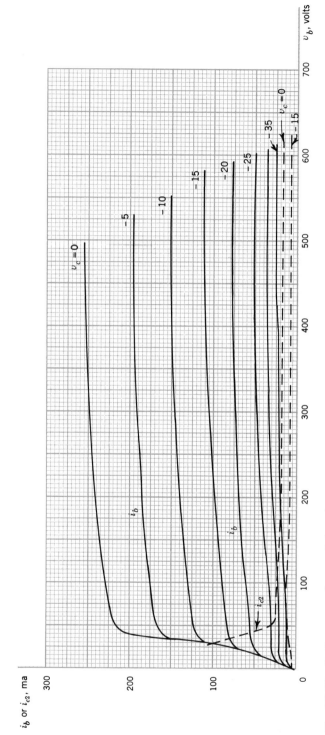

Fig. 10-28 Static output characteristics of the type 7027-A beam power pentode. The screen-grid voltage is 300 volts. (*Radio Corporation of America.*)

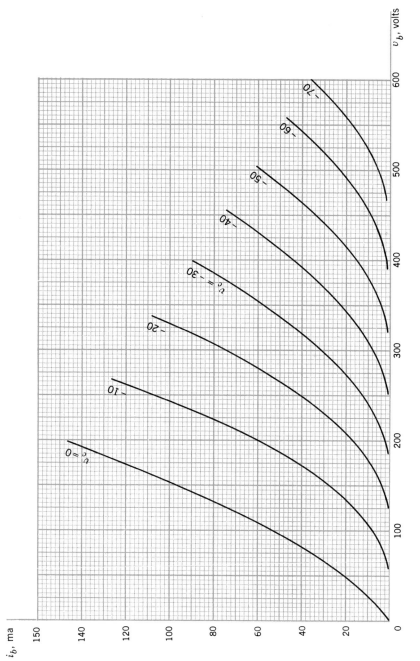

Fig. 10-29 Static output characteristics of the triode-connected type 7027-A. (*Radio Corporation of America.*)

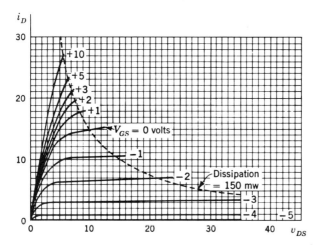

Fig. 10-30 Static output characteristics of the 3N139 FET. (*Radio Corporation of America.*)

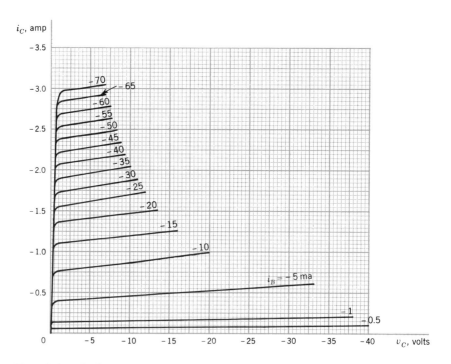

Fig. 10-31 Static output characteristics of the type 2N301 *p-n-p* (common-emitter) transistor. (*Radio Corporation of America.*)

PROBLEMS

In the following problems, the type 7027-A beam power tube will be used. It can also be used as a triode by connecting the screen grid to the plate. The ratings of this vacuum tube are $V_{b,\max} = 600$ volts, $V_{g2,\max} = 500$ volts, maximum plate dissipation = 35 watts, maximum screen-grid dissipation = 5 watts. The heater requires a voltage of 6.3 volts rms and a current of 0.9 amp rms. The output characteristics for the pentode are given in Fig. 10-28. Note that some screen-grid characteristics are included in this characteristic. The output characteristics for the triode connection are given in Fig. 10-29. In the triode connection, the $V_{g2,\max}$ rating limits the plate voltage. We shall also use a 3N139 FET. The ratings of this FET are $V_{DS,\max} = 35$ volts, $|V_{GS,\max}| = 10$ volts, $I_{D,\max} = 50$ ma, maximum channel dissipation 0.15 watt. The output characteristics are given in Fig. 10-30. We shall also use the type 2N301 p-n-p transistor. Ratings of this transistor are $|V_{C,\max}| = 40$ volts, peak collector current = 3 amp, $|I_{CQ,\max}| = 1.5$ amp, maximum collector dissipation = 11 watts, maximum case temperature = 85°, thermal resistance between collector and case 1°C/watt. The common-emitter output characteristics are given in Fig. 10-31 and the common-emitter input characteristics are given in Fig. 10-32.

Assume that all bypass and coupling capacitors are short circuits at all signal frequencies.

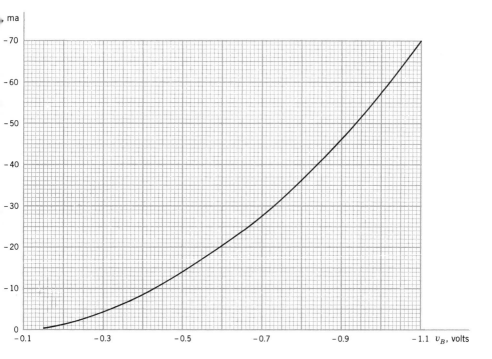

Fig. 10-32 Static input characteristics of the type 2N301 p-n-p (common-emitter) transistor. (*Radio Corporation of America.*)

10-1. A triode-connected type 7027-A vacuum tube is connected into the circuit of Fig. 10-33. The coordinates of the quiescent operating point are $V_{bQ} = 350$ volts and

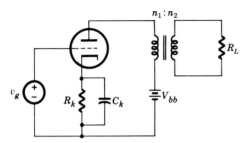

Fig. 10-33

$V_{cQ} = -30$ volts. The value of R_L is 16 ohms and the turns ratio $n_1/n_2 = 14.2$. The input signal is $v_g = 30 \cos \omega t$ volts. Compute the power output, plate circuit efficiency, plate dissipation under quiescent conditions and under maximum signal conditions, the power-supply voltage V_{bb}, and the value of R_k. Compute the percent second, third, fourth, and total harmonic distortion. What is the efficency of operation if the heater power and the power dissipated in R_k are taken into account?

10-2. Repeat Prob. 10-1, but now use a value of $R_L = 8$ ohms.

10-3. A type 7027-A beam power tube is connected into the circuit of Fig. 10-34.

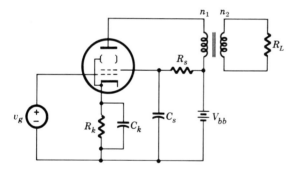

Fig. 10-34

The coordinates of the quiescent operating point are $V_{bQ} = 300$ volts, $V_{cQ} = -15$ volts, $V_{c2Q} = 300$ volts. The load resistance is 16 ohms, the transformer turns ratio $n_1/n_2 = 11.2$, and the input signal is $15 \cos \omega t$ volts. Compute the power output, plate current efficiency, plate dissipation under quiescent conditions and under maximum signal conditions, the power-supply voltage V_{bb}, the value of R_k, and the value of R_s (zero is an acceptable value). Compute the percent second, third, fourth, and total harmonic distortion. What is the efficiency of operation if the heater power, the power dissipated in R_k and R_s, and the screen-grid dissipation are taken into account? Hint: All the power, except the heater power, is supplied by the battery.

10-4. Repeat Prob. 10-3, but now use a turns ratio of $n_1/n_2 = 15.4$.

10-5. Repeat Prob. 10-3, but now use a value of $V_{cQ} = -10$, and $v_g = 10 \cos \omega t$. Why would this circuit not be used?

10-6. A 3N139 FET is connected into the circuit of Fig. 10-35. The coordinates of the quiescent operating point are $V_{DSQ} = -15$ volts and $V_{GSQ} = -2$ volts, the value of

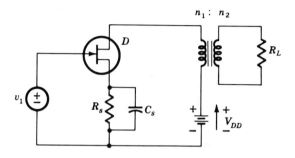

Fig. 10-35

R_L is 16 ohms, and $n_1/n_2 = 7.9$. The input signal is $v_1 = 3 \cos \omega t$ volts. Compute the power output, output circuit efficiency, channel dissipation under quiescent conditions and under maximum conditions, the power-supply voltage V_{DD}, and the value of R_s. Compute the percent second, third, fourth, and total harmonic distortion.

10-7. Repeat Prob. 10-6 but use $R_L = 8$ ohms.

10-8. A 2N301 transistor is connected into the circuit of Fig. 10-36. The coordinates of the quiescent operating point are $V_{CQ} = -5$ volts, $I_{BQ} = -20$ ma. The values of the circuit elements are $R_E = 1$ ohm, $R_L = 4$ ohms, and $n_1/n_2 = 0.89$. If the base signal

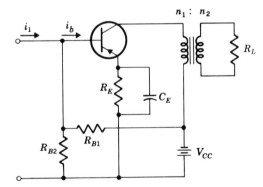

Fig. 10-36

current $i_b = 10 \cos \omega t$ ma, compute the power output, collector-circuit efficiency, overall efficiency, (i.e., output power/P_{OO}), collector-junction dissipation under quiescent conditions and under maximum signal conditions, and the percent second, third, fourth, and total harmonic distortion. What is the value of V_{CC}? If $\alpha = 0.985$ and the stability factor is to be less than 15, compute the values of R_{B1} and R_{B2}. What is the current i_1 in this case? Is it sinusoidal?

10-9. Repeat Prob. 10-8, but now assume that $i_b = 19.5 \cos \omega t$ ma.

10-10. Repeat Prob. 10-8, but now assume that $i_1 = 19.5 \cos \omega t$ ma. Now use a value of i_1 so that the peak-to-peak swing of i_b is 40 ma. Do not neglect the input circuit distortion. Assume that the operating point is the same and that R_B, the parallel combination of R_{B1} and R_{B2}, is 20 ohms. Repeat all the calculations for $R_B = 1000$ ohms. Neglect any changes in the operating point.

10-11. Design a single-ended amplifier using a triode-connected 7027-A vacuum tube that meets the following specifications: $P_2 = 1.6$ watts, $V_{bQ} = 300$ volts, $R_L = 4$ ohms, and total harmonic distortion equal to or less than 10 percent. The design should be of the form of Fig. 10-33. The values of V_{bb}, n_1/n_2, R_k, and v_g should be specified and the ratings should not be exceeded. (Note that the maximum screen-grid voltage limits the maximum plate voltage here.)

10-12. Design a single-ended amplifier using a 7027-A beam power tube that meets the following specifications: $P_2 = 10$ watts, $V_{bQ} = 300$ volts, $V_{c2Q} = 300$ volts, $R_L = 16$ ohms, and the total harmonic distortion less than 10 percent. The design should be of the form of Fig. 10-34. The values of R_k, R_s, n_1/n_2, V_{bb}, and v_g should be specified (zero is an acceptable value of R_s). The tube ratings should not be exceeded.

10-13. Design a single-ended amplifier using a 3N139 FET that meets the following specifications: $P_2 = 0.036$ watt, $V_{DSQ} = 15$ volts, $R_L = 4$ ohms, and total harmonic distortion less then 10 percent. The design should be of the form of Fig. 10-35. V_{DD}, n_1/n_2, R_s, and v_1 should be specified. The ratings of the FET should not be exceeded.

10-14. Design a single-ended amplifier, using a 2N301 transistor, that meets the following specifications: $V_{CEQ} = -12$ volts, $P_2 = 4.5$ watts, $R_L = 4$ ohms, stability factor less than 5, and total harmonic distortion less than 15 percent. The circuit should be of the form of Fig. 10-36. The values of V_{CC}, R_E, R_{B1}, R_{B2}, n_1/n_2, and i_b should be specified. Now assume that the ideal current generator i_b is replaced by one whose internal impedance is R_B (the parallel combination of R_{B1} and R_{B2}) and repeat the problem. What should be the value of i_1?

10-15. Modify the design of Prob. 10-12 by connecting two type 7027-A vacuum tubes in parallel so that the power output is doubled without increasing the distortion.

10-16. Modify the design of Prob. 10-14 by connecting two type 2N301 transistors in parallel so that the power output is doubled without increasing the distortion.

10-17. A pair of triode-connected type 7027-A vacuum tubes are connected into the push-pull circuit of Fig. 10-10a (the circuit is modified so that triodes can be used), where $V_{bb} = 380$ volts and direct voltage drop across R_k is 30 volts. Obtain the composite characteristics of this device. Plot curves P_2 and percent second, third, and total harmonic distortion versus $R_{pp} = R_{dd} = 4(n_1/n_2)^2 R_L$. Use the maximum signal voltage that can be applied without causing grid current or causing the ratings to be exceeded. What should the value of R_k be?

10-18. A pair of type 7027-A vacuum-tube pentodes are connected into the push-pull circuit of Fig. 10-10a, where $V_{bb} = 315$ volts, $V_{c2Q} = 300$ volts, and $V_{cQ} = -15$ volts. Obtain the composite characteristics of this device. Plot curves of P_2 and percent second, third, and total harmonic distortion versus $(n_1/n_2)^2 R_L$. Use the maximum signal voltage that can be applied without causing grid current or causing the ratings to be exceeded. What should the value of R_k be?

10-19. A pair of 3N139 FETs are connected into the circuit of Fig. 10-10b where $V_{DD} = 15$ volts; the direct voltage drop across R_s is 2 volts. Obtain the composite characteristics of the device. Plot curves of P_2 and percent second, third, and total harmonic distortion versus $(n_1/n_2)^2 R_L$. Use an input signal of $v_{gs} = 1 \cos \omega t$ volt. Then repeat the calculations for $v_{gs} = 3 \cos \omega t$ volts. What should the value of R_s be?

10-20. A pair of 2N301 transistors are connected into the push-pull circuit of Fig.

10-10c, where $V_{CC} = -6$ volts, the voltage drop across R_E is 1 volt, and R_B is adjusted so that the quiescent base current of each transistor is 25 ma. Obtain the composite characteric of this device. Plot curves of P_2 and percent second, third, and total harmonic distortion versus $(n_1/n_2)^2 R_L$. Use the maximum signal current that can be applied without causing the instantaneous magnitude of the base current to exceed 45 ma. What is the value of R_E? Now assume that two resistors are used to obtain base current for each transistor (see Fig. 10-36). Find values of R_{B1} and R_{B2} such that the stability factors of each device are less than 5. Ignore the input circuit distortion. Repeat this problem, but now do not let the instantaneous magnitude of the base current exceed 65 ma. Assume that $I_C = 0$ if $I_B = 0$.

10-21. Design a push-pull amplifier using a pair of triode-connected 7027-A vacuum tubes. (Modify Fig. 10-10a.) The quiescent plate voltage of each tube is to be approximately 300 volts, $R_L = 4$ ohms, the total harmonic distortion is to be equal to or less than 2.5 percent, the grid current is to be zero, and the operation is to be class A. The power output is to be 6.5 watts. Determine V_{cQ}, R_k, n_1/n_2, the plate-circuit efficiency, and v_{g1} for this amplifier.

10-22. Design a push-pull amplifier using a pair of 7027-A vacuum tubes. The quiescent plate voltage of each tube is to be 300 volts, $V_{c2Q} = 300$ volts, $R_L = 4$ ohms, the total harmonic distortion is to be equal to or less than 1.5 percent, the grid current is to be zero, and the operation is to be class A. The power output is to be 22 watts. Find V_{cQ}, R_k, n_1/n_2, the plate-circuit efficiency, and v_g for this amplifier (see Fig. 10-10a). Assume that the curve for $v_c = -40$ volts lies along the 15-ma ordinate for $v_b > 200$ volts.

10-23. Design a push-pull amplifier using a pair of 3N139 FETs. The quiescent drain-to-source voltage for each FET is to be 15 volts, $R_L = 4$ ohms, the total harmonic distortion is to be less than 15 percent, and the operation is to be class A. The power output is to be 0.06 watt. Find V_{DD}, R_s, n_1/n_2, the output circuit efficiency, and v_{gs} for the amplifier (see Fig. 10-10b).

10-24. Design a push-pull amplifier using a pair of 2N301 transistors. The average collector voltage of each transistor is to be -5 volts, $R_L = 4$ ohms, and the total harmonic distortion is to be equal to or less than 7 percent; the operation is to be class A, and the stability factor is to be less than or equal to 8. The power output is to be 4 watts. Find the values of I_{BQ}, V_{CC}, R_E, R_{B1}, R_{B2}, and the collector-circuit efficiency, and i_B. (Neglect input-circuit distortion.)

10-25. Design a push-pull amplifier using type 7027-A vacuum tubes with $V_{bQ} = 400$ volts, $V_{c2Q} = 300$ volts, and $R_L = 16$ ohms, and the total harmonic distortion less than 2.5 percent. The power output should be 20 watts. The operation should be class AB and the grid current should be zero. All the elements of the circuit, the plate-circuit efficiency, and the input signal should be specified (see Fig. 10-10a). The plate-circuit efficiency should be as large as possible.

10-26. Design a push-pull amplifier using type 7027-A vacuum tubes with $V_{bQ} = 300$ volts, $V_{c2Q} = 300$ volts, and $R_L = 4$ ohms. The operation is to be class ABB. Use the projected cutoff method to obtain the grid bias. Assume that the curve of i_b for $e_c = -40$ volts lies along the 10-ma ordinate and that $i_b = 0$ if $e_c < -40$ volts. Distortion should be considered when this bias is obtained. (Note that the transfer characteristics can be obtained from the plate characteristics.) The total harmonic distortion is to be less than 10 percent. (The distortion should also be checked using a small signal.) The grid current is to be zero and the ratings of the vacuum tube are not to be exceeded. The output power is to be 22 watts. Specify all of the elements of the ciruit (see Fig. 10-10a), η_2, and the input signal.

10-27. Design a push-pull amplifier using 3N139 FETs with $V_{DSQ} = 15$ volts and $R_L = 4$ ohms. The operation is to be class ABB. Use the projected cutoff method to obtain the gate bias. Distortion should be considered when the bias is obtained. The harmonic distortion should be less than 15 percent. (This distortion should also be checked using a small signal.) The ratings of the FET should not be exceeded. The power output is to be 0.08 watt. Specify all the elements of the circuit (see Fig. 10-10b) and the input signal. (Assume that $i_o = 0$ if $V_{GS} \leq -6$ volts.)

10-28. Design a push-pull amplifier using type 2N301 transistors with $V_{CEQ} \approx -12$ volts, $R_L = 4$ ohms, $P_2 = 8$ watts, and the total harmonic distortion less than 10 percent. The operation can be either class A or class AB. All the elements of the circuit and the input signal should be specified (see Fig. 10-10c). Neglect input-circuit distortion.

10-29. Design a push-pull amplifier using type 2N301 transistors with $V_{CEQ} = -10$ volts, and $R_L = 4$ ohms. The operation is to be class ABB. Use the projected cutoff method to determine the bias. Distortion should be considered when this bias is obtained. (Determine the transfer characteristics from those which are specified.) The total harmonic distortion is to be less than 12 percent, and the ratings of the transistor are not to be exceeded. The output power is to be 20 watts. Specify all the elements of the circuit and the input signal (see Fig. 10-10c). Neglect the input-circuit distortion. Then determine the input signal if $R_B = R_{B1}R_{B2}/(R_{B1} + R_{B2}) = 10$ ohms. Assume that $R_E = 0$ in all these calculations. (Check distortion at small-signal levels also.)

10-30. The collector-base junction of a 2N301 transistor is to operate at a temperature of 85°C when it is dissipating 10 watts. The ambient temperature is 20°C. It is to be insulated from the heatsink by a mica spacer 0.05 mm thick. The effective area of the transistor case in contact with the mica is 5 cm². What must be the effective resistance of the heatsink $\theta_H + \theta_R \theta_C/(\theta_R + \theta_C)$? Note that the internal thermal resistance of the transistor is given in the specifications.

10-31. Design the heatsink required in Prob. 10-30. Assume that it is made of a metal with a very high thermal conductivity, so that $\theta_H \approx 0$ and its surface temperature is constant. Also assume that it is lacquered a dull black.

10-32. The transistor of Prob. 10-30 is to be operated at a value of $V_{CEQ} = -5$ volts and at a temperature of 85°C, $dI_{CO}/dT_J = 0.01$. What is the maximum value that the stability factor may have if the operation is to be stable? Assume that the collector voltage is independent of the collector current.

10-33. For the phase inverter of Fig. 10-19a, compute the percentage of R_g that is to be tapped if perfect phase inversion is to result. Assume that the upper and lower circuits are identical. The answers should be in terms of the circuit elements and the parameters of the FETs.

10-34. Repeat Prob. 10-33, for the percentage of R_{B2} that is to be tapped in the circuit of Fig. 10-19b. The answer should be in terms of the circuit elements and the h parameters of the transistors. The input impedance of each half of the push-pull amplifier is R_i. To simplify the analysis assume that $h_{re} = 0$.

10-35. The phase inverter of Fig. 10-20a is such that the two FETs are identical. If $R = R_L R_g/(R_L + R_g)$ and $R' = R'_L R'_g/(R'_L + R'_g)$, what relation must exist among R, R', R_s, and the parameters of the FETs if phase inversion is to be ideal?

10-36. Repeat Prob. 10-35 for the circuit of Fig. 10-20b. Here, let $R = R_C R_B/(R_C + R_B)$ and $R' = R'_C R'_B/(R'_C + R'_B)$. The answer should be in terms of R, R', R_E, and the h parameters of the transistors. Assume that R_B and R'_B include the input resistance of the next stage. To simplify the analysis assume that $h_{re} = 0$.

10-37. Compute the output impedance of both outputs of the phase inverter of Fig. 10-21a. The answers should be in terms of the circuit elements and the parameters of the FETs.

10-38. Repeat Prob. 10-37 for the phase inverter of Fig. 10-21b. The answers should be in terms of the circuit elements and the h parameters of the transistors.

10-39. Discuss procedures for obtaining the composite characteristics for the push-pull amplifier of Fig. 10-23.

10-40. Repeat Prob. 10-39 for Fig. 10-24.

10-41. Repeat Prob. 10-39 for Fig. 10-26.

11

Tuned Large-signal Amplifiers

The maximum output-circuit efficiency of an amplifier increases as the operation is shifted from class A to class B (see Sec. 8-6). If class C operation is used, the maximum theoretical output-circuit efficiency can approach 100 percent. The untuned power amplifiers of Chap. 10 were not operated class C, since excessive (harmonic) distortion would have resulted. However, if an amplifier is only to provide gain at a single frequency or over a narrow band of frequencies, tuned circuits, which reject the unwanted harmonics, can be used. Highly efficient operation is then possible. These amplifiers are usually used as the output stages in radio transmitters. The output power often exceeds 50,000 watts, and the efficiency is of prime importance. The operation of these amplifiers is nonlinear, and hence they are called large-signal amplifiers. Since they are tuned and operate at radio frequencies, they are also called *tuned radio-frequency power amplifiers*.

11-1 GENERAL DISCUSSION OF
CLASS B AND CLASS C OPERATION

We shall now consider some typical tuned power amplifiers. Figure 11-1 illustrates a simple vacuum-tube, FET, and transistor amplifier. Note that there are vacuum-tube amplifiers capable of outputs in excess of 50,000 watts.

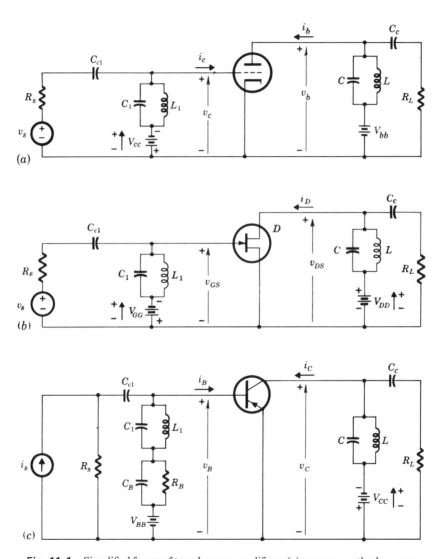

Fig. 11-1 Simplified forms of tuned power amplifiers: (*a*) common-cathode vacuum-tube-triode amplifier; (*b*) common-source FET amplifier; (*c*) common-emitter-transistor amplifier. Neutralization networks have been omitted from these amplifiers.

The transistor amplifiers are limited to outputs of about several hundred watts. FET amplifiers are limited, at present, to outputs of 1 watt or less. Thus, these are not often used as radio-frequency power amplifiers.

Now let us discuss Fig. 11-1. To simplify the diagrams, the emitter-stabilizing circuit and the neutralizing networks (see Sec. 9-26) have been omitted. Battery bias is shown; other methods of bias will be discussed in Sec. 11-6. A common-emitter transistor amplifier is illustrated; however, common-base circuits are also often used. Much of the analysis of the various amplifier configurations is the same, and so we shall base our discussion on the generalized device shown in Fig. 11-2. It will be assumed that the effective Q of the resonant circuit is high enough so that v_O consists only of the direct voltage and the fundamental component of the signal. That is, the tuned circuit effectively eliminates the harmonics (see Secs. 9-20 and 9-21). We also assume that the input quantity, e.g., the grid voltage for a vacuum tube, or the gate-source voltage for an FET, or the base current for a common-emitter transistor, is sinusoidal. The capacitors C_{c1}, C_c, and C_B are considered to be short circuits at the signal frequency. Figure 11-3a illustrates typical curves of output voltage and current for a tuned class C amplifier. Note that the ωt axis has been labeled so that the voltage is a cosine wave. A typical input voltage and current are shown in Fig. 11-3b. If the device is a vacuum tube, then x_I represents the grid voltage and y_I the grid current. Although the output voltage is sinusoidal, the output current is very distorted. It is not zero for only a portion of a cycle; even then, it is not part of a sinusoid. If the device output dissipation P_{OD} were zero, then the output circuit efficiency would be 100 percent. The instantaneous power dissipated within the output circuit of the device is

$$p_{OD} = v_O i_O \qquad (11\text{-}1)$$

so that

$$P_{OD} = \frac{1}{2\pi} \int_{-\pi}^{\pi} p_{OD}\, d(\omega t) \qquad (11\text{-}2)$$

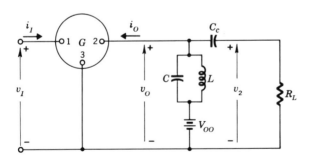

Fig. 11-2 A generalized-device representation of a tuned power amplifier.

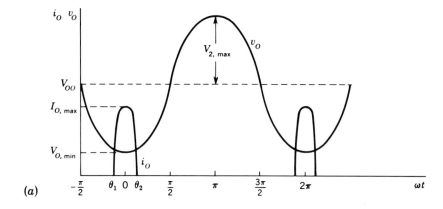

(a)

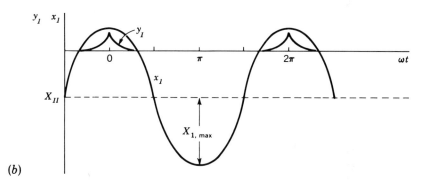

(b)

Fig. 11-3 (a) Typical curves of output voltage and current for a tuned class C amplifier and (b) typical curves of input voltage and current.

but $i_O = 0$ unless $\theta_1 \le \omega t \le \theta_2$, so that

$$P_{OD} = \frac{1}{2\pi} \int_{\theta_1}^{\theta_2} p_{OD} \, d\omega t \qquad (11\text{-}3)$$

We shall define the conduction angle θ_c as

$$\theta_c = \theta_2 - \theta_1 \qquad (11\text{-}4)$$

where θ_1 is measured in negative degrees or radians from zero. The power supplied by the battery is

$$P_{OO} = \frac{1}{2\pi} \int_{\theta_1}^{\theta_2} i_O V_{OO} \, d\omega t = \frac{V_{OO}}{2\pi} \int_{\theta_1}^{\theta_2} i_O \, d\omega t \qquad (11\text{-}5)$$

and the output power is

$$P_2 = \frac{V_2^2}{R_{ac}} \qquad (11\text{-}6)$$

where

$$V_2 = \frac{V_{2,\max}}{\sqrt{2}} \tag{11-7}$$

(see Fig. 11-3a).

The output-circuit efficiency is given by

$$\eta_2 = \frac{P_2}{P_{OO}} = \frac{P_{OO} - P_{OD}}{P_{OO}} \tag{11-8}$$

If θ_c is small enough (ideally zero), we can consider that v_O is constant at $V_{O,\min}$ for values of $\theta_1 \le \omega t \le \theta_2$, so that Eq. (11-3) becomes

$$P_{OD} \approx \frac{V_{O,\min}}{2\pi} \int_{\theta_1}^{\theta_2} i_O \, d\omega t \tag{11-9}$$

Then, substituting Eqs. (11-5) and (11-9) into Eq. (11-8), we obtain

$$\eta_2 = 1 - \frac{V_{O,\min}}{V_{OO}} \tag{11-10}$$

If the output circuit is properly adjusted, $V_{O,\min}$ can approach zero. Thu ,
η_2 can approach 100 percent as θ_c approaches zero. The efficiency is always less than 100 percent, since $V_{O,\min}$ and θ_c are always greater than zero. From the law of conservation of energy, we can write

$$P_2 \le P_{OO} = V_{OO} \int_{\theta_1}^{\theta_2} i_O \, d\omega t \tag{11-11}$$

Thus, as $\theta_2 - \theta_1$ decreases, $I_{O,\max}$ must increase if the output power is not to decrease. The peak current of electronic devices is limited and, hence, the minimum value of θ_c is limited. However, efficiencies of 85 percent or higher are possible.

In order to obtain the quantities of interest, the instantaneous value of i_O must be found and integrated. We shall consider a procedure for doing this in the next section.

We have assumed that the parallel resonant circuit is tuned to the frequency of the input signal. However, if it is tuned to an integral multiple of this frequency instead, then the output will approximately be a sinusoid at the frequency to which the resonant circuit is tuned. This is true because i_O is very distorted and, hence, contains many harmonics of relatively large amplitude. Such circuits are called *frequency multipliers*. Their analysis is similar to that of the conventional amplifier. These circuits cannot be used to multiply the fundamental by an arbitrarily large number, since the amplitude of the higher harmonics falls off with increasing frequency.

11-2 ANALYSIS OF TUNED CLASS B AND CLASS C AMPLIFIERS

In the graphical analysis of Chap. 10, the load impedance was purely resistive, so that, with the exception of a phase reversal, the output voltage and current waveforms were the same. Thus, the plot of i_O versus v_O was a straight line, i.e., the ac load line. For the tuned class B or class C amplifiers, the waveform of v_O does not resemble that of i_O (see Fig. 11-3). Hence, the locus of operation on the device output characteristics is not a straight line. Thus, any analysis using these characteristics would be very tedious. However, by using an appropriate set of characteristics, we can obtain a locus of operation that is a straight line. Assume that, because of the resonant circuit, the output voltage is sinusoidal,

$$v_O = V_{OO} - \sqrt{2} V_2 \cos \omega t \tag{11-12}$$

If we also assume that the device input consists of a sinusoidal signal superimposed upon a direct bias, we have

$$x_I = X_{II} + \sqrt{2} X_1 \cos \omega t \tag{11-13}$$

where, as is usually the case, x_I represents either the input voltage or the input current. Since v_O and x_I have the same waveforms, a plot of v_O versus x_I is a straight line. Therefore, instead of working with a plot of i_O versus v_O with x_I as a parameter, let us use a plot of x_I versus v_O with i_O as a parameter. These are called *constant-current characteristics* and a typical set is given in Fig. 11-4. The dashed curves represent an input quantity. For instance, in a vacuum tube, x_I would be grid voltage and y_I would be grid current. The curves resemble those for a vacuum-tube triode. If a vacuum-tube pentode is used, there would be another set of constant-current characteristics for the screen-grid current. (A typical set of transistor characteristics is given in Fig. 11-13.) The scales are given in normalized form. If high-power vacuum tubes are used, the voltage scale would be in kilovolts and the current scale in amperes. Transistors are not operated at very high power levels. Transistor voltage scales would be in volts and the current scales in amperes or milliamperes. FETs can be operated only at very low power levels. The voltage scales would be in volts and the current scales in milliamperes. The parametric equations for the locus of operation are given by Eqs. (11-12) and (11-13). The locus is drawn between points P and Q in Fig. 11-4. Actually, the locus should be twice this length and should be extended beyond point Q to another point called P', which is not shown on the diagram. That is, as ωt varies from $-\pi/2$ to 0, to $\pi/2$, to π, to $3\pi/2$, the instantaneous operating point moves from point Q to P, to Q, to P', to Q, respectively. However, since the operation is class B or C, the output current will be zero for operation along QP'; hence it is not drawn.

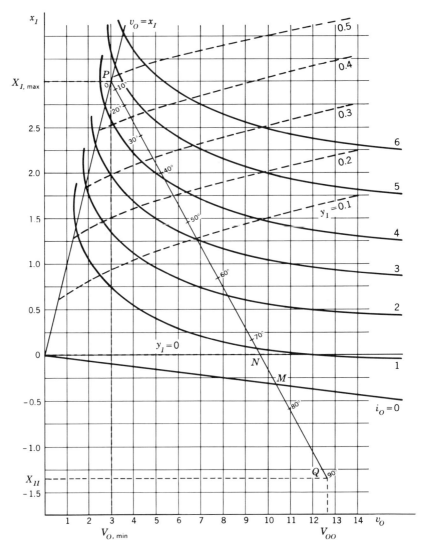

Fig. 11-4 Constant-output-current characteristics for a generalized device. Constant y_I curves are also shown. Note that the $i_O = 0$ curve actually is a boundary. All points below it represent $i_O = 0$.

The voltages and currents are even functions of time, and thus if the response for $0 \leq \omega t \leq \pi/2$ is known, the reponse for $-\pi/2 \leq \omega t \leq 0$ is also known. The locus from point Q to P is marked in lengths proportional to $\cos \omega t$ as indicated. That is, each length is $\overline{PQ} \cos \omega t$, $\omega t = 0, 10, 20, 30,$ $\dots, 90°$. The point Q is the quiescent operating point. Its coordinates are X_{II} and V_{OO}. Point P has the coordinates $X_{I,max}$ and $V_{O,min}$. From Eqs. (11-12) and (11-13), we have

$$X_{I,max} = X_{II} + \sqrt{2}X_1 \qquad (11\text{-}14)$$

$$V_{O,min} = V_{OO} - \sqrt{2}V_2 \qquad (11\text{-}15)$$

These values are unknown. They depend not only upon the device but also upon the resonant circuit. Point P is often chosen as a design parameter. In Sec. 11-5, we shall discuss how this can be done. For the time being, let us assume that it is known. Once the points P and Q are determined, the locus can be drawn between them and marked in degrees. Then, i_O and y_I as functions of ωt can be obtained by interpolating between the constant i_O and y_I curves, respectively. The degree markings on the line $\overline{PQ}$ are used to do this.

If the output current is given by the Fourier series

$$i_O = I_{OA} + 2(I_{o1} \cos \omega t + I_{o2} \cos 2\omega t + \cdots) \qquad (11\text{-}16)$$

then I_{OA} is the average value of i_O

$$I_{OA} = \frac{1}{2\pi} \int_{\theta_1}^{\theta_2} i_O \, d\omega t \qquad (11\text{-}17)$$

Since i_O is an even function of time, we can write

$$I_{OA} = \frac{1}{\pi} \int_0^{\theta_2} i_O \, d\omega t \qquad (11\text{-}18)$$

The fundamental component of plate current can be obtained from the relation

$$\sqrt{2}I_{o1} = \frac{2}{\pi} \int_0^{\theta_2} i_O \cos \omega t \, d\omega t \qquad (11\text{-}19)$$

Since we do not have an analytical expression for i_O, approximation techniques must be used to perform the desired integrations. Consider the curve of $f(\omega t)$ shown in Fig. 11-5a. We can approximate its integral from 0 to A by adding the area of the trapezoids obtained by connecting points on the curve by straight lines. Actually, for i_O and y_I, we do not have a smooth curve, but only a set of discrete points determined at distinct values of ωt. *Thus, a straight-line approximation is as good as any other.* The area of the trapezoid of Fig. 11-5b is $c(a + b)/2$. Thus, we can approximate the integral by

$$\int_0^{\pi/2} f(\omega t) \, d\omega t = \Delta \omega t \left\{ \frac{f(0) + f(\Delta \omega t)}{2} + \frac{f(\Delta \omega t) + f(2\,\Delta \omega t)}{2} \right. $$
$$\left. + \cdots + \frac{f[(n-1)\,\Delta \omega t] + f(n\,\Delta \omega t)}{2} \right\}$$

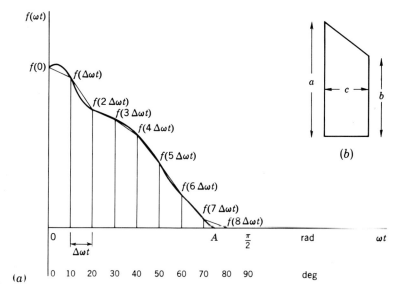

Fig. 11-5 (a) Integration using trapezoidal approximations; (b) a trapezoid.

where $\Delta\omega t = \pi/2n$ rad. Combining terms, we have

$$\int_0^{\pi/2} f(\omega t)\, d\omega t = \Delta\omega t \left\{ \frac{f(0)}{2} + f(\Delta\omega t) + f(2\,\Delta\omega t) \right.$$
$$\left. + \cdots + f[(n-1)\,\Delta\omega t] + \frac{f(n\,\Delta\omega t)}{2} \right\} \quad (11\text{-}20)$$

If we chose $n = 9$, so that $\Delta\omega t = \pi/18$ rad, or $10°$, we obtain

$$\int_0^{\pi/2} f(\omega t)\, d\omega t = \frac{\pi}{18} \left[\frac{f(0°)}{2} + f(10°) + f(20°) \right.$$
$$\left. + \cdots + f(80°) + \frac{f(90°)}{2} \right] \quad (11\text{-}21)$$

Thus, Eqs. (11-18) and (11-19) become, for $10°$ increments,

$$I_{OA} = \frac{1}{18} \left[\frac{i_o(0°)}{2} + i_o(10°) + i_o(20°) + \cdots + i_o(80°) + \frac{i_o(90°)}{2} \right]$$
$$(11\text{-}22)$$

and

$$\sqrt{2}I_{o1} = \frac{1}{9} \left[\frac{i_o(0°)}{2} + i_o(10°)\cos 10° + i_o(20°)\cos 20° \right.$$
$$\left. + \cdots + i_o(80°)\cos 80° + \frac{i_o(90°)\cos 90°}{2} \right] \quad (11\text{-}23)$$

Table 11-1

ϕ, deg	$\cos \phi$	$i_o(\phi)$	$i_o \cos (\phi)$	y_I	$y_I \cos \phi$
0	1.000				
10	0.985				
20	0.940				
30	0.866				
40	0.766				
50	0.643				
60	0.500				
70	0.342				
80	0.174				
90	0.000				

If greater accuracy is desired, smaller increments can be used. We shall also be interested in obtaining the corresponding input quantities.

$$y_I = Y_{IA} + \sqrt{2}(Y_{i1} \cos \omega t + Y_{i2} \cos 2\omega t + \cdots) \tag{11-24}$$

Then, to obtain Y_{IA} and Y_{i1}, we can proceed exactly as in Eqs. (11-18), (11-19), (11-22), and (11-23) except that y_I is used instead of i_o. The simplest way of performing these calculations is to set up a table. A sample one is given here. The values of i_o and y_I are interpolated from the curve of Fig. 11-4 and are substituted into the first and third blank columns of the table. The second and fourth columns are then calculated. The values from the table are then substituted into Eqs. (11-22) and (11-23) or into modifications of them where i_o is replaced by y_I.

The other quantities we shall need in our computations can be obtained directly from Fig. 11-4. The peak signal output voltage is given by $V_{OO} - V_{O,\min}$. Thus, if the output voltage is expressed by Eq. (11-12), then the rms value of the output signal voltage is given by

$$V_2 = \frac{V_{OO} - V_{O,\min}}{\sqrt{2}} \tag{11-25}$$

Similarly, the rms value of the signal component of x_I is

$$X_1 = \frac{X_{I,\max} - X_{II}}{\sqrt{2}} \tag{11-26}$$

We are now in a position to calculate the quantities of interest. Assume that the resonant circuit is adjusted so that it appears as a pure resistance at the signal frequency. Then the output power is

$$P_2 = V_2 I_{o1} \tag{11-27}$$

The effective resistance of the output circuit is just the ratio of the fundamental component of the voltage to the current. Hence,

$$R_{ac} = \frac{V_2}{I_{o1}} \tag{11-28}$$

The power supplied by V_{OO} is

$$P_{OO} = V_{OO}I_{OA} \tag{11-29}$$

If we assume that the zero-frequency resistance of the inductance L is negligible, the device output dissipation is given by

$$P_{OD} = P_{OO} - P_2 \tag{11-30}$$

The output-circuit efficiency is

$$\eta_2 = \frac{P_2}{P_{OO}} \tag{11-31}$$

The output quantities have now been obtained. At times, we are interested in similar output quantities. The average power dissipated in the input of the device is given by

$$P_{ID} = \frac{1}{2\pi} \int_0^{2\pi} x_I y_I \, d\omega t$$

If $x_I = X_{II} + \sqrt{2}X_1 \cos \omega t$ and y_I is given in Eq. (11-24), we have

$$P_{ID} = \frac{1}{2\pi} \int_0^{2\pi} (X_{II} + \sqrt{2}X_1 \cos \omega t)$$
$$\times \, [Y_{IA} + \sqrt{2}(Y_{i1} \cos \omega t + Y_{i2} \cos 2\omega t + \cdots)] \, d\omega t$$

Solving, we obtain

$$P_{ID} = X_{II}Y_{IA} + X_1 Y_{i1} \tag{11-32}$$

If a power supply X_{II} is used to produce an input bias, then the power supplied by it will be

$$P_{II} = X_{II}Y_{IA} \tag{11-33}$$

This assumes that all the direct component of y_I passes through or appears across the power supply. Note that P_{II} is often negative. That is, the power supply actually dissipates power. For instance, in the circuit of Fig. 11-1a the battery V_{cc} dissipates power when the grid draws current. The input generator, e.g., the generators v_s and i_s in Fig. 11-1, must supply any power that is absorbed by the power supply or in the input of the device.

The conduction angle θ_c can be obtained by noting where the $i_o = 0$ curve crosses the locus of operation. This is point M in Fig. 11-4. Thus,

$$\theta_c = 2 \cos^{-1} \frac{\overline{MQ}}{\overline{PQ}} \tag{11-34}$$

In this case, $\theta_c = 152.8°$. The factor of 2 is used, since the output current is an even function of time (see Fig. 11-3a). Similarly, we can define

$$\theta_y = 2 \cos^{-1} \frac{\overline{NQ}}{\overline{PQ}} \tag{11-35}$$

as an input conduction angle. If transistors are used and y_I represents a voltage, it becomes meaningless to speak of a conduction angle θ_y. There is no input current if a MOSFET is used.

When vaccum-tube pentodes are used, the screen-grid dissipation is given by $V_{c2}I_{c2A}$, where I_{c2A} is found by the same type of graphical procedure as we have discussed. The screen-grid voltage contains only a direct component because of the bypass capacitor.

At the start we assumed that the location of points P and Q (see Fig. 11-4) were known. Point Q is obtained from the quiescent operating point. The x_i intercept of point P is determined from Eq. (11-13) and the input quantities. However, the v_O axis intercept is unknown. The procedure is to guess at this coordinate of P and then compute R_{ac} [see Eq. (11-28)]. If the calculated and actual values of R_{ac} agree, the guess was correct; otherwise, choose another value of P and try again. If the calculated value of R_{ac} is less than the actual value, shift the location of point P to the right.

For a frequency multiplier, the procedures of this section can be used to calculate the harmonic component of i_O. Equations (11-19) and (11-23) can be used here with $\cos \omega t$ replaced by $\cos n\, \omega t$, where n is the order of the harmonic.

11-3 THE RESONANT CIRCUIT

The function of the resonant circuit in a tuned amplifier is to provide the correct load impedance to the amplifier, to reject the unwanted harmonics, and to couple the power to the load. The first two functions can be studied using the techniques of Secs. 9-20 to 9-25. The resonant circuits in tuned power amplifiers are sometimes called *tank circuits*. Such a circuit is shown in Fig. 11-6a. The efficiency of all the components of a high-power amplifier are important. Let us compute the efficiency of Fig. 11-6. It is

$$\eta = \frac{I_L^2 R_L}{I_L^2 R_L + I_a^2 R} \tag{11-36}$$

where we have neglected the losses in the capacitor. The analysis is considerably simplified if we use the equivalent circuit of Fig. 11-6b, where

$$R_L' = \frac{\omega_0^2 L^2}{R_L} \tag{11-37}$$

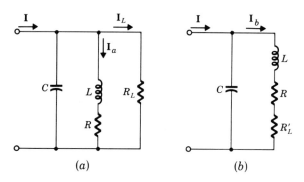

Fig. 11-6 (a) A simple output network and (b) the equivalent circuit of this network.

This assumes that $R_L \gg \omega_0 L$ and is derived as is Eq. (9-261). It is also assumed that the capacitor is adjusted to resonance at ω_0, the frequency of operation. Then the efficiency will be

$$\eta = \frac{I_b^2 R_L'}{I_b^2 (R + R_L')} = \frac{R_L'}{R + R_L'} \tag{11-38}$$

Let Q_0 be the Q of the coil itself at resonance

$$Q_0 = \frac{\omega_0 L}{R} \tag{11-39}$$

and Q_{eff} is the Q of the coil shunted by R_L

$$Q_{\text{eff}} = \frac{\omega_0 L}{R + R_L'} \tag{11-40}$$

These definitions are compatible with those of Secs. 11-20 and 11-21. Then, substituting in Eq. (11-38), we obtain

$$\eta = \frac{1/Q_{\text{eff}} - 1/Q_0}{1/Q_{\text{eff}}} = 1 - \frac{Q_{\text{eff}}}{Q_0} \tag{11-41}$$

Thus, if the efficiency of the tank circuit is to be high, $Q_0 \gg Q_{\text{eff}}$. If R_L can be varied, then Q_{eff} can be made as small as desired. The value of Q_0 is usually several hundred. The circuit is usually adjusted so that Q_{eff} ranges between 10 and 20. The efficiency of the tank circuit is then 90 percent or more. The selectivity is a function of Q_{eff}. However, the only frequencies that must be rejected are harmonics of ω_0 which are far removed from ω_0. Even at low values of Q_{eff}, the harmonic rejection can be very good, so the assumption of Sec. 11-2, that the device output voltage v_O is sinusoidal, is justified. If the amplifier is to be the output stage of a commercial radio transmitter, then the radiation of unwanted frequencies must be kept to a minimum, and additional filtering often is added to the circuit. The efficiency of this filter also must be considered.

We have assumed that the value of R_L can be varied. Usually it is fixed by the design requirements. The tank circuit of Fig. 11-7a is often used to provide a means of controlling the effective value of R_L. We shall assume that $R_L \gg \omega_0 L_2$. Then, proceeding as in Sec. 9-23, we obtain the equivalent circuit of Fig. 11-7b. The power dissipated in R_2 and R_L is

$$P' = I_a^2 \frac{(\omega_0 M)^2}{R_2 + R_L} \tag{11-42}$$

The power dissipated in R_L can be obtained by multiplying Eq. (11-42) by $R_L/(R_2 + R_L)$. Thus, the efficiency of operation is

$$\eta = \frac{(\omega_0 M)^2/(R_2 + R_L)}{R_1 + (\omega_0 M)^2/(R_2 + R_L)} \frac{R_L}{R_2 + R_L} \tag{11-43}$$

Defining

$$Q_{01} = \frac{\omega_0 L_1}{R_1} \tag{11-44}$$

$$Q_{\text{eff},1} = \frac{\omega_0 L_1}{R_1 + (\omega_0 M)^2/(R_2 + R_L)} \tag{11-45}$$

$$Q_{02} = \frac{\omega_0 L_2}{R_2} \tag{11-46}$$

$$Q_{\text{eff},2} = \frac{\omega_0 L_2}{R_2 + R_L} \tag{11-47}$$

and substituting into Eq. (11-43) yields

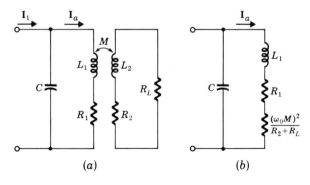

(a) (b)

Fig. 11-7 (a) A mutual-inductance-coupled output network and (b) its equivalent circuit.

$$\eta = \left(1 - \frac{Q_{eff,1}}{Q_{01}}\right)\left(1 - \frac{Q_{eff,2}}{Q_{02}}\right) \qquad (11\text{-}48)$$

To obtain high efficiencies, the coupled resistance must be much greater than the primary resistance and R_L must be much greater than R_2. As in the case of the simple coil of Fig. 11-6, the Q_{01} will usually be several hundred and $Q_{eff,1}$ will be between 10 and 20. The load resistance is usually such that Q_{02} is 50 (or more) times $Q_{eff,2}$. The efficiencies obtainable with the mutual-inductance-coupled circuit compare quite favorably with those of Fig. 11-6. Efficiencies of 90 percent or higher are obtainable. The selectivity of this tuned circuit is given by the relations of Sec. 9-23.

If the impedances in transistor circuits are too small, then tapped coils can be used to obtain the desired selectivity (see Secs. 9-22 and 9-23).

We have assumed that the circuits of Figs. 11-6 and 11-7 are adjusted for resonance. This is usually accomplished by varying C, since air-core coils are used to keep the losses low. The proper value of C must be determined. This can be done by measuring the power delivered to R_L. However, this requires the use of radio-frequency measuring equipment. A simpler technique is to measure I_{OA}, the average value of i_O (see Fig. 11-3). This can be done by placing a simple d'Arsonval ammeter in series with the power-supply lead to the tank circuit. From Fig. 11-3 we can see that the voltage v_O is a minimum between θ_1 and θ_2. If the tank circuit is detuned, the output signal voltage will decrease and v_O will increase for those times that $i_O \neq 0$. This will increase i_O. Thus, the capacitor C is adjusted for a *minimum* in I_{OA}. This is an approximate adjustment, but it is usually accurate enough.

11-4 EFFECTS OF INPUT-CIRCUIT DISTORTION ON CLASS B AND CLASS C AMPLIFIERS

We have thus far neglected the effects of input-circuit distortion in the analyses. If such distortion is present, it cannot be assumed that x_I varies sinusoidally [see Eq. (11-13)], so that the locus of operation is no longer a straight line as is shown in Fig. 11-4. We shall modify the procedure to take input distortion into account. Two typical input circuits are shown in Fig. 11-8. The generators v_s and i_s are the cosinusoidal input generators, and V_{SS} and I_{SS} are bias generators. The voltages and currents v_B and i_B are of the form

$$x_B = X_{SS} + x_s = X_{SS} + \sqrt{2}X_s \cos \omega_0 t \qquad (11\text{-}49)$$

Thus, the locus of operation on a plot of x_B versus v_O will be a straight line. It is desirable to alter the characteristics of Fig. 11-4 so that the ordinate is expressed in terms of x_B instead of x_I. Before we do this, let us consider the approximations that will be made. If the impedance $\mathbf{Z}$ contains inductances

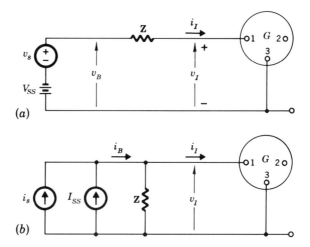

Fig. 11-8 Generalized input circuit: (*a*) voltage source and (*b*) current source.

and capacitances, then a nonlinear differential equation must be solved to obtain v_O and i_O. Usually, tuned circuits, adjusted to be a pure resistance at the frequency ω_0, are used. We shall assume that $\mathbf{Z}$ is constant at this value and is equal to R. We also assume that the impedance is constant down to zero frequency. This is usually not the case. The generator X_{SS} may have to be adjusted to obtain the proper bias. Let us assume that in Fig. 11-4, x_I represents a voltage and y_I represents a current. Then, for each constant-y_I curve, we can write

$$v_B = Ri_I + v_I \tag{11-50}$$

The constant-i_I curves can now be plotted on an v_B, v_O set of axes. Thus, if we used the same scales as in Fig. 11-4, the constant-i_I curves would be shifted upward by an amount equal to Ri_I. Similarly, if x_I represents a current and y_I a voltage, we have

$$i_B = Gv_I + i_I \tag{11-51}$$

where $G = 1/R$.

We must now plot the constant-output-current characteristics of the x_B, v_O axes. The procedure of Sec. 5-11 can be used. To obtain x_B in terms of x_I, the dynamic characteristic of Fig. 5-29b must be drawn. This requires a knowledge of the locus of operation, which cannot be found until x_B is known in terms of x_I. As a first trial, assume that the straight line $\overline{PQ}$ is the locus of operation (see Fig. 11-4). The dynamic input characteristic is then drawn and x_B is obtained in terms of x_I. The characteristics of Fig. 11-4 can then be replotted on an x_B versus v_O axis.   The locus of operation on these curves will be a straight line.   The actual locus of operation is now known, and the assumed dynamic input characteristic can be checked.   If it is severely in error, draw a new one using the new locus of operation.   Repeat the procedure until the assumed dynamic input characteristic agrees with the calculated one.   Once the new characteristics are drawn, the analysis proceeds essentially as in Sec. 11-2.   When the device input quantities are computed, the value of x_I and not of x_B should be used.   The results of this analysis are very approximate and should be treated as such.   However, they are often accurate enough to check the feasibility of a design and to estimate the operating conditions.   If the generator impedance is changed, a new set of characteristics must be drawn.

   If x_I represents an input voltage and if the output impedance of the circuit that drives the power amplifier is very much less than the input impedance of the power amplifier, then the input-circuit distortion can be ignored.   On the other hand, if x_I represents an input current, then for undistorted operation, the output impedance of the driving stage should be very much greater than the input impedance of the power amplifier.   Thus, the design of the driver amplifier can do much to eliminate the need for the approximate analysis of this section.

11-5   DESIGN OF CLASS B AND CLASS C AMPLIFIERS

We shall assume in this discussion that the stage preceding the amplifier is designed so that the input-circuit distortion can be neglected.   If this is not the case, then the characteristics of the device should be modified in accordance with Sec. 11-4.   We shall begin with a discussion of vacuum-tube-triode amplifiers.   These results will be extended to the beam power tube, the vacuum-tube tetrode, the vacuum-tube pentode or FET, and the transistor.

Vacuum-tube triode   The design of the amplifier consists of the proper choice of the points P and Q of Fig. 11-4.   The location of point P depends to a great extent upon the variation of plate current with grid bias.   To obtain high efficiency, the grid is always driven positive to obtain large swings in output voltage and current.   As the grid voltage is increased from the cutoff value, the total current from the cathode increases steadily.   However, as the grid becomes positive, some of it is diverted to the grid.   If the grid voltage is increased sufficiently, it will begin to take a larger and larger proportion of the cathode current.   As the grid voltage is increased above the plate voltage, the plate current does not usually increase and, eventually, will decrease. Point P should be chosen so that $V_{O,\min} \geq X_{I,\max}$, that is, $V_{b,\min} \geq V_{c,\max}$. A line whose equation is $v_O = x_I$ ($v_b = v_c$) is often drawn on the constant-current characteristic, and point P is chosen to lie on it.   Such a line is shown in Fig. 11-4. Often, to limit the grid current, the grid voltage is not allowed to become equal to the plate voltage. The point P is then made to lie on a line $v_O = kx_I$ ($v_b = kv_c$). The value of k usually lies between 1 and 2. The intersection of this line and the constant-i_O curve that represents the desired peak output current determines the location of point P. The peak values of grid voltage and grid current should be checked to see if they have been exceeded.

The location of point Q requires that V_{OO} and X_{II} be specified. The peak output voltage is given by $V_{OO} - V_{O,\min}$. Thus, the peak tube voltage is

$$V_{O,\max} = 2V_{OO} - V_{O,\min} \tag{11-52}$$

This should not exceed rated values. The voltage $V_{O,\min}$ is known, because point P is fixed. Thus, a value of V_{OO} can be chosen. The first trial of $V_{O,\max}$ should be somewhat less than the rated value. The value of $X_{II}(V_{CQ})$ must now be picked. The $i_O = 0$ curve is used here. If class B operation is desired, then the intersection of the $i_O = 0$ curve with a vertical line drawn through V_{OO} determines the bias X_{IIB}. If class C operation is desired, then a more negative grid voltage should be used. Ordinarily, values of X_{II} are chosen so that the conduction angle lies between 120 and 150 degrees.[1] Note that the maximum magnitude of the grid voltage occurs when the signal becomes negative and is equal to

$$X_{I,\min} = 2X_{II} - X_{I,\max} \tag{11-53}$$

This should not exceed the peak negative-grid-voltage rating of the vacuum tube. The driver amplifier will have to supply the power dissipated by the grid and the bias current. Thus, the grid swing may be limited, so the driver stage will not have to supply large amounts of power. This will affect not only the value of X_{II}, but also the position of point P. In general, if the maximum value of i_O remains constant, the driving power decreases as $V_{O,\min}$ increases. Once the values of P and Q are chosen, the load power and the input and output dissipation of the device can be determined. If the required power output is obtained without exceeding any ratings, the design is complete. The design can be modified in the following ways if it is unsatisfactory. The output-circuit efficiency can be increased and the dissipation decreased by reducing the conduction angle θ_c and/or $V_{O,\min}$. However, the output power is also decreased if θ_c is decreased, unless the peak output current is increased. Increasing the plate voltage will increase the output power and plate dissipation. If the design is still unsatisfactory, a larger tube will be required. Once the design is complete, the effective resistance of the tank circuit can be obtained from Eq. (11-28). The tank circuit can then be designed using the results of Secs. 9-20 to 9-25 and 11-3. The power dissipated in the tank circuit must be considered in the design.

Vacuum-tube tetrodes and pentodes, beam power tubes, and FETs The design of circuits using these devices is similar to that of the vacuum-tube triode. The constant-current characteristics for the pentode and beam power tube include an additional set of constant screen-grid current characteristics. The screen-grid input power is analyzed in the same way as the control-grid input power is, except that the screen-grid voltage is usually constant, so that its dissipation is the product of the direct screen-grid voltage and the average screen-grid current. The screen-grid voltage is usually chosen to be considerably larger than the maximum control-grid voltage. This limits the control-grid current. Consequently, tetrodes, pentodes, and beam power tubes require less grid-driving power than vacuum-tube triodes. If a pentode is not used, then the minimum plate voltage must be equal to or greater than the screen-grid voltage. Otherwise, the plate current falls off and the screen-grid current rises greatly because of secondary emission effects. This increases screen dissipation and reduces output power. The MOSFET takes no input current. Thus, the driver stage does not have to supply power. Otherwise, the design concepts are essentially the same. Note that at present the FET can supply only small amounts of power.

Transistor amplifiers The constant-current characteristics of a common-emitter transistor (i_B versus v_C; see Fig. 11-13) are quite horizontal and linear, except at knees which occur at very small values of collector voltage. The operation can be restricted to lie just above this value of v_C. This determines the value of $V_{O,\min}$. (Note that for a p-n-p transistor, the scales of Fig. 11-4 would be negative.) The point P can be chosen at any value of x_I that does not exceed peak base- and collector-current ratings, or base-voltage ratings. The driving power, supplied by the preceding stage, increases as $|I_{B,\max}|$ increases. The remainder of the design, including the choice of point Q, is similar to that of the vacuum-tube triode.

11-6 INPUT BIAS IN CLASS B AND CLASS C AMPLIFIERS

In vacuum tubes, grid bias is usually not obtained by means of a cathode resistance in class B or class C amplifiers, because the plate current is zero for at least one half-cycle. A separate negative power supply can be used to obtain the bias. However, this is often undesirable. If the grid is driven positive, so that there is grid current, we can obtain the negative bias by means of the grid-leak bias circuit of Fig. 11-9a. The grid and cathode of the vacuum tube can be considered to be a vacuum-tube diode. When v_g is positive, the capacitor is charged with the polarity shown. Since grid current can be only in the direction indicated, the capacitor can discharge only through R. The capacitor will not discharge completely, and there will always be a voltage across it which produces a negative grid bias. The average

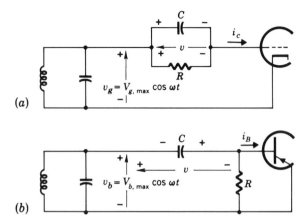

Fig. 11-9 (*a*) A vacuum-tube grid-leak bias circuit and (*b*) a transistor input-bias circuit.

value of this voltage is the direct-grid bias. If R were an open circuit, the capacitor would charge to a voltage of $V_{g,\max}$. Thereafter, v would remain constant at that value. This would provide too much grid bias, since the grid would never again be driven positive. However, R is not an open circuit, and it can be adjusted to obtain the proper grid bias. To design this circuit, compute the Fourier series for the grid current given by Eq. (11-24)

$$i_c = I_{cA} + \sqrt{2}(I_{c1} \cos \omega t + I_{c2} \cos 2\omega t + \cdot \cdot \cdot) \qquad (11\text{-}54)$$

All the direct current passes through R; hence,

$$R = \frac{-V_{cQ}}{I_{cA}} \qquad (11\text{-}55)$$

The value of the capacitor C should be chosen large enough so that it is effectively a short circuit at the signal frequencies.

One advantage of grid-leak bias is that if the value of v_g changes *slightly*, the direct grid bias changes in a way that tends to keep the amplifier operation constant. For instance, if $V_{g,\max}$ is reduced, the value of V_{cQ} becomes less negative. This also is a disadvantage of the circuit. If the exciting signal v_g should become zero (which is a large change), the grid bias also would become zero. This results in large values of plate current and usually causes the plate-dissipation rating to be greatly exceeded. A circuit breaker is sometimes placed in series with the power supply to prevent this. A cathode-bias circuit (R_k shunted by C_k) is at times included. It is designed so that it does not provide substantial bias if the operation is normal.

However, should the excitation fail and the plate current increase, the voltage drop across R_k would provide sufficient negative bias to prevent the plate current from becoming excessive.

Cathode bias can be used with class C vacuum-tube amplifiers, even though the plate current is zero for substantial portions of the time, if a large enough bypass capacitor is used. However, a large value of R_k would be required to obtain the bias, and it would have to be in series with the power supply. Thus, cathode bias would be expensive and inefficient.

The two power supplies in the transistor circuit of Fig. 11-1c are not required if the circuit of Fig. 11-9b is used. The operation there is essentially the same as that of Fig. 11-9a. In the case of the transistor, the emitter-base junction performs the same function that the cathode-grid diode does in the vacuum tube. Thus, when v_b is negative, the capacitor C will be charged with the polarity shown. When v_b becomes less negative than v, the net base-emitter voltage will be positive and the transistor will be cut off. The charge can then leak off the capacitor C through both the high impedance of the transistor and the resistor R. Similar to the case of the vacuum tube, the direct bias can be controlled by varying R.

The circuit of Fig. 11-9b would function in essentially the same way if the resistor R were placed across the capacitor. Then Fig. 11-9a and b would have the same form. Conversely, the resistor R of Fig. 11-9a could be placed across the grid-cathode leads. In the arrangement of Fig. 11-9a, very little signal voltage will appear across the bias resistor. Hence, the circuit of Fig. 11-9a will require less signal power than the circuit of Fig. 11-9b. In Fig. 11-9b, no direct current passes through the signal source. This can be an advantage at times. The circuits of Fig. 11-9a and b are used with either vacuum-tube or transistor circuits. However, the circuit of Fig. 11-9a is more common.

In the MOSFET, there is no direct input current. Thus, these bias circuits cannot be used unless a diode is added. They can be used with the junction FET. However, the MOSFET is much more common than the junction FET.

11-7 NEUTRALIZATION

The neutralization of radio-frequency power amplifiers is essentially the same as the neutralization of small-signal radio-frequency amplifiers, so that the discussions and circuits of Sec. 9-26 apply here also. If an amplifier is designed to operate at only one frequency, neutralization usually does not provide too much trouble; hence, radio-frequency power amplifiers are often neutralized vacuum-tube triodes. Vacuum-tube tetrodes and pentodes and

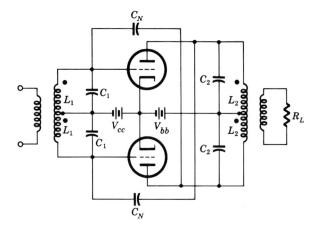

Fig. 11-10 A tuned push-pull vacuum-tube-triode amplifier (a single tuning capacitor can also be used).

beam power amplifiers rarely require neutralization. Even so, triodes are very often used as high-power amplifiers, because they do not have screen-grid dissipation.

The neutralizing capacitor (see Fig. 9-69) is connected between the input and the output of the amplifier. The difference of potential there may be of the order of tens of kilovolts or more. The capacitor must be able to withstand this voltage without breaking down. Of course, breakdown voltages should be considered whenever components are chosen.

11-8 PUSH-PULL CLASS B AND CLASS C AMPLIFIERS

Radio-frequency push-pull power amplifiers are constructed in a manner similar to the push-pull circuit of Figs. 10-9 and 10-10 except that the ferromagnetic-core transformers are replaced by tuned circuits. A typical vacuum-tube-triode amplifier is shown in Fig. 11-10. The capacitors C_N are for neutralizing purposes. Since one tube is always cut off, it might appear that the output could be analyzed by considering each tube separately. However, this is not the case, since the two circuits interact in the tank circuit. The amount of this interaction depends upon the coefficient of coupling between the two coils L_2 and also upon the circuit elements. It manifests itself in a change in the effective load impedance. Note that, because of resonance, the signal components of the two plate voltages are negatives of each other, as they should be.

REFERENCE

1. Terman, F. E.: "Electronic and Radio Engineering," 4th ed., p. 464, McGraw-Hill
   Book Company, New York, 1955.

BIBLIOGRAPHY

Alley, C. L., and K. W. Atwood: "Electronic Engineering," 2d ed., chap. 12, John
   Wiley & Sons, Inc., New York, 1962.
Gray, T. S.: "Applied Electronics," 2d ed., pp. 629–652, John Wiley & Sons, Inc., New
   York, 1954.
Terman, F. E.: "Electronic and Radio Engineering," 4th ed., chap. 13, McGraw-Hill
   Book Company, New York, 1955.

PROBLEMS

*The following problems use the two vacuum tubes and the transistor whose character-
istics and ratings are supplied. (The ratings have been adjusted for illustrative purposes.)
An FET is also considered.*

*Type 5671 vacuum-tube triode: The ratings of this vacuum tube are maximum plate
voltage 30,000 volts, maximum negative grid voltage* − 5000 *volts, plate dissipation 25 kw,
peak cathode current 50 amp, grid dissipation 2500 watts. The heater voltage is 11 volts*

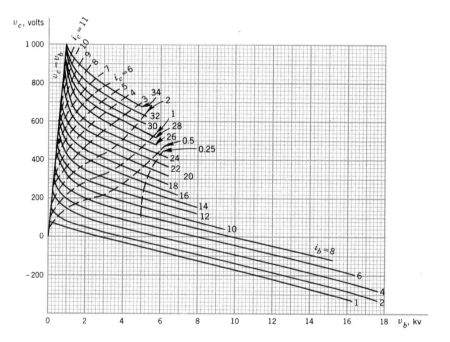

Fig. 11-11 The constant-current characteristics of the type 5671 vacuum-tube
triode. Assume that $i_b = 0$ if $v_b < -40v_c$, where v_c is negative. (*Radio Corporation
of America.*)

rms, and the heater current is 285 *amp rms. The constant-current characteristics are supplied in Fig.* 11-11.

Type 6166 *beam power tube: The ratings of this vacuum tube are maximum plate voltage* 14,000 *volts, maximum direct screen-grid voltage* 2000 *volts, maximum negative control-grid voltage* −2400 *volts, plate dissipation* 10 *kw, screen-grid dissipation* 400 *watts, control-grid dissipation* 100 *watts. The rated filament voltage is* 5 *volts rms and the filament current is* 181 *amp rms. The constant-current characteristics are given in Fig.* 11-12a *and b. To avoid confusion, the constant plate-current curves are on one characteristic and the constant control- and screen-grid curves are on the other.*

Type 2N301 *transistor: The ratings of this transistor are maximum (negative) collector voltage* −40 *volts, maximum (negative) base-emitter voltage* −20 *volts, maximum (negative) collector current* −3 *amp, collector dissipation* 11 *watts. An idealized set of constant-collector current and constant base-voltage characteristics is given in Fig.* 11-13.

11-1. A type 5671 vacuum-tube triode is connected into the circuit of Fig. 11-1a. The values of the voltages are $V_{bb} = 12,500$ volts, $V_{cc} = -1250$ volts, $v_s = 1800 \cos \omega t$ volts. The operation is such that the peak plate current is 18 amp. Determine the average values of i_b and i_c, the rms values of the fundamental components of i_b and i_c, the plate dissipation, the grid dissipation, the conduction angle, the plate-circuit efficiency, the effective load resistance, and the power output. Are any ratings exceeded? Assume that $R_s = 0$. What is the efficiency if all the power dissipated in the tube and in the circuit is considered?

11-2. Repeat Prob. 11-1, but now assume that $V_{cc} = -1000$ volts and that the peak plate current is 30 amp.

11-3. A type 6166 beam power tube is connected into the circuit of Fig. 11-1a. The screen grid is connected in the usual way. The values of the circuit voltages are $V_{bb} = 5000$ volts, $V_{c2Q} = 1200$ volts, $V_{cc} = -300$ volts, $v_g = 500 \cos \omega t$ volts. The peak tube current is 8 amp. Determine the power output; the average values of i_b, i_{c2}, and i_c; the rms values of the fundamental components of i_b and i_c; the plate dissipation; the screen-grid dissipation; the control-grid dissipation; the conduction angle; and the effective load resistance. Are any ratings exceeded? What should the value of the screen-grid resistance be? Assume that the generator resistance $R_s = 0$.

11-4. Repeat Prob. 8-3, but now assume that $v_g = 600 \cos \omega t$ volts and that the peak tube current is 12 amp.

11-5. A 2N301 transistor is connected into the circuit of Fig. 11-1c. The values of R_B and V_{BB} are such that the base current will be zero if $i_s > -20$ ma. Assume that the base current is $i_B = i_s + 20$ ma if $i_s < -20$ ma and $i_B = 0$ if $i_s > -20$ ma. This assumes that i_B cannot be positive (or, equivalently, $I_{CO} = 0$) and that there is no signal current in R_s when $i_B < 0$. The value of V_{CC} is -25 volts and $i_s = 55 \cos \omega t$ ma. Assume that R_s is an open circuit and that C_B acts as a short circuit at the signal frequency. The operation is to be such that the peak collector current is -2 amp. Determine the output power, the average values of i_C and v_B, the rms values of the fundamental components of i_C and v_B, the collector junction dissipation, the emitter junction dissipation, and the effective load resistance. Are any ratings exceeded?

11-6. A 3N139 FET is connected into the circuit of Fig. 11-1b. The voltages are $V_{DD} = 10$ volts, $V_{GG} = -10$ volts, $v_s = 12 \cos \omega t$ volts. The operation is such that the peak drain current is 15 ma. Determine the average value of i_D and the rms value of the fundamental component of i_D, the output power, channel dissipation, output circuit efficiency, and load resistance. Obtain the constant-current characteristics of the 3N139 FET from the static plate characteristics of Fig. 10-30. Assume that $i_D = 0$ if $v_{GD} \leq -6$ volts.

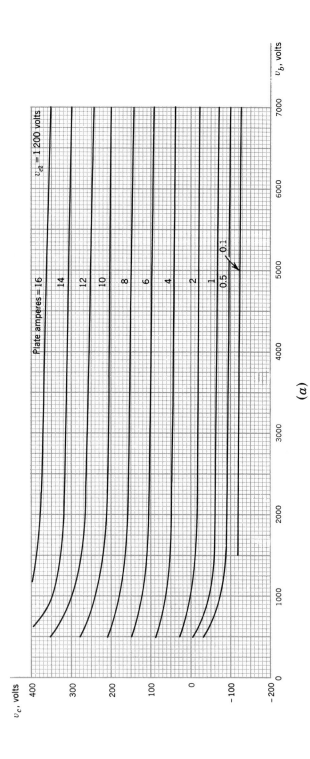

(a)

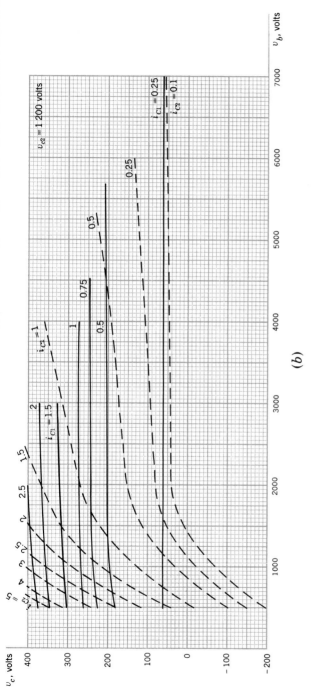

Fig. 11-12 The constant-current characteristics of the type 6166 beam power tube. (*a*) Constant-plate-current curves. Assume that $i_b = 0$ if $v_c < -150$ volts. (*b*) Constant control-grid and screen-grid current curves. Assume that $i_{c2} = 0$ if $v_c < -150$ volts. (*Radio Corporation of America.*)

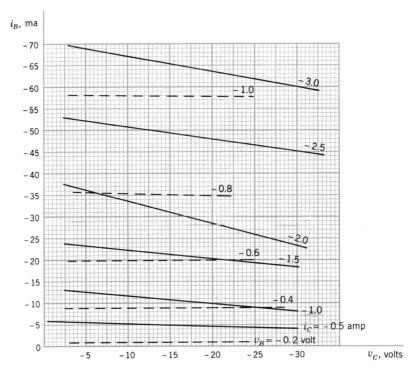

Fig. 11-13 Idealized constant-collector-current and constant-base-voltage curves for a 2N301 transistor in the common-emitter configuration. Assume that $i_C = 0$ if $i_B = 0$.

11-7. The tank circuit of Fig. 11-6a is to operate at a frequency of 10 MHz. The capacitor C is 50 pf. The Q of the coil alone is 300. If the efficiency of the tank circuit is to be greater than 90 percent, what is the maximum value of R_L?

11-8. The tank circuit of Fig. 11-7a is to operate at a frequency of 10 MHz. The capacitor C is 50 pf, and the Q of L_1 alone is 300. $R_L = 50$ ohms. Assume that $R_2 \ll R_L$. The efficiency of the tank circuit is to be 90 percent or more. Compute the minimum value of the mutual inductance. If the coefficient of coupling between the two coils is 0.8 ($k = M/\sqrt{L_1 L_2}$), what is the minimum value of L_2?

11-9. The input resistance of the tank circuit of Fig. 11-7a is to be 4000 ohms at 10 MHz. The value of R_L is 50 ohms, and the efficiency of the tank circuit is to be equal to or greater than 90 percent. The Q of L_1 alone is 300. Design the tank circuit. Neglect R_2. Assume that the coefficient of coupling of the coils is 0.8 ($k = M/\sqrt{L_1 L_2}$).

11-10. Repeat Prob. 11-9, but now assume that $R_2 = 2$ ohms.

11-11. Consider the design of Prob. 11-9, but now assume that $C \geq 500$ pf. What is the maximum efficiency that can be obtained?

11-12. Design a class C amplifier using a type 5671 vacuum-tube triode to meet the following specifications: $V_{bb} = 15{,}000$ volts, output power 36,000 watts, and $R_L = 50$ ohms. Determine the values of V_{cc}, v_g, the power supplied by v_g, and the elements of the tank circuit. $R_s = 0$ (see Fig. 11-1a). The tank circuit of Fig. 11-7a is to be used. Assume that the Q of the primary coil alone is 300, $R_2 = 1$ ohm, and the minimum value of C is 50 pf. The frequency of operation is 10 MHz. Verify that no ratings have been exceeded. What is the conduction angle?

11-13. Redesign the amplifier of Prob. 11-12 to obtain the maximum output power without exceeding ratings.

11-14. Design a class C amplifier using a type 6166 beam power tube to meet the following specifications: $V_{bb} = 6500$ volts, $V_{c2Q} = 1200$ volts, output power 11,000 watts, and $R_L = 50$ ohms. Use the tank circuit of Fig. 11-7a. Assume that it has an efficiency of 90 percent. Determine the values of V_{cc}, v_g, and the power supplied by v_g. $R_s = 0$ (see Fig. 11-1a). What is the conduction angle? Verify that no ratings have been exceeded.

11-15. Redesign the amplifier of Prob. 11-14 to obtain the maximum output power without exceeding ratings.

11-16. Design a class C amplifier using a type 2N301 transistor that is to meet the following specifications: $V_{CC} = -15$ volts, output power 7 watts, and $R_L = 50$ ohms. Assume that R_s is an open circuit (see Fig. 11-1c), that $i_B = i_s + I_o$ when $i_s < -I_o$, and that $i_B = 0$ when $i_s > -I_o$ (see Prob. 11-5 and Fig. 11-1). Determine I_o, i_s, and the power supplied by i_s. Use the tank circuit of Fig. 11-7 and assume that it is ideal.

11-17. Redesign the amplifier of Prob. 11-16 to obtain the maximum output power without exceeding ratings.

11-18. Design a class C amplifier using a 3N139 FET that is to meet the following specifications: $V_{DD} = 10$ volts, output power 0.140 watt, and $R_L = 50$ ohms. Assume that R_s is a short circuit (see Fig. 11-1b). Use the tank circuit of Fig. 11-7 and assume that it is ideal. Determine the value of V_G, v_s, and the power supplied by v_s. Use the constant-current characteristics determined in Prob. 11-6.

11-19. Redesign the amplifier of Prob. 11-18 to obtain the maximum output power without exceeding ratings. The ratings for the FET are given at the start of the problems of Chap. 10.

11-20. Assume that the amplifier of Prob. 11-1 obtains its grid bias by means of a grid-leak circuit. If v_s were to become zero, what would the plate current and plate dissipation become? Assume that the tank circuit has zero resistance for direct current.

12

Introduction to Signal-flow Graphs

In this chapter, we shall introduce a diagrammatic procedure for representing and evaluating a set of linear simultaneous equations, such as those found in linear amplifier problems. These representations are called *signal-flow graphs* or *signal-flow diagrams*.[1,2] They help in the study of general network configurations as well as in the solution of specific network problems. The signal-flow graph will be introduced here with some simple techniques for its construction and analysis. The bibliography at the end of this chapter contains much additional reference material.

12-1 DEFINITION OF A SIGNAL-FLOW GRAPH AND ITS RELATION TO A BLOCK DIAGRAM

Many times in the discussion of amplifiers it is convenient to reduce their representations to *block diagrams*. That is, the amplifier is represented simply by a set of blocks which are labeled with specific gains. For instance, consider the cascade of three amplifier stages shown in Fig. 12-1a. The voltage gains of the three stages are A_{v1}, A_{v2}, and A_{v3} when they are connected as shown. Thus, the overall voltage gain is

$$A_v = \frac{V_2}{V_1} = A_{v1}A_{v2}A_{v3} \tag{12-1}$$

A_{v1}, A_{v2}, and A_{v3} could be any of the appropriate gain expressions of Chap. 9. The blocks could also represent more complex amplifier stages. Block diagrams are thus a convenient method of representing the performance of a complex amplifier without obscuring the details with a large number of circuit elements. There is no need to draw the two wires. For instance, the block diagram of Fig. 12-1b conveys the same information as Fig. 12-1a. The arrows indicate the direction of the transmission of the signal. For instance

$$V_3 = A_{v1}V_1 \tag{12-2}$$

but

$$V_1 \neq A_{v1}V_3 \tag{12-3}$$

For convenience, block diagrams should be as simple as is possible. Figure 12-1c conveys all the information of Fig. 12-1a or b in an abbreviated form. This representation is called a *signal-flow graph*. A block diagram of a more

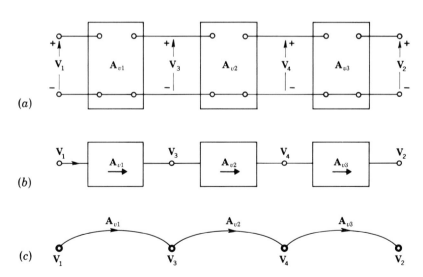

Fig. 12-1 (a) Block-diagram representation of a cascade of voltage amplifiers; (b) simplified block-diagram representation; and (c) a signal-flow-graph representation.

complex amplifier structure is shown in Fig. 12-2a.   This is called a *feedback amplifier*, since a portion of the output signal is fed back to the input.   These amplifiers will be discussed in great detail in the next chapter.   The small circle of Fig. 12-2a is called a *summing point*, wherein the output voltage (or current) is the algebraic sum of the applied voltages (or currents).   The plus and minus signs indicate whether a sum or difference is used.   The voltages are all indicated in the diagram.   The signal-flow-graph representation is shown in Fig. 12-2b.   In each case

$$\mathbf{V}_2 = \mathbf{A}_v(\mathbf{V}_1 - \beta\mathbf{V}_2)$$

or

$$\frac{\mathbf{V}_2}{\mathbf{V}_1} = \frac{\mathbf{A}_v}{1 + \mathbf{A}_v\beta} \tag{12-4}$$

The significance of this relation will be discussed in the next chapter.

Thus far we have presented some simple signal-flow graphs.   Let us now formalize the representation so that procedures for evaluating complex networks can be developed.   We shall use the signal-flow diagram of Fig. 12-3 in this discussion.   The small circles are called *nodes*.   These are given *node values* that represent the variables of the system.   For instance, y_0, x_1, x_2, and x_3 could represent voltages and/or currents.   The signal-flow graph can be used to represent any set of simultaneous equations; hence, the node values can represent any set of variables.   The line segments are called *branches*.   They are given a direction by the arrows and are sometimes called *directed branches*.   Each branch is assigned a value a_{ij} called the *branch gain*,

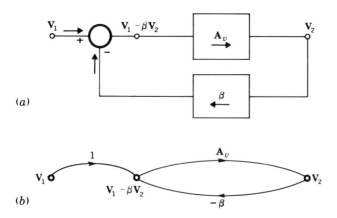

(a)

(b)

Fig. 12-2 A simple feedback amplifier: (a) block-diagram representation and (b) signal-flow-graph representation.

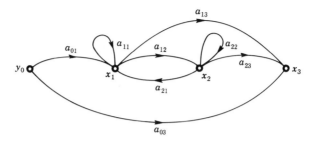

Fig. 12-3 A signal-flow graph.

or the *branch transmittance*. The *output end of a branch* is the end of the branch towards which the arrow points. The *input end of a branch* is the other end. The *signal transmission* along a branch is defined as the product of the node value at the input end of a branch times the branch transmittance. A branch is said to *enter*, or to be *incident* on, a node if it is connected to the node and its arrow points towards the node. It is said to *leave* the node if it is connected to the node and its arrow points away from the node.

To write the equations of a signal-flow graph, we use the following rule: *Any node value is equal to the sum of all the signal transmissions of all the branches incident on the node.* For instance, for Fig. 12-3

$$x_1 = a_{01}y_0 + a_{11}x_1 + a_{21}x_2 + 0x_3$$
$$x_2 = 0y_0 + a_{12}x_1 + a_{22}x_2 + 0x_3 \tag{12-5}$$
$$x_3 = a_{03}y_0 + a_{13}x_1 + a_{23}x_2 + 0x_3$$

Note that a branch, such as a_{11} or a_{22}, can be connected from a node to itself. However, it is treated as any other branch.

If no branches enter a node, then that node is called a *source node*, or simply a *source*. Node y_0 is a source. It represents an independent variable. If the signal-flow graph represents a set of network equations, then the source nodes represent the independent driving generators. If a node has no branches leaving it, then it is called a *sink node* or simply a *sink*. Node x_3 of Fig. 12-3 is a sink.

Equations (12-5) represent a set of linear simultaneous equations. To obtain a form that can be readily solved by determinants, they should be rearranged as follows

$$-a_{01}y_0 = (a_{11} - 1)x_1 + a_{21}x_2 + 0x_3$$
$$0 = a_{21}x_1 + (a_{22} - 1)x_2 + 0x_3 \tag{12-6}$$
$$-a_{03}y_0 = a_{13}x_1 + a_{23}x_2 - x_3$$

The quantity y_0 is considered to be known.   In this way, a set of simultaneous equations can be written for any signal-flow graph, and all variables can be obtained in terms of the driving function and the branch transmittances.

12-2   METHOD FOR OBTAINING A SIGNAL-FLOW GRAPH FROM A SET OF SIMULTANEOUS EQUATIONS

In the last section it was demonstrated that a set of simultaneous equations could be written for a signal-flow graph.   Let us now consider the inverse procedure and obtain the signal-flow graph that represents a set of simultaneous equations.   For instance, consider

$$
\begin{aligned}
y_1 &= b_{11}x_1 + b_{12}x_2 + b_{13}x_3 \\
y_2 &= b_{21}x_1 + b_{22}x_2 + b_{23}x_3 \\
y_3 &= b_{31}x_1 + b_{32}x_2 + b_{33}x_3
\end{aligned}
\tag{12-7}
$$

We would like to convert this into the form of Eqs. (12-5).   This can be done simply by adding x_1 to each side of the first equation, x_2 to each side of the second equation, etc., and by bringing the known quantities over to the right-hand side.   Thus,

$$
\begin{aligned}
x_1 &= -y_1 + (b_{11} + 1)x_1 + b_{12}x_2 + b_{13}x_3 \\
x_2 &= -y_2 + b_{21}x_1 + (b_{22} + 1)x_2 + b_{23}x_3 \\
x_3 &= -y_3 + b_{31}x_1 + b_{32}x_2 + (b_{33} + 1)x_3
\end{aligned}
\tag{12-8}
$$

The signal-flow graph can now be drawn.   The node values are y_1, y_2, y_3, x_1, x_2, and x_3.   The coefficients on the right-hand side of the first equation yield the branch transmittance of the branches incident on node x_1.   Similarly, the second equation yields the branch transmittances of the branches incident on node x_2, etc.   Thus, the signal-flow graph for the set of simultaneous equa-

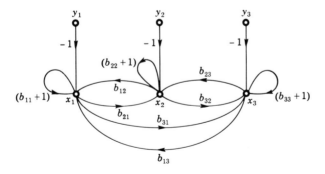

Fig. 12-4   A signal-flow graph obtained from Eqs. (12-7).

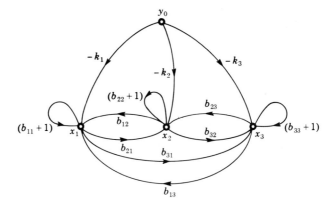

Fig. 12-5 A modification of Fig. 12-4 which can be used when there is only one independent generator.

tions of Eqs. (12-7) is given in Fig. 12-4. There are three independent quantities y_1, y_2, and y_3 and thus three source nodes. (Note that the order of the subscripts of the branch transmittances of Fig. 12-4 is different from that of Fig. 12-3.) In amplifier theory, there is usually only one independent generator y_0, and we can write

$$y_1 = k_1 y_0$$
$$y_2 = k_2 y_0 \qquad\qquad (12\text{-}9)$$
$$y_3 = k_3 y_0$$

In this case, the three nodes y_1, y_2, and y_3 can be replaced by a single node y_0, as shown in Fig. 12-5. We have demonstrated these techniques with a set of third-order simultaneous equations. However, the same procedures would be used for simultaneous equations of any order.

12-3 SOME ELEMENTARY SIMPLIFICATIONS OF SIGNAL-FLOW GRAPHS

In this section we shall consider some techniques of simplifying a signal-flow graph without altering the relations among any of the variables. We shall use a set of signal-flow-graph equations similar to Eqs. (12-5) in our discussion:

$$x_1 = a_{01} y_0 + a_{11} x_1 + a_{21} x_2 + \cdots + a_{n1} x_n$$
$$x_2 = a_{02} y_0 + a_{12} x_1 + a_{22} x_2 + \cdots + a_{n2} x_n \qquad (12\text{-}10)$$
$$\cdots \cdots \cdots \cdots \cdots \cdots \cdots \cdots \cdots \cdots \cdots \cdots \cdots$$
$$x_n = a_{0n} y_0 + a_{1n} x_1 + a_{2n} x_2 + \cdots + a_{nn} x_n$$

where it is assumed that there is only one independent source, y_0. (Note that this assumption is not necessary to obtain the results of this section.) The branches incident on a node affect only the equation for that node (for example, a_{02}, a_{12}, a_{22} $\cdots$ a_{n2} are the only branches that affect the value of x_2). Thus, we can make the following simplifications, which are illustrated in Fig. 12-6.

Combination of two parallel branches   If two or more branches are connected from node x_i to node x_j and *all* are incident on x_j, then they can be replaced by a single branch whose transmittance is the sum of the transmittances of the individual branches.   For instance, in Fig. 12-6a this is true since $a_{ij1}x_i + a_{ij2}x_i = (a_{ij1} + a_{ij2})x_i$ and the transmittances a_{ij1} and a_{ij2} only appear in the equation for x_j [see Eqs. (12-10)].   Note that the branch from node x_j *to* node x_i is not included here.

Elimination of a self-loop   A branch that starts and ends on the same node is called a *self-loop*.   For instance, branches a_{11} and a_{22} of Fig. 12-3 are self-loops.   We shall see in the next section that it is often desirable to have a signal-flow graph that does not contain such loops.   They can be eliminated without altering any of the variables by the following procedure. Consider Eqs. (12-10); solve the jth equation for x_j by bringing the $a_{jj}x_j$ term to the left-hand side.   Thus,

$$x_j = \frac{a_{0j}}{1 - a_{jj}} y_0 + \frac{a_{1j}}{1 - a_{jj}} x_1 + \cdots + \frac{a_{j-1,j}}{1 - a_{jj}} x_{j-1}$$

$$+ 0x_j + \frac{a_{j+1,j}}{1 - a_{jj}} x_{j+1} + \cdots + \frac{a_{nj}}{1 - a_{jj}} x_n \quad (12\text{-}11)$$

where we have assumed that

$$a_{jj} \neq 1 \qquad\qquad\qquad\qquad\qquad\qquad\qquad\qquad\qquad\qquad (12\text{-}12)$$

Equation (12-11) could replace the equation for x_j in Eqs. (12-10).   This would still represent a valid set of equations for all the variables even though the signal-flow graph has been changed.   (Note that the jth equation has only been rearranged.)   However, x_j no longer has a self-loop, since the coefficient of x_j on the right-hand side of the equation is now zero.   *Only those branches of the signal-flow graph that are incident on x_j will be changed.*   They will be multiplied by $1/(1 - a_{jj})$.   All the other branches are unchanged.   Thus, the equivalency indicated in Fig. 12-6b is valid.   By repeating this procedure at each node in turn, all the self-loops can be eliminated.   This procedure breaks down if $a_{jj} = 1$, since $1/(1 - a_{jj})$ becomes infinite.   In the type of network that we shall consider, this is not usually a problem.   In the next section, a procedure that may cause some of the a_{jj}'s to become equal to unity

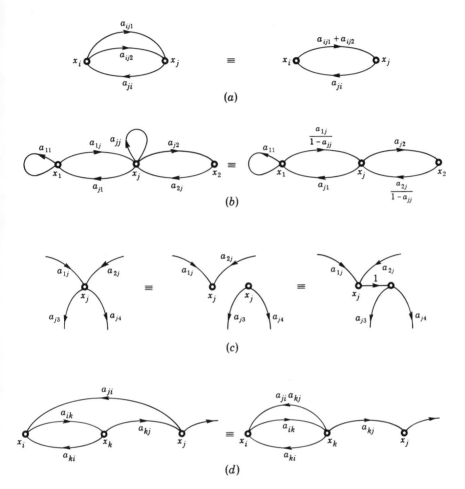

Fig. 12-6 Techniques for the modification of signal-flow graphs which do not change the values of any of the variables: (*a*) elimination of parallel branches; (*b*) elimination of self-loops; (*c*) node splitting; and (*d*) shift of the input end of a branch.

will be considered.   However, we shall later explain that this will not cause any problem in any practical case.

Node splitting   There are times when it is convenient to represent all nodes as sources or sinks.   This can be done simply by splitting each node into two nodes, one with all the incident branches and the other with the remaining branches.   This has been done in the portion of the signal-flow graph of Fig. 12-6*c*.   In the second diagram, the node x_j has been split into two nodes, both with the same variable. Thus Eqs. (12-10) will be unaffected by the splitting of the node. The value of x_j remains unchanged because the branches incident upon it are unchanged. The signal transmission from node x_j is unchanged, since we have made the value of the second node equal to x_j. The third network of Fig. 12-6c accomplishes this by means of a branch of unity transmittance.

Shift of the input end of a branch   If the input end of a branch is shifted from one node to another and this does not change the *product* of its branch transmittance and input-node value, then the node values of the signal-flow graph will be unchanged. In general, this procedure will require changing the branch transmittance. Consider Fig. 12-6d. The signal transmission along one branch incident on node x_i is $a_{ji}x_j$. However, $x_j = a_{kj}x_k$. Thus, we can shift the input end of the branch to x_k provided that the branch transmittance is changed to $a_{ji}a_{kj}$. In both cases the signal transmission is $a_{ji}x_j = a_{ji}a_{kj}x_k$. If another branch were incident on node x_j, then we could not express x_j in terms of x_k alone and this procedure could not be used. Note that the two branches incident on node x_i in the second figure of Fig. 12-6d can be combined by the procedure of Fig. 12-6a.

12-4 REDUCTION OF SIGNAL-FLOW GRAPHS

In most amplifier applications, the output voltage or current in response to an input signal is to be determined. Hence only one of the unknowns in a set of mesh or nodal equations need be found. Similarly, when signal-flow graphs are considered, we often wish to calculate only one of the node values in terms of the independent generators. Assume that there is only one independent generator, so that a signal-flow graph similar to that of Fig. 12-5 results. If the signal-flow graph consisted of only two nodes and one branch as shown in Fig. 12-7, then the desired solution could be obtained by inspection.

$$x_1 = a_{01}y_0 \tag{12-13}$$

The procedure to be developed next will eliminate a node of a dependent variable from the signal-flow graph without changing the value of any of the other variables. Successive applications of this procedure and elimination of self-loops will produce a signal-flow graph of the form of Fig. 12-7, and the problem will be solved. We shall assume that the node to be

y_0 x_1 **Fig. 12-7**   A simple signal-flow graph.

removed does not have a self-loop. If it does, it can be eliminated by the procedure of Sec. 12-3.

The procedure for eliminating a node is called *node pulling* and can be done as follows. Choose the equation for the node in question from the signal-flow graph equations (12-10). If node x_j is to be eliminated, write

$$x_j = a_{0j}y_0 + a_{1j}x_1 + \cdots + a_{j-1,j}x_{j-1} + 0x_j + a_{j+1,j}x_{j+1}$$
$$+ \cdots + a_{nj}x_n \quad (12\text{-}14)$$

Now use this equation to eliminate x_j from all the other equations. For instance, for $h \neq j$

$$x_h = a_{0h}y_0 + a_{1h}x_1 + a_{2h}x_2 + \cdots + a_{jh}x_j + \cdots + a_{nh}x_n \quad (12\text{-}15)$$

or

$$x_h = a_{0h}y_0 + \sum_{\substack{k=1 \\ k \neq j}}^{n} a_{kh}x_k + a_{jh}x_j \quad (12\text{-}16)$$

Substituting Eq. (12-14) and combining terms, we obtain

$$x_h = (a_{0h} + a_{0j}a_{jh})y_0 + \sum_{\substack{k=1 \\ k \neq j}}^{n} (a_{kh} + a_{kj}a_{jh})x_k \quad (12\text{-}17)$$

If we repeat this operation for $h = 1, 2, \ldots, j - 1, j + 1, \ldots n$, then the variable x_j will be eliminated from the equations and a new signal-flow graph can be drawn with one less node. Note that there is now one equation less.

Let us determine the significance of Eq. (12-17). Consider the transmittance from node x_r to node x_h. The original transmittance a_{rh} is still present, but the transmittance $a_{rj}a_{jh}$ has been added. This can be considered to be the transmittance from node x_r to node x_h through node x_j. For instance, consider the simple signal-flow graph of Fig. 12-8a. The node x_2 can be eliminated simply by adding $a_{12}a_{23}$ to the transmittance of the branch from node 1 to node 3 (see Fig. 12-8b). In general, a node is eliminated by replacing it by branches which supply the branch transmittances of all possible transmission paths through the node. A transmission path through a node consists of *one* branch entering and *one* branch leaving the node. Note that exactly two branches are used. A signal-flow graph more complex than the previous one is shown in Fig. 12-8c. The resultant signal-flow graph with node x_2 eliminated is shown in Fig. 12-8d. Although the node that is removed cannot have a self-loop, all the other nodes can. In fact, self-loops can be created by this procedure. The node-pulling technique can be applied to each node in turn. Of course, any self-loops must be eliminated by the

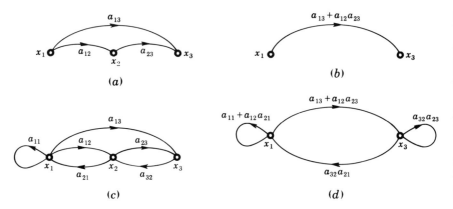

Fig. 12-8 (*a*) A simple three-node signal-flow graph; (*b*) the equivalent signal-flow graph with one node eliminated; (*c*) a more complex signal-flow graph; and (*d*) the elimination of node x_2 of this signal-flow graph.

procedure of Sec. 12-3 before this can be done. If any of the transmittances of a self-loop are unity, then that procedure will not work. (Node pulling can cause unity self-loops.) Two things can be done in this case. The first is to eliminate other nodes, if possible. This may change the value of the self-loop. The second is to rearrange the original simultaneous equations by renumbering the variables and rearranging the equations. It can be shown[3] that if the original system of simultaneous equations is linearly independent then the branch transmissions of the self-loops always can be made not equal to unity by such a procedure.

Now let us consider an example of node pulling. We wish to obtain x_2 in terms of y_0 and the branch transmittances for the signal-flow graph of Fig. 12-9*a*. Since node x_3 has no self-loop, it is eliminated first. This is shown in Fig. 12-9*b*, where 1×3 is added to the self-loop of node x_1, 1×4 is added to the branch transmittance from node x_1 to x_2, 1×3 is added to the branch transmittance from node x_2 to x_1, and a self-loop of transmittance 1×4 is added to node x_2. The self-loop at node x_1 is removed in Fig. 12-9*c* by multiplying the transmission of all the branches incident on node x_1 by $1/(1 - 2) = -1$. Node x_1 is eliminated in Fig. 12-9*d*. Finally, to solve the problem, the self-loop is eliminated from node x_2. The reduced network is shown in Fig. 12-9*e*, and the solution is

$$x_2 = -\tfrac{9}{21} y_0 \tag{12-18}$$

Thus, it can be seen that signal-flow graphs provide a systematic means of representing and solving electric network problems.

If more than one variable is desired, this procedure need not be repeated. For instance, if x_1 is desired, it can be found from Fig. 12-9*c* after

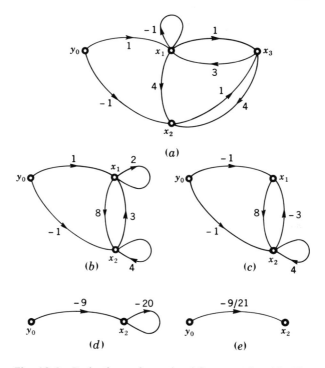

Fig. 12-9 Reduction of a signal-flow graph: (*a*) The signal-flow graph; (*b*) node x_3 removed; (*c*) the self-loop of node x_1 removed; (*d*) node x_1 removed; and (*e*) the self-loop of node x_2 removed.

x_2 is found. That is, substitute the values of x_2 and y_0 into Fig. 12-9*c* and then solve for x_1. This yields

$$x_1 = -y_0 - 3x_2$$

REFERENCES

1. Mason, S. J.: Feedback Theory: Some Properties of Signal Flow Graphs, *Proc. IRE*, vol. 41, pp. 1144–1156, 1953.
2. Mason, S. J.: Feedback Theory: Further Properties of Signal Flow Graphs, *Proc. IRE*, vol. 44, pp. 920–926, 1956.
3. Seshu, S., and N. Balabanian: "Linear Network Analysis," p. 415, John Wiley & Sons, Inc., New York, 1959.

BIBLIOGRAPHY

Chirlian, P. M.: "Basic Network Theory," chap. 10, McGraw-Hill Book Company, New York, 1969.
Mason, S. J.: Feedback Theory: Some Properties of Signal Flow Graphs, *Proc. IRE*, vol. 41, pp. 1144–1156, 1953.

Mason, S. J.: Feedback Theory: Further Properties of Signal Flow Graphs, *Proc. IRE*,
   vol. 44, pp. 920–926, 1956.
Mason, S. J., and H. J. Zimmerman: "Electronic Circuits, Signals, and Systems," chaps.
   4 and 5, John Wiley & Sons, Inc., New York, 1960.
Peskin, E.: "Transient and Steady State Analysis of Electric Networks," chap. 8, D.
   Van Nostrand Company, Inc., Princeton, N.J., 1961.
Seshu, S., and N. Balabanian: "Linear Network Analysis," pp. 407–425, John Wiley &
   Sons, Inc., New York, 1959.
Truxal, J. G.: "Automatic Feedback Control System Synthesis," pp. 88–113, McGraw-
   Hill Book Company, New York, 1955.

PROBLEMS

12-1. Obtain the signal-flow graph which represents the equations

$$x_1 = y_0 + 2x_1 + 3x_2 + x_3$$
$$x_2 = 2y_0 + x_1 + 7x_2 + 9x_3$$
$$x_3 = -y_0 - x_1 - x_2 + 4x_3$$

12-2. Obtain a set of equations which characterize the signal-flow graph of Fig. 12-10.

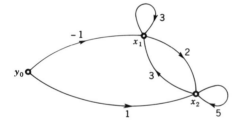

Fig. 12-10

The equations should be in a form suitable for solution by determinants.   Assume that
y_0 is known.

12-3. Repeat Prob. 12-2 for the signal-flow graph of Fig. 12-11.

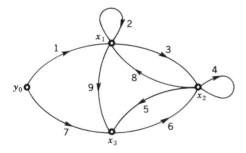

Fig. 12-11

12-4. Obtain a signal-flow graph which represents the linear simultaneous equations

$$y_0 = 3x_1 + 2x_2$$
$$-2y_0 = 2x_1 + x_2$$

12-5. Obtain a signal-flow graph which represents the linear simultaneous equations

$$y_0 = x_1 + x_2 + x_3$$
$$0 = x_1 - 2x_2 + x_3$$
$$-y_0 = x_1 + x_2 - 3x_3$$

12-6. Eliminate all the parallel branches from the signal-flow graph of Fig. 12-12.

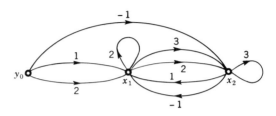

Fig. 12-12

12-7. Eliminate all the self-loops from the signal-flow graph of Fig. 12-12.

12-8. Repeat Prob. 12-7 for the signal-flow graph of Fig. 12-11.

12-9. Use signal-flow-graph reduction techniques to solve the simultaneous equations of Prob. 12-5 for x_2. Assume that y_0 is known.

12-10. Use node-pulling techniques to obtain x_2 in terms of y_0 for the signal-flow graph of Fig. 12-10.

12-11. Repeat Prob. 12-10, but now assume that the branch transmittance between node y_0 and node x_1 is $+1$.

12-12. Repeat Prob. 12-10 for the signal-flow graph of Fig. 12-11.

13

Feedback Amplifiers

If a signal at the output of any stage of an amplifier affects its earlier stages, then the complete circuit is called a *feedback amplifier*. The process of returning the signal to an earlier stage is called *feedback*. We have thus far considered the disadvantages of feedback in such things as the Miller effect in FET and transistor amplifiers. However, there are many times when feedback is deliberately introduced and substantial benefits result. In fact, many amplifier applications depend upon feedback for their success. For example, feedback can reduce nonlinear distortion and some undesirable signals and can eliminate much of the variation of gain caused by changes in the parameters of FETs or transistors. In this chapter we shall use signal-flow graphs to study the general concepts of feedback. In addition, we shall develop techniques for analyzing specific feedback amplifiers. Linear models will be used here.

13-1 BASIC PRINCIPLES OF FEEDBACK AMPLIFIERS

A typical feedback amplifier is characterized by the block diagram of Fig.
13-1a.   The variables X_1, X_2, and X_3 can represent voltages and/or currents.
X_1 represents the input signal; X_2 represents the output signal.   The gain of
the amplifier without feedback is **A**, and β represents the fraction of the output signal that is returned to the input.   (Note that the conventional notation
is conflicting; β as used in this chapter is *not* the short-circuit current gain of
the common-emitter transistor amplifier.)

The small circle is a *summer*.   Its output is the algebraic sum of its
inputs connected to the terminals marked + and −.   The positive sum is
used for the signal connected to the + terminal and the negative sum is taken
for the signal connected to the − terminal.   Thus, the output is the difference between the two input signals.   A signal-flow-graph representation
of Fig. 13-1a is shown in Fig. 13-1b.   In each case,

$$X_3 = X_1 - \beta X_2 \tag{13-1}$$

Note that X_3 is the actual input to the amplifier.   It is the *difference* between
the input signal X_1 and a fraction of the output signal X_2.

The notation used here conforms with that used in a large body of
literature relating to feedback amplifiers and control systems.   However, it
is often found that in an actual feedback amplifier the configuration is somewhat different.   In these cases, the summer algebraically adds both the
input signal and the feedback signal, i.e., both its signs are +.   However,
the gain of the amplifier **A** is negative.   (In this case, Fig. 13-1 would still be

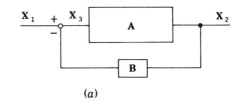

(a)

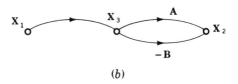

(b)

Fig. 13-1 (*a*) A block-diagram representation of a
feedback amplifier and (*b*) a signal-flow-graph representation of a feedback amplifier.

applicable if β is a negative number so that $-\beta$ is positive.) Thus, there still will be a $180°$ phase difference between X_2 and X_1. Then X_3 will again consist of the difference *between* two signals.

Now let us compute the gain of the feedback amplifier. The output of the amplifier X_2 is defined as the product of the input X_3 and the gain A. Thus,

$$X_2 = AX_3 \tag{13-2}$$

Eliminating X_3 from Eq. (13-1), we obtain

$$X_2 = X_1 \frac{A}{1 + A\beta} \tag{13-3}$$

We shall define the gain K of the amplifier in the usual way as X_2/X_1. Hence,

$$K = \frac{A}{1 + A\beta} \tag{13-4}$$

Note that there are two gains to be considered. A is the gain of the amplifier alone without feedback, while K is the gain of the entire feedback amplifier. Many times, the feedback network, which we shall call the β *network*, is simply a resistive voltage or current divider. In this case, β will be a real number. For much of the useful frequency range, A may be a real number. Let us consider Eq. (10-4), assuming that we have such an amplifier and that X_3 actually consists of a *difference* of signals (e.g., both A and B are negative). If

$$|A\beta| \gg 1 \tag{13-5}$$

then we can approximate K as

$$K \approx \frac{1}{\beta} \tag{13-6}$$

If β is a purely resistive network, then the gain of the amplifier seems to be constant, independent of all the parameters of the active elements, e.g., the FETs, vacuum tubes, or transistors, and independent of frequency. This would be ideal in that there would be no frequency distortion or nonlinear distortion. (Nonlinear distortion can be considered to be a variation of the parameters of the active elements with signal level.) Also the gain would not change as the active elements aged. However, the amplifier is not completely free of distortion or variation in gain, since Eq. (13-6) is only approximate. In addition, if $|A|$ falls off for any reason such as the presence of frequency distortion or because of aging of the active elements, then the inequality of relation (13-5) may no longer be valid so that Eq. (13-6) may no longer apply. However, in a well-designed feedback amplifier, the dependence of the amplification upon the characteristics of the active elements can be greatly reduced. We shall study all of these effects in great detail subsequently.

If $\mathbf{A}$ is a real negative number, $\boldsymbol{\beta}$ is a real negative number, and $\mathbf{A}\boldsymbol{\beta} \gg 1$, then $-\mathbf{A} \gg -1/\boldsymbol{\beta}$. Thus, the introduction of this type of feedback reduces the overall gain of the amplifier [see Eq. (13-6)]. For this reason, a feedback amplifier may have more stages than a nonfeedback amplifier that has the same gain. Usually, this is a small price to pay for the advantages of feedback. The type of feedback that we have been discussing is called *negative feedback*, because the signal $-\mathbf{X}_2\boldsymbol{\beta}$ is $180°$ out of phase with the input signal $\mathbf{X}_1$. (Note that $\mathbf{A}$ is negative.) Thus, $\mathbf{X}_3$, the signal at the input to the amplifier portion of the feedback amplifier, is actually the difference between two signals. This can be seen from Eq. (13-1). In general, $|\mathbf{X}_1| > |\mathbf{X}_2\boldsymbol{\beta}|$. We can now discuss why the gain of the feedback amplifier can be almost independent of $\mathbf{A}$. Suppose that $|\mathbf{A}|$ increases; then $|\mathbf{X}_3|$ will decrease, because the signal subtracted from $\mathbf{X}_1$ will increase. This tends to counteract the effect of the increase in $|\mathbf{A}|$ and to stabilize the gain.

Let us now consider a somewhat different amplifier. Assume that $\mathbf{A}$ *or* $\boldsymbol{\beta}$ is a real negative number and that $|\mathbf{A}\boldsymbol{\beta}| < 1$. Then Eq. (13-4) shows that $|\mathbf{K}| > |\mathbf{A}|$. Thus, we have actually increased the gain by the introduction of feedback. This is called *positive feedback*, since the signal $-\mathbf{X}_2\boldsymbol{\beta}$ is in phase with $\mathbf{X}_1$. At first glance, positive feedback may appear to be very attractive, since it results in an increased gain. However, it is very rarely used in amplifiers for two reasons: (1) The advantages gained when negative feedback is used become disadvantages. That is, the distortion and the dependence of the gain of the amplifier upon the parameters of the active elements are greater than they are in the nonfeedback case. (2) Positive-feedback amplifiers have a tendency to oscillate, which renders them useless as amplifiers.

In the discussion of negative and positive feedback, we neglected the variation of the phase shift of $\mathbf{A}$ or $\boldsymbol{\beta}$ with frequency. Because of this, true negative or positive feedback amplifiers do not exist. In fact, the feedback can be negative at some frequencies and positive at others. We shall discuss this in greater detail when Nyquist plots are considered.

Feedback can be classified as *voltage feedback* or *current feedback*. In voltage feedback, the signal fed back (which can be either a voltage or a current) is proportional to the output voltage. In current feedback, the signal fed back is proportional to the output current. If voltage-negative feedback is used, the output voltage of the amplifier tends to become independent of the value of $\mathbf{A}$, while current-negative feedback tends to stabilize the value of the output current.

This will be discussed in much greater detail in Sec. 13-6.

To illustrate the ideas of voltage feedback and current feedback further, we shall consider the block diagrams of Fig. 13-2. Figure 13-2*a* and *b* illustrate voltage feedback. The $\boldsymbol{\beta}$ circuit samples the output voltage and returns it to the input. In Fig. 13-2*a* the signal fed back can be considered to

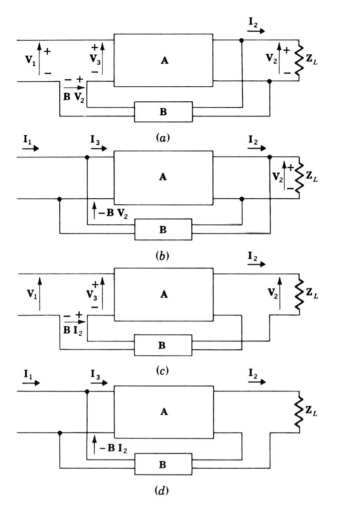

Fig. 13-2 (*a*) Voltage series feedback; (*b*) voltage shunt feedback; (*c*) current series feedback; (*d*) current shunt feedback.

be a voltage, and it is connected in *series* with the input. Thus, this is called *voltage series* feedback. In Fig. 13-2*b* the signal fed back can be considered to be a current $-\beta V_2$. (Note that the dimensions of β are mhos in this case.) The feedback signal is placed in parallel, or *shunt*, with the input generator. Thus, this is called *shunt feedback*. Since the feedback signal is proportional to a voltage, the circuit of Fig. 13-2*b* is called *voltage shunt* feedback.

In Fig. 13-2*c* and *d* the β circuit samples the output current. Thus, Fig. 13-2*c* is called *current series* feedback, while Fig. 13-2*d* is *current shunt* feedback.

Each amplifier of Fig. 13-2 can be considered to be one of four types. It is a voltage amplifier if the input and outputs are both voltages. In this case, $\mathbf{A}$ would be written as $\mathbf{A}_v$. If the input and output signals are currents, then the amplifier is a current amplifier. In this case, $\mathbf{A}$ would be written as

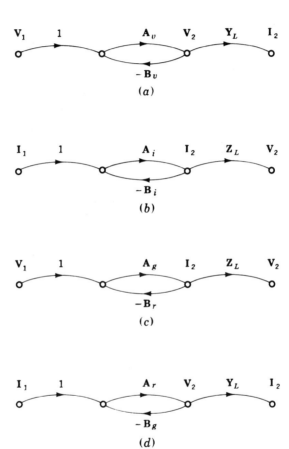

(a)

(b)

(c)

(d)

(e)

Fig. 13-3 Signal-flow-graph representation of feedback amplifiers: (a) voltage series feedback; (b) current shunt feedback; (c) current series feedback; (d) voltage shunt feedback; (e) general configuration.

A_i. The input could be a voltage and the output a current. In this case, the dimensions of A would be mhos and A would be written as A_g. Finally, the input could be a current and the output a voltage. The dimensions of A would be ohms, and we would write A as A_r. In general, the symbol A will represent all four of these gains. Note that four types of β can be defined in an analogous fashion.

The output voltage and current of an amplifier are related by the equation

$$\mathbf{V}_2 = \mathbf{I}_2 \mathbf{Z}_L \tag{13-7}$$

Note that, for convenience, we have defined $\mathbf{I}_2$ as *out* of the amplifier. It is a simple procedure to relate the output voltage and current. Let us adopt the convention that the amplifier output is a voltage if voltage feedback is used and a current if current feedback is used. The signal-flow diagrams of Fig. 13-3a to d can then represent the four types of feedback amplifiers. Figure 13-3e is a general representation of all four of these configurations, where $\mathbf{X}_1$, $\mathbf{X}_2$, and $\mathbf{X}_{2a}$ represent voltages and/or currents and $\mathbf{W}_L$ represents either an impedance or an admittance. Since the output voltage or current are related by Eq. (13-7), one can easily be determined from the other. Then, the node $\mathbf{X}_{2a}$ and the branch $\mathbf{W}_L$ will often be omitted from our studies of feedback amplifiers. That is, Fig. 13-1b will be used for much of these studies.

13-2 ANALYSIS OF SOME VERY SIMPLE FEEDBACK AMPLIFIERS

Before proceeding with a general discussion of feedback amplifiers, let us study some very simple ones. Consider the FET amplifier of Fig. 13-4. Equation (13-4) will be used here to obtain the amplification. We will assume that the capacitor C_s is a short circuit at the signal frequency. The

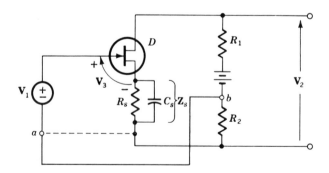

Fig. 13-4 A very simple FET voltage series feedback amplifier.

gain without feedback is that which would be obtained if the wire from a to b were broken and the dotted connection were made. In this case

$$A = \frac{V_2}{V_3} = -g_m R_{sh} \tag{13-8}$$

where

$$R_{sh} = \frac{r_d(R_1 + R_2)}{r_d + R_1 + R_2} \tag{13-9a}$$

This is a voltage-feedback amplifier, since $V_3 = V_1 + V_2 R_2/(R_1 + R_2)$. The value of β is defined in Eq. (13-1). Thus

$$\beta = \frac{-R_2}{R_1 + R_2} \tag{13-9b}$$

Note that β is negative since the negative summer of Fig. 13-1a is not included; that is $-\beta$ is positive in Fig. 13-1b. The feedback is negative since A is also negative. Hence, using Eq. (13-4)

$$K = \frac{V_2}{V_1} = \frac{-g_m R_{sh}}{1 + g_m R_{sh} R_2/(R_1 + R_2)} \tag{13-10}$$

If

$$g_m R_{sh} R_2/R_1 + R_2 \gg 1 \tag{13-11}$$

then

$$K \approx -\frac{R_1 + R_2}{R_2} \tag{13-12}$$

This agrees with the discussion of Sec. 13-1. This example seems to indicate that Eq. (13-4) will be useful in the analysis of specific amplifier circuits. *Actually, this is not the case. In all but the simplest amplifier circuits, $A/(1 + A\beta)$ cannot be used to obtain expressions for the gain.* For instance, if $A = 0$ because the g_m of the FETs becomes zero, then Eq. (13-4) predicts that $K = 0$. However, if there is *direct transmission* between the input and output (through a feedback network), the gain K will not become zero even if A does. A direct transmission path would occur in Fig. 13-4 if the gate-to-drain capacitance were considered. Let us discuss another case where Eq. (13-4) cannot be used. If C_s is not considered to be a short circuit, then there will be an additional feedback term. That is, the voltage drop across $Z_s = R_s/(1 + j\omega C_s R_s)$ will affect V_3. To obtain the gain of this circuit, we shall use the model of Fig. 13-5. Then

$$V_{gs} = V_3 = V_1 - I(R_2 + Z_s) \tag{13-13}$$

$$\mu V_3 = I(r_d + Z_s + R_1 + R_2) \tag{13-14}$$

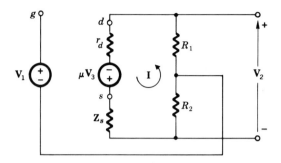

Fig. 13-5 A linear model for the circuit of Fig. 13-4.

and

$$V_2 = -I(R_1 + R_2)$$

Then, solving, we obtain

$$K = \frac{-\mu(R_1 + R_2)}{r_d + Z_s + R_1 + R_2 + \mu(Z_s + R_2)} \tag{13-15}$$

Manipulating, we have

$$K = \frac{-\mu(R_1 + R_2)/(r_d + Z_s + R_1 + R_2)}{1 + \mu(Z_s + R_2)/(r_d + Z_s + R_1 + R_2)} \tag{13-16}$$

If $\mu(Z_s + R_2)/(r_d + Z_s + R_1 + R_2) \gg 1$,

$$K \approx -\frac{R_1 + R_2}{Z_s + R_2} \tag{13-17}$$

Note that Eq. (13-16) has been put in the form of $A/(1 + A\beta)$. However, until the problem was solved, we did not know what to call A or β. For instance, why should β be defined as $-(Z_s + R_2)/(R_1 + R_2)$? In an example as simple as this, reasons for choosing A and β as indicated by Eq. (13-16) might be found *once the answer is known*. In more complex feedback amplifiers, even this cannot be done. This will be illustrated further in Sec. 13-7. In general, linear-model analysis is the proper procedure to use to obtain the gain of a feedback amplifier. If the gain expression is put in the form $G/(1 + GB)$, then this is of the form of Eq. (13-4); hence, the discussions of Sec. 13-1 may apply. For instance, if GB is real and positive and $GB \gg 1$, then

$$K \approx \frac{1}{B} \tag{13-18}$$

If B is independent of the parameters of the active elements, we still obtain the advantages of feedback.

In summary, the relation $A/(1 + A\beta)$ is very useful in studying the general concepts of a feedback amplifier. However, it is of only limited use in obtaining the gain of an actual feedback amplifier. If the actual gain can be put in the form $G/(1 + GB)$, it may prove very helpful to the understanding of the feedback amplifier.

The amplifier of Fig. 13-4 uses both voltage and current feedback. The voltage feedback results from the voltage drop across R_2, while the current feedback is due to the voltage drop across Z_s. Since Z_s and R_2 are in series, it may appear strange that two different kinds of feedback result. To explain this, assume that Z_s is purely resistive and that a load resistance is placed across the output terminals. This will tend to decrease V_2 and to increase I, which in turn will decrease the feedback voltage across R_2 and increase the feedback voltage across Z_s. The first of these effects tends to reduce the feedback voltage and the second tends to increase it. Thus, the first effect is voltage feedback while the second is current feedback. Note that the presence of R_2 tends to stabilize the output voltage, while the presence of Z_s tends to stabilize the output current.

The feedback voltage in each case is applied in series with the input voltage [see Eq. (13-13)]. Thus, this is an example of both voltage series feedback and current series feedback.

Now consider the simple transistor amplifier of Fig. 13-6a. Its linear model is given by Fig. 13-6b. Applying nodal analysis, we have

$$I_1 = \left[\frac{1}{r_{b'e}} + \frac{1}{r_{b'c}} + j\omega(C_{b'e} + C_{b'c})\right]V_1$$

$$- \left(\frac{1}{r_{b'c}} + j\omega C_{b'c}\right)V_2 - \left(\frac{1}{r_{b'e}} + j\omega C_{b'e}\right)V_3$$

$$0 = \left(g_m - \frac{1}{r_{b'c}} - j\omega C_{b'c}\right)V_1 + \left(\frac{1}{r_{b'c}} + j\omega C_{b'c} + \frac{1}{r_{ce}} + \frac{1}{R_c}\right)V_2$$

$$- \left(\frac{1}{r_{ce}} + g_m\right)V_3 \quad (13\text{-}19)$$

$$0 = -\left(g_m + \frac{1}{r_{b'e}} + j\omega C_{b'e}\right)V_1 - \frac{1}{r_{ce}}V_2$$

$$+ \left(g_m + \frac{1}{r_{b'e}} + \frac{1}{r_{ce}} + j\omega C_{b'e} + Z_E\right)V_3$$

These equations can be solved for the gain of the amplifier. Let us consider the type of feedback that occurs here. The voltage across Z_E is proportional to the output current (actually $I_2 - I_1$). Thus, it introduces current feedback. This voltage is in series with the input signal. Thus, this is current series feedback. On the other hand, the current through the parallel combination of $r_{b'c}$ and $C_{b'c}$ is proportional to the output voltage (actually $V_2 - V_1$). The signal fed back is in parallel with the input signal.

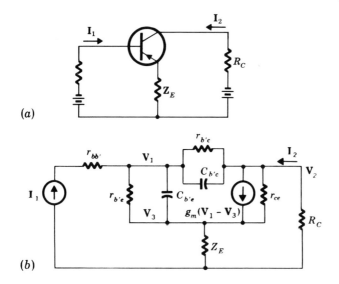

Fig. 13-6 (*a*) A simple common-emitter transistor amplifier and (*b*) its linear model.

Thus, this introduces voltage shunt feedback.   Hence, both types of feedback are incorporated in these devices.

Note that even if g_m becomes zero, $\mathbf{I}_2$ will not be zero because of the presence of $r_{b'c}$ and $C_{b'c}$ and $\mathbf{Z}_E$.   Thus, there is direct transmission here.

13-3 EFFECT OF FEEDBACK ON NONLINEAR DISTORTION AND NOISE—IMPORTANCE OF OPEN-LOOP GAIN, RETURN RATIO, AND RETURN DIFFERENCE

Nonlinear distortion results in the production of harmonic or intermodulation terms (see Sec. 5-10).   Thus, we can represent distortion by a linear system with an additional generator that produces these distortion signals.

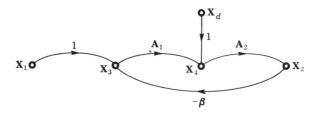

Fig. 13-7 The signal-flow graph of a feedback amplifier with a distortion or noise signal applied to one of the intermediate stages.

Such a circuit is shown in Fig. 13-7.   Usually the nonlinear distortion occurs
in the output stages where the signal swings are larger.   For this reason, we
have split the **A** branch into two branches, $\mathbf{A}_1$ and $\mathbf{A}_2$, and injected the
distortion signal at their junction.

Extraneous signals called *noise*, which can prove very troublesome, are
often introduced at some point in the amplifier.   For instance, the power
supply may not produce a pure direct voltage.   It may have components of
the power-line frequency (usually 60 Hz. and its harmonics) present in its
output.   This will act just as a signal voltage and will appear in the output
signal.   The active elements themselves produce random fluctuations in
signal level, and this also will result in an output noise.   In some cases, noise
can completely obscure the signal (see Sec. 9-27).   The signal $\mathbf{X}_d$ can be
considered to be a noise signal as well as a distortion signal.

The output signal $\mathbf{X}_2$ for the amplifier of Fig. 13-7 can be found by
successively eliminating nodes of the signal-flow graph.   This is shown in
Fig. 13-8.   Thus, we have

$$\mathbf{X}_2 = \mathbf{X}_{2s} + \mathbf{X}_{2d} = \frac{\mathbf{A}_1\mathbf{A}_2\mathbf{X}_1}{1 + \mathbf{A}_1\mathbf{A}_2\beta} + \frac{\mathbf{A}_2\mathbf{X}_d}{1 + \mathbf{A}_1\mathbf{A}_2\beta} \tag{13-20}$$

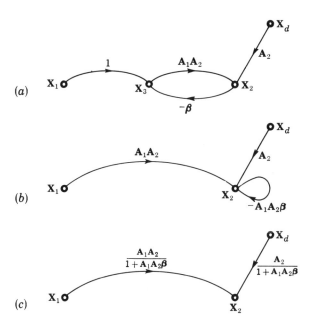

Fig. 13-8 Solution of Fig. 13-7 for x_2: (*a*) elimination
of node x_4; (*b*) elimination of node x_3; (*c*) elimination of
the self-loop of node x_2.

Let us now consider the advantage gained by using feedback. If the β branch were not present in Fig. 13-7, the output would be

$$\mathbf{X}_2' = \mathbf{X}_{2s}' + \mathbf{X}_{2d}' = \mathbf{A}_1\mathbf{A}_2\mathbf{X}_1' + \mathbf{A}_2\mathbf{X}_d' \tag{13-21}$$

where the primes indicate the nonfeedback case. It is the ratio of the distortion or noise to the signal that is of importance, not their absolute values. We shall denote this ratio by $\mathbf{D} = \mathbf{X}_{2d}/\mathbf{X}_{2s}$. In the feedback case,

$$\mathbf{D} = \frac{\mathbf{X}_d}{\mathbf{X}_1}\frac{1}{\mathbf{A}_1} \tag{13-22}$$

and in the nonfeedback case,

$$\mathbf{D}' - \frac{\mathbf{X}_d'}{\mathbf{X}_1'}\frac{1}{\mathbf{A}_1} \tag{13-23}$$

These ratios are complex numbers. It is their magnitude in which we are interested. Comparing Eqs. (13-22) and (13-23), it appears as though no advantage is gained by using feedback. However, this is often not the case. The value of the output signal is usually specified, e.g., the output voltage, current, or power. The signal swings of the last stage, hence, the distortion signal $\mathbf{X}_d$, are then fixed, whether or not feedback is used. Hence,

$$\mathbf{X}_{2s} = \mathbf{X}_{2s}' \tag{13-24}$$

and

$$\mathbf{X}_d = \mathbf{X}_d'$$

Thus, the input signals must be different in the feedback and in the nonfeedback cases. Substituting Eqs. (13-20) and (13-21) into Eq. (13-24), we have

$$\frac{\mathbf{X}_1\mathbf{A}_1\mathbf{A}_2}{1 + \mathbf{A}_1\mathbf{A}_2\beta} = \mathbf{X}_1'\mathbf{A}_1\mathbf{A}_2$$

Hence,

$$\mathbf{X}_1 = \mathbf{X}_1'(1 + \mathbf{A}_1\mathbf{A}_2\beta) \tag{13-25}$$

Substituting, and taking the ratio of Eqs. (13-22) and (13-23), we obtain

$$\frac{\mathbf{D}}{\mathbf{D}'} = \frac{1}{1 + \mathbf{A}_1\mathbf{A}_2\beta} \tag{13-26}$$

Therefore, if the input signal can be increased to compensate for the loss in gain due to feedback, the distortion and noise can be reduced by the factor $1/(1 + \mathbf{A}_1\mathbf{A}_2\beta)$. In a good negative-feedback amplifier, the magnitude of $1 + \mathbf{A}_1\mathbf{A}_2\beta$ might be 100 or more, so that amplifiers with very low distortion can be built. In fact, if power amplifiers are to have harmonic distortion of less than 1 percent, it is impractical to build them without using feedback.

The input signal must be increased when feedback is used. If this cannot be done, then additional amplification may be needed. This can be in the form of a preamplifier that precedes the feedback amplifier. The distortion will be very small here, since the signal levels will be low. The entire feedback amplifier can be designed to give the required gain, in which case the feedback amplifier would probably have more stages than the non-feedback amplifier. We shall discuss the design of feedback amplifiers in Sec. 13-12.

If X_d represents a noise signal, then the discussion is complicated somewhat. In general, if the signal level can be raised, feedback will reduce the effects of noise just as it reduces the distortion. However, there are circumstances when the input-signal level is fixed and the interfering noise is produced in the first amplifier stage. In this case, the input-signal level cannot be increased unless it is amplified. The amplification will increase the noise level equally. Then, the ratio of $|D/D'|$ will be unity, and no advantage is gained by using feedback.

The reduction of noise and distortion that can be obtained by the use of feedback is given by the magnitude of Eq. (13-26). If the feedback is negative, then $-A_1A_2\beta$ will be a real negative number. When its magnitude is large, then $1/|1 + A_1A_2\beta|$ will be small and the distortion will be greatly reduced. If positive feedback is used, then $-A_1A_2\beta$ will be a real positive number. In most circumstances with positive feedback, $|A_1A_2\beta|$ must be less than 1 if oscillation is not to occur. In these cases, $1/|1 + A_1A_2\beta|$ will be greater than unity, and the distortion will be increased if the output signal is kept constant.

The quantity $-A_1A_2\beta$ is called the *open-loop gain* of the feedback amplifier. Consider Fig. 13-9. This is the signal-flow graph of the feedback amplifier of Fig. 13-1, except that the β branch has been removed from node X_3, so that the feedback loop has been broken. Let us compute the gain X_3'/X_3.

$$\frac{X_3'}{X_3} = -A\beta \tag{13-27}$$

Thus, the open-loop gain for the simple feedback amplifiers that we have been considering is obtained by breaking the feedback loop, and taking the ratio of a signal applied at the input of the **A** circuit to the signal returned to the

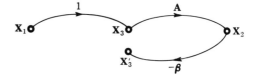

Fig. 13-9 A signal-flow diagram of the feedback amplifier of Fig. 13-1 with the feedback loop opened.

output of the β circuit.   For this reason, the negative of the open-loop gain is called the *return ratio*.   A quantity that is often of interest is $1 + A\beta$.   If a unit signal is applied ($X_3 = 1$), then $X_3' = -A\beta$, so that $1 + A\beta$ is the difference between the applied signal and the returned signal.   Hence, $1 + A\beta$ is called the *return difference*.   This is a measure of the advantage gained when feedback is used.

Note that in feedback amplifiers, often A is negative and β is also negative; that is, $-\beta$ is positive.   Thus, the feedback circuit actually introduces no phase reversal.   However, the amplifier does.   Hence, the feedback and open-loop gain are negative and the return difference is positive.

13-4   EFFECT OF FEEDBACK ON THE SENSITIVITY OF THE GAIN OF AN AMPLIFIER TO CHANGES IN PARAMETER VALUES

If the parameters of the active elements of an amplifier vary, then the gain of the amplifier will change.   For the transistor or FET, the parameter variations are usually due to changes in either the temperature or the power-supply voltage.   On the other hand, for the vacuum tube, they are often due to aging or changes in the power-supply voltage.   Many electronic instruments require amplifiers with a very constant gain.   The use of feedback can make the gain of an amplifier almost insensitive to changes in the parameters of the active elements.   The gain of a feedback amplifier is given by Eq. (13-4) as

$$K = \frac{A}{1 + A\beta}$$

Now let us assume that A changes by an amount ΔA.   Then K will change by an amount ΔK.   Thus,

$$K + \Delta K = \frac{A + \Delta A}{1 + (A + \Delta A)\beta} \tag{13-28}$$

Then

$$\Delta K = \frac{A + \Delta A}{1 + (A + \Delta A)\beta} - \frac{A}{1 + A\beta} \tag{13-29}$$

Usually, it is not the actual change that we are interested in but the fractional change.   Then, dividing Eq. (13-29) by Eq. (13-4) and rearranging, we obtain

$$\frac{\Delta K}{K} = \frac{\Delta A/A}{1 + (A + \Delta A)\beta} \tag{13-30}$$

The quantity $\Delta A/A$ represents the fractional change in the amplification without feedback.   Hence, the fractional change in the gain has been reduced by the return difference of the feedback amplifier computed *after* the change in **A** has occurred. If negative feedback is used and $-(\mathbf{A} + \Delta\mathbf{A})\beta$ is a large negative number, then a considerable improvement in the sensitivity to parameter value changes is obtained by using feedback. If $\Delta\mathbf{A}$ results because of aging, then eventually $|(\mathbf{A} + \Delta\mathbf{A})\beta|$ will become small and the advantages of feedback will be lost. Feedback amplifiers should be checked from time to time to see that this has not occurred. (Note that $|A|$ can decrease greatly while $|K|$ does not, and, hence, the amplifier can have sufficient gain but yet not function properly.)

Differences, rather than derivatives, were used in the analysis of this section, so that the results would be accurate for large changes in **A** and not just for infinitesimal ones.

13-5 EFFECT OF FEEDBACK ON FREQUENCY RESPONSE

Let us now consider the effect of feedback on the frequency distortion of a simple amplifier. We shall assume that the gain formula of Eq. (13-4) can be used, and that

$$\mathbf{A} = \frac{A_{\mathrm{mid}}}{1 + jf/f_2} \tag{13-31}$$

Then

$$\mathbf{K} = \frac{A_{\mathrm{mid}}}{1 + A_{\mathrm{mid}}\beta} \frac{1}{1 + jf/[f_2(1 + A_{\mathrm{mid}}\beta)]} \tag{13-32}$$

The half-power bandwidth has been increased by a factor $1 + A_{\mathrm{mid}}\beta$ while the gain has been reduced by the same factor. It is assumed that $-A_{\mathrm{mid}}\beta$ is a negative number. The gain-bandwidth product has not changed. It might appear that no advantage has been gained by using feedback. However, the use of feedback allows gain to be traded for bandwidth where it might not have been convenient to do so, such as in the case of the variation of $\mathbf{h}_f$ with frequency in a transistor. In addition, if feedback is used to improve the frequency response, it will also provide the advantages discussed in Secs. 13-3 and 13-4. If the frequency response of the amplifier is more complex than that given by Eq. (13-31), then a gain-bandwidth trade using feedback may prove more advantageous than other types of gain-bandwidth trades.

If feedback is used to achieve any of the advantages discussed in Secs. 13-3 and 13-4, then it becomes somewhat academic to speak of its greatly improving the frequency response. This is because the magnitude of the open-loop gain must be high to obtain the advantages of feedback. Hence, in a well-designed feedback amplifier, $|A\beta|$, and as a consequence $|A|$, should not fall off over any frequencies of interest. Since the use of feedback does increase the bandwidth, a good feedback amplifier usually has a bandwidth much greater than that required by the bandwidth of the input signals.

For instance, a high-quality audio amplifier should have a frequency response that is essentially flat for frequencies from 20 to 20,000 Hz. However, the frequency response of the overall feedback amplifier that is designed to amplify these signals may be essentially flat for frequencies from 2 to 200,000 Hz.

13-6 EFFECT OF FEEDBACK ON IMPEDANCE LEVELS

Feedback can have a profound effect on the output and input impedance of an amplifier. We shall use the representation discussed in Sec. 8-2, where an amplifier was represented by its Thévenin's or Norton's equivalent circuit to determine the output impedance. Two typical amplifier representations are shown in Fig. 13-10. Note that $A_{v,oc}$ and $A_{i,sc}$ are open-circuit and short-circuit amplifications respectively, and *do not change* if Z_L changes. The output impedance Z_o accounts for changes in gain with load impedance. We shall assume that feedback is added to these amplifiers and see how the output impedance is changed. Consider the voltage-feedback amplifier of Fig. 13-11a. Assume that the β circuit is ideal so that $V_a = V_1 - \beta V_2$ and Z_β is infinite. Then we can compute the effective output impedance using the relation (from Thévenin's theorem) $Z_{o,vfb} = V_{oc}/I_{sc}$. (The subscript *vfb* stands for voltage feedback.) Note that we have assumed the positive direction of I_2 as out of the amplifier. Under open-circuit conditions, the gain of the amplifier is given by Eq. (13-4). Then

$$V_{2oc} = \frac{A_{v,oc}V_1}{1 + A_{v,oc}\beta} \tag{13-33}$$

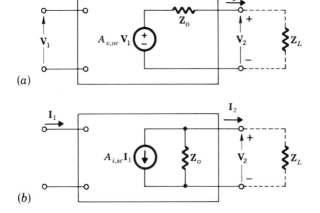

(a)

(b)

Fig. 13-10   (a) A Thévenin's equivalent circuit of a voltage amplifier and (b) a Norton's equivalent circuit of a current amplifier.

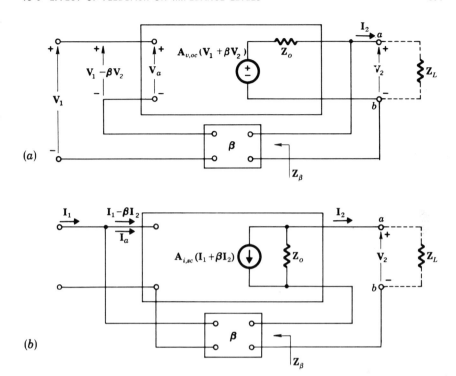

Fig. 13-11 (a) An ideal voltage-feedback amplifier and (b) an ideal current-feedback amplifier.

If a short circuit is placed across terminals ab, then $V_2 = 0$, so that the feedback voltage has been eliminated, and

$$\mathbf{I}_{2sc} = \frac{\mathbf{A}_{v,oc}\mathbf{V}_1}{\mathbf{Z}_0} \tag{13-34}$$

Thus

$$\mathbf{Z}_{0,vfb} = \frac{\mathbf{Z}_0}{1 + \mathbf{A}_{v,oc}\beta} \tag{13-35}$$

If negative feedback is used, the output impedance is divided by the *return difference under open-circuit conditions*. (Note that this is the maximum return difference for a voltage-feedback amplifier.)

In the case of negative-feedback, the output impedance with feedback is less than the output impedance without feedback.

Remember that in many negative-feedback amplifiers, *both* **A** and **β** are negative.

We have analyzed a circuit using voltage series feedback. However the same type of result would occur if we used voltage shunt feedback. In either case, we would have

$$\mathbf{V}_{2oc} = \frac{\mathbf{A}_{oc}\mathbf{X}_1}{1 + \mathbf{A}_{oc}\boldsymbol{\beta}}$$

where $\mathbf{X}_1$ is the input voltage *or* current. When the output is short-circuited, $\mathbf{V}_2 = 0$. Since voltage feedback is being considered, the feedback signal will be zero. Hence,

$$\mathbf{I}_{2sc} = \frac{\mathbf{A}_{oc}\mathbf{X}_1}{\mathbf{Z}_o}$$

Therefore,

$$\mathbf{Z}_{o,vfb} = \frac{\mathbf{Z}_o}{1 + \mathbf{A}_{oc}\boldsymbol{\beta}}$$

The important fact here is that *the feedback is present when the terminals are open-circuited and it is removed when the terminals are short-circuited.*

Now consider the current-feedback amplifier of Fig. 13-11b. We shall again assume that the $\boldsymbol{\beta}$ circuit is ideal, so that $\mathbf{I}_a = \mathbf{I}_1 - \boldsymbol{\beta}\mathbf{I}_2$ and $\mathbf{Z}_\beta = 0$. Then, when a short circuit is placed across terminals *ab*

$$\mathbf{I}_{2sc} = \mathbf{I}_1 \frac{\mathbf{A}_{i,sc}}{1 + \mathbf{A}_{i,sc}\boldsymbol{\beta}} \tag{13-36}$$

Under open-circuit conditions, $\mathbf{I}_2 = 0$ and the feedback current becomes zero. Thus,

$$\mathbf{V}_{2oc} = \mathbf{A}_{i,sc}\mathbf{I}_1\mathbf{Z}_o \tag{13-37}$$

Hence

$$\mathbf{Z}_{o,ifb} = \mathbf{Z}_o(1 + \mathbf{A}_{i,sc}\boldsymbol{\beta}) \tag{13-38}$$

When negative-current feedback is used, the output impedance is multiplied by the *return difference under short-circuit conditions.* (Note that this is the maximum return difference for a current-feedback amplifier.) This relation was derived using current shunt feedback. However, a similar result would be obtained using current series feedback. The important fact is that *the feedback signal becomes zero when the terminals are open-circuited and the feedback is present when the terminals are short-circuited.*

If $\mathbf{Z}_o$ is the output impedance of a device and $\mathbf{Z}_L$ is the load impedance and $|\mathbf{Z}_o| \ll |\mathbf{Z}_L|$, then the output voltage will be almost independent of $\mathbf{Z}_L$. On the other hand, if $|\mathbf{Z}_o| \gg |\mathbf{Z}_L|$, then the output current will be almost independent of $\mathbf{Z}_L$. Thus, it is to be expected that voltage feedback will reduce the output impedance, whereas current feedback will increase it.

Now let us determine the effect of feedback on the input impedance of an amplifier. Figure 13-12a illustrates a shunt-feedback amplifier. The output connections are not shown since this figure can represent *either* current shunt feedback or voltage shunt feedback. Now assume that the input current is $\mathbf{I}_1$. The current actually entering the amplifier $\mathbf{A}$ is $\mathbf{I}_1 - \beta\mathbf{X}_2$, where $\mathbf{X}_2$ represents either the output voltage or current. The input voltage is then

$$\mathbf{V}_1 = \mathbf{Z}_i(\mathbf{I}_1 - \beta\mathbf{X}_2)$$

Note that we have assumed that $\mathbf{Z}'_\beta = \infty$. Then, for the amplifier

$$\mathbf{X}_2 = \mathbf{A}(\mathbf{I}_1 - \beta\mathbf{X}_2) \tag{13-39}$$

That is, the amplifier output can always be expressed in terms of the input current. Substituting and noting that $\mathbf{Z}_{i,\text{shfb}} = \mathbf{V}_1/\mathbf{I}_1$, we have

$$\mathbf{Z}_{i,\text{shfb}} = \frac{\mathbf{Z}_i}{1 + \mathbf{A}\beta} \tag{13-40}$$

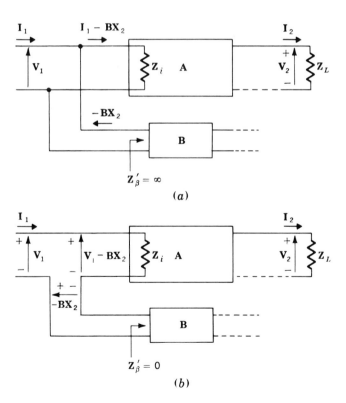

Fig. 13-12 (a) A shunt-feedback amplifier and (b) a series-feedback amplifier.

where the subscript shfb stands for shunt feedback, β is defined in Fig. 13-12a, and A is defined in Eq. (13-39). Thus, the input impedance of an amplifier using shunt feedback is given by the input impedance of the amplifier without feedback divided by the return difference. Note that it does not matter whether voltage or current feedback is used.

Now consider Fig. 13-12b, which represents a series-feedback amplifier. Again note that this can be *either* a voltage series feedback or a current shunt feedback. The current I_1 is

$$I_1 = \frac{V_1 - \beta X_2}{Z_i}$$

where we have assumed that $Z'_\beta = 0$. Then

$$X_2 = A(V_1 - \beta X_2) \tag{13-41}$$

Here the amplifier output is expressed in terms of its input voltage. Substituting and manipulating, we obtain

$$Z_{i,\text{sefb}} = Z_i(1 + A\beta) \tag{13-42}$$

where the subscript sefb stands for series feedback, β is defined in Fig. 13-12b, and A is defined in Eq. (13-41). Thus, the input impedance of an amplifier using series feedback is given by the product of the input impedance of the amplifier without feedback and the return difference.

The results for the effect of feedback on the input and output impedances appear to be very different. However, they are related. In the case of voltage feedback or shunt feedback, the feedback is present if the terminals in question are open-circuited, but the feedback becomes zero if the terminals are short-circuited. The impedance viewed into such a pair of terminals is equal to the impedance without feedback divided by the appropriate return difference.

On the other hand, in the case of current feedback or series feedback, the feedback is present if the terminals in question are short-circuited, but it becomes zero if they are open-circuited. The impedance viewed into such a pair of terminals is equal to the impedance without feedback multiplied by the appropriate return difference.

13-7 CALCULATION OF THE GAIN OF FEEDBACK AMPLIFIERS

Linear models will be used to analyze feedback amplifiers. Thus, there is really nothing new involved, and the procedures we have been using can now be applied to feedback amplifiers. Several feedback amplifiers will be analyzed in this section to illustrate some useful techniques. We shall not analyze every possible type of feedback amplifier here, but the procedure we use can be applied to all feedback amplifiers.

Consider the three-stage FET voltage-shunt feedback amplifier shown in Fig. 13-13a. The voltage gain from the gate of the first FET to the gate of the third FET $\mathbf{A}_{v1} = \mathbf{V}_3/\mathbf{V}_1$ is just the voltage gain of a two-stage RC-coupled voltage amplifier. Thus, the procedures of Chap. 9 can be used to analyze it. Note the feedback *does not* affect the ratio $\mathbf{V}_3/\mathbf{V}_1$, although it does affect the value of $\mathbf{V}_1$. The gain $\mathbf{A}_{v1}$ should include the effects of the parasitic capacitances even though they have not been drawn in Fig. 13-13a. The linear model for the complete amplifier is shown in Fig. 13-13b. The first two stages of the amplifier are accounted for by the $\mathbf{A}_{v1}\mathbf{V}_1$ term, which appears in the model of the third FET. The capacitances C_1 and C_2 represent the input and the output capacitances of the amplifier, respectively. To simplify the analysis, we shall assume that, in the last stage, the coupling capacitor C and the source bypass capacitor C_{s2} are short circuits at the signal frequency. The analysis would be essentially the same if we did not do this, but some of the concepts would be obscured by unnecessary detail. The conductance G_2 represents the parallel combination of R_2', R_2'', and r_d of the FET.

Before we analyze the FET amplifier, let us consider the transistor amplifier of Fig. 13-14a. Its linear model is shown in Fig. 13-14b. The effects of the first two stages have been accounted for by the expression $\mathbf{A}_{i1}\mathbf{I}_1$. The current gain $\mathbf{A}_{i1}$ can be found by the methods of Chap. 9. As we discussed in Sec. 9-6, the emitter impedance primarily affects the current entering the transistor stage. If the emitter impedance of the third stage is considered when $\mathbf{A}_{i1}$ is calculated, we can, to a high degree of accuracy, ignore it otherwise. A similar statement can be made for the feedback elements $r_{b'c}$ and $C_{b'c}$ in the hybrid-pi model. These calculations have been made in Fig. 13-14b. We have also assumed that the last coupling capacitor C is a short circuit. The conductance G_2 represents the parallel combination of R_2', R_2'', and $1/h_{oe}$ for the last stage. The admittance $\mathbf{Y}_O$ represents all of h_{oe} given in Fig. 6-43 except for h_{oe}, which has been combined in G_2. Note that we have used the h-parameter linear model which was defined from, and is equivalent to, the hybrid-pi model. It is convenient to use the h-parameter model here. In addition, a feedback analysis was performed using the hybrid-pi model (see Fig. 6-48). The capacitors C_1 and C_2 represent external stray capacitances. The admittance $\mathbf{Y}_i$ represents the input admittance of the first amplifier stage (including R_{B1} and R_{B2}). The feedback will affect the values of $\mathbf{V}_1$ and $\mathbf{I}_1$ but not their ratio, so that $\mathbf{Y}_i$ is calculated as though the feedback loop were not present. (It does act as a load upon the last stage, but this effect is negligible here.) Equations (9-76) to (9-78) can be used for this purpose. (The feedback does affect the impedance seen at terminals ab by the external generator $\mathbf{I}_s$, since it affects the value of $\mathbf{V}_1$.) The models of Figs. 13-13b and 13-14b are the same except for the $g_m\mathbf{A}_{v1}\mathbf{V}_1$ and the $h_{fe}\mathbf{A}_{i1}\mathbf{I}_1$ terms. (Assume that $\mathbf{Y}_i = 0$ and $\mathbf{Y}_o = 0$ in the FET case.) In the transistor circuit,

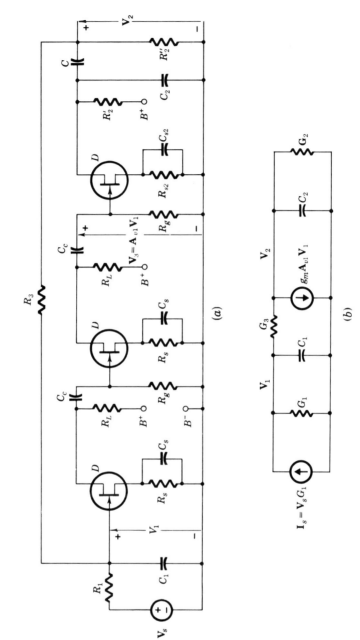

Fig. 13-13 (*a*) A three-stage FET voltage-shunt feedback amplifier and (*b*) a linear model for this amplifier which uses the approximations and substitutions discussed in the text. Note that the input generator has been replaced by Norton's theorem.

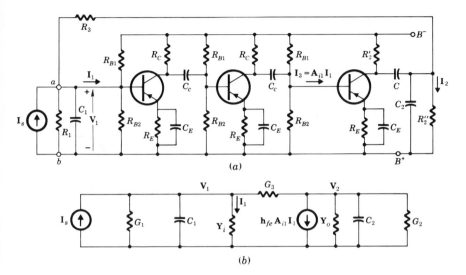

Fig. 13-14 (a) Three-stage transistor voltage-shunt feedback amplifier and (b) a linear model for the amplifier which uses the approximations and substitutions discussed in the text.

$$\mathbf{I}_1 = \mathbf{V}_1\mathbf{Y}_i \tag{13-43}$$

Now let us use the substitutions

$$\mathbf{A} = g_m\mathbf{A}_{v1} \tag{13-44a}$$

for the FET amplifier, and

$$\mathbf{A} = \mathbf{h}_{fe}\mathbf{A}_{i1}\mathbf{Y}_i \tag{13-44b}$$

for the transistor amplifier. If Eqs. (13-43) and (13-44) are substituted, then the models of Figs. 13-13b and 13-14b become identical. This model is shown in Fig. 13-15. The following nodal analysis is applicable to both amplifiers.

$$\mathbf{I}_s = (G_1 + G_3 + j\omega C_1 + \mathbf{Y}_i)\mathbf{V}_1 - G_3\mathbf{V}_2 \tag{13-45a}$$

$$0 = (\mathbf{A} - G_3)\mathbf{V}_1 + (G_2 + G_3 + \mathbf{Y}_o + j\omega C_2)\mathbf{V}_2 \tag{13-45b}$$

Solving for $\mathbf{V}_2/\mathbf{I}_s$ yields

$$\frac{\mathbf{V}_2}{\mathbf{I}_s} = \frac{-(\mathbf{A} - G_3)}{(G_1 + G_3 + \mathbf{Y}_i + j\omega C_1)(G_2 + G_3 + \mathbf{Y}_o + j\omega C_2) + G_3(\mathbf{A} - G_3)} \tag{13-46}$$

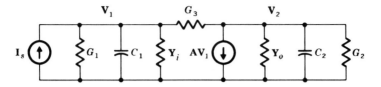

Fig. 13-15 A linear model which is equivalent to Figs. 13-13*b* and 13-14*b* when the substitutions discussed in the text are made.

To obtain the voltage gain of the FET amplifier, multiply Eq. (13-46) by G_1 and substitute Eq. (13-44*a*). To obtain the current gain of the transistor amplifier, multiply Eq. (13-46) by G_2'' and substitute Eq. (13-44*b*). Thus, the gain of both amplifiers has been obtained.

In order to interpret Eq. (13-46) more easily, we shall make some approximations. The conductance G_3 is usually very much less than unity, while **A** is essentially a gain very much greater than unity. We shall approximate $\mathbf{A} - G_3$ by **A**. This is equivalent to ignoring the direct transmission through the resistance R_3. Making the approximation and manipulating Eq. (13-46), we obtain

$$\frac{\mathbf{V}_2}{\mathbf{I}_s} = \frac{-\mathbf{A}/[(G_1 + G_3 + j\omega C_1 + \mathbf{Y}_i)(G_2 + G_3 + \mathbf{Y}_o + j\omega C_2)]}{1 + \mathbf{A}G_3/[(G_1 + G_3 + \mathbf{Y}_i + j\omega C_1)(G_2 + G_3 + \mathbf{Y}_o + j\omega C_2)]}$$

(13-47)

If

$$\left|\frac{\mathbf{A}G_3}{(G_1 + G_3 + \mathbf{Y}_i + j\omega C_1)(G_2 + G_3 + \mathbf{Y}_o + j\omega C_2)}\right| \gg 1 \qquad (13\text{-}48)$$

we have

$$\frac{\mathbf{V}_2}{\mathbf{I}_s} \approx -\frac{1}{G_3} \tag{13-49}$$

Thus, the voltage gain of the FET amplifier is approximately

$$\mathbf{K}_v \approx -\frac{G_1}{G_3} \tag{13-50a}$$

while the current gain of the transistor amplifier is approximately

$$\mathbf{K}_i \approx -\frac{G_2''}{G_3} \tag{13-50b}$$

Thus, the gain of both these amplifiers can be made essentially independent of the parameters of the active elements over a band of frequencies. Note that the inequality of relation (13-48) will not be valid at all frequencies. At very low frequencies, **A** falls off because of the effects of the coupling and bypass capacitors. At high frequencies, $\mathbf{A}$ falls off because of parasitic capacitance and the variation of $\mathbf{h}_{fe}$ with frequency. In addition, the $j\omega C_1$ and $j\omega C_2$ terms cause the left-hand side of relation (13-48) to become small at high frequencies.

Let us interpret Eq. (13-48). We shall break up the product on the left-hand side and consider each term separately. $G_3/(G_1 + G_3 + j\omega C_1 + \mathbf{Y}_i)$ is the voltage-divider ratio $\mathbf{V}_1/\mathbf{V}_2$ if the generator $\mathbf{I}_s$ is replaced by an open circuit. This is what could be called $\boldsymbol{\beta}$. Note that the gain *does not* approach $1/\boldsymbol{\beta}$. The quantity $\mathbf{A}/(G_2 + G_3 + \mathbf{Y}_o + j\omega C_2)$ is a measure of the gain from the gate of the first FET, or the base of the first transistor, to the output. Note that it does not take into account the fact that the $\boldsymbol{\beta}$ circuit can load down the output. Thus, we can roughly say that

$$\frac{AG_3}{(G_1 + G_3 + j\omega C_1 + \mathbf{Y}_i)(G_2 + G_3 + \mathbf{Y}_o + j\omega C_2)}$$

is the open-loop gain of the amplifier. This discussion tends to substantiate the fact that the relation $\mathbf{A}/(1 + \mathbf{A}\boldsymbol{\beta})$ can be used to study the general principles of feedback amplifiers, but this relation cannot be used to compute the gain of specific ones.

13-8 OSCILLATION IN FEEDBACK AMPLIFIERS

Whenever a feedback amplifier is constructed, there is always a danger that it will be *unstable*. That is, that it may oscillate. Consider the feedback amplifier of Fig. 13-9. If the open-loop gain is equal to $+1$ at some frequency, then a signal of that frequency, originating at any point in the feedback loop, will be returned to the same point with an equal magnitude. Thus, this signal will persist indefinitely, and oscillation will result. (Note that signals of all frequencies are always present because of random fluctuation in currents and voltages.) A question that can be asked is: If the phase angle of the open-loop gain is zero, and if its magnitude is greater than 1, will such a persistent signal build up? The answer is that it often will. *However, there are circumstances when it will not.* Oscillation is a complex phenomenon that can best be understood from a mathematical study rather than from simple physical arguments.

Before proceeding with this mathematical discussion, let us consider why oscillation is so undesirable. It can produce an interfering signal that will obscure the desired one. The "howl" that is often heard in public address systems is typical of this. Oscillation in an amplifier is harmful even if it does not obscure the signal (e.g., an audio amplifier may oscillate at the inaudible frequency of 100,000 Hz) because the oscillation usually builds up until the amplifier is driven into highly nonlinear regions where it cannot function properly. Of course, there are instances when a circuit is designed to generate a signal.   In such cases, an oscillator is built deliberately.   Such circuits will be discussed in Chap. 14.

To analyze the stability of an amplifier, we shall consider the Laplace transformed form of the gain.   This subject was introduced in Secs. 9-13 to 9-15.   In particular, we are interested in the location of the poles of the transformed gain function $\mathbf{K}(s)$.   As we demonstrated in Sec. 9-15, if these poles lie in the left half-plane, the transient response of the amplifier will decay exponentially.   On the other hand, if the poles lie in the right half-plane, then the transient response will consist of terms which build up exponentially; consequently, oscillation will result.   If the poles lie exactly on the $j\omega$ axis, then the response will consist of sinusoids which build up with time if the poles are not simple (of first order).   If the $j\omega$-axis poles are of first order, then the transient response will contain a sinusoid which neither builds up nor decays.   This condition is the borderline case of oscillation.   It is unsuitable in an amplifier since, once excited, these sinusoids will persist.   In addition, any slight change in any of the parameters of the amplifier may shift the poles into the right half-plane.   Thus, we shall say that a feedback amplifier is *stable* if *all* its poles lie in the left half-plane and that it is *unstable* if *any* of its poles lie on the $j\omega$ axis or in the right half-plane.   If a practical amplifier oscillates, then the output signal does not build up indefinitely.   In actual amplifiers, the voltages and currents are limited by cutoff and saturation phenomena in the active elements.

To determine if a feedback amplifier is stable, we need only obtain the gain (as was done in Sec. 13-7), replace $j\omega$ by s, and then clear fractions so that the gain with feedback $\mathbf{K}(s)$ is expressed as the ratio of two polynomials in s.   (It is assumed that any common factors in the numerator and denominator are canceled.)   The denominator polynomial is then examined to see if it has any roots on the $j\omega$ axis or in the right half-plane.   If it does not, then the amplifier is stable.   The most straightforward manner of determining the location of the roots of a polynomial is to factor it.   However, the polynomials encountered in feedback amplifiers are ordinarily of fairly high degree, and factoring will usually require an extremely tedious cut-and-try procedure.   We do not need to know the location of the poles of the gain function, but only whether they lie on the $j\omega$ axis or in the right half-plane.   Fortunately, there are several procedures that will supply this information without factoring the polynomial.   These will be considered in the next sections.

13-9 ROUTH-HURWITZ TESTS FOR THE LOCATION OF THE ROOTS OF A POLYNOMIAL

The Hurwitz test is a simple procedure to determine if a polynomial has roots in the right half-plane or on the $j\omega$ axis.   It will be stated without proof.

Consider a polynomial $\mathbf{D}(s)$, which has no roots at $s = 0$.

$$\mathbf{D}(s) = s^k + d_{k-1}s^{k+1} + \cdots + d_1 s + d_0 \tag{13-51}$$

All the coefficients $d_{k-1}, \ldots, d_1, d_0$ must be positive. If any are negative or zero, then the polynomial will have right half-plane roots and we need proceed no farther. An exception to this is if the polynomial contains only even (or only odd) powers. Then $\mathbf{D}(s)$ *may* have $j\omega$-axis roots instead of right half-plane roots. However, we consider this to be borderline instability. Thus, if any coefficients are nonpositive, we can state that the amplifier is not stable. If all the coefficients are positive, then the test must be applied. Break up $\mathbf{D}(s)$ into the sum of two polynomials.

$$\mathbf{D}(s) = \mathbf{m}(s) + \mathbf{n}(s) \tag{13-52}$$

where $\mathbf{m}(s)$ is an even polynomial, i.e., contains only even-powered terms, including the constant, and $\mathbf{n}(s)$ is an odd polynomial. Then, form the improper fraction.

$$\Phi = \frac{\mathbf{m}(s)}{\mathbf{n}(s)} \tag{13-53a}$$

$$\Phi = \frac{\mathbf{n}(s)}{\mathbf{m}(s)} \tag{13-53b}$$

Choose either Eq. (13-53a) or (13-53b) so that the highest power of the numerator is greater than the highest power of the denominator. Let us assume that Eq. (13-53a) is used. The degree of $\mathbf{m}(s)$ is one greater than $\mathbf{n}(s)$. [Note that $\mathbf{m}(s)$ contains all the even powers while $\mathbf{n}(s)$ contains all the odd powers.] Thus, we can write

$$\Phi = a_1 s + \frac{\mathbf{R}_1(s)}{\mathbf{n}(s)} \tag{13-54}$$

The polynomial $\mathbf{R}_1(s)$ will be even and one degree less than $\mathbf{n}(s)$. (This will be illustrated in the subsequent example.) Then take the reciprocal of the remainder term and divide once

$$\frac{\mathbf{n}(s)}{\mathbf{R}_1(s)} = a_2 s + \frac{\mathbf{R}_2(s)}{\mathbf{R}_1(s)} \tag{13-55}$$

Continue this procedure with successive remainders.

$$\frac{\mathbf{R}_1(s)}{\mathbf{R}_2(s)} = a_3 s + \frac{\mathbf{R}_3(s)}{\mathbf{R}_2(s)} \tag{13-56}$$

The degrees of the numerator and the denominator of the remainder will decrease and the procedure will eventually terminate. If any of the $a_1, a_2, \ldots$ are not positive, then $\mathbf{D}(s)$ will contain right half-plane roots. If all the $a_1, a_2, \ldots$ are positive, then $\mathbf{D}(s)$ will only contain left half-plane roots, except in a special case which will be discussed subsequently.   Let us consider some examples of this procedure.

$$\mathbf{D}(s) = s^4 + 6s^3 + 9s^2 + 12s + 4$$
$$\mathbf{m}(s) = s^4 + 9s^2 + 4$$
$$\mathbf{n}(s) = 6s^3 + 12s$$

The division can be set up in compact form.

$$
\begin{array}{r}
\frac{1}{6}s \\ \hline
6s^3 + 12s \,|\, s^4 + 9s^2 + 4 \\
s^4 + 2s^2 \qquad\qquad \frac{6}{7}s \\ \hline
7s^2 + 4 \,|\, 6s^3 + 12s \\
6s^3 + \frac{24}{7}s \qquad \frac{49}{60}s \\ \hline
\frac{60}{7}s \,|\, 7s^2 + 4 \\
7s^2 \qquad\qquad \frac{15}{7}s \\ \hline
4 \,|\, \frac{60}{7}s \\
\frac{60}{7}s \\ \hline
0
\end{array}
$$

The a's are $\frac{1}{6}, \frac{6}{7}, \frac{49}{60}, \frac{15}{7}$.   The polynomial $\mathbf{D}(s)$ has all its roots in the left half-plane.   If any of the a's had been negative, then the procedure could have been stopped, because it would have been known that $\mathbf{D}(s)$ had right half-plane roots.

If the original polynomial is such that $\mathbf{m}(s)$ and $\mathbf{n}(s)$ both have the same factor, then when the ratio $\mathbf{m}/\mathbf{n}$ or $\mathbf{n}/\mathbf{m}$ is formed, this factor will be lost. However, if the common factor is not canceled from $\mathbf{m}(s)$ and $\mathbf{n}(s)$, then it will be carried through the division and will appear as the last divisor.   For instance, if

$$\mathbf{D}(s) = (s^2 + 1)(s^2 + 2s + 2) = s^4 + 2s^3 + 3s^2 + 2s + 2$$

then

$$\mathbf{m}(s) = s^4 + 3s^2 + 2 = (s^2 + 1)(s^2 + 2)$$
$$\mathbf{n}(s) = 2s^3 + 2s = (s^2 + 1)(2s)$$

$$
\begin{array}{r}
\frac{1}{2}s \\ \hline
2s^3 + 2s \,|\, s^4 + 3s^2 + 2 \\
s^4 + s^2 \qquad\qquad s \\ \hline
2s^2 + 2 \,|\, 2s^3 + 2s \\
2s^3 + 2s \\ \hline
0
\end{array}
$$

Note that the test terminated prematurely, i.e., the last divisor is not a constant.   We can then state that $2s^2 + 2$ is a factor of $\mathbf{D}(s)$, $\mathbf{m}(s)$, and $\mathbf{n}(s)$.   The test proceeds as before, except that the common factor of $\mathbf{m}(s)$ and $\mathbf{n}(s)$ is not evaluated.   For example, $s^2 + 2s + 2$ is all that is tested in the last example.   The only factor that an even and an odd polynomial can have in common is an even polynomial; i.e., the product of two even polynomials is an even polynomial and the product of an even and an odd polynomial is an odd polynomial.   Let us consider an even polynomial

$$\mathbf{E}(s) = s^{2k} + b_{k-1}s^{2(k-1)} + \cdot \cdot \cdot + b_1 s^2 + b_0 \qquad (13\text{-}57)$$

If s_0 is a root of such a polynomial, then $-s_0$ will also be a root.   Hence, if $\mathbf{E}(s)$ has left half-plane roots, it must also have right half-plane roots.   The only way that $\mathbf{E}(s)$ cannot have right half-plane roots is for all its roots to lie on the $j\omega$ axis.   This does not lead to a stable condition.   Thus, we can state that if a polynomial is to have all its roots in the left half-plane, then all the $a_1, a_2, \ldots$ in the Hurwitz test must be positive and the test must not terminate prematurely.   A polynomial that has all its roots in the left half-plane is called a *Hurwitz polynomial*.

The Routh test is another procedure to determine if the roots of a polynomial lie in the right half-plane.   It is essentially the same as the Hurwitz test, except that an array is used in place of the long division.   To perform this test, break the polynomial $\mathbf{D}(s)$ up into its even and odd parts as indicated in Eq. (13-52).   Then

$$\mathbf{m}(s) = a_0 s^{2k} + a_1 s^{2k-2} + \cdot \cdot \cdot + a_k \qquad (13\text{-}58)$$

$$\mathbf{n}(s) = b_0 s^{2k-1} + \cdot \cdot \cdot + b_{k-1}s \qquad (13\text{-}59)$$

We have assumed that $\mathbf{m}(s)$ is of higher degree than $\mathbf{n}(s)$ and have formed the following array [if this is not the case, then the coefficients of $\mathbf{n}(s)$ will form the first row of the array]:

$$
\begin{array}{llllll}
a_0 & a_1 & a_2 & \cdot \cdot \cdot & a_k \\
b_0 & b_1 & b_2 & \cdot \cdot \cdot & \\
c_0 & c_1 & \cdot \cdot \cdot & & & (13\text{-}60) \\
d_0 & d_1 & \cdot \cdot \cdot & & \\
\cdot \cdot \cdot \cdot \cdot \cdot \cdot \cdot \cdot \cdot \cdot \cdot \cdot \cdot
\end{array}
$$

The first two rows are obtained from Eqs. (13-58) and (13-59).   The third row is obtained using the following relations:

$$c_0 = \frac{b_0 a_1 - a_0 b_1}{b_0}$$

$$c_1 = \frac{b_0 a_2 - a_0 b_2}{b_0} \qquad (13\text{-}61)$$

$$c_2 = \frac{b_0 a_3 - a_0 b_3}{b_0}$$

$$\cdot \cdot \cdot \cdot \cdot \cdot \cdot \cdot \cdot \cdot$$

In a similar way, any row is generated from the two preceding it. The operations of Eq. (13-61) are essentially those of long division. In fact, the third row contains the coefficients of the remainder of the first division of the Hurwitz test. Similarly, the fourth row contains the coefficients of the second remainder, and so on. Thus, this array will eventually terminate. The first column in the array is then examined. If any of the coefficients $a_0, b_0, c_0, \ldots$ are not positive, then the polynomial $D(s) = m(s) + n(s)$ will have right half-plane roots. The number of right half-plane roots is equal to the number of sign changes in the sequence $a_0, b_0, c_0, d_0, \ldots$. Multiple roots are counted as the order of their multiplicity; e.g., a double root is counted twice. Let us evaluate the previous example using the Routh procedure.

$$D(s) = s^4 + 6s^3 + 9s^2 + 12s + 4$$

Then form the array

$$
\begin{array}{ccc}
1 & 9 & 4 \\
6 & 12 & \\
7 & 4 & \\
\frac{60}{7} & & \\
4 & & \\
0 & &
\end{array}
$$

All the coefficients of the first column are positive. Thus, there are no roots in the right half-plane. Note the similarity of this array and the long division of the first example. Since we are only interested in the signs of the coefficients, any row can be multiplied by a positive coefficient if this proves convenient.

If the Hurwitz test terminates prematurely, then the Routh test will also. The implications are the same in both cases.

The Hurwitz and Routh tests provide very simple means of determining whether or not an amplifier is stable. However, they do not provide any information about how to stabilize an amplifier if it does oscillate, nor do they indicate any procedures for the successful design of feedback amplifiers. The Nyquist criterion, which will be discussed in the next section, will do all of this.

13-10 THE NYQUIST CRITERION FOR THE STABILITY OF A FEEDBACK AMPLIFIER

In this section we shall discuss a test which not only determines whether an amplifier is stable but also will indicate means for properly designing feedback amplifiers. This procedure is called the *Nyquist criterion*. We shall restrict ourselves to single-loop feedback systems. A single-loop amplifier

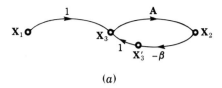

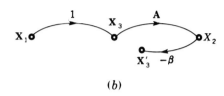

Fig. 13-16 (a) Modification of the signal-flow diagram of the feedback amplifier of Fig. 13-1 and (b) the modification that results when the feedback loop is broken.

is one in which there is only one feedback path. If the feedback loop is broken at *any* point, then all signal feedback will cease. For instance, the feedback amplifier of Fig. 13-1 is a single-loop system. We shall modify this diagram by splitting node X_3 as is shown in Fig. 13-16a. This node splitting does not change the operation of the amplifier. Now let us break the feedback loop by removing the branch between node X_3' and X_3. The configuration of Fig. 13-16b results. The open-loop gain L is given by

$$L(j\omega) = \frac{X_3'(j\omega)}{X_3(j\omega)} \tag{13-62}$$

The return difference will be denoted by $F(j\omega)$ and is

$$F(j\omega) = 1 - L(j\omega) \tag{13-63}$$

According to our previous notation, $L = -A\beta$. Since the return difference $F = 1 + A\beta$, then $F = 1 - L$. In a negative-feedback amplifier, the open-loop gain L is (nominally) negative; e.g., in Fig. 13-16, both A and β are negative. Note that we are expressing F and L as functions of $j\omega$ rather than of s.

The Nyquist criterion will involve a plot of $L(j\omega)$ or $F(j\omega)$ as a function of ω. We must plot both the magnitude and phase of $L(j\omega)$. To do this, a polar plot shall be used. That is, evaluate $L(j\omega)$ at a particular value of frequency ω_a. Then, using polar coordinates, plot the magnitude and phase angle of $L(j\omega_a)$. Repeat this operation for all frequencies. The frequency scale does not show up in this polar plot. However, points on the graph can be marked to indicate the frequency, although this is usually not necessary. A typical polar plot is shown in Fig. 13-17. The vector $L(j\omega)$ is drawn from the origin 0 to the curve. The solid curve represents the polar plot. The gain has been assumed to be zero at $\omega = 0$ and $\omega = \infty$. The arrows on the solid curve indicate the direction of increasing frequency. We

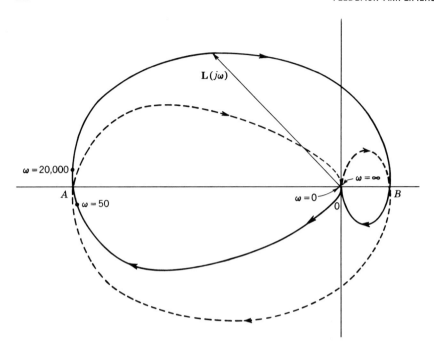

Fig. 13-17 A polar plot of the open-loop gain of a feedback amplifier.

have assumed a negative-feedback amplifier, so that the phase angle in the midband region is 180°. (The phase angle has been assumed to be $-90°$ at $\omega = 0$ and at $\omega = \infty$.) The dotted curve represents a plot of the conjugate of $L(j\omega)$. It is just a mirror image of the plot of $L(j\omega)$. The Nyquist criterion states the following.

Given a function $F(s)$ which is equal to $N(s)/D(s)$, where $N(s)$ and $D(s)$ are polynomials in the complex variable s. If a polar plot of $F(j\omega)$ and its conjugate is made for all frequencies, then the number of times that the plot encircles the origin is equal to the number of right half-plane zeros of $F(s)$ minus the number of right half-plane poles of $F(s)$.

The word "encircles" should be clarified. Consider Fig. 13-18; a radius vector $F(j\omega)$ is drawn from the origin to a point on the polar plot. Now let this point trace out the curve corresponding to the following path. Start at the point corresponding to $\omega = 0$ and increase ω to $\omega = \infty$, then return on the conjugate curve from $\omega = \infty$ to $\omega = 0$. Such a path is shown by the arrows of Fig. 13-18. Count the net number of *complete* revolutions that this radius vector makes when the complete contour is traced. (Counterclockwise revolutions should be subtracted from clockwise ones.) This net number of revolutions is called the number of encirclements. In Fig. 13-18

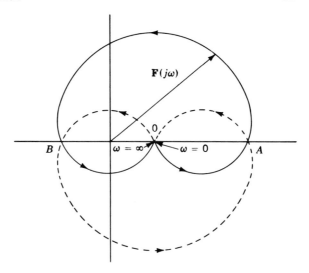

Fig. 13-18 A polar plot of $F(j\omega)$.

for frequencies between point O and A, the net rotation of the vector is zero. From A to B to O, there is one counterclockwise revolution; from O to B to A on the dashed curve, there is another counterclockwise revolution; and finally, from A to O on the dashed curve, there is no net rotation. Therefore, this function has two more poles than zeros in the right half-plane.

Let us now see how this criterion can be applied to feedback amplifiers. From Eq. (13-4), the gain of the feedback amplifier of Fig. 13-1 is

$$K(s) = \frac{A(s)}{1 + A(s)\beta(s)} \tag{13-64}$$

But $-A(s)\beta(s)$ is the open-loop gain. Thus, using Eq. (13-63), we have

$$K(s) = \frac{A(s)}{F(s)} \tag{13-65}$$

Note that $A(s)$ and $F(s)$ are both ratios of two polynomials in s. The amplification $A(s)$ is the gain of a nonfeedback amplifier and will have all its poles in the left half-plane. Hence, if $K(s)$ is to have right half-plane poles, then $F(s)$ must have right half-plane zeros. [We shall assume that $A(s)$ does not have right half-plane zeros that cancel the zeros of $F(s)$. Simple amplifier configurations do not produce right half-plane (or $j\omega$-axis) zeros. For instance, none of the interstage networks of Chap. 9 has right half-plane zeros. If more complex coupling networks are used, then such zeros may result.] The open-loop gain $L(s)$ is the gain of a nonfeedback amplifier and hence will not have right half-plane poles. Thus,

$$F(s) = 1 - L(s)$$

will not have right half-plane poles, since the only poles that it can have are
those of $\mathbf{L}(s)$. That is, $\mathbf{F}(s)$ can be infinite only if $\mathbf{L}(s)$ is. However, $\mathbf{F}(s)$
can have right half-plane zeros even though $\mathbf{L}(s)$ does not.

For most simple amplifier structures, we can state that if $\mathbf{F}(s)$ has zeros
in the right half-plane (or on the $j\omega$ axis), then the amplifier is unstable. If
all the zeros of $\mathbf{F}(s)$ lie in the left half-plane, then the amplifier will be stable.
Thus, to determine the stability of an amplifier, we need only make a polar
plot of the return difference $\mathbf{F}(j\omega)$. If this encircles the origin, then the
amplifier will be unstable. If it passes through the origin, then this is the
borderline case of instability, i.e., poles on the $j\omega$ axis. It is slightly more
convenient to obtain the open-loop gain than the return difference. From
Eq. (13-63), we have

$$\mathbf{L}(j\omega) = 1 - \mathbf{F}(j\omega) \tag{13-66}$$

If $\mathbf{F}(j\omega) = 0$, then $\mathbf{L}(j\omega) = 1$. Thus, if the curve of $\mathbf{F}(j\omega)$ encircles the
origin, the curve of $\mathbf{L}(j\omega)$ will encircle the point $+1$. Thus, the previous
criterion can be stated in the following way. If a simple feedback amplifier
is to be stable, then the polar plot of $\mathbf{L}(j\omega)$ and its conjugate must not encircle or pass through the point $+1$. This point is called the *critical point* and
is sometimes labeled (1,0). Consider that Fig. 13-17 contains such a plot.
The amplifier will be stable if the length $\overline{OB}$ is less than unity; otherwise it
will be unstable.

Let us now consider some practical procedures for obtaining the return
difference. We shall illustrate these with the common-source FET amplifier
and the common-emitter transistor amplifier. The same basic procedure
can be used for the other amplifier configurations. Consider that the FET
of Fig. 13-19a is in a feedback loop. To measure the open-loop gain,

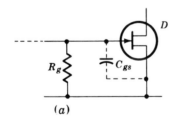

(a)

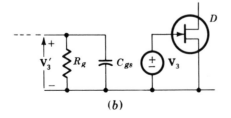

(b)

Fig. 13-19 (a) The gate circuit of an
FET in a single-loop feedback amplifier
and (b) the circuit to be used in computing the open-loop gain. Note that C_{gs}
cannot actually be disassociated from the
FET. If an actual measurement is made
this capacitance must be added to the
circuit.

"break" the lead to the gate and apply a generator V_3 between gate and source. The returned voltage appears across the other side of the break and the source of the FET. Note that any impedance between the gate and the source, including the gate-to-source capacitance, is placed on the V_3' side of the circuit. When this measurement is made, any *independent* generators, other than V_3, for example, the input generator, must be replaced by their internal impedances.

We have assumed that there is only one feedback loop present in the amplifier. However, in almost all cases, there are unavoidable local feedback loops around each amplifier stage. The gate-to-drain capacitance always constitutes a feedback loop. (When dual-gate FETs are used, this can usually be ignored.) Sufficient, accuracy is often obtained if we consider that C_{gd} affects the input and output impedances (see Sec. 9-1) and neglect its effect as a feedback element. The source-bias impedance Z_s also produces feedback (see Fig. 13-20). Usually [see, for instance, Eq. (13-15)], the only action of this feedback is to make Z_s appear as an impedance $(1 + \mu)Z_s$. In most circumstances, we can replace Fig. 13-20a by Fig. 13-20b in any *linear signal analysis* and thus eliminate the feedback due to Z_s. In most practical cases, the effect of "local" feedback loops can be eliminated, and the single-loop procedures can be used.

Figure 13-21 will be used to illustrate the procedure for determining the open-loop gain in a common-emitter transistor amplifier. The lead to the base terminal is broken, and a current generator I_3 is applied between the base and the emitter. For computation the input impedance of the transistor Z_i is placed external to the transistor as shown in Fig. 13-21b. The current in it is I_3'. The open-loop gain is I_3'/I_3. Any independent generators, except I_3, should be replaced by their internal impedances. There is local feedback around each transistor-amplifier stage. For instance, the $r_{b'c}$ and $C_{b'c}$ produce feedback. The emitter-stabilizing impedance also introduces feedback (see Sec. 13-2). However, in both of these cases, the primary effect is on Z_i. If Z_i is computed considering the emitter-stabilizing impedance $r_{b'c}$ and

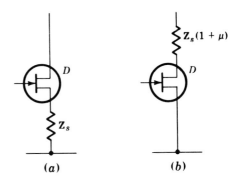

Fig. 13-20 (*a*) An FET with a source bias impedance and (*b*) a modification of this circuit to be used in calculations eliminating the local feedback loop.

(*a*)   (*b*)

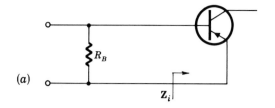

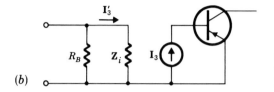

Fig. 13-21 (a) The base circuit of a transistor in a single-loop feedback amplifier and (b) the circuit to be used in computing the open-loop gain. (Note that $I_b = I_3$.)

$C_{b'c}$ and it is then assumed that Z_E, $r_{b'c}$, and $1/C_{b'c}$ are zero, sufficient accuracy usually results. Thus, the local feedback loops can be eliminated from transistor-amplifier calculations.

When the feedback loop is broken, it is assumed that this is done in relation to signal frequencies but that the operating point of the FETs or transistors is not disturbed.

The Nyquist diagram can be used to establish a definition for positive or negative feedback. If $|F(j\omega)| > 1$, then the gain of the amplifier with feedback will be less than the gain without feedback. If $|F(j\omega)| < 1$, then the introduction of feedback will increase the gain. In the Nyquist diagram $L(j\omega) = 1 - F(j\omega)$ is plotted. A circle of radius 1 whose center is at $+1$ is called the *circle of regeneration*. For those frequencies where the plot of $L(j\omega)$ lies within this circle, the gain with feedback will be greater than the gain without feedback, and the feedback can be considered to be positive. For those frequencies where $L(j\omega)$ lies outside of the circle of regeneration, the feedback is negative. Positive feedback is sometimes called *regenerative feedback*, and negative feedback is sometimes called *degenerative feedback*.

The procedures we have discussed apply to single-loop feedback amplifiers. If a multiple-loop feedback amplifier, such as that of Fig. 13-22,

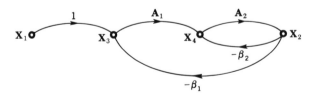

Fig. 13-22 The signal-flow diagram of a multiple-loop feedback amplifier.

is used, then the Nyquist procedures must be modified.   The procedure consists of opening all feedback loops and then closing successive ones, making polar plots and comparing them.   The procedure will not be discussed here but it is given in the first and seventh references of the bibliography.   In any event, the procedures of Sec. 13-9 can be used to determine the stability of any feedback amplifier.

13-11   ABSOLUTE STABILITY, CONDITIONAL STABILITY, GAIN MARGIN, AND PHASE MARGIN

If the midband value of the open-loop gain is changed without affecting the frequency response, then only the size of the Nyquist diagram will vary. Let us determine how the stability is affected by such changes.   Consider the plot of Fig. 13-23a.   To simplify the diagram, we have assumed that the mid-frequency response extends down to zero frequency.   A low-frequency response similar in shape to the dotted conjugate curve can be included.   The length $\overline{OA}$ is the magnitude of the open-loop gain in the midband region.   If $\overline{OB}$ is equal to or greater than 1, then the amplifier is unstable.   Since the ratio $\overline{OB}/\overline{OA}$ is constant, the magnitude of $\overline{OA}$ is limited.   Hence, the maximum value of the open-loop gain is limited.   Now consider the Nyquist plot of Fig. 13-23b.   No matter how large it becomes, the plot will always be to the left of the origin, and the critical point, $+1$, cannot be encircled. Thus, this amplifier will be stable, independent of the midband open-loop gain.   Such amplifiers are called *absolutely stable*.   It may seem as though all amplifiers should be constructed so that they are absolutely stable.   However, this type of stability is usually obtained only with simple amplifiers, which often do not provide enough gain.

Consider the Nyquist diagram of Fig. 13-23c.   If $\overline{OC} < 1$, the amplifier will be stable.   If the gain is increased so that $\overline{OC} \geq 1$ and $\overline{OB} \leq 1$, the amplifier will oscillate.   However, if the gain is increased still further so that $\overline{OB} > 1$, the amplifier will again be stable.   (See Sec. 13-10 for the definition of encirclement.)   If an amplifier is stable but can become unstable if the gain *decreases*, it is said to be *conditionally stable*.   The advantage of conditional stability is that the midband open-loop gain $\overline{OA}$ can be made very large. The interstage coupling networks of these amplifiers must be fairly complex to obtain the desired Nyquist plot.   For this reason, conditional stability is usually not used unless very large open-loop gains are required.

The most commonly used Nyquist plot resembles that of Fig. 13-23a. Let us consider some practical problems related to it.   If $\overline{OB}$ is very close to unity, then any slight shift in power-supply voltage or element values might cause the amplifier to oscillate.   To establish some design criteria, we shall

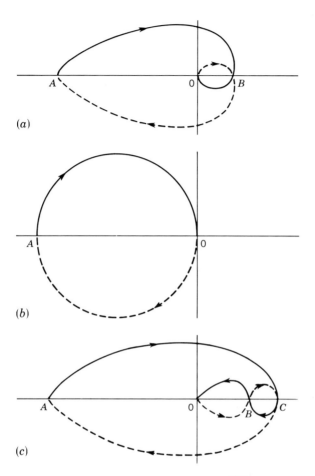

Fig. 13-23 Nyquist diagrams: (*a*) stable if $\overline{OB} < 1$, unstable if $\overline{OB} \geq 1$; (*b*) absolutely stable; (*c*) stable for $\overline{OC} < 1$, unstable, for $\overline{OC} \geq 1$ and $\overline{OB} \leq 1$, conditionally stable if $\overline{OB} > 1$.

assume that the open-loop gain is such that the phase shift decreases (or increases) monotonically and the amplitude decreases monotonically as the frequency is increased above (or decreased below) the midband value. We can then state that the amplifier will be stable if the open-loop gain falls below unity before the phase shift becomes zero degrees or that the amplifier will be stable if the phase shift has not become zero degrees when the open-loop gain has fallen off to unity. Consider the portion of the Nyquist diagram shown in Fig. 13-24. The circle is drawn with a radius of 1 and with

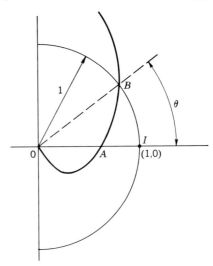

Fig. 13-24 An illustration of gain margin and phase margin. The portion of the Nyquist diagram near the critical point is shown.

its center at the origin. The critical point (1,0) is marked on the diagram at point I. The Nyquist plot intersects the unit circle at point B. The phase angle at point B is θ degrees. The angle θ is called the *phase margin*. When the phase angle is zero degrees, then the magnitude of the open-loop gain is $\overline{OA}$. This is called the *gain margin*. The gain margin is usually specified in decibels as follows:

$$GM\big|_{db} = -20 \log \overline{OA} \qquad (13\text{-}67)$$

If $GM\big|_{db}$ and θ are large, then there will be very little tendency for the amplifier to oscillate if the parameter values change. These margins are just an indication of two points on a curve, and consequently do not completely specify it. However, for the usual interstage networks, the specification of adequate gain and phase margins provides stable operation for most changes in parameter values.

If the gain margin and/or the phase margin is small, the open-loop gain may be very close to $+1$ at some frequencies. Thus the return difference will be small at these frequencies. This may cause the gain at these frequencies to become very large, thus producing an undesirable peak in the frequency response. Adequate gain and phase margins may prevent this from occurring.

13-12 BASIC DESIGN OF FEEDBACK AMPLIFIERS

We shall now consider some basic aspects in the design of feedback amplifiers. In the next section, additional aspects of their design will be considered.

At first we shall devote much of our attention to the high-frequency aspects of the design of feedback amplifiers; i.e., we shall assume that the mid-frequency range starts at zero frequency. However, the low-frequency considerations are similar to the high-frequency ones and will be discussed subsequently. We shall consider some simple expressions for the open-loop gain. A single-stage amplifier could have an open-loop gain of the form

$$\mathbf{L_1}(j\omega) = -\frac{L_0}{1 + jf/f_2} \tag{13-68}$$

A Nyquist plot of this expression is given in Fig. 13-25a. Similarly, for two, three, and four stages, we obtain

$$\mathbf{L_2}(j\omega) = -\frac{L_0}{(1 + jf/f_2)^2} \tag{13-69}$$

$$\mathbf{L_3}(j\omega) = -\frac{L_0}{(1 + jf/f_2)^3} \tag{13-70}$$

$$\mathbf{L_4}(j\omega) = -\frac{L_0}{(1 + jf/f_2)^4} \tag{13-71}$$

We have called the magnitude of the midband open-loop gain L_0 and assumed that the feedback is negative. The Nyquist plots for Eqs. (13-69) to (13-71) are sketched in Fig. 13-25b, c, and d. Let us now compare these four to determine the maximum magnitude of the midband open-loop gain L_0. In each case, L_0 is equal to the length $\overline{OA}$. The Nyquist diagram of Fig. 13-25a is absolutely stable. Thus, in theory, the value of L_0 can be as large as desired. In practice, a response of the form of Eq. (13-68) is only obtainable with a single-stage amplifier, which usually does not supply sufficient gain. The diagram of Fig. 13-25b is also absolutely stable. This type of response could be obtained from two identical stages. If common-source FET amplifiers or common-emitter transistor amplifiers are used in a feedback amplifier, then an odd number of stages is usually used to obtain the desired 180° phase shift (negative feedback) in the midband region. Note that the common-emitter transistor amplifiers have 180° phase shifts in their midband current gain. The reason that expressions such as Eq. (9-28) do not have a minus sign is because of the convention used in assigning a direction to the output current. Transformers can be used to obtain a 180° phase shift. However, there are many instances when it is not desirable to use them.

The Nyquist diagram of Fig. 13-25c is the most practical that we have discussed thus far. The amplifier will be stable if $\overline{OB} < 1$. Rewriting Eq. (13-70), we obtain

$$\mathbf{L_3}(j\omega) = \frac{L_0}{[1 + (f/f_2)^2]^{3/2}} \quad \underline{/180° - 3 \tan^{-1}(f/f_2)} \tag{13-72}$$

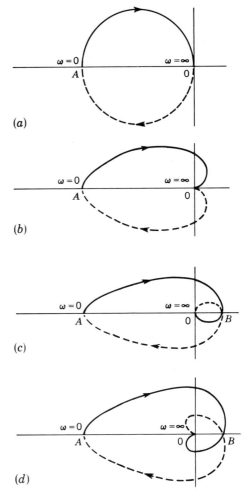

Fig. 13-25 Nyquist diagrams for the open-loop gains given by (*a*) Eq. (13-68); (*b*) Eq. (13-69); (*c*) Eq. (13-70); and (*d*) Eq. (13-71).

The frequency which corresponds to point B will have a phase shift of zero degrees. Thus,

$$180° - 3 \tan^{-1}\frac{f_B}{f_2} = 0 \tag{13-73}$$

Solving, we obtain

$$\frac{f_B}{f_2} = \sqrt{3} \tag{13-74}$$

The magnitude of the gain at $f = f_B$ must be equal to or less than 1. Hence

$$\frac{L_0}{[1 + (f_B/f_2)^2]^{3/2}} \leq 1$$

Substituting Eq. (13-74), and solving, we have

$$L_0 \leq 8 \tag{13-75}$$

Thus, the maximum open-loop gain is 8 (or 18 db). This is usually not large enough for most practical cases. The assumption that all three stages have identical frequency responses limits the maximum value of L_0. This will be illustrated in a subsequent example.

The maximum open-loop gain for the Nyquist diagram of Fig. 13-25d can be obtained using the procedures of Eqs. (13-72) to (13-75). Note that $180° - 4 \tan^{-1}(f_B/f_2) = 0$. Thus,

$$L_0 \leq 4 \tag{13-76}$$

If the cascade of additional identical stages is considered, still smaller values of L_0 will result.

To illustrate some procedures for increasing the open-loop gain let us consider the high-frequency design of a feedback amplifier. The design specifications are as follows: the voltage gain in the midband region $K_0 = -50$, the open-loop gain in the midband region $L_0 = -100$, and the amplifier is to amplify frequencies up to 10,000 Hz. We shall use the amplifier of Fig. 13-13a, which was analyzed in Sec. 13-7, and assume that the approximate expressions of Eqs. (13-47) to (13-50) are valid. Then, from Eq. (13-50a),

$$\frac{G_1}{G_3} = \frac{R_3}{R_1} = 50 \tag{13-77}$$

The approximate expression for the open-loop gain is given by Eq. (13-78) as

$$\mathbf{L} = \frac{-g_m \mathbf{A}_{v1} G_3}{(G_1 + G_3 + j\omega C_1)(G_2 + G_3 + j\omega C_2)}$$

The gain of the first two amplifier stages can be written as

$$\mathbf{A}_{v1} = \frac{A_0}{(1 + jf/f_{21})(1 + jf/f_{22})}$$

The approximate gain of the third amplifier stage is

$$\frac{g_m}{G_2 + G_3 + j\omega C_2} = \frac{g_m/(G_2 + G_3)}{1 + jf/f_{23}}$$

where

$$f_{23} = \frac{G_2 + G_3}{2\pi C_2}$$

In addition,

$$\frac{G_3}{G_1 + G_3 + j\omega C_1} = \frac{G_3/(G_1 + G_3)}{1 + jf/f_{24}}$$

where

$$f_{24} = \frac{G_1 + G_3}{2\pi C_1} \tag{13-78}$$

The complete expression for the open-loop gain is

$$\mathbf{L} = \frac{-L_0}{(1 + jf/f_{21})(1 + jf/f_{22})(1 + jf/f_{23})(1 + jf/f_{24})}$$

where

$$L_0 = \frac{g_m A_0 G_3}{(G_1 + G_3)(G_2 + G_3)}$$

If $f_{21} = f_{22} = f_{23} = f_{24}$, then the maximum value that L_0 can have is 4 [see Eq. (13-76)]. Thus, we cannot have all the half-power frequencies equal. For convenience, let us assume that

$$f_{21} = f_{22} = f_{2a} \qquad \text{and} \qquad f_{23} = f_{24} = f_{2b} \tag{13-79}$$

Thus

$$\mathbf{L} = \frac{-L_0}{(1 + jf/f_{2a})^2(1 + jf/f_{2b})^2}$$

For a moment, let us assume that f_{2b} is so much greater than f_{2a} that the second term in the denominator can be ignored. We shall determine the frequency f_c where the open-loop gain is 1. The specified value of L_0 is -100. Hence

$$\frac{100}{1 + (f_c/f_{2a})^2} = 1$$

Solving, we obtain

$$f_c = 9.95 f_{2a}$$

The phase angle of $\mathbf{L}$ at this frequency, due to these two stages, is given by $180° - 2\tan^{-1}9.95$.

$$\angle L_1(j\omega_c) = 11.5°$$

Since the amplifier is to work with frequencies of up to 10,000 Hz, the open-loop gain should be essentially flat up to that frequency. Thus, let us choose $f_{2a} = 10 \times 10,000 = 100,000$ Hz. (The magnitude of the open-loop gain will be approximately equal to 99 at a frequency of 10,000 Hz.) Then $f_c = 0.995 \times 10^6$ Hz. Now let us choose f_{2b} so that the phase margin is at least 5°. If the magnitude of $\angle[1/(1 + jf_c/f_{2b})^2] \leq 6.5°$, then this will be obtained. Note that $-6.5 + \angle L_1 = 5°$. [Actually, the phase margin will be greater than 5° since $|1/(1 + jf_c/f_{2b})|$ will be slightly less than unity.] Then

$$\tan^{-1} \frac{f_c}{f_{2b}} = \frac{6.5°}{2} = 3.25°$$

so that $f_c/f_{2b} = 0.057$ and $f_{2b} = 17.46 \times 10^6$ Hz. We have arbitrarily divided the half-power frequencies in Eqs. (13-79). Actually, all that is required is that two of the half-power frequencies be 100,000 Hz and that the other two be 17.46×10^6 Hz. Three of the half-power frequencies, f_{21}, f_{22}, and f_{23}, are half-power frequencies of the amplifier stages, while f_{24} is the half-power frequency of the β network. Both the gain of the amplifier stages and the resistances R_1 and R_3 of the β network will decrease if their respective half-power frequencies increase. If R_1 and R_3 are too small, then they will load down the output circuit. In addition, R_1 may represent the internal impedance of the signal generator, and hence, have a minimum value. As a compromise, we shall choose $f_{23} = f_{24} = 100,000$ Hz and

$$f_{21} = f_{22} = 17.46 \times 10^6 \text{ Hz}$$

To determine the value of R_1 and of R_3, let us assume that the input capacitor is 50 pf. Then, substituting in Eqs. (13-77) and (13-78), we have $G_1/G_3 = 50$ and $(G_1 + G_3)/(2\pi \times 50 \times 10^{-12}) = 100,000$. Solving, we obtain $R_3 = 1.623 \times 10^6$ ohms and $R_1 = 32,460$ ohms. Since we wish a midband open-loop gain of -100 and the midband loss of the β network is $R_1/(R_1 + R_3) = \frac{1}{51}$, the required midband gain of the amplifier is 5100. The methods of Chap. 9 are used in obtaining the amplifier design.

The 5° phase margin achieved in the design is very small. Often, phase margins of about 50° are desired. The gain margin of this amplifier is also small. We shall now redesign the amplifier to obtain a larger gain and phase margins. In the previous design, almost all the falloff in open-loop gain, up to f_c, was produced by two stages. These contributed 168.5° of phase shift, which resulted in the small phase margin. Now let us use essentially only one stage to reduce the gain to unity. This can contribute at most 90° of phase shift. Hence, we can have a greater phase margin. The notation of the previous design will be used. Then

$$f_{21} = f_{2a}$$
$$f_{22} = f_{23} = f_{24} = f_{2b}$$

and we have

$$\frac{100}{\sqrt{1 + \left(\dfrac{f_c}{f_{2a}}\right)^2}} = 1$$

Solving, we obtain $f_c/f_{2a} = 100$. As before, we choose $f_{2a} = 10^5$ Hz. Then, $f_c = 10^7$ Hz. At f_c, the phase shift due to one stage is

$$\angle L_1 = 180° - \tan^{-1} 100 = 90.4° \approx 90°$$

If the phase margin is to be 45°, then each of the other three stages can contribute 15° of phase shift at $f = f_c$. Hence,

$$\tan^{-1} \frac{f_c}{f_{2b}} = 15°$$

Thus, $f_{2b} = 37.32 \times 10^6$ Hz. Actually, we have achieved a phase margin that is somewhat greater than 45° for the reasons discussed in the last example. Let us now calculate the gain margin. For frequencies equal to or greater than f_c, the phase shift of the first stage is essentially 90°. Thus, the overall phase shift becomes 0° when the normalized phase shift of each stage of the other three stages is 30°. Let us call the frequency where this occurs f_d. Then,

$$\tan^{-1} \frac{f_d}{f_{2b}} = 30°$$

Hence, $f_d = 21.55 \times 10^6$ Hz. The magnitude of the open-loop gain at this frequency is

$$|L(j\omega)| = \frac{100}{(1 + 215.5^2)[1 + (21.55/37.32)^2]^3} = 0.301$$

Substituting in Eq. (13-67), we obtain a gain margin of 10.4 db.

The actual parameters of the amplifier are obtained as before. This calculation will not be repeated.

We have improved the gain and phase margins of the amplifier greatly. However, the half-power frequency of one stage has been increased from 10^5 to 37.32×10^6 Hz. In the other two stages, the half-power frequencies were increased from 17.46×10^6 to 37.32×10^6 Hz. As the half-power frequency is increased, the midband gain is reduced. In general, increasing the open-loop gain, the gain margin, and/or the phase margin imposes more stringent requirements on the bandwidth of the active devices. At times, increasing these quantities will make it impossible to build the amplifier with particular active devices. In such cases, FETs or transistors with higher g_m and/or lower shunt capacitances should be chosen if they are available.

In the next section we shall discuss a procedure for improving gain and phase margins which does not require as much bandwidth although large values of open-loop gain, gain margin, and/or phase margin will always require relatively broad bandwidth devices.

We have omitted the low-frequency design from this discussion. If we neglect the effect of the source bias impedance, then this design is essentially the same as the high-frequency design, except that there are only three RC-coupled stages rather than the four that were considered in the high-frequency case. Of course, increasing the low-frequency bandwidth does not reduce the midband gain. At times, direct-coupled amplifiers are used to achieve the low-frequency aspects of the design.

Actually, the effects of the source impedance must be considered. The results of Sec. 9-5 can be used here. The frequency response of these networks can be of help in obtaining the required design. In fact, the response of these networks is very similar to that of the corrective networks that will be discussed in the next section.

The design procedure for transistors is similar to that for FETs. The principles that were discussed in this section are applicable. The functions for the current gain of a transistor amplifier replace those for the voltage gain of an FET amplifier. The reactance of the external stray capacitance C_2 will affect the frequency response of the last stage. However, C_2 is often small enough to be ignored. Then the form of the frequency response of the transistor amplifier is similar to the FET amplifier, and thus the basic principles of design are the same. The major difference is that gain and bandwidth cannot be traded in exactly the same way in a FET amplifier as in a transistor amplifier.

13-13 CORRECTIVE NETWORKS

If the open-loop frequency response of a feedback amplifier is designed properly, then the midband magnitude of the open-loop gain can be made as large as desired. However, as was illustrated by the design of the last section, the upper (lower) half-power frequencies of the amplifier stages can become very high (low). Thus, it may prove difficult to construct amplifiers with the required gain. If networks could be devised that would cause the gain of an amplifier to fall off with increasing (or decreasing) frequency but would not introduce any phase shift, then they would be ideal. These could be used to reduce the magnitude of the open-loop gain below unity without causing its phase angle to approach zero degrees. Unfortunately, amplitude and phase response are interrelated, so that we cannot obtain such ideal networks. However, there are some networks which are not ideal but prove very helpful. Consider the two networks drawn in Fig. 13-26a and b. If we let $\mathbf{G} = \mathbf{V}_2/\mathbf{V}_1$ for the network of Fig. 13-26a and $\mathbf{G} = -\mathbf{I}_2/\mathbf{I}_1$ for the network of Fig. 13-26b, we have

$$\mathbf{G} = \frac{1 + jf/f_{2a}}{1 + jf/f_{2b}} \tag{13-80}$$

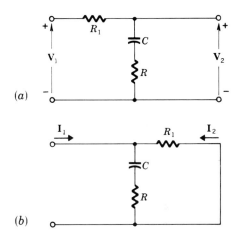

Fig. 13-26 Phase-lag-compensating networks: (a) voltage type and (b) current type.

where

$$f_{2a} = \frac{1}{2\pi RC} \tag{13-81}$$

and

$$f_{2b} = \frac{1}{2\pi(R_1 + R)C} \tag{13-82}$$

This network does not reduce the response to zero, but to f_{2b}/f_{2a} of its midband value. Plots of the asymptotes of the amplitude response of this function and its phase shift are given in Fig. 13-27. These networks are called *phase-lag networks* since they produce a lagging phase angle. As the frequency increases above $\sqrt{f_{2b}f_{2a}}$, the magnitude of the phase shift decreases toward zero. Thus, the circuit has some aspects of an ideal interstage network.

To illustrate the use of these corrective networks, let us consider that one is *added* to a feedback amplifier. The magnitude, in decibels, and phase angle of the open-loop gain $\mathbf{L}(j\omega)$ of this amplifier before correction are plotted in Fig. 13-28. The gain margin and phase margin are shown there.

Now consider that a corrective network, of the type shown in Fig. 13-26, is added. The overall gain and phase shift of the resulting open-loop gain are obtained by adding a response of the type of Fig. 13-27 to the solid curves of Fig. 13-28. This results in the dashed curves of Fig. 13-28. Note that the gain and phase margins have both been increased significantly.

In this example, the gain and phase margin have been increased without increasing the bandwidth of the amplifier stages. However, this will not always be the case. For instance, suppose that the corrective network had

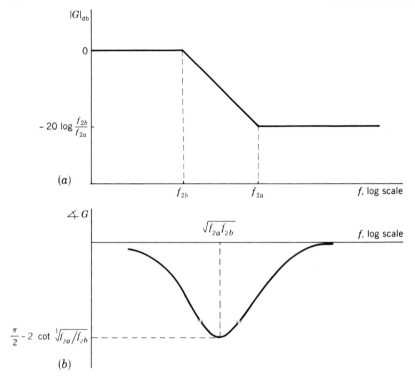

Fig. 13-27 (*a*) The asymptotes of amplitude response in decibels for the networks of Fig. 13-26 and (*b*) the phase response of these networks.

to introduce more loss than it did. In this case, f_{2b} would have to be increased (see Fig. 13-27). This will increase both the magnitude of the maximum phase shift of the compensating network and the frequency where this maximum occurs. This could lead to oscillation or low gain and phase margins. To prevent this, the bandwidth of the amplifier itself may have to be increased.

Several corrective networks could be added. In this case, the f_{2a} (or f_{2b}) of one network is not made the same as the f_{2a} (and f_{2b}) of the other; for example, $f'_{2b} > f'_{2a} > f_{2b} > f_{2a}$ where the primes refer to one of the corrective networks. This is done so that the maximum phase shifts do not occur at the same frequency. Thus, the overall phase shift is kept low. However, this requires a relatively broad bandwidth to work within. Again, this may require that the bandwidth of the amplifier itself be increased.

Compensating networks can be used to correct the low-frequency response. Two such networks are shown in Fig. 13-29. If $\mathbf{G} = \mathbf{V}_2/\mathbf{V}_1$ for

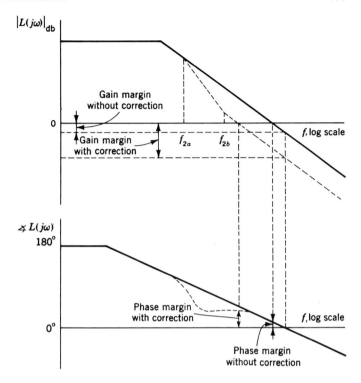

Fig. 13-28 An illustration of the use of a corrective network; the dashed curve represents the gain and phase margins after the corrective networks have been added. The asymptotes of the curves are drawn.

the network of Fig. 13-29a and $\mathbf{G} = -\mathbf{I}_2/\mathbf{I}_1$ for the network of Fig. 13-29b, we have

$$\mathbf{G} = \frac{f_{1a}}{f_{1b}} \frac{1 + jf/f_{1a}}{1 + jf/f_{1b}} \tag{13-83}$$

where

$$f_{1a} = \frac{1}{2\pi RC} \tag{13-84}$$

$$f_{1b} = \frac{R_1 + R}{2\pi R_1 RC} \tag{13-85}$$

The response of this network is similar to that of the networks of Fig. 13-26, except that the amplitude response falls off with decreasing frequency and the phase angle leads instead of lags. (The reason for the difference is that in

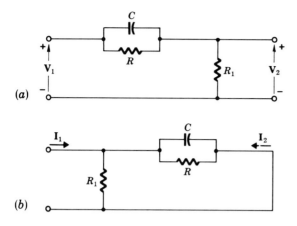

Fig. 13-29 Phase-lead-compensating networks: (a) voltage type and (b) current type.

these networks $f_{1b} > f_{1a}$.) This is called the *phase-lead network*. Its application in the low-frequency region is similar to that of the phase-lag network in the high-frequency region.

The source, cathode, or screen-grid bias impedances and the emitter-stabilizing impedance (see Secs. 9-5 and 9-6) produce a frequency response that is essentially the same as that of the phase-lead network. Thus, these impedances can serve the same functions as the frequency-corrective networks.

13-14 OPERATIONAL AMPLIFIERS

Feedback can be used to obtain electronic devices that perform mathematical operations. These devices are called *operational amplifiers*. One application of them is in analog computers, where an electric circuit is set up so that its response is the solution of a differential equation. In this section, we shall develop amplifiers that can be used to solve linear integrodifferential equations.

Multiplication by a constant; addition and subtraction Consider the block diagram of the amplifier of Fig. 13-30a. We shall assume that the amplifier is ideal in that $\mathbf{Z}_i$ is infinite and $v_2/v_a = A$. In general, v_a will be very small. Usually, the open-loop gain of the feedback amplifier is high. Then, $|v_a| \ll |v_1|$ and $|v_a| \ll |v_2|$. This also tends to keep any current entering the amplifier small, even if $\mathbf{Z}_i$ is not infinite. Then, the current i must be through R_1 as well as R_2. Hence

$$i = \frac{v_1 - v_a}{R_1} = \frac{v_a - v_2}{R_2} \tag{13-86}$$

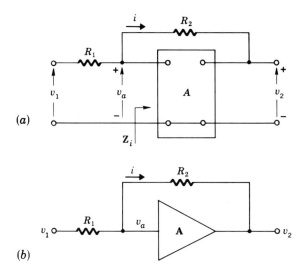

Fig. 13-30 (*a*) An operational amplifier that multiplies by a constant and (*b*) a simplified representation of this amplifier.

but

$$v_a = \frac{v_2}{A} \tag{13-87}$$

Substituting, we obtain

$$\frac{v_2}{R_2}\left[1 - \frac{1}{A}\left(1 + \frac{R_2}{R_1}\right)\right] = -\frac{v_1}{R_1} \tag{13-88}$$

If the voltage gain is sufficiently high so that

$$1 \gg \left|\frac{1}{A}\left(1 + \frac{R_2}{R_1}\right)\right| \tag{13-89}$$

then we can approximate v_2 by

$$v_2 = -\frac{R_2}{R_1}v_1 \tag{13-90}$$

Thus, we have achieved multiplication by a constant. The representation of Fig. 13-30*b* is the one that is usually used in analog-computer circuits.

Now consider the circuit of Fig. 13-31. Here

$$i = \frac{v_{11} - v_a}{R_{11}} + \frac{v_{12} - v_a}{R_{12}} + \cdots + \frac{v_{1n} - v_a}{R_{1n}} = \frac{v_a - v_2}{R_2}$$

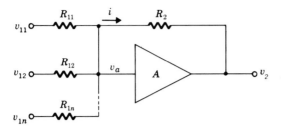

Fig. 13-31 An electronic circuit that performs the mathematical operation of addition and multiplication by a constant.

Then, substituting Eq. (13-87), we obtain

$$\frac{v_2}{R_2}\left[1 - \frac{1}{A}\left(1 + \frac{R_2}{R_{11}} + \frac{R_2}{R_{12}} + \cdots + \frac{R_2}{R_{1n}}\right)\right]$$

$$= -\left(\frac{v_{11}}{R_{11}} + \frac{v_{12}}{R_{12}} + \cdots + \frac{v_{1n}}{R_{1n}}\right)$$

If

$$1 \gg \left|\frac{1}{A}\left(1 + \frac{R_2}{R_{11}} + \frac{R_2}{R_{12}} + \cdots + \frac{R_2}{R_{1n}}\right)\right| \tag{13-91}$$

then

$$v_2 = -R_2\left(\frac{v_{11}}{R_{11}} + \frac{v_{12}}{R_{12}} + \cdots + \frac{v_{1n}}{R_{1n}}\right) \tag{13-92}$$

Thus, we can multiply a number of voltages by arbitrary constants and add them. The constant multiplier can be adjusted by varying the input resistors. Note that the input circuits do not interact with each other.

These amplifiers introduce a minus sign. If this is not desired, then two amplifier stages should be cascaded. Two signals can be subtracted by multiplying them by −1 before they are added.

Differentiation   Consider the circuit of Fig. 13-32. We have

$$i = C\frac{d}{dt}(v_1 - v_a) = \frac{v_a - v_2}{R} \tag{13-93}$$

Then, substituting Eq. (13-87), we obtain

$$-C\frac{dv_1}{dt} = \frac{v_2}{R} - \frac{1}{A}\left(\frac{v_2}{R} + C\frac{dv_2}{dt}\right)$$

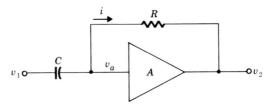

Fig. 13-32 A differentiator.

If

$$\left|\frac{v_2}{R}\right| \gg \left|\frac{1}{A}\left(\frac{v_2}{R} + C\frac{dv_2}{dt}\right)\right| \tag{13-94}$$

then

$$v_2 = -RC\frac{dv_1}{dt} \tag{13-95}$$

Thus, the output is proportional to the derivative of the input. The inequality of relation (13-94) requires some comment. There may be times when $dv_2/dt \gg v_2$, and the inequality will not be valid no matter how large A is. The value of A should be made large enough so that relation (13-94) is satisfied for almost all the time and in practical cases (with bounded derivatives) is invalid only when v_2 is very small. Usually the inequality is satisfied in this way in practical analog computers.

Integration Consider the circuit of Fig. 13-33. For the time being, ignore the battery V_0. Then

$$i = \frac{v_1 - v_a}{R} = C\frac{d}{dt}(v_a - v_2) \tag{13-96}$$

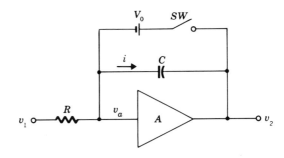

Fig. 13-33 An integrator.

Substitute Eq. (13-87); this yields

$$C \frac{dv_2}{dt} - \frac{1}{A} \left(\frac{v_2}{R} + C \frac{dv_2}{dt} \right) = -\frac{v_1}{R}$$

If

$$\left| C \frac{dv_2}{dt} \right| \gg \left| \frac{1}{A} \left(\frac{v_2}{R} + C \frac{dv_2}{dt} \right) \right| \tag{13-97}$$

then

$$v_2 = -\frac{1}{RC} \int v_1 \, dt \tag{13-98}$$

This circuit provides a convenient means of establishing the initial value of a variable. Assume that the switch sw of Fig. 13-33 is closed prior to $t = 0$ and is opened at $t = 0$. Then, at $t = 0+$, just after the switch is opened, the voltage across the capacitors is V_0 and, thus,

$$v_{20} - v_{a0} = V_0$$

Substituting Eq. (13-87) and assuming that $1 \gg |1/A|$, we have

$$v_{20} = V_0 \tag{13-99}$$

Thus, the battery and switch are a simple means of establishing the initial value of a variable.

To illustrate the use of these operational amplifiers, let us use them to solve a simple differential equation

$$\frac{d^2y}{dt^2} + A \frac{dy}{dt} + By = f(t) \tag{13-100}$$

Rewrite this equation as

$$\frac{d^2y}{dt^2} = -A \frac{dy}{dt} - By + f(t) \tag{13-101}$$

Consider the circuit of Fig. 13-34. For the time being, assume that the connection between points a and b is broken and that a generator equal to the unknown d^2y/dt^2 is available and connected to point a. The analog computer should provide a means for generating the driving function $f(t)$. Then the voltages will be as marked on the diagram. Using Eq. (13-101), we have that the voltage at point b equals d^2y/dt^2. If the d^2y/dt^2 generator is removed and points a and b are connected as shown, then, since an equilibrium must be established and the required $f(t)$ is supplied, the circuit voltages will be the required ones. The unknown y can be obtained from the terminal so marked. The voltages equal to d^2y/dt^2 and $-dy/dt$ can also be obtained from the appropriate terminals.

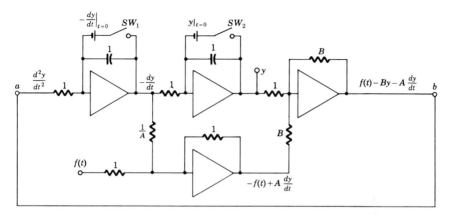

Fig. 13-34 A circuit for the solution of the differential equation (13-100). The values of resistance and capacitance are given in megohms and microfarads, respectively.

The initial values of y and dy/dt are established by means of the appropriate batteries. At $t = 0$, switches sw_1 and sw_2 are opened and $f(t)$ is applied. Note that writing the differential equation in the form of Eq. (13-101) allows us to use integrating circuits and, thus, to conveniently establish initial values.

We have worked with voltage amplifiers in this section. We could have proceeded on a dual basis and used current amplifiers.

BIBLIOGRAPHY

Bode, H. W.: "Network Analysis and Feedback Amplifier Design," chap. 7, D. Van Nostrand Company, Inc., Princeton, N.J., 1945. (A difficult graduate-level book.)

Chirlian, P. M.: "Analysis and Design of Electronic Circuits," chap. 10, McGraw-Hill Book Company, New York, 1965.

Gibbons, J. E.: "Semiconductor Electronics," chap. 14, McGraw-Hill Book Company, New York, 1966.

Gray, T. S.: "Applied Electronics," pp. 570–600, John Wiley & Sons, Inc., New York, 1954.

Millman, J., and C. C. Halkias: "Electronic Devices and Circuits," chap. 17, McGraw-Hill Book Company, New York, 1967.

Schilling, D. L., and C. Belove: "Electronic Circuits: Discrete and Integrated," chap. 8, McGraw-Hill Book Company, New York, 1968.

Truxal, J. G.: "Automatic Feedback Control System Synthesis," pp. 143–159, McGraw-Hill Book Company, New York, 1955.

PROBLEMS

13-1. A feedback amplifier has a gain that is given by Eq. (13-4). If $A = -20$ and $\beta = -0.1$, comment on the accuracy of Eq. (13-6). Repeat this problem for values of A equal to -100 and -1000.

13-2. The gain of a feedback amplifier is given by Eq. (13-4), where $A = -9$ and $\beta = -0.1$. If $|A|$ increases by 10 percent, what will the percentage change in K be?

13-3. Repeat Prob. 13-2, but now use values of $A = -1000$ and $A = +9$.

13-4. Obtain an exact expression for the voltage gain of the amplifier of Fig. 13-35.

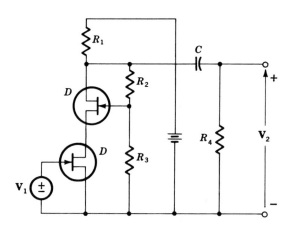

Fig. 13-35

The answer should be in terms of the parameters of the FETs and the circuit elements. Assume that the reactance of C is zero at the signal frequency.

13-5. Repeat Prob. 13-4 but now use the vacuum-tube amplifier of Fig. 13-36.

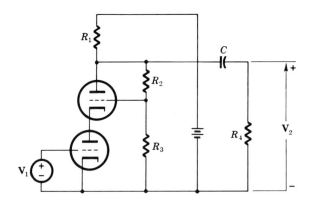

Fig. 13-36

13-6. Obtain an exact expression for the current gain of the amplifier of Fig. 13-37. The answer should be in terms of the low-frequency h parameters of the transistor and the circuit elements. Assume that the reactance of C is zero at the signal frequency.

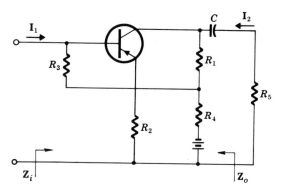

Fig. 13-37

13-7. Repeat Prob. 13-6 but now use the hybrid-pi model for the transistor. Assume that the capacitors of the model can be considered to be open circuits.

13-8. Compare the ratio of the distortion to the signal X_{2d}/X_{2s} for the feedback amplifier of Fig. 13-38. Use the following three cases: $\beta_1 = 0$ and $\beta_2 = 0$; $\beta_1 = 0$ and

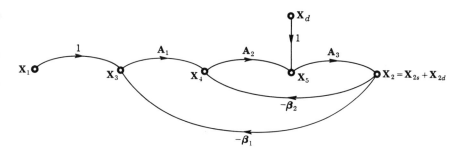

Fig. 13-38

$\beta_2 = \beta_2$; $\beta_1 = \beta_1$ and $\beta_2 = \beta_2$. Assume that the input signal X_1 can be varied so that X_{2s} remains constant.

13-9. Repeat Prob. 13-8, but now assume that X_1 is constant.

13-10. If, for the amplifier of Fig. 13-22, $K = X_2/X_1$ and A_1 changes by an amount ΔA_1, what will the fractional change $\Delta K/K$ be?

13-11. Repeat Prob. 13-10 for a fractional change ΔA_2 in A_2.

13-12. A feedback amplifier is such that its gain expression is given by Eq. (13-4). If $A = -A_0/[(1 + jf/f_a)(1 + jf/f_b)]$, how does the midband-gain–half-power-bandwidth product vary with β?

13-13. Compute the output impedance of the amplifier of Fig. 13-4. Assume that C_s is a short circuit.

13-14. Repeat Prob. 13-13, but now do not assume that C_s is a short circuit.

13-15. Compute an expression for the input impedance Z_i of the amplifier of Fig. 13-37.

13-16. Compute an expression for the output impedance $\mathbf{Z}_0$ of the amplifier of Fig. 13-37. Assume that the impedance of the input generator is infinite.

13-17. Compute the voltage gain of the amplifier of Fig. 13-13a, was done in Sec. 13-7, but do not consider that the coupling capacitor C is a short circuit.

13-18. Repeat Prob. 13-17 but now do not consider that any capacitor acts as a short circuit.

13-19. Compute the current gain of the amplifier of Fig. 13-14a, as was done in Sec. 13-7, but do not assume that the coupling capacitor C is a short circuit.

13-20. Compute the voltage gain $\mathbf{V}_2/\mathbf{V}_1$ of the amplifier of Fig. 13-39. Neglect the effect of all coupling, bypass, and parasitic capacitors.

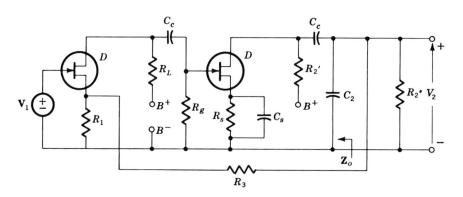

Fig. 13-39

13-21. Repeat Prob. 13-20, but do not neglect the coupling, bypass, and parasitic capacitors.

13-22. Compute the output impedance $\mathbf{Z}_0$ of the amplifier of Fig. 13-39. Neglect the effects of the coupling, bypass, and parasitic capacitors.

13-23. Repeat Prob. 13-20 for the amplifier of Fig. 13-40.

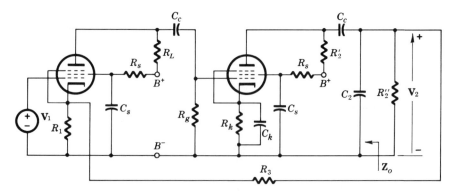

Fig. 13-40

13-24. Repeat Prob. 13-21 for the amplifier of Fig. 13-40.

13-25. Repeat Prob. 13-22 for the amplifier of Fig. 13-40.

13-26. Compute the current gain I_2/I_1 of the amplifier of Fig. 13-41. Assume that all coupling and bypass capacitors are short circuits and that high-frequency effects can be ignored.

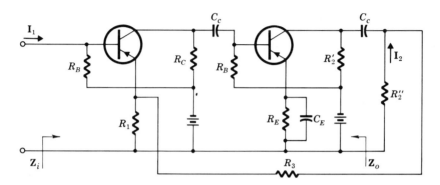

Fig. 13-41

13-27. Repeat Prob. 13-26 but do not consider that the coupling and bypass capacitors are short circuits or that the high-frequency effects can be ignored.

13-28. Compute the input and output impedances for the amplifier of Fig. 13-41. Use the assumptions of Prob. 13-26.

13-29. The following polynomials are the denominator polynomials of the transformed form of the gain expression of a feedback amplifier. There are no common factors in the numerators. Use the Hurwitz test to determine which amplifiers are stable.

(a) $s^3 + 5s^2 + 8s + 6$
(b) $s^3 - 4s^2 + 9s + 7$
(c) $s^3 + 9s + 2$
(d) $s^4 + 2s^3 + 3s^2 + 2s + 2$
(e) $s^4 + s^3 + s^2 + 12s + 6$

13-30. Repeat Prob. 13-29, but now use the Routh procedure.

13-31. The open-loop gain of a feedback amplifier is given by $-6/(1 + jf/10,000)^3$. Draw the Nyquist diagram for this amplifier. Is it stable?

13-32. Repeat Prob. 13-31 for an open-loop gain of $-3/[(1 + jf/10,000)^4(1 + j10/f)^3]$.

13-33. Repeat Prob. 13-31 for an open-loop gain of $-6(1 + jf/10,000)^4$.

13-34. A feedback amplifier has an open-loop gain of $-8/(1 + jf/f_2)^4$. Will this amplifier be stable for any finite and nonzero value of f_2?

13-35. Obtain exact expression for the open-loop gain of the amplifier of Fig. 13-13a. Assume that all bypass capacitors are short circuits. Neglect any parasitic capacitances that are not shown.

13-36. Repeat Prob. 13-35 for the amplifier of Fig. 13-14a. Neglect any high-frequency effects.

13-37. Determine the gain and phase margins for the amplifier of Prob. 13-31.

13-38. Repeat Prob. 13-37 for the amplifier of Prob. 13-32. Note that there are actually two sets of gain and phase margins, one for the high frequencies and one for the low frequencies.

13-39. The low-frequency response of the open-loop gain of a feedback amplifier is given by $-100/[1(+ jf_a/f)(1 + jf_b/f)(1 + jf_c/f)]$ and the amplifier is to work with frequencies down to 20 Hz. The magnitude of the open-loop gain is not to be less than 75 over the useful range of frequencies. Design the amplifier, in regard to the low-frequency response, so that it will be stable and have at least a $10°$ phase margin.

13-40. Repeat Prob. 13-39 for a $45°$ phase margin. What is the gain margin in this case?

13-41. The current gain of a single transistor amplifier stage is $A_i = A_0/(1 + jf/f_2)$. Three of these are to be used in a single-loop feedback amplifier whose open-loop gain is $A_{i1}A_{i2}A_{i3}\beta$. The midband open-loop gain is to have a magnitude of at least 100 and $\beta = -\frac{1}{50}$. Design the amplifier. For each stage, $A_{i,\text{mid}} = 100R_{\text{sh}}/R_i$ and $f_2 = 1/2\pi C(R_1 + R_{\text{sh}})$, where $C = 100$ pf and the maximum value of f_2 is 200×10^6 Hz. $R_i = 2000$ ohms. The open-loop gain should be essentially constant up to a frequency of 10^5 Hz. The three stages are not to be identical. Design the amplifier so that it is stable. There should be a $5°$ phase margin.

13-42. Repeat Prob. 13-41 but now use a $45°$ phase margin if possible.

13-43. The open-loop gain of a feedback amplifier is $100/[(1 - jf_a/f)(1 - jf_b/f)^2 (1 + jf/f_c)^2(1 + jf/f_d)^2]$. What relations must exist among f_a, f_b, f_c, and f_d if this amplifier is to be stable? Assume that f_a and f_b are both very much less than f_c and f_d.

13-44. Discuss how a bias impedance or an emitter-stabilizing impedance can be used in the design of a feedback amplifier.

13-45. Modify the design of Prob. 13-39 by adding corrective networks to increase the phase margin to $20°$.

13-46. Repeat Prob. 13-45 for the amplifier of Prob. 13-41.

13-47. Set up a circuit which can be used to solve the differential equation

$$\frac{d^3y}{dt^3} + 3\frac{d^2y}{dt^2} - 5\frac{dy}{dt} + 6y = f(t)$$

where

$$y\Big|_{t=0} = 0 \qquad \frac{dy}{dt}\Big|_{t=0} = -3 \qquad \text{and} \qquad \frac{d^2y}{dt^2}\Big|_{t=0} = 7$$

Assume that a generator whose output voltage is equal to $f(t)$ is available.

13-48. Repeat Prob. 13-47, but now assume that $f(t) = e^{-3t} \sin 2t$ and that no such generator is available. [Hint: Set up a differential equation whose solution is $f(t)$.]

14

Sinusoidal Oscillators

Very often such electronic devices as receivers, transmitters, and a great variety of electronic test equipment must generate a sinusoid of specified frequency. To obtain these signals, an *oscillator* is built. That is, we deliberately construct an unstable feedback amplifier. The basis for much of the analysis of oscillator circuits has been developed in the last chapter. However, simplifications and modifications can be made for the usual oscillator circuits. These will be discussed in this chapter.

14-1 CRITERIA FOR OSCILLATION

The criteria for the stability of feedback amplifiers, which were discussed in Secs. 13-9 and 13-10, can also be applied to determine if a circuit will oscillate. For instance, if a feedback circuit has the Nyquist plot of Fig. 13-23a, we can state that it will oscillate if the gain is such that $\overline{OB} > 1$. In general, if the open-loop gain of a feedback amplifier is equal to $L_a \underline{/0}$ at some frequency ω_a

and $L_a > 1$, we *cannot* state that the amplifier will oscillate (see Fig. 13-23c). However, if we restrict ourselves to relatively simple circuits, where the amplitude response decreases monotonically and the phase angle increases or decreases monotonically as we depart from a midband region, then Nyquist diagrams such as those of Fig. 13-25 result. *In such cases, we can state that a device will oscillate if the magnitude of its open-loop gain is greater than* 1 *when its phase angle is zero.* Most oscillator circuits fit into this category; thus, the criterion for their oscillation is very simple. As a corollary, if there is oscillation for one value of gain, then increasing the magnitude of the open-loop gain (without changing the frequency response) will not cause the oscillation to cease. The Nyquist diagrams for oscillator circuits often differ from those for amplifiers in that there is positive feedback in the midband region. Thus, often, the Nyquist diagram of Fig. 13-25 would be reflected about the vertical axis if the devices were to be oscillators. This would allow the critical point to be included more easily; i.e., the gain of the amplifier could be lower. For instance, in any of Fig. 13-25, oscillation would then occur if $\overline{OA}$ were greater than 1.

In order for our analysis to apply to FETs and transistors, we shall use the generalized active element of Fig. 14-1. The impedance $\mathbf{Z}_i$ is the input impedance of the active element. In a common-source FET, it could include the input capacitance. However, it is often convenient to treat the interelectrode capacitances as external elements. For the transistor, $\mathbf{Z}_i$ represents the input impedance (see Fig. 9-63). In the common-source FET, $\mathbf{Y}_{fb}$ represents C_{gd} while in the transistor $\mathbf{Y}_{fb}$ represents the parallel interconnection of $r_{b'c}$ and $C_{b'c}$.

For the common-source FET, $\mathbf{Y}_o$ represents r_d in parallel with C_{ds}. For the transistor $\mathbf{Y}_o$ can be represented as shown in Fig. 9-64. If, as is often the case, the transistor is operated at frequencies far below ω_β, then $\mathbf{Y}_i$ and $\mathbf{Y}_o$ can be considered as resistors in shunt with capacitors (see Figs. 9-63 and 9-64).

In the case of the FET or vacuum tube, the current of the current generator is proportional to the voltage $\mathbf{V}_1$. In the case of the transistor,

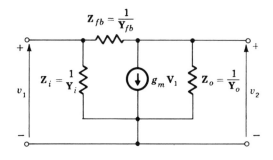

Fig. 14-1 Generalized linear device to be used in the study of oscillation.

that current is proportional to $V_{b'e}$ (see Fig. 6-42). However, at frequencies far below ω_β, $V_{b'e} \approx V_1$. [Actually, $V_{b'e} \approx V_1 r_{b'e}/(r_{b'e} + r_{bb'})$. Thus, g_m can be replaced by $r_{b'e} g_m/(r_{b'e} + r_{bb'})$. Often this is not necessary since $r_{b'e} \gg r_{bb'}$.]

Frequently the output capacitance will be included as an external element. In this case $\mathbf{Y}_o$ is written as g. We shall now consider two procedures to determine whether a simple structure will oscillate.

Infinite gain An oscillator may be thought of as an amplifier with zero input signal. Then if there is to be an output, the gain must be infinite. Consider the typical oscillator structure shown in Fig. 14-2. Let us write the nodal equations for this circuit.

$$0 = (\mathbf{Y}_1 + \mathbf{Y}_i + \mathbf{Y}_3)\mathbf{V}_1 - \mathbf{Y}_3\mathbf{V}_2 \tag{14-1}$$

$$0 = (g_m - \mathbf{Y}_3)\mathbf{V}_1 + (\mathbf{Y}_3 + \mathbf{Y}_2 + g)\mathbf{V}_2 \tag{14-2}$$

The solution for $\mathbf{V}_2$ in determinant form is

$$\mathbf{V}_2 = \frac{\begin{vmatrix} \mathbf{Y}_1 + \mathbf{Y}_i + \mathbf{Y}_3 & 0 \\ g_m - \mathbf{Y}_3 & 0 \end{vmatrix}}{\begin{vmatrix} \mathbf{Y}_1 + \mathbf{Y}_i + \mathbf{Y}_3 & -\mathbf{Y}_3 \\ g_m - \mathbf{Y}_3 & \mathbf{Y}_3 + \mathbf{Y}_2 + g \end{vmatrix}} \tag{14-3}$$

The numerator determinant is zero. If there is to be any output, the denominator determinant must also be zero. Hence,

$$g_m = -\frac{(\mathbf{Y}_1 + \mathbf{Y}_i)(\mathbf{Y}_2 + \mathbf{Y}_3 + g) + \mathbf{Y}_3(\mathbf{Y}_2 + g)}{\mathbf{Y}_3} \tag{14-4}$$

This equation is not as simple as it may seem. The right-hand side is usually a complex number which is a function of frequency. Thus,

$$g_m = G(\omega) + jB(\omega) \tag{14-5}$$

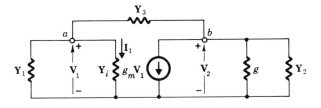

Fig. 14-2 A basic oscillator structure. $\mathbf{Y}_3$ represents the parallel combination of $\mathbf{Y}_{fb}$ and an external element connected from a to b; g represents the conductive component of $\mathbf{Y}_o$. $\mathbf{Y}_2$ represents the susceptive component of $\mathbf{Y}_o$ in parallel with an external element connected from point b to the reference.

If g_m is a real number, the criteria for oscillation become

$$g_m = G(\omega) \tag{14-6}$$

$$B(\omega) = 0 \tag{14-7}$$

In general, there is only one value of ω, called ω_0, that will satisfy Eq. (14-7); thus, this equation is used to determine the frequency of oscillation. This value can then be substituted into Eq. (14-6). Thus, for the simple Nyquist plots that we have been considering,

$$g_m \geq G(\omega_0) \tag{14-8}$$

is the condition that must be imposed upon the active element if oscillation is to occur. We shall see examples of this procedure in the next section.

For a transistor if the frequency of operation is not well below ω_β, g_m will have to be replaced by a complex function of frequency. Thus, it may not always be possible to consider that g_m is a real number. However, the basic procedure is the same.

Zero impedance, negative resistance Another procedure for determining the criterion for oscillation of a simple structure is to establish a loop with zero impedance for some value of ω. A sinusoidal current can then persist indefinitely in this loop. For instance, consider the basic oscillator structure of Fig. 14-2. We wish to determine the impedance looking into terminals ab when $\mathbf{Y}_3$ is removed. A simple analysis yields

$$\mathbf{Z}_{ab} = \frac{1}{\mathbf{Y}_1 + \mathbf{Y}_i} + \frac{1}{g + \mathbf{Y}_2} + \frac{g_m}{(\mathbf{Y}_1 + \mathbf{Y}_i)(g + \mathbf{Y}_2)} \tag{14-9}$$

If

$$\frac{1}{\mathbf{Y}_3} + \mathbf{Z}_{ab} = 0 \tag{14-10}$$

for some value of ω, then there will be oscillation. Substituting Eq. (14-9) into Eq. (14-10), we obtain

$$g_m = -\frac{(\mathbf{Y}_1 + \mathbf{Y}_i)(\mathbf{Y}_2 + \mathbf{Y}_3 + g) + \mathbf{Y}_3(\mathbf{Y}_2 + g)}{\mathbf{Y}_3} \tag{14-11}$$

Thus, the criterion for oscillation is the same as Eq. (14-4), and the discussion following it holds here also. Note that the impedance around any loop could have been set equal to zero to determine this criterion.

To obtain some physical insight into this procedure, let us examine a specific example. Assume that $\mathbf{Y}_i = 0$, $g = 0$, g_m is a real number, and $\mathbf{Y}_1$ and $\mathbf{Y}_2$ represent capacitance admittances. Thus,

$$\mathbf{Y}_1 = j\omega C_1 \qquad \mathbf{Y}_2 = j\omega C_2$$

Substitution in Eq. (14-9) yields

$$\mathbf{Z}_{ab} = -\frac{g_m}{\omega^2 C_1 C_2} + \frac{1}{j\omega C_1} + \frac{1}{j\omega C_2}$$

This represents the series connection of two capacitors C_1 and C_2, and a *negative* resistance $-g_m/\omega^2 C_1 C_2$. Now let us assume that $\mathbf{Y}_3$ represents an inductance with a series resistance.

$$\frac{1}{\mathbf{Y}_3} = R + j\omega L$$

Then, substituting in Eq. (14-10) and using Eqs. (14-5) to (14-8), we obtain the criterion for oscillation.

$$g_m \geq \omega_0{}^2 C_1 C_2 R \qquad \text{or} \qquad \omega_0 = \frac{1}{\sqrt{LC_1 C_2/(C_1 + C_2)}}$$

Thus, we can consider that oscillation results when there is a negative resistance of proper magnitude to offset the losses of the circuit elements.

Both procedures presented in this section are equivalent to setting the open-loop gain equal to unity. Note that in the case of the FET most insight is usually gained if the open-loop voltage gain is considered. For the transistor the open-loop current gain provides the most insight. This will be illustrated in Sec. 14-3.

14-2 TYPICAL RADIO-FREQUENCY OSCILLATOR CIRCUITS

Some representative oscillator circuits are shown in Fig. 14-3. In Fig. 14-3a and b, the feedback takes place between the coupled coils. There are modifications of this circuit wherein the input circuit is tuned or where both input and output circuits are tuned. The oscillators of Fig. 14-3c and d are called *Colpitts oscillators*. The tuned circuit consists of the two capacitors C_1 and C_2 and the inductor L. The counterpart of this circuit is the *Hartley oscillator*, which is shown in Fig. 14-3e and f. Here the tuned circuits consist of the inductors L_1 and L_2, and the capacitor C. Some of these circuits use an inductor labeled RFC (radio frequency choke). It is designed so that it is essentially an open circuit at the frequency of operation. The elements R_g, C_g, R_B, R_{B1}, R_{B2}, C_B, R_E, C_E, and C_a are included for bias or stabilization purposes. In these circuits, the operation is often nonlinear. The tuned circuits are used to reject any unwanted harmonics. Linear and nonlinear operation of oscillators is discussed in Sec. 14-4. We have illustrated the transistor circuits in the common-emitter configuration. Common-base and common-collector circuits can also be used, and their circuits are similar.

The MOSFET can often be operated in the enhancement and depletion node. Thus, in theory, it can be operated without bias. In this case, R_g in

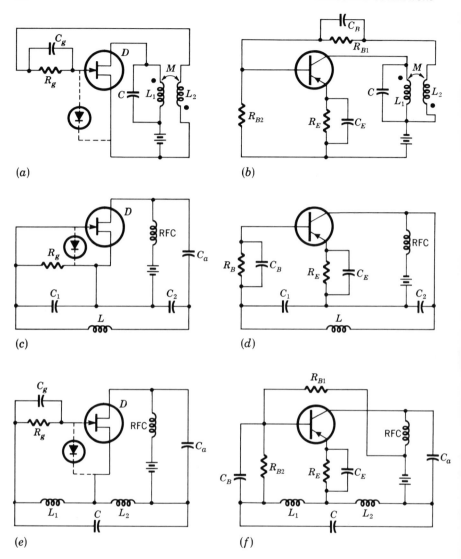

Fig. 14-3 Some basic radio-frequency oscillator circuits: (a) and (b) tuned output; (c) and (d) Colpitts; (e) and (f) Hartley. If MOSFETS are used, the R_g can be replaced by a short circuit in Figs. 14-3a to e. The level of oscillation will be reduced if R_g and the diodes shown dashed are included in each circuit.

Fig. 14-3a and e can be replaced by short circuits. However, it is often desirable to have the oscillation produce a bias and this bias reduce the g_m of the device. This then will limit the magnitude of the oscillator's signal. This will be discussed in greater detail in Sec. 14-4. The inclusion of R_g and the diodes, shown dashed in Fig. 14-3a, c, and e, will accomplish this. The bias that results is similar to grid leak bias (see Sec. 11-6).

Let us demonstrate how the criterion for oscillation developed in the last section can be applied to these circuits. For instance, let us apply the infinite-gain procedure to Fig. 14-3b. We shall assume that C_B and C_E are short circuits at the signal frequency and that R_{B2} can be considered to be an open circuit. Then, using the approximate model discussed in Sec. 14-1, we obtain the linear model of Fig. 14-4a. In Fig. 14-4b a voltage generator is used instead of a current generator. In general, $R_i \ll 1/\omega C_i$. Thus, C_i is omitted from Fig. 14-4b. We shall assume that $R_i + R_2 \gg \omega L_2$ and $R_i + R_2 \gg \omega M$. Then,

$$I_1 = -\frac{j\omega M I_3}{R_i + R_2}$$

The circuit of Fig. 14-4c can be obtained using the procedure of Sec. 9-23. Then

$$0 = \left(\frac{1}{g_o} - \frac{j}{\omega C}\right) I_2 - j\left[-\frac{1}{\omega C} + \frac{g_m \omega M R_i}{g_o(R_i + R_2)}\right] I_3$$

$$0 = +\frac{j}{\omega C} I_2 + \left[R_1 + \frac{\omega^2 M^2}{R_i + R_2} + j\left(\omega L_1 - \frac{1}{\omega C}\right)\right] I_3$$

Setting the real and imaginary parts of the determinant of the equations equal to zero, we obtain

$$R_1 + \frac{\omega^2 M^2}{R_i + R_2} + \frac{g_o L_1}{C} - \frac{g_m R_i M}{C(R_i + R_2)} = 0 \tag{14-12}$$

and

$$\omega^2 L_1 C - \frac{\omega^2 M^2 g_o}{R_i + R_2} - 1 - R_1 g_o = 0 \tag{14-13}$$

Solving Eq. (14-13) for ω^2, we obtain, for the frequency of oscillation,

$$\omega_0 = \sqrt{\frac{1 + R_1 g_o}{L_1 C - M^2 g_o/(R_i + R_2)}} \tag{14-14}$$

Then

$$g_m \geq \frac{C(R_i + R_2)}{R_i M}\left(R_1 + \frac{\omega_0^2 M^2}{R_i + R_2} + \frac{g_o L_1}{C}\right) \tag{14-15}$$

This gives the minimum value of g_m that can be used if the circuit is to oscillate. Note that the frequency of oscillation depends upon the parameters of the circuit and the transistor as well as on the resonant circuit.

Now let us analyze the circuit of Fig. 14-3c. We shall assume that $1/\omega C_1 \ll R_g$ and that the RFC acts as an open circuit at the signal frequency. Thus, the equivalent circuit for this oscillator is given in Fig. 14-2. The

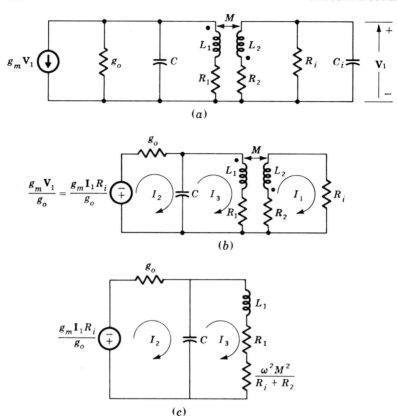

Fig. 14-4 (a) Linear model of the oscillator of Fig. 14-3b. The capacitor C represents the output capacitance of the transistor in parallel with any external capacitance. (b) A modification of this circuit. It has been assumed that $R_i \ll 1 \ \omega C_i$. (c) A further modification of this circuit.

criterion for oscillation for this circuit is Eq. (14-4) where $g = 1/r_d$, $\mathbf{Y}_1 = j\omega C_1$, $\mathbf{Y}_2 = j\omega C_2$, $\mathbf{Y}_3 = 1/(R + j\omega L)$, and $\mathbf{Y}_i = 0$. Note that we have included a resistance in series with the coil and assumed that the capacitors are lossless. This is usually justified in practice. Then, substituting in Eq. (14-4) or (14-11) and setting the real and imaginary parts equal to zero, we obtain

$$\omega_0 = \sqrt{\frac{C_1 + C_2}{C_1 C_2 L} + \frac{R}{C_2 L r_d}} \tag{14-16}$$

$$g_m \geq \omega_0^2 C_1 C_2 R + \frac{\omega_0^2 L C_1 - 1}{r_d} \tag{14-17}$$

The two circuits that we have analyzed in this section are typical of many radio-frequency oscillator circuits.

14-3 THE *RC* OSCILLATOR

The frequency of oscillation of the oscillators that were discussed in the last section is close to the resonant frequency of the tuned circuit. However, at low frequencies the resonant circuit elements become very large. In Sec. 13-12, it was demonstrated that a simple three-stage *RC*-coupled amplifier with identical stages would oscillate if the magnitude of the midband open-loop gain were greater than 8. This provides a simple means of obtaining a low-frequency oscillator without using large resonant circuits. Consider the circuits shown in Fig. 14-5. They are, effectively, three-stage *RC*-coupled amplifiers with only one active element. If fewer than three *RC* sections are used, these circuits will not oscillate. This can be seen from a study of the Nyquist plots of Fig. 13-25. The procedure of Sec. 14-1 can be used to determine the frequency of oscillation and the criterion for oscillation. These structures are sometimes called *phase-shift* oscillators because of the phase shifts introduced by the *RC* circuits. (Note that all oscillator circuits have elements that introduce phase shift.) These *RC* oscillators have no tuned circuits to reject harmonics; thus, the operation should be linear to prevent excessive distortion. In the next section, we shall discuss linear and nonlinear operation of oscillators.

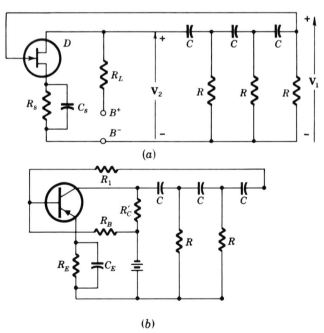

(a)

(b)

Fig. 14-5 *RC* phase-shift oscillators: (a) common-source FET as the active element; (b) common-emitter transistor as the active element.

Let us analyze the FET oscillator of Fig. 14-5a.   The gate of the FET will essentially act as an open circuit.   In addition, to obtain maximum voltage gain and also minimum capacitance, R is made as large as possible.   Then in general, $R \gg R_L$, and the open-loop gain is given by

$$\mathbf{L}(j\omega) = \frac{A_v}{1 - 5(f_1/f)^2 - j[6f_1/f - (f_1/f)^3]}$$ (14-18)

where

$$f_1 = \frac{1}{2\pi RC}$$ (14-19)

and, making use of the fact that $R \gg R_L$, we have

$$A_v = -g_m R_{\text{sh}}$$ (14-20)

Note that

$$\frac{1}{R_{\text{sh}}} = \frac{1}{R_L} + \frac{1}{r_d}$$

It is assumed that C_s acts as a short circuit for signal frequencies.   If there is to be oscillation, then, at the value of f where $\mathbf{L}(j\omega)$ is a real positive number, $|L(j\omega)| \geq 1$.   (Note that A is a negative number.)   Equation (14-18) is real and positive when

$$6\frac{f_1}{f} - \left(\frac{f_1}{f}\right)^3 = 0$$ (14-21)

Solving Eq. (14-21), we obtain $f = 0$, $f = \pm f_1/\sqrt{6}$.   The gain of the β network is zero at $f = 0$.   Thus, the second root must be used.   Hence, the frequency of oscillation is

$$f_0 = \frac{f_1}{\sqrt{6}}$$ (14-22)

Substituting into Eq. (14-20) and setting $\mathbf{L}(j\omega) = 1$, we obtain

$$A_v = -29$$ (14-23)

Thus, this circuit will oscillate if A_v is negative and $|A_v| \geq 29$.

If the transistor phase-shift oscillator had the same configuration as the FET oscillator, the third resistor would be shunted by the relatively low input resistance of the transistor.   This would lead to improper operation.   To avoid this, the circuit is modified as shown in Fig. 14-5b.   A linear model for this amplifier is shown in Fig. 14-6.   Since the frequencies of operation of these oscillators is low, usually in the audio range, the shunt capacitances of the model can be omitted.   The value of R_1 is chosen so that

$$R_1 + r_{b'b} + r_{b'e} = R$$ (14-24)

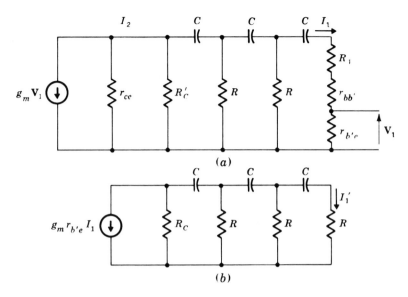

Fig. 14-6 (*a*) Model of the *RC* phase-shift oscillator of Fig. 14-5*b* and (*b*) model used to obtain the open-loop gain I_1'/I_1. $R_1 + r_{bb'} + r_{b'e} = R$.

The transistor should fundamentally be considered as a current amplifier. Thus the open-loop current gain is of importance.   If $R_C' \ll R$, then the current gain will be low.   If R_C (R_C' in parallel with the r_{ce} of the transistor) is made too large, the effect of the first capacitor will be nullified.   Thus, there is an optimum value of R_C that must be used.   Let us analyze the open-loop current gain of this circuit.   To do this we use the model of Fig. 14-6*b*. Solving for the open-loop gain, I_1'/I_1, we obtain

$$L(j\omega) = \frac{-g_m r_{b'e}}{3 - \left(\dfrac{f_1}{f}\right)^2 - j4\dfrac{f_1}{f} + \dfrac{R}{R_C}\left[1 - 5\left(\dfrac{f_1}{f}\right)^2 - j\left(6\dfrac{f_1}{f} - \dfrac{f_1^3}{f^3}\right)\right]} \quad (14\text{-}25)$$

where f_1 is defined in Eq. (14-19).   Setting Eq. (14-25) equal to 1, we obtain

$$4\frac{f_1}{f} + \frac{R}{R_C}\left[6\frac{f_1}{f} - \left(\frac{f_1}{f}\right)^3\right] = 0 \quad (14\text{-}26a)$$

$$g_m r_{b'e} = -3 + \left(\frac{f_1}{f}\right)^2 - \frac{R}{R_C}\left[1 - 5\left(\frac{f_1}{f}\right)^2\right] \quad (14\text{-}26b)$$

Solving Eq. (14-26*a*) for f, we have

$$f = \frac{f_1}{\sqrt{6 + 4R_C/R}} \quad (14\text{-}27)$$

This is the frequency of oscillation. Substituting in Eq. (14-26b) and manipulating, we obtain

$$g_m = \frac{1}{r_{b'e}} \left(23 + 4\frac{R_C}{R} + 29\frac{R}{R_C} \right) \tag{14-28}$$

It is desirable that g_m be as small as possible. Let us minimize this expression with respect to R_C. Differentiate Eq. (14-28) with respect to R_C/R and set the derivative equal to zero. This yields

$$4 - 29\left(\frac{R}{R_C}\right)^2 = 0$$

Thus, the optimum value of R_C is given by

$$\frac{R_C}{R} = \sqrt{\frac{29}{4}} \tag{14-29}$$

Substitution in Eq. (14-22) yields

$$g_m = \frac{44.54}{r_{b'e}}$$

Thus, the criterion for oscillation is

$$g_m \geq \frac{44.54}{r_{b'e}} \tag{14-30}$$

At times, two transistors are used in phase-shift oscillators. This lowers the requirements on the g_m of the individual transistors.

In addition to phase-shift oscillators considered here, more complex RC oscillators are built. They often use bridge structures in their feedback circuits. The principles of Sec. 14-1 can also be applied to these.

14-4 LINEAR AND NONLINEAR OPERATION OF OSCILLATORS

In an oscillator, the amplitude of the oscillation builds up until an equilibrium condition is reached. If this amplitude is small, then the operation can be very linear and the output will be a sinusoid with a relatively small amount of distortion. On the other hand, if the amplitude of oscillation is very large, then the output may be very distorted. Linearity of operation is related to the efficiency of operation, just as it is in amplifiers. If an oscillator operates class C, then its efficiency and distortion will be considerably higher than if the operation is class A. Many times, oscillators are designed to supply high power, and in such cases class C operation is often used. Tuned circuits are then often used to reject harmonics.

If the active elements of the oscillator circuits were really linear, the amplitude of the oscillation would build up indefinitely.   All active elements have cutoff and saturation regions which limit the amplitude of the oscillation. For instance, in a transistor, the collector current effectively becomes zero when the emitter current is zero; in an FET, the drain current is essentially zero if the gate-source voltage is negative enough.   The FET and the transistor have knees in their output characteristics where the curves crowd together.   This represents a saturation region.   As the instantaneous operating point moves into the highly nonlinear region, the effective gain of the active element decreases.   For instance, consider the phase-shift oscillators of Fig. 14-5.   If the open-loop gain is adjusted so that it is just slightly higher than the minimum value required for oscillation, then the oscillation will not proceed far into the nonlinear region.   On the other hand, if the magnitude of the open-loop gain is increased greatly, then the amplitude of oscillation will be considerably larger and the output will be distorted.   It may appear as though the magnitude of the open-loop gain should be the minimum that produces oscillation.   However, any slight reduction in gain, which could be caused by aging of the elements or by a change in power-supply voltage, would then cause the oscillation to cease.   There are several procedures that will yield both linear operation and a certainty of oscillation. One is to use a nonlinear resistance which varies in such a way that it reduces the open-loop gain as the amplitude of oscillation increases.   For instance, if Y_3 in Fig. 14-2 is a conductance whose value decreases when the current through it increases, then the open-loop gain falls off as the signal level increases.   An ordinary tungsten-filament lamp is often used for these purposes.

If very linear operation is desired, the procedure illustrated in Fig. 14-7 can be used.   The signal output of the oscillator is amplified and then applied to a simple diode rectifier circuit.   A direct voltage will appear across C_g.   It will have the indicated polarity so that V will be negative. This acts as a negative gate bias for the amplifier.   Increasing the negative gate bias will reduce the open-loop gain.   Thus, the amplitude of the oscillation will decrease as A_v increases and can be made very small.   This is called an *amplitude-stabilized oscillator circuit*.   Although an FET circuit is illustrated, the same basic procedure can be applied to transistors.   Note that the amplitude-stabilizing circuit introduces a feedback loop of its own. Care should be taken that this does not cause extraneous oscillation.   This is usually of a very low frequency and causes the amplitude of the output signal to vary periodically.

Let us now consider how input bias is obtained for a class C oscillator. In the case of the FET oscillator, the equivalent of grid-leak bias is often used.   For the MOSFET the diodes shown in Fig. 14-3a, c, and e are added. The discussion of Sec. 11-6 applies here.   Initially, the gate bias will be zero and the transconductance will be high.   Thus, the oscillation will build up.

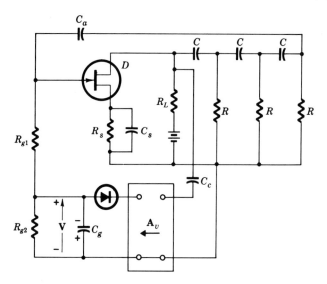

Fig. 14-7 Amplitude-stabilized oscillator; C_a and C_c are direct current blocking capacitors. ($C_a R_{gl} \gg CR$ and $R_{gl} \gg R$.)

This will increase the negative gate bias and, thus, reduce the transconductance. Hence, the amplitude of oscillation will be limited.

In the case of the transistor, the problem is somewhat different. If the bias circuits of Fig. 11-9 were used, there would be, initially, zero base current. Hence, the transistor would almost be cut off, and oscillation probably would not build up. Thus, transistor oscillator circuits are usually constructed so that there is a negative direct base-current bias produced by the power supply. The circuits of Fig. 14-3b, d, and f illustrate this. Bias circuits similar to those of Fig. 11-9 can be added to the circuit (see Fig. 14-3b and d). This circuit will tend to produce a positive base-current bias as oscillation builds up and thus will limit the amplitude of oscillation.

The device nonlinearities as well as the gate or base bias will limit the amplitude of oscillation in FET, vacuum-tube, and transistor oscillators. These nonlinearities should be considered in any circuit where the amplitude of oscillation is large.

14-5 FREQUENCY STABILITY

The frequency of operation of an oscillator circuit will not remain constant but will drift. The magnitude of these drifts is a measure of the frequency stability of the oscillator. In many applications, a shift of 1 or 2 percent is tolerable. However, there are many other times when the frequency must be held to extremely close tolerances. For instance, it is not uncommon to specify oscillator frequencies plus or minus several hertz per megahertz. In fact, specifications are often much more restrictive. For the time being, let us assume that the operation of the oscillator is linear and examine the causes of the frequency drift. The frequencies of oscillation of two representative radio-frequency oscillator circuits are given by Eqs. (14-14) and (14-16). Note that ω_0 depends not only upon the elements of the tuned circuit but also upon the parameters of the active element and the resistances of the circuit. The parameters of the active element vary with bias voltages, temperature, and age. Thus, it is desirable to minimize their effects. For instance, in Eq. (14-16), it would be desirable to make the ratio $R/r_d L C_2$ as small as possible. In addition, the power-supply voltages should be stabilized so that they do not introduce a source of parameter change.

The dependence of the frequency of oscillation on the parameters of

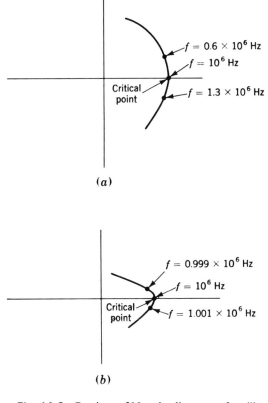

(a)

(b)

Fig. 14-8 Portions of Nyquist diagrams of oscillator circuits: (a) slow variation of phase angle with frequency and (b) rapid variation of phase angle with frequency.

the oscillator can be studied with the aid of the Nyquist diagram. Once an equilibrium has been reached, the parameters of the active device are such that the open-loop gain $L(j\omega)$ is exactly 1 at the frequency of oscillation. Now let us consider two different Nyquist diagrams. Their pertinent features are shown in Fig. 14-8. If the phase angle $\theta(\omega)$ of $L(j\omega)$ varies slowly with frequency, the diagram is of the form of Fig. 14-8a, while a rapid variation of the $\theta(\omega)$ with frequency results in a Nyquist diagram such as that of Fig. 14-8b. Note that in Fig. 14-8a points which are relatively close to the critical point correspond to frequencies *far* from the frequency of oscillation. The converse is true in Fig. 14-8b.

If there is a group of elements, such as a resonant circuit, which cause $\theta(\omega)$ to vary very rapidly with frequency, these elements will have much more effect on the frequency of oscillation than will parameters which cause $d\theta(\omega)/d\omega$ to be small. For instance, in Fig. 14-8b, the large value of $d\theta(\omega)/d\omega$ could be due to a high-Q resonant circuit. The Q of the resonant circuit of Fig. 14-8a would be much lower.

Now assume that the parameters of the active device change. This will cause the Nyquist diagram to change slightly. A point corresponding to a different frequency of oscillation will now pass through the critical point. Thus, the shift in frequency will be greater in the circuit corresponding to Fig. 14-8a than in the one corresponding to Fig. 14-8b. Thus, the frequency of oscillation of the oscillator corresponding to Fig. 14-8b depends less upon the parameters of the active device than does the oscillator of Fig. 14-8a.

In LC oscillators it is desirable to make the Q of the resonant circuit as large as possible to reduce the dependence of the frequency of oscillation on the parameters of the active device.

The frequency of oscillation primarily depends upon the elements of the resonant circuit. For instance, if r_d is sufficiently large, then Eq. (14-16) can be approximated by

$$\omega_0 = \sqrt{\frac{C_1 + C_2}{C_1 C_2 L}} \qquad\qquad (14\text{-}31)$$

Thus, these elements should not vary. Temperature fluctuations will change the dimensions of the elements and cause ω_0 to shift. This may sound trivial, but remember that we are dealing with changes on the order of parts per million or less. If a great deal of frequency stability is desired, the resonant circuits are often put into temperature-controlled ovens to maintain their stability. The capacitance of the active elements also appears in the expression for ω_0. To be specific, let us discuss the Colpitts oscillator circuits of Fig. 14-3c and d. The capacitors C_1 and C_2 consist not only of the capacitance shown, but also of the gate-to-source and drain-to-source capacitance of the FET or the effective capacitance between the emitter and base and between the emitter and collector of the transistor. In the transistor, these capacitances fluctuate with temperature and voltage. In the FET, any changes in operating temperature or voltage will change C_{gs} and C_{ds}. If possible, the effect of these fluctuations should be minimized. To simplify our discussion, let us assume that the series combination of C_1 and C_2 is replaced by a capacitor C such that

$$C = \frac{C_1 C_2}{C_1 + C_2} \tag{14-32}$$

and that the capacitances of the active element change such that the percentage change in both C_1 and C_2 is the same. Let us call ΔC the net change in C. We shall compute the change in ω_0^2. (For convenience, we shall work with ω_0^2 rather than with ω_0.) From Eq. (14-31)

$$\Delta \omega_0^2 = \frac{1}{L(C + \Delta C)} - \frac{1}{LC} \tag{14-33a}$$

$$\Delta \omega_0^2 = -\frac{L \, \Delta C}{LC(LC + L \, \Delta C)} \tag{14-33b}$$

In general, $C \gg \Delta C$, so that this can be approximated by

$$\frac{\Delta \omega_0^2}{\omega_0^2} = -\frac{\Delta C}{C} \tag{14-34}$$

If ΔC is a change due to the active element, then it will be independent of the external capacitances. Thus, if C_1 and C_2 and, thus, C, are made larger, the frequency shift will decrease. This requires that L be decreased, if ω_0 is not to change. There is a minimum value of L that can be used practically. If we replace the tuned circuit of the Colpitts oscillator by the one shown in Fig. 14-9, the stability can be increased. The oscillator is now called a *Clapp (or series-tuned) oscillator*. In the Colpitts oscillator, one limitation on the maximum value of C is the minimum value of L that can conveniently be used. However, in the Clapp circuit, C_1 and C_2 can be made as large as desired, since the effective capacitance of the circuit is given by

$$C_{\text{eff}} = \frac{C_3 C}{C_3 + C} \tag{14-35}$$

where C is defined by Eq. (14-32). (We shall see that the choice of capacitance is complicated by the requirements for oscillation.) If we assume that the changes in capacitance are all due to the active element, then only C will change. Thus,

$$\Delta C_{\text{eff}} = \frac{C_3(C + \Delta C)}{C_3 + C + \Delta C} - \frac{C_3 C}{C_3 + C} \tag{14-36}$$

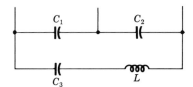

Fig. 14-9 The resonant circuit of a Clapp oscillator.

Then, if these terms are placed over a common denominator and *then* it is assumed that $\Delta C \ll C$, we obtain

$$\frac{\Delta C_{eff}}{C_{eff}} = \frac{\Delta C}{C} \frac{C_{eff}}{C} \tag{14-37}$$

The value of C can be much greater for the Clapp oscillator than for the Colpitts oscillator and C_{eff}/C can be very much less than 1. Thus, the frequency stability of the Clapp circuit can be very much greater than that of the Colpitts oscillator. If the capacitors C_1 and C_2 could be made arbitrarily large, then ω_0 could be made insensitive to changes in the active-element capacitance. However, the criterion for oscillation limits the maximum values of C_1 and of C_2. For instance, in an FET circuit, Eq. (14-17) places limits upon $C_1 C_2$.

In either the Colpitts or the Clapp circuit, the values of C_1 and C_2 need not be equal. If one of the capacitances of the active element tends to vary more than the other, then the larger capacitance should be placed across it. For instance, in the transistor circuit, C_2 is usually larger than C_1. If exceptional frequency stability is not required, then the Colpitts circuit is used, since it is simpler.

Thus far, we have ignored nonlinear effects in our discussion of stability. In general, the parameters of the active element will vary with the nonlinearities. As a consequence, ω_0 will be sensitive to them. Since the nonlinearities change with shifts in the operating point, linear oscillators have less frequency drift than nonlinear ones.

14-6 CRYSTAL OSCILLATORS

If an oscillator is to operate at only one frequency, exceptional stability can be obtained by using *piezoelectric crystals*. These crystals, which are often made of quartz, will deform if a voltage is applied to their opposite faces. Conversely, if they are deformed, a voltage will appear across their opposite faces. The symbol for a crystal and its linear model are shown in Fig. 14-10. The crystal acts as a resonant electric circuit of very high Q. Its resonant frequency is essentially the mechanical resonant frequency of the crystal,

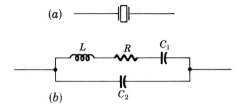

Fig. 14-10 (*a*) The symbol for a piezoelectric crystal and (*b*) its linear model.

which is exceptionally stable. Because of the very high effective Q, the frequency of oscillation is essentially determined by the resonant frequency of the crystal (see Sec. 14-5). To further improve their stability, crystals are often placed in temperature-controlled ovens. Crystals can be used to replace the resonant circuits in many oscillator configurations. A typical crystal oscillator called the *Pierce oscillator* is shown in Fig. 14-11. It is essentially a Colpitts (or Clapp) oscillator with the inductance replaced by the crystal.

The output of an oscillator may be taken across the resonant circuit. However, changes in output impedance will vary the resonant frequency. To prevent this, a buffer amplifier can be placed between the oscillator and the load.

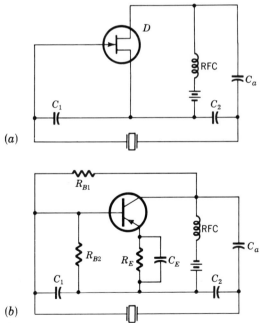

Fig. 14-11 Pierce crystal oscillators: (*a*) FET oscillator and (*b*) transistor oscillator.

14-7   DESIGN OF AN OSCILLATOR CIRCUIT WITH A SPECIFIED AMPLITUDE OF OSCILLATION

Let us consider the design of transistor and FET oscillator circuits. The transistor oscillator will be considered first. The specifications are as follows: frequency of oscillation is to be $f_0 = 10^7/2\pi$ Hz ($\omega_0 = 10^7$ rad/sec), amplitude of oscillation should be such that the operation is very linear; a Colpitts oscillator circuit is to be used.

We shall use a transistor with the following characteristics: $R_i = r_{bb'} + r_{b'e} = 100 + 1900 = 2000$ ohms, $r_{ce} = 1/g = 20,000$ ohms, $g_m = 26,842$ μmhos. The following operating point is to be used: $V_{CEQ} = -10$ volts, $I_{CQ} = -5.0$ ma, $I_{BQ} = -100$ μa, and $V_{BEQ} \approx 0$ volts. The frequency of operation is to be far below ω_β so that the capacitors can be ignored. The value of $r_{b'c}$ is assumed to be so large that it does not affect the input impedance of the transistor. We shall also assume that g_m falls off as I_{BQ} increases positively for sufficiently positive values of I_B; for example, $g_m = 100$ μmhos if $I_{BQ} = +2$ ma. We shall also assume that g_m increases as I_{BQ} becomes more negative to a value of 30,000 μmhos.

The amplitude-stabilized oscillator of Fig. 14-12 will be used. Equation (14-4) will be used to determine the criterion of oscillation. We shall correct the values of g_m (see Sec. 14-1). The value to be used in the equation is

$$g_m = \frac{26,842 r_{b'e}}{r_{b'e} + r_{bb'}} = 25,500 \ \mu\text{mhos}$$

It will be assumed that the capacitances C_1 and C_2 are lossless and that the RFC acts as an open circuit. Thus, in Eq. (14-4), $\mathbf{Y}_1 = j\omega C_1$, $\mathbf{Y}_2 = j\omega C_2$, $\mathbf{Y}_i = 1/R_i$, and $\mathbf{Y}_3 = 1/(R + j\omega L)$. The inductance has been assumed to

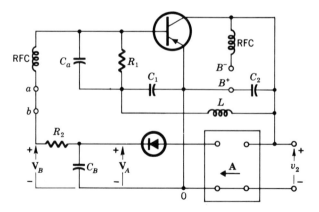

Fig. 14-12   An amplitude-stabilized Colpitts transistor oscillator.

have a series resistance R. Substituting in Eq. (14-4) and rearranging, we obtain

$$\omega_0 = \sqrt{\frac{C_1 + C_2}{LC_1C_2} + \frac{gR}{LC_2} + \frac{Lg + C_2R}{R_iLC_1C_2}} \qquad (14\text{-}38)$$

and

$$g_m \geq \omega_0^2 C_1 C_2 R + \frac{\omega_0^2 LC_2 - gR - 1}{R_i} + g(\omega_0^2 LC_1 - 1) \qquad (14\text{-}39)$$

To simplify the analysis, choose $C_1 = C_2 = C$. Assume that

$$\omega_0 \approx \sqrt{\frac{C_1 + C_2}{LC_1C_2}} = \sqrt{\frac{2}{LC}}$$

This assumption must be subsequently verified. Then, substituting in Eq. (14-39), we obtain,

$$g_m \geq \omega_0^2 C^2 R + \frac{1 - gR}{R_i} + g \qquad (14\text{-}40)$$

In general, $1 \gg gR$, so that we can neglect the gR term. Actually, this approximation is on the safe side, since it causes the requirements for oscillation to become more stringent. The resistance of the coil can be expressed in terms of its Q at resonance: $R = \omega_0 L/Q_0 = 2/(Q_0\omega_0 C)$. Substituting in Eq. (14-40) and solving for C, we obtain

$$C \leq \left(g_m - \frac{1}{R_i} - g\right)\frac{Q_0}{2\omega_0} \qquad (14\text{-}41)$$

This value represents the minimum value that $C_1 = C_2 = C$ can have if the circuit is to oscillate. Let us assume that $Q_0 = 10$.

$$C \leq 12{,}475 \text{ pf}$$

To obtain the best possible stability, the largest value of C should be used. Since g_m can become considerably greater than 25,500 μmhos, this relation can be used with the equals sign. However, to obtain a practical value, we shall use

$$C_1 = C_2 = 12{,}000 \text{ pf}$$

Note that C_1 and C_2 are effectively in shunt with the input and output capacitances of the transistor. C_1 and C_2, respectively, should be reduced by these amounts. This small change can often be ignored. Actually, some means of adjusting the frequency (by varying L or C) is usually included so that the desired frequency can be obtained precisely. The value of inductance can be found by using the relation $\omega_0 \approx \sqrt{2/LC}$. Solving this yields 1.667 μh. This is a relatively small inductance, although it is readily obtainable.   If it is desirable to use a larger inductance, then the value of C should be reduced.   However, we shall use the specified value.   Thus,

$$L = 1.667 \,\mu\text{h}$$

Since $Q_0 = 10$, the resistance of the coil is 1.667 ohms.   Let us now substitute into Eq. (14-38) to see if the approximation $\omega_0 \approx \sqrt{2/LC}$ is justified. This substitution yields

$$\omega_0 = \sqrt{10^{14}(1.00046)} = 1.00023 \times 10^7 \approx 10^7$$

Thus, the assumption is justified.

Now consider the design of the amplitude-stabilizing circuit.   The specified amplitude of oscillation will depend upon the nonlinearities of the characteristics of the transistor.   Let us assume that these are such that the operation will be linear enough if $V_{2,\text{max}} \leq 0.05$ volt, where

$$v_2 = V_{2,\text{max}} \sin \omega_0 t$$

The required base-current bias is $I_{BQ} = -100 \,\mu\text{a}$.   The base current depends upon the voltage V_B, which in turn depends upon the power-supply voltage V_{CC} and the direct voltage V_A that appears across C_B.   Applying Thévenin's theorem between the base and the reference terminal, we obtain the effective bias circuit which consists of a voltage V_T in series with a resistance R_T where

$$V_T = \frac{V_A R_1 + V_{CC} R_2}{R_1 + R_2} \tag{14-42}$$

and

$$R_T = \frac{R_1 R_2}{R_1 + R_2} \tag{14-43}$$

It has been assumed that the direct voltage V_A, of the polarity indicated, appears across C_B.   The direct base-current bias is given by $I_{BQ} = V_T/R_T$. Let us assume that $R_1 = R_2 = 30,000$ ohms.   Then $R_T = 15,000$ ohms and to obtain the proper base current $V_T = -1.5$ volts.   Since $V_{CEQ} = -10$ volts, let us set the power-supply voltage V_{CC} equal to -10 volts.   Then, substituting in Eq. (14-42), we obtain

$$V_A = 7 \,\text{volts}$$

If the capacitance C_B is chosen large enough so that the time constant $C_B R_2$ is very much larger than the period of the alternating voltage applied to the input of the diode, then V_A will be equal to the peak value of this alternating voltage.   Thus,

$$V_A = |A| V_{2,\text{max}}$$

Hence

$$|A| = 140$$

To obtain a value of C_B set $C_B \times 30,000 \gg 1/10^7$. A typical value is $C_B = 0.01 \ \mu\text{f}$.

Note if the Q of the circuit is greater than 10, then oscillation can occur at a lower value of g_m. This will mean that the amplitude of oscillation will increase. To prevent this, either C or the gain of the amplifier can be increased.

A bias-stabilizing impedance R_E in parallel with C_E can be placed in series with the emitter lead. In this case, the magnitude of V_{CC} and of V_T should be increased by an amount equal to the direct voltage drop across R_E. The capacitance should be large enough so that $h_{fe}/\omega_0 C_E \ll h_{ie}$ [see Eq. (9-78)]. Note that $h_{fe} \approx g_m R_i$ and $h_{ie} \approx R_i$.

The value of C_a should be large enough so that it acts as a short circuit in comparison with R_i. Thus, $C_a \gg 1/\omega_0 R_i$. A typical value is $C_a = 0.01 \ \mu\text{f}$.

One fact that has been ignored thus far is that the feedback loop of the amplitude-stabilization circuit may cause instability. This usually manifests itself in a slow periodic variation in the bias current I_B, which, in turn, causes the magnitude of v_2 to vary periodically. To determine if such oscillation can occur, the feedback loop should be broken between points a and b. The open-loop gain can then be obtained by considering that a current generator is applied between point a and the reference terminal 0. The ratio of the returned current, i.e., the current in an impedance equal to the transistor circuit's input impedance, which is placed between point b and the reference terminal, to the generator current yields the open-loop gain. A Nyquist plot then is used to determine the stability of the amplifier. The Nyquist plot can be varied by changing R_1, R_2, C_B, or the frequency response of the voltage amplification $\mathbf{A}$. In general, $\mathbf{A}$ will be the amplification of a tuned amplifier. Even though it is only required to amplify signals of frequency ω_0, it may have to be a broadband amplifier. The basic principles of the design of Sec. 13-21 can be applied to stabilize this system. Care must be taken because the amplifier $\mathbf{A}$ is a bandpass system that operates about the frequency ω_0, while the applied signal generator and the output voltage across C_B will only contain relatively low-frequency components.

Now let us consider the design of the oscillator using an FET. Since many of the details are identical, we shall omit some of the explanatory statements. An FET with the following characteristics will be used: $g_m = 5000 \ \mu\text{mhos}$, $r_d = 10^6$ ohms, $C_{\text{in}} = C_{\text{out}} = 10$ pf. To obtain these characteristics, the following operating point is used: $V_{DSQ} = 30$ volts, $V_{GSQ} = -5$ volts. In addition, we shall assume that the transconductance falls off as the negative gate bias is increased, so that $g_m = 100 \ \mu\text{mhos}$ when $V_{DSQ} = -10$ volts and $g_m = 10,000 \ \mu\text{mhos}$ when $V_{GSQ} = -0.1$ volt.

The oscillator circuit is shown in Fig. 14-13.   We shall again assume that the capacitances are lossless and that R is the resistance of the inductance. To simplify the analysis, we shall choose $C_1 = C_2 = C$ so that $\omega_0 \approx \sqrt{2/LC}$. Thus, substituting in Eq. (14-17), we obtain

$$g_m \geq \omega_0^2 C^2 R + \frac{1}{r_d} \tag{14-44}$$

Solving for C and writing R in terms of Q_0, we obtain

$$C \leq \frac{Q_0}{2\omega_0}\left(g_m - \frac{1}{r_d}\right)$$

If $Q_0 = 10$, then

$$C \leq 2499.5 \text{ pf}$$

This value should include C_{in} and C_{out} of the FET.   The frequency of oscillation is given by Eq. (14-16).   Substituting and solving for L, we obtain

$$L = \frac{2}{\omega_0^2 C}\left(1 + \frac{1}{\omega_0 C Q_0 r_d}\right)$$

Hence

$$L = 8 \ \mu\text{h}$$

Now let us consider the amplitude-stabilizing circuit.   If

$$v_2 = V_{2,\max} \sin \omega t$$

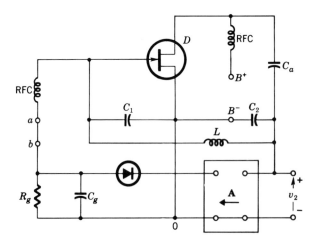

Fig. 14-13   An amplitude-stabilized Colpitts vacuum-tube oscillator.

then the gate bias will be equal to

$$V_{GS} = -|A|V_{2,\max}$$

The required gate bias is -5 volts. Let us assume that the operation will be linear enough if $V_{2,\max} \leq 0.05$ volt. Hence, $|A| = 100$.

The value of R_g should be chosen as large as possible. However, it should be small enough so that the voltage across C_g can decrease in magnitude if $V_{2,\max}$ decreases. A value of $R_g = 10^6$ ohms is typical. The value of C_g then should satisfy the inequality $R_g C_g \gg 1/\omega_0$ or $C_g \gg 10^{-13}$. A typical value is $C_g = 100$ pf. The value of C_a should be chosen so that $\omega_0 C_a \gg 1/r_d$ and $C_a \gg C_{\text{out}}$ (of the FET). A typical value is $C_a = 1,000$ pf.

Since the V_{DSQ} is 30 volts, the power-supply voltage should be 30 volts.

The stabilization of the bias feedback loop proceeds in the same way as in the transistor circuit. The Nyquist diagram is obtained on a voltage basis in this case. That is, the feedback loop is broken between points a and b. A voltage generator is placed between point a and the reference terminal. The returned voltage is that between point b and the reference terminal.

BIBLIOGRAPHY

Alley, C. L., and Atwood, K. W.: "Electronic Engineering," 2d ed., chap. 13, John Wiley & Sons, Inc., New York, 1966.

Chirlian, P. M.: "Analysis and Design of Electronic Circuits," chap. 11, McGraw-Hill Book Company, New York, 1965.

Gibbons, J. F.: "Semiconductor Electronics," pp. 575–594, McGraw-Hill Book Company, New York, 1966.

Greiner, R. A.: "Semiconductor Devices and Applications," chap. 17, McGraw-Hill Book Company, New York, 1961.

Millman, J., and C. C. Halkias: "Electronic Devices and Circuits," pp. 525–540, McGraw-Hill Book Company, New York, 1967.

Seely, S.: "Electronic Circuits," chap. 8, Holt, Rinehart and Winston, Inc., New York, 1968.

Terman, F. E.: "Electronic and Radio Engineering," chap. 14, McGraw-Hill Book Company, New York, 1955.

PROBLEMS

14-1. Derive the criterion for oscillation given by Eq. (14-4), using the fact that the open-loop gain must equal $+1$.

14-2. Obtain the minimum value of g_m that the FET of Fig. 14-3a can have if there is to be oscillation. Assume that each inductance has a resistance in series with it and that any bypass capacitors are short circuits. Determine the frequency of oscillation. The answers should be in terms of the parameters of the FET and the circuit elements.

14-3. Repeat Prob. 14-2 for the circuit of Fig. 14-3e. Assume that the RFC is an open circuit.

14-4. Repeat Prob. 14-2 but assume that the FET is replaced by a vacuum-tube triode.

14-5. Derive the minimum value of g_m that the transistor of Fig. 14-3d can have if there is to be oscillation.   Assume that each inductance has a resistance in series with it, that at the signal frequency any bypass capacitors are short circuits, and that the RFC is an open circuit.   Also assume that the parameters of the transistor are real numbers. Determine the frequency of oscillation.   The answers should be in terms of the parameters of the transistor and the circuit elements.   Now assume that g_m varies as $g_m/(1 + j\omega/\omega_\beta)$ and repeat the problem.   What is the maximum frequency at which oscillation can be maintained?

14-6.   Repeat Prob. 14-5 for the circuit of Fig. 14-3*f*.

14-7.   Design a phase-shift oscillator which is to oscillate at 1000 Hz.   The circuit of Fig. 14-5*a* is to be used.   The parameters of the FET are $g_m = 10,000$ μmhos, $r_d = 100,000$ ohms.   The coordinates of the quiescent operating point are $V_{DSQ} = 30$ volts, $I_{DQ} = 1$ ma, $V_{GSQ} = -2$ volts.   Assume that $R_{\max} = 10^6$ ohms.

14-8.   Repeat Prob. 14-7 but now use a transistor with the following parameters: $g_m = 70,000$ μmhos, $r_{b'e} = 900$ ohms, $r_{bb'} = 100$ ohms, $r_{b'c} = 10^{12}$ ohms, $r_{ce} = 10^7$ ohms.   The coordinates of the quiescent operating point are $V_{CEQ} = -10$ volts, $I_{CQ} = -10$ ma, $I_{BQ} = -100$ μa.

14-9.   Determine the criterion for oscillation for both the FET and the transistor Clapp oscillator.   Assume that $\omega C_2 \gg 1/r_d$ and that $\omega C_2 \gg r_{ce}$.

14-10.   Compare the frequency drift of the Hartley, Colpitts, and Clapp oscillator circuits to changes in the capacitance of the active elements.   Assume that the total inductance is constant in all three circuits.

14-11.   Relate the frequency stability of the vacuum-tube Clapp oscillator to the transconductance of the FET, the inductance, and the resistance of the inductance. Assume that r_d is infinite and that the frequency drift is due to changes in interelectrode capacitances of the FET.

14-12.   Determine the criterion for oscillation and the frequency of oscillation of the circuits of Fig. 14-11.   Use the model of Fig. 14-10*b* for the crystal.   What does the frequency of oscillation become as R approaches zero?

14-13.   Design a Hartley oscillator which meets the specifications and uses the transistor of Sec. 14-7.

14-14.   Repeat Prob. 14-13 but now use the FET of Sec. 14-7 as the active element.

15

Pulse, Switching, and Digital Circuits

Many electronic devices, such as digital computers, function on the basis of the presence or absence of a signal. The active elements, e.g., transistors, diodes, and FETs, are operated as switches. In fact, they take over operations that were performed by relays in earlier devices. In digital computers, the active elements are switched from an on to an off state or vice versa and, in so doing, generate signals which perform mathematical operations. Electronic devices are also used as switches in many electronic instruments. For instance, they are used as time-base generators in oscilloscopes. The circuits that are used in these cases are different from those designed as linear amplifiers. We shall present some of their fundamentals here. In Secs. 15-1 and 15-2 we shall discuss the transient response of general switching devices. In subsequent sections, we shall introduce some fundamental switching circuits. Additional details of the subject of pulse, switching, and digital circuits are given in the references cited in the bibliography at the end of the chapter.

15-1   SOME FUNDAMENTAL CONSIDERATIONS IN THE OPERATION OF ACTIVE DEVICES AS SWITCHES

In many applications, we are interested in whether or not a signal is present. Actually, there may be two signal levels, corresponding to whether or not the device is "on" or "off," and we may wish to know which level is present at any given time and to be able to switch rapidly from one level to the other. In such cases, the active element, at times, is driven to cutoff so that it acts essentially as an open circuit or it is driven into a saturation region where it acts essentially as a short circuit.   The active elements are driven between these extreme limits (rather than using them as linear amplifiers with low-level pulses) in order to improve reliability.   The characteristics of active elements vary from device to device, with time, and with the operating point. If these circuits are to reliably distinguish between the on and off levels, then these levels should be greatly separated.   Actually, at times, we go one step further and overdrive the electronic device.   We shall illustrate these concepts using Fig. 15-1, which will also define the *saturation and cutoff regions*. Some of these statements will subsequently be modified for semiconductors. The switching of semiconductor devices from saturation to cutoff region (or vice versa) is complex.   We shall consider these complexities in the next section, confining ourselves here to some fundamental aspects of switching.

For the FET, x_{I1} would correspond to zero or a positive bias while x_{I7}

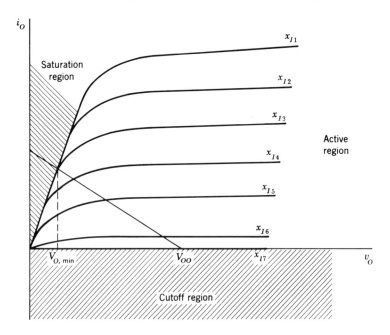

Fig. 15-1   An illustration of the cutoff, active, and saturation regions.

would be a sufficiently large negative gate bias to cut off the drain current. For a common-emitter transistor, x_{I7} would approximately correspond to $-I_{co}$. Now consider the load line. If the input signal swings the bias from x_{I3} to x_{I7}, then the output voltage will vary from V_{OO} to $V_{O,min}$. However, if the input signal is increased, then the output will be unchanged. Thus, for reliable operation, the input signal swing could be somewhat greater than $x_{I7} - x_{I3}$. The region between the cutoff and saturation regions is called

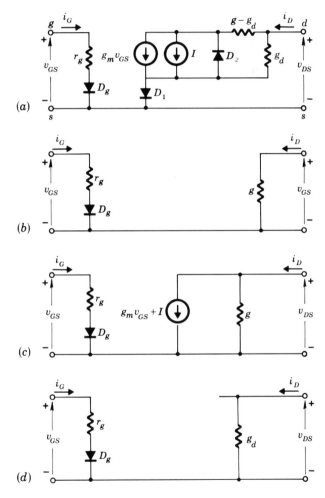

Fig. 15-2 (a) Piecewise-linear model for the FET (or the vacuum-tube pentode); (b) saturation-region linear model; (c) active-region linear model; and (d) cutoff-region linear model. Note for the MOSFET that the input should be an open circuit.

the *active region.* Note that the terms cutoff and saturation regions do not really refer to the crosshatched area of Fig. 15-1, since the operating point never enters them. Actually, the saturation region is the *line* where all the characteristics crowd together. For instance, the operating point corresponding to $V_{O,\min}$ actually lies on the curve for x_{I1}, x_{I2}, and x_{I3}. In a similar way, the cutoff region is the abscissa axis and corresponds to x_{I7}, x_{I8}, x_{I9}, ...

We are often interested in the transient response of these amplifiers. Linear models cannot be used because of the large swings into highly nonlinear regions. However, piecewise-linear models are useful. To use the piecewise-linear model, the characteristics in the active region are linearized. Such a procedure is illustrated in Fig. 7-11 for the FET. The model is redrawn in Fig. 15-2. The details of this model are explained in Sec. 7-5. For the time being, we shall ignore the high-frequency and transient aspects of these models. The models of Fig. 15-2b, c, and d are valid in the saturation, active, and cutoff regions, respectively. The analysis of Chap. 7 can be used to determine when each model should be used. Sometimes it is simpler

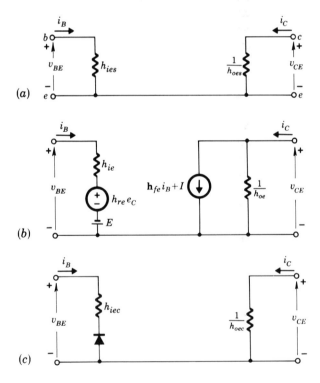

Fig. 15-3 Piecewise-linear linear models for the common-emitter transistor: (*a*) saturation region; (*b*) active region; and (*c*) cutoff region.

to inspect the characteristics to determine when the operation shifts from one region to the other. In a similar fashion, models for the common-emitter transistor that are valid, at low frequencies, in each of the three regions can be obtained from Fig. 7-17. These are shown in Fig. 15-3, where we have substituted for the parameters of Fig. 7-17. We have neglected any inter-action between the input and the output circuits in the saturation and cutoff regions, which considerably simplifies the form of these circuits. The diode shown in Fig. 15-3c conducts for base current in the normal direction. It should be reversed for the n-p-n transistor. At times the diode can be replaced by a short circuit in an analysis procedure. The large value of h_{iec} accounts for the junction impedance. For both the FET and the tran-sistor, the output impedance in the cutoff region is very high, while in the saturation region it is very low and can often be considered to be a short circuit.

Now consider the generalized device of Fig. 15-4, the characteristics of which are shown in Fig. 15-5. We shall assume that the input parameter is instantly varied from x_{I1} to x_{I5}. A capacitance is shown connected across the output. For an FET, this could be approximately considered as the output capacitance. For the transistor, for a first approximation, the capacitance should be included, as it is in Fig. 6-43. Actually, the switching of a tran-sistor must be represented by a more complex model, as we shall discuss in Sec. 15-2. For the time being, let us consider the effect of a simple shunting capacitor. This will illustrate some fundamental results.

Because of the capacitance C_o, the output voltage cannot change instantaneously. Thus, the locus of operation will not be along the load line. However, the end points of the operation, after transients have died away, will be on the load line. Let us define a voltage $V_{O,\text{crit}}$ as the value of v_O at the breakpoint of the x_{I1} curve. Now assume that the power-supply voltage is $V_{OO1} > V_{O,\text{crit}}$. When x_I is switched, the operating point will instanta-neously shift to point a and then, in a finite time, move to points b, c, and d. For those times when the operation is between points a and b, the active model is used. When the operation is between points b and d, the saturation model should be used. On the other hand, if we shift V_{OO} to $V_{OO2} < V_{O,\text{crit}}$,

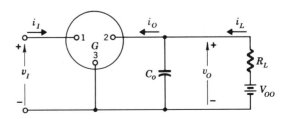

Fig. 15-4 A generalized-device pulse amplifier.

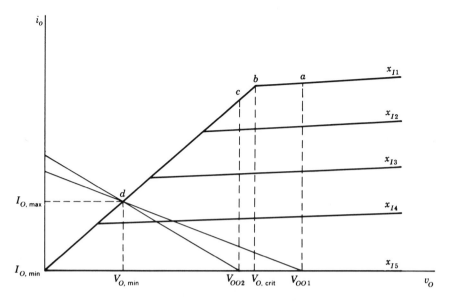

Fig. 15-5 Generalized piecewise-linear-device output characteristics showing the locus of operation in response to an input pulse when output capacitance is present.

then the locus of operation is along the line cd and the saturation model should always be used. In this circuit, the current i_O changes instantaneously with time. However, the load current does not.

$$i_L = \frac{V_{OO} - v_O}{R_L} \tag{15-1}$$

Note that i_O is not an external current, since some of the capacitance may be associated with the active device. Finally, note that $V_{O,\text{crit}}$ does not just depend upon the generalized device; it is a function of the "maximum" value of x_I.

Now let us compute the pulse response of the generalized device of Fig. 15-4. (This analysis is actually oversimplified for the transistor. It will be extended in the next section.) We shall assume that $V_{OO} < V_{O,\text{crit}}$. Let $1/h_{oes}$ and $1/g = r_s$. Also let $1/h_{oec}$ and r_d of the FET when it is cut off be represented by r_c. The models for the operation are shown in Fig. 15-6a and b. Let us assume that a step is applied to the input so that operation is switched from the cutoff to the saturation regions. That is, using Fig. 15-5,

$$x_I = \begin{cases} x_{I5} & \text{for } t < 0 \\ x_{I1} & \text{for } t > 0 \end{cases} \tag{15-2}$$

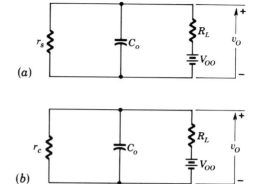

Fig. 15-6 (a) Saturation model of the generalized device of Fig. 15-4 and (b) cutoff model of this device. **(b)**

Then, from Fig. 15-6b, at $t = 0$,

$$v_0(0) = V_c = V_{oo} \frac{r_c}{r_c + R_L} \tag{15-3}$$

Thus, using Fig. 15-6a, the final value of the response is given by

$$v_0(\infty) = V_s = V_{oo} \frac{r_s}{r_s + R_L} \tag{15-4}$$

Thus, the transient response is

$$v_0(t) = V_s - (V_s - V_c)e^{-t/R_{sh,s}C_o} \tag{15-5}$$

where

$$R_{sh,s} = r_s R_L/(r_s + R_L) \tag{15-6}$$

This waveform is shown in Fig. 15-7a. The time constant is $R_{sh,s}C_o$.

Now let us consider that the device has been operating in the saturation region and at $t = 0$, it is switched to the cutoff region. That is,

$$x_I = \begin{cases} x_{I1} & \text{for } t < 0 \\ x_{I5} & \text{for } t > 0 \end{cases} \tag{15-7}$$

Then, standard transient-analysis techniques yield

$$v_0(t) = V_c - (V_c - V_s)e^{-t/R_{sh,c}C_o} \tag{15-8}$$

where

$$R_{sh,c} = \frac{r_c R_L}{r_c + R_L} \tag{15-9}$$

This waveform is shown in Fig. 15-7b. Its time constant is $R_{sh,c}C_o$. Note that the time constants of the buildup and decay are considerably different,

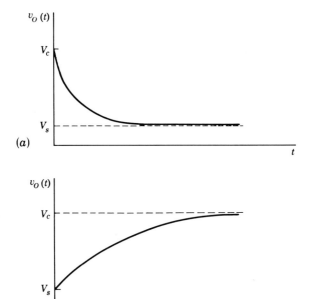

Fig. 15-7 The step response of a simple pulse amplifier: the response when the active device is switched (a) from cutoff to saturation and (b) from saturation to cutoff.

since $r_c \gg r_s$ for most electronic devices. In an ideal case, $r_s = 0$ and $r_c = \infty$. Then, Eq. (15-5) becomes

$$v_0(t) = 0 \tag{15-10}$$

and Eq. (15-8) becomes

$$v_0(t) = V_{00}(1 - e^{-t/R_L C_o}) \tag{15-11}$$

The previous analysis has been simple because the active region was not used (i.e., $V_{00} > V_{0,\text{crit}}$). If it is, then the segment of the output characteristic that is used will not pass through the origin. Hence, the device cannot be treated as a simple resistance but, while it is in the active region, can be represented as a resistance in shunt with a current generator. Its current is equal to the ordinate intercept of the segment in question. The preceding analysis will be valid if the initial and/or final values are taken from the intercept of the segment and the load line. (It will be necessary to extend the segment in those cases where the operation passes from the active to the saturation region.) In general, if $V_{00} > V_{0,\text{crit}}$, then when x_I is switched from x_{I5} to x_{I1}, two steps will have to be used to obtain the transient response.

That is, one equation will apply while $v_O > V_{O,\text{crit}}$ and another for $v_O < V_{O,\text{crit}}$.

The response to a pulse is a combination of Eqs. (15-5) and (15-8). This assumes that the pulse width is long enough so that one transient dies away before the other starts. A typical input pulse and its response are given in Fig. 15-8. If a number of stages are cascaded, the pulse response will deteriorate, e.g., the rise time will increase, for the reasons presented in Sec. 9-15.

In computer circuits, the speed at which a mathematical operation can be performed depends upon the total time that it takes for it to respond to a pulse. This includes any delay time. Let us discuss some causes of delay time. Consider that x_I represents a voltage and that $v_O(t)$ is used to drive another stage. If $V_c = x_{I1}$ and $V_s = x_{I5}$, then no delay time is added. (This assumes that the device leaves the saturation region if $x_I > x_{I1}$.) However, if

$$V_{O,\text{max}} - V_{O,\text{min}} = V_c - V_s > x_{I1} - x_{I5}$$

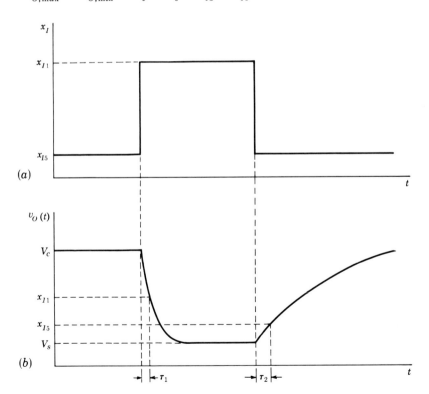

Fig. 15-8 Pulse response of the amplifier of Fig. 15-4: (a) input pulse and (b) output pulse.

then there will be periods of time when no response occurs in the next stage. For instance, if x_{I1} and x_{I5} are as indicated in Fig. 15-8b, then τ_1 and τ_2 will be such delay times as far as the next stage is concerned. Thus overdriving a stage will introduce a delay time, which is undesirable. However, it also introduces reliability. Hence, a compromise must sometimes be reached.

15-2 SWITCHING IN SEMICONDUCTOR DEVICES— CHARGE STORAGE AND CHARGE CONTROL

When semiconductor devices are switched, the simple models discussed in the last section usually are not adequate. We shall now consider switching in various semiconductor devices in greater detail.

Switching in a p-n-junction diode If an ideal diode were forward-biased for a time and then the voltage across it were reversed, the resistance of the diode would become infinite instantaneously. However, in actual diodes, this does not occur. In practical diodes, the resistance does become a very large value. However, the transition from low resistance to high resistance does not take place instantaneously. Let us consider why this is so.

When a p-n junction is forward-biased, the minority-carrier density on either side of the junction is greater than the equilibrium value of the minority-carrier densities in the bulk of the material. For instance [see Eq. (3-17b)], the hole density in the n-type region is

$$p_n = p_{n0} + P(0)e^{-x/L_{pn}} \tag{15-12a}$$

where p_{n0} is the equilibrium hole density in the bulk of the n-type region, x is the distance measured from the junction, and L_{pn} is the diffusion length of holes in the n-type material. $P(0)$ is the difference between the actual hole density immediately adjacent to the junction and the equilibrium density in the bulk of the n-type region. $P(0)$ increases as the forward bias is increased. Analogously, we can write the free-electron density in the p-type region as

$$n_p = n_{p0} + N(0)e^{x/L_{pn}} \tag{15-12b}$$

where $-x$ is the distance measured into the n-type material.

Typically, $N(0)$ and $P(0)$ will be very much greater than n_{p0} and p_{n0}, respectively, when the junction is strongly forward-biased. They increase as the forward bias is increased.

The total charge (due to holes) in excess of equilibrium is defined in Eq. (3-51). It is given by

$$Q_p = AeP(0) \int_0^{L_T} e^{-x/L_{pn}} \, dx \tag{15-13}$$

where A is the cross-sectional area of the junction and L_T is the length of the sample.

In Sec. 3-7 we discussed the charge-control concept. The equilibrium steady-state current due to holes was found to be [see Eq. (3-63)]

$$I_p = \frac{Q_p}{\tau_{pn}} \tag{15-14}$$

where τ_{pn} is the lifetime of the holes in the n-type region. An analogous equation results for the current due to the free electrons.

Equation (15-14) is derived on the basis of an equilibrium when I_p and Q_p do not vary with time. However, now let us assume that they both are functions of time. In this case, an additional term must be added to Eq. (15-14), which now becomes

$$i_p(t) = \frac{q_p(t)}{\tau_{pn}} + \frac{dq_p(t)}{dt} \tag{15-15}$$

The last term must be added for the following reasons. Suppose that external conditions change the equilibrium value of $q_p(t)$. It will then change its value by the recombination of holes with free electrons. This change of charge constitutes a current which is not given by the first term on the right-hand side of Eq. (15-15). Thus, the second term is added. It is difficult to solve this equation if the voltage across the junction is known. However, a solution can be obtained if the diode is assumed to be connected to a current generator. Consider the circuit of Fig. 15-9a. The diode is connected to a current generator which has provided a current I_0, with a hole component I_{0p}, for a very long time. Then, the excess stored charge is given by Eq. (15-14) as

$$Q_{0p} = I_{0p}\tau_{pn} \tag{15-16}$$

At $t = 0$ the current generator reverses polarity and produces the current $-I_1$. (It is assumed that I_1 is equal to or less than the reverse saturation current of the diode.) Then, for $t > 0$, Eq. (15-15) becomes

$$\frac{dq_p(t)}{dt} + \frac{1}{\tau_{pn}}q_p(t) = -I_{1p} \tag{15-17}$$

where $-I_{1p}$ is the component of current due to holes. Solving this and making use of the fact that $q_p(0) = Q_{0p}$ [see Eq. (15-16)], we obtain

$$q_p(t) = -\tau_{pn}I_{1p} + (Q_{0p} + \tau_{pn}I_{1p})e^{-t/\tau_{pn}} \tag{15-18}$$

A plot of this is shown in Fig. 15-9c. Note that the equilibrium value of excess stored charge now is negative $(-\tau_{pn}I_{1p})$. Physically this means that there are regions in the n-type material where the hole density is less than the equilibrium value.

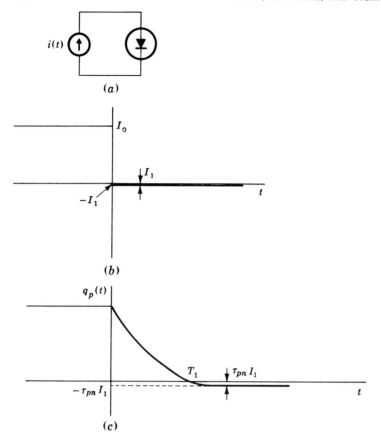

Fig. 15-9 (*a*) A *p-n*-junction diode connected to a current generator; (*b*) the current of the current generator; (*c*) the excess hole charge in the *n*-type material as a function of time.

For those times when $q_p(t)$ is positive, the junction still "acts as though it were forward-biased." That is, the potential across it is low. Once the excess charge becomes negative, the voltage across the junction reverses and eventually becomes large. Thus, the junction responds exponentially. The time constant of this response for holes is τ_{pn}.

Now let us consider the circuit of Fig. 15-10*a*. A voltage generator in series with a resistance is connected to the diode. The voltage generator applies a forward bias V_1 for a very long time. If R is much greater than the forward resistance of the diode, i will attain the equilibrium value V_1/R. Then $q_p(t)$, the excess hole charge in the *n*-type region, attains the equilibrium value $k\tau_{pn}V_1/R = Q_{0p}$ [see Eq. (15-16)], where k is the fraction of the total

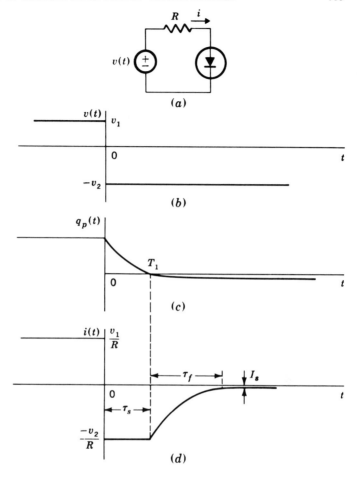

Fig. 15-10 (a) A simple diode circuit; (b) the waveform of $v(t)$; (c) the excess hole charge in the n-type material as a function of time; (d) the current $i(t)$.

current that is due to holes. At $t = 0$ the voltage generator instantaneously switches to a reverse bias voltage $-V_2$. Let us assume that this voltage is sufficiently negative to cause i to become the reverse saturation current $-I_s$. The current immediately becomes negative, but its magnitude is much larger than I_s. It becomes equal to $-V_2/R$. (This assumes that R is much larger than the forward resistance of the diode.) This can be explained by the following. At the first instant after switching, the value of $q_p(t)$ remains unchanged at Q_{0p}. Then the value of $q_p(t)$ falls off and becomes negative, as in Fig. 15-9c. While this transition is taking place, the magnitude of $dq_p(t)/dt$ [see Eq. (15-15)] is large. This allows a reasonably large current to pass through the diode. Thus, the diode resistance remains low, and the current is essentially limited by the resistor R. At time T_1, the value of $q_p(t)$ becomes negative. At this time, $dq_p(t)/dt$ decreases. The effective resistance of the diode becomes large, and the current falls off exponentially and approaches the value of $-I_s$. The curves of Fig. 15-10, especially Fig. 15-10d, are idealized somewhat, and the sharp corners really do not appear.

It is desirable for the diode to switch rapidly, i.e., go from a short circuit to an open circuit. However, the diode cannot be considered to be an open circuit until the current has fallen to a very small value. There are two phenomena which limit the switching speed. In the time between $t = 0$ and $t = t_1$, the reverse diode current remains constant (and large). This is the time required for the $q_p(t)$ to become zero. It is said that for $0 \leq t \leq T_1$ there is *excess positive charge stored* and this must be removed. The time for this to occur, called the *storage time* τ_s, is a function of the external parameters as well as of those of the diode. The value $q_p(0) = Q_{0p} = kV_1\tau_{pn}/R$. Thus, the larger V_1 is, that is, the more the diode is overdriven in the forward direction, the greater Q_{0p} will be. This results in more excess charge storage and thus in a larger value of τ_s [see Eq. (15-18)].

If V_2 is increased, then V_2/R is also increased. This increases $dq_p(t)/dt$. Hence the excess stored charge is removed at a faster rate. Thus, increasing V_2, that is, making $-V_2$ more negative, will reduce τ_s.

The second factor which limits the switching speed is the time it takes for the current to rise from $-V_2/R$ to $-I_s$. This is called the *fall time* τ_f. Actually, since the curves are rounded and exponentially approach $-I_s$, the fall time is usually defined as the time it takes for i to vary between $-0.9V_2/R$ and $-1.1I_s$. Similarly, the saturation time is defined as the time required for i to fall to $-0.9V_2/R$. The fall time also tends to decrease with increasing V_2/R for reasons similar to the reasons for the decrease in τ_s. Manufacturers often supply curves of τ_s and τ_f for various operating conditions.

In the discussion we have considered $q_p(t)$, the excess hole charge in the n-type region. Analogously there is a $q_n(t)$ which is the excess free-electron charge in the p-type region. The discussion proceeds in an equivalent fashion for this charge and the current due to free electrons.

We have discussed switching a diode from its on condition to its off condition. Let us now consider that the bias is switched from reverse to forward. If the circuit of Fig. 15-9a is used (with the polarity of the current reversed), the form of Eq. (15-18) will be unchanged. The polarities of the currents and initial charges will be reversed. The one essential difference is that the equilibrium Q_{0p} prior to switching will be very small in magnitude. Thus, the storage time will be very much smaller in this case. If the circuit of Fig. 15-10a is used (with the polarity of the voltage reversed), the current will now rapidly start to rise to the equilibrium value V/R. If V/R is increased, the equilibrium value will be attained more rapidly.   Again, manufacturers provide curves of switching time.   In switching from the reverse to forward direction, storage times are usually not expressed, and a 10 to 90 percent rise time τ_r is given.

Switching in a junction transistor   The basic phenomena which govern switching in a transistor will now be considered.   Actually, much of the previous discussion of the diode applies to the transistor.   To study transistor switching let us consider the circuit of Fig. 15-11a and b.   Here the base current is set up by a voltage generator in series with a resistance. Equivalently, this can be considered to be a current generator in shunt with a resistance.   Let us consider the emitter-base junction.   To a first approximation, this is a diode.   The input generator has been assumed to reverse-bias the junction for a long time.   Thus, the reverse saturation current I_{BO} results.   (Note that an n-p-n transistor is used.   This is done to make the reverse currents negative.)   At $t = t_1$, the polarities of the input generator reverse to forward-bias the junction.   If the resistance of the forward-biased junction is much less than R, then i_B will rise to the value $I_{Bs} = V_1/R$ (or $I_{Bs} = I_1$).   As discussed in the beginning of this section, the current will rise from I_{BO} to I_{Bs} exponentially.   However, the time constant involved in this rise is usually very much shorter than other time constants in the transistor circuit we shall discuss, and thus for all practical purposes we can consider the rise to be instantaneous.   The input generator remains constant at V_1 (or I_1) until $t = t_2$, at which point it switches and reverse-biases the junction; i.e., it becomes $-V_2$ (or $-I_2$).   The diode then switches as shown in Fig. 15-11d.   Note that the waveform is almost essentially the same as that of Fig. 15-10d for the p-n-junction diode.   The explanatons of the shape of Fig. 15-11d are essentially the same as those for Fig. 15-10d.

The response of the transistor we are usually concerned with is the output, i.e., collector, current i_C.   Let us now consider it.   When the base current is switched from off to on, i.e., the emitter-base-junction diode is switched from cutoff to conduction, the charges near the emitter-base junction rearrange themselves, as we have discussed.   However, the collector current does not change until the charge distribution in the vicinity of the collector-base junction is modified appropriately.   This requires charges to diffuse across the base and then modify the distribution near the collector-base junction.   This process takes time.   Thus, the collector current i_C does not increase instantaneously but rises as shown in Fig. 15-11e.   A 10 to 90 percent rise time τ_r, called the *switching rise time*, is defined for this switching time.   We have indicated that the collector current rises to a saturation value I_{Cs}.   Since this is a saturation value, increasing the base current I_{Bs} will not increase the value of I_{Cs}.   However, τ_r will be reduced when I_{Bs} is increased.   This is because more excess charge q_n will be introduced.   (Note

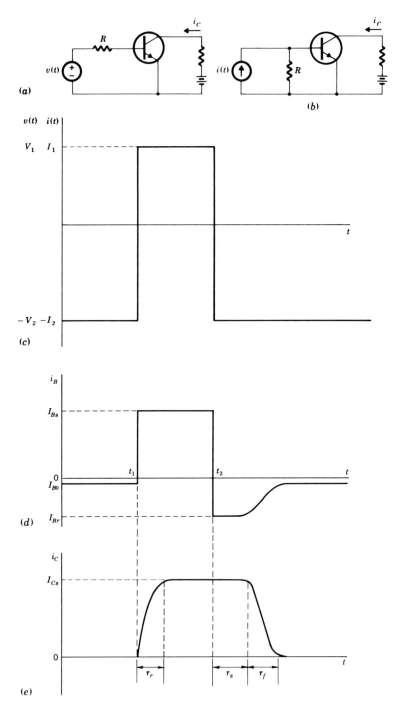

Fig. 15-11 (*a*) A transistor driven by a voltage pulse generator; (*b*) an equivalent circuit driven by a current pulse generator; (*c*) the voltage and current generator waveforms; (*d*) the resulting base current; (*e*) the resulting collector current.

that the base is assumed to be p type.)   Thus, the diffusion currents will be greater.   Manufacturers often supply curves of switching rise time.   Such a curve is given in Fig. 15-12a.   Note that τ_r decreases as I_{Bs} increases.

Now let us consider time t_2 when the input generator reverses polarity so that the emitter-base-junction diode is reverse-biased.   As discussed, the waveform of i_B is as shown in Fig. 15-11d.   During the period when excess charge is present, the base current remains essentially constant at I_{Br}.   As long as excess charge is present, the action of the charges near the emitter-base junction on the collector current is the same as if a positive i_B were present.   Thus, the collector current does not change during this time. This is illustrated in Fig. 15-11e.   The time it takes for i_C to fall to 90 percent of I_{Cs} is called the storage time τ_s.   At a time corresponding to T_1 of Fig. 15-10c, all the excess stored charge is removed from the vicinity of the collector-base junction; that is, $q_n(t)$ changes sign, and the magnitude of the base current begins to decrease exponentially from I_{Br} to I_{BO}.   Since the excess charge $q_n(t)$ has changed sign, the collector current will be reduced. Thus, i_C falls off during the time that the magnitude of i_B is decreased.

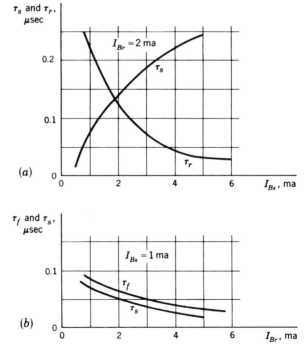

Fig. 15-12   (a) Switching rise time and storage time versus I_{Bs} for a typical transistor and (b) fall time and storage time versus I_{Br} for this transistor.

Again, the change in i_C lags after the change in i_B somewhat. The time it takes for i_C to fall from $0.9i_{Cs}$ to $0.1i_{Cs}$ is called the *switching fall time*. It is illustrated in Fig. 15-11e. Typical plots of τ_s and τ_f are given in Fig. 15-12. Note that τ_s is increased as I_{Bs} is increased. This occurs for the same reasons that it does in the case of the junction diode. However, increasing I_{Bs} reduces τ_r. Thus, some compromise is necessary.

Let us now consider the effect of increasing the value of V_2 and I_2. This will increase I_{Br} (see Fig. 15-10). As discussed in the case of the diode, this will shorten both τ_s and τ_f, as indicated in Fig. 15-12b for the transistor. Note that the total time required to turn the transistor off is $\tau_s + \tau_f$. Thus, large values of V_2 or I_2 are desirable.

The storage time is reduced if I_{Bs} is reduced and can be almost completely eliminated by making I_{Bs} small enough. However, this also increases τ_r. A circuit which tends to reduce both τ_s and τ_r is shown in Fig. 15-13. At the first instant that the pulse is applied, the capacitor acts as a short circuit. This results in a very large base current. However, this falls off exponentially and eventually the resistor R limits the current to V_1/R and thus I_{Bs} is limited. In this case, i_B rises above I_{Bs} and then falls exponentially to it. The RC time constant should be much shorter than the pulse width so that $i_B \approx I_{Bs}$ for much of the period. In this case, i_B can be kept small for much of the period but has a large initial value. When v_1 reverses polarity, a similar effect occurs. Then i_B becomes more negative than $-V_2/R$ (see Fig. 15-10) and exponentially decays to it. Thus, the inclusion of the capacitor increases the switching speed.

Switching in an FET In a junction FET, the operation involves setting up a depletion layer in the channel. Thus, the gate-channel diode is switched from forward to reverse bias and vice versa. The action involved here is similar to switching an ordinary junction diode, and the switching times involved are similar.

Switching in a MOSFET is somewhat more complicated since no actual junction is involved. However, charge configurations similar to those of a depletion layer are set up. When switching occurs, the electric field which sets up these charge distributions is changed. The free electrons

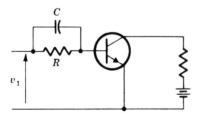

Fig. 15-13 A circuit which reduces τ_r and τ_s.

and/or holes then must move to establish a new equilibrium condition. This constitutes the time required for switching. Curves of switching times for the FET can be obtained so that FET switching circuits can be designed.

15-3 MULTIVIBRATORS

In this section we consider an oscillator which can be used to generate a continuous train of pulses. Such circuits are called *regenerative switching circuits* since they generate their own switching pulses. The oscillator is called a *multivibrator*. Two such circuits are shown in Fig. 15-14. The operation of both these circuits is similar, and they will be described simultaneously. The waveforms of T_a are given in Fig. 15-15. We shall consider that the resistance of the active device when it is saturated is very much less than R_1. Conversely, when the active device is cut off, its output resistance is very much greater than R_1. Thus, during cutoff, $v_O = V_{OO}$, and when the active device is saturated, $v_O = 0$. The base emitter voltage of the transistor will be assumed to be zero when the emitter-base diode is forward-biased. In a MOSFET the gate can always be considered to be an open circuit. The waveforms of T_b differ from those of T_a by one half-cycle. Assume that T_a and T_b are both conducting equally but that some random fluctuation increases the output current of T_a. This will decrease v_{Oa}. The voltage

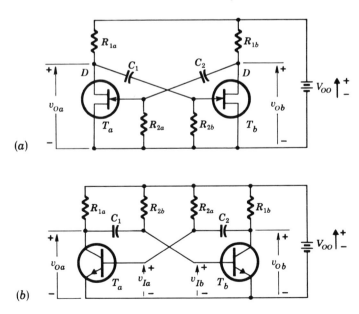

Fig. 15-14 Free-running multivibrators: (a) FET circuit and (b) transistor circuit. Note that *n-p-n* transistors are used.

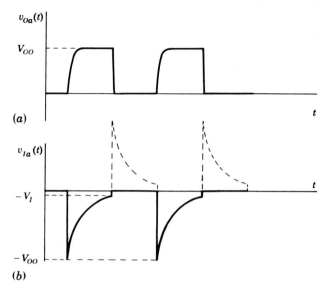

Fig. 15-15 Waveforms in a free-running multivibrator: (*a*)
output voltage and (*b*) input voltage. The dashed curves apply
to a MOSFET. For the transistor $V_1 \approx 0$.

across C_1 and C_2 cannot change instantaneously. Thus, the gate or base
voltage of T_b will decrease. This will increase v_{Ob}. Hence, the gate or base
voltage of T_a will increase, and, hence, its output current will increase further.
This process will continue until T_b is cut off. At this time, T_a should be
saturated. If the active elements could respond instantaneously and there
were no parasitic capacitance, this process would take place in zero time.
Actually, the switching considerations discussed in Secs. 15-1 and 15-2 cause
this time to be greater than zero. If T_a is a MOSFET, its gate may be driven
positive.

The capacitor C_1 will discharge so that eventually T_b will no longer be
cut off. As its current increases, v_{Ob} decreases, which tends to drive T_a
toward cutoff. The procedure outlined above repeats itself until T_b is
saturated and T_a is cut off, whereupon the cycle starts again. The rate of
oscillation depends upon the discharge of the capacitors C_1 and C_2. For the
FET, if the effective drain resistance of the active element in the saturation
region is r_s, and if we define

$$R'_{2a} = R_{2a} + \frac{r_s R_{1b}}{r_s + R_{1b}} \approx R_{2a}$$

and

$$R'_{2b} = R_{2b} + \frac{r_s R_{1a}}{r_s + R_{1a}} \approx R_{2b}$$

then the time constant for one half-cycle is $R'_{2b}C_1$, while the time constant for the other half-cycle is $R'_{2a}C_2$. For the transistor,

$$R'_{2a} = \frac{R_{2a}h_{iec}}{R_{2a} + h_{iec}} + \frac{R_{1b}}{1 + h_{oes}R_{1b}} \approx R_{2a}$$

and

$$R'_{2b} = \frac{R_{2b}h_{iec}}{R_{2b} + h_{iec}} + \frac{R_{1a}}{1 + h_{oes}R_{1a}} \approx R_{2b}$$

where the approximate relations are true if $h_{iec} \gg R_2$ and $1/h_{oes} \ll R_2$. Let us solve for the time of one half-cycle. We shall consider the transistor here. It remains cut off until its v_I has risen from $-V_{OO}$ to 0 volts. A model for the input circuit, subject to the approximations that we have discussed, is shown in Fig. 15-16. The initial voltage across C_2 is $v_I(0) = -V_{OO}$. Thus, for the first half-cycle

$$v_I(t) = V_{OO} - 2V_{OO}e^{-t/R_{2a}C_2} \tag{15-19}$$

The half-cycle is from $t = 0$ to $t = T_b$, where $v_I(T_b) = 0$. Thus,

$$T_b = R_{2a}C_2 \ln 2 \tag{15-20}$$

Similarly,

$$T_a = R_{2b}C_1 \ln 2 \tag{15-21}$$

A similar set of calculations can be applied to the FET circuit. Note that switching then starts when $v_I = -V_1$ (see Fig. 15-15).

It is possible for both T_a and T_b to become saturated when their circuits are turned on, in which case no oscillatory action will take place. More complex circuitry is sometimes used to ensure that oscillations will start.

If an external signal is applied to the gate or base of the cutoff device such that it drives it from the cutoff region, the cycle will be initiated. This often proves convenient, since it allows the multivibrator to be *synchronized* by an external signal. For instance, suppose that the multivibrator is adjusted to oscillate at a frequency just slower than that of a signal applied to one grid or base. The cycles will be initiated each time the signal drives the

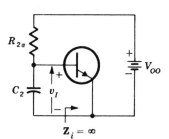

Fig. 15-16 A circuit used to obtain the cutoff time of T_b of Fig. 15-14b.

device from the cutoff region and the multivibrator will run in exact synchro-nism with the signal.   If the period of the input signal is approximately an integral multiple or submultiple of the frequency of the multivibrator, it will also synchronize it.   In this case, the frequency of the multivibrator will be an exact harmonic or subharmonic of the applied signal.   The circuit of Fig. 15-14 is called a *free-running multivibrator*, since it is not necessary to apply an external signal to obtain operation.

15-4   BISTABLE MULTIVIBRATORS—COUNTER CIRCUITS

If the coupling capacitors of the free-running multivibrator are replaced by direct coupling, very different operation results.   Consider the circuits of Fig. 15-17.   We shall again describe both circuits simultaneously.   The magnitudes of the voltages and currents will be discussed here.   Assume that T_a and T_b are conducting equally but that some disturbance increases the out-put current of T_a.   The voltage v_{Oa} will decrease and the input bias of T_b will be driven toward cutoff.   This will increase v_{Ob} and further increase the output

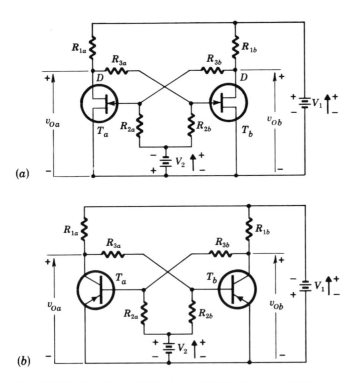

Fig. 15-17   Bistable multivibrators: (*a*) FET circuit and (*b*) transis-tor circuit.

current of T_a. This process will continue until T_b is cut off and T_a is saturated as in the case of the free-running multivibrator. However, the circuits are direct-coupled; hence, this condition will be maintained indefinitely. Now suppose that a pulse whose polarity tends to drive the device toward cutoff is applied to both gates or to both bases. Since T_b is cut off, the pulse applied to it will have no effect. However, if the pulse applied to T_a is sufficiently large to drive it from the saturation region, then v_{Oa} will rise. If this rise is sufficiently large, it will increase the output current of T_b and decrease v_{Ob}. This will further decrease the current through T_a and increase v_{Oa}. This will repeat itself until T_b is saturated and T_a is cut off. Thus, this circuit will change its state whenever the proper input pulse is applied. (Pulses which tend to saturate the devices can also change the state.) ·

Now let us consider the circuit of Fig. 15-18, which provides such triggering action, and consider some of its applications. It consists basically of the circuit of Fig. 15-17b. The diodes D_a and D_b are called *steering diodes*. They cause the triggering pulse to be applied to the proper transistor. If this were not done, a cutoff pulse would be applied to the bases of both transistors. This would waste energy and tend to interfere with proper triggering. Let us consider that T_a is cut off and T_b is saturated. Then D_a will be reverse-biased, since its anode essentially will be at the large negative potential of the collector of T_a and its cathode will be at the positive potential of the base of T_a. On the other hand, if the transistors are ideal, then D_b will act as a short circuit, since the collector voltage of T_b is zero, while the base of T_b will be at a negative potential. (In an actual circuit, the collector voltage will not be zero so that D_b may be *slightly* reverse-biased.) Thus, if a positive pulse is applied at v_i, D_a will prevent it from being applied to the base of T_a while D_b

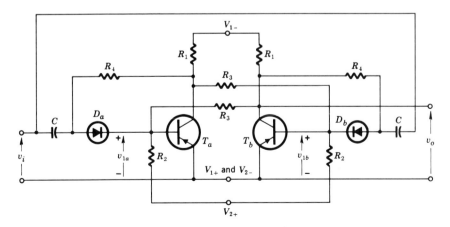

Fig. 15-18 A basic counter circuit.

will allow it to be applied to the base of T_b. In general, a positive pulse will always be applied to the base of the cutoff transistor. The diodes also perform another function. *They prevent a negative pulse from affecting either transistor*, since they can only conduct in one direction.

Now let us assume that the input voltage v_i is the train of pulses shown in Fig. 15-19a. If this voltage were applied to a series circuit consisting of C and R_2 alone, then the fictitious voltage v_1 across R_2 would have the form shown in Fig. 15-19b. Actually, neither v_{1a} nor v_{1b} has this waveform. The diodes will eliminate all negative pulses and alternate positive pulses. That is, v_{1a} and v_{1b} will only consist of positive pulses; when one is positive, the other will be zero because of steering action. In general, the waveform will not even have the shape of v_1, because the base and collector currents will affect v_{1a} and v_{1b}. However, positive pulses will be present at the base of the saturated transistor, if v_i has the waveform of Fig. 15-19a.

Now let us assume that T_a is cut off and that T_b is saturated. When v_1 has a positive pulse, it will be applied as v_{1b} to the base of T_b. Then T_b will

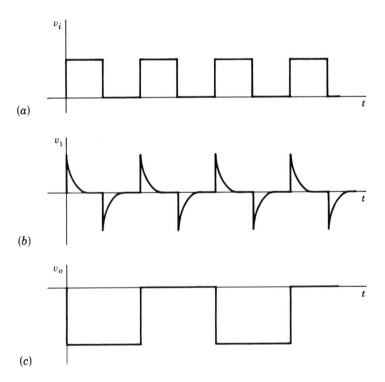

Fig. 15-19 Some typical waveforms for the circuit of Fig. 15-18: (a) the input voltage; (b) the idealized voltage v_1; and (c) the output voltage, neglecting transients.

become cut off and T_a will be saturated. The next positive pulses in v_1 will saturate T_b and cut off T_a. In this way, successive positive pulses of v_1 will change the state of the circuit. (Note that the RC input circuit provides positive and negative pulses even if the input pulses are of only one polarity. In addition, the RC circuit and the diodes prevent the input pulses from interfering with switching action once the cycle has been initiated.) If we consider that T_b is ideal, then its collector voltage is zero when it conducts and will be a negative value when it is cut off. This voltage is the output voltage v_o. It is shown plotted in Fig. 15-19c. Transients have been neglected here. Since the state only changes on successive positive pulses, the frequency of v_o will be one-half of that of v_i. For this reason, this is called a *scale-of-two circuit*. If v_o becomes the input of another scale-of-two circuit, then its output will have a frequency that is one-quarter of the input frequency, and so on.

Frequency scaling is a useful application of these circuits, but a far more important one is counting pulses. Consider that some indication is placed in the collector circuit of T_b to show when it is cut off, and that a great many circuits of the form of Fig. 15-18 are cascaded; i.e., the output of one is used as the input of the next. Assume that all the T_b's are initially conducting. We shall use the notation that a transistor is on if it is saturated and off if it is cut off. In addition, T_{a1} and T_{b1} will be the transistors of the first counter; T_{a2} and T_{b2} will be the transistors of the second counter, etc. The leading edge of each pulse of v_i will produce a positive pulse of v_1. The first such pulse will switch T_{a1} on and switch T_{b1} off. This produces a negative-going pulse in v_o which will not affect the next counter. The polarity of the output of the RC circuit will depend upon the derivative of the input voltage (see Sec. 15-7). The leading edge of the next pulse of v_i will switch T_{a1} off and T_{b1} on. This will produce a positive-going pulse that activates the next counter, and turns T_{b2} off. In a similar way, the leading edge of each of the input pulses will activate the first counter. Every second input pulse will activate the second counter; every fourth pulse will activate the third counter, etc. If all the T_b's are on at the start, then Table 15-1 can be used to determine the number of pulses. These counters operate in the *binary number system*. If there are n counters, then $2^n - 1$ pulses can be counted. Thus, circuits can be constructed that will count large numbers of pulses. Some means should be provided to reset the counter. One means of doing this is to apply a momentary cutoff bias onto all the bases of transistors T_a.

In FET and transistor circuits, if the cutoff output voltage is sufficiently high, a simple means of indicating if an active element is cut off is a neon bulb in series with a resistance. This is connected from plate to cathode or collector to emitter. If the device is cut off, the potential across the bulb will be high and it will glow. If the device is saturated, the bulb will be dark. The current drawn by these bulbs is not large enough to disturb the circuit opera-

Table 15–1

Number of pulses	T_b cutoff			
0	None			
1	T_{b1}			
2		T_{b2}		
3	T_{b1}	T_{b2}		
4			T_{b3}	
5	T_{b1}		T_{b3}	
6		T_{b2}	T_{b3}	
7	T_{b1}	T_{b2}	T_{b3}	
8				T_{b4}

tion. Other indicating devices are also used. One of the most important applications of counter circuits is in digital computers. In this case, the outputs from the various counters are used in the solution of the desired problem.

The counter circuits that we have presented are very basic and they are usually modified. For instance, capacitors are often placed across the resistances R_{3a} and R_{3b} in Fig. 15-17 to speed the operation (see Sec. 15-2). Transistor counters are often operated so that they do not actually enter the saturation region; this eliminates the problem of storage time. In digital computers, an exceptionally large number of operations are usually carried out, and speed of operation is extremely important. Thus, it is desirable to have counters that respond very rapidly.

15-5 LOGIC CIRCUITS

Digital-computer circuits operate between saturation and cutoff levels. Let us call the saturation level 1 and the cutoff level 0. Thus, a counter circuit

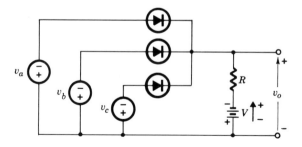

Fig. 15-20 An AND circuit.

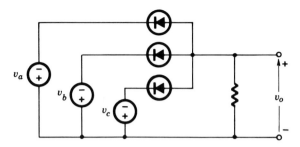

Fig. 15-21   An OR circuit.

will count the number of times that the level switches from 1 to 0, or vice versa. In order to function, a digital computer must perform certain logical operations on these 1 or 0 signals.   We shall consider several of these here.   In the next section we shall discuss an application of these logic circuits.

The AND circuit   It is often desirable to build up a circuit called an AND circuit that will have an output of 1 if all of several input circuits have outputs equal to 1.   However, if *any* of the input circuits has an output of 0, then the output of the AND circuit should be zero.   For instance, if there are three inputs *A*, *B*, and *C*, then the output of the AND circuit is 1 if *A and B and C* are 1.   In order to demonstrate the operation of the circuitry, let us assume that 1 corresponds to a negative voltage and 0 is zero volts.   (Thus, 1 will saturate a *p-n-p* transistor and 0 will cut it off.)   The logical AND operation can be performed by the circuit of Fig. 15-20.   Assume that when v_a, v_b, or v_c represents 1, their magnitudes will be slightly greater than V.   If v_a, v_b, and v_c are all 1, then all three diodes will be cut off and $v_o = V$.   Thus, the output is a 1.   On the other hand, if v_a, v_b, or v_c is zero, then the diode in series with it will conduct and v_o will, effectively, be zero.   Thus, the circuit performs the desired function.

The OR circuit   An OR circuit is one which produces an output if *any* of its inputs is 1.   That is, its output is 1 if v_a *or* v_b *or* v_c is 1.   Such a circuit is shown in Fig. 15-21.   If any generator is 1, then its diode will conduct; otherwise it will not.   Thus, if any generator is 1, it will be directly connected to the output and the output will be 1.

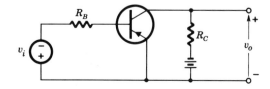

Fig. 15-22   A   NEGATE,   or NOT, circuit.

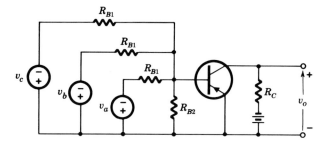

Fig. 15-23   A NOR circuit.

The NEGATE circuit   This is a circuit that will convert a 1 to a 0 and vice versa.   This can be done very simply with a common-emitter transistor amplifier such as that shown in Fig. 15-22.   If v_i is 0, then the transistor will be cut off and v_o will be a large negative value and, hence, 1.   If v_i is 1, then the transistor will saturate and v_o will be a 0.   This is also called a NOT circuit.

The NOR circuit   If several inputs are included in the circuit of Fig. 15-22, the circuit will perform the functions of an OR circuit cascaded with a negate circuit.   Hence, it is called a NOR circuit.   This is illustrated in Fig. 15-23. If v_a, or v_b, or v_c is 1, then v_o will be 0.   If v_a, v_b, and v_c are all zero, then v_o will be 1.

The logic circuits presented in this section are representative of circuits of this type.   However, there are many variations.

15-6   ADDERS

Let us now use the logic operations discussed in the last section to obtain a circuit that performs the mathematical operation of addition.   Remember that we are working with a binary system, so that the only digits are zero or one.

At first we shall consider a simple circuit called a *half adder*.   It has two inputs.   If both the inputs are zero, then the output should be zero.   If either of the inputs is a one, then the output should indicate one; if both the inputs are ones, then the output should indicate the (decimal number) 2.   This is done in a binary fashion.   To do this, the adder has two outputs labeled v_s and v_c.   If both are zeros, the output is zero.   If v_s is a one and v_c is a zero, then the output is one.   If v_s is a zero and v_c is a one, then the output is 2 (decimally).   If both v_s and v_c are ones, the output is 3 (decimally).   (The half adder will not be able to make use of this.)   This is similar to the operation of counters in cascade, see Sec. 15-4.   That is, v_s corresponds to the first counter, and v_c corresponds to the output of the second counter.

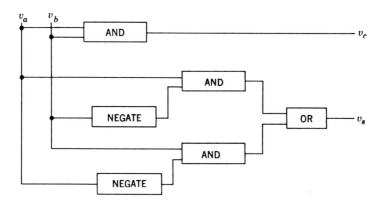

Fig. 15-24 A half adder. The input of each logic circuit is on the left.

Now let us consider Fig. 15-24, which is a simple half adder.[1] Block diagrams are used here. That is, each logic circuit of Sec. 15-5 is represented by a block. The input is the left-hand side. All the circuits have a common lead, which is omitted from the block diagrams.

In Fig. 15-24, if both inputs v_a and v_b are zeros, then both v_c and v_s will be zeros. Note that at least one input to each AND circuit will be a zero. If both inputs are ones, then v_c will be a one while v_s will be a zero. The negate circuits cause one of the inputs to each of the lower AND circuits to be zeros. Similarly, if one of the inputs is a one and the other is a zero, then v_c is a zero while v_s is a one.

The half adder can accommodate only two inputs while its output can indicate up to 3 (decimally). A circuit which can accommodate three inputs is called a *full adder*. One is shown in Fig. 15-25.[1] If all the inputs v_α, v_β, and v_γ are zero, then both v_s and v_c are zeros. If one of the inputs is a one, then

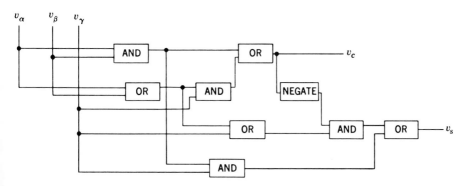

Fig. 15-25 A full adder. The input of each logic circuit is on the left.

v_s is a one and v_c is a zero. If any two of the inputs are ones, the v_c will be a one while v_s will be a zero. Finally, if all three inputs are ones, then both v_s and v_c will be ones.

Complex digital computers are made up of interconnections of adders, logic circuits, and memory circuits. Their interconnections involve the *software* of the computer.

15-7 DIFFERENTIATING AND INTEGRATING CIRCUITS

There are many applications where it is desirable to obtain a signal that is approximately the derivative of the input signal. (This can be done with an operational amplifier. However, if great accuracy is not desired, then much simpler circuits can be used.) For instance, consider the counter circuit of Fig. 15-18. The waveforms for this circuit are shown in Fig. 15-19. If the voltage v_i consists of square positive pulses, then v_1 will contain both negative and positive spikes. If these negative spikes were not present, then the counter would not function properly. The input RC circuit approximately differentiates the input voltage v_i to obtain the voltage v_1. Consider the circuit of Fig. 15-26. Its differential equations are

$$v_i = \frac{1}{C} \int i \, dt + iR \tag{15-22}$$

and

$$v_o = iR \tag{15-23}$$

If the RC time constant is considerably smaller than the period of the input signals (assuming they are periodic), then we can often state

$$\frac{1}{C} \int i \, dt \gg iR \tag{15-24}$$

This inequality is not always true no matter how small RC is. However, since the function of these circuits is only to obtain an *approximate* derivative, the accuracy is usually sufficient if RC is much smaller than one period.

If relation (15-24) is valid, we can state

$$i = C \frac{dv_i}{dt} \tag{15-25}$$

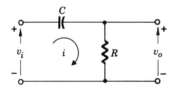

Fig. 15-26 A differentiating circuit.

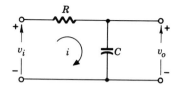

Fig. 15-27 An integrating circuit.

Substituting in Eq. (15-23), we obtain

$$v_o = RC \frac{dv_i}{dt} \tag{15-26}$$

Typical input and output waveforms for this circuit are shown in Fig. 15-19a and b.

A circuit which will approximately integrate an input waveform is shown in Fig. 15-27. Its differential equations are

$$v_i = Ri + \frac{1}{C} \int i \, dt \tag{15-27}$$

$$v_o = \frac{1}{C} \int i \, dt \tag{15-28}$$

If

$$Ri \gg \frac{1}{C} \int i \, dt \tag{15-29}$$

then

$$v_o = \frac{1}{RC} \int v_i \, dt \tag{15-30}$$

The approximation of relation (15-29) usually depends upon the fact that RC is much larger than the period of the input signal if it is periodic.

15-8 CLIPPING AND CLAMPING CIRCUITS

A circuit that limits the amplitude of an output signal is called a *clipping circuit*. One application of such a circuit is in the generation of an approximate square wave from a sine-wave input. Consider the circuit of Fig. 15-28. If $V_b \le v_i \le V_a$, where V_b is a negative voltage, then neither diode will conduct and $v_o = v_i$. If $v_i > V_a$, then D_a will conduct and act as a short circuit. Thus, $v_o = V_a$. If $v_i < V_b$, then D_b will conduct, and, thus, $v_o = V_b$. Figure 15-28b illustrates the behavior of this circuit. If $V_a = -V_b$ and $v_1 = V_{1,\max} \sin \omega t$, where $V_{1,\max} \gg V_a$, then the output of this circuit will be a fairly good square wave. The relative amplitude of the positive and negative peaks can be changed by varying V_a and V_b.

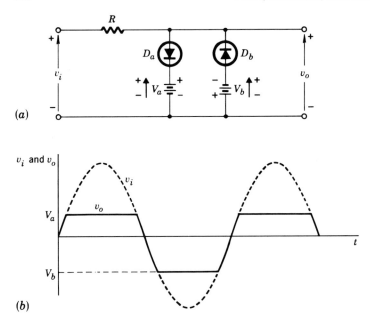

Fig. 15-28 (*a*) A diode clipping circuit; (*b*) the waveforms in this circuit when a sinusoid signal is applied.

We have illustrated a clipping circuit that uses diodes. These circuits are also built using FETs or transistors. These are, essentially, amplifiers that are driven between saturation and cutoff.

Another application of clipping circuits is in devices that are required to respond to changes in a signal's frequency but not in its amplitude. Frequency-modulation systems are an example of this. These will be discussed in Chap. 16.

It is often desirable to convert an alternating signal to one which is unidirectional without altering its waveform. A circuit which performs this operation is called a *clamping circuit* or a *dc restorer*. A typical one is shown in Fig. 15-29*a*. Consider the input voltage shown in Fig. 15-29*b*. On the first negative cycle, the diode will conduct and the capacitor C will charge to the voltage $v = V_{i,\max}$, with the polarity shown. The capacitor can discharge only through the resistor R. If the product RC is much larger than the period of the signal, then v will remain essentially constant at $V_{i,\max}$. The output voltage will then be given by

$$v_o = V_{i,\max} + v_i \qquad (15\text{-}31)$$

Thus, v_o will not be negative at any time. The output waveform of this circuit is shown in Fig. 15-29*c*. If $V_{i,\max}$ changes, the circuit will readjust itself

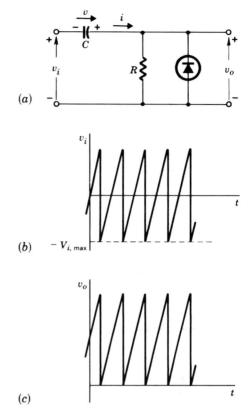

Fig. 15-29 (*a*) A diode clamping circuit; (*b*) an input waveform; (*c*) the output waveform.

so that the minimum voltage is zero. If $V_{i,\max}$ is decreased, then it may require many cycles for the capacitor to discharge before equilibrium conditions are established.

The preceding discussion assumes that the diode is ideal, and that $RC \to \infty$. In actual cases, this is not true, and v_o will be slightly negative at the negative peak of v_i. Often, the resistance R is omitted and the shunt leakage resistance of the diode takes its place. If R is made very large, then the circuit will not respond quickly if the input signal is reduced. This is usually not a serious consequence.

Once an equilibrium condition is established, the charge lost by the capacitor over any one cycle is equal to the charge gained by it over the same cycle. Thus,

$$\int_0^{2\pi} i \, d\omega t = 0 \tag{15-32}$$

If the time scale is adjusted so that v_o is positive for $0 < \omega t < \theta_1$ and v_o is negative for $\theta_1 < \omega t < 2\pi$, then Eq. (15-32) becomes

$$\int_0^{\theta_1} i \, d\omega t = \int_{\theta_1}^{2\pi} i \, d\omega t$$

Let us assume that the diode has a forward resistance of r_f and a reverse resistance of r_r. Let

$$R_1 = \frac{r_r R}{r_r + R} \tag{15-33}$$

If $r_f \ll R$, then we can write

$$\frac{1}{R_1} \int_0^{\theta_1} v_o \, d\omega t = \frac{1}{r_f} \int_{\theta_1}^{2\pi} v_o \, d\omega t \tag{15-34}$$

or

$$\frac{\int_{\theta_1}^{2\pi} v_o \, d\omega t}{\int_0^{\theta_1} v_o \, d\omega t} = \frac{r_f}{R_1} \tag{15-35}$$

Thus, the area under the negative v_o curve will decrease as r_f/R_1 decreases. In the limit, as this ratio approaches zero, v_o never becomes negative. If $r_f = 0$, there will be no time when v_o is negative. However, if $R_1 C$ is not sufficiently large, then the diode will conduct over a finite portion of the cycle and the waveform will be clipped and distorted. Thus, to obtain good nondistorted clamping action, $R_1 \gg r_f$ and $R_1 C$ must be very much larger than one period.

REFERENCES

1. Marcus, M. P.: "Switching Circuits for Engineers," 2d ed., pp. 162–164, Prentice-Hall Inc., Englewood Cliffs, N.J., 1967.

BIBLIOGRAPHY

Alley, C. L., and K. W. Atwood: "Electronic Engineering," 2d ed., chap. 16, John Wiley & Sons, Inc., New York, 1966.

Gibbons, J. F.: "Semiconductor Electronics," chap. 15, McGraw-Hill Book Company, New York, 1966.

Greiner, R. A.: "Semiconductor Devices and Applications," chaps. 18–20, McGraw-Hill Book Company, New York, 1961.

Joyce, M. V., and K. K. Clarke: "Transistor Circuit Analysis," chaps. 10–15, Addison-Wesley Publishing Company, Inc., Reading, Mass., 1961.

Marcus, M. P.: "Switching Circuits for Engineers," 2d ed., chaps. 5 and 11, Prentice-Hall, Inc., Englewood Cliffs, N.J., 1967.

Millman, J., and H. Taub: "Pulse, Digital, and Switching Waveforms," chaps. 7–20, McGraw-Hill Book Company, New York, 1965.

Pettit, J. M.: "Electronic Switching, Timing, and Pulse Circuits," chaps. 1–3 and 5–8, McGraw-Hill Book Company, New York, 1959.

Ryder, J. D.: "Engineering Electronics," chap. 9, McGraw-Hill Book Company, New York, 1957.

PROBLEMS

15-1. The output capacitance of the generalized device of Fig. 15-4 is 20 pf. Its static output characteristics are given in Fig. 15-30. The circuit is operated such that $V_{OO} = 50$ volts and $R_L = 33,330$ ohms. The input bias is $x_I = -8$ for $t < 0$ and $x_I = 0$ for $t > 0$. Determine the step response of the amplifier.

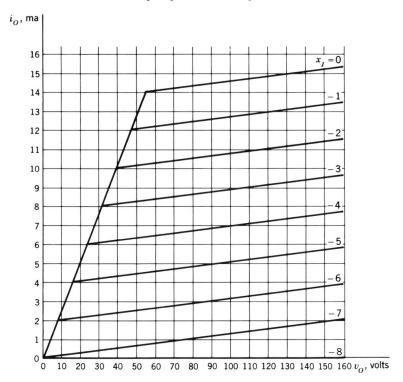

Fig. 15-30

15-2. Repeat Prob. 15-1 but now assume that $V_{OO} = 120$ volts.

15-3. Repeat Prob. 15-1 but now assume that $V_{OO} = 120$ volts and $R_L = 8000$ ohms.

15-4. Repeat Prob. 15-1 but now assume that $x_I = 0$ for $t < 0$ and $x_I = -8$ for $t > 0$.

15-5. Repeat Prob. 15-4 but now assume that $V_{OO} = 120$ volts.

15-6. For the amplifier of Prob. 15-1, $x_I = -8$ for $t < 0$, $x_I = 0$ for $0 \leq t \leq 10^{-6}$ sec, and $x_I = -8$ for $t > 10^{-6}$ sec. Obtain and plot the transient response of the amplifier.

15-7. Repeat Prob. 15-6 but now assume that $V_{OO} = 120$ volts.

15-8. Use the quantities defined in Eq. (15-18) to determine the time T_1 it takes for excess stored holes to be removed from a junction diode.

15-9. A transistor whose switching characteristics are given in Fig. 15-12 is to be pulsed from cutoff to saturation and then back to cutoff as shown in Fig. 15-11. It is desired that the sum of τ_r, τ_s, and τ_f be a minimum. Determine the value of I_{Bs} which allows this to be accomplished. Assume that $I_{Br} = 2$ ma. Only use values of current that are specified in the curves. Use the curves of Fig. 15-12.

15-10. The multivibrator of Fig. 15-14a has the following element values: $R_{1a} = R_{1b} = 10,000$ ohms, $R_{2a} = R_{2b} = 10^6$ ohms, $C_1 = C_2 = 0.01$ μf, $V_{OO} = 30$ volts. Assume that the FETS cut off when $v_{GS} < -2$ volts and that the plate resistance of the FET is 100 ohms when it is saturated, and that it is an open circuit when the FET is cut off. Compute the frequency of operation of the multivibrator. Assume that the parasitic capacitances can be neglected, so that the FETs can instantaneously switch from saturation to cutoff.

15-11. The multivibrator of Fig. 15-14b has the following element values: $R_{1a} = R_{1b} = 1000$ ohms, $R_{2a} = R_{2b} = 10^6$ ohms, $C_1 = C_2 = 0.01$ μf, and $V_{OO} = 30$ volts. The transistor parameters are (see Fig. 15-3) $h_{ies} = 10$ ohms, $h_{iec} = 10^8$ ohms, $h_{oes} = \frac{1}{10}$ mho, and $h_{oec} = 2 \times 10^{-6}$ mho. Assume that the transistor cuts off when its base-to-emitter voltage is 0 volts or less. Compute the frequency of oscillation of the multivibrator. Assume that the transistors instantaneously switch from the cutoff to the saturation regions.

15-12. Design a counter circuit that will count up to 2000 pulses. (Use block-diagram form.)

15-13. Discuss the operation of the logic circuit of Fig. 15-31.

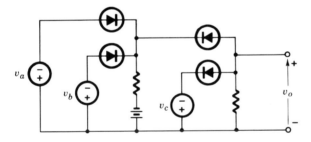

Fig. 15-31

15-14. Verify the operation of the half adder of Fig. 15-24.

15-15. Verify the operation of the full adder of Fig. 15-25.

15-16. For the circuit of Fig. 15-26, assume that v_i is a square wave with a period of 0.002 sec. Determine and plot v_o for the first cycle if $R = 10^6$ ohms and $C = 0.0001$ μf.

15-17. Repeat Prob. 15-27 if $C = 10$ pf.

15-18. For the circuit of Fig. 15-27, assume that v_i is a square wave with a period of 0.001 sec. Determine v_o for the first cycle if $R = 10^6$ ohms and $C = 0.01$ μf.

15-19. Repeat Prob. 15-18 for $C = 1.0$ μf.

15-20. What is the output of the circuit of Fig. 15-32 if the input is given by Fig. 15-29b

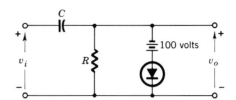

Fig. 15-32

where $V_{i,\text{max}} = 300$ volts. Assume that the diode is ideal, that RC is very long compared to the period of the signal, and that the positive and negative peaks of the signal are equal in magnitude.

15-21. Repeat Prob. 15-20 but assume that the diode is reversed.

15-22. Repeat Prob. 15-20 but assume that the polarity of the 100-volt battery is reversed.

15-23. Repeat Prob. 15-20 but now assume that the forward resistance of the diode is 100 ohms and its reverse resistance is 10^6 ohms, that $R = 10^9$ ohms, and that C is such that $0.5 \times 10^6 C$ is very much larger than one period of the input signal.

15-24. Discuss the changes that would occur in Prob. 15-20 if RC is not very long in comparison with the period of the input signal.

16

Modulation and Demodulation

A communications system is designed to convey information from one point to another. To accomplish this, a signal is made to vary in response to the information. Thus, a periodic signal, whether it be a sinusoid, a square wave, or any other waveform, does not transmit information. If the amplitude, frequency, or phase of a periodic signal is varied by intelligence, then a signal is obtained that can convey information. The process by which a function is made to vary in accordance with some specified intelligence is called *modulation*. The inverse process, that is, the recovering of the information from the signal, is called *demodulation* or *detection*. It is often inconvenient to transmit a signal directly. For instance, spoken messages carry for only a few feet. It is also difficult to transmit low-frequency electrical signals for any great distance. However, frequencies of 100 kHz or higher can be transmitted over great distances using electromagnetic waves. To take advantage of this, the modulation process often consists of varying the amplitude, frequency, or phase of a radio-frequency sinusoid.

Modulation may take on other forms. For instance, telegraph signals can be considered to be the modulation of a direct voltage. There are other modulation schemes where the amplitude, length, or position of pulses are varied. In this chapter we shall discuss modulation and demodulation procedures.

16-1 MODULATION OF A SINUSOID

The waveform that is most often modulated is the sinusoid. For instance suppose that we have a signal

$$x(t) = A \cos (\omega_c t + \phi) \tag{16-1}$$

If A and ϕ are constants, then this signal is unmodulated and $x(t)$ is called the *carrier*. Its frequency is given by $f_c = \omega_c/2\pi$. Now let us assume that we wish to transmit some information $x_m(t)$. We can do this by varying A such that

$$A = A(t) = A_c + k_1 x_m(t) \tag{16-2}$$

then

$$x(t) = [A_c + k_1 x_m(t)] \cos (\omega_c t + \phi) \tag{16-3}$$

This process is called *amplitude modulation* (a-m) since the amplitude of the carrier is varied. The information $x_m(t)$ is called the *modulating signal*. The quantity k_1 is a constant.

Let us see how the modulation could be applied to the frequency or phase of the carrier. The instantaneous phase angle of the cosinusoid of Eq. (16-1) is given by

$$\theta(t) = \omega_c t + \phi(t) \tag{16-4}$$

where we have assumed that ϕ could be a function of time. The instantaneous angular frequency ω_i is defined as the rate of change of the phase angle. Hence,

$$\omega_i = \frac{d\theta}{dt} \tag{16-5}$$

Thus, Eq. (16-4) yields

$$\omega_i = \omega_c + \frac{d\phi}{dt} \tag{16-6}$$

Note that if ϕ is a constant, then

$$\omega_i = \omega_c \tag{16-7}$$

which is the frequency of the unmodulated sinusoid. Now let us assume that we vary the instantaneous frequency in accordance with the modulating signal. That is,

$$\omega_i = \omega_c + k_2 x_m(t) \tag{16-8}$$

where k_2 is a constant. Note that the instantaneous *frequency* varies with the *amplitude* of the modulating signal. This is called *frequency modulation* (f-m). Equating Eqs. (16-6) and (16-8), we obtain

$$\phi(t) = k_2 \int x_m(t)\, dt \tag{16-9}$$

Thus

$$x(t) = A \cos \left[\omega_c t + k_2 \int x_m(t)\, dt \right] \tag{16-10}$$

If $\phi(t)$ is made to vary directly in accordance with the modulating signal, the process is called *phase modulation*. In this case,

$$\phi(t) = k_3 x_m(t) \tag{16-11}$$

and

$$x(t) = A \cos \left[\omega_c t + k_3 x_m(t) \right] \tag{16-12}$$

In the following sections of this chapter, we shall consider these modulation systems in detail.

16-2 AMPLITUDE MODULATION

Let us now consider amplitude modulation in detail. To simplify the analysis, we shall, for the time being, assume that the modulating signal is a cosinusoid such that

$$x_m(t) = A_m \cos \omega_m t \tag{16-13}$$

This will be extended to more complex modulating signals subsequently. Substituting into Eq. (16-3), we obtain

$$x(t) = (A_c + k_1 A_m \cos \omega_m t) \cos \omega_c t \tag{16-14}$$

Thus

$$x(t) = A_c(1 + m \cos \omega_m t) \cos \omega_c t \tag{16-15}$$

where

$$m = \frac{k_1 A_m}{A_c} \tag{16-16}$$

The quantity m is called the *index of modulation*. It is sometimes multiplied by 100 and called the *percent modulation*. A plot of Eq. (16-15) is given in Fig. 16-1. The curves marked *envelope of modulation* represent upper and lower limits on the value of $x(t)$. The equation for the envelope of modulation is

$$\pm A_c(1 + m \cos \omega_m t)$$

where the plus sign is used for the upper envelope and the minus sign is used for the lower one. If $m = 1$, then $x(t)$ must be zero when $\omega_m t = \pi$, 3π, 5π, ... If $m > 1$, then the expression for the upper (lower) envelope will become negative (positive) for some values of time. Mathematically, this is acceptable and values of $m > 1$ can be used in Eq. (16-15). However, most electronic devices are such that their output is zero for those values of time that $1 + m \cos \omega_m t < 0$. Thus, if $m > 1$, the modulated signal $x(t)$ will be zero for some periods of time. The envelope of $x(t)$ will no longer have the shape of the modulating signal and distortion will result. This is analogous to cutting off the active elements in an audio amplifier. (Even if the electronic devices do not introduce distortion, the envelope will not have the shape of the modulating signal if $m > 1$. This would introduce problems when the information is to be recovered from the signal.) To avoid excessive distortion, we shall assume that $0 \le m \le 1$.

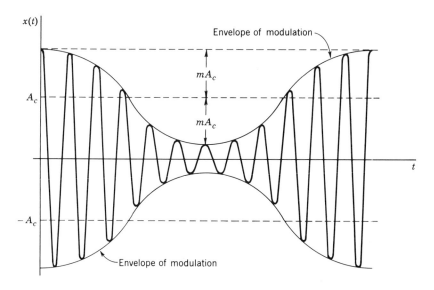

Fig. 16-1 An amplitude-modulated wave.

Consider Eq. (16-15). Using the trigonometric identity for the product of two cosines, we have

$$x(t) = A_c \cos \omega_c t + \frac{mA_c}{2} \cos (\omega_c + \omega_m)t + \frac{mA_c}{2} \cos (\omega_c - \omega_m)t$$

$$(16\text{-}17)$$

Thus, we see that the modulation process produces additional frequency components above and below the carrier frequency. These are called *sidebands* and differ from the carrier frequency by (plus or minus) the modulating frequency. The carrier itself is *unaffected by the modulation*. Its amplitude remains constant at the value A_c. A plot called a *frequency spectrum* is sometimes made to indicate the relative magnitudes of the frequencies of a waveform. Such a plot is shown in Fig. 16-2a.

Let us now consider that the waveform is not sinusoidal. Assume that $x_m(t)$ has the frequency spectrum shown in Fig. 16-2b. If this is used to amplitude-modulate a wave, then the resultant waveform will have the frequency spectrum shown in Fig. 16-2c. There is a pair of sidebands for each frequency of $x_m(t)$. The frequency scales of Fig. 16-2b and c are the same, and there is a break in the frequency axis of Fig. 16-2c.

Modulated signals are usually amplified by tuned amplifiers. For instance, in radio receivers, such amplifiers are necessary to reject unwanted signals. If the relative amplitudes or phase angles of the sidebands are changed, it is equivalent to altering the relative amplitudes or phase angles of the frequencies of the modulating signal. Thus, any tuned amplifier that is used to amplify the modulated signal can introduce frequency distortion in the same way that an *RC*-coupled amplifier can distort the modulating signal. A discussion of the frequency response of tuned amplifiers is given in Secs. 9-20 to 9-25. If amplitude modulation is desired with frequencies up to f_a, then any amplifier should have, essentially, a flat response for frequencies from $f_c - f_a$ to $f_c + f_a$.

Let us again consider that the carrier is modulated by a cosinusoid and obtain the relative power of the carrier and the sidebands. If $x(t)$ is either a voltage or a current, then the power will be proportional to the square of its rms value. Thus, P_c, the carrier power, will be proportional to $A_c^2/2$ while the total power contained in both sidebands will be proportional to $m^2 A_c^2/4$ [see Eq. (16-17)]. Thus, the ratio of the power of both sidebands to the carrier power is

$$\frac{P_{sb}}{P_c} = \frac{m^2}{2} \qquad\qquad (16\text{-}18)$$

If there is 100 percent modulation, then the sideband power will be one-half of the carrier power. This analysis is only true if there is a single sinusoid modulating the carrier. For instance, if the carrier is 100 percent modulated

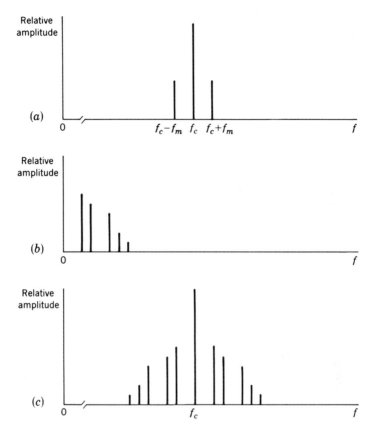

Fig. 16-2 (*a*) The frequency spectrum of an amplitude-modulated wave where the modulating frequency is a sinusoid; (*b*) the frequency spectrum of another modulating signal; (*c*) the frequency spectrum of an amplitude-modulated wave where the frequency spectrum of the modulating signal is given in (*b*).

by a square wave, then the maximum amplitude will be $2A_o$ for half the time and zero for the other half of the time. Since the carrier power is unchanged by modulation,

$$\frac{P_{sb}}{P_c} = 1 \qquad (16\text{-}19)$$

There are special amplitude-modulation procedures wherein the carrier is suppressed. This reduces the power transmitted. However, it makes detection of the signal more complex.

16-3 AMPLITUDE-MODULATING CIRCUITS

The output stage of a high-power radio-frequency amplifier is usually operated class C (see Chap. 11). Its output in response to the input radio-frequency signal is very nonlinear. Thus, if the driving signal of a class C amplifier is modulated, the output signal will be very distorted; i.e., the envelopes of the input and output signals will not be the same. Thus, it is usually desirable to introduce the modulation in the final class C amplifier stage itself. We shall consider several techniques for accomplishing this. Another modulation technique will also be discussed.

Output-voltage-modulated class C amplifiers Consider the class C radio-frequency amplifier of Fig. 11-2, which was analyzed in Sec. 11-2. If the power-supply voltage V_{OO} is varied while all the other quantities remain fixed, then the radio-frequency power delivered to the load P_2 and the rms radio-frequency output voltage V_2 will change. Thus, if V_{OO} is varied about its quiescent value, a modulated wave will result. The relationship between V_{OO} and V_2 is often fairly linear, so that the modulation is obtained without too much distortion. Before proceeding further, let us consider some assumptions. Modulation results in the generation of sidebands. We shall assume that the tuned output circuits of the class C amplifier have a frequency response that is constant for frequencies from the lowest sideband frequency to the highest sideband frequency. In general, responses of this type can be obtained, since $\omega_m \ll \omega_c$. We shall also assume that the impedance of the power supply is constant from zero frequency up to the highest modulating frequency.

We must now consider how the power-supply voltage can be varied in accordance with a modulating signal. A simple way of doing this is to place a generator which produces the modulating voltage in series with a direct power supply. Such a circuit is shown in Fig. 16-3. The instantaneous power-supply voltage is v_{OO}, and it is given by

$$v_{OO} = V_{OO} + \sqrt{2}V_m \cos \omega_m t \tag{16-20}$$

If the rms value of v_2 varies linearly with v_{OO}, then the output voltage of the amplifier will be of the form

$$v_2 = k(V_{OO} + \sqrt{2}V_m \cos \omega_m t) \cos \omega_c t \tag{16-21}$$

and we will have achieved amplitude modulation. Let us now consider the power supplied by the two generators of v_{OO}. The capacitor C_{OO} should be effectively a short circuit for the radio-frequency signals, but an open circuit for the modulating frequencies. Thus,

$$i_{OO} = I_{OA} + \sqrt{2}(I_{m1} \cos \omega_m t + I_{m2} \cos 2\omega_m t + \cdots) \tag{16-22}$$

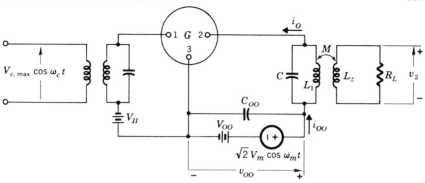

Fig. 16-3 An output-voltage-modulating circuit.

Then, using Eq. (16-20), the power supplied by the power supply is

$$P_{OO} = V_{OO}I_{OA} \tag{16-23}$$

while the power supplied by the modulating generator is

$$P_m = V_m I_{m1} \tag{16-24}$$

If the effects of distortion are ignored, then I_{OA} will be independent of V_m, and, hence, the power supplied by the direct power supply is unchanged by modulation. In general, the output-circuit efficiency remains essentially constant as v_{OO} varies.[1] The carrier power remains constant independent of modulation [see Eq. (16-17)]. Thus, for both the modulated and the unmodulated cases,

$$P_c = P_{OO}\eta \tag{16-25}$$

where η is the output-circuit efficiency. If P_{sb} is the total sideband power, then

$$P_{sb} + P_c = (P_{OO} + P_m)\eta \tag{16-26}$$

Thus

$$P_{sb} = P_m\eta \tag{16-27}$$

Thus, if the amplifier is 100 percent modulated by a sinusoid, the modulating generator supplies one-half of the power P_{OO}. The modulating generator usually is an audio power amplifier and can be designed using the methods of Chap. 10. An amplifier whose function is to supply a modulating voltage is called a *modulator*. A transistor output-modulated class C amplifier circuit is shown in Fig. 16-4. The audio amplifier is usually operated class B or class ABB for reasons of efficiency. This circuit is called a *collector-modulated class C amplifier*. The equivalent vacuum-tube device is called *a plate-modulated class C amplifier*. Similarly, an analogous FET device would be called a

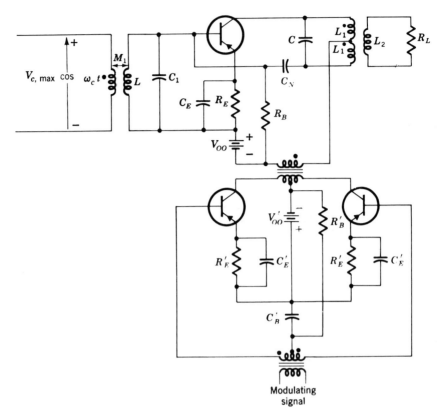

Fig. 16-4 A collector-modulated class C amplifier.

drain-modulated class C amplifier. Note that FET devices are limited to very low power levels at present.

The device output dissipation increases when a modulating signal is applied. If we assume that the circuit elements are ideal, then we have

$$P_{sb} + P_c + P_{OD} = P_{OO} + P_m \qquad (16\text{-}28)$$

That is, any power supplied by the direct power supply or by the modulator must be delivered to R_L as output power or be dissipated within the active element. Then, using Eq. (16-26), we have

$$P_{OD} = (P_c + P_{sb})\left(\frac{1}{\eta} - 1\right) \qquad (16\text{-}29)$$

The output-circuit dissipation increases with modulation. For sinusoidal modulators, P_{sb} can be as much as one-half of P_c. Thus, the introduction of modulation can increase P_{OD} by a factor of 1.5. If the modulating signal is not a sinusoid, then the sideband power can be more than one-half of the carrier power and modulation can increase P_{OD} by more than the factor of 1.5. In the transmission of speech or music, 100 percent modulation is rarely achieved for long periods of time, so that the rated device output dissipation can be 1.5 times (or less) the value of P_{OD} with no modulation.

Input-voltage-modulated class C amplifiers If the input bias (V_{II} of Fig. 16-3) of a class C amplifier is varied, the output voltage $\mathbf{V}_2$ will also vary. We can obtain modulation by modifying the circuit of Fig. 16-3 in the following way. Replace the modulating generator by a short circuit and reconnect it in series with V_{II}. The power that the modulating generator must supply is thereby greatly reduced. The modulating amplifier can thus use smaller active elements and dissipate less power. However, this type of operation usually results in greatly reduced efficiency of the class C amplifier. In addition, the nonlinear distortion of the envelope is greater for input-circuit than for output-circuit modulation. Finally, it is somewhat more difficult to adjust the circuit when this type of modulation is used.[1] For these reasons, output-circuit modulation is much more common than input-circuit modulation.

Nonlinear modulation If two signals of different frequencies are applied to a nonlinear element, modulation will result. For instance (see Sec. 5-10), consider a device with the transfer characteristic

$$x_0 = a_0 + a_1 x_i + a_2 x_i^2 \tag{16-30}$$

where x_i represents the input signal and x_0 is the output signal. If

$$x_i = X_{ic,\max} \cos \omega_c t + X_{im,\max} \cos \omega_m t$$

then

$$x_o = a_0 + \frac{a_2}{2}(X_{ic,\max}^2 + X_{im,\max}^2) + a_1(X_{ic,\max} \cos \omega_c t + X_{im,\max} \cos \omega_m t)$$

$$+ \frac{a_2}{2}(X_{ic,\max}^2 \cos 2\omega_c t + X_{im,\max}^2 \cos 2\omega_m t)$$

$$+ a_2 X_{ic,\max} X_{im,\max}[\cos(\omega_c + \omega_m)t + \cos(\omega_c - \omega_m)t] \tag{16-31}$$

If this signal is amplified by a tuned amplifier so that only those frequencies close to ω_c are passed, we obtain

$$x_0' = a_1 X_{ic,\max}\left[\cos \omega_c t + \frac{a_2 X_{im,\max}}{a_1} \cos(\omega_c + \omega_m)t\right.$$

$$\left. + \frac{a_2 X_{im,\max}}{a_1} \cos(\omega_c - \omega_m)t\right] \tag{16-32}$$

Thus, amplitude modulation has been achieved. This is called *square-law modulation* because of the form of Eq. (16-30).   To obtain such a nonlinear characteristic, an amplifier is operated class A but is biased into a nonlinear region.   The actual Taylor's-series expansion for x_0 will contain cubic and higher terms.   These will result in additional sideband frequencies and will produce harmonic distortion of the envelope.   It is to reduce these effects that the active element is operated class A.   Because of the limited efficiency that results, nonlinear modulation is only used in very low-level applications.

16-4   DETECTION OF AMPLITUDE-MODULATED SIGNALS

The intelligence contained in an amplitude-modulated wave must be con-verted to its original state if the system is to be of use (i.e., the output of the system should be a signal of the same waveform as that of the input).   A circuit which recovers the modulating signal from a modulated wave is called a *detector*.   We shall consider several techniques for the detection of ampli-tude-modulated signals in this section.

Linear detection   A simplified form of a very commonly used detector circuit is shown in Fig. 16-5.   This is called a *linear-diode detector* since it utilizes either a vacuum-tube or a semiconductor diode.   The term linear is used since it is assumed that the diode has a constant forward resistance and a constant reverse resistance, neither of which changes with signal level.   Actually, such a characteristic is not linear, since the forward and reverse resistances are not equal.   If elements that were linear in the strict sense were used, then detection would not result.   Let us assume that the waveform of v_I is given by the dashed curve of Fig. 16-6 and that the diode is ideal (i.e., its back resistance is infinite and its forward resistance is zero).   During the first cycle, v_O becomes the value shown by the solid curve.   The capacitor can only discharge through the resistor R.   We shall assume that the rate of decay of the voltage $v^{-t/RC}$ is considerably less than the maximum rate of falloff of the sinusoid of frequency ω_c.   Thus, at a time slightly later than the peak of the cycle $v_I < v_O$ and the diode will not conduct.   Hence, v_O will decay exponentially until the next cycle when the value of $v_I = v_O$.   The diode then acts as a short circuit, so that $v_O = v_I$ until a point slightly past the peak, and then the cycle repeats itself.   The resulting output voltage is shown in the solid curve of Fig. 16-6.   It has a jagged appearance.   If the

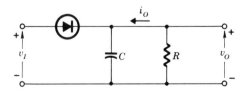

Fig. 16-5 A basic linear-diode detector circuit.

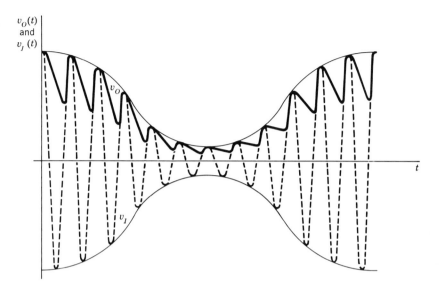

Fig. 16-6 The input and output waveforms of Fig. 16-5. (v_i is dashed.)

carrier frequency is increased while the modulating frequency is held constant, then the time that the capacitor discharges will be reduced and the jaggedness of the curve will be lessened. In Fig. 16-6, $\omega_c = 12\,\omega_m$. Usually, ω_c is 100 or more times ω_m so that the output voltage follows the envelope of modulation very closely.

If the output voltage is not to be distorted, then the RC product must be properly chosen. For instance, if it is too small, then v_O will fall off too much between successive cycles of the carrier and the jagged result of Fig. 16-6 will result. To eliminate this effect,

$$RC \gg \frac{1}{\omega_c} \tag{16-33}$$

On the other hand, if RC is too large, then v_O will not be able to fall off fast enough to follow the envelope of the modulation. To prevent this from occurring

$$RC \ll \frac{1}{\omega_m} \tag{16-34}$$

where ω_m should be the highest frequency that is contained in the modulation. If relations (16-33) and (16-34) are to be compatible

$$\omega_c \gg \omega_m \tag{16-35}$$

This is usually the case and the circuit of Fig. 16-5 yields very good results.

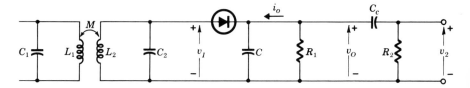

Fig. 16-7 A diode rectifier circuit with *RC* coupling.

The output voltage of the circuit of Fig. 16-5 has a direct component which may interfere with the bias of the next amplifier stage. Resistance-capacitance coupling is often used to eliminate this. Such a circuit is shown in Fig. 16-7. The ac and the dc load impedances are now different. To analyze this circuit the *detection characteristic* of the diode must be obtained. This is a plot of demodulated output voltage versus demodulated output current with the carrier voltage as a parameter. To obtain this characteristic, the circuit of Fig. 16-5 can be used. An *unmodulated* carrier is applied. The direct output voltage and current v_o and i_o are measured for various values of R and plotted. It is assumed that the capacitor C is large enough so that relation (16-33) is satisfied. The peak carrier voltage is then changed and the procedure is repeated. A typical set of characteristics is shown in Fig. 16-8. (Note that $-i_o$ is plotted.) Now let us analyze the circuit of

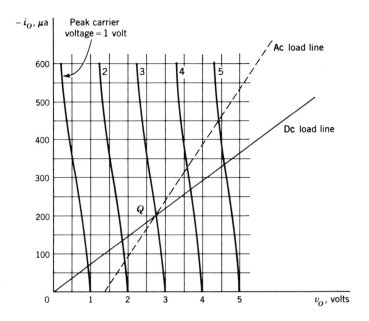

Fig. 16-8 A typical demodulation characteristic.

Fig. 16-7. We shall assume that the capacitor C_c is a short circuit at all frequencies of interest. The equation for the dc load line is

$$i_O = -\frac{v_O}{R_1} \tag{16-36}$$

It is shown in Fig. 16-8. The slope of the ac load line is $-1/R_{ac}$, where

$$R_{ac} = \frac{R_1 R_2}{R_1 + R_2} \tag{16-37}$$

It is drawn through the quiescent operating point. In this case, the quiescent operation results when the carrier is unmodulated. For instance, if the peak unmodulated carrier voltage is 3 volts, then point Q is the quiescent operating point. The ac load line is shown dashed in Fig. 16-8. The instantaneous value of v_O can be obtained from the intersection of the ac load line with the characteristic curves. (The peak carrier voltage varies with the modulation.) Note that if the peak carrier voltage falls below 1.4 volts, the output will be clipped. Thus, if excessive distortion is not to result, the maximum modulation index is limited. The slopes of the ac and dc load lines are R_{ac} and $R_1 = R_{dc}$, respectively. Thus, the maximum index of modulation that can be used without causing clipping is

$$m_{max} = \frac{R_{ac}}{R_{dc}} \tag{16-38}$$

If this is to approach 100 percent, $R_{ac} \approx R_{dc}$. To accomplish this in the circuit of Fig. 16-7, $R_2 \gg R_1$.

The input impedance of the detector circuit is of importance, since a tuned circuit usually precedes it (see Fig. 16-7). Let us compute the input impedance, assuming that the diode is ideal and that relations (16-33) and (16-34) are satisfied. The output voltage v_2 will then have the shape of the envelope of the modulation. If

$$v_I = V_{max} \cos \omega_c t$$

(that is, if the signal is unmodulated) then the output power will be

$$P_2 = \frac{V_{max}^2}{R_1}$$

(If R_1 is sufficiently large, then $v_O = V_{max}$.) Note that the output voltage is of zero frequency. Since the components are ideal, the input power is equal to the output power. If R_i is the effective input resistance, then

$$\frac{V_{max}^2}{R_1} = \frac{V_{max}^2}{2R_i}$$

Thus

$$R_i = \frac{R_1}{2} \tag{16-39}$$

If modulation is applied to the carrier, the effective input resistance will change, since the ac and dc load resistances are not equal. If $R_2 \gg R_1$ in Fig. 16-7, as it often is, then these resistances will be almost equal and Eq. (16-39) can be used to compute the input resistance. In general, the effective input resistance can be found by equating the input and output powers.

Another form of detection makes use of an ordinary amplifier that is biased class B. Its output consists of only the upper (or lower) half of the waveform of Fig. 16-1. The "average" value of this waveform can be considered to vary with the modulation. It will be of the same waveform as that of the envelope. If such a waveform is amplified by a circuit that rejects frequencies close to or greater than the carrier frequency, as well as ω_c, the output will have the same waveshape as the envelope. Thus, demodulation results. The primary disadvantage of this type of detection is that it tends to introduce distortion, because of the curvature of the characteristics of electronic devices near cutoff. However, the input resistance of this detector can be very high.

Nonlinear detection A square-law circuit can be used for demodulation as well as for modulation. Consider that a square-law detector has the transfer characteristics given by Eq. (16-30) and that the input signal is the amplitude-modulated wave of Eq. (16-17). Assume that the output of the detector is passed through an amplifier that rejects all frequencies except those close to the modulating frequency. The output of this amplifier will then be

$$x_o(t) = a_2 A_c^2 m \left(\cos \omega_m t + \frac{m}{4} \cos 2\omega_m t \right) \tag{16-40}$$

Thus, detection has been achieved but $25m$ percent harmonic distortion has been introduced. If higher terms are included in the Taylor's series of Eq. (16-30), then still more distortion will result. If more than one modulating frequency is present, then intermodulation distortion terms will result. For these reasons, square-law detectors are used in applications where the amount of distortion is unimportant or where the value of m is kept small. One of the advantages of square-law detection is that it uses an amplifier circuit and, hence, produces gain. The input impedance of the detector can be very high, also.

16-5 FREQUENCY AND PHASE MODULATION

In Sec. 16-1 we discussed that intelligence can be transmitted by varying the instantaneous frequency of the signal. This is defined as frequency modulation and it is characterized by Eq. (16-10). Let us assume that the modulating signal is a cosinusoid given by

$$x_m(t) = X_{m,\max} \cos \omega_m t \tag{16-41}$$

Substitution in Eq. (16-10) yields

$$x(t) = A \cos \left(\omega_c t + \frac{k_2 X_{m,\max}}{\omega_m} \sin \omega_m t \right) \tag{16-42}$$

where we have assumed that the constant of integration is zero. The rate of variation of the instantaneous frequency is ω_m, and the amount of frequency deviation is proportional to $X_{m,\max}/\omega_m$. Thus, the instantaneous frequency variation can be kept within any limit desired simply by limiting $X_{m,\max}$. It was thought at one time that wideband signals could be transmitted over an extremely narrow bandwidth using frequency modulation. However, we shall see that this is *not* the case. Before proceeding with our discussion of frequency modulation, let us consider the phase-modulated signal of Eq. (16-12). Now let us assume that the modulating signal is a sinusoid given by

$$x_m(t) = X_{m,\max} \sin \omega_m t \tag{16-43}$$

Substituting in Eq. (16-12) yields

$$x(t) = A \cos (\omega_c t + k_3 X_{m,\max} \sin \omega_m t) \tag{16-44}$$

Equations (16-42) and (16-44) can be put into the same form. Thus, we can simultaneously analyze frequency modulation by a cosinusoid and phase modulation by a sinusoid using the following equation:

$$x(t) = A \cos (\omega_c t + m_F \sin \omega_m t) \tag{16-45}$$

where m_F is either the *frequency- or the phase-modulation index* and is given by

$$m_F = m_f = \frac{k_2 X_{m,\max}}{\omega_m} \tag{16-46}$$

for the frequency-modulation system and

$$m_F = m_p = k_3 X_{m,\max} \tag{16-47}$$

for the phase-modulated system. Then, for both systems Eq. (16-45) is valid. Using the identity for the sum of the cosines of two angles, we obtain

$$x(t) = A[\cos \omega_c t \cos (m_F \sin \omega_m t) - \sin \omega_c t \cdot \sin (m_F \sin \omega_m t)] \tag{16-48}$$

Two other trigonometric identities that are needed are:

$$\cos (m_F \sin \omega_m t) = J_0(m_F) + 2J_2(m_F) \cos 2\omega_m t$$
$$+ 2J_4(m_F) \cos 4\omega_m t + \cdots \tag{16-49}$$

and

$$\sin (m_F \sin \omega_m t) = 2J_1(m_F) \sin \omega_m t + 2J_3(m_F) \sin 3\omega_m t + \cdots \tag{16-50}$$

where $J_0(m_F)$, $J_1(m_F)$, $\ldots$, $J_k(m_F)$, $\ldots$ are Bessel's functions of the first

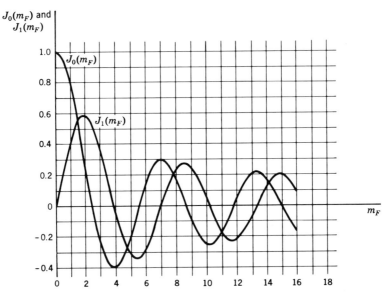

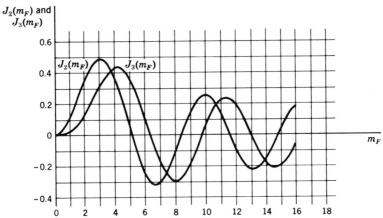

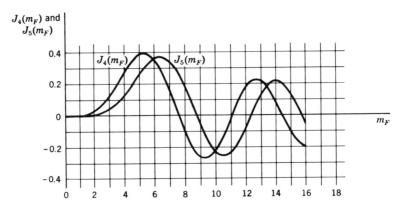

Fig. 16-9 Plots of Bessel's functions of the first kind. (*From F. E. Terman, "Radio Engineers' Handbook." Copyright 1943. McGraw-Hill Book Company. Used by permission.*)

kind of order k. The first six of these functions are given in Fig. 16-9. Substituting Eqs. (16-49) and (16-50) into Eq. (16-48) and manipulating, we obtain

$$x(t) = A\{J_0(m_F) \cos \omega_c t + J_1(m_F)[\cos(\omega_c + \omega_m)t - \cos(\omega_c - \omega_m)t]$$
$$+ J_2(m_F)[\cos(\omega_c + 2\omega_m)t + \cos(\omega_c - 2\omega_m)t] + \cdots\} \quad (16\text{-}51)$$

Thus, a carrier and an *infinite* set of sidebands result. The carrier amplitude is a function of the modulating signal. The frequency of the sidebands depends only upon the frequency of the modulating signal. If a transmission system is to be useful, it must have a limited bandwidth. Fortunately, in the case of frequency and phase modulation, the sidebands far removed from the carrier are usually small and can be neglected. Note that the higher order Bessel's functions remain close to zero for small values of m_F. An empirical rule[2] for determining the number of sideband pairs that are of importance is to use $m_F + 1$ pairs of sidebands if $m_F > 1$. This can be verified from an inspection of Fig. 16-9. The bandwidth required by a frequency- or phase-modulated system is equal to or greater than that required by an amplitude-modulated system where the modulating signals are the same.

One of the primary advantages of frequency or phase modulation over amplitude modulation is that the effects of interfering noise can easily be reduced in these systems. To study these effects, let us consider an un-modulated carrier and a sinusoidal noise signal at a frequency near the carrier frequency. The total signal is given by

$$x(t) = X_{c,\max} \cos \omega_c t + X_{a,\max} \cos(\omega_c + \omega_a)t \quad (16\text{-}52)$$

where X_a represents the noise. The instantaneous amplitude and phase of $x(t)$ can be determined from a phasor diagram such as that of Fig. 16-10. The phasor $\overline{OA}$ represents the carrier $X_{c,\max} \cos \omega_c t$. Thus, the phasor $\overline{AB}$, representing the noise, must "rotate" at an angular frequency ω_a. The resultant phasor is $\overline{OB}$. The amplitude of $\overline{OB}$ will vary from $X_{c,\max} + X_{a,\max}$ to $X_{c,\max} - X_{a,\max}$. Hence, the index of amplitude modulation is given by $X_{a,\max}/X_{c,\max}$. If we assume that the transmitter's output power is constant, then the ratio $X_{a,\max}/X_{c,\max}$ will be fixed. The relative interference depends upon the ratio of the index of modulation of the noise to the index of modu-lation of a "signal." In amplitude modulation, the index of modulation cannot be increased at will. It must be adjusted so that the largest modulating signal will not result in more than 100 percent modulation. Now let us consider the amount of frequency modulation produced by the noise. The instantaneous value of the angle θ is given by

$$\theta = \tan^{-1} \frac{X_{a,\max} \sin \omega_a t}{X_{c,\max} + X_{a,\max} \cos \omega_a t} \quad (16\text{-}53)$$

The frequency-modulated signal will have the instantaneous frequency

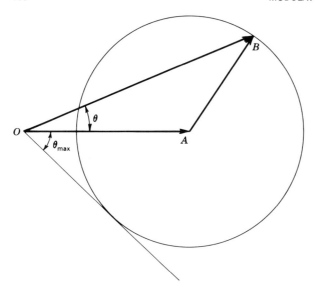

Fig. 16-10 A phasor diagram that can be used to calculate
the effect of an interfering signal.

$\omega_c t + d\theta/dt$.   If this is compared with Eq. (16-45), we see that the amount of
interference depends upon the relative magnitudes of $m_F \sin \omega_m t$ and $d\theta/dt$.
In a frequency-modulated system, the value of m_F can be made as large as
desired without introducing distortion or increasing the power of the transmitter.   Thus, if large values of m_F are used, the effects of interference can
be made to be much less than those in a comparable amplitude-modulated
system.   However, large values of m_F result in a relatively large number of
important sidebands.   If small values of m_F are used (0.5 or less), the
effective bandwidths of the frequency- or phase-modulation systems will be
no greater than a corresponding amplitude-modulated system.   However,
there will also be no improvement in noise performance.   In fact, the noise
performance of the amplitude-modulated system may actually be better.   On
the other hand, if m_F is much greater than unity, the noise performance
will be greatly improved, but the bandwidth required will be high.   In
general, the relative noise reduction increases with bandwidth.

There are broadband noise-reducing systems that can be used with
amplitude-modulated systems.   However, these are extremely complex.
Thus, frequency modulation is used for low-noise commercial broadcasting.

16-6   FREQUENCY- AND PHASE-MODULATING CIRCUITS

A very close relationship exists between frequency and phase modulation.
The same circuits can be used to produce both if minor modifications are

made. Before considering actual modulating circuits, we shall demonstrate how a phase modulator can produce frequency modulation, and vice versa. If a circuit produces phase modulation, then Eqs. (16-10) and (16-12) demonstrate that it will also produce frequency modulation if the modulating signal is integrated before it is applied to the phase modulator. Integrating circuits were discussed in Secs. 15-14 and 15-7. A simple integrating circuit is shown in Fig. 15-27. The output of these circuits is inversely proportional to frequency, which is in accordance with Eqs. (16-46) and (16-47). In a similar way, phase modulation can be obtained from a frequency-modulation system if the modulating signal is differentiated. Differentiating circuits are also discussed in Secs. 13-14 and 15-7. Now let us consider some modulating circuits.

Variable-reactance circuits The frequency of oscillation of all of the circuits of Fig. 14-3 are approximately equal to the resonant frequencies of their tank circuits. Thus, if we could construct a capacitor or inductor whose reactance could be made to vary in accordance with a modulating signal, frequency modulation would be produced. Consider the circuits of Fig. 16-11a and b. Their linear model is given in Fig. 16-11c, where $k = g_m$, r_i is an open circuit, and $r_o = r_d$ for the FET (or vacuum-tube) circuit; and $k = h_{fe}/h_{ie}$, $r_i = h_{ie}$, and $r_o = h_{oe}^{-1}$ for the transistor circuit. The operating frequency is assumed to be well below ω_β. (We have assumed that $h_{re} = 0$.) For the time being, high-frequency effects and parasitic capacitances will be ignored. We have assumed that the bypass capacitors C_s and C_E are short circuits and that the radio-frequency choke is an open circuit at the carrier frequency. Consider that the voltage generator $\mathbf{V}_m$ is replaced by a short circuit. Then the output admittance is given by

$$\mathbf{Y}_0 = \frac{kR + 1}{R - j/\omega C} + \frac{1}{r_o} \tag{16-54}$$

where

$$R = \frac{R_1 r_i}{R_1 + r_i} \tag{16-55}$$

If

$$\frac{1}{\omega C} \gg R \quad \text{and} \quad kR \gg 1 \tag{16-56}$$

then

$$\mathbf{Y}_o = \frac{1}{r_o} + jkR\omega C \tag{16-57}$$

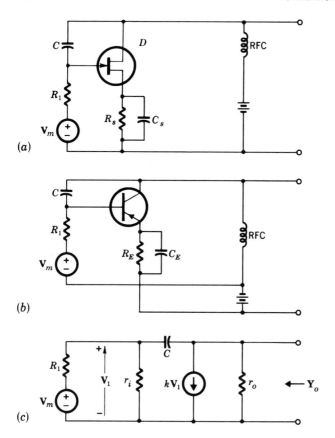

Fig. 16-11 (*a*) A reactance FET modulator; (*b*) a reactance-transistor modulator (the generator V_m is assumed to have zero impedance at the carrier frequency); (*c*) their linear model.

Thus, the output impedance is a resistance in shunt with a capacitance. If the g_m of the FET or the h_{fe} of the transistor could be varied, then the effective capacitance would also vary. Now consider that V_m is the modulating voltage. Its frequency ω_m is very much less than the carrier frequency. The magnitude of $1/\omega_m C$ will be very large and the reactance of the RFC will be small at ω_m. Thus, V_m will essentially affect only the input bias of the active element. This will change g_m and h_{fe} and, hence, the effective output capacitance. This circuit is called a *reactance modulator*. In use, it is connected in parallel with the capacitance of any of the tank circuits of Fig. 14-3. An equivalent tank circuit is shown in Fig. 16-12. Resistive elements have been neglected. The capacitor C_1 consists of any fixed capacitor plus

Fig. 16-12 An equivalent tank circuit where one of the capacitances is the output of a reactance modulator. Losses have been neglected.

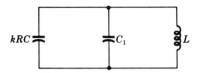

the parasitic-output capacitance of the active element of Fig. 16-11. The resonant frequency is

$$\omega_0 = \frac{1}{\sqrt{L(C_1 + kRC)}}$$

If $kRC \gg C_1$, then

$$\omega_0 \approx \frac{1}{\sqrt{kRCL}} \tag{16-58}$$

If the frequency modulation is to be without distortion, then $g_m^{-\frac{1}{2}}$ or $h_{fe}^{-\frac{1}{2}}$ should vary linearly with the modulating signal plus the direct bias. If kRC is not much greater than C_1, then g_m or h_{fe} should vary so that $1/\sqrt{1 + kRC/C_1}$ is a linear function of the modulation. Neither of these variations usually occurs. However, if the modulating signal is kept small, very little distortion usually results.

In the previous discussion, we have assumed that the $\mathbf{h}_{fe}$ of the transistor is a real number. If this is not the case, then the input admittance will not be a constant resistance in parallel with a capacitance. We have also assumed that the other parameters of the transistor do not vary with the modulating voltage.

A semiconductor diode can also be used in a variable-reactance modulator circuit. Consider the circuit of Fig. 16-13a. The direct voltage should be large enough so that the diode is always reverse-biased. The model is given in Fig. 16-13b. The capacitor C_j is the junction capacitance of the diode, and r_b is the back resistance of the diode (see Sec. 3-6). Let us assume that the capacitor C can be considered to be a short circuit at the carrier frequency. If the voltage v is constant, then the output admittance of this circuit, for frequencies at or near the carrier frequency, is

$$Y_o = \frac{1}{R} + j\omega C_j \tag{16-59}$$

where

$$R = \frac{R_1 r_b}{R_1 + r_b} \tag{16-60}$$

The junction capacitance varies with the potential across the depletion layer. This potential is approximately given by v. Then,

$$C_j \approx k_1 v^{-n} \tag{16-61}$$

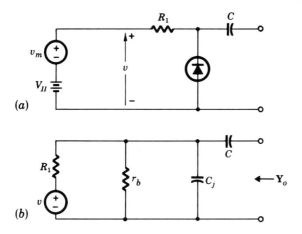

Fig. 16-13 (*a*) A reactance diode modulator and (*b*) its linear model.

where k_1 is a constant and n is a positive constant less than unity. If v varies in accordance with the modulating signal, then (since C is essentially an open circuit at ω_m) its primary effect is to vary C_j. Then

$$C_j = k_1(V_{II} + v_m)^{-n} \tag{16-62}$$

Thus the resonant frequency is

$$\omega_0 = k_2 V_{II}^{n/2}\left(1 + \frac{v_m}{V_{II}}\right)^{n/2} \tag{16-63}$$

where k_2 is a constant. Expanding in a Taylor's series, we have, if

$$\frac{v_m}{V_{II}} < 1$$

then

$$\omega_0 = k_2 V_{II}^{n/2}\left[1 + \frac{nv_m}{2V_{II}} + \frac{n}{4}\left(\frac{n}{2} - 1\right)\frac{v_m^2}{V_{II}^2} + \cdots\right] \tag{16-64}$$

Thus, if the ratio v_m/V_{II} is kept small, ω_0 will vary almost linearly with v_m and the distortion will be minimized.

In most reactance-modulator circuits, the frequency deviation must be kept small to avoid distortion. To increase the frequency deviation, the output of the frequency-modulated oscillator is applied to one or more stages of frequency multipliers (see Sec. 11-1). This will increase both the carrier frequency and the frequency deviation.

Phase-shifting circuits We shall now discuss a circuit[3] that can be used to produce phase modulation. Consider the amplifier of Fig. 16-14. The voltage V_1 is assumed to be a sinusoidal generator whose frequency is ω_c. The voltage V_m is the modulating signal. We shall assume here, as we did for the reactance-modulator circuit, that V_m only affects the transconductance of the FET. A linear model for this amplifier is shown in Fig. 16-14b. It has been assumed that C_c and C_s are short circuits and that the two radio-frequency chokes are open circuits at ω_c. The r_d has also been assumed to be an open circuit. The voltage gain V_2/V_1 of this circuit is

$$\mathbf{A}_v = \frac{\omega C + jg_m}{\omega C - jg_m} = 1 \quad \underline{/2 \tan^{-1} g_m/\omega C} \tag{16-65}$$

The magnitude of the voltage gain is independent of g_m and is equal to unity. The phase shift is a function of g_m and, hence, of the modulating voltage. Thus, phase modulation is produced. The phase angle does not vary linearly with g_m. In addition, the relation between the modulating signal and g_m is not linear. Sometimes these two nonlinearities can offset one another. In general, if the phase deviation is kept small, the distortion will be low. To obtain additional phase shift, several of these amplifiers are often cascaded with the same modulating signal applied to each amplifier. Usually, isolating amplifiers are placed between them. Frequency multipliers can also be used to increase the phase shift.

The variable-reactance modulators are used to change the frequency of an oscillator. Consequently, a crystal oscillator cannot be used with them

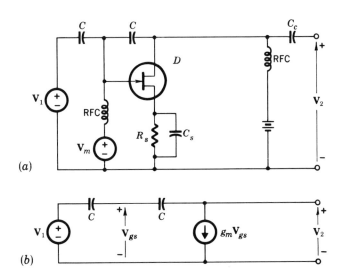

Fig. 16-14 (a) A phase modulator and (b) its model.

(see Sec. 14-6). In many commercial applications, crystal oscillators are required because of their frequency stability. The phase-shift circuit of Fig. 16-14 can be used in conjunction with a crystal oscillator, since the frequency of V_1 always remains constant.

16-7   DETECTION OF FREQUENCY- AND PHASE-MODULATED SIGNALS

The similarity of frequency and phase modulation allows similar circuits to be used in their detection. The converse of the methods discussed at the beginning of Sec. 16-6 can be used to convert one type of detector to the other. We shall consider some basic methods for detection here.

Slope detection   An ordinary amplitude-modulation detector of the type shown in Fig. 16-7 can be used to detect frequency modulation if the tuned circuit is properly adjusted. For instance, assume that the resonance curve of the tuned circuit is given by Fig. 16-15. If the circuit is tuned so that ω_1, and not ω_0, is the unmodulated carrier frequency, then v_I, the input voltage to the diode detector of Fig. 16-7, will vary as the frequency is changed and this circuit will demodulate a frequency-modulated signal. The circuit is called a *slope detector*. The slope of the resonance curve is not constant. As a consequence, this type of detector produces a great deal of distortion. It is not often used, except in systems where the frequency deviation is kept very small. We shall now discuss detector circuits that can be used for large frequency deviations.

The discriminator circuit   Frequency-modulation detectors usually produce a radio-frequency voltage whose amplitude varies with frequency. Amplitude-modulation detectors can then be used to obtain the demodulated output. Before we consider actual detector circuits, let us discuss the tuned circuit of Fig. 16-16. The primary and secondary circuits are each tuned to resonance at the carrier frequency ω_c. We shall assume that the Q of the

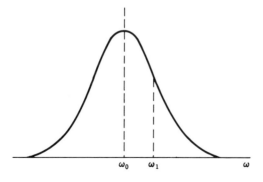

Fig. 16-15   A resonance curve used to illustrate slope detection.

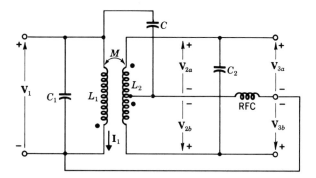

Fig. 16-16 A phase-shift discriminator.

tuned circuits is such that the peak of the resonance curve is essentially flat over the frequency deviation of the input signal. The capacitor C is considered to be a low impedance and the radio-frequency choke a very high impedance at all input frequencies. If the impedance coupled into L_1 is much less than $\omega_c L_1$, we have

$$I_1 = \frac{V_1}{j\omega L_1} \tag{16-66}$$

At resonance, the secondary impedance is purely resistive and is equal to R. Hence (consider that C_2 is composed of two equal capacitors in series),

$$V_{2a} = \frac{jMV_1}{2\omega C_2 L_1 R} = \frac{j\omega L_2 M V_1}{2L_1 R} \tag{16-67}$$

$$V_{2b} = \frac{-jMV_1}{2\omega C_2 L_1 R} = -\frac{j\omega L_2 M V_1}{2L_1 R} \tag{16-68}$$

Thus, at resonance, the phase angle of V_1 differs from that of V_{2a} and V_{2b} by 90°. Now consider the voltages V_{3a} and V_{3b}. These are given by

$$V_{3a} = V_1 + V_{2a} \tag{16-69}$$

$$V_{3b} = V_1 + V_{2b} \tag{16-70}$$

A phasor diagram illustrating these voltages is shown in Fig. 16-17a. Now let us assume that the input frequency shifts above ω_c. The relative amplitude of the voltages will not change, because it is assumed that the resonance curve is flat. However, the phase angle is very sensitive to frequency shifts, so the phasor diagram becomes that of Fig. 16-17b. The magnitude of V_{3a} has been reduced while that of V_{3b} has increased. Similarly, for frequencies below ω_c we have the phasor diagram of Fig. 16-17c. Now, the magnitude of V_{3a} has increased while that of V_{3b} has decreased. We have thus achieved

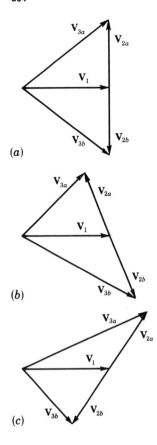

(a)

(b)

(c)

Fig. 16-17 Phasor diagrams for the phase-shift discriminator of Fig. 16-16: (a) $\omega = \omega_0$; (b) $\omega > \omega_0$; and (c) $\omega < \omega_0$.

a circuit wherein the magnitude of the voltages varies with frequency. If we add two amplitude-modulation detectors to the circuit of Fig. 16-16, a frequency-modulation detector results. This is shown in Fig. 16-18. The output voltage of each of the detectors will be approximately equal to their peak input voltages, $|V_{3a,\max}|$ and $|V_{3b,\max}|$. The diodes are connected so that the output voltage v_o is the difference between the two output voltages. Thus,

$$v_o = |V_{3a,\max}| - |V_{3b,\max}| \tag{16-71}$$

This voltage will vary linearly with frequency until the voltage falls off because of the resonance curve. A typical plot of v_o versus frequency is given in Fig. 16-19. This circuit is called a *Foster-Seeley discriminator*. (It has been assumed here that the resistors R are large enough so that the resonant circuit is not affected by the detector.)

   If the amplitude of the input signal of a discriminator varies, then the amplitude of v_o will also vary. In Sec. 16-5 we discussed that one of the

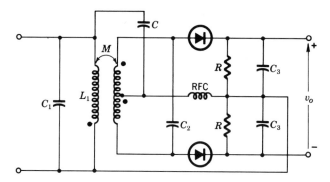

Fig. 16-18 A Foster-Seeley discriminator for the detection of frequency-modulated signals.

advantages of frequency modulation was its relative freedom from interference. However, if the detector responds to amplitude modulation, one advantage gained by using frequency modulation will be lost, since the interference will amplitude-modulate the signal. To remove the amplitude modulation from the signal, a circuit called a *limiter* is used. This performs the same function as the clipper circuits of Sec. 15-8. In frequency-modulation receivers, the limiters are usually just amplifiers that are driven between their saturation and cutoff regions. As a consequence, the peak value of the voltage will not vary, and the signal essentially will not be amplitude-modulated. Of course, the limiter precedes the detector stage.

The ratio detector If the Foster-Seeley discriminator circuit is modified somewhat, a circuit can be obtained that is relatively insensitive to variations in amplitude. Such a circuit is shown in Fig. 16-20. Note that the con-

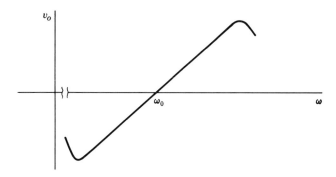

Fig. 16-19 The output characteristic of a Foster-Seeley discriminator.

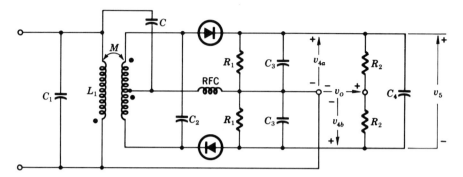

Fig. 16-20   A ratio detector.

nections of one of the diodes have been reversed.   For the time being, neglect the capacitor C_4.   Thus, Eq. (16-71) becomes

$$v_5 = v_{4a} - v_{4b} = |V_{3a,\max}| + |V_{3b,\max}| \tag{16-72}$$

where $\mathbf{V}_{3a}$ and $\mathbf{V}_{3b}$ are defined in Fig. 16-16.

The output is taken as shown.   Since the two resistors R_2 are equal, we have

$$v_o = v_{4a} - \frac{v_5}{2} \tag{16-73}$$

$$v_o = |V_{3a,\max}| - \frac{|V_{3a,\max}| + |V_{3b,\max}|}{2}$$

$$v_o = \frac{|V_{3a,\max}| - |V_{3b,\max}|}{2} \tag{16-74}$$

(It is assumed that the resistors are large enough so that they do not affect the resonant circuit.)   The voltage v_5 varies only slightly with changes in the instantaneous frequency, because increases in $|V_{3a,\max}|$ are accompanied by decreases in $|V_{3b,\max}|$, and vice versa (see Fig. 16-17).   Now let us consider the effect of C_4.   It is made very large, so that the time constant R_2C_4 is much larger than the longest period encountered in the modulating signal (for example, 0.25 sec for an audio system).   Thus, v_5 will tend to remain constant as the frequency shifts because of modulation.   Hence, the sum of $|V_{3a,\max}|$ and $|V_{3b,\max}|$ is fixed.   However, as the instantaneous frequency changes, their *ratio* will vary essentially in accordance with Fig. 16-17.   The value of v_o given by Eq. (16-74) will be almost one-half of that produced by the Foster-Seeley discriminator.   (Note that $|V_{3a,\max}|$ and $|V_{3b,\max}|$ are changed somewhat because of the constraint that v_5 is constant.)   Now let us consider that noise amplitude-modulates the signal (at an audio rate).   The sum of $|V_{3a,\max}|$ and $|V_{3b,\max}|$ is constant, and their ratio is fixed by the frequency deviation. Hence, v_o will not vary with amplitude modulation. In actual circuits, there is some variation of v_5 with amplitude modulation, since the components are not ideal and since the time constant R_2C_4 is not infinitely long. This circuit does tend to reject amplitude modulation fairly well. The discriminator tends to produce somewhat less distortion, however.

16-8 PULSE MODULATION

Let us now consider another type of modulation where information is transmitted as a series of pulses. This is called *pulse modulation*. If the pulses are transmitted by radio waves, the pulses are usually used to amplitude-, frequency-, or phase-modulate a carrier.

Let us consider one type of pulse modulation called *pulse-amplitude modulation* (PAM). In this system, a signal is sampled at equal intervals in time. A sequence of pulses is generated. The amplitude of each pulse is proportional to the amplitude of the signal at the time when it is sampled. Such a representation is shown in Fig. 16-21. In general, the time between pulses and the width of the pulses are much less than is shown in Fig. 16-21. If the time between pulses is made small enough and the pulses are made narrow enough, the original signal can be recovered from the pulses very accurately.

Let us consider an application of PAM. Suppose that we wish to transmit two different signals over the same communication channel, e.g., a telephone line. Both sets of signals are converted to pulses. However, one signal is sampled at times corresponding to $t = 0, 1, 2, 3, 4, \ldots$ while the other is sampled at times corresponding to $t = 0.5, 1.5, 2.5, 3.5, \ldots$. All the pulses are transmitted over the same channel. However, at the receiving end of the channel there are two devices, one constructed so that it responds only to pulses occurring at times corresponding to $t = 0, 1, 2, \ldots$ and the other responding only to pulses occurring at times corresponding to $t = 0.5, 1.5, 2.5, \ldots$. Thus, the output of each device contains only the pulses for one signal, and the two signals are separated. If the widths of the pulses are made very narrow, many sets of signals can be transmitted over the same channel using this procedure. This is called *multiplexing*. As the pulse width becomes narrower, the bandwidth of the amplifiers of the transmission channel must become greater (see Sec. 9-14). Thus, as the number of separate signals is increased, the bandwidth of the channel must be increased.

Pulse modulation is not the only way that signals can be multiplexed. For instance, at any time, many amplitude- and/or frequency-modulated signals are transmitted by many radio stations simultaneously. However, they all have different carrier frequencies. Then, tuned amplifiers are used to select the desired signal and reject all others. This also is *multiplexing*.

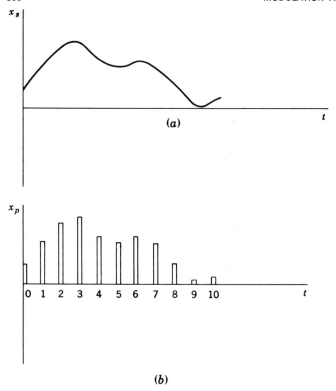

Fig. 16-21 (*a*) A signal; (*b*) a pulse-amplitude-modulation representation of this system.

The system of multiplexing using pulses occurring at different times is called *time-division multiplexing*, while the one using different frequencies is called *frequency-division multiplexing*.

There are other pulse-modulation schemes where the amplitude of all the pulse is constant. In these, the signal is again sampled at equally spaced intervals of time. In one such procedure the width (time duration) of the pulse varies proportionally with the signal level. This is called *pulse-width modulation* (PWM) or *pulse-duration modulation* (PDM). In another procedure, the pulse is displaced in time from the time that it would normally occur. The displacement is proportional to the signal level. This is called *pulse-position modulation* (PPM).

One advantage of transmitting signals which are of constant amplitude is that nonlinearities of any devices which amplify the pulses do not change the signal. This is sometimes of importance in systems such as transcontinental telephone lines, where the signal may pass through hundreds of amplifiers, each of which can add its own nonlinear distortion.

There is another type of pulse modulation called *pulse-code modulation* (PCM). Here the signal is sampled as in PAM (see Fig. 16-21); however, the pulses are allowed only specified levels, called *quantized levels.* If the signal is not exactly equal to a quantized level, the level closest to the signal is chosen. This introduces an error called *quantizing error* in the output signal. Enough allowed levels should be chosen so that this error can be kept small. The pulses themselves are not transmitted. There is a fixed number of allowed levels, each given a code representation. This code is transmitted. Usually binary systems are used. That is, the code consists of a sequence of pulses, equally spaced in time. If a pulse is present, this is said to be a one; if a pulse is absent, it is said to be a zero. For instance, suppose that each quantized level is assigned four pulses. Then the quantized level 0 could be represented by 0000. That is, four zeros are transmitted. The level 0.01 could be represented by 0001, etc. Thus, there are 16 levels which can be represented by a sequence of four pulses.

Then, in a PCM procedure, the signal is sampled. The quantized pulses are obtained, and the code sequence is transmitted. At the receiving end, the signal is decoded, and then the original signal is reconstructed.

This type of system is used when noise is a problem (see Sec. 9-28). Consider that a very weak signal is being transmitted, e.g., from a satellite far out in space. Noise could completely obscure it. Now suppose that the signal is transmitted by pulse-code modulation. The noise will tend to obscure that also. That is, the noise can make ones appear as zeros and vice versa. However, no matter how large the noise is, the probability that the correct signal will be received will always be (at least slightly) greater than the probability that an incorrect signal will be received. This procedure can then be used to reduce the effect of the noise. The code can be made redundant, i.e., repeat itself. As a simple example, consider that each digit is repeated 11 times, i.e., each quantized level is represented by a sequence of 44 pulses. Suppose that a one is to be transmitted, i.e., a sequence of 11 ones. If the signal is obscured by noise, the signal which should be 11 ones in sequence might appear as 11011010111. The majority of pulses (eight) are ones. Then, the receiver is designed to make a decision that the pulse actually is a one. If a majority of the 11 pulses are zeros, then the receiver is designed to decide that the pulse is a zero. Redundancy does not eliminate noise errors. However, by making the system redundant *enough*, extremely weak signals can be received in the presence of noise with an arbitrarily low frequency of errors. The redundancy illustrated here is very simple. Far more sophisticated procedures are usually used.

REFERENCES

1. Gray, T. S.: "Applied Electronics," 2d ed., pp. 710–714, John Wiley & Sons, Inc., New York, 1954.

2. Terman, F. E.: "Radio Engineers' Handbook," p. 579, McGraw-Hill Book Company, New York, 1943.
3. Beleskas, S. M.: Phase Modulation Circuit, *Proc. Natl. Electron. Conf.*, vol. 3, pp. 654–661, 1947.

BIBLIOGRAPHY

Gray, T. S.: "Applied Electronics," 2d ed., chap. 12, John Wiley & Sons, Inc., New York, 1954.
Ryder, J. D.: "Electronic Fundamentals and Applications," 2d ed., chaps. 15 and 16, Prentice-Hall, Inc., Englewood Cliffs, N.J., 1959.
Seely, S.: "Electronic Circuits," chap. 9, Holt, Rinehart and Winston, Inc., New York, 1968.
Terman, F. E.: "Electronic and Radio Engineering," 4th ed., chaps. 15–17, McGraw-Hill Book Company, New York, 1955.

PROBLEMS

16-1. A sinusoidal carrier of frequency ω_c is amplitude-modulated by a sinusoidal signal of frequency ω_m. The index of modulation is 0.5. Plot the resulting waveform and the frequency spectrum. Determine the amount of power contained in the sidebands relative to the carrier power.

16-2. Repeat Prob. 16-1 but now assume that the index of modulation is 2. Assume that the output becomes zero when the upper envelope is negative. How many pairs of sidebands are produced? Hint: Find the Fourier series of the envelope.

16-3. Repeat Prob. 16-1 but now assume that the modulating signal is a square wave.

16-4. Repeat Prob. 16-2 but now assume that the modulating signal is a square wave.

16-5. For the amplifier of Prob. 11-1, determine and plot the magnitude of the output radio-frequency voltage if V_{bb} is varied from 5000 to 15,000 volts. Assume that the peak plate current remains constant. Discuss how this plot could be used in the design of an amplitude modulator.

16-6. Repeat Prob. 16-5 but do not assume that the peak plate current remains constant. Use $R_{ac} = 1960$ ohms. Note: A cut-and-try procedure will be required.

16-7. For the amplifier of Prob. 11-1, determine and plot the magnitude of the output voltage if V_{cc} varies from -1000 to -1700 volts. (A cut-and-try procedure will be required.) Discuss how this plot could be used in the design of an amplitude modulator.

16-8. A square-law modulator has the characteristic

$$x_0(t) = 1.0x_i + 1.0x_i^2$$

If $x_i = 1 \sin \omega_c t + 1 \sin \omega_{m1} t + 0.5 \sin \omega_{m2} t$, what will the output signal be? If $x_0(t)$ is amplified by a circuit that rejects all signals except those close to ω_c, what will the output of this circuit be? Discuss any distortion that is produced.

16-9. Repeat Prob. 16-8 but now assume that the modulator has the characteristic

$$x_0(t) = 1.0x_i + 1.0x_i^2 + 0.5x_i^3 + 0.5x_i^4$$

16-10. A cosinusoidal carrier of frequency f_c is 50 percent modulated by a cosinusoid of frequency f_m. This is then detected by the circuit of Fig. 16-5. The time constant $RC = 1/\sqrt{f_m f_c}$. If $f_m = 10,000$ Hz and $f_c = 20,000$ Hz, sketch the output waveform. Assume that the diode is ideal.

16-11. Repeat Prob. 16-10 but now assume that $f_c = 10^6$ Hz.

16-12. The diode of Fig. 16-7 has the detection characteristic of Fig. 16-8. The resistance of R_1 is 16,667 ohms, and the peak voltage of the unmodulated carrier is 3 volts. What is the minimum value of R_2 that can be used if a 50 percent modulated signal is to be detected without clipping?

16-13. Repeat Prob. 16-12 but now assume that the peak unmodulated carrier voltage is 5 volts.

16-14. An amplitude-modulated wave consists of a carrier of frequency ω_c and two pairs of sidebands at frequencies $\omega_c + \omega_{m1}$, $\omega_c - \omega_{m1}$, $\omega_c + \omega_{m2}$, and $\omega_c - \omega_{m2}$. Assume that the carrier and all sidebands are cosinusoids and that the peak amplitude of the carrier is 1.0 while that of the sidebands is 0.5. The signal is applied to a square-law detector with the characteristic

$$x_0 = 1.0x_i + 1.0x_i^2$$

If x_0 is amplified by a circuit that rejects frequencies close to or greater than ω_c, what will the output be? Discuss any distortion produced.

16-15. Repeat Prob. 16-14 but now assume that the detector has the characteristic

$$x_0 = 1.0x_i + 1.0x_i^2 + 0.5x_i^3 + 0.5x_i^4$$

16-16. Discuss the instantaneous frequency variation of a sinusoid that is frequency-modulated by a square wave.

16-17. Repeat Prob. 16-16 for a sinusoid that is phase-modulated by a square wave. What practical limitation occurs here?

16-18. A frequency-, or phase-, modulated wave has the form given by Eq. (16-45). The value of m_F is 0.5. Plot a frequency spectrum showing the relative values of the carrier and the five pairs of sidebands.

16-19. Repeat Prob. 16-18 for values of $m_F = 1, 5, 9$, and 10.

16-20. Repeat Prob. 16-18, but assume that the term $\cos \omega_m t$ of Eq. (16-41) is replaced by a square wave which is an even function of time and varies at a frequency ω_m. Assume that the square wave can be expressed by two terms of its Fourier series. The value of m_F obtained from the fundamental component is 1.0.

16-21. Repeat Prob. 16-20 for a value of $m_F = 3$.

16-22. The output capacitance of a reactance modulator is $k_1 C$. The quantity k_1 is a function of the modulating voltage and is given by

$$k_1 = 1 + v_m$$

This reactance device is to be used to control the frequency of an oscillator, whose frequency of oscillation is given by

$$\omega_0 = \frac{1}{\sqrt{k_1 CL}}$$

Expand the value of ω_0 in a power series. Assume that $v_m = V_{m,\max} \cos \omega_m t$. What is the maximum value of $V_{m,\max}$ that can be used if the second-harmonic component of the variation of ω_0 is to be less than 10 percent? To simplify the analysis assume that terms whose powers are greater than the second can be ignored.

16-23. The diode-reactance modulator of Fig. 16-13 is used to frequency-modulate an oscillator whose instantaneous frequency is given by Eq. (16-64). The value of $n = \frac{1}{2}$. Assume that $v_m = V_{m,\max} \cos \omega_m t$ and that all the terms not shown in Eq. (16-64) can be ignored.   Compute the maximum value that $V_{m,\text{max}}/V_{ll}$ can have if the second-harmonic distortion of the frequency deviation is to be less than 2 percent.

16-24.   Compute the voltage gain of the phase modulator of Fig. 16-14a if the plate resistance is not considered to be infinite.   What relation must there be among the FET parameters and the circuit elements if the circuit is to be a good phase modulator?

16-25.   Obtain a power-series expansion for the phase shift as a function of $g_m/\omega C$ for the phase modulator of Fig. 16-14a.   Assume that Eq. (16-65) is valid.

16-26.   Compute an analytical expression for V_{3a} and V_{3b} for the discriminator of Fig. 16-16.   Assume that the inductances have series resistance associated with them.

16-27.   Use the results of Prob. 16-26 to obtain an expression for the output voltage of the Foster-Seeley discriminator circuit of Fig. 16-18.   Assume that the detector portion of the circuit is ideal and does not affect the resonant circuit.

16-28.   Use the results of Prob. 16-26 to obtain an expression for the output voltage of the ratio detector of Fig. 16-20.   Assume that the detector portion of the circuit is ideal and does not affect the resonant circuit.

16-29.   Discuss the use of redundancy in reducing the effects of noise.

17
Power Supplies

Almost all electronic devices require direct voltage sources to establish bias voltages and currents. The voltages can be obtained from batteries, but this is often inconvenient. It would be desirable to obtain the direct-bias voltages from the commercial electric power lines. They usually supply an alternating voltage. Thus, circuits must be designed to convert the alternating voltage to a direct voltage of the proper value. Such circuits are called *power supplies*. The process of converting the alternating voltage and currents to pulsating direct current is called *rectification*. In addition, the pulsating direct current must be *filtered* so that the output voltage is essentially constant. We shall consider the rectifier circuit first and then analyze filter circuits.

17-1 IDEALIZED DIODE CHARACTERISTICS

Rectifiers usually use a semiconductor diode. A piecewise-linear model for this element that we shall use is given in Fig. 17-1. The resistor r_b is the re-

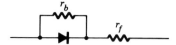

Fig. 17-1 A piecewise-linear model of a vacuum-tube or semiconductor diode.

verse or back resistance of the diode, while r_f is its forward resistance. In almost all power-supply applications, the back resistance can be considered to be an open circuit. The forward resistance of actual diodes is nonlinear. However, for most power-supply applications, sufficient accuracy is obtained using the circuit of Fig. 17-1. One exception is the gas diode, which has a practically constant voltage drop when it is conducting in the forward direction. Its piecewise-linear equivalent circuit has a battery in place of r_f.

The symbol for an ideal diode and the solid-state diode is the same. To differentiate between the two, we shall omit the circle from the ideal diode.

17-2 THE HALF-WAVE RECTIFIER

A very simple rectifier circuit is shown in Fig. 17-2a. The diode permits the current to be in only one direction. Thus,

$$i = \begin{cases} \dfrac{V_{max}}{r_f + R_L} \sin \omega t = I_{max} \sin \omega t & 0 \le \omega t \le \pi \\ 0 & \pi \le \omega t \le 2\pi \end{cases} \tag{17-1}$$

This waveform is shown in Fig. 17-2b. The direct current is the average value of this waveform. Hence,

$$I_{L,dc} = \frac{I_{max}}{\pi} \tag{17-2}$$

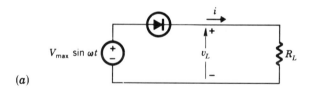

(a)

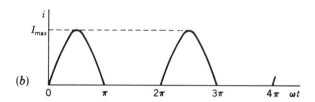

(b)

Fig. 17-2 (a) A half-wave-rectifier circuit and (b) its load current.

and the average value of the load voltage v_L is

$$V_{L,\mathrm{dc}} = \frac{V_{\max}R_L}{\pi(r_f + R_L)} = \frac{I_{\max}R_L}{\pi} = \frac{V_{L,\max}}{\pi} \tag{17-3}$$

Although this circuit produces a direct voltage across the load resistance, it would be unacceptable as a bias supply for many electronic devices because the voltage v_L has alternating, as well as direct, components. These alternating components would act as spurious signals and mask the desired ones. For instance, in an audio amplifier, such a power supply would produce a loud *hum*. Filter circuits which eliminate this hum will be discussed in Secs. 17-4 to 17-9. A criterion that is often used to specify the amount of alternating voltage present in the output of a power supply is the *ripple factor* γ. This is defined as

$$\gamma = \frac{\text{rms value of alternating components of } v_L}{V_{L,\mathrm{dc}}} = \frac{V_{L,\mathrm{ac}}}{V_{L,\mathrm{dc}}} \tag{17-4}$$

Many times, $V_{L,\mathrm{eff}}$, the effective (rms) value of v_L, can be easily obtained ($V_{L,\mathrm{eff}}$ has both alternating and direct components), so that it is convenient to obtain γ in terms of it. Consider the following. If

$$v_1 = v_2 + v_3 \tag{17-5}$$

where v_2 and v_3 are of *different* frequencies, then

$$V_{1,\mathrm{eff}}^2 = V_{2,\mathrm{eff}}^2 + V_{3,\mathrm{eff}}^2 \tag{17-6}$$

Thus

$$V_{L,\mathrm{ac}}^2 = V_{L,\mathrm{eff}}^2 - V_{L,\mathrm{dc}}^2 \tag{17-7}$$

and

$$\gamma = \sqrt{\left(\frac{V_{L,\mathrm{eff}}}{V_{L,\mathrm{dc}}}\right)^2 - 1} \tag{17-8}$$

If the load resistance has no reactive components, then load currents can replace the load voltages in these relations. Since the voltages and currents are half-sinusoids, their effective values are given by

$$V_{L,\mathrm{eff}} = \frac{V_{L,\max}}{2} \tag{17-9}$$

$$I_{L,\mathrm{eff}} = \frac{I_{L,\max}}{2} \tag{17-10}$$

Then, using Eqs. (17-3) and (17-8), we obtain

$$\gamma = \sqrt{\frac{\pi^2}{4} - 1} = 1.21 \tag{17-11}$$

This is quite large. For many electronic devices, γ must be much less than 0.001. This is why filtering is required.

The power dissipated within the diode is

$$P_{oD} = I_{L,\text{eff}}^2 r_f \tag{17-12}$$

It is often unnecessary to use Eq. (17-12) to obtain the dissipation, since manufacturers rate the diodes in terms of the direct load voltage and load current. We shall also see that the power-supply filter enters into the choice of the diode.

The maximum voltage that appears across the diode occurs when it is not conducting. This is called an inverse voltage. The maximum value of this voltage is the *peak inverse voltage*. For the circuit of Fig. 17-2, the peak inverse voltage is V_{max}.

We shall subsequently see that the inclusion of a filter can markedly change the values of all the quantities that we have discussed.

The half-wave rectifier without a filter is not a very good power supply for most electronic devices. Before studying filters, we shall consider a circuit whose performance is considerably better than that of the half-wave rectifier.

17-3 THE FULL-WAVE RECTIFIER

Consider the circuit of Fig. 17-3a. It consists basically of two half-wave rectifiers with a common load resistance. Since v_1 and v_2 are 180° out of phase, each diode will conduct on alternate half-cycles. Thus, the load current of Fig. 17-3b results. This circuit is called a *full-wave rectifier*. Proceeding as in the last section, we obtain

$$i_L = \frac{V_{\text{max}}|\sin \omega t|}{r_f + R_L} = I_{L,\text{max}}|\sin \omega t| \tag{17-13}$$

$$v_L = \frac{V_{\text{max}}R_L|\sin \omega t|}{r_f + R_L} = V_{L,\text{max}}|\sin \omega t| \tag{17-14}$$

$$V_{L,\text{dc}} = \frac{2V_{L,\text{max}}}{\pi} \tag{17-15}$$

$$I_{L,\text{dc}} = \frac{2I_{L,\text{max}}}{\pi} \tag{17-16}$$

$$V_{L,\text{max}} = \frac{V_{L,\text{max}}}{\sqrt{2}} \tag{17-17}$$

$$\gamma = \sqrt{\pi^2/8 - 1} = 0.48 \tag{17-18}$$

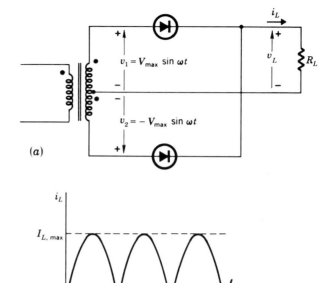

Fig. 17-3 (*a*) A full-wave-rectifier circuit and (*b*) its load current.

The power dissipated in each diode is

$$P_{oD} = \frac{I_{L,\text{eff}}^2 r_f}{2} \tag{17-19}$$

since the current in each diode is zero for one half-cycle. Note that for the same value of $I_{L,\text{dc}}$, the value of P_{oD}, for each diode, is one-quarter of that for the half-wave rectifier.

When one diode is cut off, the other is essentially a short circuit. Thus, the peak inverse voltage is $2V_{\text{max}}$.

Again note that filtering can change all the values presented here.

The full-wave rectifier provides substantial improvement over the half-wave rectifier. It is more complex, in that two diodes and a transformer are required. In many applications, the transformer is required to vary the value of the input voltage so that the required value of $V_{L,\text{dc}}$ can be obtained. The transformer also provides isolation between the power line and the circuit. A transformer can be used with a half-wave rectifier, but the direct current through it would tend to saturate the core. Thus, a large, expensive transformer would be required (see Sec. 17-19). In the full-wave rectifier, the net direct flux through the core is zero, and the direct current does not saturate it. This is an important advantage of the full-wave rectifier.

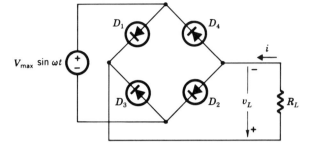

Fig. 17-4   A full-wave bridge rectifier.

In some applications, a transformer is not required to vary the power-line voltages. In such circumstances, it would be desirable to construct a transformerless full-wave rectifier. Such a circuit is shown in Fig. 17-4. When the voltage $V_{max} \sin \omega t$ is positive, diodes D_1 and D_2 will conduct. When this voltage is negative, diodes D_3 and D_4 will conduct. Thus, the current i_L will have the form shown in Fig. 17-3b, and we shall have achieved full-wave rectification. Because of the circuit configuration, this is called a *bridge rectifier*. It uses four diodes instead of the two used in Fig. 17-3a. However, especially when semiconductor diodes are used, their cost, size, and weight are much less than those of a transformer.

17-4   GENERAL DISCUSSION OF POWER-SUPPLY FILTERS

The ripple factor of a rectifier circuit is very high. A power-supply filter reduces these alternating components. A typical power-supply filter circuit is shown in Fig. 17-5. v_I is the output voltage of the rectifier, and v_O is the output voltage of the filter. Note that the direct component of v_I is unaffected by the filter, while the alternating components of v_I are attenuated by it. The series elements of the filter should present a high impedance to the alternating components, while the shunt elements should present a low impedance to these components. The converse should be true for the direct components. If v_I is known, then it can be expanded in a Fourier series.

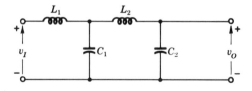

Fig. 17-5   A   typical   power-supply filter.

Ordinary network analysis can then be used to obtain v_O.   If v_I has a waveform such as that of Fig. 17-2b, then its Fourier series is

$$v_I = V_{max} \left[\frac{1}{\pi} + \frac{1}{2} \sin \omega t - \frac{2}{\pi} \sum_{k=1}^{\infty} \frac{\cos 2k\omega t}{(2k+1)(2k-1)} \right] \qquad (17\text{-}20)$$

Similarly, the Fourier series for Fig. 17-3b is given by

$$v_I = V_{max} \left[\frac{2}{\pi} - \frac{4}{\pi} \sum_{k=1}^{\infty} \frac{\cos 2k\omega t}{(2k+1)(2k-1)} \right] \qquad (17\text{-}21)$$

The lowest frequency of Eq. (17-21) is twice the power-line frequency.   It is important to realize that the output voltage of a half-wave or full-wave rectifier will depend upon the type of filter that is used and will *not* always be of the form of Figs. 17-2b or 17-3b, respectively.   Thus, Eqs. (17-20) and (17-21) cannot always be used in the analysis of power-supply filters.

17-5   THE CAPACITOR FILTER

A simple power-supply filter consists of a capacitor placed in parallel with the load resistance.   Such a circuit is shown in Fig. 17-6.   We shall assume in our discussion that the forward resistance of the diode is zero.   The load voltage v_L, after the first cycle, will have the form shown in Fig. 17-7a. Because of the diode, the capacitor C can only discharge through R_L.   When $\omega t = \pi/2$, the voltage $v_L = V_{max}$.   As v_I decreases, v_L falls off with v_I for a time.   However, the rate of falloff of $\epsilon^{-t/R_L C}$ will become less than that of $\sin \omega t$.   Thus, v_L will tend to be higher than v_I.   At this time, the diode will cut off, i.e., become an open circuit.   This occurs at $\omega t = \theta_2$ in Fig. 17-7a. The voltage v_L then has the form

$$v_L = V_{max} \sin \theta_2 \epsilon^{-t/R_L C} \qquad \theta_2 \le \omega t \le \theta_1 + 2\pi \qquad (17\text{-}22)$$

During the next cycle, v_I will eventually become equal to v_L and the diode will conduct.   Thus, the output voltage will have the form

$$v_L = V_{max} \sin \omega t \qquad \theta_1 \le \omega t \le \theta_2 \qquad (17\text{-}23)$$

This waveform is repeated periodically.   Let us consider the currents in the

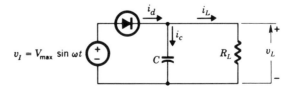

Fig. 17-6   A half-wave rectifier with a capacitor filter.

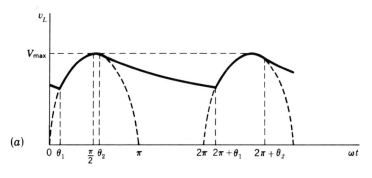

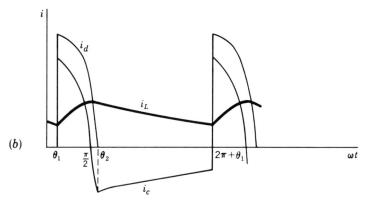

Fig. 17-7 (a) The load voltage of the circuit of Fig. 17-6 and (b) the currents in this circuit.

circuit. The load current i_L will have the same waveform as the load voltage. During the time that the diode is not conducting

$$i_c = -i_L = -\frac{v_L}{R_L} \qquad \theta_2 \le \omega t \le \theta_1 + 2\pi \tag{17-24}$$

When the diode does conduct, the current through C is just what it would be if the capacitor were connected directly across v_I. (There are no transients, since the diode starts to conduct at the instant $v_I = v_L$.) Thus

$$i_c = V_{max} \omega C \cos \omega t \qquad \theta_1 \le \omega t \le \theta_2 \tag{17-25}$$

The diode current is

$$i_d = i_c + i_L \tag{17-26}$$

These waveforms are shown in Fig. 17-7b. The peak current through the diode occurs at $\omega t = \theta_1$ (this assumes that $R_L \gg 1/\omega C$) and is

$$I_{d,max} = E_{max}\left(\omega C \cos \theta_1 + \frac{\sin \theta_1}{R_L}\right) \tag{17-27}$$

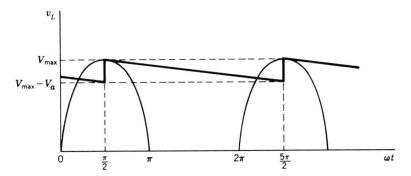

Fig. 17-8 The approximate load voltage that is to be used in the analysis of the capacitor filter.

The diode must be capable of passing this peak current. If the value of C is increased, the decay of v_L in the period $\theta_2 \leq \omega t \leq \theta_1 + 2\pi$ will decrease. In the limit, as C approaches infinity, v_L will approach a pure direct voltage. Increases in C are accompanied by increases in $I_{d,\max}$.

In order to obtain the direct load voltage and the ripple factor, the value of θ_1 and of θ_2 must be known. A transcendental equation must be solved to obtain them. This is very tedious. We shall now make some approximations that simplify the calculations. [Note that the Fourier series of Eq. (17-20) cannot be used here, since the output of the rectifier is *not* of the form of Fig. 17-2b.] We shall assume that the load voltage varies linearly[1] with time as shown in Fig. 17-8. This waveform appears to be considerably different from that of Fig. 17-7a. However, the results obtained using it compare very favorably with those obtained using actual measurements. The average value of Fig. 17-8 is

$$V_{L,\text{dc}} = V_{\max} - \frac{V_a}{2} \tag{17-28}$$

If ΔQ represents the change in charge stored in C between $\pi/2$ and $5\pi/2$, then

$$V_a = \frac{\Delta Q}{C} \tag{17-29}$$

Since the voltage is assumed to vary linearly with time, the charge stored in C must decrease at a constant rate. Thus, current i_C is constant over this period. (Note that this leads to a paradox since $i_L = i_C$ during the discharge period of the capacitor. If i_L is constant, then v_L must be constant and not vary as shown. This paradox results because we have not assumed that the capacitor voltage varies exponentially with time. However, the results obtained with this analysis are accurate.) The constant value of i_C is $I_{L,\text{dc}}$, the direct load current.   Since the time of one period is the reciprocal of the frequency, we have

$$V_a = \frac{I_{L,\text{dc}}}{fC} \tag{17-30}$$

Thus

$$V_{L,\text{dc}} = V_{\text{max}} - \frac{I_{L,\text{dc}}}{2fC} \tag{17-31}$$

Even though we have assumed that all the components of this circuit are ideal, its voltage regulation is not.   That is, the output voltage will fall off as the output current increases.   The direct load current and voltage are related by

$$I_{L,\text{dc}} = \frac{V_{L,\text{dc}}}{R_L} \tag{17-32}$$

Substituting in Eq. (17-31), we obtain

$$V_{L,\text{dc}} = \frac{V_{\text{max}}}{1 + 1/(2fR_LC)} \tag{17-33}$$

To calculate the ripple factor, we must determine $V_{L,\text{ac}}$, the rms value of the alternating component of v_L.   This is a triangular waveform that varies from $-V_a/2$ to $V_a/2$.   Thus

$$V_{L,\text{ac}} = \frac{V_a}{2\sqrt{3}} \tag{17-34}$$

Substituting Eqs. (17-32), (17-34), and (17-30) into Eq. (17-4), we have

$$\gamma = \frac{1}{2\sqrt{3}fR_LC} \tag{17-35}$$

To calculate the peak diode current, we must determine the value of θ_1 [see Eq. (17-27)].   The angle θ_1 can be approximately obtained[1] by assuming that the diode starts to conduct when $v_I = V_{\text{max}} - V_a$.   Thus,

$$V_{\text{max}} \sin \theta_1 = V_{\text{max}} - V_a \tag{17-36}$$

Substituting for V_a using Eqs. (17-30), (17-32), and (17-33) and solving, we obtain

$$\theta_1 = \sin^{-1} \frac{2fR_LC - 1}{2fR_LC + 1} \tag{17-37}$$

The peak diode current is found from Eq. (17-27).   If the value of fR_LC is increased, the value of $V_{L,\text{dc}}$ will more closely approach V_{max} for all values of time, the ripple factor will be reduced, and the peak diode current will be increased.

The ripple factor is usually very small, so that $v_L \approx V_{max}$. Thus, the peak inverse voltage for this circuit is $2V_{max}$.

When a single capacitor filter is used with a full-wave rectifier, the results are very similar to those of the half-wave rectifier. The approximate output voltage for the full-wave rectifier is shown in Fig. 17-9. The approximate waveform is the same as that of Fig. 17-8, but its period is halved. Thus, the half-wave rectifier relations can be applied to the full-wave rectifier if we replace f by $2f$. Then

$$V_{L,dc} = V_{max} - \frac{I_{L,dc}}{4fC} \tag{17-38}$$

$$V_{L,dc} = \frac{V_{max}}{1 + 1/4fR_LC} \tag{17-39}$$

$$\gamma = \frac{1}{4\sqrt{3}fR_LC} \tag{17-40}$$

and

$$\theta_1 = \sin^{-1}\frac{4fR_LC - 1}{4fR_LC + 1} \tag{17-41}$$

The peak diode current is again found by substituting in Eq. (17-27).

When a power supply is designed, the values of $V_{L,dc}$, $I_{L,dc}$, and γ are specified and the values of V_{max} and C are to be found. This can be done for the half-wave rectifier by simultaneously solving Eqs. (17-33) and (17-35). This calculation yields

$$C \geq \frac{1}{2\sqrt{3}fR_L\gamma} \tag{17-42}$$

and

$$V_{max} = V_{L,dc}(1 + \sqrt{3}\gamma) \tag{17-43}$$

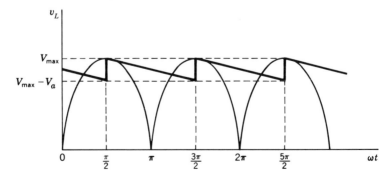

Fig. 17-9 The approximate load voltage that is to be used in the analysis of a full-wave rectifier with a capacitor filter.

If the greater-than sign is used in Eq. (17-42), the actual value of γ should be used in Eq. (17-43). If the amount that $V_{L,\text{dc}}$ is allowed to vary as $I_{L,\text{dc}}$ varies between given limits is specified, then Eq. (17-31) may actually specify the minimum value of C.

For the full-wave rectifier, these design relations become

$$C \geq \frac{1}{4\sqrt{3}fR_L\gamma} \tag{17-44}$$

$$V_{\max} = V_{L,\text{dc}}(1 + \sqrt{3}\gamma) \tag{17-45}$$

and Eq. (17-38) is used to determine the minimum value of C if voltage regulation is specified. Note that the value of C that is required when the full-wave rectifier is used is one-half of the value required when the half-wave rectifier is used. Typical values of C range from 10 μf to several hundred microfarads. Electrolytic capacitors are usually used.

This analysis has neglected the voltage drop in the forward resistance of the diode. The primary effect of this voltage drop is to reduce the value of $V_{L,\text{dc}}$. Experimentally determined plots of $V_{L,\text{dc}}$ versus $I_{L,\text{dc}}$ for various values of C are often supplied by diode manufacturers. Thus, the effect of the forward resistance as well as the resistances of the circuit can be determined by measurements.

17-6 THE INDUCTOR-INPUT FILTER

In theory, the simple capacitor filter can be used to obtain as small a ripple factor and as good a voltage regulation as desired. However, the size of the capacitor can become extremely large. This may result in a filter that is too large, too heavy, and too expensive. In addition, the peak diode currents can be very high, and, thus, a high-current-capacity diode will be required. In such cases, it is often desirable to use more-complex filter circuits. A typical one is shown in Fig. 17-10. This is called an *inductor-input filter*, since the input element is an inductance. This is also called an *L-section filter*, since its shape resembles that of an inverted *L*. If the design requirements are stringent enough to require an inductance, then it usually is desirable to obtain the advantages of a full-wave rectifier. [There is less alternating voltage in the output of a full-wave rectifier, and this voltage is of higher frequency than it is in the half-wave rectifier; see Eqs. (17-20) and (17-21).]

The output current of a full-wave rectifier, with a resistance load, equals zero only twice during any one cycle (see Fig. 17-3b). The presence of the inductance tends to maintain the current at all times. For the time being, let us assume that i_l is never zero. Thus, one of the diodes must be conducting at all times. If we neglect the voltage drop in the diode, then v_l

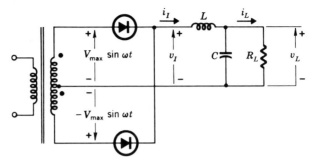

Fig. 17-10 A full-wave rectifier with an inductor-input filter.

will have the form of Fig. 17-3b, and it can be expanded in the Fourier series of Eq. (17-4).   That is,

$$v_I = V_{max} \left(\frac{2}{\pi} - \frac{4}{3\pi} \cos 2\omega t - \frac{4}{15\pi} \cos 4\omega t - \cdots \right) \tag{17-46}$$

To determine the output voltage v_L, we can use the circuit of Fig. 17-11 and consider that v represents each of the components of Eq. (17-46) in turn. Thus, the direct load voltage is given by

$$V_{L,dc} = \frac{2V_{max}}{\pi} \tag{17-47}$$

The load voltage is not a function of the load current if the components are ideal.   Hence, the voltage regulation will be ideal.   If the inductance has a series resistance R, then the direct load voltage is given by

$$V_{L,dc} = \frac{2V_{max}}{\pi} - I_{L,dc}R \tag{17-48}$$

The effective series resistance of the diodes can also be included in R.

Now let us determine the alternating components of output voltage.   In general

$$\frac{1}{\omega C} \ll R_L \tag{17-49}$$

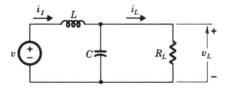

Fig. 17-11 The filter circuit of Fig. 17-10.

so that we can ignore R_L in these calculations. Thus, the component of the load voltage at frequency 2ω is

$$v_{L2} = \frac{-4V_{max}}{3\pi(1 - 4\omega^2LC)} \cos 2\omega t \tag{17-50}$$

In general, the element values are such that

$$\omega L \gg \frac{1}{\omega C} \tag{17-51}$$

so that $4\omega^2LC \gg 1$. Thus, the rms value of the second-harmonic voltage is

$$V_{L2} = \frac{V_{max}}{3\pi\sqrt{2}\omega^2LC}$$

Similarly, the rms value of the fourth harmonic is

$$V_{L4} = \frac{V_{max}}{60\pi\sqrt{2}\omega^2LC}$$

Thus V_{L4} is one-twentieth of V_{L2}. The higher harmonics are even smaller fractions of V_{L2}. Hence, very little error is introduced by assuming that the rms alternating voltage is given by V_{L2}. Therefore, the ripple factor is

$$\gamma = \frac{1}{6\sqrt{2}\omega^2LC} \tag{17-52}$$

where it is assumed that the direct voltage drop in the resistance R is negligible.

In this analysis, we assumed that the current i_I was never zero. It cannot be negative, because of the diodes. However, if the load current becomes sufficiently small, then i_I will become zero for finite periods of time. The previously developed relations for $V_{L,dc}$ and γ will no longer be valid, since v_I can no longer be expressed by Eq. (17-46). A typical curve of $V_{L,dc}$ versus $I_{L,dc}$ for an inductor-input filter is given in Fig. 17-12. If the load current drops below a critical value, the load voltage rises and the regulation is no longer ideal. If R_L becomes an open circuit, the voltage across the capacitor becomes V_{max}, as it does in the capacitor filter. The capacitor cannot discharge and, thus, neither diode in the rectifier circuit will conduct. Let us determine the constraints that must be imposed on the circuit elements if the previous analysis is to be correct. We shall again assume that relations (17-49) and (17-51) are valid. Then, harmonics above the second can be neglected. Therefore,

$$i_I = \frac{2V_{max}}{\pi R_L} - \frac{2V_{max}}{3\pi\omega L} \cos\left(2\omega t - \frac{\pi}{2}\right) \tag{17-53}$$

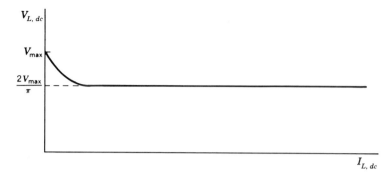

Fig. 17-12 A curve of direct output voltage versus direct output current for an inductor-input filter.

Since i_I cannot become negative, this expression is only true for positive values. If it is negative, then $i_I = 0$. If $i_I > 0$ for all times (except possibly for intervals of zero length), then

$$\frac{2V_{max}}{\pi R_L} = \frac{2V_{max}}{3\pi\omega L}$$

or

$$L \geq \frac{R_L}{3\omega} \tag{17-54}$$

The value of $L = R_L/3\omega$ is called the *critical inductance* L_c. Thus, the value of the inductance should always be greater than the critical value. At times, R_L is a variable. (This can occur instantaneously when an ordinary amplifier circuit is the load, and the signal level varies with time.) The maximum value of R_L should be used in Eq. (17-54). If the maximum value of R_L is very large, then the value of the critical inductance will be excessive. In these cases, a resistance can be placed in parallel with the load resistance. This effectively limits the maximum value of the load resistance and thus the value of L_c. This resistance is called a *bleeder resistance*. It serves another function. If high-quality capacitors are used in a power supply, the capacitors can hold their stored charge for a long time if the load resistance becomes disconnected. *Thus, the power supply can present a serious shock hazard even if it is turned off.* The bleeder resistance provides a discharge path for the capacitors, and should be connected directly across them. Resistors used for this purpose should be carbon resistors, rather than wire-wound resistors, since carbon resistors are less likely to open-circuit.

The design of the filter consists of the choice of V_{max}, L, and C when $V_{L,dc}$, $I_{L,dc}$, and γ are specified. The value of $V_{L,dc}$ determines V_{max} and, hence, the turns ratio of the transformer. $R_L = V_{L,dc}/I_{L,dc}$. This can then

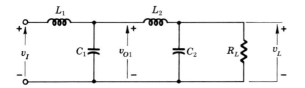

Fig. 17-13   A two-section inductor-input filter.

be substituted into Eq. (17-54) to determine the minimum value of L.   If this is excessive (or for safety reasons), a bleeder resistance should be included. The value of the product LC can then be determined from Eq. (17-52). L and C are then chosen so that size, and/or weight, and/or cost will be minimized.

If the value of γ is very small, then the sizes of L and/or C can become unreasonably large.   A smaller, cheaper, and lighter filter may then be constructed if more filter elements are used.   Such a filter structure is shown in Fig. 17-13.   In general, the element values are chosen so that

$$\omega L \gg \frac{1}{\omega C} \tag{17-55}$$

and

$$\frac{1}{\omega C} \ll R_L \tag{17-56}$$

where L and C refer to either inductor and either capacitor, respectively.   As a consequence of these assumptions, v_{O1} will have the same form as v_L of Fig. 17-10.   The filter section consisting of L_2 and C_2 acts in essentially the same way as the one consisting of L_1 and C_1.   Thus, the rms value of the alternating component of v_L can be obtained by multiplying the rms value of the alternating component of v_{O1} by $1/4\omega^2 L_2 C_2$.   Hence, the ripple factor is

$$\gamma = \frac{1}{24\sqrt{2}\,\omega^4 L_1 L_2 C_1 C_2} \tag{17-57}$$

If this analysis is to be valid, the current i_I must never be zero.   Then L_1 should be greater than the critical value given by Eq. (17-54).   Even though this two-section filter has more elements than the one-section filter, the overall filter can have less volume.   Note that Eq. (17-57) is smaller than Eq. (17-52) by a factor of $4\omega^2 L_2 C_2$.

17-7   THE CAPACITOR-INPUT FILTER

If an additional capacitor is added to the inductor-input filter as shown in Fig. 17-14, the ripple factor will be reduced.   However, the direct voltage across the capacitor will be essentially the same as that given by Eq. (17-38).

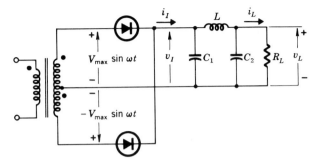

Fig. 17-14 A full-wave rectifier with a capacitor-input filter.

Hence, we have reduced γ at the expense of voltage regulation. The direct load voltage is equal to the direct voltage across C_1 minus the drop in R, the series resistance of the inductor. Thus, using Eq. (17-38), we have

$$V_{L,\text{dc}} = V_{\max} - \frac{I_{L,\text{dc}}}{4fC} - I_{L,\text{dc}}R \qquad (17\text{-}58)$$

Substituting the relation $I_{L,\text{dc}} = V_{L,\text{dc}}/R_L$, we obtain

$$V_{L,\text{dc}} = \frac{V_{\max}}{1 + 1/4fR_LC + R/R_L} \qquad (17\text{-}59)$$

In order to analyze the effect of the filter section consisting of L and C_2, we shall determine the Fourier series of the current i_I. This is

$$i_I = I_{L,\text{dc}} + I_{2,\max} \cos 2\omega t + I_{4,\max} \cos 4\omega t + \cdots \qquad (17\text{-}60)$$

Note that the full-wave rectifier produces only even harmonic components and that i_I will be an even function of time. Using the usual Fourier-series relationships, we obtain

$$I_{\text{dc}} = \frac{1}{2\pi} \int_0^{2\pi} i_I \, d\omega t \qquad (17\text{-}61)$$

$$I_{2,\max} = \frac{1}{\pi} \int_0^{2\pi} i_I \cos 2\omega t \, d\omega t \qquad (17\text{-}62)$$

The current i_I in a capacitor filter is nonzero only for short periods of time near $\omega t = \pi/2$ and $\omega t = 3\pi/2$. The value of $\cos 2\omega t$ is approximately -1 during these intervals. Thus,

$$|I_{2,\max}| \approx \frac{1}{\pi} \int_0^{2\pi} i_I \, d\omega t = 2I_{\text{dc}} \qquad (17\text{-}63)$$

We shall assume that the filter components are such that

$$\omega L \gg \frac{1}{\omega C_1} \tag{17-64}$$

$$\omega L \gg \frac{1}{\omega C_2} \tag{17-65}$$

and

$$\frac{1}{\omega C_2} \ll R \tag{17-66}$$

Thus, the magnitude of the second-harmonic component of v_I can be obtained by multiplying Eq. (17-63) by $1/2\omega C_1$. Then the rms value of the second harmonic of V_I is

$$V_{I2} = \frac{I_{dc}}{\sqrt{2}\omega C_1} = \frac{V_{L,dc}}{\sqrt{2}R_L\omega C_1} \tag{17-67}$$

The attenuation of the filter section consisting of L and C_2 can be obtained using the procedures of Eqs. (17-49) to (17-52). Thus,

$$V_{L2} = \frac{V_{L,dc}}{4\sqrt{2}R_L\omega^3 C_1 C_2 L} \tag{17-68}$$

As in the case of the inductor-input filter, the higher harmonics can usually be neglected. Then, the ripple factor is given by

$$\gamma = \frac{1}{4\sqrt{2}R_L\omega^3 C_1 C_2 L} \tag{17-69}$$

The design of this filter proceeds in a manner similar to that of the inductor-input filter. The value of V_{max} and the minimum value of C_1 for the required voltage regulation are obtained from Eqs. (17-58) and (17-59). Then, Eq. (17-69) is used to determine the product $C_1 C_2 L$. The capacitor-input filter is sometimes called a *pi-section filter* because it resembles the Greek letter π.

The ripple factor of this filter can be further reduced if a multiple-section filter is used. Each additional LC section will reduce the ripple factor by $1/4\omega^2 LC$.

17-8 RESISTANCE-CAPACITANCE FILTERS

An inductor is a relatively expensive, large, and heavy component. At times, it can be replaced by a resistor in a filter section. This tends to increase the ripple factor and worsen the voltage regulation. However, sometimes it may be feasible to use several sections of filtering instead of one

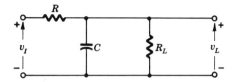

Fig. 17-15 An RC filter section.

when a resistance replaces the inductance. A typical RC filter section is shown in Fig. 17-15. We shall assume that

$$R \gg \frac{1}{\omega C} \tag{17-70}$$

$$R_L \gg \frac{1}{\omega C} \tag{17-71}$$

Then, if we are dealing with a full-wave rectifier and assume that all the harmonics above the second can be neglected, the alternating component of the voltage will be reduced by a factor of approximately $1/2\omega RC$.

Resistance-capacitance filter sections are usually not used by themselves but are cascaded with other filter sections. Such a filter is shown in Fig. 17-16. The ripple factor can be obtained by multiplying Eq. (17-52) by $1/2\omega RC$ and accounting for the direct voltage drop in R. Thus,

$$\gamma = \frac{1 + R/R_L}{12\sqrt{2}\omega^3 RLC_1C_2} \tag{17-72}$$

This is not as small as the ripple factor of the two-section inductor-capacitor filter given by Eq. (17-57), but it is considerably smaller than the ripple factor of Eq. (17-52). Note that Eq. (17-72) takes the direct voltage drop in R into account.

There will be a voltage drop $I_{L,\text{dc}}R$ in the filter resistance. This worsens the voltage regulation of the power supply. However, sometimes it is an advantage. Many times a power supply is required to produce several different output voltages. For instance, in an amplifier, the output stages often require larger direct voltages than the input stages. The ripple voltage

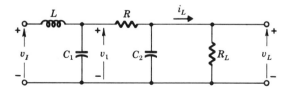

Fig. 17-16 A cascade of an inductor-input filter and RC filter section.

must be much lower at the input stages, since the signal levels are lower here. The filter of Fig. 17-16 could be used in this case. The power supply is designed to produce the required value of $V_{1,\text{dc}}$. The value R is then chosen so that $V_{L,\text{dc}}$ is reduced to the required amount. The direct-voltage drop across R is $I_{L,\text{dc}}R$. The ripple factor of v_L will be less than that of v_1. If it is desired to reduce the ripple factor at v_L still further, the value of C_2 can be increased, or additional RC sections can be used. The total series resistance should be kept constant so that the correct output voltage will be obtained.

17-9 OUTPUT IMPEDANCE OF FILTERS

A power supply for an electronic device should ideally present a zero impedance to all signal components. For instance, in the analysis of amplifier circuits, we replaced the power supply by a short circuit in the linear models. When several cascaded amplifier stages use the same power supply, it is especially important that the power-supply impedance be low, since if it is not, signal voltages may appear across it. Thus, feedback can be introduced between the various stages and the amplifier may oscillate. The output element of a power-supply filter is a shunt capacitance. Hence, the impedance down to fairly low frequencies can be kept small. The zero (or very low) frequency impedance of the filter is determined by the voltage-regulation equation. For instance, for an inductance-input filter, Eq. (17-48) gives the low-frequency resistance as

$$R_{\text{dc}} = R \tag{17-73}$$

while for the capacitor-input filter we can use Eq. (17-58) to obtain

$$R_{\text{dc}} = \frac{1}{4fC} + R \tag{17-74}$$

Note that f is the power-line frequency and not the signal frequency. If this low-frequency impedance is too high, the voltage regulation will be poor, and an amplifier which uses this power supply may oscillate. If the voltage regulation is ideal, then the low-frequency resistance will be zero. Voltage-regulator circuits are used to reduce this low-frequency power-supply impedance. These will be discussed in the next section.

17-10 VOLTAGE-REGULATED POWER SUPPLIES

In many applications, it is necessary to construct a power supply whose output voltage remains very constant even if the load resistance changes or if the supply-line voltage varies. For instance, oscillators and direct-coupled amplifiers often require such power supplies. A well-regulated power supply will have a low output resistance (see Sec. 17-9). We shall consider several circuits that can be used to regulate the voltage of a power supply.

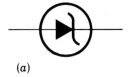

(a)

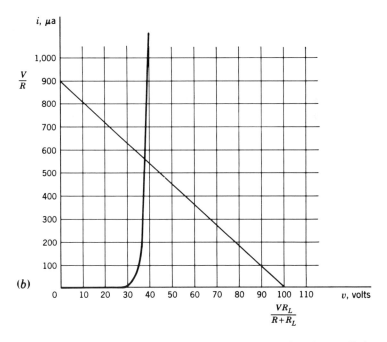

(b)

Fig. 17-17 (a) The symbol for a voltage-regulator semiconductor diode and (b) its voltage-current characteristics.

Voltage-regulator diodes When the reverse bias voltage of a semiconductor diode is increased sufficiently, it breaks down. Its breakdown voltage-current characteristic is such that the voltage across the diode is almost independent of the current through it, so the diode can be used as a voltage regulator (see Sec. 3-9). The symbol for such a diode is given in

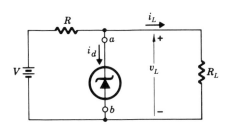

Fig. 17-18 A simple voltage-regulator circuit.

Fig. 17-17a. It is sometimes called a *zener diode* and its voltage-current characteristic is given in Fig. 17-17b. A typical circuit that uses this device is given in Fig. 17-18. Its operation is as follows. If V or R_L should increase, then i_d would increase (see Fig. 17-17b) and the voltage drop across R would rise. This would tend to maintain v_L constant. Similarly, if V or R_L decreases, then i_d would decrease. To analyze this circuit, replace the circuit consisting of V, R, and R_L as viewed looking into terminals ab by its Thévenin's equivalent circuit. A load line can then be drawn on the characteristics as shown. The voltage across the diode and, hence, the load voltage, is given by the intersection of the load line and the characteristic. Thus, v_L will remain essentially constant for large variations in V or R_L.

This circuit has two disadvantages: (1) It is very inefficient. Power is dissipated in both the resistor R and in the diode. If the regulation is to be good, $i_d > i_L$, so that the current through R depends on i_d to a great degree. Thus, the efficiency will be very small. (2) The output voltage cannot be chosen at will but is a function of the available diode breakdown voltages. We shall next consider some more complex circuits that eliminate these difficulties and, in addition, provide better voltage regulation.

Series voltage regulator Consider the circuit shown in Fig. 17-19. We have used *n-p-n* transistors here since this is conventional. A regulator using FETs could also be built. At present, however, the operation would be limited to very low load current values. The battery V represents the ouput of a filtered, but unregulated, power supply. The resistance of T_3 is in series with the power supply and the load. The variation of this resistance produces the voltage regulation. This resistance is a function of the base-to-emitter voltage of T_3. This, in turn, depends upon the current through T_2. The base voltage of T_2 depends upon the difference between v_a and the

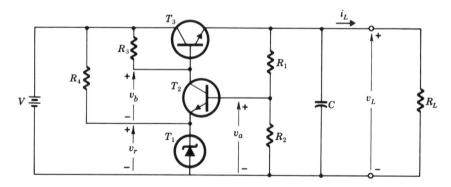

Fig. 17-19 Voltage-regulated power supply using a series transistor.

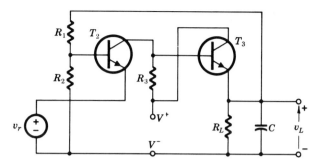

Fig. 17-20 The circuit of Fig. 17-19 redrawn.

reference voltage v_r. Device T_1 is included to establish a fixed reference voltage with which the output voltage is compared. (R_4 and T_1 form a simple voltage-regulator circuit of the type of Fig. 17-18.) The voltage v_a is a fraction of the output voltage v_L. If v_L increases, then the bias of T_2 will shift so that T_2 draws more current. This will increase the current through R_3 and cause v_b to decrease. Thus, the base-to-emitter voltage of T_3 will change in such a way as to increase the resistance of T_3 and, thus, to reduce v_L. Thus, the variation in v_L will be reduced. In a similar way, a reduction in v_L will be accompanied by a decrease in the resistance of T_3. Increases in the gain of T_2 or of T_3 tend to reduce the variations in v_L, since they make the change of the resistance of T_3 more sensitive to these variations. The function of the capacitor C is to provide a low output impedance at high frequencies. If the relative sizes of R_1 and R_2 are changed, the effective input bias of T_2 will be varied. This will result in a change in v_L. Thus, the voltage of this power supply can be adjusted. An alternative way of considering this circuit is to redraw it as in Fig. 17-20. The generator v_r symbolically replaces the voltage-reference diode. Thus, this is a two-stage direct-coupled amplifier whose input is v_r and whose output is v_L. Negative voltage feedback is incorporated, so the output voltage tends to remain independent of the fluctuations in the load resistance and the power-supply voltages (see Secs. 13-3, 13-4, and 13-6). If the open-loop gain is increased, the fluctuations in v_L and the output impedance will be reduced. The voltage-regulator circuit is a feedback amplifier; hence, it may oscillate. The procedures of Secs. 13-8 to 13-13 should be used to ensure that the circuit is stable.

17-11 CONTROLLED RECTIFIERS

There are many high-power applications where it is desirable to vary the output voltage of a power supply without introducing a series resistance that dissipates power. One means of doing this is to control the rectifier so that

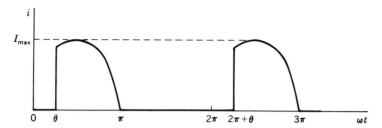

Fig. 17-21 Current in a controlled rectifier.

it conducts for only a fraction of the cycle.   For instance, consider Fig. 17-2.
If the diode conducted for only a portion of the half-cycle, the average value
of i would be reduced and control would have been achieved.   Consider that
the diode circuit of Fig. 17-2 can be controlled so that the current i has the
form shown in Fig. 17-21.   We shall assume that the time of the diode's
initial conduction occurs θ rad after the start of each cycle.   The current i_L
is then

$$i_L = \frac{V_{max}}{r_f + R_L} \sin \omega t \qquad \theta \le \omega t \le \pi$$

The direct load current is given by the average value of i_L.   Thus

$$I_{dc} = \frac{V_{max}(1 + \cos \theta)}{2\pi(r_f + R_L)} \tag{17-75}$$

If θ can be varied from π to 0, the direct load current will vary from zero to a
maximum value of $V_{max}/\pi(r_f + R_L)$.   If the diode were ideal $(r_f = 0)$, then
no power would be dissipated in it even though control had been achieved.
The output waveform of this circuit is very rich in harmonics if θ is close to π
and the ripple factor will change as θ is varied.   These circuits are usually
used in applications where low ripple factors are not required (and filters are
not used).   Let us now briefly consider a device that can be used as a controlled rectifier.

The _p-n-p-n_ controlled rectifier   Consider the _p-n-p-n_ structure shown
in Fig. 17-22a.   It has three leads labeled _anode_, _cathode_, and _gate_, and its
symbol is shown in Fig. 17-22b.   This device can be considered to be the
interconnection of a _p-n-p_ and an _n-p-n_ transistor as shown in Fig. 17-22c.
To explain the operation, consider the simple circuit of Fig. 17-22d.   Assume
that i_g is zero or negative, so that T_1 is almost cut off.   Then i_1 will be almost
zero and T_2 will also be essentially cut off.   If i_g is made positive, so that T_1
conducts, i_1 will be nonzero and T_2 will start to conduct.   The current i_2 will
divide into i_2' and i_2''.   If R is much larger than the base-emitter impedance of

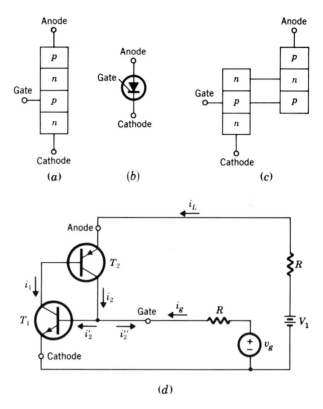

Fig. 17-22 (a) A *p-n-p-n* controlled rectifier; (b) its symbol; (c) a "two-transistor" representation of this device; (d) the schematic representation of part (c) connected into a simple circuit.

T_1 when it is conducting, most of this current will pass through T_1. This will increase i_1, which will increase i_2. Thus, this process will repeat itself until both T_1 and T_2 are saturated. Hence, the gate current can switch the connection between the anode and cathode from a very high to a very low impedance. Once conduction has started, the gate loses control. Consider that i_g is reduced to zero. The base current of T_2 will still be maintained by i_2 and the device will not switch off. Thus, the gate can be used to initiate conduction but not to terminate it. However, if V_1 is reduced to zero or made negative, i_L will become zero and the gate will regain control. (The anode current cannot be in the reverse direction because of the *p-n* junctions.) Thus, if this device is used in a half-wave rectifier circuit (with the anode and cathode connected as though they were the anode and the cathode, respectively, of an ordinary diode) and the gate voltage was turned on at the same angle θ of each cycle, the output current would have the form shown in Fig. 17-21. Thus, the desired controlled-rectifier action would be achieved.

There are several ratings that must be considered. If the anode-to-cathode voltage is made too large, conduction will be initiated by breakdown phenomena even though gate current has not been applied. Breakdown can result from the application of too large an inverse voltage also. Power dissipation is very important, since the current in a *p-n* junction varies markedly with temperature. Thus, the turn-on characteristic will vary greatly with junction temperature.

Let us describe a controlled-rectifier circuit. Such a circuit is shown in Fig. 17-23. Assume that two sinusoidal voltages are available and that the phase angle between them can be varied. When v_g just becomes positive, the rectifier will switch on provided that v_a is positive. Actually, v_g may have to be slightly positive, but if V_{max} is very much greater than this voltage, very little error is introduced by assuming that the controlled rectifier conducts when v_g just becomes positive. Thus, the current i will have the waveform shown in Fig. 17-21. Now consider Fig. 17-24, which can be used to produce a varying phase angle θ. The two transformers are used for isolation purposes. Assume that the resistance R_i is infinite. If $R_2 = R_3$, then in complex form, we have

$$\mathbf{V}_1 = \frac{\mathbf{V}_I}{2} \frac{1 - j\omega R_1 C}{1 + j\omega R_1 C} = \frac{\mathbf{V}_I}{2} \underline{/-2 \tan^{-1} \omega R_1 C} \tag{17-76}$$

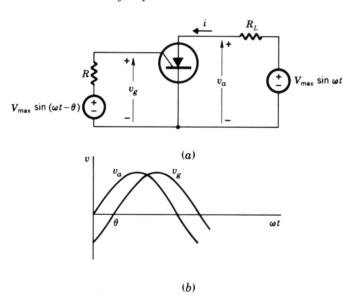

(a)

(b)

Fig. 17-23   (a) A simple controlled-rectifier circuit and (b) waveforms in this circuit (assuming that the controlled rectifier is not conducting).

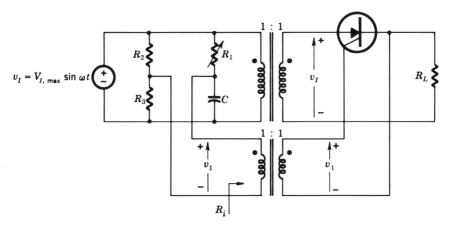

Fig. 17-24 A controlled rectifier which uses a phase-shifting circuit.

Thus, as R_1 is varied from a short circuit to an open circuit, the phase angle θ between v_I and v_1 will vary from 0 to 180° and the current can be varied continually from a maximum value to zero. We have, thus, achieved the desired control.

REFERENCE

1. Happell, G. E., and W. M. Hesselberth: "Engineering Electronics," pp. 417–423, McGraw-Hill Book Company, New York, 1953.

BIBLIOGRAPHY

Greiner, R. A.: "Semiconductor Devices and Applications," chap. 16, McGraw-Hill Book Company, New York, 1961.

Happell, G. E., and W. M. Hesselberth: "Engineering Electronics," chap. 14, McGraw-Hill Book Company, New York, 1953.

Millman, J., and C. C. Halkias: "Electronic Devices and Circuits," chap. 20, McGraw-Hill Book Company, New York, 1967.

Seely, S.: "Electronic Circuits," chap. 15, Holt, Rinehart and Winston, Inc., New York, 1968.

PROBLEMS

In all the following problems that call for numerical answers, assume that the power-line frequency is 60 Hz. If it is not specified otherwise, the diodes can be assumed to be ideal in these problems.

17-1. Compute expressions for $I_{L,\text{dc}}$, $V_{L,\text{dc}}$, γ, and η_r for the half-wave rectifier of Fig. 17-2*a*. Do not assume that the back resistance of the diode is infinite or that the forward resistance is zero.

17-2. Repeat Prob. 17-1 for the full-wave rectifier of Fig. 17-3*a*.

17-3. Repeat Prob. 17-1 for the full-wave bridge rectifier of Fig. 17-4 but now assume that the back resistance of the diodes is infinite. Do not assume that the forward resistance of the diodes is zero.

17-4. Find an expression for the load current in the full-wave bridge rectifier of Fig. 17-4. Do not assume that the back resistance of the diodes is infinite or that the forward resistance is zero.

17-5. Determine the output voltage v_O for the circuit shown in Fig. 17-25. How will the output voltage vary if a load resistance is placed across terminals ab?

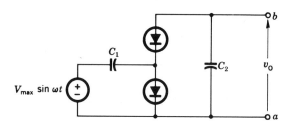

Fig. 17-25

17-6. Repeat Prob. 17-5 for the circuit of Fig. 17-26.

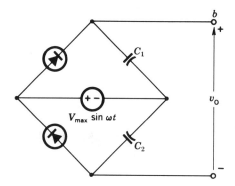

Fig. 17-26

17-7. The half-wave rectifier with a capacitor filter shown in Fig. 17-6 has the following circuit values: $V_{max} = 150$ volts, $C = 20$ μf, and $R_L = 10,000$ ohms. Compute the values of $V_{L,dc}$, $I_{L,dc}$, γ, the peak diode current, and the peak inverse voltage.

17-8. Repeat Prob. 17-7, but now consider that a full-wave rectifier is used and that 150 sin ωt is the voltage across one-half of the transformer secondary.

17-9. Design a power supply using a half-wave rectifier with a capacitor filter as shown in Fig. 17-6. The specifications of the filter are: $V_{L,dc} = 150$ volts, $I_{L,dc} = 20$ ma, and $\gamma = 0.01$. Determine the values of C and V_{max}. What is the peak diode current? Assume that the diode is ideal.

17-10. Repeat Prob. 17-9 but now use a full-wave rectifier.

17-11. Repeat Prob. 17-10 but now assume that the design specifications are $V_{L,dc} = 350$ volts, $I_{L,dc} = 100$ ma, and $\gamma = 0.001$.

17-12. The full-wave rectifier with an inductor-input filter shown in Fig. 17-10 has the following circuit values: $R_L = 1000$ ohms, $C = 20$ μf, and $V_{max} = 300$ volts. The inductance is the minimum value that satisfies relation (17-54). Compute the values of $V_{L,dc}$, $I_{L,dc}$, and γ. Assume that the resistance of the inductance is 20 ohms.

17-13. For the circuit of Fig. 17-10, the circuit values are $V_{max} = 300$ volts, $L = 2$ henrys, $C = 20$ μf, and $R_L = 10,000$ ohms. What is the minimum value of bleeder resistance that can be used if the inductance is not to be less than the critical value?

17-14. Assume that there is no bleeder resistance, that the load resistance is removed from the power supply of Prob. 17-13, and that the power supply is turned off at some later time. The leakage resistance of the capacitor is 10^9 ohms. At the instant that the power supply is turned off, what will the output voltage be? How long will it take for the output voltage to drop to 10 volts? Repeat the calculations if a 10^5-ohm bleeder resistance is connected across the capacitor.

17-15. Design a power supply using a full-wave rectifier and an inductor-input filter that meets the following specifications: $V_{L,dc} = 350$ volts, $I_{L,dc} = 100$ ma, and $\gamma = 0.001$. Use a value of inductance that satisfies relation (17-54) but is less than 20 henrys. The values of V_{max}, L, and C should be specified. Compare these results with those of Prob. 17-11. Assume that the inductance has no resistance associated with it.

17-16. Repeat Prob. 17-15 but now use a two-section inductance-input filter. Assume that the values of both inductances and of both capacitances are equal.

17-17. Repeat Probs. 17-15 and 17-16 but now assume that $\gamma = 0.00001$.

17-18. Repeat Prob. 17-15 but now assume that the inductance has a series resistance of 500 ohms.

17-19. Repeat Prob. 17-16 but now assume that each inductance has a series resistance of 500 ohms.

17-20. The capacitor-input filter of Fig. 17-14 has the following element values: $C_1 = 20$ μf, $C_2 = 30$ μf. $L = 10$ henrys, $R_L = 1000$ ohms, and the series resistance of the inductance is 100 ohms. If $V_{max} = 350$ volts, what are the values of $V_{L,dc}$, $I_{L,dc}$, γ, and the peak diode currents?

17-21. Repeat the design of Prob. 17-15 but now use the capacitor-input filter of Fig. 17-14. Assume that $C_2 = 2C_1$ and that the resistance of the inductance is zero. What is the peak diode current? Does the critical inductance have any significance here?

17-22. Repeat Prob. 17-21 but now assume that the resistance of the inductance is 500 ohms.

17-23. Repeat Prob. 17-21 but now assume that an additional LC section is added to the filter. Assume that the values of both inductances are equal and that the three capacitors have equal values. The maximum allowed value for the inductances is 20 henrys.

17-24. A filter of the type shown in Fig. 17-16 is to be used in a power supply with two different outputs. The first output is to be such that $V_{L1,dc} = 350$ volts, $I_{L1,dc} = 100$ ma, and $\gamma_1 = 0.001$. The second output is to be such that $V_{L2,dc} = 250$ volts, $I_{L2,dc} = 10$ ma, and $\gamma_2 = 0.00001$. Design the power supply using a full-wave rectifier. Note that the power supply must supply a total current of 110 ma.

17-25. The output resistance of the capacitor-input filter of Fig. 17-14 is to be equal to or less than 10 ohms. What is the minimum value that C_1 can have? Assume that the inductance has zero resistance.

17-26. Assume that the characteristics of the voltage-regulator diode of Fig. 17-18 are given in Fig. 17-17b. Plot a curve of v_L versus V as V varies from 0 to 220 volts. The values of the circuit elements are $R = 200,000$ ohms and $R_L = 200,000$ ohms.

17-27. Obtain an expression for the voltage gain of the circuit of Fig. 17-20. The answer should be in terms of the parameters of the transistors and the circuit elements.

17-28. Use the results of Prob. 17-27 to discuss the voltage regulation of the circuit.

17-29. Assume that the controlled rectifier of Fig. 17-24 conducts when the gate voltage exceeds $bV_{1,\max}$, where b is a constant that is less than $\frac{1}{2}$. Derive an expression for the angle θ of Fig. 17-21. Assume that all components are ideal and that R_i is infinite.

17-30. Consider Fig. 17-24. Derive an expression for v_1. Do not assume that R_i is infinite. What relation must there be among R_i and the circuit elements if Eq. (17-76) is to be valid?

Index

Index